French Painting 1774-1830:
The Age of Revolution

French Painting 1774-1830:
The Age of Revolution

Grand Palais, Paris
16 November 1974 - 3 February 1975

The Detroit Institute of Arts
5 March - 4 May 1975

The Metropolitan Museum of Art, New York
12 June - 7 September 1975

Exhibition sponsored by
Founders Society The Detroit Institute of Arts,
The Metropolitan Museum of Art
and the Réunion des Musées Nationaux, Paris.

The exhibition was made possible through the generous assistance of
the Edsel B. and Eleanor C. Ford Exhibitions Fund,
a gift from Mrs. Allan Shelden
and a grant from the New York State Council on the Arts.

English language edition distributed by
Wayne State University Press,
5980 Cass Avenue, Detroit, Michigan, 48202.

Cover illustration, Eugène Delacroix (1798-1863)
Detail of *Liberty Leading the People*, 1830
Paris, Musée du Louvre
No. 41

Organizers of the Exhibition

Frederick J. Cummings
Director, The Detroit Institute of Arts

Pierre Rosenberg
Conservateur au Département des Peintures, Musée du Louvre

Robert Rosenblum
Professor of Fine Arts, New York University

Consulting Committee

Jean-Pierre Cuzin
Conservateur au Département des Peintures, Musée du Louvre

Jacques Foucart
Conservateur au Département des Peintures, Musée du Louvre

Geneviève Lacambre
Conservateur au Département des Peintures, Musée du Louvre

Jean Lacambre
Conservateur à l'Inspection Générale des Musées Classés et Contrôlés

Antoine Schnapper
Professor of the History of Art, University of Dijon

Jacques Vilain
Conservateur à l'Inspection Générale des Musées Classés et Contrôlés

Curators in Charge of the Exhibition

Anthony M. Clark
Chairman, Department of European Paintings, The Metropolitan Museum of Art

Dewey F. Mosby
Curator of European Art, The Detroit Institute of Arts

John Walsh
Curator, Department of European Paintings, The Metropolitan Museum of Art

Coordinator of the Exhibition, Paris

Isabelle Julia

Commentaries and documentation have been prepared by:

Arnaud Brejon de Lavergnée	A. B. L.
Marie-Claude Chaudonneret	M.-Cl. C.
Jean-Pierre Cuzin	J.-P. C.
Jacques Foucart	J. F.
Thomas Gaehtgens	Th. G.
Isabelle Julia	I. J.
Anne Leclair	A. L.
Geneviève Lacambre	G. L.
Jean Lacambre	J. L.
Sylvain Laveissière	S. L.
Jean-François Méjanès	J.-F. M.
Laure Pélicer and Philippe Bordes	L. P. and Ph. B.
Pierre Rosenberg	P. R.
Robert Rosenblum	R. R.
Sarah Robertson	S. R.
Antoine Schnapper	A. S.
Katrin Simons	K. S.
Jacques Vilain	J. V.
Nathalie Volle	N. V.
Nicole Wilck-Brocard	N. W.-B.
Norman Ziff	N. Z.

Table of Contents

Acknowledgments

"French Painting 1774-1830: The Age of Revolution" represents the first joint effort of the Réunion des Musées Nationaux of France, the Metropolitan Museum of Art and the Detroit Institute of Arts. Recently the Administration of the French Museums, due to the efforts of its former director Jean Chatelain and his successor, Emmanuel de Margerie, and the Metropolitan have pooled their resources to present a series of exhibitions of major significance. The Detroit Institute of Arts became a logical partner of these institutions, having established a tradition of organizing exhibitions that encompass both the familiar and the less familiar in order to create a better understanding of the total artistic climate of a period.

A truly international endeavor, "French Painting 1774-1830: The Age of Revolution" brings together for the first time four different epochs of French painting. Many of the artists are unknown to American and European publics, but deserve wider recognition. The exhibition is timely, coming on the eve of the Bicentennial of the United States of America; the subtitle "The Age of Revolution" will immediately suggest the connections between the intellectual, social and political currents here and in France, currents we must understand in order to grasp the Revolutions of 1776 and 1789. The role that France played in our own Revolution was a matter of ideas as well as action. In fact, this exhibition marks the first official event of Detroit's Bicentennial celebration.

The concept of the exhibition was formulated five years ago by Frederick J. Cummings and Robert Rosenblum; Professor Rosenblum's provocative book, *Transformations in Late Eighteenth Century Art* (Princeton, 1967), had already initiated a reassessment of late 18th and early 19th-century art. Pierre Rosenberg quickly joined them, "in the spirit of '76," to help overcome the formidable obstacles presented, paradoxically enough, by the general obscurity of the period and the rarity of the works of art themselves. The enthusiasm and dedication of Rosenblum, Rosenberg and Cummings, as well as the generosity of so many, are revealed in the splendid exhibition that has been assembled.

A Scientific Committee, listed on page 5, was organized to help select the objects, secure the loans and write the catalog. We wish to express our gratitude to the members of this illustrious group, who, in turn, gladly acknowledge their debt to the late Professor Walter Friedlaender for his pioneering efforts in the field.

To our own curators, Anthony M. Clark, John Walsh, Jr. and Dewey F. Mosby, who have worked so diligently to make this show a reality, we owe thanks and congratulations.

In Detroit, the generosity of numerous individuals has made the exhibition possible. We particularly note the dedication of Mrs. Edsel B. Ford, whose vision and magnanimity are universal exemplars for all who dream of great exhibitions of this type. Mrs. Allan Shelden has also earned our heartfelt thanks for her unusually generous and sympathetic support of this exhibition. We deeply appreciate the financial assistance provided by the Edsel B. and Eleanor C. Ford Exhibitions Fund. In New York the expenses of the exhibition have been defrayed, in part, by a generous grant from the New York State Council on the Arts.

It would have been difficult to undertake this exhibition without the extensive cooperation of the French and American governments. The heavy administrative burden was carried in France with the greatest skill and grace by the devoted team from the Réunion des Musées Nationaux of France—Hubert Landais, Irène Bizot, Marguerite Rebois, Ute Collinet and Claude Soalhat.

Our greatest debt of gratitude is owed to the collectors (several of whom wish to remain anonymous), museums and institutions listed on pages 708-710, who generously agreed to part with their precious works of art for nearly a year.

It would be impossible to express sufficient thanks to Isabelle Julia, who assisted with all details of the organization of the exhibition in Paris and coordinated the French catalog, or to Susan F. Rossen, coordinator of the English edition of the catalog. Also to be thanked are Susan K. Weinberg, Terry Ann R. Neff and Judith Schub, each of whom diligently read parts of the English manuscript.

In addition, members of our staffs in Detroit and New York were especially involved in this complex venture, in particular Philippe de Montebello, Ronald Winokur, James Pilgrim, Donald Rosenthal, Stuart Silver, John Buchanan, Herbert Moskowitz, Melanie Snedcof, Alain Goldrach, Christine Faltermeier and Shelley Perlove.

We are deeply grateful as well for the exceptional efforts of the conservation, photographic, education, bookstore, publicity and installation personnel of our institutions. Though they remain unnamed here, their hard work was essential to the success of the exhibition and is greatly appreciated.

Frederick J. Cummings
Director
The Detroit Institute of Arts

Thomas Hoving
Director
The Metropolitan Museum of Art

French Painting 1774-1830: The Age of Revolution

Pierre Rosenberg

Why this exhibition, this title, these dates?

Over the past two decades there has been a succession of monographs and exhibitions dedicated to Ingres, Delacroix, Géricault, less famous painters such as Girodet or Prud'hon, or even lesser masters such as Jean-Louis Demarne, Mmes Labille-Guiard and Vallayer-Coster. Various exhibitions in France, and especially outside of France, have been devoted to the artistic trends of the period, commonly known as Neo-Classicism and Romanticism. The two most important exhibitions, both organized by the Council of Europe and held in London in 1959 and 1972, attempted to give a definition of a style in its most varied artistic expressions.

The purpose of this exhibition is entirely different. It is limited to the study of the painting of a single country, France. During the 56 years separating the death of Louis XV (which occurred exactly two centuries ago) from the fall of Charles X, France was shaken by the most important political events of its history. The public consciousness was profoundly transformed and, of course, painting did not remain static.

In 1774, David was 26 years old. But Fragonard, Hubert Robert and Greuze had not yet lived half their lives. In 1830, Prud'hon and Géricault had been dead for seven and six years respectively. Ingres was 50 years old and had produced his most important masterpieces; Delacroix was still only 32! Gros died in 1835, Gérard two years later. It is this disunity, so essential to the period, which we have attempted to suggest, avoiding any classifications such as the artificial bipolarity of Romanticism and Neo-Classicism. The exhibition in France bears the title "de David à Delacroix, La Peinture Française de 1774 à 1830," which we borrowed from a famous work by Walter F. Friedlaender originally published in German over 40 years ago. Thus, we have tried to bring together the names of the era's two greatest French painters, born exactly a half-century apart, who have become convenient if not accurate archetypes of two different approaches to painting, which to this day can still claim their own adherents.

How does one give an objective idea of the pictorial production of this epoch? How does one choose among the thousands of paintings of all genres, formats and styles that have survived, too often in poor condition?

Although we have assembled thirteen works by David, eight by Ingres, five by Géricault and four by Prud'hon, one of our major concerns has been not to limit our choice to the most illustrious of the period. We wanted to bring out of obscurity many artists, some famous during their lifetimes but who today are only names in specialized dictionaries. This catalog contains works by about 125 painters. And yet this list cannot be considered complete. It may surprise some that the exhibition does not include works by Bilcoq, Blondel, Boulanger, Coupin de la Couperie, Debucourt, Doyen, Ducis, Duplessis-Bertaux, Hue, Laurent, Menjaud, Pajou *fils*, Picot, Pillement, Roland de La Porte or Roques. Some artists, such as Henri-Pierre Danloux or Étienne-Barthélemy Garnier, for example, are insufficiently represented. It was impossible to be encyclopedic in an era where the number of painters seemed to multiply from year to year. We can only hope that those who will reproach this or that omission will not be those who think the exhibition too vast and the number of paintings excessive.

The 56 years under consideration here are divided into four very distinct political periods: the reign of Louis XVI, the Revolution, the Consulate and the Empire, and the Restoration of Louis XVIII and Charles X. The four periods have been examined from the strict viewpoint of French painting in separate essays which function both as prefaces to the catalog itself and make use of the exhibited works to analyze the artistic tendencies of the epoch. From each of these eras we have intentionally selected a similar number of paintings.

A second organizing principle of the exhibition was the hierarchy of subject matter, important throughout the 18th century and surviving until the second half of the 19th. The *grand genre*, history painting—a broad term that embraced religious themes, ancient history and, more frequently toward the end of the 18th century, modern history—was the most highly regarded category, followed by portraiture, genre and still life. Within each period we have attempted to present a balance of these categories. While this hierarchy of content is not understood today, it had a profound significance during an epoch in which paintings sought to, at times had to, have a profound meaning, elevate the spirit, present a moral lesson or serve as an example.

Two final remarks: because of the unfamiliarity of the period, we thought it advisable where possible to follow the judgment of the artists themselves; consequently, we have attempted to exhibit works that were shown at the Salons. Maligned today, the Salon was the crucial institution for the period, its doors open to most artists during the reign of Louis XVI and to all of them during the Revolution. The Salon was the only means, besides the Church which commissioned religious pictures, by which painters could present their work to the public. It matters little that Fragonard did not exhibit there often, or that Greuze refused to exhibit his works after the affront he received for his *Caracalla* in 1769. One can scarcely find a major work of the period, from David's *Belisarius* (No. 30) and Géricault's *Wounded Cuirassier* (No. 74) to Delacroix' *Liberty Leading the People* (No. 41), that had not been shown at the Salon. The artists considered the works they sent to the Salon to be their very best. This holds true for some of the minor paintings as well, by Pierre-Henri de Valenciennes (No. 179), Jean-Louis Demarne (No. 46), and Jean-Laurent Mosnier (which was initially included in the exhibition only for its quality, but the compiling of the catalog revealed that it too had been exhibited at the Salon; see No. 135).

We might also receive criticism for not including enough studies, for purposely selecting, with a few exceptions (Nos. 147, 167), the finished work rather than the sketch. Our own era prefers the first expression of an artist and scorns the finished product. No doubt this attitude would have shocked not only the contemporaries of David, but also those of Greuze and Delacroix, who believed that true judgment of an artist's merits could be made only on the basis of the completed work. Presented with a choice between two sets of attitudes—those of our contemporaries, whose taste for the period is not well-defined and too often rests on fragmentary knowledge of the time, and those of the period in question—we have deliberately opted for the second. An exhibition which first and foremost respects historical veracity must banish those dogmas that so often distort the truth by relating the most disparate of works and yield to the will of the artists whom it should serve above all.

The most striking quality of painting in this period is its variety, the reflection of a time which sought to be open to every kind of exploration. The numerous themes, showing that iconography had assumed a new importance, range from the most unusual still lifes like the curious collection of birds and eggs painted by Leroy de Barde (No. 122), to genre, rendered convincing both by their content and technique (e.g. the detailed description of Louis-Léopold Boilly's *Galleries of the Palais Royal* [No. 8], which is a trompe-l'œil imitation of an engraving; from thrilling scenes such as the moonlit *Young and his Daughter* by Pierre-Auguste Vafflard [No. 178] to symbolical and deliberately hidden allegory, as in the self-portrait as a Free Mason by Jean-Baptiste Regnault [No. 151] and the careful rendering of an actual event, both political and macabre, *Vivant Denon Returning the Remains of El Cid to his Tomb* by A.-E. Fragonard [No. 57] to the psychological audacity of the homosexual *Death of Hyacinth* by Jean Broc [No. 6]). The variety of subjects was accompanied by a diversity of styles; the painters of our period referred more than ever to the masters of the past, as Robert Rosenblum has so aptly pointed out here in his essay on the Napoleonic period. They looked, naturally, to antiquity, which occupied a privileged position; to Poussin and Raphael; to the Italian primitives; and to the little Dutch masters, whose technical virtuosity they frequently imitated; to Rembrandt's golden brown *sfumato* and to Rubens' dramatic compositions. In a word, there are very few arts of the past that the artists did not explore. Nevertheless, whatever the inspiration, nothing was parodied or slavishly imitated (see, for example, the paintings of Fleury Richard [Nos. 154, 155] and the *troubadour* painters).

The co-existence during the period of a variety of artistic trends also destroys the myth, invented by lazy art historians more eager for simplistic ideas than the truth, of David's sectarian reign over his period (as false a legend as that of the so-called blind tyranny of Lebrun over his contemporaries in the 17th century). David accepted, even while not understanding, Girodet's *Ossian* (No. 80) and Ossianic themes in general. It is significant that at the time of David's greatest power, the movement of *troubadour* painting developed under the patronage of the Empress Josephine. Moreover, in his own studio two countertrends blossomed: the curious "Barbus" and the Primitifs, who in Ingres, found their ultimate and most glorious incarnation. If we have attempted to represent this period in its most diverse aspects, we nevertheless made our selections on the basis of quality. Here we are indeed on uncertain ground, and yet less slippery than it would seem, because of the existence during the period of a large number of unanimously accepted objective criteria (such as technical accuracy and the supremacy of drawing). Nothing is more relative than "quality," nothing more changeable than taste, of which it has so often (and perhaps so justly) been said that only those who share our attitudes have good taste. By exhibiting the most celebrated paintings of the era and spreading the scale of choice as widely as possible to include the most diverse tendencies— *grand genre* and still life, thickly and vigorously brushed paintings as well as smooth canvases executed without shadow, as brittle and crackling as glass or porcelain—we hope to give the public an idea of an epoch whose variety has not ceased to surprise us, to make clear the immense ambitions of artists for whom painting was not a gratuitous play of lines, an image more or less freely captured of the scenery around the Ile-de-France. Alas, so many paintings of this period have disappeared! So many paintings, precisely those most praised at their appearance in the Salon, are rolled up and stored in museum reserves, never even having been photographed. A great number of these neglected canvases, many of them extremely large, are at present impossible to judge, on account of dirt, grime and lack of restoration. Such problems explain some of the reasons why this exhibition, first projected by Frederick J. Cummings and Robert Rosenblum, had to be a cooperative effort by a team of scholars whose names appear on page 4, which selected and researched the works, often supervised their restoration and produced the major part of this catalog. The scholarly committee wishes to acknowledge its indebtedness to the many archivists, museum curators, private collectors, specialists, curators and photographers without whom this exhibition would not have been possible.

We are aware that this exhibition is only a beginning, an initial exploration of an unknown and inadequately studied period. Few eras of French painting have been so rich in diverse talent or have seen so many attempts—sometimes thwarted—in so many directions. In 1830, French painting was not, could no longer be what it had been in 1774. The line that led from one point to the other was far from straight, and was there in fact only one? Through the illustrations in this catalog (they accompany each of the introductory essays and are arranged in chronological order) the reader will be able to judge the changes for himself, transformations that summarize, still sketchily perhaps, 56 years in the history of French painting.

J.-H. Fragonard
The Lock, c. 1780
Paris, Musée du Louvre
No. 59

Drouais
Marius at Minturnae, 1786
Paris, Musée du Louvre
No. 52

David
Portrait of the Marquise de Pastoret, c. 1792
The Art Institute of Chicago
No. 34

Gauffier
Portrait of Doctor Penrose, s.d. 1798
Minneapolis Institute of Arts
No. 66

Girodet
Portrait of an Indian, 1807
Montargis, Musée Girodet
No. 81

Meynier
Napoleon on the Battlefield of Eylau, 1807
Versailles, Musée National
No. 128

Taunay
French Army Crossing the Saint-Bernard Pass, 1808
Versailles, Musée National
No. 173

Boilly
The Galleries of the Palais Royal (detail), s.d. 1809
Paris, Musée Carnavalet
No. 8

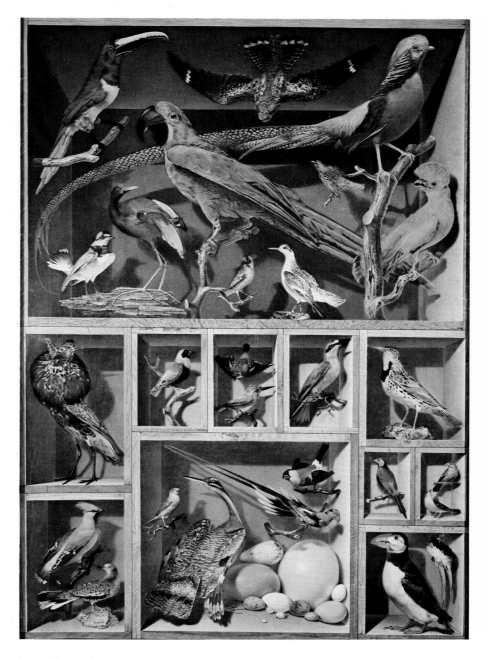

Leroy de Barde
Still Life with Birds, s.d. 1810
Paris, Musée du Louvre, Cabinet des Dessins
No. 122

Franque
Allegory of the Condition of France Before the Return from Egypt, Salon of 1810
Paris, Musée du Louvre
No. 61

Ingres
Death of Leonardo da Vinci (detail), s.d. 1818
Paris, Musée du Petit Palais
No. 106

Gudin
Devotion of Captain Desse, 1828-29
Bordeaux, Musée des Beaux-Arts
No. 92

28

Painting Under Louis XVI
1774-1789

Frederick J. Cummings

On the 10th of May, 1774, Louis XV died of smallpox at the age of 64, and his 20-year-old grandson, Louis Augustus, became King of France. In the same year, the 26-year-old Jacques-Louis David learned that the State had awarded him the Prix de Rome which he greatly coveted, having attempted to obtain it on three previous occasions. These events initiated the careers of the two personalities who were to dominate the following 15-year period in governance and the arts in France. While Louis XVI assumed center stage reluctantly, David worked assiduously to achieve full command of his rare personal powers, eventually obtaining the hegemony of the arts that was to make him absolute arbiter in his field.

Throughout the reign of Louis XVI, dramatic intellectual and social changes undermined the carefully elaborated absolutism created under Louis XIV. Unable to cope with overwhelming taxes and inequitable laws, glaring class distinctions and increasing government debts, the established order became the target for the searing and brilliant criticism of *philosophes* like Jean-Jacques Rousseau and Jean Le Rond d'Alembert.

The dynamics of change were hastened by new intellectual attitudes, providing keys to unlock new worlds of feeling and imagination, a process in which the arts assumed the leading role. Voltaire's emphasis on reason, his belief in the sufficiency of human capacity to cope with man's physical and social environment, was basic to a new self-confidence and self-consciousness that would ultimately lead modern man literally "to the stars." Rousseau's essay on the *Contrat Social* (1762) paved the way for questioning the responsibilities of the citizen and the state to one another. His equally important *Rêveries du promeneur solitaire (Essays of a Solitary,* 1782) examined the boundaries and resources of feelings. This was the greatest contribution of late 18th-century France to European civilization. French painting during the 1770s and '80s thus underwent rapid changes of great magnitude. While this may have reflected the shattering events of contemporary life, its implications extended far beyond pre-Revolutionary France.

In the world of art, change itself became a continuous feature. This was due in part to an ever-varying selection among historical sources, developed in turn by a greater awareness of former epochs. The past was presented as a world where vital struggles of *virtù*, social obligation, personal conduct involving moral courage were enacted. Like the *philosophes*, who at first dealt with these issues in abstract treatises, the painters felt most comfortable with dramatic subjects from antiquity and medieval history—worlds quite removed from current events. These subjects were used as a means of exploring values in political and social realms. Ultimately, the same artists would paint in heroic guise with equally compelling implications such contemporary events as the oath of the Tennis Court or the death of Marat. In this way, the heroic aspects of contemporary life became so closely identified with the achievements of antiquity that the two were at times interchangeable. The possibilities of exploration of man's dilemmas through historical incidents were infinite, ranging from questions of social obligation to the state to suicide. Emotional drama in the face of decisions about human values remains the constant and unifying factor in the paintings of this period.

The secularization of subject matter could be, and was, fostered by the King, through his patronage of the most powerful artists and his concern to link the arts with national history and goals. Since royal patronage was by far the most important single force during this period, this essay will consider only the major phases of painting, to the exclusion of developments in portraiture, landscape, still life and genre—each of which flourished and provided unique contributions.

The period is divisible into three nearly chronological currents. The first comprises the commission of paintings for the Chapel of the École Militaire Royale in 1773-74 and includes several royal commissions awarded well into the 1780s. A second begins with the younger generation of history painters working in Rome, to which Joseph-Marie Vien took the young Jacques-François Peyron and Jacques-Louis David as students in 1775. The new pictorial rationale and subject matter created by these students of Vien found climactic expression in David's *Belisarius* of 1781 (No. 30). The third phase, beginning in 1781 and continuing through David's masterful works of the '80s, established his ultimate authority and resulted in a new school of younger artists committed to his style.

The impact of heroic clarity and vibrancy of the Davidians forced contemporaries like François-André Vincent and Jean-Baptiste Regnault, among others, to change their approaches significantly.

The diaphanous charades of Boucher and the irrepressible wit of Fragonard dominated the arts even after Boucher's death in 1769 and the appointment in 1770 of Jean-Baptiste-Marie Pierre as First Painter to the King and Director of the Academy. Madame du Barry and the Marquis de Marigny, the King's Director General of Buildings, continued to encourage the court style of the 1750s and '60s. During the later years of Louis XV, royal commissions had decreased in number and importance. The final great series was for the dining room of the Petit Trianon; first awarded in 1768, it was completed over the next ten-year period by Louis Lagrenée the Elder (1769), Vien (1773), Jean-François Doyen (1775) and Noël Hallé. It is significant to keep in mind that the Royal Chapel commission was given by the Church. Only in ecclesiastical circles was painting of a more serious nature possible; during the reign of Louis XV, the Church had consistently engaged the most proficient artists, such as Hallé, Carle Van Loo and Jean Restout. The Royal Chapel commission thus privileged the nine participating artists, including Jean-Antoine Beaufort *(Death of Saint Louis)*, Lagrenée the Elder *(Meeting of Pope Innocent IV and Saint Louis at Lyon)*, Hallé *(Saint Louis Taking the Crown of Thorns to the Sainte Chapelle)*, Nicolas-Guy Brenet *(Saint Louis Receiving the Ambassadors of the King of the Tartars)*, Louis-Jean-Jacques Durameau *(Saint Louis Washing the Feet of the Poor)* and Vien *(Saint Louis Transferring the Regency of the Kingdom to his Mother)*. The series further included a secondary painting by Amedée Van Loo and the altarpiece by Doyen *(Last Communion of Saint Louis)*. All of these men were linked with the Academy in some way and the majority had a royal appointment. Most were either students or close friends of Pierre.

The paintings prepared for the Royal Chapel are dated 1773 and were shown in the Salon, with the exception of that by Jean Restout of the year following. While their French medieval subjects presage *troubadour* themes that would abound from this moment on, they are nevertheless painted in the style of the early years of Louis XVI. It is only much later that *troubadour* painting utilized not only medieval subjects but also the miniaturizing technique of medieval illuminations.

Upon his succession in 1774, Louis XVI retired the Marquis de Marigny, favorite of Madame du Barry and close friend of his father the Dauphin; the Comte d'Angiviller was now appointed Director General of the King's Buildings. D'Angiviller was responsible for the extensive reorganization of the administration of the fine arts which, seen in retrospect, was the most decisive force in the impending

Durameau
Saint Louis Washing the Feet of the Poor, Salon of 1773
Paris, École Militaire, Chapelle Saint-Louis

alteration in style. In this process, royal patronage of the schools and the royal commissions were of the greatest importance, leading to the dramatic changes in painting which characterized the entire reign of Louis XVI. Under D'Angiviller, those artists gathered for the Royal Military Academy commission were given further, extensive patronage; their domination of the fine arts well into the 1780s ultimately led to considerable tension with the developing Davidian current.

In 1775, D'Angiviller devised a plan for awarding a major series of commissions to illustrate the history of France. In a letter to Pierre of 27 June, he mentioned four subjects from Rollin's medieval history, each of which was to celebrate some noble or virtuous act. At first, Durameau, a pupil of Pierre, was selected to complete the entire series; in the end he painted only the superb *Continence of Bayard* (No. 55). This subject was specifically designated by D'Angiviller to illustrate chivalrous respect for virtue. Brenet, a pupil of Boucher, professor at the Academy and participant in the Royal Chapel commission, was among those chosen to prepare one of the subjects for this series. His enormous picture of the *Death of Du Guesclin* (No. 15) illustrates the victory of the French over the British and serves as a tribute to personal courage. A fourth subject, the *Capture of President Molé*, was undertaken by Vincent (Salon of 1779; now in Paris, Chambre des Députés). Also included in this exhibition is Suvée's *Death of Admiral Coligny* (No. 169). These paintings, and others added later, were finally reproduced as tapestries at the Gobelins Manufactory.

Each painting in the series is commanding. While retaining the pastel and roseate colors of the Rococo, the artists drew upon their knowledge of French medieval and renaissance history. Their concern for careful historical presentation is evidenced by the rich costumes, the medieval settings, the attention to surfaces and textures that identify and establish the tangibility of each object. Flying cherubs dropping flowers give way to richly-gowned ladies and armored knights with feet planted firmly on the ground. Madame de Pompadour is transformed with grace and charm into the companion of Bayard. Both the historic accuracy and sense of gravity of the figures form a startling contrast to the casual mythologies, fantasies, the cloud people and airy theaters of Boucher's imagination.

In a general way, these large paintings—serious in theme but secular in subject—reflect the taste of Louis XVI himself and, in turn, that of his chosen arbiter of taste, the rather stern Comte d'Angiviller. The inaugural Salon of the new reign (1775) quite specifically excluded the libertine subjects that had dominated French art since Watteau introduced light-hearted themes early in the century with his *Embarkation from Cytherea*, the Isle of Love (Louvre).

Very precise instructions to the jury from D'Angiviller, Pierre and the King barred licentious subjects and nudity of an indecent sort (indeed, the nudes of the preceding reign disappear—the characters in Durameau's *Continence of Bayard* are literally laden with draperies) and further recommended respect for propriety. As a result, in the Salon of 1775 actual historical events were the preferred subjects—mythologies were virtually nonexistent.

While a transformation of taste in official painting was occurring in Paris, a veritable revolution was underway in the French Academy in Rome. Since the early 18th century, this school had been crucial to the creation of superlatively trained French painters, sculptors and printmakers. Its basic premise was that students could best learn through contact with the great works of art from antiquity, the Renaissance and the 17th century that could be seen in Rome. Under Louis XV, the leadership of the Academy in Rome had weakened for two reasons. Charles Natoire, director of the school from 1751 to 1774, was neither a strong nor a vital teacher. Although an excellent painter in his own right, the program of studies under his aegis was lacking in stringency and vigor. The other factor was the establishment in Paris in 1748 of the Royal Drawing School (École des Élèves Protégées). To an important degree, it had supplanted the need for academic training in Rome during those years.

By 1775, D'Angiviller nonetheless viewed the French Academy in Rome as the key to the revival of the arts and the purification of taste in France. Accordingly, one of his first acts was to abolish the Royal Drawing School in Paris and to insist that the Academy provide outstanding young artists with a period of carefully programmed study at the fountainhead of art that was Rome. Noël Hallé replaced Natoire as director of the Academy in 1775, winning the confidence of the students and, more important, re-establishing the vigorous routine of studies that he believed characterized the Academy in the 17th century. Precise instructions from D'Angiviller sought to regulate each day for the students: they were to rise at 5 a.m. in the summer, the male model was to be in position at 6 a.m. or a little later, drawing from life was to continue until 8 a.m., and so forth. It was hoped that these measures would modify the lax habits (*"reformer le luxe"*) and the over-socializing of the pensioners.

When Vien was appointed director of the Academy late in 1775, he took David, Peyron and Jean Bonvoisin with him to Rome. In the following year, Regnault won the Prix de Rome with his *Diogenes Visited by Alexander* (Paris, École des Beaux-Arts), and he also joined this group. Under Vien, the regulation of daily work was made even more specific, and life drawing, anatomy and perspective were all enforced as substantial aspects of the course. The *écorché* made by Houdon for the Academy was recommended for

Regnault
Diogenes Visited by Alexander, 1776
Paris, École des Beaux-Arts

anatomical studies. It seems probable that the students were urged to complement and surpass this model, for it will be recalled that Houdon did, in fact, take anatomy lessons from Dr. Seguier at the hospital of S. Luigi dei Francesi near the Colosseum.

In 1776, D'Angiviller added a further directive to his reforms when he instructed Vien to re-establish the practice of having each student send a painting back to Paris for review by a committee of academicians. In addition, each student was to submit four works from the nude model, one of these a life-size painting after the nude, and one a painted sketch; the others could be drawings. The nude figure, preferably male, now to make its reappearance in a more severe context, was to be "correctly" drawn. Two of these four works were to be selected for exhibition at the Academy in Rome, where they could be viewed by other artists and the general public.

The vigorous routine pursued in Rome by Vien and his pupils caused a dramatic change in the very types of paintings produced by these young artists. Peyron's *Belisarius* (No. 139) of 1779 was the first work to embody the new pictorial concepts in the form that established the style of David in his magisterial productions of the 1780s. It contrasts sharply with David's slightly earlier *Funeral of Patroclus* (No. 27), which while heroic in conception, retains the swirling currents of Boucher and must be considered a transitional work.

Justinian's general, Belisarius (c. 505-564), became a popular figure in paintings of the 1770s and '80s (see also No. 30). Taken from the *Chiliades* or *Book of Histories* by Tzetzes, the 12th-century Byzantine poet and grammarian who lived in Constantinople, the story describes a man who, treated ungratefully by his king, became blind and was forced to beg for sustenance. Peyron showed Belisarius, his helmet on a table, his shield hung on the wall, receiving children brought to him by the people. Underlying this emblematic painting is the Rousseauian theme of leading children at a tender age to an exemplar of virtue. It also echoes the message of Jean-François Marmontel's novelette of 1767, *Belisarius*, that whoever paid homage to the general, a man without rancor and envy, would be raised to virtue. It was Tzetzes who first repeated the words of Belisarius, "He who gives a coin to Belisarius, who emulated virtue, has suppressed jealousy and envy."

In composing this painting, Peyron took several radically new steps. He adopted the principles of ancient relief sculpture by allowing the corners and sides of the painting to be open, spacious and free, in direct contrast to rococo paintings such as Durameau's, with their complex groupings built up from the corners of the painting and arranged figure by figure into depth. The paleness and fragility of Hallé's relaxed and graceful academic idiom are here rejected for the sober presentation of antique life. Peyron used simplified poses—profiles, full front and full back views—and regularized groupings with ample, intricately folded draperies. Behind Belisarius, the young Tiberius, his guide and companion, is clad like a young Greek, his profile head reminiscent of those on ancient vase paintings. The somber mood and severe Attic composition were further underlined by the architectural setting—rectilinear, obdurate, stony—laid out with great clarity. In the background, stone arches delineate the left and center groupings, and the corner of a wall frames the principal figures of Belisarius and Tiberius. The raking cellar light and severe staging link this painting suggestively with Caravaggio's *Calling of Saint Matthew* in the Contarelli Chapel of S. Luigi dei Francesi, certainly a major inspiration to the young French pensioners in Rome. Like his baroque forebears, Peyron used light for dramatic emphasis and to unify individual groupings. The inclusion of the still life on the table helps relate this antique drama to everyday life, just as Caravaggio's use of such things as a plucked chicken in the still life of his *Supper at Emmaus* (London, National Gallery) makes this Christian drama a credible reality.

David could declare, "Peyron showed me the way." Indeed, the principles of form and color employed by Peyron in the *Belisarius* (and already heralded in his *Death of Seneca* of 1773) were not ignored by David, who drew heavily upon this highly original example for his great works of the '80s. The fine color sensibility which Peyron exhibited here—the grayed blues and whites embellished by delicate passages of pink and rose—would serve as inspiration for David's even blonder and more simplified palette of local colors. From Peyron springs the architectural setting of the *Horatii*, as does the network of linear perspective containing a reduced relief plane of figures.

At the same time that Peyron painted his forward-looking *Belisarius*, another type of picture, as revolutionary and as critical for developments in the 1780s, made its appearance. This is the series of studies of male nudes (or academies) painted in the Academy during those cold morning hours of study. None of the male figures from this group is lyrically or decoratively conceived. On the contrary, each is presented as an intense, dramatic exercise in which light and a single expressive figure are the sole components. An important tradition for such figures had been established in Paris at the Royal Drawing School, where Brenet excelled in rendering them in mythological guise (*Morpheus*, Worcester Art Museum); and Vien, himself, painted similar figures (Toulouse) in a strong, raking light.

While in Rome, David painted at least two such figures: *Hector*, a seated male nude seen from the back (Cherbourg) and *Patroclus*

(Montpellier). He was criticized for his use of opaque shadows and the Caravaggesque lighting that create an emotional tension while enhancing the sculptural qualities of the figures. In his *Saint Sebastian* of 1778, now in the Musée Ochier in Cluny, David's fellow student, Bonvoisin, exhibited a similar predilection for Caravaggesque lighting, although the heroic anatomy of his figure recalls Michelangelo's nudes on the Sistine ceiling.

David
Patroclus, c. 1778
Montpellier, Musée Fabre

In his first commissioned painting, *Saint Roch Interceding for the Plague-Stricken* (No. 28), David first employed the new artistic concepts he learned in Rome. In a field strewn with victims of the plague, the kneeling pilgrim saint implores the aid of the Madonna. Despite the dominant presence of the Madonna, who is seated with her infant Son on solid, rock-like clouds, the pensive man in the foreground, a semi-nude Michelangelesque figure, and his desperate, writhing companions remain entirely unaware of the supernatural event occurring in their midst. The larger scale of the saint and Madonna and her own imperviousness to the earthly torment surrounding her further isolate and intensify the psychological responses of the figures. The simple massing of large forms and concentration of dramatic elements, as well as the concern for depicting intensified emotional states, distinguish this work from the diffused agitation of the earlier *Funeral of Patroclus* (No. 27). David was now concerned with a new set of pictorial values arising from his study of the art of Caravaggio and Poussin. From these baroque masters, in particular, he learned that a reasoned and sober clarification of emotional response is the key to credibility and the chief component of "heroic" art.

Understandably, those accustomed to the delightfully erotic and fashionable art of Boucher and Fragonard were rather shaken by the paintings of David in the Salon of 1781, an event which opens the third and last phase of painting under Louis XVI. David was certainly conscious of the innovative and even revolutionary character of his entries to this Salon. Rather than gradually exposing the public sensibility to his new-found idiom, David chose to take the Salon by storm, bringing forth for the exhibition all of his major paintings from the Roman period. No doubt his submissions were exhibited because both D'Angiviller and Vien recognized his talent. They include the three academic male nudes—*Hector, Patroclus* and *Saint Jerome* (Quebec, Cathedral)—as well as the *Saint Roch*, the *Funeral of Patroclus* (No. 27) and the *Belisarius* (No. 30), the latter most certainly his finest painting to that time and one of the greatest works of 18th-century French art.

We have already seen how much David gleaned from the earlier version of the same subject by Peyron, but it is important at this point to clarify the differences between their approaches in order

Bonvoisin
Saint Sebastian, 1778
Cluny, Musée Ochier

to underscore David's achievement. If Peyron's goal was to revive a Poussinesque pictorial clarity, David set out to make the drama a real and present event; in so doing, he relied on the example of Raphael, whose pictorial images were conceived as extensions of the existing world. In his *Belisarius*, a few life-size figures are set onto a huge stage, whose architectural elements, column bases and stone paving seem contiguous with our own space. The principals are in profile, arranged as in a relief sculpture, across the immediate foreground, so that we cannot help but be confronted immediately with their presence and physical reality. While Peyron's composition and David's earlier pictures themselves are populated with many figures, the cast of characters is here reduced to four. The marvelous and superbly-clad figure of the blind Belisarius stretches forward, his right hand in supplication, his left gripping tightly the waist of a child who extends the general's helmet toward a woman proferring a coin, her leaning figure and features marked with sympathetic tenderness for the plight of the mendicant. The secondary figure of the soldier is relegated to a background plane. The entire scene takes place in the open air, the stark light made more palpable by rich shadows. The vivid blues, yellows and clear whites create startling impressions of tangibility. Everything David had learned at the Academy in Rome was here brought together in a work having the greatest implications for 19th-century and modern art.

David's *Hector and Andromache* (No. 31), painted as his reception piece for the Academy and shown at the Salon of 1783, is the climax of his impulse to give tangible existence to the dramas of antique life. The vigor of Poussin's *Death of Eudamidas* (Copenhagen, National-museum) is present here, but rather than in that twilight zone, the drama plays itself out in broad daylight within our immediate presence and space. Andromache sits before the dead Hector, his feet rough and bony and his powerful rib cage protruding starkly through taut skin. Only a laurel wreath identifies him as an antique hero. The grief-stricken Andromache, her face stained with tears, reaches toward the corpse of her husband and implores us, however indirectly, to participate in this tragedy.

This event is seen through the highly focused, brilliantly colored consciousness of the epoch of Louis XVI. It becomes at once real and larger than life, an expression of the world of virtue and heroic action. These ideals, found in Homer and other ancient sources and which the Enlightenment linked with an abiding concern for human sensibility and dignity, are best expressed in the writings of Rousseau. David succeeded in visualizing these concepts so that the viewer felt personally concerned and deeply involved, the paintings themselves serving as guides to action in a present just as tumultuous and " historic " as the past.

David leads us to the verge of emotional participation in his compositions of the '80s, through our knowledge of the events and his convincing and dramatic portrayals of them. This is pertinently effected by his analysis of the emotional extremes and stress which the events call forth. Brutus condemning his children to death, Socrates killing himself, Andromache weeping at the deathbed of her husband, the Horatii preparing to kill the brothers of their wives and husband of their sister—in each, drama is sustained by the tension of momentary emotional duress brought about and heightened by the actuality and necessity of the event itself. Stoicism, virtue, social obligation are all made concrete in austere, clearly rectilinear forms, buttressing the multivalent emotions of these wide-screen, sharply-focused dramas.

Vincent
The Sabine Women, Salon of 1781
Angers, Musée des Beaux-Arts

David's achievement was neither immediately understood nor taken up. The continuing production of Peyron represents a personal contribution of the highest originality, although it was not sufficiently heroic to command a following once the absorption of his ideas by others had taken place. Other artists in the early 1780s pursued separate directions; in fact, the period is virtually characterized by a multiplicity of stylistic approaches. For example, Regnault's *Education of Achilles* (Avignon), Vincent's *Sabines* of 1781 (Angers), Jean-Simon Berthélemy's *Apollo and Sarpédon* of 1781 (Langres) or François Ménageot's *Learning Holding Back Time* of the same year (No. 126) illustrate trends somewhat divergent from the tradition of the 1770s. However, after the enormous success of David's royal commission in 1785, the *Oath of the Horatii,* the younger generation —Anne-Louis Girodet, Pierre-Narcisse Guérin, François-Xavier Fabre— and others could not escape his influence. By the 1790s, even Regnault and Vincent would feel the attraction of David's clarity and tangibility.

Berthélemy
Apollo and Sarpedon, Salon of 1781
Langres, Musée

David's revolutionary style was first felt in the work of his students who, impressed by his strong personality and the passionate heroism of his art, directly emulated him in their choice of subjects and composition. Indeed, his students were uniquely capable of following David's ideas, since he himself taught them the necessary and special technical devices required of the style. Thus, Davidianism in its most potent form was restricted to a group of unusually talented students who, in turn, were to influence a series of lesser artists, thereby completely altering the course of French art and modern art as well.

In the examination of the works of David's immediate pupils, we may then determine what he considered important in his teaching. It is clear that he stressed the lessons learned in Rome from Greek and Roman art, Raphael and the Baroque, emphasizing two major skills: superb, linear drawing of the nude figure and a profound understanding of linear perspective. His students came to prefer

David
Oath of the Horatii, 1784
Paris, Musée du Louvre

large-scale rectilinear compositions with life-size figures arranged in relief across the frontal plane. Compositions were simplified to include only the most essential elements; objects were defined as separate areas of color (often a primary, a half-tone or a hue closely related to a primary), each with its own outline and integrity. Historical research and accuracy were a central concern: students were taught that a single dramatic focus served as the unifying component, that intense feeling could draw together the work of art.

Among David's most talented pupils, the first to absorb these principles was Jean-Germain Drouais. In 1782, he had painted the *Return of the Prodigal Son* (Paris, Saint Roch), while strongly under the influence of Peyron. Late in 1784, he had accompanied David to Rome and worked at Palazzo Mancini, where he painted a series of academies, of which the finest example is a little-known canvas in La Fère, the *Wounded Gladiator* (1785).

J.-G. Drouais
Wounded Gladiator, 1785
La Fère, Musée

Under David's tutelage, Drouais completed in Rome his first "Davidian" painting: *Marius at Minturnae* (No. 52). Despite his humble origins and illiteracy, Gaius Marius became a Consul of Rome. Drouais' painting illustrates the extraordinary personal force and courage of this Roman general when confronted by a would-be assassin with drawn sword. He challenges him with the simple question, "Fellow, darest thou kill Gaius Marius?" Astonished by such audacity and taken aback by the force of the Consul's hawk-like face and piercing eyes, the terrified young soldier throws his cloak over his face and recoils in shock and fear. Drouais, in a brilliant invention, washed the face of the soldier in shadow to create a dramatic silhouetted profile. Two life-size combattants are bound together in an elaborate composition of interlocking diagonals and triangular forms, all in a closed space that seem to be a projection of our own. This painting, electrified by the opposition of obdurate courage with terrified perception, is one of the masterpieces to emerge from the immediate circle of David. Exhibited in Rome on 25 August 1786, this large composition can rightfully be called Drouais' *Horatii*. The premature death of Drouais in 1788 removed one of the finest talents of the period. His equal is not found until Ingres assumed a similar role more than a decade later.

Before his 20th year, Anne-Louis Girodet had established himself as one of David's finest and most original pupils, excepting Drouais. His first works include the copy of David's *Horatii*, now in the Toledo Museum of Art. Other early paintings, all identical in size and technique, the finest of these being the work which earned him the Prix de Rome, *Joseph Recognized by his Brothers* (Paris, École des Beaux-Arts), are closely related to David's *Death of Socrates* (No. 32). In the same year, Girodet painted a large altarpiece for a Capuchin convent in Paris, the *Deposition* (No. 78). This powerful and beautiful composition, thought to have been lost until the Girodet exhibition in 1967, is certainly second only to Drouais' *Marius*. Among the masterpieces produced by the Davidian school, its direct inspiration is David's *Hector and Andromache*, with Christ and the Virgin substituted for the antique figures. The stark, raking light and somber shadows are far removed from the delicate flickering shade of Peyron's semi-darkness and much closer to David's *Socrates*. The Christ figure recalls David's early academies. His body, limp in a temporary unconsciousness, will regain its heroic vitality with the forthcoming resurrection. The profound solemnity and emphasis on personal grief in this work derive from that side of David's art that stresses interior emotional response. Behind the hooded grief and shaded despair of the Virgin are the tears of Andromache and the supplication of Belisarius.

Comparison of this painting with Regnault's *Deposition* (No. 148) of the same year, painted for the Royal Chapel at Fontainebleau, illustrates how much Girodet had learned from David and to what extent his art presages romantic developments. While Girodet relied on Caravaggesque lighting and the austere silhouettes of the shrouded and bowed heads of antique processional reliefs, Regnault's carefully orchestrated groupings and pastel light recall Annibale Carracci and traditional academic pictorialism. The superb *Death of the Virgin* by Jean-Charles-Nicaise Perrin (No. 137) in the Chapel of the Grand Trianon, also from the Salon of 1789, depended even more on the Neo-Classicism of Vien and Peyron. The Virgin is shown stretched out on the *lit de mort* like an antique heroine whom the angel, a classical winged genius, covers with roses.

These three paintings are the last great religious compositions of the 18th century. Comparison with the Saint Louis series commissioned for the École Militaire Royale in the first years of the reign of Louis XVI illustrates how compelling was the hold of David's severe republicanism over his younger followers. By the mid-1780s, the pre-eminence of the Church and the ability of Christian themes to move the public had declined in favor of secular dramas presenting a new emotional sensibility. Until 1789, the King's patriotic interests generally encouraged the secularization of subject matter. After 1789, the process was carried on by the artists themselves and the Academy. The paintings by David, for example, do not follow a strict iconography prescribed by the Church, by traditional images, or even by a workshop style, introducing instead a different repertory of subjects.

The 1790s present an artistic scene more volatile than ever before. The cohesive character of David's art of the previous decade had given way to a dramatic series of experiments in which he applied his powerful style to the presentation of the startling events of his own social and political context. While the profound sense of this effort must be discussed in terms of the Republic that followed, the groundwork was laid during those last, significant years of the Ancien Régime, when French painting was dedicated to one principal theme: the human condition and the regeneration of society. While English painting of the period resembles a rocket exploding in several directions at once, in its unprecedented investigation of the physical, emotional and intellectual worlds, painting in France remains more concentrated. For this unparalleled exploration of intense feeling, we can thank David and those working around him.

Vien
Saint Louis and Marguerite de Provence, s.d. 1774
Versailles, Musée National
No. 193

J. Vernet
Construction of a Highway, s.d. 1774
Paris, Musée du Louvre
No. 189

J. Vernet
Fair of Beaucaire, s.d. 1774
Montpellier, Musée Fabre
No. 190

Lépicié
Interior of a Customhouse, s.d. 1775
Lugano, Thyssen-Bornemisza Collection
No. 121

Vincent
Belisarius, s.d. 1776
Montpellier, Musée Fabre
No. 199

Durameau
Continence of Bayard, Salon of 1777
Grenoble, Musée de Peinture et de Sculpture
No. 55

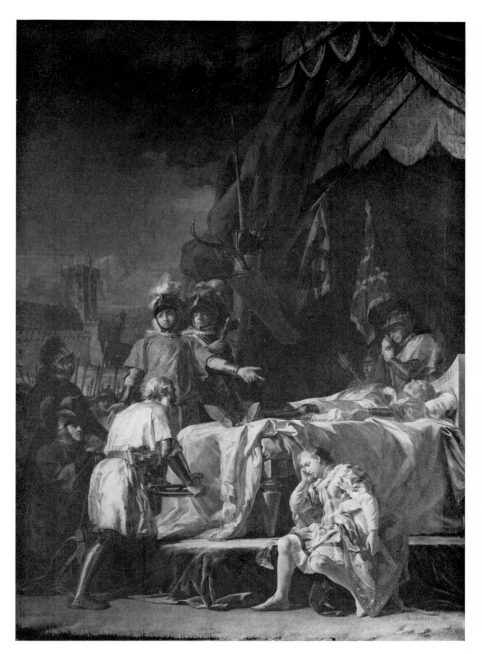

Brenet
Death of Du Guesclin, s.d. 1777
Versailles, Musée National
No. 15

Hallé
Cornelia, Mother of the Gracchi, Salon of 1779
Montpellier, Musée Fabre
No. 96

Gamelin
The Deluge, s.d. 1779
Carcassonne, Église Saint-Vincent
No. 63

David
Funeral of Patroclus, s.d. 1779
Dublin, National Gallery of Ireland
No. 27

54

Peyron
Belisarius, s.d. 1779
Toulouse, Musée des Augustins
No. 139

Peyron
Hagar and the Angel, s.d. 1779
Paris, Private Collection
No. 138

J.-H. Fragonard
The Lock, c. 1780
Paris, Musée du Louvre
No. 59

Greuze
Distributor of Rosaries, c. 1780
Montclair, N.J., Art Museum
No. 83

M. Gérard
The First Step, c. 1780
Cambridge, Mass., Fogg Art Museum
No. 71

Volaire
Eruption of Mount Vesuvius, c. 1780
Richmond, Virginia Museum of Fine Arts
No. 203

David
Saint Roch Interceding for the Plague-Stricken, s.d. 1780
Marseilles, Musée des Beaux-Arts
No. 28

David
Portrait of Count Potocki, s.d. 1780
Warsaw, National Museum
No. 29

Duplessis
Portrait of André Dupré de Billy (?), c. 1781
San Francisco, California Palace of the Legion of Honor
No. 54

J.-F.-L. Lagrenée
Pygmalion and Galatea, s.d. 1781
The Detroit Institute of Arts
No. 115

64

Ménageot
Learning Holding Back Time, Salon of 1781
Paris, École des Beaux-Arts
No. 126

David
Belisarius, s.d. 1781
Lille, Musée des Beaux-Arts
No. 30

P.-A. Wille
Double Reward, s.d. 1781
Blérancourt, Musée National du Château
No. 205

Greuze
Return of a Drunkard, c. 1782
The Portland Art Museum
No. 85

David
Hector and Andromache, s.d. 1783
Paris, École des Beaux-Arts
No. 31

Vigée-Lebrun
Portrait of Madame Grant, s.d. 1783
New York, The Metropolitan Museum of Art
No. 196

Vigée-Lebrun
Portrait of the Comte de Vaudreuil, 1784
Richmond, Virginia Museum of Fine Arts
No. 197

Greuze
A Widow and her Priest, c. 1780-85
Leningrad, State Hermitage Museum
No. 84

Spaendonck
Basket and Vase of Flowers, s.d. 1785
Fontainebleau, Château
No. 168

Greuze
Self-Portrait, c. 1785
Paris, Musée du Louvre
No. 86

Labille-Guiard
Portrait of Madame Labille-Guiard and her Pupils, s.d. 1785
New York, The Metropolitan Museum of Art
No. 112

Mosnier
Portrait of the Artist in his Studio, s.d. 1786
Leningrad, State Hermitage Museum
No. 135

Vestier
Portrait of Brenet, s.d. 1786
Versailles, Musée National
No. 192

Drouais
Marius at Minturnae, 1786
Paris, Musée du Louvre
No. 52

H. Robert
Project for the Arrangement of the Grand Gallery of the Louvre, c. 1786
Paris, Musée du Louvre
No. 157

Suvée
Death of Admiral de Coligny, s.d. 1787
Dijon, Musée des Beaux-Arts
No. 169

Berthélemy
Entry of the French into Paris, s.d. 1787
Versailles, Musée National
No. 2

David
Death of Socrates, s.d. 1787
New York, The Metropolitan Museum of Art
No. 32

P.-A. Wille
Death of the Duke of Brunswick, s.d. 1787
Moscow, State Pushkin Museum
No. 206

Bidauld
Roman Landscape, s.d. 1788
Basel, Kunstmuseum
No. 4

84

H. Robert
Demolition of the Houses on the Pont au Change, c. 1788
Paris, Musée Carnavalet
No. 156

J.-H. Fragonard
The Kiss, c. 1785-88
Leningrad, State Hermitage Museum
No. 60

David
Portrait of Lavoisier and his Wife, s.d. 1788
New York, The Rockfeller University
No. 33

Perrin
Death of the Virgin, s.d., 1788
Versailles, Grand Trianon, Chapelle
No. 137

Vien
Love Fleeing Slavery, s.d. 1789
Toulouse, Musée des Augustins
No. 194

Girodet
Deposition, s.d. 1789
Montesquieu-Volvestre (Haute-Garonne), Église
No. 78

Regnault
Deposition, s.d. 1789
Paris, Musée du Louvre
No. 148

Regnault
The Deluge, Salon of 1789
Paris, Musée du Louvre
No. 149

J. Vernet
Death of Virginie, s.d. 1789
Leningrad, State Hermitage Museum
No. 191

Houel
View of the Entrance to a Cave, 1789
Rouen, Musée des Beaux-Arts
No. 101

94

Moreau the Elder
Landscape, c. 1780-90
Nîmes, Musée des Beaux-Arts
No. 134

Vallayer-Coster
Still Life with Sea Shells, Salon of 1789
Paris, Baronne de Saint-Palais Collection
No. 180

J.-B. Huet
Spaniel Attacking a Turkey, s.d. 1789
Leningrad, State Hermitage Museum
No. 102

Boissieu
Children's Dance, c. 1789
Paris, Musée du Petit Palais
No. 10

Callet
Portrait of Louis XVI, Salon of 1789
Clermont-Ferrand, Musée Bargoin
No. 17

Painting During the Revolution
1789-1799

Antoine Schnapper

Since the publication in 1912 of Jean Locquin's great book, *La peinture d'histoire en France de 1747 à 1785,* it is generally agreed that the Revolution did not seriously affect the development of French painting, which since mid-century had progressively begun to show all the characteristics of what is now called Neo-Classicism. The logical conclusion of this development, the great paintings of David—from his *Belisarius* (No. 30) to his *Brutus* (Louvre)—appeared between 1781 and 1789. Nevertheless, an upheaval like the Revolution could not fail to have repercussions on the intellectual life and daily existence of artists. The pictures they painted are relatively little-known—although it is to be hoped that this exhibition may stimulate further studies. In the meantime, we must examine whether the pictures presented here faithfully reflect the state of painting during the active stage of the Revolution, between the taking of the Bastille and the beginning of the Napoleonic era.

Even if the Revolution did not fundamentally change painting styles, it unleashed an acute crisis in the art world by highlighting the problem of how this world should be organized, how artists should be trained and what should be their material circumstances. For a century and a half, French artistic life had centered around the Royal Academy (Académie Royale de Peinture et de Sculpture). This institution had been founded to free artists from the cumbersome regulations of the medieval guilds, to insure them higher intellectual and social status and to permit beginners to learn their trade under reasonable conditions. From the beginning, it preserved the great tradition, always emphasized by its defenders, of admitting an unlimited number of members. True, with an average of 80 to 100 painters, engravers and sculptors as full members and 30 or so associates *(agréés),* it could not escape being regarded as an art aristocracy: this was indeed what its protector, the Director General of

Royal Buildings (Surintendant Général des Bâtiments du Roi) intended it to be, guarding closely the Academy's prestige.

This aristocratic, or rather meritocratic, body was itself organized on rigid hierarchical lines, in the well-known French tradition. There were a *directeur, recteurs, adjoints à recteur, professeurs, adjoints à professeurs, conseillers* (the officers of the Academy); then came the ordinary academicians, and lastly at the bottom of the scale the *agréés,* associate members who had not yet submitted an acceptable *morceau de réception,* or qualifying work. At the beginning of 1789, there were 52 officers (excluding the secretary, Antoine Renou, but including 16 honorary and non-practicing patrons) and 63 academicians.

Membership in the Academy was not only a matter of prestige; more importantly, its members enjoyed the monopoly of royal commissions and free access to the Salon. This official exhibition, which had been held regularly every two years since the 1740s, was an unparalleled way for an artist to become known and to find patrons. It was attended by thousands of people and thousands of catalogs were sold; it stimulated a flood of critical articles, brochures and pamphlets, and the resultant publicity, although sometimes displeasing to sensitive ears, was certainly preferable to silence for an artist's career. Such privileges would have sufficed to explain a revolt of non-academicians against the Academy, but further reasons must be sought to explain the internal dissensions that arose. One cause was that access to the Salon was really free only for the officers. A selection committee, chosen from among the officers, was set up in 1748; it examined the pictures submitted and took care that those accepted formed a *"beau choix."* It could reject at will in 1773, and did so particularly on moral criteria. We know from a letter written by the King's First Painter, Jean-Baptiste-Marie Pierre, that officers escaped this censure, which inevitably caused discontent among the academicians and *agréés.* Another privilege of the officers, equally irritating to the other members, was their sole right to elect new members.

The need for more easily accessible exhibitions, in which young artists or those who had failed admission to the Academy could show their works, had already been voiced on several occasions and was to become more pressing under the Revolution. Although D'Angiviller succeeded, soon after becoming Director General of Royal Buildings, in destroying the old Academy of Saint Luke, the former painters' guild which had organized exhibitions up to that time, and had also prohibited the Colisée exhibitions, it was clear from the number of new ventures like the Salon de la Jeunesse and the Salon de la Correspondance that a real need existed. In 1789, just before the outbreak of the Revolution, the astute art dealer

Lebrun created a new Salon for young artists, and offered them the use of his premises on the Rue de Cléry. In 1777, the *Journal de Paris* published "a plan for an establishment to provide young artists with facilities for exhibiting their works to the public." D'Angiviller's sharp reaction showed that there were supporters for the idea within the Academy itself: "The order that I am seeking to restore in this Academy, and the severity that I preach and demand in respect of admittance standards, is distressing for certain very eminent artists who were once too much the master and now are less so. They would like to attract the young people to themselves."

"Order... and severity." D'Angiviller, to whom French art owes so much, was not without responsibility for the violence of the crisis, if not the crisis itself, that between 1790 and 1793 split artistic circles. His attempt to restore the prestige and privileges of the Academies was made to support the cause of the *grand genre,* which had always been difficult for the public to accept. As a royal declaration of 15 March 1777 recalled, it was from the King that academicians received both protection and royal commissions *(travaux d'encouragement).* There is ample evidence of the force of D'Angiviller's "reactionary" policy—if not from the *Procès-verbaux de l'Académie (Records of the Academy),* which are sometimes too discreet, at least from the memoirs of the imperturbable Pierre-Georges Wille. The Academy frequently rejected applications for associate membership, and often even the submissions of approved associates. Apart from these rejections voted in the official sessions, there were in fact others of which we know nothing, since prospective candidates came for preliminary interviews before declaring themselves. In the years immediately preceding the Revolution, the portraitist Joseph Ducreux had his application refused three times. In 1787, Jacques Bertault was rejected, and in 1788 so were the landscape artists Pierre-Alexandre Pau de Saint-Martin and Louis-Gabriel Moreau the Elder. Without going into detail, Wille mentions several withdrawn applications and refusals in July 1789. In August, Louis-Richard Trinquesse, who had already been refused admission twice, withdrew his third application. Several admissions were granted justly despite a large minority of negative votes, for example, Marie-Marc-Antoine Bilcoq in 1785 and Jean-Jacques Forty in 1788.

As for qualification for full membership, Jean-Jacques-François Lebarbier had to apply twice in 1785, as did Nicolas-André Monsiau in 1789. This was more than simply aggravating; it was a serious matter, since, as Wille relates, according to the rules imposed by D'Angiviller, "an associate member whose work submitted for qualification is refused shall be struck out and his associate membership shall be declared null and void." In fact, this rule was so harsh that it could hardly ever be applied. On 28 August 1789,

Lebarbier
Jupiter on Mount Ida, 1785
Paris, Musée du Louvre

the Academy voted to suspend it, to the immediate benefit of Charles Echard and the sculptor Louis-Pierre Deseine.

But this did not stop the crisis. It erupted in September with demands made by pupils concerning honors they wished to confer posthumously on their fellow-student, Jean-Germain Drouais. At the beginning of October, there was an open dispute between the academic authorities, represented by the director Vien and the secretary Renou and a faction of "young Turks" led by David and Jean-Bernard Restout, whose initial demand was for students' pictures to be exhibited in the Salon. This is not the place to describe the lengthy quarrels that were to rend the Academy right up to its abolition in 1793, and which produced a profusion of letters, memoranda, petitions, addresses and reports, many of which were tabled at the general meetings of the National Assemblies. The principal theme of the demands was, simply, equality, which to the moderates meant equality among all Academy members; to the radicals it meant among all artists. The result was a de facto split within the Academy, which led to the creation of the Commune des Arts qui ont le dessin pour base (Commune of the Arts Based on Drawing), whose first meeting on 27 September 1790 was attended by 300 artists. This group's immediate demands for the destruction of the Academy were to be answered by the Constitution of 1791 which, by outlawing the Academy along with other privileged bodies, provided the necessary ammunition for its eventual abolition.

Was the Academy of 1789 really the assembly of senile half-wits characterized by David when he described a typical member as an "old academician who had gone through all the innumerable dignities of the Academy, and who had by his unfailing and lethargic attendance worn out all the seats, from the stool to the great arm-chair"? The officers who exhibited at the Salon of 1789 were Vien, the two Lagrenées, Brenet, Durameau, Suvée, Vincent, Joseph Vernet, Roslin, Duplessis, Hubert Robert and Gérard van Spaendonck. The academicians included Roland de la Porte, Mme Vallayer-Coster, the architect De Wailly, Jollain (who, rightly or wrongly, was to become during the Revolution a symbol of academic mediocrity), Callet, Berthélemy, Hue, Sauvage, Mme Vigée-Lebrun, Mme Labille-Guiard, David, Regnault, Taillasson, César Van Loo, Lebarbier, Vestier, Peyron, L'Espinasse, Perrin, Valenciennes, Girout, Mosnier, Dumont, Legillon, Cornélius van Spaendonck and Bilcoq. The associate members were Hall, Houel, Demarne, Nivard, Taunay, Lemonnier, Monsiau, Lavallée-Poussin and La Fontaine. The visitor to the present exhibition can form his own opinion of their achievement. The quality of academic instruction and standards of judgment seem to have been satisfactory, if we examine the results of the Prix de Rome for the same year. The first prize went to Anne-Louis Girodet, second first prize to Charles Meynier and second prizes to François Gérard and Charles Thévenin.

Another way of looking at this is to compare the two catalogs for the Salon of 1791: one reserved for academicians and associate members, the other open to all. There are very few names rejected by the Academy that subsequent generations have remembered. Who were the "underground" stars of the period who had at last been accorded the right to public expression—both at the Salon and at the meetings of the Société Populaire des Arts? Parseval, Petit-Coupray, Cazin, Lefebvre (not to be confused with Robert Lefèvre), Desoria, Potain, Taurel, Bazin, Mouchet, P.J. Bocquet, Chéry (who, fired with Revolutionary zeal, became a chief of police but returned to portraiture after 1815). It hardly seems appropriate to add to this modest array of talent the names of Armand Caraffe, who was born in 1762, or of François-Xavier Fabre, born in 1766. Only in still life (Antoine Berjon) and in landscape (Jean-Joseph-Xavier Bidauld, who was in fact in Italy from 1785 to 1791, Georges Michel and Louis-Gabriel Moreau the Elder) do we find painters of greater distinction. In any case, the Academy had just made a gesture in favor of this type of painting, which was not its own, by granting associate membership to Charles-François Nivard, Charles Echard and the Flemish painters Jean-François Legillon and Pierre-Joseph La Fontaine.

To question the existence of the Academy naturally implied a total re-examination of the problems involved in training artists and recognizing talent, with the inevitable question of how state commissions should be allocated. Teaching in the Academy was based not on a body of doctrine, but on general principles that had been scrutinized by theoreticians for more than two centuries. The emphasis was on drawing, first from classical sculpture and later from life. From quarterly competitions *(petits prix)*, successful pupils advanced to painting studies and could compete for the principal award, the Prix de Rome. Since its foundation, the chief advantage provided by the Academy had always been the free availability of live models; painting instruction proper was obtained from a master, who was generally an academician In the years just preceding the Revolution, the sought-after masters were Joseph-Marie Vien, Jacques-Louis David and François-André Vincent.

David never ceased his virulent campaign against the academic teaching system. What was the cause of his implacable hatred? The simplest explanation, which must not be overlooked, however, is the rancor he felt for an institution that had treated him harshly. We know that David competed three times unsuccessfully for the Prix de Rome before finally winning it in 1774. His unfinished memoirs, written after 1808, were still marked by this bitterness:

"Early in my life, I suffered from being forced to learn how unjust men can be." According to David, who even before the Revolution hardly ever attended the sessions of the Academy, the basis for the discrimination against him, was not complicated: it centered around the obvious jealousy of mediocre talents for the rising star of genius. But the acrimony evident in David's report to the Convention of 8 August 1793, in which he called for the abolition of the Academies, is not self-explanatory. His artistic career was marked by a profound change of style, which appears today all the more pronounced because many of his early pictures, unlike those of the majority of great artists, are preserved. One must admit that the canvases David submitted for the Prix de Rome are of little merit. He became himself in Rome between 1778 and 1780, and it was entirely the result of his own efforts and not all due to his training. He tells us himself that his real master in Rome was Raphael, whose work drew him to studies of classical antiquity—thus, his strong conviction that young artists were wasting their time at the Academy. And yet the criticisms contained in his report are not sound; the only one which is not anecdotal in nature concerns his objection to the multiplicity of teachers, each of whom taught classes one month out of the year.

David's fellow members of the Commune des Arts agreed with him on the disadvantages of the multiple teaching system in the *Mémoire et plan relatifs à l'organisation d'une École nationale des Beaux-Arts,* published in 1791. The pupil was here compared to a traveler seeking his way: "and since everyone he asks points in a different direction, he walks aimlessly, and usually gets lost." But they were just as wary of instruction by a single master, who imparts to his pupils "his opinion as principles, his works as models, and his method as technique." This explains the importance David and his colleagues attached to the idea of a museum, in which young artists could study not only antiquity but also great painters of various schools: "the pictures would be grouped in such a way that the different schools could be compared, and their different eras and progress could be appreciated."

Within the Academy itself, efforts were being made to revise and even completely redraft its statutes. Most of the officers, on the one hand, and the academicians and associate members, on the other—with landscape and genre painters advancing their own special claims—remained attached to the privileges they enjoyed. The plan published (also in 1791) by the second faction, which called itself "the majority" of the Academy, while proclaiming the principle of equality among all members of the "central" Academy, proposed that they alone should have access to the Salon. As Quatremère de Quincy responded in his *Suite aux considérations sur les arts du dessin en France:* "The authors have been guided by a single viewpoint and moved by a single purpose, which is to achieve participation for all in the elite that was formerly confined solely to the professors."

Such an attitude, despite the eloquence of the Academy's advocates, Renou and Deseine, could only contribute to its momentary downfall. In the meantime, there was a harvest of new proposals. We have already mentioned those of the two factions within the Academy and that of the Commune des Arts. "The first party wishes to retain its authority, the second wants a share in it, and the third wishes to destroy it," wrote Quatremère de Quincy in presenting his own plan. He had little trouble exposing the vagueness of the proposal of the Commune des Arts, which only proclaimed in general terms the need for a free national school. He also pointed out that the principal drawback of the old Academy was that it had tried to combine two quite different capabilities: it functioned both as an honorary body, rewarding merit and indulging egos, and as an active training institution for young artists. The former role, he felt, should be abandoned, the latter retained and entrusted to a restricted group of professors, chosen from a body of academicians three times larger. In dealing with teaching methods, he suggested that more models be made available and that a gallery of antique statuary be formed. He proposed that *petits prix* be abolished and the Prix de Rome maintained. Finally, he devoted a chapter to the principal problem of the moment: that of prizes and incentives.

To choose its elite, France replaced the system of privilege by that of competition which, when properly used, still remains the fairest, or at any rate the least unfair, method of rewarding merit with distinction. In the art world, as elsewhere, everyone was concerned with this issue. The plan of the Commune des Arts, otherwise so vague, proposed a system that was extraordinarily slow and complicated: it stipulated that the artists would elect judges, who would make recommendations which the artists would then have to approve unanimously. Quatremère de Quincy was less naïve; he suggested that the judges themselves be excluded from competition and that they should take into account public opinion before arriving at any decisions, which could not be expected to satisfy everyone.

The problem was most serious and urgent, since the traditional sources of patronage had collapsed and the very livelihood of artists, especially of history painters, was at stake. The shocks that society had suffered were profoundly changing the patterns of artistic life. In a letter published in the *Journal Général de France* of 21 December 1791 about that year's Salon, an anonymous artist expressed the general anxiety, stating that art needed powerful protectors. He questioned whether royal authority, now so weakened, would have the incentive and means to encourage people of talent, at a time when church commissions were disappearing along with the traditional patronage of the rich nobility, wealthy lawyers and financial magnates.

There were various new private ventures; one, a Société des Amis des Arts founded as a corporation by the architect Charles de Wailly, organized exhibitions, commissioned engravings and bought pictures (including Jean-Joseph Taillasson's *Despair of Hercules,* Salon of 1795) and drawings, in particular. According to Bruun-Neergard in 1801, the Society had spent in ten years 180,000 francs for paintings and drawings and 40,000 francs for engravings. Above all, the State attempted to fulfill its traditional function: the Assemblies voted funds to subsidize state commissions *(travaux d'encouragement),* which were restricted to artists who had become known through the Salons. This resulted in the selection by the artists of a jury from the exhibitors in the Salon of 1791, including both members and non-members of the Academy who, disregarding the wishes of Quatremère de Quincy, voted themselves a considerable part of the awards. Among the state commissions thus distributed, we find works by Taillasson *(Raising to Life of Pauline, Wife of Seneca,* Salon of 1793, Blaye), by Vincent *(William Tell Overturning Gesler's Boat,* Salon of 1795, Toulouse), Hue *(View of Lorient,* Salon of 1793, Louvre), Berthault *(The Tenth of April,* Salon of 1793, Versailles), Belle the Younger *(Anaxagores and Pericles,* Salon of 1793) and Lefebvre *(Death of Seneca,* Salon of 1793). The system was continued for subsequent Salons but replaced in 1801 by state awards: purchases of pictures, medals and the Legion of Honor. Among the artists thus "encouraged" during the Revolution were Peyron, Prud'hon, Taillasson once again (for his *Hero and Leander*, No. 172), Lagrenée, Garnier, Lethière, Taunay and Bidault.

Some of the initiatives taken by the Convention were thwarted by the volatile political situation. Such was the case of the decree of 6 Floréal, Year II, which called upon painters to immortalize the glorious moments of the Revolution and sculptors to design monuments in honor of the Republic; the 9 Thermidor and the fall of Robespierre occurred just before the exhibition of these works was scheduled to open. Another competition, instituted in October 1793, was hardly more successful. For the painters the fixed subject was "Brutus being brought back to Rome after his death in battle," and that for the sculptors was "the schoolmaster of Falerii." This restructured Prix de Rome proved disappointing: in painting only a second prize was awarded (to Fulchran-Jean Harriet), and no prize was awarded to the sculptors, who were accused of lacking patriotism or of having produced a figure resembling a flagellated Christ.

Life became more and more difficult for painters, history painters in particular. We know that Prud'hon, for example, survived by drawing ornamental illustrations for publishers. But times had already changed. The year 1790 had seen the formation of the Commune des Arts; 1793, the abolition of the Academy; and 1795, the creation of the Institute, with David among the initial 48 government-appointed members. Rarely has the irony of history been so immediately apparent. This is largely due to the violent acceleration of events which transpired during revolutionary times. In 1791, the world was flooded with the light of reason and equality. "The system of the arts must change just like the political system.... There will be no more style nor academic manner; these will be replaced by the true and the natural" (Explanation by numerical order... in coll. Deloynes, XVII, p. 121, Salon of 1791). In 1793, the preface to the Salon catalog proclaimed that "artists are free by definition; the essence of genius is independence." But at that very moment, it became necessary to abolish the Commune des Arts because it was beginning to resemble the former Academy. The mysterious forces of reality were busy restoring a hierarchical order. It is ironic that David's Institute was less like the old Academy of Painting than the Académie Française itself, the institution he had ridiculed in 1793 as "40 immortals issued from the inexhaustible spring of Hypocrene that Richelieu had founded, whose children can never increase and, above all, never decrease in number."

* *
*

An interesting article by Mme Caubisens-Lasfargues (*Information d'Histoire de l'Art*, 1960) on the Salons during the Revolution has pointed out that although reality and utopia seemed to coincide at all levels at this moment, they were actually separated by an immense gap. A paradox of the Revolution is that while all the official voices (including the critics) were extolling the virtues of large-scale historical painting drawn from antiquity in order to influence public morality, the artists were in fact painting what they could sell. This finally revealed the existence of a situation which the organization of pre-Revolutionary artistic life had heretofore hidden. At a time when it should have been harvesting the fruit of 40 years of effort on the part of the monarchical administration, history painting was in fact being drowned in a flood of genre pictures, a mode which until then had been virtually repressed by the regulations of the Academy and the Salons. From the first signs of unrest in the Academy, we find the genre painters claiming a more significant position: they would actually obtain one-third of the sums distributed as official commissions after the Salon of 1791 !

From 1791 on, access to the Salon was unrestricted. In general, this doubled or tripled the number of exhibitors and works shown. Significantly, history paintings did not show this increase. In 1789, there were only 17 paintings with classical subjects out of a total 206; in 1795, there were 16 out of 535. According to the calculations of Mme Caubisens-Lasfargues, of 3,078 Salon entries between 1789 and 1799, only 147 bore subjects taken from classical antiquity. François Benoît came to similar conclusions in 1897: he estimated that subjects from ancient history represented 9 per cent of the pictures shown in the Salons during the period 1775-89 and less than 4 per cent for the subsequent years up to 1808. State patronage, which for the most part had been concentrated on large-scale historical works, was limited by political uncertainties, and the middle class did not seem much interested in historical subjects, or even contemporary ones. In any case, for this kind of painting, the pace of events was too rapid. The impetus of painting between 1789 and 1799 was more than ever toward portraiture, landscape and genre.

David
Brutus, Salon of 1789
Paris, Musée du Louvre

For portraits, precise figures are hard to establish, since very frequently the catalog entries refer to multiple groupings; this was especially true of miniatures, which were exhibited together several to a frame. In 1794, the *Journal de Paris* estimated that there were 200 portraits in that year's Salon, although there were only 135 portraits listed in the catalog. Benoît puts the proportion of portraits at 25 per cent in the Salons from 1775 to 1789 and at 40 per cent for the periods of the Revolution and Empire. During the Revolution alone, the figure seems to have dropped to around 25-30 per cent. It should not be forgotten that David himself, between *Brutus* and the *Sabines,* painted mostly portraits. Baron Gérard, despite the success of his *Belisarius* in the Salon of 1795 and of his *Cupid and Psyche* in the Salon of 1797 (Louvre), did not find buyers for these pictures and was forced to turn to portraiture. The number of landscapes exhibited in the Salons was comparable (about 200 in the Salon of 1793). On the whole, portraits and landscapes account-ed for more than half the paintings on exhibition. Whereas just before the Revolution genre scenes were relatively few in number, they now became more numerous than ever, reaching a peak in the Salon of 1796.

Critics, nevertheless, remained faithful to the established hierarchy of subject matter. They deplored the popularity of portraits and landscapes and reserved most of their comments for the *grand genre,* usually beginning their comments with a tribute to the illustrious veteran, Joseph-Marie Vien, who had done so much to bring the French school of painting back to the grand manner. In point of fact, he rarely exhibited in the Salon and had not succeeded in chang-ing his style. *Love Fleeing Slavery* (No. 194), shown in the Salon of

Gérard
Cupid and Psyche, Salon of 1797-98
Paris, Musée du Louvre

David
Study for the Oath of the Tennis Court, c. 1791
Versailles, Musée National

David
Madame Trudaine, c. 1792
Paris, Musée du Louvre

David
Barra, 1794
Avignon, Musée Calvet

David
Death of Marat, 1793
Brussels, Musées Royaux des
Beaux-Arts de Belgique

1789, is little more than a colorful reworking of earlier compositions. In drawing, however, he developed a new approach, with minutely detailed compositions in pen and ink that give a view of antiquity at once graceful and cool. The most famous painters were born after 1740 and had become known just before the Revolution: Berthélemy, Suvée, Vincent, Regnault and, finally, David, whose fame eclipsed them all.

The amount of David's work surviving from Revolutionary days has been somewhat diminished by politics and misfortune. His great undertaking of 1791, the *Oath of the Tennis Court,* which was to have given contemporary history the prestige of antiquity, was still-born. This immense canvas, now at Versailles, remains largely uncovered; only a few heads were ever completed. His *Death of Le Pelletier de Saint-Fargeau* (1793) has unfortunately disappeared. An unforgettable composition, dominated by the strong vertical of the sword, it is now known only from drawn copies and a fragment of an engraving. The swift pace of Revolutionary events also explains why many canvases were unfinished; but these including not only the portraits of the Marquise de Pastoret (No. 34) and Mme Trudaine (c. 1791; Louvre), but also the extraordinary *Joseph Barra* (1794; Avignon), who lies like an ambiguous Greek hero in a silvery net of brushstrokes—become all the more attractive in this state. The archetypal painting of the Revolutionary martyr, however, which we were unfortunately not able to borrow for this exhibition, remains David's *Death of Marat* of 1793 (Brussels, Musées Royaux des Beaux-Arts). Using the device of the dedication, the painter conducts a solemn dialogue with the Revolutionary leader, who lies removed from time as he is from the tribulations of the flesh, and whose virtues of simplicity and commitment to the public cause correspond mysteriously to David's qualities as a painter. The wooden chest is as much a symbol of the painter's total commitment to reality, interpreted objectively and without excessive detail or adornment, as it is of Marat's devotion. And the bare background of the picture, which David used extensively in portraiture, here takes on a new spiritual meaning.

With the end of the Reign of Terror and the fall of Robespierre, David found himself in prison with time on his hands. While he was interned in the Luxembourg, he made a first sketch for the *Sabines ;* it would not be completed until 1799, by which time he was already thinking of a pendant, the *Leonidas at Thermopylae* (1814; Louvre). The *Sabines* is a solemn homage to antiquity; the picture shows Hersilia, bathed in an orange and blue light, separating the warring brothers, whose naked bodies seem to form an immense and elegant bas-relief. In this masterpiece, David achieved a perfect harmony between the pictorial qualities and the intellectual ambitions of his style, a balance missing in the overly heroic *Leonidas*.

David's brillance shines like a beacon over the whole of this period. But one of the aims of this exhibition is to remind us that he was not alone. Among the painters whose rehabilitation is long overdue is Jean-François Peyron, for many years considered David's equal; we would be mistaken to think of him, because of the similarity of their subject matter only, as a failed David. He is, in fact, quite a different kind of artist. His imagination was not fertile; he meditated at length over his few compositions, frequently revising them, carefully building up a smooth, brilliant surface of intense, deep colors. His admirable technique, in fact, links him to a distinctly different artistic current of the period, of which we shall have more to say later.

Portraiture engaged a very large number of artists, both specialists and others. The greatest history painters did not disdain this source of income. David, for example, was paid 7,000 *livres* by the Lavoisiers in 1788 for their portrait (No. 33), more than the King paid for a major history painting. Vincent also painted more and more portraits toward the end of his career. In the Salon of 1795, he showed four portraits and only one history painting, admittedly an enormous canvas (*William Tell Overturning Gesler's Boat,* Toulouse).

The most famous portraitists just before the Revolution were women. The artistocratic leanings of Mme Vigée-Lebrun forced her to emigrate, like the painters Henri-Pierre Danloux and Joseph Boze, and she continued to enjoy brilliant success in all the courts

David
The Sabines, 1799
Paris, Musée du Louvre

Vestier
Portrait of Latude, Salon of 1789
Paris, Musée Carnavalet

of Europe, including Russia. Mme Labille-Guiard, on the other hand, had no trouble adapting from the princes of the Court to the personalities of the new epoch. The series of pastel portraits of deputies she showed at the Salon of 1791 ranged, in alphabetical order, from Barnave to Robespierre and Talleyrand. Pastels like these often served as studies for more important pictures; such was the case with her *Portrait of Robespierre* (No. 113) and that of *Mirabeau* by Boze (No. 13). At the same time, Antoine Vestier was quietly pursuing a fertile career, objectively recording the changing signs of the times. The Bastille is present in the background of his *Portrait of Latude* (Paris, Musée Carnavalet), as a prison from which people escaped. The uniform of the veteran Thourel (Tours) was meant to symbolize the wars from which soldiers returned laden with honors and military virtue. The typically rococo technique of pastel portraiture had not lost its appeal. The pastellist Ducreux had long been kept out of the Academy but became a most fashionable painter. In the Salon of 1793, his entries included both portraits of obscure, bourgeois citizens and famous Jacobins (e.g. Couthon and Robespierre). In 1795, he exhibited a portrait of *Citoyenne Beauharnais,* together with those of a half-dozen political and artistic celebrities, including a self-portrait; at the same time, his daughter began a painting career, also in portraiture. In 1796, he exhibited a portrait whose title is worth mentioning: *Boissy d' Anglas Presiding over the Convention of the First Prairial. With one hand, he thrusts aside with horror the head of the Deputy Ferraud, which is being proffered to him on the end of a pike, while he restores calm to the Assembly with the other.* In the catalogs of the Salons, we read a host of obscure names: Marie Bouliar (a pupil of Duplessis), P. Davesne, Henri J. François, Louis Landry, François-Marie Neveux. Some were no doubt from the circle of David, which provided names that have not been completely forgotten: Mme Marie Guilhelmine Benoist, and especially Jean-Louis Laneuville, whose beautiful *Portrait of Barère de Vieuzac* (voting the death of the King), long attributed to David, is included here (No. 117). Some names have only been remembered by chance: one is Courteille, whose extensive travels led him to Russia, where many of his mediocre, signed and dated portraits have been preserved.

The 19th century was the century of landscape. Its popularity began with the Revolution and marked the decline of the hierarchy of styles. This development was reluctantly acknowledged by the critics. "We must concede that landscape has reached the highest level it has ever achieved in our school, since Claude Lorrain, Poussin, La Hyre, Gaspard Dughet, and their contemporaries," wrote the critic of the *Petites Affiches* during the Salon of 1793. And yet, the tradition of historical landscape, reworked in the studio, stood firm against the onslaught of landscape painted from nature and assumed even new strength, as the paintings of Pierre-Henri de Valenciennes attest. Working from beautiful studies painted directly from life, he built up firm architectural compositions in the manner of Poussin for the Salons. Fortunately, works of an intermediate stage that successfully combine the artist's occasionally contradictory qualities still exist (No. 179).

The Academy itself had been besieged, even before the Revolution, by other landscape artists, some of them less decorous. It rejected Moreau the Elder, whose canvases must have seemed too small, but it accepted César Van Loo, a painter whose efforts at realism, it must be admitted, soon become stereotyped (his snow landscapes, for example, despite their high quality). The Academy granted associate membership to Taunay and Demarne, who revived in France the scarcely academic tradition of the *Bamboccianti* and accepted painters now forgotten, like the 18th-century Flemish artists, Légillon (who filled his tiny landscapes with animals) and the prolific Pierre-Joseph La Fontaine. The latter, a painter from Courtrai, specialized in church interiors, often nocturnal views, in which the figures were occasionally painted by Demarne or Taunay. Perhaps the success of these little landscapes, typically northern in style, foreshadowed the popularity of Granet.

The Salons during the Revolution brought to light a number of other landscape artists who, with the exception of Alexandre-Hyacinthe Dunouy, Jean-Joseph-Xavier Bidault and one or two others, remain more or less unknown. Not many people today are familiar with the works of René-Louis Chancourtois or Pierre-Jean Boquet, to cite only two names that recur frequently. Although Charles-François Nivard, an associate member of the Academy, seems to have painted historical landscapes (to judge from the size and subjects of the canvases he exhibited), many others worked directly from nature and appear to have followed the advice given by Chateaubriand in his famous *Lettre sur l'art du dessin dans les paysages,* written in 1795 but not published until 1828. Many artists took the trouble to identify the site represented; thus, Pierre-Marie Gault felt it useful to place his Gauls at the foot of the Puy de Dôme. Others were less precise: see especially the views of Italy by Bidault, Florent-Fidèle-Constant Bourgeois and Pierre-Joseph Petit; of Switzerland by Alexandre Duperreux, Jean-Joseph Schmid and Georges Michel; of Normandy by Demarne, Pau de Saint-Martin and François Cotibert; of Savoy by Dunouy; or of the countryside around Paris. Petit, Duval and Pau de Saint-Martin followed the odd example of Bruandet and penetrated the remote and lonely expanses of the forest of Fontainebleau. In a large volume addressed to landscape artists published in 1800, Valenciennes strongly advised

Valenciennes
Roman Landscape, c. 1786
Paris, Musée du Louvre

a trip to the Pyrenees: "You should go especially to these mountains to study Nature and paint her sublime movements."

Genre painting could become portraiture as easily as landscape. In the Salon of 1795, Martin Drolling showed a "portrait of a woman with her child at the window of a prison, pointing to another window where she supposed the child's father to be"; also listed by the artist are two other pictures, "one showing a young woman freeing a captured bird, while a little boy watches it fly away; and the other, a young woman seated at a casement, playing a guitar, alongside a little boy holding a bouquet of roses." While Greuze and Wille had been forgotten by then, sentimental subjects remained fashionable. Both Drolling and Boilly were also landscapists, as were Demarne, Taunay and Jacques-François Swebach, names that contemporary critics favored and posterity has remembered.

Whatever the subject they attempted, painters like Boilly or Taunay earn our admiration for their delicate and elegant sense of detail. In all the painting of the Revolutionary period, the pendulum swings between two contradictory trends. On the one hand, the great history painters dreamed of returning to classical simplicity, rejecting the tinsel charms of beautiful color and masterful technique, preferring strong opposition of light and shade, emphasizing the pure intellectual beauty of line (the impetus toward the *tabula rasa* which has been so well analyzed by Robert Rosenblum, 1967). On the other hand, in still life, genre painting, landscape and even some history painting, we have the rich colors and porcelain-like finish that made Boilly so famous. Even a "primitive" and fanatical Jacobin like Caraffe was seduced by brilliant color, which he sometimes set against a black background. The same trend appears in the little highly-polished wood panels, so popular at the time, done not only by genre painters like Taunay, but also by others as "modern" as Peyron or Charles Landon, and later on by the *troubadours*.

This meticulous technique is clearly northern in origin. We know how fond French collectors in the second half of the 18th century were of Flemish and Dutch painting: people enthused over the elegant little pictures of such artists as Frans van Mieris, Gerard Dou, and Adrian van der Werff (whose works in particular fetched astronomical prices in the great sales at the end of the century). Just as sought after were the little landscapes in the Italian style by Bartholomeus Breenbergh and Cornelis van Poelenburg, which had a strong influence on Taunay. In the realm of history painting, the northern influence was combined with that of Louis Lagrenée, who had made his reputation with tiny, exquisitely painted pictures, often on copper. While the stark, bare style suited large surfaces and grand classical subjects, minor subjects and small scale invited meticulous finish and brilliant color—"jewels to feast the eye on."

The taste for the *beau métier* seemed to spread contagiously; it even attracted the comments of critics at the Salon of 1795: "It seems that today the taste for high finish or polish in painted works is not confined to *tableaux de cabinet,* to which, as we have remarked, it seems more suited. History painting itself is acquiring it and the smaller pictures of painters who normally exercise this discipline seem to be inspired rather by the works of Layresse or of Monsieur Van der Werff than by those of Albani, Paul Veronese or even of Poussin and Lebrun" (coll. Deloynes, XVIII, pp. 472-473). In 1801, Bruun-Neergard was excessive in his praise of a little picture by Duvivier, *The Sorrow of Andromache,* which had preoccupied the painter for seven years and in which "everything is as highly finished as in the most beautiful of Van der Werff's pictures"; such a result was worth the incredible sum of 7,000 francs to the collector who purchased it.

As early as the Salon of 1795, the critic Polyscope (Amaury Duval) raised the criticism later aimed at the Davidians by the Romantics and by Stendhal in particular after the Salon of 1824. Polyscope objected to the exclusive choice of classical subjects on the ground that they led to "dry, cold pictures," and that the affectations of French painting at the time of Boucher were simply being replaced by a second, nobler but equally pernicious artifice. He urged that nature, and nature alone, be imitated.

The blossoming of the *style troubadour* under the Empire derived to some extent from a systematic application of the *beau métier* and small scale to history painting, pictorially speaking. While poles apart from the Primitifs, who followed Maurice Quai, this movement nevertheless began among the pupils of David, who were perhaps more in tune with the ideas of their time. They made a very conscious effort, as we learn from the memoirs of Granet and even more, those of Fleury Richard, to combine "historical interest" and "ideal beauty" with a renewed feeling for color, based on studies of Dutch painting. Granet followed much the same current, although with less subtlety, in his efforts to express the poetry of ruins and cloisters and to contrast the fragility of man with the grandiose and picturesque permanence of architecture.

For the traditional classification by "genres," which was still clearly made during the Revolutionary period, we may now substitute a simpler one, based on pictorial technique, in which we may associate those specialists in landscape, still life, genre and history who valued more highly the example of early Dutch art than that of David and antiquity, above all. We are here a long way from the *tabula rasa* toward which the Neo-Classicicists gravitated. We are not dealing, however, with a group of unrepentant "rococo" painters; their reaction took other paths. In fact, they rejected

Boucher's artificial, delicate coloring and Fragonard's beautifully-worked impasto for the sake of an objectivity that cared little for *la belle nature* and emulated reality by means of a smooth, glazed painted surface, taking full advantage of the charms of color. In this group, no doubt larger than that of the pure Neo-Classicists, Peyron approached the Van Spaendoncks and Caraffe came close to Taunay. But the greatest of them all was surely Louis-Léopold Boilly, whose triumphant virtuosity did not scorn even the use of trompe-l'œil. At the end of 1793, speaking at the Société Populaire et Républicaine des Arts, the Revolutionary Jean-Baptiste-Joseph Wicar denounced artists who had lived too long in Italy, who behaved like émigrés and who he felt should be treated as such (he called for the destruction of the works submitted for entry to the Academy by François-Xavier Fabre and Denis Gauffier, acknowledged painter to the "infamous" Lord Harvey). But he also reproached genre painters for their incurable admiration for Flemish painting and for their obscenity, singling out Boilly in particular for public censure. In fact, Wicar was correct in denouncing Boilly as a counter-Revolutionary who had undermined the esthetics of painting.

Reaching this point, one might think this conclusion paradoxical, that history painting in the *grand genre,* so venerated by government officials and men of letters alike under Louis XVI and during the Revolution, was really a secondary phenomenon. Finally, the history painting that best expressed the deepest inclinations of French painting was not David's *Leonidas at Thermopylae* but rather his *Coronation of Napoleon.*

Boze and Lefèvre
Portrait of Mirabeau, 1789-90
Aix-en-Provence, Musée Granet
No. 13

Boilly
Impromptu Concert, 1790
Saint-Omer, Musée-Hôtel Sandelin
No. 6

Vigée-Lebrun
Self-Portrait, 1790
Florence, Galleria degli Uffizi
No. 198

Drolling
Self-Portrait, c. 1791
Orléans, Musée des Beaux-Arts
No. 49

Labille-Guiard
Portrait of Robespierre, c. 1791
Private Collection
No. 113

Roslin
Portrait of Daubenton, s.d. 1791
Orléans, Musée des Beaux-Arts
No. 161

Caraffe
Oath of the Horatii, s.d. 1791
Arkangelski Castle
No. 18

Laneuville
Portrait of Barère de Vieuzac, c. 1792
Bremen, Kunsthalle
No. 117

Vincent
Portrait of the Actor Dazincourt, s.d. 1792
Marseilles, Musée des Beaux-Arts
No. 200

Sablet
Portrait of Thomas Hope Playing Cricket, s.d. 1792
London, Cricket Memorial Gallery
No. 162

David
Portrait of the Marquise de Pastoret, c. 1792
The Art Institute of Chicago
No. 34

Garnier
Consternation of Priam and his Family, s.d. 1792
Mâcon, Musée Municipal des Ursulines
No. 64

Valenciennes
Biblis Changed into a Fountain, s.d. 1792
Quimper, Musée des Beaux-Arts
No. 179

Meynier
France Encouraging Science and the Arts, 1793
Boulogne-Billancourt, Bibliothèque Marmottan
No. 127

Réattu
Triumph of Civilization, c. 1793-98
New York, Private Collection
No. 147

David
Portrait of a Youth, s.d. 1793
Paris, Private Collection
No. 35

Schall
Heroism of William Tell, s.d. Year II (1793-94)
Strasbourg, Musée des Beaux-Arts
No. 163

Gagnereaux
Spirit of Peace Halting the Horses of Mars, s.d. 1794
Geneva, Musée d'Art et d'Histoire
No. 62

Regnault
Liberty or Death, s.d. Year III (1794-95)
Hamburg, Kunsthalle
No. 150

Trinquesse
Portrait of an Architect, s.d. 1794
Paris, Private Collection
No. 176

Suvée
Cornelia, Mother of the Gracchi, s.d. 1795
Paris, Musée du Louvre
No. 170

Michel
Storm, s.d. Year III (1794-95)
Nantes, Musée des Beaux-Arts
No. 131

Gauffier
Vallombrosa, near Florence, c. 1796
Montpellier, Musée Fabre
No. 65

H. Robert
Ruins of the Grand Gallery of the Louvre, c. 1796
Paris, Musée du Louvre
No. 158

F. Gérard
Portrait of Larevellière-Lépeaux, c. 1797
Angers, Musée des Beaux-Arts
No. 67

Guérin
Death of Cato, 1797
Paris, École des Beaux-Arts
No. 93

144

Harriet
Oedipus at Colonus, s.d. Year VI (1797-98)
Paris, Private Collection
No. 97

Desoria
Portrait of Élisabeth Dunoyer, s.d. 1797
The Art Institute of Chicago
No. 47

Gauffier
Portrait of Doctor Penrose, s.d. 1798
Minneapolis Institute of Arts
No. 66

J.-J. Lagrenée
Psyche in her Palace, s.d. Year VI (1797-98)
Paris, Private Collection
No. 114

Delafontaine
Portrait of Andrieux or *The Skater,* s.d. 1798
Paris, Hôtel de la Monnaie
No. 42

Taillasson
Hero and Leander, Salon of 1798
Blaye, Musée d'Histoire et d'Art
No. 172

Lethière
Philoctetes at Lemnos, c. 1798
Brest, Musée Municipal
No. 123

H. Robert
Young Girls Dancing Around an Obelisk, s.d. 1798
Montreal, Museum of Fine Arts
No. 159

152

F. Watteau
Battle of the Pyramids, s.d. Year VII (1798-99)
Valenciennes, Musée des Beaux-Arts
No. 204

Landon
Daedalus and Icarus, Salon of 1799
Alençon, Musée de la Maison d'Oze
No. 116

Bonnemaison
Young Woman Surprised by a Storm, Salon of 1799
New York, The Brooklyn Museum
No. 11

Peyron
Time and Minerva, Salon of 1799
Paris, Ministère des Armées
No. 140

Girodet
Portrait of Bourgeon, s.d. 1800
Saint-Omer, Musée-Hôtel Sandelin
No. 79

Boilly
Studio of a Young Artist, s.d. 1800
Moscow, State Pushkin Museum
No. 7

Van Loo
Ruins of a Gothic Church, s.d. Year IX (1800-01)
Fontainebleau, Château
No. 184

Painting Under Napoleon
1800-1814

Robert Rosenblum

David
Napoleon at Saint Bernard, 1800
Rueil-Malmaison, Château

When Jacques-Louis David painted the military fact of Napoleon crossing the mountain pass of the Grand Saint Bernard on 20 May 1800, he posed, in one unforgettable image, the problems that would beset every ambitious French artist confronted with the interpretation of contemporary events in a world first shattered by the Revolution and then to be reconstructed under the leadership of a 30-year-old officer who had just become the First Consul of France.   At a time of such swift and drastic changes, David, like Napoleon himself, was compelled to create a new mythology which could convince his compatriots that, after the extinction of a moribund tradition of monarchy, the true grandeur of the historical past could be resurrected in the service of the present and the future.   In *Napoleon at Saint Bernard* (1800; Versailles, Musée National), David provided, as it were, a rich and heroic historical pedigree for the Corsican upstart. On the ascent of icy rocks in the left foreground are inscribed, just below Bonaparte's own name, the names of Hannibal and Karolus Magnus, classical and medieval military leaders who had also succeeded in an arduous Alpine expedition.   But even without the explicit propaganda of such a newly invented historical dynasty, the image of Napoleon himself resonates with the glories of past leadership. Represented crossing the precarious mountain pass not on a mule, as was actually the case (and as would later be seen in mid-19th-century illustrations of the event by such artists as Paul Delaroche and Adolphe Yvon), but rather, in the Consul's own words, on a fiery steed *("un cheval fougueux"),* Napoleon suddenly looms up as a passionate heir to a long tradition of equestrian figures that echo across history from the processions of classical antiquity through the baroque energies of rearing horses and royal riders by a Bernini, a Rubens, a Falconet.   There is, to be sure, something willful, and hence artificial about David's message.   A great man has come from nowhere to fulfill an historical destiny, which is not his by genealogical right, but by virtue of his duplication of the great deeds of the past and by virtue of the almost supernatural energy and control that he promises as the great new leader of France. Resolutely, he masters his horse and his will as he points upwards against a dramatic crescendo of icy winds and stormy sky that act as a romantic foil of wild nature against his firm exercise of reason and discipline.

David's myth-making was supported in the many Napoleonic portraits necessary for the dissemination of the new faith. In his own pupil Antoine-Jean Gros' *Portrait of Bonaparte as First Consul* (No. 89), the military hero is transformed into the great statesman. Here Bonaparte stands coolly in a costume that, like the brocaded cloth on the table, is both spare and sumptuous, his head turned toward an unseen future whose grandeur is ascertained by the virtual catalog of Napoleonic achievements to which he points—military feats, like the crossing of the Grand Saint Bernard; peace treaties, like that of Amiens; religious reconciliations with the Pope, like the Concordat; and the memorable date, 18 Brumaire, of the coup d'état. But, however staged and explicitly propagandistic David's and Gros' images of the First Consul may seem, they still belong to the empirical world. Within a few years, even this could change. After Napoleon ascended to the imperial throne on 2 December 1804, another student of David, Jean-Auguste-Dominique Ingres, was capable of elevating his ruler from the flesh-and-blood man whom he, too, had painted as First Consul, to a terrifying deity who seems to have issued both natural and supernatural law for eternity (No. 104). Combining the image of supreme beings in both classical and Christian mythologies, Napoleon, in Ingres' iconic portrait, is at once Jupiter and God the Father, a remote and omnipotent divinity whose luxurious realm and fearsome immobility transcend the mundane data of earthly history. Five years later, Ingres would relocate this terrifying god in his proper mythological domain in the Olympian *Jupiter and Thetis* (No. 105).

The range of these Napoleonic portraits—from literal fact to hallucinatory visions, from a pictorial style of scrupulous, almost Eyckian realism to one of ghostly unreality—characterized the equal diversity of conception and style in the abundance of painting inspired by the 15-year history of Napoleon's reign over the destiny of the Western world. At times, artists could transpose the military facts of Napoleonic history into airborne fantasies, where the data of contemporary costume and portraits collide with ethereal personages. Such is the case in Anne-Louis Girodet's deliriously congested confrontation of ectoplasmic figures from Macpherson's *Ossian* with an assembly of specifically identifiable Napoleonic military heroes (No. 80), a painting that, among other things, immediately proves inadequate any simple-minded distinction between the so-called neo-classic and romantic. If its chiseled, marmoreal contours

Ingres
Bonaparte as First Consul, 1804
Liège, Musée des Beaux-Arts

still suggest the classicizing training of Girodet's master David and the abstract Homeric outlines of Flaxman, the composition as a whole stems from Rubens (the *Arrival of Marie de' Medici at Marseilles*, Louvre) and the ambiance is one of a moon-struck irrationality that defies Davidian laws of gravity and perspective. Such is the case, too, in Jean-Pierre Franque's equally lunar allegory of Bonaparte in Egypt (No. 61), where the young Corsican officer, mysteriously silhouetted against a cloudy night sky, contemplates a crystalline apparition of allegorical figures that represent evil divinities assailing La France, who desperately beckons the young general to return home to solve her domestic problems.

The view, in Franque's painting, of a cloud-capped pyramid on the horizon is worthy of Claude-Nicolas Ledoux' and Étienne-Louis Boullée's most sublime architectural fantasies; but it is also a record of an exotic topographical fact associated with Napoleon's military career. Indeed, the pictorial record of the Napoleonic campaigns continually provided a combination of journalistic fact and imaginative fiction that could appeal simultaneously to the need for knowledge about contemporary events and the need to glamorize these brutal military truths with an aura of remoteness and adventure. In the paintings of the many artists commissioned to illustrate for domestic consumption the foreign expeditions of Napoleon and his troops, one finds an expanding encyclopedia of geographic and cultural curiosities culled from the strangest reaches of Europe and the Arab world. Within this exhibition, there are even the thermal extremes of the dusty heat of Egypt (Vincent, No. 201) or Palestine (Gros, No. 88), and the bitter cold of the Alpine pass of the Grand Saint Bernard (Taunay, No. 173) or the wintry plains of Eylau (Meynier, No. 128), where the temperature was recorded at —19° C (2° F). Natural wonders also abound, not only in the spectacular desert scenes of the Near East or the sublime mountain summits of the Alps, but less dramatically, in the ravishing vista of Lake Garda, which forms the unexpected backdrop for Hippolyte Lecomte's pictorial record of the hair-raising adventure of Josephine, whose carriage was attacked there by enemy ships in August 1796 (No. 118). This gazetteer of the world's wonders included, of course, other peoples, other costumes, other styles of architecture so that, for example, the Egyptian campaign permitted the dissemination to an audience at the Paris Salons of information about the picturesque dress and racial characteristics of Arabs as well as about Muslim and ancient Egyptian architecture. Although this appetite for knowledge about the wonders of nature and of man was here presented through the vehicle of Napoleonic history painting, it nevertheless was soon to be satisfied outside the recording of Napoleonic events. Thus, many later paintings in this exhibition

—for example, Louis-Jacques Daguerre's view of Romanesque ruins in Scotland (No. 25) or Delacroix' tribute to Greek heroism at Missolonghi (No. 39)—extend, a decade after Napoleon's demise, the popular curiosity about remote architectural wonders and exotic peoples that was first made so abundantly accessible to French spectators through the paintings of Napoleonic military history.

For all the newness of the environments transmitted through these paintings, their dramatic structure was often based on traditional formats and moral values. In Jean-François Peyron's depiction of the *Death of General Valhubert* at the Battle of Austerlitz on 2 December 1805 (No. 141), the journalistic fact of this event is ennobled not only by the language of gestures borrowed from the frozen theatrical rhetoric of a David or a Poussin, but by the uncommon heroism of the general himself. Like one of the Spartan warriors venerated in neo-classic paintings, Valhubert, after being wounded by an enemy shell, rejected his aides-de-camp's offers of help, for a military order decreed that the wounded were not to be removed until after the battle, and Valhubert, though an officer, refused to exempt himself from this rule. More generally, such demonstrations of unusual virtue preserved, through multiple classical and Christian allusions, the sense that the grim means of war, plague and famine were finally justified by the noble ends of Napoleon's benevolence, wisdom and mercy. Under the aegis of a vast machine for pictorial propaganda, headed by Dominique-Vivant Denon, whose portrait by Prud'hon (No. 142) and whose mysterious adventures in Spain (A.-E. Fragonard, No. 57) figure in this exhibition, many artists attempted to interpret Napoleon's campaigns in the light of the age-old traditions of noble warriors who die, like Peyron's Valhubert, a perfectly staged death; or more characteristically, of great warriors—that is, like Napoleon himself—who bring to a conquered people the moral good and physical comforts associated with beneficent Roman emperors and even with Christ. Charles Meynier's interpretation of the aftermath of the battle of Eylau (No. 128) offers, like Gros' more famous painting of the same scene, a shocking, ostensibly eye-witness account of a freezing battlefield littered with naked and half-naked corpses, accompanied even by the miseries of starving dogs and horses. Yet this insistence on gruesome fact is finally expiated in the figure of the Emperor himself, whose saintly calm in the face of death and whose benevolent concern with the healing of the enemy wounded promise a new and better world of moral values worth dying for. Even the benighted enemies finally realize the virtues of the Napoleonic enlightenment, turning as they do toward Napoleon as if converted to a true religion, and repeating with their war-torn bodies those gestures of allegiance that were illustrated in such scenes of oath-taking to

Gros
Battle of Eylau, Salon of 1808
Paris, Musée du Louvre

David
Distribution of the Eagles, Salon of 1810
Versailles, Musée National

the flags of the imperial army as David's *Distribution of the Eagles* of 1810 (Versailles, Musée National) or Meynier's painting of Marshal Ney with the 76th regiment (No. 129).

However, not all Napoleonic history paintings preserved the rhetoric of morality, of patriotism, of higher causes inherited from the idealism of French Revolutionary propaganda and its counterpart in the Greek and Roman historical narratives chosen previously by David and his school as paragons of stoical virtue. Gros himself, in the *Battle of Nazareth* (No. 88), the painting that won for him the 1801 competition to record General Junot's stunning defeat (8 April 1799) of some 6,000 Turks and Arabs with only 500 French soldiers, tells us less about victory and heroism than about an orgy of violent bloodshed, where struggling men and horses, thrusting sabers and exploding guns erupt volcanically in a turbulent atmosphere of gun powder and desert sand. It was a painting that, in its emphasis upon uncommon suffering rather than noble leadership, and in its dynamic but unfocused composition, was later to inspire Géricault, who copied it, and Delacroix, who praised it extravagantly in his essay on Gros (1848).

Other artists, less pretentiously, ignored Napoleon and his generals and recorded, instead, the plight of anonymous foot-soldiers, of those men who, like drones in the Napoleonic hive, are seen only in the background of David's *Napoleon at Saint Bernard,* where their diminutive size is dramatically contrasted to the monumentally scaled figure of Napoleon himself. In a painting of the same event by Nicolas-Antoine Taunay (No. 173), we lose sight of Napoleon in this Alpine pass and consider instead the unheroic hardships of a military campaign set against a ravishing landscape of snow-covered rocks and pine trees. The rigors of survival—attending the wounded, making bonfires, seeking primitive shelter—are quietly observed against the spectacular mountain setting. Taunay's record of these common miseries of war set against uncommon environments was finally to usurp the grandeur of heroes and abstract ideals, just as his view of the *Entry of the Imperial Guard into Paris* (No. 174) tells us more about the response of ordinary Parisian men, women and children to the pageant than about the pageant itself. In effect, those later battle paintings of Théodore Géricault (No. 74), Nicolas Charlet, Horace Vernet (No. 188), Auguste Raffet, where we see only the suffering of anonymous people, are among the heirs of Taunay's modest, but poignant records of modern war viewed as fact, not fiction.

In looking at paintings of Napoleonic history, spectators often had the choice of focusing upon the journalistic facts of the heroism and misery of war or of subordinating these human actualities to the almost picaresque adventures provided by such dramatic and unfamiliar settings as the Alps, the Near East, Spain. Thus, A.-E. Fragonard's somewhat fictionalized record of Napoleon's artistic advisor, Vivant Denon, contemplating, like Hamlet or the shepherds of Arcadia, the skull of the 11th-century Spanish hero, El Cid, as it had been preserved near Burgos, ignores the grim military facts of the French invasion of Spain in favor of a mysterious meditation upon death, medieval heroes and gloomy gothic vaults (No. 57). Other kinds of history painting—that culled from Greco-Roman history or mythology, from the Bible, from medieval history, from literature—could also venture farther and farther away from the immediacy of current historical events which, in the 1780s and 1790s, especially in the work of David, had so often been interpreted through the narrative metaphors of historical legend. For David, before 1800, the martyrdoms of Marat and Socrates (No. 32) were almost interchangeable examples from past and present of noble lives sacrificed to a cause. But gradually, in the years following the Revolution, subjects inspired by the historical past and by imaginative literature began to lose their didactic relation to the historical present, and offered a growing abundance of escapist fantasies that concentrated on the joys and sorrows of Eros or on the thrills provided by particularly morbid or bizarre themes. Even David himself, when choosing classical subject matter after 1800, turned more and more often to such erotically complex narratives as Sappho's ecstatic love for the disguised boatman, Phaon (No. 36), or Apelles' inspiration by Alexander's mistress, Campaspe, for his painting of the new-born Venus rising from the sea (No. 37). But among the generation of his students and younger contemporaries, that is, those artists first emerging around 1800, the search for the emotional extremes of love and desperation was far more intense. In three works included here from the Salon of 1801, this more passionate pulse can already be felt. There is, for one, Gros' painting of the legend of Sappho's literally suicidal despair (No. 87), an interpretation even more fervent than that by Jean-Joseph Taillasson (1791; Brest), which introduced Parisian spectators to this tragic conclusion to a tale of unrequited love. In Gros' picture of 1801 the poetess, after her final libation, is silhouetted like a Greek maenad against a weird luminary drama of moonlight, dark clouds and shimmering sea, a nocturnal ambiance of ghostly mystery that would be no less appropriate for the Ossian illustrations being painted in the same year by Gérard and Girodet (Nos. 68, 80).

Another kind of pathetic love-death could be found at the same Salon in Broc's elegiac vision of Apollo lamenting his beloved Hyacinth, tragically felled by the god's own discus (No. 16). Here again, as in Gros' *Sappho,* the rational lessons of Davidian Classicism are turned inside out in an irrational world of erotic and visual fantasy.

Taillasson
Sappho, Salon of 1791
Brest, Musée des Beaux-Arts

Reflecting the sophisticated primitivism of that sect of radical young Davidians, the Primitifs, who aspired to the formal and emotional simplicities of archaic art and literature, Broc interprets the pathos of this homoerotic Greek myth in a strange pictorial language. Sharply outlined against the sun's rays, Apollo and Hyacinth transform the heroic muscularity of David's sculptural nudes into creatures of smooth, limp flesh that is at once molten in its physical and emotional fluidity and frozen in the precision of its abstract contours.

Similarly, another painting from the Salon of 1801, Mme Constance Charpentier's *Melancholy* (No. 19), alters the lessons of David to a point that thoroughly confounds the arbitrary boundaries between the neo-classic and the romantic. The heroine's melancholy, which one presumes to be caused by the tragedies of unrequited love or untimely death, belongs to the same emotional realm as Sappho's and Apollo's grief; and the landscape of weeping willows resonates, like the setting of a pastoral idyl in Broc's *Death of Hyacinth* or of a sublime, moonlit precipice in Gros' *Sappho*, with the feelings evoked by the figures. That Mme Charpentier's despondent woman is based closely on the subordinate figure of Camilla in David's *Horatii* is a telling indication of how artists of the next generation could change their master's emphasis upon public, politically oriented emotions to a new exploration of states of private feeling unrelated to the social goals that activated so many artists at the time of the Revolution.

The major directions of these excursions into a new emotional terrain were toward the erotic and the horrific. Even conventional mythological subjects could be interpreted, as in Guérin's *Iris and Morpheus* of 1811 (No. 94), with a new inflection of voluptuous, nocturnal fantasy that locates them less in a public domain of shared myth than in a private realm of the spectator's own erotic dreams. And in the work of a great master like Prud'hon, the most ordinary erotic mythologies take on subjective overtones of mystery and privacy (Nos. 143, 144). Like Jacques-Antoine Vallin's *Diana and Actaeon* (No. 181), Prud'hon's mythological lovers and zephyrs exist in a twilight world, where light and substance have given way to elusive, shadowy visions of the joys and sorrows of love. It is the world of night and of dreams of sensuality and terror that begins to permeate the interpretation of classical mythology, as it does, indeed, the choice of themes from other sources.

Small wonder that the Biblical motif of the Deluge, which already had made an appearance in Jean-Baptiste Regnault's painting at the Salon of 1789 (No. 149), and still earlier in Gamelin's painting of 1779 (No. 63), became so prominent at the beginning of the century. Sometimes inspired directly by the Bible, sometimes by such modern literary sources as Salomon Gessner's *Idyls,* the Deluge—as in Henri-Pierre Danloux' version at the Salon of 1802 (No. 26)

David
Oath of the Horatii (detail), 1784
Paris, Musée du Louvre

—permitted a full-scale empathy with a primal terror in the face of malevolent nature, a terror that would reach its apogee in Géricault's *Raft of the Medusa* (1819, Louvre). Similarly, another Biblical narrative transformed into modern literature—the Italian poet Alfieri's tragedy, *Saul*—inspired François-Xavier Fabre to paint such a spine-chilling drama as *Saul Crazed by Remorse,* a painting of 1803 (No. 56) that obliges Davidian figures to enact a scene of supernatural horror and grisly bloodshed, where the vengeful ghost of the high priest Abimelech appears above the bodies of his slaughtered family.

Often, the search for these extremities of feeling led French artists to foreign literary texts, especially from England, where writers and artists had been so precocious in investigating those new emotions commonly associated with the dawn of Romanticism in the mid-18th century. Thus, it is Macpherson's Ossianic poems of the 1760s (and first published in France in 1777) that not only inflamed Napoleon's imagination but that of many French artists like Gérard, Girodet (Nos. 68, 80) and Ingres (1813; Montauban, Musée Ingres), who, by a strange pictorial alchemy, were able to transform the earthbound, Greco-Roman figures of their master, David, into Nordic specters that float by moonlight in a misty, irrational space. Less well-known, but equally astounding among these French responses to the English fascination for the fantastic and the macabre, is Pierre-Auguste Vafflard's harrowing vision inspired by Edward Young's *Night Thoughts* of the 1740s (and first published in France in 1769-70), where the poet carries his dead daughter into a moonlit graveyard a kind of pictorial "gothic novel" that already announces the most blood-curdling moments in the 20th-century horror film (No. 178). That this large and imposing painting appeared at the Salon of 1804 is yet another indication of the need to reconsider the proper definition and chronological boundaries of French romantic painting, which is often considered to be primarily a post-Napoleonic development.

In the same way, a fascination with the art and history of the Middle Ages, usually associated with the romantic generation of Eugène Delacroix and Louis Boulanger, can already be traced in history paintings executed during the Napoleonic years, especially in the many works collected by Josephine, who favored what came to be known as the *style troubadour.* To be sure, themes from medieval French history had already appeared before 1789, as pictures of the 1770s like Vien's *Saint Louis and Marguerite de Provence* (No. 193), Durameau's *Continence of Bayard* (No. 55), and Brenet's *Death of Du Guesclin* (No. 15) make clear; but the anti-Christian passions of the Revolution interrupted what might otherwise have been an exploration of medieval subject matter as continuous as it had been in such other countries as England or Germany. Yet, under Napoleon, and after the Concordat of 1801, subjects associated with the Middle Ages in general and with Christianity in particular again began to make their appearance. Fleury-François Richard's *Deference of Saint Louis to his Mother* (No. 154), exhibited at the Salon of 1808 and then again in 1814, is typical of these new interpretations of the gothic world, for its narrative, taken from Joinville's *Vie de Saint Louis*, concerns Saint Louis' own painful response to the bitter conflict between his mother, Blanche de Castille, and his beloved wife, Marguerite de Provence. Emphasizing indoor scenes of familial or amorous drama, rather than outdoor scenes of military conflicts and Christian miracles, these domesticated visions of the Middle Ages also attempted to recreate a pictorial style appropriate to their subject. Unlike the medieval scenes of Brenet, Vien or Durameau, which still depend upon the conventions of baroque style, these paintings willfully revive the clarity of detail and the smallness of scale which Richard could admire in the paintings and illuminated manuscripts of the late Middle Ages. Just as other students of David tried to reconstruct with growing accuracy the archaeological data relevant to their scenes of Greek and Roman history, so too did these little masters of the *style troubadour*—Richard, Jean-Antoine Laurent, Jean-Baptiste Vermay, Pierre-Sylvestre Coupin de la Couperie —attempt to include a maximum of precise information about costume, furniture and decor for the period they illustrated. Indeed, at times, as in Richard's painting, we feel that the artist is taking the standard neo-classic deathbed scene, with its traditional rectilinear ordering of parallel planes and strong alternations of light and shadow, and transposing it to the Middle Ages simply by a change in the theatrical paraphernalia of clothing and setting.

Such pictures provided a medieval counterpart to the passion for Greco-Roman history and art; for they extended the historicizing attitudes of David into the domain of medieval art, history and legend, offering not only the sharp-focus rendering of such Gothic artifacts as those collected by Alexandre Lenoir for his Musée des Monuments Français, but also a taste for the pictorial style of the late Middle Ages, with its miniaturist scale and exquisitely wrought description of the variegated textures of the seen world. Moreover, these paintings often reintroduced, in an unexpected way, those Christian motifs that had almost been eclipsed between 1789 and 1801, the year in which Napoleon reaffirmed Catholicism as the official religion of France. But now, rather than paintings of traditional Christian themes—the Virgin and Child or the Crucifixion— one finds instead historical recreations of a long lost medieval world, where such images were lovingly made and devoutly believed in. This retrospective view, like Chateaubriand's *Génie du christianisme*

(1802), nostalgically estheticized the Middle Ages, focusing on such artifacts as the sculptured gothic Virgin and Child in Richard's painting, or even choosing a crucifix as the subject of an illusionistic tour de force, as in Louis-Léopold Boilly's composition of 1812 (No. 9) which like so many 19th-century paintings, is not really religious, but rather a secular view of a religious object made in a pre-Revolutionary world where Christian piety was unquestioned. The consequences of this new kind of spectator Christianity, which included views, like François-Marius Granet's, of famous Christian shrines, were enormous for modern art: even Gauguin's paintings of pious Breton peasants worshiping their rustic Calvaries are direct descendents of this attitude first revealed at the beginning of the 19th century.

Such references to a Christian medieval past, seen from a secular present, could take on many new guises. César Van Loo's view of gothic church ruins in the snow (No. 184), exhibited at the Salon of 1801, chooses the picturesque motif of crumbling gothic vaults that must have been a particularly familiar sight in France after the ravages of anti-Christian vandalism fomented by the Revolution. But Van Loo now parallels these decaying, skeletal forms with the leafless branches of a snow-covered tree, a melancholy metaphor of winter and death that, outside France, was soon to be given more intensely mystical implications in the art of Caspar David Friedrich, among others. In quite another vein, the gothic could provide not so much a religious, but an exotic setting for an erotic motif, as in Jean-Baptiste Mallet's *Gothic Bath* from the Salon of 1810 (No. 124), which takes the Ingresque theme of a marmoreal yet voluptuous nude bather, but locates her in a cloistered interior that is gothic rather than Near Eastern.

Mallet's painting, like that of Richard, revives not only the milieu of the Middle Ages in its architectural setting, but also a miniaturist style that seems to belong to the pictorial art of both the French and Netherlandish primitives and the little Dutch masters. The painting of 17th-century Holland, in fact, provided an important inspiration for a quiet current of painting under Napoleon that included not only occasional still lifes, like those by Antoine Berjon, Jan-Frans Van Dael and Alexandre-Isidore Leroy de Barde (Nos. 1, 182, 122), which virtually revive the microscopic precision with which Netherlandish masters recorded the wonders of shells, minerals, flowers, fruits, birds and insects, but even more important, the illustration of modest scenes of daily life or of charming anecdote. After the more idealist and heroic tenor of so much art and life of the 1790s, many artists seemed to turn with relief to genre painting, often describing the diverse visual phenomena of the everyday world with a brush that could rival the painters of 17th-century Holland.

Berjon
Shells and Madrepores, Salon of 1810
Lyon, Musée des Beaux-Arts

Boilly's own scenes of more casual modern experience, whether an artist's studio or the bustle of pedestrians in the *Galleries of the Palais Royal, Paris* (No. 8), are miracles of the painter's mimetic skill in their glossy, mirror-like reflections of the prosaic truths of indoor and outdoor Paris. Such painstaking craftsmanship and unpretentious subject matter seemed particularly appropriate to what the early 19th century viewed as the proper domain for women artists, whose numbers, especially in David's studio, increased at a startling rate around 1800. In general, these women perpetuated the sentimental mode of Greuze, at times aggrandizing the popular theme of sorrow to the grandiose dimensions of Mme Charpentier's *Melancholy* (No. 19), but more commonly diminishing them to the domestic proportions of Mme Chaudet's tearful contemplation of a girl mourning a dead pigeon (No. 20) or of Marguerite Gérard's neo-Dutch glimpse of a moment of swooning amorous disappointment in *Bad News* (No. 72). In works like these, as in those of Boilly himself, a style of intense, sharp-focus realism begins quietly to undermine the pretensions of those ideal, classicizing forms promoted by David. Yet it should be noted that even within David's own domain of Greco-Roman subjects, a strong undercurrent of an almost Netherlandish realism can be sensed, so that, curiously, paintings like Ingres' *Jupiter and Thetis* (No. 105) seem to combine the opposite extremes of abstract formal invention and the most close-eyed description of surface appearances, as if the worlds of Phidias and Gerard Dou had been combined.

In landscape, too, the extremities of an ideal vision, based primarily on Poussinesque precedent, and an empirical one, based on a growing curiosity about the recording of diverse phenomena in a world whose scientific and geographic boundaries kept widening, could be felt. Although in theoretical terms, pure landscape in the years around 1800 was much maligned as an inferior genre of painting, the number of landscapes executed and exhibited in those years kept increasing. In terms of an almost underground development of informal landscape painting, it was the many French painters in Italy—Pierre-Henri de Valenciennes, Jean-Victor Bertin, Jean-Joseph-Xavier Bidauld, Théodore Turpin de Crissé—who preserved 17th-century classicizing formulas while, at the same time, quietly introducing fresh perceptions of weather and topography (see Nos. 3, 4, 177), a fusion of opposites that would later be explored by Jean-Baptiste Corot (Nos. 22, 23), among others. Yet the development of landscape in these years is to be found as well in the backgrounds of both journalistic and fictional subject paintings. Thus, the many painters who illustrated the drama of Napoleonic military history against specific landscape settings introduced a taste for visual knowledge about everything from parched desert wastes in Palestine to limpid lakes and snow-covered mountains in the Alps. More-over, painters who explored literary and mythological subjects tend-ed to emphasize more and more, as did Gros in his *Sappho* (No. 87) and Mme Charpentier in her *Melancholy* (No. 19), the importance of a landscape background that could communicate the emotions expe-rienced by the figures themselves. Drooping trees, rushing cata-racts, jagged precipices, moonlit skies, luminous meadows could underline the feelings enacted in the dramatic narrative. The École des Beaux-Arts may have waited until 1817 to recognize landscape as a sufficiently important category to inaugurate, at last, a Prix de Rome in historical landscape, but the conditions of this new award were, in fact, prepared in the first decade of the century and often, almost surreptitiously in the backgrounds of subject paintings.

The growing complexity and diversity of subject, style and emotion so common to the years around 1800 were reflected as well in portraiture. The range, as before, moved from the intimacy and directness of informal portraits to the glitter and official gran-deur demanded by the formal portraits of the Napoleonic adminis-tration and family; and the fashionable record of elegantly-costumed ladies and gentleman was also perpetuated, as in Mulard's Ingresque portrait of an unidentified woman whose charms extend from a coquettish expression to the circuitous rhythms of an Indian shawl (No. 136). But even within this traditional scope many new psycho-logical experiences were recorded. Thus, within the group of artists' portraits in this exhibition, one is surprised to turn from the secure, matter-of-fact personalities of Martin Drolling (No. 49) or Pierre-Narcisse Guérin (No. 95) to the uncommon intensity of Abel de Pujol's self-portrait of 1806 (No. 146), where tousled hair, staring eyes and a curious combination of assertion and withdrawal already announce the deeper psychological mysteries of Géricault's portraits of the insane (No. 77). And there is, too, Regnault's extraordinary allegorical portrait, *Physical Man, Moral Man...* (No. 151), in which the features of the hermit-mystic are probably to be identified with those of the artist himself who, like a sorcerer, points to the weird, Ossianic apparition of allegorical figures associated with the secret rites of freemasonry.

Even in the domain of more public portraiture, like Gros' records of Napoleonic officers, one is startled to discover, as in the portrait of the young son of General Legrand (No. 90), a strange melancholy and passivity foreign to the outer demands of warfare. If some of these portraits, like Gérard's of the Comte de Fries, with his wife and child (No. 69), seem to conform to an official aristocratic type that blends hauteur with a studied informality, others are surprisingly fresh in their curiosity about less familiar human beings. Thus, Joseph-Marie Vien *fils'* portrait of Frion (No. 195) documents a biological oddity, a giant seen dressing after his swim, just as Girodet's portrait of a turbaned man from the East (No. 81) gives a precise account of the exotic features and costume of an unfamiliar human being who must have offered to Parisian spectators the anthropological equivalent of the Near Eastern landscape and architecture introduced in so many Napoleonic military paintings.

In fact, by the end of the Napoleonic era, French painting had become more complex and diverse than at any earlier point in its history. In subject alone, the new range was immense. Napoleonic history itself provided occasions for recording everything from traditional heroism and nobility to ignoble suffering and slaughter, and stimulated an insatiable curiosity about the exotic data of peoples, architecture, landscape far from the world of modern Paris. But even within the realm of more traditional history painting, the introduction of unexplored themes was no less rapid. The record of national history from Saint Louis through the 18th century, the illustration of imaginative literature from Dante to Ossian, the search for unfamiliar Biblical and Greco-Roman narratives of uncommon pathos and mystery, and the invention by the artist of private fictions—such a rapid expansion of a traditional iconographic repertory was typical of the period. Typical, too, of this enriching of experience was the pursuit of ever more intense emotional extremes, whether in the subjective reading of human psychology through portraiture or even through new interpretations of conventional mythologies culled from classical sources. Moreover, this widening scope of subject and feeling was accompanied by an equally widening diversity of styles, whereby almost the entire history of Western art became accessible as a stimulus for artists working in a world where earlier traditions had been ruptured. Not only were such conventional sources as Raphael, Poussin and Rubens used, but also Greek vase painting, gothic miniatures, Flemish and Italian primitives, the little Dutch masters. For artists, as for everyone who lived through the Napoleonic era, the world was changing with breathtaking rapidity, and the historical past loomed larger and larger as a source of security upon which new yet venerable traditions could be constructed. But at the same time, the unfamiliar experiences of the 19th-century present often demanded the breaking of these traditional molds. Beneath the public facade of the official myths of the Napoleonic reign, there were disturbing undercurrents of private emotions and observations that demanded definition. It was a tension between inherited myths and unprecedented realities, between the historical past and contemporary actualities that would become even more acute in the next effort to reconstruct the shattered yet continuous traditions of French politics, life and art: the Bourbon Restoration.

Gros
Portrait of Bonaparte, First Consul, s.d. Year X (1801-02)
Paris, Musée de la Légion d'Honneur
No. 89

Gros
Battle of Nazareth, s.d. Year IX (1800-01)
Nantes, Musée des Beaux-Arts
No. 88

Vincent
Battle of the Pyramids, c. 1800-03
Gisors, Private Collection
No. 201

Lefèvre
Portrait of Guérin, s.d. Year IX (1800-01)
Orléans, Musée des Beaux-Arts
No. 119

Charpentier
Melancholy, s.d. Year X (1801-02)
Amiens, Musée de Picardie
No. 19

Broc
Death of Hyacinth, Salon of 1801
Poitiers, Musée des Beaux-Arts
No. 16

Gros
Sappho at Leucadia, s.d. 1801
Bayeux, Musée Baron-Gérard
No. 87

F. Gérard
Ossian, 1801
Hamburg, Kunsthalle
No. 68

Girodet
Ossian Receiving Napoleonic Officers, Salon of 1802
Rueil-Malmaison, Château
No. 80

Danloux
The Deluge, Salon of 1802
Saint-Germain-en-Laye, Musée Municipal
No. 26

Fabre
Saul Crazed by his Remorse, s.d. 1803
Montpellier, Musée Fabre
No. 56

Van Dael
The Tomb of Julie, s.d. Year XII (1803-04)
Rueil-Malmaison, Château
No. 182

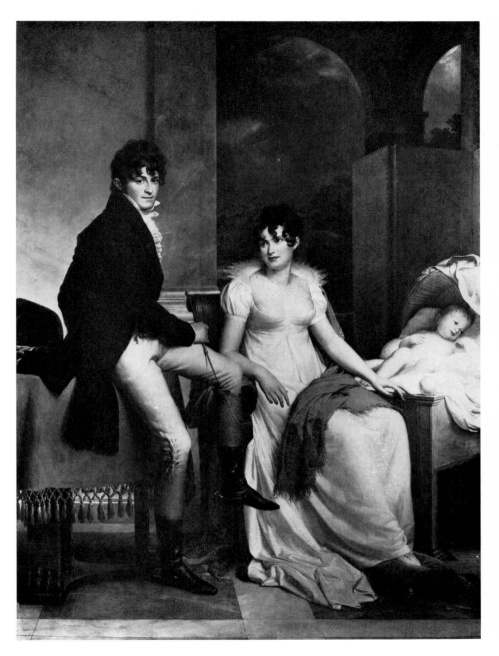

F. Gérard
Portrait of the Comte de Fries and his Family, c. 1804
Vienna, Kunsthistorisches Museum
No. 69

M. Gérard
Bad News, Salon of 1804
Paris, Musée du Louvre
No. 72

Vafflard
Young and his Daughter, Salon of 1804
Angoulême, Musée National
No. 178

Vien *fils*
Portrait of Frion, Salon of 1804
Perpignan, Musée Hyacinthe Rigaud
No. 195

Vincent
Allegory of the Freeing of the Prisoners of Algiers, s.d. 1806
Kassel, Museum
No. 202

Abel de Pujol
Self-Portrait, s.d. 1806
Valenciennes, Musée des Beaux-Arts
No. 146

192

Ingres
Portrait of Napoleon I on his Imperial Throne, s.d. 1806
Paris, Musée de l'Armée
No. 104

Lecomte
Josephine at Lake Garda, s.d. 1806
Rueil-Malmaison, Château
No. 118

Turpin de Crissé and Demarne
Landscape with Animals, s.d. 1806
Boulogne-Billancourt, Bibliothèque Marmottan
No. 177

Girodet
Portrait of an Indian, 1807
Montargis, Musée Girodet
No. 81

Meynier
Napoleon on the Battlefield of Eylau, 1807
Versailles, Musée National
No. 128

Meynier
Marshal Ney and the Soldiers of the 76th Regiment, s.d. Year XV (1808)
Versailles, Musée National
No. 129

Chaudet
Young Girl Mourning the Death of her Pigeon, Salon of 1808
Arras, Musée
No. 20

Peyron
Death of General Valhubert, s.d. 1808
Versailles, Musée National
No. 141

Taunay
French Army Crossing the Saint-Bernard Pass, 1808
Versailles, Musée National
No. 173

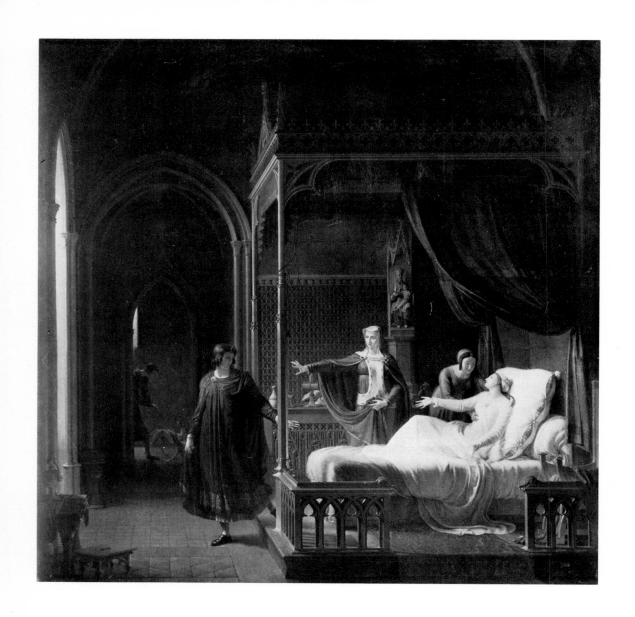

F. Richard
Deference of Saint Louis to his Mother, Salons of 1808 and 1814
Arenenberg, Napoleonmuseum
No. 154

David
Sappho and Phaon, s.d. 1809
Leningrad, State Hermitage Museum
No. 36

GALERIES DU PALAIS ROYAL.

Boilly
The Galleries of the Palais Royal, s.d. 1809
Paris, Musée Carnavalet
No. 8

Leroy de Barde
Still Life with Birds, s.d. 1810
Paris, Musée du Louvre, Cabinet des Dessins
No. 122

Mallet
Gothic Bath, Salon of 1810
Dieppe, Musée
No. 124

Granet
Stella in Prison, s.d. 1810
Moscow, State Pushkin Museum
No. 82

Franque
Allegory of the Condition of France Before the Return from Egypt, Salon of 1810
Paris, Musée du Louvre
No. 61

Taunay
Entry of the Imperial Guard into Paris, Salon of 1810
Versailles, Musée National
No. 174

Vallin
Diana and Actaeon, s.d. 1810
Roanne, Musée Joseph Dechelette
No. 181

Bertin
Italian Landscape, c. 1810
Boulogne-Billancourt, Bibliothèque Marmottan
No. 3

Gros
Portrait of Second-Lieutenant Legrand, Salon of 1810
The Los Angeles County Museum of Art
No. 90

Mulard
Portrait of a Woman, c. 1810
Fort Worth, Kimbell Art Museum
No. 136

Ingres
Jupiter and Thetis, s.d. 1811
Aix-en-Provence, Musée Granet
No. 105

Guérin
Iris and Morpheus, s.d. 1811
Leningrad, State Hermitage Museum
No. 94

David
Napoleon in his Study, s.d. 1812
Washington, National Gallery of Art
No. 36 bis

216

Géricault
Portrait of a Carabinier, c. 1812
Rouen, Musée des Beaux-Arts
No. 73

A.-E. Fragonard
Vivant Denon Returning the Bones of El Cid to his Tomb, c. 1812
Saint-Quentin, Musée A. Lecuyer
No. 57

Prud'hon
Portrait of Vivant Denon, 1812
Paris, Musée du Louvre
No. 142

Regnault
Physical Man, Moral Man..., c. 1810-15
Brest, Musée des Beaux-Arts
No. 151

Regnault
Judgment of Paris, 1812
The Detroit Institute of Arts
No. 152

Boilly
Crucifix, Salon of 1812
Oxford, The Dulverton Trustees: on loan to Magdalen College
No. 9

Berjon
Basket of Flowers, s.d. 1814
Paris, Musée du Louvre
No. 1

Prud'hon
Young Zephyr, c. 1814
Paris, Musée du Louvre
No. 143

David
Apelles and Campaspe, c. 1814
Lille, Musée des Beaux-Arts
No. 37

Swebach
Unloading of a Ship, c. 1810-20
Private Collection
No. 171

Demarne
Hay Pitchers' Lunch, Salon of 1814
Cherbourg, Musée Thomas-Henry
No. 46

Heim
Defense of Burgos, c. 1814
Versailles, Musée National
No. 99

Géricault
Wounded Cuirassier, Salon of 1814
Paris, Musée du Louvre
No. 74

Painting During the Bourbon Restoration, 1814-1830

Robert Rosenblum

Lordon
Marie-Antoinette in the Conciergerie
Salon of 1817
Engraving.

The years 1814-15, with their bewildering political alternations between a restored king and a restored emperor, both of whom had been exiled, were too unsettled to define, in artistic terms, the kind of programmatic propaganda that had accompanied Napoleon's reign. But by the time of the Salon of 1817, the first to be held after Louis XVIII's definitive return from Ghent after the upheaval of the Hundred Days, the character of the Bourbon Restoration was clearly reflected in the pictures there exhibited. Most conspicuously, an enormous effort was made to re-establish the proper dynastic connections with the Bourbon monarchy of the 18th century, whether in terms of tearful remorse for the victims of the Terror (a sentiment that was given architectural form in Paris in the Chapelle Expiatoire for the commemoration of Louis XVI and Marie-Antoinette) or an assertion of the qualities of charity, heroism and public enterprise to be found under the reign of Louis XVI. Seen at the Salon of 1817, together with such paintings as Pierre-Jérôme Lordon's *Marie-Antoinette, Queen of France, in the Prison of the Conciergerie*, two paintings in this exhibition—Louis Hersent's *Louis XVI Distributing Alms to the Poor* (No. 100) and Fleury Richard's *Madame Élisabeth de France Distributing Milk* (No. 155)—attempted to make clear that the return of Louis XVIII to the throne meant the return of a Bourbon dynasty which, even on the eve of the Revolution, was capable of a humility that extended as far as rural benevolence. In the painting by Hersent, Louis XVIII's brother is seen bestowing gifts of affection and money upon the Greuze-like inhabitants of a hamlet, just outside the château of Versailles, which has been blighted by the severities of the rigorous winter that preceded the fall of the Bastille; in the composition by Richard, Louis XVI is replaced, as it were, by his sister, Mme Élisabeth de France who, shading herself with a parasol in her home at Montreuil, attends to the charitable distribution of milk to peasant children, a philanthropy, so the Salon catalog explained, that also involved Mme Élisabeth's considerate arrangement to have the girlfriend of the Fribourg cowherd, Jacques, come from Switzerland to France to join him in marriage. Such images of humble charity in the country must have evoked, for spectators in 1817, a long-lost, pre-Revolutionary world of almost Arcadian sweetness and simplicity; and in the case of the Richard, this retrospective glimpse of Rousseauian goodness among rich and poor, aristocrat and peasant, was further enriched by the prominent intrusion of a picturesquely shadowed gothic arcade, a motif often explored by Richard in his earlier illustrations to French medieval history (No. 154). But here, gothic architecture carries with it more modern Christian associations, quietly underlining the conjunction of virtue and the preservation of Christianity and its values.

Indeed, the return of the Bourbons, first with Louis XVIII and then, in 1824, with his brother Charles X, stimulated what was virtually a revival of religious art, though often in the disguised form of French national history and genre. Thus, scenes from the religious life of Saint Louis figured large under the Restoration, providing as they did exactly that coincidence of Christian piety and Bourbon pedigree propagandized between 1815 and 1830; and other scenes of French national history would similarly emphasize the miraculous aspects of Catholicism. Nicolas-André Monsiau's *Devotion of Monsigneur de Belzunce* (No. 133), at the Salon of 1819, removes, as it were, the miracle-working Napoleon of Gros' *Napoleon in the Pesthouse at Jaffa* (1804; Louvre) and replaces him with a legitimate Christian healer, the courageous and noble bishop, Monsigneur de Belzunce, who attended the suffering residents of Marseilles during the devastating plague of 1720. Often, this new Bourbon piety would find its expression not in Biblical or historical illustration but rather in vignettes from the life of devout peasants, especially in Italy, where the faith of these simple souls had never been challenged by the intellectual and physical desecration of the Church experienced in France during the Revolution, and where picturesque local costumes gave an exotic distance to these people comparable to the effect of medieval costumes in paintings of the *style troubadour*.

Gros
The Pesthouse at Jaffa, Salon of 1804
Paris, Musée du Louvre

Two paintings in this exhibition, both of 1827, may make this point clearer. In Léopold Robert's *Pilgrims Returning from the Feast Day of the Madonna dell'Arco* (No. 160), a religious procession bursts upon us. These Neapolitan peasants, led by a festooned ox-cart, have returned from a visit to the shrine of the Madonna dell'Arco during the festival of Pentecost; and their sensuous, colorful exuberance—the shaking of tambourines, the strumming of a mandolin, the dancing of the tarantella—evokes an almost pagan world that is further echoed in the distant silhouette of Vesuvius. We would hardly know this was a scene associated with Christian piety were it not for the primitive broadsheet of the Madonna held by the dark-skinned urchin at the front of the cart. The other emotional extreme of this tourist view of Christian faith may be seen in Victor Schnetz's painting from the Salon of 1827-28, *Vow to the Madonna* (No. 166), where a pathetic drama—a Raphaelesque grouping of an older woman who prays for a sick young girl—is played out in a humble Italian church. But in both cases, the world of Christianity is associated with a childlike innocence that seemed more appropriate to peasants in exotic, Mediterranean climes than to the sophisticated urbanites in Paris who could only enjoy as spectators these glimpses of rural piety. In later French painting, this image of pious peasants would move from Italy to the generalized soil of Millet's northern French countryside or to the more picturesque terrain of Gauguin's Britanny.

The efforts to revitalize the Church during the Bourbon Restoration meant not only these new, and often peripheral views of a primitive world still united by Christian faith, but also more traditional attempts to sustain the great themes of Christian art. The Church provided many new commissions for religious painting from hosts of major and minor artists, most of whom could do little more than paraphrase, with varying degrees of personal inflection, the Christian prototypes offered by Raphael, Poussin, the Carracci or Rubens. Ingres himself, working in Italy during the reigns of both Napoleon and Louis XVIII, created for a Roman church, S. Trinità dei Monti, his ambitious *Jesus Delivering the Keys to Saint Peter* of 1820 (No. 108), whose close dependence upon Raphael's interpretation of the same theme in the tapestry cartoons may exemplify the degree to which so many artists of the time—from Picot to Prud'hon—were obliged, after the disruption of a long tradition of Christian art, to imitate closely the old masters' representations of these time-honored subjects.

Yet the official, public façade of Ingres' religious paintings, with their respectful quotations from the timeless beauty of Raphael's Christian images, could occasionally be altered in the work of his contemporaries by more personal and passionate inflections. Such was the case in Ary Scheffer's wildly dramatic submission to the Salon of 1824, a scene of a storm-tossed boat, so ubiquitous in romantic imagery, but one now guided by the medieval piety of Saint Thomas Aquinas who, in this moment of terror, preaches faith in divine benevolence (No. 164). This tempestuous mood turns inward in Delacroix' commission for the Paris church of Saint-Paul-Saint-Louis, a *Christ in the Garden of Olives* (No. 40), which was first seen at the Salon of 1827-28. Unlike his earlier religious commissions, with their awkward repetitions of Raphaelesque formulas, this painting is saturated with the same heart-felt drama of loneliness, suffering and desperation which, in the 1820s, he could also convey in the more secular terms of a writer alienated from society, as in his illustrations to *Tasso in the Madhouse*. For Delacroix and other painters of the 1820s, religious subjects could often provide, as they did for Prud'hon in his late *Crucifixion* (1822; Louvre), a vehicle for expressing personal sorrows. Delacroix's close contemporary, Alfred de Vigny, was to do the same in his own later poetic interpretation of *Le Mont des Oliviers* (1843), which similarly transforms a public drama into a private confession. Even older Davidians, like Baron Gérard, occasionally essayed Christian subjects with surprisingly personal results. Thus, in his *Saint Theresa* (No. 70), executed for a Catholic hospice founded by Chateaubriand's wife and named Marie-Thérèse after the Duchesse d'Angoulême, an image of fervent mysticism and piety is projected as the Carmelite nun, framed by a gothic arch and kneeling on a column base in a spare and gloomy church interior, looks outward and upward beyond the spectator to an invisible world of spiritual revelation.

Delacroix
Tasso in the Madhouse, c. 1824
Zurich, Bührle Collection

Even within the more traditional realm of Greco-Roman subject matter, still promulgated by those artists whose ambitions were first defined by the art of David, a mood of greater irrationality was often conveyed. Already under Napoleon, classical history and mythology were frequently interpreted with an emphasis upon the pathetic, the morbid or the erotic; and these tendencies were, if anything, intensified after 1815, when such themes seemed to be increasingly shrouded in an aura of nocturnal mystery that turned substance to shadow, public myth to private reverie. Exiled in Brussels after the Restoration and dissociated from the heroic causes of the Revolution and the Empire, David himself turned fully in his late years to such erotic mythologies as *Mars Disarmed by Venus and the Three Graces* (No. 38), where the goddess of love has conquered the god of war, and where David's figural style, in its voluptuous attenuations, ironically reverts to the rococo esthetic he had so vigorously rejected in the 1780s. Such is the case as well in Pierre-Claude Delorme's *Cephalus and Aurora* (No. 45), from the Salon of 1822, where the cloudborne world of classical erotic fantasy created by Delorme's own master Girodet is pursued even further. Similarly, Claude-Marie Dubufe's *Apollo and Cyparissus* (No. 53), also exhibited at the Salon of 1822, is yet another example of these belated interpretations of classical myth, in this case expanding the homoerotic theme of Jean Broc's *Death of Hyacinth* (No. 16) to a large-scale elegy in which, against a twilight landscape, the Apollo Belvedere seems to have come to life to kneel tearfully at the limp body of Cyparissus, whose hopeless grief at the accidental shooting of his own beloved stag has been assuaged by the god's granting him the solace of death.

These bizarre and lugubrious themes from classical antiquity

Prud'hon
Crucifixion, 1822
Paris, Musée du Louvre

Sigalon
Locusta, Salon of 1824
Nîmes, Musée des Beaux-Arts

were further expanded by the growing interest in Racine's own interpretations of Greco-Roman history and legend. At times, it is difficult to discern, as in Prud'hon's *Andromache* (No. 145), completed by the artist's student, Charles Boulanger de Boisfremont, and exhibited at the Salon of 1817, whether the source is Homer or Racine, although in this case, the stoical dedication of the widowed Andromache to her son Astyanax is predicated, as Chateaubriand would have emphasized, upon Racine's Christian ethic rather than upon that of the pagan Homer. In the works of younger artists like Xavier Sigalon, however, classical themes unfamiliar to a traditional repertory are clearly culled from Racine. His *Locusta,* which made so deep an impression at the Salon of 1824 and which is represented here by a sketch (No. 167), is a macabre subject inspired by the drama *Britannicus,* where the grim tale is told of Nero's sorceress, Locusta, who tries her poison on a slave before attempting the assassination of Britannicus. Such a grisly narrative, which includes, in Sigalon's interpretation, the malevolent Nero's confidant, Narcissus, his hideous sorceress and a slave's nude body racked with pain, stretches beyond the breaking point the boundaries of any definition of neo-classic painting, and corresponds far more closely to the overt investigation of states of passion and irrationality associated with the welling forces of an official school of Romanticism. These forces seemed at last to triumph at the Salon of 1824, where Delacroix' *Scenes of the Massacre of Chios* (Louvre), which wallows in contemporary accounts of the barbaric Turkish suppression of the Greeks fighting for their independence, so vigorously challenged Ingres' official homage to a secure past, the *Vow of Louis XIII* (Montauban, Cathédrale) which looks back to Raphael, to Philippe de Champaigne and to the Bourbon dynasty's traditional fusion of Church and State.

Yet in retrospect, this hostile, black-and-white opposition between classic and romantic factions propagated by artists during the Bourbon Restoration can no longer satisfy our modern view of the period's complexities. Thus, artists thoroughly trained in the canons of Davidian Classicism could often stray into foreign territories, including that of French national history. Two paintings in the exhibition, both from the Salon of 1824, demonstrate students of David—Pierre-Henri Révoil and Jean-Auguste-Dominique Ingres— venerating the world of François I, whose image as a great king and patron of the arts could help to underline the Bourbon efforts at recalling the glories of the French monarchic past. Perpetuating the miniaturist, almost Netherlandish precision of descriptive surfaces that had been the stylistic earmark of earlier *troubadour* masters like Fleury Richard (No. 154), both Révoil and Ingres record, with intensely sharp focus, the particularities of 16th-century faces, costume, furniture, architectural decoration. In the case of Révoil's *François I Knighting his Grandson François II* (No. 153), the scene of renaissance pageantry and monarchic rights is one that glamorizes the ancestry of the Bourbon Restoration; and in the case of Ingres' *Death of Leonardo da Vinci* (No. 106), the idea of monarchic grandeur and authority is combined with the idea, increasingly popular in the 19th century, of recording, in the manner of Vasari, a moment in the legend of a great artist's life. At times, as in Granet's earlier illustration of *Stella in Prison* (No. 82), the anecdote could be picaresque; but in the case of Ingres, the moment chosen is a noble one that equates the grandeur of the dying Leonardo with that of his patron, François I. It was a concept that flattered both the 19th-century artist, whose official stature kept rising, and the 19th-century royal patron, who felt it his duty, as did François I, to encourage the arts in his country.

Other pictures, once more the work of nominally neo-classic painters, display even more fully the inadequacy of the neo-classic-romantic polarity. Ingres' own *Roger and Angelica* (No. 107), exhibited at the Salon of 1819, has, if anything, fewer Davidian aspects than even Géricault's *Raft of the Medusa*, seen at the same Salon. Not only is its treatment of the female nude eccentric to the point of being grotesque, but its subject is inspired by a weird, fairy-tale narrative in Ariosto's *Orlando Furioso*, a legend of fantastic creatures (here an orc and a hippogriff), of a maiden in distress, of a knight in shining armor, of moonlight, foaming sea and craggy rocks, all executed in a bizarre, miniaturist style that recalls Flemish and Italian primitives. The male counterpart to Ingres' tortured female prisoner is found in Horace Vernet's *Mazeppa* of 1826 (No. 187). Inspired, like so many artists of the 1820s (Géricault, Boulanger, Delacroix) by Byron's poetic metamorphoses of erotic and sadistic themes, Vernet shows us the brutal punishment of the Polish page, Mazeppa who, discovered as the lover of a nobleman's wife, is tied to a wild horse for a nightmarish ride made all the more terrifying by the presence of packs of wolves, whose eyes glisten in the darkness. In fact, the growing taste for the supernatural, the morbid and the spinechilling could be found throughout narrative painting under the Bourbon Restoration. Thus, A.-E. Fragonard can also terrify us by illustrating the ghostly statue of the commander of Seville grasping the shoulder of his fleeing murderer, Don Juan, before dragging him to hell (No. 58). Elsewhere, the evocative sketchiness of Fragonard's painting of an apparition is replaced by a quasi-photographic accuracy that is equally intended to enlist the belief of the spectator. Thus, through glassy precision of detail and erudite historical reconstruction of faces and decor, Paul Delaroche can transport us to 15th-century England, where we watch,

Boulanger
Mazeppa, Salon of 1827-28
Rouen, Musée des Beaux-Arts

horrified, as if we were spectators in the theater, the ominous approach of the henchman who will murder the children of Edward IV, pathetically imprisoned in the bloody Tower of London (No. 44).

The terror and the pathos of such paintings, whether inspired by Ariosto, Byron, Mozart, Shakespeare or historical legend, penetrated as well the recording of contemporary history, from which moments of uncommon hardship and desperation were certain to inflame artists' imaginations. To be sure, human misery had been prominent in many paintings of Napoleonic history, but in general, it was subsumed and expiated by heroic leaders whose noble ends justified the ignoble means of war. But after the fall of Napoleon, these myths turned into deceptions, and often only pointless suffering remained. Géricault's *Wounded Cuirassier,* from the Salon of 1814 (No. 74), may be the first great painting to turn inside out these Napoleonic ideals, for the excitement of battle and of abstract causes is now replaced by the agony of an anonymous cavalry soldier of almost allegorical character, wounded in an unspecified Napoleonic battle whose goals, in 1814, must have seemed tragically anachronistic. It was a disillusion conveyed more modestly in many of the paintings from the post-Napoleonic era—in works not only by Géricault but by Horace Vernet (No. 188), Nicolas-Toussaint Charlet and Auguste Raffet—which reflect, in their focus upon weary foot-soldiers and the unidealized miseries of battle, the sad end of an epic dream.

The exploration of human beings reduced to a state of animal despair, unguided by ideals embodied in great heroes or in high-minded sacred or secular beliefs, was a recurrent motif in painting during the Bourbon Restoration and one that reached its most sensational expression in Géricault's *Raft of the Medusa* at the Salon of 1819. Even when Ary Scheffer tells us of Saint Thomas Aquinas' faith in God during a storm (No. 164), we are somehow more impressed by human terror than by divine benevolence; and when the shipwreck is a contemporary one, as in Théodore Gudin's *Devotion of Captain Desse* of 1828-29 (No. 92), nominally commemorating the courageous French captain of the *Julia* who, in 1822, managed to save 25 souls from a Dutch boat, the *Columbus,* which had lost its mast, the hero and his ship are only ghostly blurs in the background. Again, we are confronted not with the agent of salvation, but rather, as in the *Medusa* and as in Turner's contemporaneous shipwreck scenes, with the full horror of the foundering ship and its cargo of pitifully helpless human beings at the mercy of an overwhelming, malevolent force.

This fascination with suffering and terror, and this desperate faith in those few vestiges of natural or supernatural benevolence that seemed to survive in an age that followed the Revolutionary and

Géricault
Raft of the Medusa, Salon of 1819
Paris, Musée du Louvre

Napoleonic Wars found a particularly stirring correlative in the Greek Wars of Independence. Beginning in 1821, this bloody conflict between Greeks and Turks quickly enlisted the passions of European intellectuals, who viewed these remote wars as a battle between the symbolic protagonists of good and evil, the forces of Western rationality and civilization versus a non-Western enemy that represented mindless barbarism. The imagination of French painters was constantly kindled by reports of unusual brutality in the Greek isles, whether in incidents of pillage and slavery, as in Delacroix' *Scenes of the Massacre of Chios*, where the image of a hero and of a force of salvation has been totally eclipsed, or in Scheffer's *Suliot Women* (Louvre) at the Salon of 1827, where the women who have survived the defeat of their husbands by the pasha's troops drive themselves like animals to a collective suicide by jumping from a precipice. Such scenes of misery, always lent a fictional enchantment through their exotic setting, are represented here by Delacroix' passionate *Greece on the Ruins of Missolonghi* (No. 39), a painting that was first seen in Paris at the Galerie Lebrun in 1826 with works by other French masters, ranging from David to Géricault, in an exhibition that was organized in order to raise public funds to support the Greek cause. Characteristically, Delacroix transformed the harrowing accounts of the Turkish extinction of virtually the entire population of Missolonghi (as well of such foreign heroes as Lord Byron, who had come to Missolonghi to defend it, only to die on its soil) into a pictorial entreaty that is more symbolic than documentary. Against a background of blackened sky, a Turkish janissary, flattened like a Persian miniature and rendered impersonal, even inhuman, by the profile view, drives his standard into the scorched Greek earth; while in the foreground, a Greek woman in white—a variant on a despairing figure in David's *Sabines*—rises heroically above the rubble, her arms extended toward the bloodstained architectural ruins that provide a poignant tomb for a male corpse (perhaps an allusion to Byron), whose dead hand protrudes limply in the foreground. It is a tripartite image—a nameless dead hero, an impassioned female survivor, a depersonalized victor—that turns contemporary fact into a symbolic plea for tears, assistance and urgent hope which prophesies by over a century Picasso's own allegorical account of the destruction of buildings and civilian populations, *Guernica*.

Delacroix, in fact, may have been the last great painter before Picasso who could create a compelling mythology from the data of contemporary history; for after the demise of Napoleon, no new flesh-and-blood head of state, whether a restored Bourbon king or the bourgeois king, Louis-Philippe, could exert the imaginative authority needed to resurrect the dreams of the Revolution or the Empire. It is hardly surprising that, after 1830, even Delacroix

A. Scheffer
The Suliot Women, Salon of 1827-28
Paris, Musée du Louvre

Callet
Louis XVIII, Salon of 1817
Versailles, Musée National

Gérard
Charles X, 1825
Versailles, Musée National

abandoned this earlier challenge, though he did so with a masterpiece that succeeds, perhaps for the last time, in joining the world of modern historical fact and traditional allegory, *Liberty Leading the People*, a painting that commemorates the July Revolution of 1830 (No. 41). It is a work that offers a curious collision of literal truth—the view of Notre Dame and old Parisian houses, the palpable reality of Parisian insurgents, whether workers or street urchins—with the ideal figure of *La France*, who, descending from the skies and from earlier classical and revolutionary allegories, leads the people of Paris toward an abstract goal. But it took Delacroix' genius to combine these two realms of the factual and the imaginary in a turbulent, explosive vision that elevates the street-fighting of Paris to a hymn to the universal ideal of liberty rather than to propaganda for a specific French political faction. Other artists, painting military scenes during the Bourbon Restoration, turned more and more to sheer documentation, recording, like François Heim, Louis-François Lejeune, or Horace Vernet (Nos. 99, 120, 188), the battles of past and present, whether Revolutionary, Napoleonic or Bourbon, with quasi-cinematic verisimilitude, or descending to the poignant level of the anonymous foot-soldier.

The conflict between contemporary realities and inherited traditions could be seen as well in Restoration portraiture. State portraits of Louis XVIII and Charles X by artists like Paulin-Guérin, Robert Lefèvre and François Gérard often attempted to revive, with feeble results, the formulas for Bourbon monarchs provided before the Revolution by Hyacinthe Rigaud, Antoine-François Callet and Joseph-Suffrein Duplessis; and historical portraits, like Pierre-Narcisse Guérin's of *Henri de la Rochejacquelin* (No. 95), tried to enlist, at the Salon of 1817, sympathy for the Royalist cause, whose motto, *"Vive le Roi"*, provides on a waving banner the explicitly propagandistic background for this image of a 21-year-old martyr who had given his life in 1794 to defend the throne of the decapitated brother of Louis XVIII. There developed, too, a revival of pre-Revolutionary aristocratic portrait formulas that could accommodate the haughty images demanded by the barons, counts and marquis of a restored monarchy, or the nouveau-riche sitters who aped the nobility. Ingres, in particular, created a brilliant, if tenuous equilibrium between the literal appearance of these patrons in their 19th century costume and jewelry and the resurrection of portraits types culled from masters like Holbein and Bronzino which could lend these sitters those qualities of chilly of aloofness and elegance to which they aspired. His *Portrait of the Comte Amédée-David de Pastoret* of 1826 (No. 111) virtually substitutes a modern head for a Bronzino prototype, just as his *Portrait of Madame Leblanc* (No. 110), executed in Florence in 1823, transforms the bourgeois respectability of a wealthy

French government official's wife into an image of Olympian detachment and abstemious luxury. And like Delacroix himself, Ingres could learn from the traditions of British aristocratic portraiture, especially that of Sir Thomas Lawrence (who so frequently exhibited at the Restoration Salons), witness his *Portrait of Count Gouriev*, the Russian ambassador to Tuscany (No. 109), whose commanding presence dominates not only the spectator but even the stormy panorama of Tuscan sky, hills and trees behind him.

But other artists could approach the facts of human personality and social position with a candor usually foreign to Ingres. Thus, even in an official portrait of a nobleman, such as that of Jean-Antoine Chaptal, Comte de Chanteloup (commissioned in 1824 for the " Société d'encouragement pour l'industrie nationale," of which the Count was president), Gros portrays this chemist and statesman at his writing table with an intense warmth and intimacy that speak of a personal dialogue between artist and sitter (No. 91). Similarly, Delaroche, in 1829, could catch the Marquis de Pastoret, Chancellor of France, in a moment of disarming informality that belies, in terms of its ephemeral mood, casual gesture and aura of privacy, the official costume worn by the Marquis for this commemorative occasion (No. 43). And outside the domain of official portraiture, the specificity of psychological revelation increased rapidly. Mme Haudebourt-Lescot, in her *Self-Portrait* of 1825 (No. 98), evokes an introspective, almost melancholic personality that, by comparison to the pleasant, public visage of Mme Vigée-Lebrun's earlier *Self-Portrait* (No. 198), is like a confession from a private diary. In the same way, the portrait of one artist by another—Ary Scheffer's *Portrait of Hersent* (No. 165)—creates a startling, close-up informality in which a pair of eyes meets our gaze with an uncommonly intense stare that eliminates questions of physical environment and profession in favor of a confrontation with a particular human psychology.

The climax of these ever deeper explorations of the human mind is found, of course, in Géricault's extravagant empathy with the mysterious, irrational world of human beings separated from normal adult behavior. This included not only his record of the desperation of the survivors of the *Medusa* but, above all, his portraits of the insane, where he offers the internal psychic counterpart of the external narrative terror exploited by so many of his contemporaries in the 1820s. Here, fascinated by the occasion to document for the psychiatrist Dr. Georget the tragic variations on the loss of reason, he not only documented the specific clinical facts of physiognomy and psychology, such as a case of kleptomania (No. 77), but he also translated this scientific enterprise into a mysterious symbol of a dark and frightening potential in all of mankind. The intensity of Géricault's observation of and compassion for these disturbed souls distills the often inflated rhetoric of romantic drama to its most direct and haunting statement.

Whatever subject Géricault turned to—portraiture, scenes of military life, landscape, animals—he could transform from prose to poetry, from fact to symbol, thereby deeply unsettling the foundations of the traditional hierarchy of subject matter, which still reigned officially under the Bourbon Restoration. One is again reminded of his genius when looking at Carle and Horace Vernets' picturesque documents of an event recorded by the many artists, and even by writers like Goethe, who visited Rome: the annual spectacle of a race of riderless horses down the Corso, the so-called *corso dei barberi* (Nos. 185, 186), which was illustrated as early as the late 1770s by a Scottish artist, David Allan. But unlike Géricault, who, in a series of paintings of 1816-17 (No. 76), miraculously succeeded in recreating this tourist attraction as a poetic metaphor of literally unbridled passion momentarily restrained and then released by the disciplining forces of man, the paintings by the two Vernets (father and son) offer only a prosaic, if vivid, account of a colorful pageant, a *festa* of rearing horses, holiday costumes, noisy crowds. Their interpretation, that is, remains still within the conventional realm of a lower order of genre and animal painting, never elevating its subject to that symbolic power which both Géricault and Delacroix attained in even their most humble themes. The Vernets' pictorial prose is like that of a tourist's diary, enlivened by the discoveries of unfamiliar sights in foreign lands, just as Louis-Jacque-Mandé Daguerre's contemporaneous record of the ruins of a Romanesque building in Scotland (No. 25) conveys, with its proto-photographic literalness of description, the enchantment of the remote in both history and geography.

But many other artists offered far more overtly matter-of-fact records of things observed at home. At times, as in Eugène Devéria's *Young Women Asleep* of 1827 (No. 48), such a charming glimpse of ladies dozing gracefully at a ball, while a suitor tiptoes in, is painted with a sketchy, vibrant warmth that lends a candlelight mystery of amorous intrigue to the scene; but more often, these vignettes of ordinary observation are executed in a technique that continues the neo-Dutch genre tradition that, with artists like Louis-Léopold Boilly and Marguerite Gérard, had become so prominent under Napoleon. Martin Drolling's two interior views of 1815 and 1816—one, a kitchen where a woman and a girl sew and a child plays with a kitten (No. 51); the second, another domestic scene where a gentleman relaxes in his house-slippers, a lady plays a piano and a servant opens a cupboard (No. 50)—may symbolize this quiet continuation of a polished style whose mimetic, mirror-like fidelity to middle-class facts suggests a revival of the little Dutch masters of the 17th century. The same might be said of Bouhot's breathtakingly accurate replication of the Salle des Pas-Perdus at the Palais de Justice (No. 12), where lawyers and visitors move about casually within vast, vaulted spaces that are rendered with the accurate, trompe-l'œil perspectives and miniaturist precision familiar to the church interiors of a 17th-century Dutch painter like Pieter Saenredam. It is hard to remember that such a picture was exhibited at the Salon of 1824, so foreign do its unpretentious, literal-minded descriptions of the commonplace appear amid the passionate esthetic programs embodied in the antagonistic faiths of Ingres and Delacroix that collided at the same Salon. Yet finally, by the middle of the 19th century, these casual images of sun-filled rooms, of people occupied in strolling or chatting and this search for fidelity to the facts of perception would begin to usurp the long reign of imaginative and historical subject matter and the equally long traditions of hierarchic compositional structure that still dominated the most ambitious painting executed before 1830. Indeed, it is the Parisian views of a master like Étienne Bouhot that, based in turn on such 18th-century scenes as those by Nicolas-Bernard Lépicié (No. 121), ultimately provide the pictorial continuity that underlies the Impressionist cityscapes of Manet, Monet, Renoir and Pissarro, just as Louis-Philippe Crépin's crystal-clear view of sea, sky and shore at Cherbourg (No. 24), shown at the Salon of 1822, offers a link to that intense observation of maritime light and weather which would be so important for artists from Jongkind and Boudin to Monet and Seurat.

It is, in fact, the landscapes of the period 1814-30 that reflect most clearly the growing tensions between the preservation of inherited attitudes and the quiet search for an almost naive truth in the recording of fresh scenes and perceptions. The duality can be seen most dramatically in a work of Géricault. Often, as in his *Landscape with a Roman Tomb*, of 1815-16 (No. 75), he turned to an Italianate tradition, in which the ideal harmonies of architecture and landscape provide an overtly poetic environment for an unspecified drama of a gloomy, even morbid cast. But he could equally turn to the counter-tradition of British and Dutch landscape painting, documenting, especially in his last years, the humble facts of vernacular architecture—stables, lime kilns, blacksmiths' shops—located in the most prosaic landscape settings. The same duality is evident, too, in the work of the short-lived Achille-Etna Michallon, whose first Salon entry in 1812 was *A Wash House, Study Made after Nature at Aunay*, but who then, in 1817, could turn from such a casual observation, presented only as a study, in order to win the Academy's first Prix de Rome competition in *paysage historique*, that is, a landscape ennobled by a mythological or historical subject, in this case, *Demo-*

critus and the Abderitans (Paris, École des Beaux-Arts). And he could continue, as seen in this exhibition, with such a bleak and stormy historical landscape as *Philoctetes at Lemnos* of 1822 (No. 130), which provides a resonant, Salvator Rosa-like environment for the agonizing drama of this wounded, abandoned Greek hero who, earlier, as in Guillaume Lethière's painting (No. 123), had so often inspired classically oriented artists in search of romantic *terribilità*. Even the young Jacques-Raymond Brascassat, an artist who after 1830 would paint primarily domestic animals in a domestic landscape, began by learning to idealize both these components of his art, as seen in his own Prix de Rome competition entry of 1825, the *Hunt of Meleager* (No. 14), where in a turbulent, Rubensian landscape a mighty fallen tree echoes the drama of the hunting and slaying of the Calydonian boar.

But other landscapes of the period could ignore these venerable academic ambitions in favor of more straightforward records of the facts of nature. Often, these facts were those of Italy, whose landscape, especially for foreigners, offered a certain remoteness and wonder, saturated as it was with an historical past without literally conforming to the academic requirements of *paysage historique*. Two works by French painters who lived almost all their lives in Italy—Pierre-Athanase Chauvin's landscape, *La Ruffinella, near Rome* (No. 21), and Nicolas-Didier Boguet's *View of the Villa Aldobrandini at Frascati,* executed in 1824 and sent to the Salon of 1827-28 (No. 5) —are cases in point, as is the painting with which Jean-Baptiste Corot made his Salon debut in 1827, his *Bridge of Narni, near Rome* (No. 22). But here, the remnants of an ancient viaduct, the herd of goats, the picturesquely costumed peasants and the deep, solemnly measured panorama of the Roman Campagna still evoke explicitly the traditions of Claude and Poussin and might still provide the setting for a bucolic passage in Theocritus or Virgil; whereas, in less official paintings of the same decade, particularly those executed in France, Corot would move from this studied meditation on the nostalgia of a landscape saturated with history and legend to more spontaneous and casual observations of ramshackle farmhouses and forest corners. And even many of his Italian landscapes of this decade, such as *La Cervara* (No. 23), an impression of a village outside Rome, are so candid in their response to changing atmospheric effects that they feel more at home in northern European landscape traditions than in those of Italy. It was the kind of innocent landscape that, in the 1820s, was to be exemplified by the British paintings and watercolors that French artists saw both at home and in England and that made their most conspicuous public appearance at the Salon of 1824. There, with some 30 other British works, was John Constable's *Haywain* (1821; London, National Gallery), whose vibrant brushwork and image of rural simplicity were soon to be echoed in France by such paintings as Paul Huet's little landscape of 1826 (No. 103), a virtual homage to this British masterpiece of the pastoral mode.

The truth and modesty of these British, as well as Dutch, landscape traditions supported those quiet aspects of French landscape painting that pursued the honest record of prosaic fact. Both Antoine-Pierre Mongin's *Curiosity* at the Salon of 1824 (No. 132) and Jan-Frans Van Dael's painting of his house of 1828 (No. 183) reflect this freshness and candor of empirical observation (" *une étude d'après nature,* " as the Salon catalog described the Mongin); but these perceptions, as in Corot's work of the 1820s, are still wedded to an intuitively abstract discipline of parallel and perpendicular alignments that unobtrusively offer a spatial skeleton of almost Davidian lucidity beneath the charming surface descriptions of the casual growth of trees, the rubble of old walls, the sparkling shimmer of light. The immediate future of French painting was, in fact, to be more and more determined by such modest glimpses of the vivid here-and-now than by the perpetuation of the grandiose historical rhetoric that, in the painting of Ingres and Delacroix and their lesser satellites, reached, by 1830, a passionate climax, but one that was as retrospective as the monarchy itself. In the decades that followed the July Revolution, the artistic conflicts of the Bourbon Restoration were finally to be resolved in favor of immediate personal truths rather than inherited public myths, of the urgent new demands of the 19th-century present rather than the veneration of a long-lost historical past.

Géricault
Landscape with a Roman Tomb: Morning, c. 1815
Paris, Musée du Petit Palais
No. 75

Lejeune
Battle of Guisando, s. d. 1815
Versailles, Musée National
No. 120

Drolling
Interior of a Kitchen, s.d. 1815
Paris, Musée du Louvre
No. 51

Drolling
Interior of a Dining Room, s.d. 1816
Paris, Private Collection
No. 50

F. Richard
Madame Élisabeth de France Distributing Milk, Salon of 1817
Versailles, Musée National
No. 155

Guérin
Portrait of Henri de La Rochejaquelein, Salon of 1817
Cholet, Musée Municipal
No. 95

Géricault
Riderless Horse Race, c. 1817
Paris, Musée du Louvre
No. 76

Hersent
Louis XVI Distributing Alms to the Poor, s.d. 1817
Versailles, Musée National
No. 100

Taunay
Sermon of Saint John the Baptist, s.d. 1818
Nice, Préfecture
No. 175

Ingres
Death of Leonardo da Vinci, s.d. 1818
Paris, Musée du Petit Palais
No. 106

Monsiau
Devotion of Monseigneur de Belzunce, s. d. 1819
Paris, Musée du Louvre
No. 133

Ingres
Roger and Angelica, s.d. 1819
Paris, Musée du Louvre
No. 107

Prud'hon
Venus, Hymen and Cupid, c. 1815-20
Paris, Musée du Louvre
No. 144

Ingres
Jesus Delivering the Keys to Saint Peter, s.d. 1820
Montauban, Musée Ingres
No. 108

Mallet
The Bathing of the Infant Saint John the Baptist, s.d. 1820
Paris, Private Collection
No. 125

H. Vernet
Riderless Horse Race, c. 1820
New York, The Metropolitan Museum of Art
No. 186

Ingres
Portrait of Count Gouriev, s.d. 1821
Leningrad, State Hermitage Museum
No. 109

Dubufe
Apollo and Cyparissus, s.d. 1821
Avignon, Musée Calvet
No. 53

264

Delorme
Cephalus and Aurora, s.d. 1822
Sens, Musée Municipal
No. 45

Crépin
Harbor of Cherbourg, s.d. 1822
Paris, Musée de la Marine
No. 24

266

Michallon
Philoctetes at Lemnos, s.d. 1822
Montpellier, Musée Fabre
No. 130

Géricault
Portrait of an Insane Man ("Kleptomaniac"), c. 1822
Ghent, Museum voor Schone Kunsten
No. 77

A.-E. Fragonard
Don Juan and the Commander's Statue, c. 1820-30
Strasbourg, Musée des Beaux-Arts
No. 58

Mongin
Curiosity, s.d. 1823
Cleveland, Mr and Mrs Noah L. Butkin Collection
No. 132

Boguet *fils*
View of the Villa Aldobrandini at Frascati, c. 1823
Aix-en-Provence, Musée Granet
No. 5

Ingres
Portrait of Madame Leblanc, s.d. 1823
New York, The Metropolitan Museum of Art
No. 110

Haudebourt-Lescot
Self-Portrait, s.d. 1823
Paris, Musée du Louvre
No. 98

Scheffer
Saint Thomas Aquinas Preaching During a Storm, s.d. 1823
Paris, Chapelle de l'Hôpital Laënnec
No. 164

Gros
Portrait of the Comte Chaptal, s.d. 1823
The Cleveland Museum of Art
No. 91

Sigalon
Locusta, c. 1824
Nîmes, Musée des Beaux-Arts
No. 167

Bouhot
Salle des Pas-Perdus, Palais de Justice, Paris, s.d. 1824
Paris, Ministère de la Justice
No. 12

Prud'hon and Boisfremont
Andromache and Astyanax, Salon of 1824
New York, The Metropolitan Museum of Art
No. 145

David
Mars Disarmed by Venus and the Three Graces, s.d. 1824
Brussels, Musées Royaux des Beaux-Arts de Belgique
No. 38

Révoil
François I Knighting his Grandson, François II, s.d. 1824
Aix-en-Provence, Musée Granet
No. 153

Brascassat
Hunt of Meleager, s.d. 1825
Bordeaux, Musée des Beaux-Arts
No. 14

Chauvin
La Ruffinella, near Rome, 1825
Paris, Musée des Arts Décoratifs
No. 21

P. Huet
Guardian's House in the Forest of Compiègne, s.d. 1826
Paris, Michel Legrand Collection
No. 103

H. Vernet
Mazeppa and the Wolves, s.d. 1826
Avignon, Préfecture
No. 187

C. Vernet
Riderless Horse Race, s.d. 1826
Avignon, Musée Calvet
No. 185

H. Vernet
Scene of the French Campaign of 1814, s.d. 1826
New York, Private Collection
No. 188

Delacroix
Greece on the Ruins of Missolonghi, 1826
Bordeaux, Musée des Beaux-Arts
No. 39

Ingres
Portrait of the Comte Amédée-David de Pastoret, s.d. 1826
The Art Institute of Chicago
No. III

Daguerre
People Visiting a Romanesque Ruin, s.d. 1826
Paris, Gérard Lévy Collection
No. 25

Delacroix
Christ in the Garden of Olives, Salon of 1827-28
Paris, Église Saint-Paul-Saint-Louis
No. 40

Devéria
Young Women Asleep, s.d. 1827
Paris, Musée du Louvre
No. 48

Schnetz
Vow to the Madonna, Salon of 1827-28
La Rochelle, Musée des Beaux-Arts
No. 166

F. Gérard
Saint Theresa, Salon of 1827-28
Paris, Infirmerie Marie-Thérèse
No. 70

Corot
Bridge of Narni, near Rome, Salon of 1827-28
Ottawa, National Gallery of Canada
No. 22

L. Robert
Pilgrims Returning from the Feast Day of the Madonna dell' Arco, s.d. 1827
Paris, Musée du Louvre
No. 160

Van Dael
Landscape: The Painter's House, s.d. 1828
Rotterdam, Museum Boymans van Beuningen
No. 183

Corot
La Cervara near Rome, c. 1828
Zurich, Kunsthaus
No. 23

Delaroche
Portrait of the Marquis de Pastoret, 1829
Boston, Museum of Fine Arts
No. 43

Scheffer
Portrait of Hersent, s.d. 1830
Grenoble, Musée de Peinture et de Sculpture
No. 165

Gudin
Devotion of Captain Desse, s.d. 1830
Bordeaux, Musée des Beaux-Arts
No. 92

Delaroche
The Children of Edward IV, s.d. 1830
Paris, Musée du Louvre
No. 44

Delacroix
Liberty Leading the People, s.d. 1830
Paris, Musée du Louvre
No. 41

Catalog

Editor's Note

The sizes of works of art are given in centimeters, with height preceding width. An artist's biography precedes the first entry in the catalog under his name. References and exhibitions have been abbreviated and can be found in the list of exhibitions and the bibliography on pp. 685 and 689, both of which have been left standing from the French edition of this catalog.

One asterisk (*) means exhibited in Paris only; two (**) mean exhibited in Paris and Detroit only; three (***) mean exhibited in Detroit and New York only; four (****) mean not exhibited.

Abbreviations

"...."	When the French title of a painting is placed between quotation marks, this indicates a Salon catalog title.
A.A.F.	*Archives de l'Art Français*
Arch. Louvre	Paris, Archives of the Musée du Louvre and National Museums
Arch. Nat.	Paris, Archives Nationales
B.S.H.A.F.	*Bulletin de la Société de l'Histoire de l'Art Français*
c.	center
Coll. Deloynes	Relates to the Salon critiques gathered by M. Deloynes, *"auditeur des Comptes,"* in 56 volumes today preserved in the Cabinet des Estampes of the Bibliothèque Nationale, Paris.
D. (d.)	Dated
h.c.	Not in catalog
Ibid. and *Idem*	Ibidem and Idem
I.G.R.A.F.	*Inventaire Général des Richesses de l'Art Français*
INV.	Inventory
l.	lower, left
m.	middle
N.A.A.F.	*Nouvelles Archives de l'Art Français*
r.	right
R.K.D.	Rijksbureau voor kunsthistorische documentatie, The Hague
S. (s.)	Signed
Salon	Indicates that the painting participated in a Parisian Salon.
u.	upper

Antoine Berjon

1754 Lyon 1843

The son of a butcher, Antoine Berjon was born in Lyon, Saint-Pierre de Vaise parish, on 17 May 1754. After having studied drawing under the Lyonnais sculptor, Antoine-Michel Perrache, and then medicine, he joined the silk industry as a fabric designer, as did many of his confreres. Working for a commercial silk manufacturer, he made many business trips to Paris, where he became friendly with the portraitists Jean-Baptiste-Jacques Augustin and Claude Hoin, and participated in the Salon for the first time in 1791 with paintings of fruit. After the siege of Lyon (1793) and the ruin of the business establishment where he was employed, he moved to Paris in 1794, leading a precarious existence in which his primary assistance came from Marceline Desbordes-Valmore. He exhibited at the Salons of 1796, 1798, 1799, 1804 and 1810.

Returning to Lyon in 1810, he worked for an embroidery-maker and, on 6 July, succeeded Jacques Barraband as professor of the flower still life class at the École des Beaux-Arts (Lyon, Arch. mun., R 1). He participated in the Parisian Salons of 1817 and 1819 (second class metal), in the Lyonnais Salons of 1822 and 1837. Forced to resign his post in 1823 because of some incidents caused by his irascibility, he was replaced by his student Antoine Thierriat; in retirement he continued to instruct several students, and to paint until his death on 25 October 1843. He showed at the Salon of 1842, and the Lyonnais exhibition of 1843-44 included 41 of his works.

Beginning with Joannès Gaubin ("Antoine Berjon, peintre de fleurs," *Revue du Lyonnais*, 1856, pp. 159-176), biographers have stressed the unsociable and hard character of this artist, who believed besides that he had been persecuted for his political beliefs.

In the French museums are about ten of his paintings, all still lifes (none are known to be in museums outside France): Bagnères-de-Bigorre: *Fleurs*; Lyon: *Le Cadeau* (fruit, s.d. 1797, dedicated to Augustin; perhaps no. 27, "*Un tableau de fruits,*" in the Salon of 1798), *Fruits et fleurs dans une corbeille d'osier* (s.d. Lyon, 1810, perhaps no. 46 in the Salon of 1810), *Coquillages et madrépores sur une table de marbre,* (s.d. Lyon, 1810, no. 47 in the Salon of 1810), *Fruits dans une coupe d'albâtre* (s., acquired in 1811), *Fleurs dans un vase d'albâtre,* (s.d., Lyon, 1813), *Fleurs peintes sur fond blanc, Raisins dans une coupe d'albâtre ;* Montpellier: (on loan to the Mairie de Montblanc, Hérault) *Fleurs dans une corbeille,* s.; Saint-Étienne: *Nature morte,* s., *Fleurs.*

Best known as a flower painter, Berjon also did portraits, sometimes in oil (the composer *J. Halévy avec son frère et sa sœur,* s.d. 1820, Lyon, Conservatoire de Musique) or in pastel (*Autoportrait,* Lyon, Musée des Beaux-Arts and Musée Lyonnais des Arts Décoratifs), but most frequently in sepia, India ink and watercolor (*Claude Hoin,* Heino, Holland, Hannema Foundation; *Autoportrait,* Saint-Étienne), *Portrait de femme,* Paris, Bibliothèque de l'École des Beaux-Arts ; *Mlle Bailly* and *Mme Augias,* Lyon, Musée). In the Salon of 1796 (Salon no. 23), he exhibited studies entitled *Victimes lyonnaises;* two compositions dating from the Directory of standing females, *La Merveilleuse aux pommes* and *La Merveilleuse au pied,* are in the Lyon museum. Berjon also did miniatures (Salon of 1804, no. 23), perhaps under the influence of his friend Augustin (who did his portrait, shown at the Exposition Universelle of 1878, and to whom in 1797 he dedicated his first known painting, *Le cadeau):* a *Portrait de femme* in the Cabinet des Dessins, Louvre, and an *Autoportrait* at the age of 65 in the Lyon museum attest to his mastery of this genre. He was an occasional engraver: the Salon of 1796 includes an engraving (" engraving; new kind invented by the artist," Salon no. 25) and 12 etchings by him were published after his death, along with some lithographs. The Musée des Beaux-Arts of Lyon contains many drawings by Berjon (*Études des Fleurs ; Le Lièvre* and *Le Coq,* Salon of 1810; *La Fouine,* 1818), as does that city's Musée Historique des Tissus (four pattern books containing 259 drawings); at Mâcon is a *Coupe de fruits.*

Born some 20 years before the principal members of the School of Lyon, Antoine Berjon stands out among the many flower painters by virtue of his originality. We have not been able to locate his landscapes, but one finds in his most vigorous portraits (e.g. *Claude Hoin*) the incisive manner of a Jean-Jacques de Boissieu; even in his miniatures, he is able to describe the model with an accuracy that avoids hardness. He shares with his fellow Lyonnais artists Michel Grobon, Pierre Révoil and Fleury Richard a "Dutch" taste for precision, smooth finish and luminous effects so well-suited to the neo-classical spirit. Like them, he lived for a long time in Paris and exhibited side-by-side with Jan-Frans Van Dael and the Van Spaendoncks at a time when flower painting was enjoying a renewed popularity. In these confrontations, and perhaps above all in the study of 17th-century Dutch masters, Berjon found stimulating examples.

S.L.

I
Basket of Flowers

"Bouquet de lis et de roses dans une corbeille posée sur une chiffonnière"
Plate p. 223
Canvas; 66 × 50; s.d.l.r. *Berjon./Lyon 1814*
Salon of 1817, no. 42 (?)
Paris, Musée du Louvre

Enriched by a prestigious heritage, still life, at the beginning of the 19th century, did not lose its popularity with the public, as the Salon catalogs indicate. Holland which inspired the painters of interiors from François Granet to Étienne Bouhot, also imposed its vision on the painters of still life: a taste for technical precision and for illusionism could be displayed in largely decorative compositions à la Van Huysum or, on the other hand, used to isolate objects which contain their own power of seduction.

The work of Berjon most often illustrates this second tendency. His most ambitious painting, *Fruits et fleurs dans une corbeille d'osier* (Salon of 1810) resembles in its exuberance a Van Spaendonck; and, despite the fact that in 1813 Berjon copied Van Dael's *La tubéreuse cassée* (see sale, Paris, Palais Galliera, 1 june 1967, no. 2, ill.; Van Dael's composition, s.d. 1807, entered the Lyon museum around 1810 as a model for fabric designers), one rarely finds in his own compositions the clever constructions of bouquets which were then so fashionable. Berjon preferred simple compositions, in which flowers and fruit are presented directly with some of that scientific precision, a characteristic of this genre of which he was in complete command, as well as a lively sense of the limpid atmosphere and soft light conducive to the harmonizing of delicate tones. Painters who intensively scrutinize reality willingly assign to it the poetry of the unreal: thus, Berjon gave to the fruit of his *Cadeau* (1797) an obsessive presence, and he was attracted to the uncommon shapes of the *Coquillages et madrépores* (1810); or even isolated in space a *Panier*

suspendu et rempli de fleurs (Salon of 1819, no. 62; perhaps the painting reproduced by S.H. Pavière, *A Dictionary of flower, fruit, and still life painters*, Leigh-on-Sea, 1963, II, fig. 3). Painted in 1814, the *Bouquet* recently acquired by the Louvre is perhaps identical to the one Berjon, then professor in Lyon, sent to the Salon of 1817 (he had not exhibited since 1810): its subject and dimensions match the description under no. 42 of the catalog (see Provenance). In opposition to the flower painting conceived as a coherant, composed image, it offered a most original formula. Everything underlines the individuality of each element; the unusual perspective, slight dissonance of sharp tones, strong definitions of light along the marble shelf and basket, precise rendering of materials, exact observations of reflections, and drops of water—one by one—each catches our eye. The mystery of the unexplained (why has the bolt of the lock fallen open; and why are the shells, which a Van der Ast would have emphasized, hidden in the shadow of a drawer ?), intended evidently to pique the curiosity, becomes a psychological game, in which the viewer is provoked by the temporary disarray of things: the flowers will soon be arranged in the albaster vase, the basket emptied, the books put in order, the drawer closed. In this intimate painting, the casual presentation of objects suggests familiar activities—reading in the garden, picking flowers—and evokes a human presence. In introducing the suggestion of sequential development into a somewhat super-realist composition whose plastic components belong fully to their period, Berjon explored one of the most original directions of still life painting.

PROVENANCE

Painted in Lyon in 1814; corresponds perhaps to title of no. 42 in Salon of 1817, which describes the principal elements of the Louvre picture. The Salon list of that year designates Berjon's entries as "4 paintings of flowers and fruits; 81 × 64 cms." (Arch. Louvre, Série X Salons). These dimensions, which must include the frames, match the present painting, which would have a border 7 cm. wide. Acquired in 1974 from the Galería Vélasquez, Madrid, by the Musée du Louvre (INV. no. R.F. 1974 - 10).

EXHIBITIONS

1817, Salon, no. 42 (?); 1843-1844, Lyon, no. 23 (?).

S.L.

Jean-Simon Berthélemy

1743 Laon - Paris 1811

Jean-Simon Berthélemy, who was born 5 March 1743, entered the studio of Noël Hallé (see O. Estournet, 1905, p. 108). Three years later, after three unsuccessful attempts, he won the Grand Prix with *Alexandre coupant le nœud gordien* (Paris, École des Beaux-Arts), which enabled him to enter the École Royale des Élèves Protégés, where he stayed until 1771 (L. Courajod, 1874, p. 175). His training was completed by the traditional stay in Rome, from October 1771 to October 1774. Berthélemy seems to have gratified the hopes of the current director of the Academy, Charles Natoire, who several times told Marigny that his pupil "is on the road to distinction in his art" (*Correspondance des Directeurs de l'Académie,* 1902 ed., XII, p. 398).

Although history tells us of his friendship with other classmates at Palazzo Mancini, the painters F.-G. Ménageot, F.-A. Vincent, and J.-B. Suvée, and the architects P.-A. Pâris and J.-J. Huvé, and of his cordial relations with certain well-known hosts such as Bergeret (see Bergeret de Grancourt, 1948, p. 70), nothing is known of his artistic activity during these years in Rome.

After his return to Paris, he began an official career which continued smoothly right up to the Revolution. *Agréé* in 1777, he became a full member of the Royal Academy of Painting on 18 August 1781 with his *Apollon et Sarpédon* (Langres). From 1779 to 1789, he regularly exhibited at the Salon works ordered by D'Angiviller for the Gobelins manufactory. These were antique subjects (*Manlius Torquatus condamnant son fils à mort,* 1785, Tours; or *La Confiance d'Eléazar,* 1789, Angers; or episodes from French history, such as

L'Action courageuse d'Eustache de Saint-Pierre au siège de Calais, 1779 (Laon); *Le Combat de Marcel et Maillard,* 1783, present location unknown; and *The Entry of the French into Paris,* 1787, (No. 2). Known as a talented painter of ceilings, he received many commissions. He worked with J.-F. Chalgrin at the Hôtel de Saint-Florentin, with Charles de La Brière at the Hôtel de Vaudreuil and with R. Mique at the Palais de Fontainebleau. All of these decorations are preserved, as is his ceiling in the Musée Napoléon, done under the Directory and Empire, as was a decoration for the Palais du Luxembourg.

Berthélemy remained in the background during the Revolution, whose excesses he soon seems to have disapproved of (Duchange, 1853, p. 15), and did not occupy a prominent place. Nevertheless, in 1791, he became the official designer of costumes for the Opera (he had been assistant designer since 1787), a post he retained until 1807 (Arch. nat., AJ XIII, 57 and 79 [7-8]).

He reappeared under the Directory, which appointed him on 14 May 1796 "Commissioner for the research of objects of science and art in Italy," along with Thouin, Berthelot, Monge, La Billardière and the sculptor J.-G. Moitte (*Correspondance des Directeurs de l'Académie,* 1907 ed., XVI, p. 417). From June 1796 to January 1798 they traveled to Milan, Piacenza, Parma, Modena, Bologna, Pavia, Ferrara, Cento, Florence, Rome, Mantua and Venice, choosing works of art that were to be paraded triumphantly on carts through Paris on 9 Thermidor, Year VI (27 July 1798) for a solemn festival (M.-L. Blumer, 1934, pp. 241-245).

On 12 August of the following year, Berthélemy

and Moitte were named "members of the artists' council at the Central Museum of the Arts" (Arch. Louvre, Z², 1798, 12 August).

Absorbed by his tasks as curator of the museum, Berthélemy became principally occupied with problems of display and of the restoration and acquisition of works of art, until Vivant Denon, appointed director of the Musée Napoléon, relieved him on 19 November 1802 of his duties as honorary administrator (Arch. Louvre, Z², 1802, 19 November). He was then given several imperial commissions (decorations for the Musée Napoléon and the senatorial Palais du Luxembourg, mentioned above). He exhibited for the last time at the Salon of 1808 with *Général Bonaparte visitant les Fontaines de Moïse* (Versailles, Musée de l'Histoire de France), which the critics described as insignificant and incorrectly drawn (coll. Deloynes, XLIII,, no. 1143, p. 54). Realizing that his art, which J.-L. David said was dull (E.-J. Delécluze, 1855, p. 113), was out of touch with the new style, and convinced of public hostility against him, Berthélemy died of melancholy on 2 March 1811 (Duchange, 1853, pp. 33-34).

Besides Berthélemy's accomplishments as a history painter and decorator, he was a fine portraitist (*Portrait de Diderot*, 1784, Paris, Musée Carnavalet). His work was sought by numbers of religious institutions (*Le Martyre de saint Pierre*, Douai, church of Saint-Pierre, painted in 1779 for the abbey of Anchin; *L'établissement de la religion chez les sauvages*, Paris, church of Saint-Sulpice, and *La Sainte Famille en Egypte*, parish church of Monthléry-Linas, painted in 1784 and 1791 for the seminary of the Saint-Esprit in Paris); but he was not able to combine correct drawing with fervent inspiration—the two qualities demanded by his contemporaries. Though Bachaumont thought that he had the "sacred fire (...) that links him with the happy period of Monsieur Doyen" (Bachaumont, 1777-89, XXIV, 25 August, Letter 1, pp. 18-19), others continued to accuse him of choosing the easy way (*Journal de Paris*, 15 September 1785, p. 1064) and of being more concerned with certain tricks of brushwork than with drawing, effect, color, expression and even reason" (coll. Deloynes, XI, no. 208, p. 25). Berthélemy's style, in which this love of *fa presto* is accompanied by a desire for grandeur and austerity, gives him a unique position in 18th-century painting.

N.V.

2
Entry of the French into Paris*

La reprise de Paris sur les Anglais: Entrée de l'armée française le 13 avril 1436
Plate p. 81
Canvas; 383 × 262; s.d.l.l. *Berthélemy 1787*
Salon of 1787 (not in the catalog)
Versailles, Musée National

Berthélemy had suggested painting for the Salon of 1787 "the delegation sent by Charles V to Duguesclin to return to him his sword as constable which he relinquished," or "the retaking of Paris from the English"; the latter subject was accepted (see F. Engerand, 1901, pp. 37-38).

The picture was probably submitted during the last few days before the close of the Salon, which would explain its absence from the catalog. J.-J. Guiffrey, in his re-edition of the Salon catalog in 1870, noted that he had found the following manuscript citation in a copy of the original catalog belonging to G. Duplessis: "The Connétable de Richemont joyfully receives Michel Le Tellier (or Lallier or Lailler) and the loyal citizens who had helped his troops enter the city. Marshal De l'Isle-Adam shows them the letters of amnesty and confirmation of privileges." This episode took place on 13 April 1436 and marked the beginning of the expulsion of the English from occupied France.

As this canvas was submitted so late, it did not receive comment by the critics, with one exception (see coll. Deloynes, XV, no. 371, p. 29), a critic who found it well composed, full of movement and taste, and thought that the artist, though lacking in precision "has the germ of a great man." The scene has indeed been well thought out: its composition skillful, and the figures historically correct in their costumes and medieval arms, the decor reconstituted with fair accuracy. However, the theatrical and somewhat exaggerated gesturing of the figures, the dramatic expressions on the faces and the too-brilliant colors did not match the rules and conventions of contemporary taste. Yet, this painting summarizes well the work of this painter who, in his desire to edify the onlooker with the contemplation of an episode of transcendent national importance, sometimes lapsed into grandiloquence.

PROVENANCE

Ordered for the King and intended for the Gobelins manufactory; valued at 3,000 *livres* on 27 October 1787 (Arch. nat. O1 - 1921, B, fol. 5), in a document published by F. Engerand (see below); appears in 1794 in the Gobelins inventory (Arch. Louvre, 40 DD 4, p. 7, no. 4); sent to Versailles by decision of the jury dated 7 March 1798 (Arch. Louvre, p. 4, 1798, 7 March; requested on 2 June 1802 by the Minister of the Interior to complete the collection in the Gallery of the Conservative Senate in the Palais du Luxembourg (Arch. nat. F²¹ [64]; in 1810, was in the Palais de Fontainebleau (Arch. Louvre I DD 18, p. 516, no. 1184); though intended from 1832 for the Versailles museum (Arch. Louvre, I DD 89, no. 1180), it remained at Fontainebleau until 6 November 1835 (Arch. Louvre, p. 12, Registre Fontainebleau, fol. 82), when it was sent finally to Versailles (INV. 2524). It was enlarged at the top above the spire probably shortly after it was placed in the Versailles museum in 1835.

REFERENCES

Coll. Deloynes, v. XV, no. 371, p. 29; (Anon.) mus. cat. of Versailles, 1801, no. 8; [Ch. Gavard], 1839-1848; v . I, no. CXVIII; Duchange, 1853, p. 44; Eud. Soulié, mus. cat. 1854-1855, v. I, no. 158; J.-J. Guiffrey, 1870, p. 60; Bellier and Auvray, 1882-1885; v. I, p. 78; J.-J. Guiffrey, 1897, p. 356; F. Engerand, 1901, pp. 37-38; M. Fenaille, 1903-1923, v. V, p. 86; R. Lanson, 1926, p. 43; A. Pérate and G. Brière, 1931, no. 158.

RELATED WORKS

Tapestries. The *Entry of the French into Paris* was one of a series of pictures intended to serve as models for a *Tenture de l'Histoire de France,* ordered in 1784 by D'Angiviller. Three of the ten episodes in this set were by Berthélemy: *L'action courageuse d'Eustache de Saint-Pierre au siège de Calais,* 1779, Laon; *Le Combat de Marcel et Maillard,* 1783, location unknown (see M. Fenaille, 1903-1923, IV, pp. 370-372). Two weavings were made from the painting exhibited here; the first was in high warp, made in the atelier at Audran between 1788 and 1791, and given to the Spanish ambassador on 18 June (30 Prairial, Year VII), the second was also begun in high warp and was abandoned by order of the jury on 18 September 1794 (27 Fructidor, Year II); it was lent in July 1825 to the painter Chabal and has not been found since (cf. M. Fenaille, *op. cit.*). *Engravings.* Engraved by Ed. Lerouge in Ch. Gavard, Paris, 1839-1848, II, 2nd series, section 3, no. 7 (cf. J. Laran, 1930, XIV, no. 8, p. 108). An example of the engraving was included in the exhibition, 1971, Bourg-en-Bresse, no. 143.

N. V.

Jean-Victor Bertin

1767 (not 1775) Paris 1842

From a family of master wig-makers that included his uncle and godfather (so, too, were the families of Louis Moreau, Pierre Valenciennes and Jean-Baptiste Corot; is this just pure coincidence !), he entered the Royal Academy of Painting at the age of 18 in 1785, as the student of Gabriel-François Doyen. In 1788 he was reported as still being there studying under Valenciennes, who made a profound impression on his education (until the age of 40, Bertin presented himself at the Salons as a student of Valenciennes) and who directed him toward the *paysage composé*, ideally Italianate and idyllic. In the first half of the 19th century, Bertin even became one of its leading representatives and most vehement advocates, to the point of

becoming tainted by the discredit into which it fell because of the slow but widespread rise of Realism (so much so that Gustave Planche could qualify his works as "absurdities of the brush").

From 1785 to 1793, Bertin took part in several *concours d'émulation* without success. His career actually began in at the Salon of 1793, the first in which he exhibited; from then on, until his death, he participated regularly in the Salons. He received awards several times, in particular at the Salons of 1799 and 1808, was decorated by the Legion of Honor in 1822, and his paintings (perhaps because of their pleasing decorative character) were often bought by the State and placed either in official palaces (Trianon, Fontainebleau, notably in 1811, 1816, 1817), or in provincial museums (purchases made at the Salons of 1833, 1836-1840).

From 1801 on, he repeatedly proposed to the Academy the creation of a Prix de Rome in the category of Historical Landscape, efforts which did not come to fruition until 1817, when the first competition in historical landscape was held, and was in fact won by one of his students, Achille-Etna Michallon. This prize would continue to be awarded in this category until 1863.

Most likely sometime between 1806 and 1808, Bertin made a trip to Italy. In any case, Italian subjects became more numerous in his work. At the height of his reputation, between 1816 and 1824, Bertin executed several lithographs for a course in landscape (*Étude de paysages*, 1823; *Recueil d'études de paysage*, appearing from 1816), for which there were such distinguished devotees as the Duc de Berry and the banker Laffitte. Passing through his fashionable atelier were André Jolivard, Corot (from 1822 on; he recalled that he did not remember it well but, in fact, he owed much to it, especially with respect to principles and the manner of transforming in the studio a study made from nature; e.g. his *Entrée du parc de Saint-Cloud*, painted exactly in Bertin's manner, c. 1800-1810). Michallon, Jules Coignet, Léon Fleury, Antoine-Félix Boisselier, Camille-Joseph-Étienne Roqueplan, Charles de la Berge and Félix-Hippolyte Lanoue who, on the eve of Bertin's death in 1841, won the prize for historical landscape.

The first catalog of his painting has recently been compiled by Mme S. Gutwirth (1974), but it most probably should be enlarged, Bertin apparently having been as productive a painter as he was in demand. Of the 147 works already cataloged, with practically no reference to works distributed through sales, only about 60 were able to be illustrated in this fundamental work. A good number of the Salon paintings remain lost; the most serious omissions being the from his early years, Bertin's first known signed and dated painting, a large landscape with a mountain, temple and weeping willow of 1800 (see Gutwirth, 1974, no. 23, p. 342, ill.). Fortunately, certain paintings are known through published engravings, especially in the *Annales du Musée* by Landon (*Paysages*, 1808). This true only of several paintings from the Salons of 1801 (*Ville de Phénéos*, which received a *prix d'encouragement*—a canvas sent by the Louvre to the Prefecture of Nice and apparently lost today; it was the first official purchase of a Bertin), 1802, 1804, 1808 (*Palestrina, Entrée de Pérouse, Olevano, Paysage italien*, all engraved by Landon), 1812,

1814, 1822 (a *Vue prise dans les Apennins, sur l'ancienne voie Valérie*, which was destroyed in 1870-71 in the fire at the Château de Saint-Cloud). Salon paintings which have been located include, for 1800, the *Statue*, or *Intérieur d'un parc*, Dijon, Musée Magnin (if the identification is correct); for 1808, *Vue de Ronciglione*, Nantes; for 1812, *Arrivée de Napoléon à Ettlingen*, Versailles; for 1817, *Pasteurs faisant des offrandes au dieu Pan*, s.d. 1816, Rennes; for 1819, *Caribert et Théodegilde*, painted for the Galerie de Diane at Fontainebleau and deposited at Béziers by the Louvre (more a sylvan neoclassical landscape than an example of the gothic *style troubadour*, despite the subject !); for 1831, *Paysage historique*, s.d. 1830, sent by the State to Toulouse. We should add that the *Vue d'Olevano* of the Salon of 1817 was burned at Saint-Cloud in 1870-71; and that the *Vue prise à Nepi, sur la route de Florence à Rome*, from the same Salon, was placed by the Louvre in the Ministry of War in 1876, but its present location is not known. It may turn up in the French provinces some day, the paintings of 1876 having been distributed to regional *hôtels des généraux*.

Because this exhibition does not extend beyond 1830, we shall mention only briefly some of the other Salon paintings by Bertin which are now in museums: Dijon (1836), Honfleur (1838), Autun (1839), Évreux (1839), Carpentras (1840), besides a painting burned at Saint-Cloud (s.d. 1831) and another placed in the Ministry of War, as had been the *Vue de Nepi*, cited above (s.d. 1834). Other museums with his paintings include Cherbourg, Sceaux (small studies made in the Ile-de-France, e.g., *Entrée du parc de Saint-Cloud*, which constitute, besides the idealized *vues composées*, the main alternative in Bertin's œuvre), Boston Museum of Fine Arts (the same type of suburban Parisian landscape). Saint-Denis (*ibid.*), La Fère, Coutances (two typical idyllic landscapes of 1810-12), Rouen and Quimper (*ibid.*), Lille (s.d. 1837), Angers (s.d. 1837), Avignon (two handsome studies of insolated trees, executed with a sense of freshness and pre-Barbizon sensibility), Reims (s.d. 1820), Phoenix and Providence. In the Louvre is a *Vue d'Essonnes*, 1800-05, of a charming modesty *à la danoise* (cf. Dahl, Koepke) and two large canvases commissioned, in 1819 by Laffitte (on loan to the Monuments Historiques from the Château de Maisons-Laffitte), the Musée and Bibliothèque Marmottan, with numerous landscapes of the environs of Paris (not all cataloged by Gutwirth). These constitute the most notable holdings of works by Bertin. This list indicates the great popularity in which Bertin was held throughout the first half of the 19th century; the later distribution of his works and the fact that most of the paintings mentioned in museums are now held in reserve points to an extreme reaction in the opposite direction.

Of a fairly consistent "idealizing" inspiration, Bertin's œuvre was marked at the beginning by a rather hard and straightforward technique; it softened and matured under the Empire and Restoration, made up equally of direct, unpretentious views and noble and elaborate compositions; after 1830, he attempted to rival Realism with an enriched palette, a more accessible imagery and a more realistic observation of nature, while never breaking with his earlier classicizing esthetic. This compromise proved to be rather inhibiting and stultifying; certainly Bertin's best works were those done before 1830.　　　　　J. F.

3
Italian Landscape

Paysage d'Italie avec un cavalier
Plate p. 211
Canvas; 60 × 96; s.l.l. *V. Bertin*
Boulogne-Billancourt, Bibliothèque Paul Marmottan

One of Bertin's finest landscapes, but also one of the least known, this painting is one of those rare views probably painted in Italy or perhaps executed from direct impressions of Italy; it can nevertheless be categorized as a *vue composée*. The locale and general disposition of elements recall the *Vue prise à Borghetto sur la route de Rome à Florence* (S. Gutwirth, 1974, no. 90, p. 351, ill.) and *Vue d'une ville dans la Sabine, soleil couchant,* exhibited in the Salon of 1814 and known by a lithograph of 1822 by J.-L.-F. Villeneuve (*ibid.,* no. 83, p. 350, ill.) where the light streams in from between the clusters of trees in a very similar way. Mme Gutwirth dates the canvas to the years 1808-10; it is true that precisely named Italian locales appear more frequently in Bertin's work after the Salon of 1808, to such an extent that it must be concluded that he made a trip to Italy about that time (although this contention cannot be absolutely proven). Besides, the soft light streaming in from the side, the fine precision of his palette and the subtlety of harmonies depart from the studied, spare quality of his early work (cf. the small *tondi* in Cherbourg; the *Statue,* Dijon, Musée Magnin, which is perhaps one of the paintings exhibited by Bertin at the Salon of 1800 [Gutwirth, *op. cit.,* no. 22, p. 342, ill.]; the *tondi* engraved by Nicolas Ransonnette; and some views of the Ile-de-France, such as the *Entrée du parc de Saint-Cloud,* Sceaux, and the *Vue d'Essonnes,* Louvre). As for the present painting, one could plausibly suggest a date slightly after 1810 because the only known Italian dated landscape, *Vue de Ronciglione,* Nantes (s.d. 1808), displays a greater dryness and stiffness, a somewhat less natural luminosity and less ambitious, more traditional organization of space (the same weaknesses are seen in the artist's other paintings in the Salon of 1808, known from the engravings of J.-M.-S. Bence). In contrast, the Boulogne painting affects us precisely by its indirect yet harmonious unfolding of planes, with a subtle yet agreeable play of coulisses and stepped planes which softens and enriches the scene.

Insofar as one can reconstruct Bertin's stylistic development, considering the number of omissions in Bertin's œuvre (see Biography above), it is clear that our painting is related to such a work as *Site de la Grèce* (Salon of 1812, known by the lithograph of P.-A. Mongin; see Gutwirth, *op. cit.,* no. 77, p. 349, ill.), which also features ingenious spatial construction, underlined by a delicate lateral lighting. A successful balance is realized in the Boulogne painting between the landscape and the small figures, who carry the anecdotal content. Their refinement and elegance, and their vaguely antique colors make the painting even more poetical and timeless. (The same effect can be found in the *Eurydice et ses compagnes,* Quimper, dated correctly by Gutwirth 1810-15; *op. cit.,* no. 80, p. 350, ill.).

The road motif and laterally elongated patterns seem to be typical of Bertin, who created here, at the beginning of his mature period, one of his most successful compositions. His academic formulas, later dismissed as stiff and tedious, are used to sustain a unified and sensitive composition, full of feeling for the observation of reality.

PROVENANCE

Donated by Paul Marmottan to the Institut de France, 1932. The collection formed by Paul Marmottan was divided by him between the museum which bears his name in Paris and his country estate at Boulogne-sur-Seine, transformed into a library devoted to Napoleon; a small collection of drawings and paintings, which are not well-known, is attached to the library (cf. the Meynier exhibited here, *France Encouraging Science and the Arts,* No. 127); a large portion of the collection has been photographed by the photographic service of the Réunion des Musées Nationaux.

REFERENCES

P. Fleuriot de Langle, 1938, no. 114, p. 81; S. Gutwirth 1974, no. 58, p. 347, ill.; B. Foucart, 1974 (in press).

J. F.

Jean-Joseph-Xavier Bidauld

1758 Carpentras - Montmorency 1846

Bidauld studied in Lyon with his brother, Jean-Pierre-Xavier (1745-1813), painter of genre and flower pieces, and traveled with him in Provence and Switzerland. In 1783, he was in Paris, where he met Joseph Vernet, Joseph-Siffred Duplessis and Jean-Honoré Fragonard. The Cardinal of Bernis and the art dealer Dulac offered to subsidize him in Rome. He accepted Dulac's offer and left for Italy in 1785. He remained there five years, frequently traveling through the Roman states of Tuscany and the Kingdom of Naples. In 1790, he returned to Paris. In 1793, he traveled to Brittany; in 1803, the Haut-Dauphiné, and later he made sure he visited Fontainebleau, Ermenonville and Montmorency, where he lived in the Petit-Montlouis, the residence of Jean-Jacques Rousseau.

He exhibited regularly in the Salon from 1791 to 1844. Faithful to the so-called neo-classical landscape, he painted essentially historical landscapes whose figures, as Marie-Madeleine Aubrun has pointed out, were occasionally painted by other artists—Guillaume Lethière, Carle Vernet, François Gérard or Louis-Léopold Boilly. Up to the July Monarchy, this type of painting was very popular. In 1812, Bidauld received a gold medal for his Salon entries and in 1823 became the first landscape painter to be named a member of the Academy of Fine Arts. But afterwards his entire output, including his Italian studies, became the object of attacks by young "realist" critics, Théophile Thoré in particular.

Suzanne Gutwirth will soon publish the catalog raisonné of Bidauld's work.

J. L.

4
Roman Landscape

Paysage romain
Plate p. 84
Canvas; 72 × 98; d.l.r. *Roma 1788*
Basel, Kunstmuseum

The imprecision of the Salon catalog and of contemporary commentaries does not permit us to establish the possibility that this painting was exhibited in 1791, the first Salon in which Bidauld took part.

While northern influence is evident, above all the work falls within the tradition of Poussinesque landscape, from which he took the principle of the vast panorama composed of harmoniously rhythmic lines; like Joseph Vernet or Jean-Michel Moreau the Younger, he added picturesque and folk elements (e.g., the group of Roman peasants in the foreground).

This type of composition, treated broadly but with careful attention to such background details as the convoy crossing the aqueduct, was to remain popular during the entire first half of the 19th century.

PROVENANCE
Bequest of Hans Burckhardt, 1923 (INV. 1395).

REFERENCES
Mus. cat., 1926, no. 1385; mus. cat., 1946, p. 98.

J.L.

Nicolas-Didier Boguet *fils*

1802 Rome - Rome ? after 1861

The only son (although with no explanation Thieme- and Becker listed a brother named Louis, a sculptor in Rome) and student of his father, Nicolas-Didier Boguet (1755 Chantilly-Rome 1839), Boguet *fils* lost his mother (a French woman from Rome, who died in 1805 after six years of marriage) and spent his whole life near his father. Several letters from Boguet *père* to François-Xavier Fabre, which were published by the dean, L. G. Pélissier in the *Nouvelle Revue Rétrospective* in 1896 and used again by Marie-Madeleine Aubrun in her recent (1974), fundamental article on Boguet *père*, indicate the harmonious association of the father and son, known as Didino, or le grand Didino by close friends of the family and by his father. Thus, "We are always two inseparable friends, never going out one without the other. He [Didino] has made progress and I am happy with him" (2 April 1820; L. G. Pélissier, 1896, p. 321) and "Le grand Didino is very open to your friendship; I can assure you that he is worthy of it and that he is not ungrateful. It is from me that he is learning to know men. All that I should like to say to you in his behalf is that you should have one like him" (31 March 1821; *ibid.,* p. 327).

On 21 June 1823 and 24 August 1825, Boguet *père* signed letters to Fabre: "the two Boguets" (*ibid.,* pp. 334, 336); again to Fabre, 8 February 1834, he wrote: "Didino has always worked little until now, but he has made progress, and his paintings are admired, which

he will be able to take advantage of if he has to: that is consolation for the future. As to the rest, for some time he has been working assiduously and is feeling well. We always lead a very solitary and rather monotonous life; we never go out in the evening, thus we see no one unless artists come in to see us, some of whom are friends, with whom we talk painting while looking at my drawings, which have greatly increased in number" (*ibid.,* p. 412).

One gathers from this letter that Boguet *fils* did not intend to be a productive artist, and that in fact after 1839 he stopped painting completely. Apart from two paintings bequeathed by Granet to the museum of Aix-en-Provence (see No. 5), there are some drawings signed by him in Montpellier and Aix. In a written communication, Marie-Madeleine Aubrun has indicated, in addition, that she has found paintings in a private collection, but she did not publish them in her recent article. It is likely, however, that Boguet *fils* was able to work in close collaboration with his father, and the distinction between the two hands appears difficult to establish, apart from the painting exhibited here.

A manuscript on Nicolas-Didier Boguet *père* written by his son on 8 June 1861 and preserved in the archives of the Château de Chantilly, attests to his profound filial devotion. He alluded to the enormous group of drawings by Boguet *père*, today mostly located in the Gabinetto Nazionale delle Stampe in Rome (1,022 watercolors and drawings), a collection which "will never," wrote the son, "be broken up, divided or dispersed so long as the desire of this same son, and of his relatives, is not overpowered" (Aubrun, 1974, p. 323). It was Boguet *fils* who, in 1840, had erected in the church of San Luigi dei Francesi in Rome a funerary monument in honor of his father, sculpted by P. Lemoine (another Frenchman in Rome whose portrait was done by Ingres). On the bas-relief of this monument, Boguet *fils* very aptly chose to engrave the names of Dughet, Poussin alongside that of his father Claude, thus linking him to his great inspirations.

The work of Boguet *père* was the subject of some studies in 1925 by P. Marmottan and especially by Aubrun in 1974 (an article with a catalog of the painted work and numerous reproductions): 88 paintings have already surfaced, but a great many evidently remain to be discovered, in view of the extent of Boguet's international clientele; all are landscapes, including some scenes of the Italian countryside commissioned by Bonaparte. The only certain painting is the *Scène de Bataille de Rivoli,* which was presented late to the Salon of 1836 and loaned to Périgueux by the Louvre in 1876. Others include *Castiglione* (Versailles), *Passage du Pô devant Plaisance* (not located but existing in a replica at Chantilly and a copy in Versailles by Bacler d'Albe), *Prise d'Ancône* (known only from Alexandre-Hyacinthe Dunouy's copy in Versailles), almost none of the Salon paintings have been recovered; one painting sold in Rotterdam in 1968 has been identified without sufficient proof as the one from the Salon of 1800; for 1819: *La Mort de la reine Andovare* commissioned for the Galerie de Diane at Fontainebleau and sent in 1864 to Amiens and then to Doullens; the *Vue du Campo Vaccino* corresponds perhaps to the painting of the same subject in the Trieste museum; the *Vue d'Albano*

is, perhaps, as believed by Bellier and Auvray, the one dated 1795, in Grenoble.

In fact, Boguet *père,* settled in Rome from 1783, exhibited little in France (Salons of 1800, 1806, 1808, 1819, 1824, 1827 and 1836), making his career in Italy. He became a member of the Academies of Rome and Florence and knew all the French artists in Rome, including Chauvin, Fabre, Ingres, Bodinier (who was to paint his portrait, Salon of 1827, formerly Munich, Messinger Collection; see the photograph preserved in the R.K.D. of The Hague), Granet; or Italian artists such as Landi, Camuccini, Tofanelli, Nardi and Pinelli. He worked for an aristocratic, international clientele living in Rome: Count Gouriev (see No. 109), Count Kinsky, generals Miollis and Davidoff, Lord Howard, the Duke of Bedford, Lord Bristol, Lady Bentinck, Prince Torlonia, Chevalier Puccini, the Countess of Albany. Boguet *père* was admired by Kotzebue, Chateaubriand, Stendhal. He decorated in fresco or distemper many Italian palaces and villas (Pistoia, Poggio Imperiale, the Quirinal Palace in Rome—a decoration lost, it seems, since 1815).

In addition to the museums already mentioned, works by Boguet *père* can be seen in the Capodimonte museum in Naples (two canvases dated 1803), in Helsinki (1796), in Florence (1792; Galleria degli Uffizi); three in Montpellier (c. 1815, 1821 and 1826), in Stockholm (copy of a Claude Lorrain).

Finally, about a half dozen etchings by Boguet *père* are known. All these works show his faithful and deep grasp of ideal and idyllic landscape in the spirit of Valenciennes, Fabre, Bidauld, Simon Denis and in a certain sense comparable to a Richard Wilson in its mastery of light and profound veneration of Claude.

J. F.

5

View of the Villa Aldobrandini at Frascati

Vue de la loge Aldobrandini à Frascati
Plate p. 271
Canvas; 31 × 37.6; s.l.l. *d. Boguet fils;* inscribed on the back of the canvas:
A Madame Néna, 1er janvier 1824
Aix-en-Provence, Musée Granet

An entry on the back of this canvas contains an allusion to Magdalena di Pietro, who was to marry the

artist F.-M. Granet in 1843. As pointed out by M.-M. Aubrun, another dedication, *"A la Signorina*

Néna," this time signed *Didino 1824,* appears on the back of a second canvas bequeathed by Granet to the museum in Aix, *Sous-bois à l'oratoire* (M.-M. Aubrun, 1974, p. 334, no. 78, ill.). In all, there are four paintings in the museum under the name Boguet, which would seem to confirm the fact that Boguet *fils* also had been a painter, although in a rather secretive way. Nevertheless, Boguet *père* wrote in a letter to Fabre, dated 29 December 1892, "Didino has done some pretty studies at Frascati" (Pélissier, 1896, p. 300—a quotation indicated in a written communication from Mme Aubrun, to whom we owe much of the information contained in this entry).

In her catalog of the painted œuvre of Boguet *père,* M.-M. Aubrun included the present painting, perhaps too cautiously, and implied that it might be the product of a collaboration between father and son, exactly like the *Sous-bois à l'oratoire,* cited above. In this respect, this latter painting, composed and idyllic, seems to exhibit more qualities of Boguet *père,* "follower of Claude Gellée," than does the painting of the Villa Aldobrandini, whose immediate and candid spontaneity reflects the art of Granet, noticeable even in the dominant architectural motif of the loggia (cf. in Aix Granet's *Réception de deux cardinaux* and the delightful painting of an Italian girl at work, both very characteristic of Granet, a painter of interiors and architecture, as well as landscapes). Granet's influence, seen in the only known canvas signed by Boguet *fils* (all the more

reason to make the present attribution to him) should not surprise us, if we remember that Granet, in Rome from 1802 to 1826, was a close friend of the Boguet family (which would explain the familiarity of the dedications by Didino as well). In another respect, the influence of Boguet *père* is noticeable in the delicate rendering of the masses of foliage, visually dissolving and evanescent, anticipating Corot's silvery landscapes.

Boguet *père* exhibited four paintings at the Salon of 1827 (Aubrun, *op. cit.,* nos. 53-56): two under no. 113, both *Vues de la Villa Aldobrandini à Frascati ;* and two under no. 114, both *Vues des environs de Frascati.* These last two, because their dimensions are known from an entry in the Louvre Archives, cannot be confused with the painting in Aix, and they remain unlocated. Also lost is a *Vue de Rome depuis la villa Aldobrandini,* bought by Bodinier, after having been in the collection of General Miollis in Palazzo Aldobrandini, Rome before 1814 (Aubrun, *op. cit.,* no. 57).

PROVENANCE
Bequeathed by the artist Granet to the museum, 1849.

EXHIBITION
1961, Rome, no. 35.

REFERENCE
M.-M. Aubrun, 1974, p. 332, no. 52, ill. (catalogued as Boguet *père*).

J. F.

Louis-Léopold Boilly

1761 La Bassée (near Lille) - Paris 1845

After a stay in Douai between 1775 and 1779, Boilly worked at Arras, where he probably got to know the painter G.-D. Doncre, who could have been responsible for imbuing in him a taste for portraits and trompe-l'œil. In 1785, he settled in Paris, where he was to spend the rest of his life, and exhibited at the Salon from 1791 until 1824. He produced an enormous corpus of paintings and drawings and yet pursued a very quiet career on the fringe of official currents. The one exceptional event of his life occurred under the Reign of Terror, when an accusation was registered

against him by his colleague and compatriot J.-B. Wicar for painting subjects contrary to acceptable moral standards. This denunciation before the Comité de Salut Public, just when J.-B. Suvée, Hubert Robert and André Chénier were in prison, would have led him to the gallows; in order to exonerate himself, he was obliged to paint a work with a patriotic theme, *Le Triomphe de Marat* (Lille).

He specialized in portraits: *L'Atelier d'Isabey,* Salon of 1798, Louvre; *A.-F. Boïeldieu,* Salon of 1800, Rouen; *Le Baron de Galz en costume de page,* 1806, Bordeaux, Musée des Arts Décoratifs; *"A la Reconnaissance,"* Paris, private collection; and in genre scenes: *Le Billard,* Leningrad, the Hermitage; *La Vaccine,* formerly in the collection of Du Bourg de Bozas; or scenes of Parisian life: *L'Arrivée d'une diligence dans la cour des messageries,* 1803, Louvre; *Le Départ des conscrits en 1807,* Salon of 1808, Paris, Musée Carnavalet; *L'Entrée de l'Ambigu-Comique,* 1819, Louvre; *La Distribution de vin et de comestibles aux Champs-Elysées,* Salon of 1822, Paris, Musée Carnavalet, *La Partie de dames au café Lamblin,* Salon of 1824, Chantilly.

He soon became well-known, through engravings and later on, lithographs; in 1823, he created a suite of humorous lithographs entitled *Les Grimaces.* If Boilly suffered a certain eclipse after 1830 because his subjects were considered too old-fashioned at that time, he remained, nonetheless, along with Martin Drolling and Marguerite Gérard, one of the best exponents of anecdotal, and at times moralizing, bourgeois painting. Working in a relatively small format, he evolved a refined, smooth and sparkling technique, inspired by some of the Dutch masters of the 17th century, such as Terborch, Gerard Dou and Metsu; moreover, he actually owned several paintings by Dutch artists (his sale, Paris, 13-14 April 1824, nos. 38-69).

Boilly was also a prolific draughtsman, often working in watercolor (*Un carrefour de Paris à l'époque des déménagements,* Lille) or in pen, heightened with ink washes (*L'Enfant puni,* formerly Paul Marmottan Collection, acquired in 1974 by the Lille museum). J. V.

6

Impromptu Concert

Le Concert improvisé or *Le Prix de l'harmonie*
Plate p. 120
Canvas; 46 × 55
Saint-Omer, Musée de l'Hôtel Sandelin

Having arrived in Paris in 1785, Boilly was soon under the protection of a connoisseur from southern France, M. Calvet de la Palun. He ordered several paintings from Boilly, indicating exactly the subjects he wished; it was under these circumstances that, in 1789, he bought *La Visite reçue* (Saint-Omer) and *La Visite rendue* (London, Wallace Collection); in 1790, *Impromptu Concert, Ce qui allume l'amour l'éteint* (Saint-Omer), *Les Malheurs de l'amour* (London, Wallace Collection) and *Le Retour de l'Infidèle* (private collection) and, finally, in 1791, *Le Danger des mariages d'amourette* or *Les Conseils maternels* (private collection) and *Le Vieillard jaloux* (Saint-Omer). The majority of these paintings have a label on the back indicating the subject and its author; on the back of this painting, for instance, we can read, "Invented by M. Calvet de la Palun. It is at the age of sensitivity that one feels all the strength of harmony. The old woman sleeps, the child plays. Painted by Louis Boilly in 1790."

This group of eight paintings is especially homogeneous, as much by content, i.e. gallant subjects tending to be moralizing, as by the polished and porcelain-like technique directly inspired by the Dutch masters, such as Franz van Mieris or Gerard Dou. Also notable are his color harmonies executed with a great sense of refinement, emphasized here by the nocturnal setting in which the yellow dress of the harpist is accented. The rendering of textures is also particularly well done, especially the satin, which would bear comparison with *The Kiss* by Fragonard (here No. 60).

PROVENANCE
Bought by M. Calvet de la Palun in 1790; Paris, Chaix d'Est-Ange Collection,; Saint-Omer, Du Teil Collection; bequeathed by Baronne du Teil to the city of Saint-Omer in 1921, in memory of her husband, Commandant Joseph du Teil.

EXHIBITIONS
1885, Paris, no. 24; 1930, Paris, no. 14; 1933, Paris, no. 24; 1955, Florence, no. 3, ill. 4.

REFERENCES
H. Harrisse, 1898, p. 9, pp. 95-96, no. 139; J. Du Teil, 1907, pp. 22, 24, 30, ill. p. 32; Thieme and Becker, v. IV, 1910, p. 225; P. Marmottan, 1913, pp. 31, 33, mus. cat., 1924, no. 12; A. Mabille de Poncheville, 1931, pp. 23-24, 170, ill. opp. p. 28; J. Joets, 1937, p. 180; J. Vergnet-Ruiz and M. Laclotte, 1962, p. 227.

RELATED WORKS
A drawing with several variations (private collection), cited by J. du Teil (1907, p. 32). J. V.

7
*Studio of a Young Artist**

L'Atelier d'une jeune artiste
Plate p. 158
Canvas; 63 × 51; s.d.l.l. *L. Boilly. 1800*
Moscow, Pushkin Museum of Fine Arts

Boilly often treated the theme of the artist's studio: e.g., *L'Atelier d'Isabey,* Salon of 1798, no. 39 (Louvre; H. Harrisse, 1898, p. 75, no. 13) and *L'Atelier de Houdon,* Salon of 1804, no. 41 (Paris, Musée des Arts Décoratifs; H. Harrisse, *op. cit.,* p. 79, no. 29) of which there is another version in Cherbourg (H. Harrisse, *op. cit.,* p. 111, no. 312). We should also point out *L'Etude du dessin,* Salon of 1796, no. 41 (H. Harrisse, *op. cit.,* p. 74, no. 9), a lost painting engraved by F. Cazenave; and especially an excellent, although unpublished, drawing in Albi, *La Leçon de dessin* (pen, ink washes, heightened with white). Finally, there is a painting in grisaille from the former collection of Georges May, *Une jeune fille assise et peignant* (H. Harrisse, *op. cit.,* p. 114, no. 342) which can be compared to the painting exhibited here.

The present painting can also be compared with *L'Intérieur d'un atelier de peinture,* exhibited in the Salon of 1800, no. 35 (Washington, National Gallery; H. Harrisse, *op. cit.,* p. 77, no. 19). These two paintings, exactly contemporary, are perfect examples of Boilly's taste for the accumulation of anecdotal and picturesque details. The same plaster torso of a Venus appears in both paintings. Both, too, are rendered in a somewhat superficial manner, producing the pleasant impression of young dilettantes indulging in an enjoyable pastime rather than artists seriously engaged in their craft.

PROVENANCE

Acquired by Prince N. B. Youssoupoff in Paris, between 1808-11; in the collection of the Youssoupoff princes, Saint Petersburg, until 1918; Palace-Museum of Prince Youssoupoff, Petrograd, 1918-24; Leningrad, Hermitage Museum, 1924, and transferred to Moscow, Pushkin Museum in 1927 (INV. no. 1260).

EXHIBITIONS

1908-1909, Saint Petersburg, no. 65; 1912, Saint Petersburg, no. 57; 1955-1956, Moscow, p. 22 (Leningrad, p. 8).

REFERENCES

Mus. cat., 1839, no. 229; A. Benois, 1908, p. 732; F. Monod, 1912, p. 196; L. Hautecœur, 1912 b, p. 24; P. Marmottan, 1913; p. 245; mus. cat., 1920, no. 74; S. Ernst, 1924, p. 200, ill.; L. Réau, 1929, p. 71, no. 451; A. Mabille de Poncheville, 1931, p. 172; mus. cat., 1948, p. 13, no. 1260; mus. cat., 1957, p. 19, no. 1260; mus. cat., 1961, p. 27, no. 1260.

J. V.

8
Galleries of Palais-Royal

"Les Galeries du Palais-Royal"
Plate p. 204 and color plate p. 24
Canvas; 50 × 63; s.l.l. *L. Boilly pinx* and d.l.r. *1809*
Paris, Musée Carnavalet

This is a replica of a brown-tint engraving made in 1809 of a painting of the same subject, exhibited by Boilly in the Salon of 1804 (no. 1043). The scene takes place in the Galerie Montpensier of the present Palais-Royal, occupied between 1800-1807 by the Tribunal, and represents, in the words of P. Marmottan; "This captivating place... [which] is a little luxurious city enclosed in a larger one; it is the temple of pleasure where bright corruptions have outlawed the very shadow of modesty. There is no *guinguette* in the world more graciously depraved; there is laughter but innocence blushes still. Make your round and you will see everything your heart desires.... Libertinage is eternal there; at every hour of the day and night its temple is open at every price. The Athenians built temples for their Phrynes, ours find their own in this enclosure" (P. Marmottan, 1913, pp. 101-102). It was on account of this description of Paris' most popular meeting place at that time that Boilly was severely criticized, i.e., when the original canvas was exhibited at the Salon of 1804. So we read in the *Ombres chinoises du Salon:*

> Mais ce sujet est trop obscène,
> Oui, Boilly; pour l'honneur des mœurs,
> Devait choisir une autre scène.
> Lui qui peint avec propreté,
> Qui lèche si bien sa peinture;
> N'a-t-il pas été dégoûté
> En léchant cette ordure ?

(coll. Deloynes, XXXI, no. 877, p. 734) and in the *Lettre adressée à messieurs les rédacteurs du journal des Sciences:* "What must we think of the ribald or trivial scenes that Monsieur Boilly has transferred to the canvas when the mark of long work proves to us that he had time to think about it... and to tear his canvas a thousand times rather than capture transitory scenes that the police can not prevent, but whose prudence has consigned them to darkness...." (coll. Deloynes, XXXII, no. 888, pp. 434-435). It is quite interesting to realize that the critics of this Salon, at which the *Pestiférés de Jaffa* by Gros was also being exhibited, were insensible to the pictorial qualities of the painting, preferring to fall back on a purely moral condemnation of the work.

Using a very personal method, Boilly repeated a previously painted subject in grisaille, "*à l'imitation de l'estampe,*" to use a contemporary phrase. We can compare this canvas, among others, to *La Jeune Femme assise sur l'appui d'une croisée* from the Salon of 1799

(London, National Gallery); *Les Petites Coquettes,* 1809 (private collection), or its pendant, *Les Petits Soldats,* 1809 (Douai), which reproduce the borders peculiar to this technique in trompe-l'œil and use a range of grays imitating engraving.

This painting is typical of Boilly's interest in anecdotal description, seen here in the figure of a Negro, or one of a small Savoyard on the extreme right showing his marmot. This latter figure was re-used in 1807 in *Les petits Savoyards montrant la marmotte* (H. Harrisse, 1898, p. 128, no. 493), and in a drawing in *Un Cadre avec six dessins* (*ibid.*, p. 138, no. 580), then lithographed by F.-S. Delpech.

PROVENANCE
Collection of the artist; his sale, Paris, 13-14 April 1829, no. 36; gift to the Museum by the Société des amis de Carnavalet, 1973.

REFERENCES
H. Harrisse, 1898, p. 53; J. Wilhelm, 1973, p. 32 ill.

RELATED WORKS
I. The original painting:
Prov.:
Paris, Coincy sale, 5 March 1812, no. 1; Paris, Préfecture de Police (?); destroyed in the 1871 fire at the Préfecture de Police (?).

Exh.:
1804, Salon, no. 43.

Ref.:
Coll. Deloynes, v. XXXI, no. 870, p. 478; no. 876, p. 668; no. 877, p. 734; no. 878, p. 12; v. XXXII, no. 880, pp. 53-54; no. 888, pp. 434-436; no. 889, pp. 513-514; no. 892, p. 605; v. XXXVI, no. 982, p. 143; Bellier and Auvray, v. I, 1882, p. 109; H. Harrisse, 1898, pp. 23, 33, 53, 80, no. 30, ill. opp. p. 108, p. 109; P. Marmottan, 1913, pp. 98-103; A. Mabille de Poncheville, 1931, pp. 89-91, ill. opp. p. 80.

II. Preparatory drawing:
A preparatory drawing for the painting in the Salon of 1804, in pen, ink washes and watercolor (31 × 48; H. Harrisse, 1898, p. 172, nos. 1000, 1001, 1002); sold in 1860 (Paris, 21 May 1860, no. 697) and 1910 (Paris, Hôtel Drouot, rooms 7 and 8, 21 April 1910, no. 1).

J. V.

9
Crucifix

"Un Christ": Trompe-l'œil
Plate p. 222
Canvas; 62 × 46; s.l.l. *L. Boilly pinx: | rue Meslée nº 12, | A Paris*
Salon of 1812, no. 110
Oxford, The Dulverton Trustees; on indefinite loan to Magdalen College

This work is typical of Boilly's preference for trompe-l'œil, executed here in monochrome harmonies based on gray and brown. It would be worthwhile to compare this painting to other trompe-l'œil works, either his *Cadre avec six dessins,* from the former collection of Du Bourg de Bozas (H. Harrisse, 1898, p. 138, no. 580), or more particularly his *Trompe-l'œil aux pièces de monnaie* (not cited by Harrisse), acquired by the museum in Lille in 1974. We see in these paintings the same meticulous quality in the rendering of details as well as the use of the *cartellino,* where the artist has written his name and address. From the time of the Salon of 1808, we know that Boilly was living at 12, rue Meslée, and this allows us to date the Lille painting sometime during the years 1808-14.

Boilly was particularly fond of employing the illusionist technique of the *cartellino,* thereby making a reference to Venetian masters, such as Giovanni Bellini.

He used this device in his trompe-l'œil paintings, as well as in his genre subjects, evident in the *Studio of a Young Artist* of 1800, exhibited here (No. 7).

PROVENANCE
Collection of the Third Lord Northwick (Northwick Park, Gloucestershire), then of his widow, until 1912; collection of Captain E.G. Spencer-Churchill (grandson of Lady Northwick); his sale, London, Christie's, 21 October 1965, no. 65; acquired by the Dulverton Trustees; placed in Magdalen College, 1966.

EXHIBITION
1812, Salon, no. 110.

REFERENCES
R.-J. Durdent, 1813, p. 54; *Catalogue...* 1864, no. 402; Bellier and Auvray, v. I, 1882, p. 109; H. Harrisse, 1898, pp. 26, 55, 82, no. 39, p. 137; P. Marmottan, 1913, pp. 134-135; T. Borenius, 1921, no. 84.

J. V.

Jean-Jacques de Boissieu

1736 Lyon 1810

Jean-Jacques de Boissieu studied drawing with an artist named Lombard and painting with the baroque painter Jean-Charles Frontier, who had been director of the École de Dessin in Lyon since 1757. For two years, Boissieu did fabric design and then, about 1759, began to work from nature. In 1758, he published his first prints, six pages of etched sketches *(Livre de Griffonnements),* and in 1759 six landscapes. In 1760, he was in correspondence with the printmaker J.-G. Wille, whose assistance he sought in Paris to sell some drawings, and execute four etchings of views of Lyon. From 1761 to 1764, he stayed in Paris where he saw regularly Wille, Greuze, Soufflot, Mariette (who included Boissieu's work in his collection), Claude-Henri Watelet

(one of the great collectors of Rembrandt prints in the 18th century and also a charming imitator and retoucher of Rembrandt's works; on Watelet, see J. de Cayeux, 1965, pp. 131-161). Boissieu specially valued Watelet's acquaintance: "We often drew from nature together," Boissieu wrote in a letter to his brother Camille (see *Notice sur la vie et les œuvres de J.-J. de Boissieu,* Paris-Lyon, 1879). And finally, he also associated with the young Duc Alexandre de La Rochefoucauld, who took the artist with him to Italy. For two years, Boissieu visited Genoa and Naples and lived in Rome, where he met Winckelmann.

However, it is possible that this trip took place from 1758-59 on (see the unedited travelog by Boissieu at the book-dealer G. Heilbrun, Paris, 1956, cat. no. 12, no. 38).

On his return from Italy in 1766, Boissieu worked at perfecting his craft as an etcher. In 1771, he established himself in Lyon, where he purchased the office of Treasurer of France. He married in 1773. The leaders of the Revolution in Lyon showed respect for his talent—David in particular intervened on his behalf—and his plates were eventually placed under the protection of the Revolutionary Law in 1793. By 1802, Boissieu was a member of the council of the conservatory for the arts in Lyon and played an active role in the organization of the museum—he was instrumental in effecting the purchase of various works, among others an excellent Zurburan. Boissieu did not exhibit in Paris, but instead at the Salon des Arts of 1786 in Lyon, where he showed a painting, *Un homme qui souffle sur un bouillon,* eight drawings and two etchings.

Boissieu is best known for his etchings, where a bold application of ink is used to create relief and a dramatic *chiaroscuro* (cf. *Notice..., op. cit.,* for 140 prints catalogued by the artist's grandson, Alphonse de Boissieu: a few views of Italy, numerous landscapes of the countryside around Lyon, scenes of interiors [*Le maître d'école,* 1780; *Les tonneliers,* 1790], studies of heads (1770-80), figures like those in *Les Pères du désert,* 1791—for this, the principal figure is borrowed from Zurburan's *Saint Francis of Assisi* which Boissieu picked up illegally at a sale in Lyon and then resold to the Musée de Lyon in 1807; the same figure was used again by Fleury Richard of Lyon in his work, *La mort de Saint Paul Ermite,* 1810, Digne). In his etchings, Boissieu also copied many 18th-century Dutch paintings, for example, *Le pêcheur à la ligne, d'après Ruisdaël* (1763); *Petit paysage, d'après Berghem* (1769); a *Paysage, d'après Van der Kabel* (1773); *Le repos des faucheurs, d'après Adrien Van de Velde* (1795); *Charlatan* (1772), after the famous painting by Dujardin at the Louvre (Boissieu's preparatory drawing is in the Musée de Chalon-sur-Saône); and *La rupture de la digue,* after Jan Asselyn (1783). Ludwig I owned a complete set of his etchings.

Boissieu's drawings are no less numerous and are of the same exceptional quality. One should point out in particular the strong red chalk sketches where the tight modeling (studies of heads, Louvre) recalls that impeccable and almost irritating technique—already classicizing in the noble and sculptural modeling—of the Italianizing artists Cornelis Bega and Adriaen Van de Velde. Even more successful are his graphite drawings *(Portrait de Jean-Baptiste de Boissieu,* Lyon, Musée des Beaux-Arts; *Homme aux bras croisés,* Narbonne) and his many wash-drawing landscapes with their subtle lighting (Orléans; Lyon, which has just acquired in 1974 the lovely drawing, *Rentrée de la moisson* [see P. Prouté, *Fontebasso,* cat., Paris, 1974, no. 36, ill.] and Pontoise [see 1971-1972, Pontoise, exh. cat., nos. 13 and 14, ill.]). There are many extant drawings by Boissieu. To the list in Audin and Vial's dictionary of most of the French museums which have Boissieu drawings can be added only Pontoise, Bourg-en-Bresse, Besançon (see 1967, Bourg, exh. cat., nos. 41, 42, 90); Paris, Musée Carnavalet (see exh. cat., 1971, Paris, no. 2, ill.) and Montpellier. The most beautiful collection of drawings known to us—in addition to the one at the Louvre (20 subjects)—is in Darmstadt where Ludwig I acquired from 1798 on 36 subjects in all, mostly from Dalberg (see Bergsträsser, 1970, pp. 89-99). It is interesting, as Bergsträsser pointed out, that Boissieu was so fully and quickly appreciated in Germany, and that he corresponded with Artaria of Frankfurt (the collection of engraved work at the Städel is one of the most beautiful in existence, rich in unique proofs), with Frauenholz of Nuremberg, and Rost and Mauser in Leipzig. Both Leipzig's and Bremen's museums own Boissieu drawings. One should also cite, without claiming to present a complete list, other drawings at the Uffizi (see P. Rosenberg, 1968, nos. 84-85, figs. 66-67), in Sacramento, Kansas City, Detroit, Baltimore, etc. (for the Boissieu drawings in the United States, see P. Rosenberg, 1972, under no. 9), at the British Museum (see 1968, London, exh. cat., no. 30, fig. 198), and in Amsterdam (see 1974, exh. cat., no. 3).

By contrast Boissieu's paintings are much rarer. It seems that he did very little painting. According to his biographers, he painted only between 1773 and 1780, offering as an explanation the artist's poor health —the odor of turpentine is supposed to have prevented him from painting in oil. One should cite the following works: three paintings at the Musée de Lyon *(Le Cellier,* 1769; *Portrait de sa femme* ; *Marché d'animaux)* ; the landscapes in the museums in Nantes and Sens; and the landscape from the Louvre on loan since 1903 to Péronne and lost during World War I; *Les bords de la Loire* from the Musée Masséna in Nice; the *Petit oratoire* preserved by the artist's descendants (Jacques de Boissieu Collection; see 1967, Bourg, exh. cat., no. 77); the *Aqueducs de Chaponost par temps de neige,* s.d. 1772, Boissieu's largest known painting (Paris, Comte de La Morinière Collection; 1967, Bourg, exh.

cat., no. 57); and a *Vieillard et enfant* (private collection, 1967, Bourg, exh. cat., no. 40). In addition, Thieme and Becker (1910) mention certain *Paysages* in Breslau (according to the 1926 museum catalog there were two, one s.d. 1773) and in Berlin (included in the museum catalog of 1883, but these paintings may have been moved to Breslau). The R.K.D. in The Hague has photographs of three paintings: a signed *Paysage* from the Karsen Collection in The Hague (1965); the *Laveuses* which was in the H. Brocard Collection in Moscow before 1917 (no. 335), very Ruisdael-like in feeling; the *Bord de rivière avec pont,* in the Walcker sale, Cologne, on 16 November 1909, as no. 10. Not mentioned in Thieme and Becker or Audin and Vial is the *Veau abattu* (a very northern theme), which Frimmel listed as belonging to a collection in Lemberg (now L'Vov and possibly in the town museum; see Frimmel, 1907, p. 101, ill. p. 103). Works that have been much better known, since the 1877 retrospective exhibition in Lyon are: the *Souffleur de bulles,* reminiscent of W. Vaillant and J. Van Oost (this may be the painting that was sold at the Palais Galliera in Paris, 28 June 1962, no. 132, unless the latter was a copy); and the *Apprêts du dîner* and the *Bouquet de fête* (collection of the artist's family). The *Portrait d'Imbert Colomes* in Roanne has only been tentatively attributed to Boissieu. Finally, one should mention the *Vue de l'Ile Barbe* in the collection of the Duchesse de Berry (Galerie de la *S.A.R.* Duchesse de Berry, 1822, II, pl. 65).

In his landscapes and scenes of interiors, Jean-Jacques de Boissieu imitated the minor Dutch masters of the 17th century (he was described as "that Dutchman wandering along the smiling banks of the Saône" cf. *Notice..., op. cit.,* p. 9. But one should not forget that many Dutch painters of the 17th century, from Asselyn to Van der Cabel, visited and even went to live in Lyon. Boissieu described in precise detail the countryside around Lyon, experimented with the contrasts between light and shade, emphasized the picturesque elements of his subjects, painted with a light touch in the manner of a Jean Pillement or a Karel Dujardin. He never did *paysages composés,* but preferred to paint from nature. Toward the end of his life, his declining health made it impossible for him to continue his outings in the country. In 1810, he wrote to C.G. Prestel of Frankfurt (1773-1830, a printmaker, musician, dealer in prints and drawings and founder of the famous Maison Prestel). He was no longer doing any drawing, he told Prestel, "having always made it a rule not to depart from a faithful imitation of nature" (see *Archives de l'Art Français,* 1874-75, p. 466). In the manner of the Dutch painters, of a Swanevelt for example, Boissieu laid out the planes of his compositions with clarity, emphasizing the role of light and of a sky filled with clouds, stressing as accents human figures and animals silhouetted against the light.

At the end of the 18th century, Jean-Jacques de Boissieu had a considerable reputation in Lyon. He guided and advised the painters who founded the school of Lyon (M. Grobon, P.-H. Révoil, F.-F. Richard, A. Berjon, A.-J. Duclaux, F. Épinat, etc.) and also F.-M. Granet and A. Forbin, who joined him in 1795. Boissieu's direct observation of nature, the desire for a precise representation of things—too precise, perhaps—the taste for the effects created by a sharp light, the polished touch, and finally the quiet and warm humanity in Boissieu's work, all were elements that influenced other painters. He thus prepared the way for Michel Grobon and for an entire school of painters of landscapes and intimate interiors (Génod, Bonnefond, Bellay, etc.) which was to last until the end of the 19th century.

M.-Cl. C. and J. F.

10
Children's Dance *

Danse d'enfants
Plate p. 98
Panel; 30 × 38
Paris, Musée du Petit Palais

This charming painting has, curiously enough, remained virtually unknown. It is not surprising that it was part of the Dutuit Collection (the most beautiful collection of its kind that has come down to us from the 19th-century in France) consisting mainly of Dutch art. The painting was not included in the 1925 catalog of the collection. It seems to have been forgotten when the museum was set up (did it then appear to be an unimportant work or perhaps a fake?). The attribution to Boissieu was not established until around the year 1967, and the painting was then brought to the attention of the organizers of the Bourg exhibition, who managed to include it *hors catalogue*.

In his *Éloge Historique de M. J.-J. de Boissieu* (Lyon, 1810, p. 9), Dugas-Montbel mentioned four paintings, one a *"Tableau de Famille"* which could be the *Children's Dance* of the Petit Palais. Since it is known that Boissieu drew from nature and that he etched a series of heads from life (old men, peasants; 1770), the characters in the painting exhibited here could be considered actual portraits. One might even identify here several members of the artist's family, according to a suggestion from Mlle Fr. Baudson, Conservator of the Musée de Bourg-en-Bresse and the organizer of the important exhibition in Bourg in 1967: the man standing at the left is apparently the artist's brother, Jean-Baptiste de Boissieu (1739-1812), judging from a drawing in the collection of Georges de Boissieu (1967, Bourg, exh. cat., no. 11) and from another in the Musée de Lyon, (s.d., 1781); the young woman with the umbrella might well be the artist's own wife, Anne La Roch de Valoux, whom Boissieu married in 1772 (cf. the closely related painting in the Musée de Lyon and the two drawings in the collection of Ch.-A. de Boissieu, one of which is dated 1776; 1967, Bourg, exh. cat., no. 7, fig. 4 and no. 8, fig. 5). Further identifications cannot be so precise. It is indeed more risky to identify the young woman with the tambourine as the artist's sister-in-law (the two Boissieu brothers married the Valoux sisters; Jean-Baptiste's marriage took place in 1782). The old grandmother, sitting next to the young tambourine player and gazing tenderly at the dancing children, resembles only vaguely—and really only insofar as she too is an old woman—the artist's mother in a drawing in the collection of Antoine de Boissieu (1967, Bourg, exh. cat., no. 5, fig. 3). One might more naturally think in terms of a psychological and chronological relationship among the figures themselves: the old woman could be the wife of the large gentleman standing behind her, and the young tambourine player possibly an elder sister to the children, a cousin or even a maid or a companion. Identifying the children with those of Jean-Jacques or Jean-Baptiste raises certain problems: in the first place, we can never make an

exact count (there are too many children in the painting! And how would one classify the eldest dancer? Or how is one to explain the old woman in the background?); secondly, in this sort of identification one would come up against chronological difficulties; the painter's nephew, Claude-Victor (Mlle Baudson would like to identify him with the little dancer in the plumed hat) was born in 1784 and this would thus make Boissieu's painting date after the period when he was supposed to have stopped painting—around 1780. Boissieu's drawings and etchings offer no means of comparison—for example in the Bourg exhibition drawings no. 13 (Louis de Boissieu and his maid Joséphine, 1783) and no. 14 (Benoist-Marie and Louis de Boissieu, the artist's two sons, 1792). In the 1783 drawing the young Louis wears his hair short, whereas in the painting the little dancer with his back turned has long hair. As for the 1792 drawing, the two young people bear absolutely no relation to the figures in the painting.

Questions of chronology are far less important here than a solid psychological and artistic understanding of the painting and of Boissieu's special world. It is certainly a *tableau de famille,* yet Dugas-Montbel cannot be certain what sort it is. We are concerned here with the family itself, the family recreated to suit the needs of genre painting—a kind of rephrased Brekelenkam or Van Ostade. Like Rembrandt, Rubens and the 17th-century northern painters of interiors, Boissieu found his models among his close relatives. Thus, there is no need to see Rembrandt's mother in each of his old women, his father in the old men, or Helena Fourment, Isabella Brandt or the latter's sister in each woman that Rubens painted. In Boissieu's work, there are many genre scenes that have no correspondence with the actual age of the people represented. The old woman in the background, borrowed from the world of Rembrandt or Greuze, already appeared in the prints of 1770 (cf. for example: 1967, Bourg, exh. cat., no. 28, fig. 6), in other words well before the time when this painting was done. Conversely, the young mother represented in the drawing *Bénédicité* of 1792 (included in the Paulme sale, Paris, 13 May 1929, no. 13, ill.) looks just like the artist's wife as she appears in a drawing dated 1776 (collection of Ch. A. de Boissieu; 1967, Bourg, exh. cat., no. 7, fig. 4; the model's clothes are the same in both drawings, a fact which proves that the artist handled his models arbitrarily). The small child learning to pray in the 1792 drawing is the same young Louis of a drawing done in 1783 (Louis and his maid Joséphine, 1967, Bourg, exh. cat., no. 13). The *Bénédicité* of 1792 and its companion piece, *Concert* (where one sees the brother of the artist, the large gentleman of the 1781 drawing, represented as a cellist), the *Lecture* on a terrace (representing once again the large-girthed brother—1967, Bourg, exh. cat., no. 94; the drawing is a companion piece to the *Repos des Travailleurs,* engraved in 1803), all these works are part of the same rather timeless and anonymous world—the world of all genre painting— as the *Écrivain public* of 1790 (print dated 1790; 1967, Bourg, exh. cat., no. 20, fig. 20) or the *Petits Tonneliers* done 20 years earlier (1967, Bourg, exh. cat., no. 103, fig. 21). It is a singularly appealing world, filled with a steady and almost naive warmth, a world where Chardin and Le Nain are fused in the crystalline light of a Karel Dujardin and a Michael Sweerts (exactly as one sees it in the work of Jean-Louis Demarne). And while the painting still has elements of Neo-Classicism, at the same time it prepares the way for the domestic world of François Bonvin. The neo-Dutch style, in the way that Bilcoq phrased it, acquires here the cool and intriguing rhythm of Boissieu's northern or German contemporaries, from Wybrand Hendriks to Friedrich (one is inclined to think also of the Russian painter Venetzianoff; nor should one forget the important precedent provided by Liotard).

Painter of landscapes and scenes of interiors, Jean-Jacques de Boissieu brings together his talents as a portraitist and as a genre painter in the *Children's Dance.* The use of brown tones, the artful rendering of the children, the expression of the simple joy (which is not without certain qualities of introspection) of a family watching the gay sport of its children, a vivid and very localized colorism (the spots of color of the children's clothes), these are all elements which call to mind the art of the Le Nain (H. Gerson described Boissieu's painting, *Le Cellier* of 1769 in Lyon, a Le Nain of the 18th-century; 1942, p. 113).

This scene, with its affected and almost acid grace, appears against a forest background described with scrupulous care. Boissieu rendered in extreme detail the bark of the trees (recalling Jacob Van Ruisdael and Wynants, artists whom he copied in etchings which often were important elements in his wash-drawings (cf. *Porte de ferme,* Lyon, Musée des Beaux-Arts). Boissieu combined here a taste for the descriptive with a polished and smooth manner, a neo-Dutch technique that had a great vogue at the end of the 18th and the beginning of the 19th century.

PROVENANCE

In the Gallery of Cardinal Fesch, 1845, Rome. Fesch sale, no. 329-1731, with the title *La Récréation Champêtre*. Bequest of Auguste Dutuit in 1902 (the painting was not listed in the inventory at this time and remained unattributed). This remarkable collection was created by the Dutuit brothers: Eugène (1807-1886) and Auguste (1812-1902). Left to the city of Paris, it formed the basis for the Petit Palais Collection and was installed in the same year (1902) in Ch. Girault's building. The collection was extremely rich in paintings and drawings by northern masters of the 17th century. It included very few French paintings of the neo-classical and romantic period (such works would not have suited the taste of the Dutuit brothers). Besides the Boissieu were three works by Hubert Robert; a sketch by X. Leprince for the *Embarquement des bestiaux à Honfleur* (Salon of 1824, Louvre); a Demarne, a Court and the *Intérieur d'église* by Balan.

EXHIBITION

1967, Bourg, not in cat. (14 bis).

REFERENCE

Dugas-Montbel, 1810, p. 9 (?).

M.-Cl. C. and J.F.

Chevalier Féréol de Bonnemaison

C. 1770 ? - Paris 1827

Féréol de Bonnemaison was born probably around 1770 in the region of Montpellier. There is no document concerning him until he won the first prize for drawing at the Montpellier Academy in 1786, at the age of 16. Henri, editor of the sales catalog of his works after his death, attested to the artist's precocity by stating that "he went straight from the student's bench to rank of masters" (sales catalog, 17 April 1827, p. 3). Soon afterwards, wishing to pursue his studies, he left for Paris and arrived there shortly before the outbreak of the Revolution. Frightened by the uprisings, he fled to England where he probably remained until some calm was restored in France.

He participated in the Salon for the first time in 1796, exhibiting three portraits of women (Salon catalog, no. 46). It was, however, with *Un Écolier étudiant sa leçon* (Salon of 1798, no. 43) and especially *La Rentière demandant l'aumône* (Salon of 1800, no. 40) that he became famous. His skill as a portraitist was recognized, and he presented many portraits at the Salons: *Autoportrait* (1798, no. 44); *Effigie de M. de Caulincourt, grand écuyer* (1806, no. 47); *Portrait du général du génie Vallongue* (1806, no. 48), which was especially singled out by the critics. The only portrait known at the present time to be by Bonnemaison is *Monsieur Segond* (1812; Louvre), where he penetrated the character of his model with great skill and candor and proved himself a worthy disciple of David.

A great connoisseur of earlier painting, Bonnemaison was appointed to direct the restoration of the paintings taken as booty during the wars under the Republic and the Empire. In 1814, Louis XVIII conferred on him the Cross of the Legion of Honor and the Cross of Saint-Charles, to reward him for having succeeded in the delicate restoration of five Raphael paintings belonging to the King of Spain, of which the *Vierge à la perle* and *Vierge au poisson* (Prado) had been taken by Napoleon. He became curator of the collection of the Duc de Berry and then director of restoration at the Royal Museum in 1816. Upon the death of his illustrious patron, he continued to work on the collection, becoming curator of the paintings of the Duchesse de Berry and her son, the Duc de Bordeaux. It is mostly this aspect of his activities that is known; indeed, he directed the publication of

lithographs of the works of which he was in charge (cf. *La Galerie de la Duchesse de Berry,* 1822), an effort that earned him a medal in 1823. Thanks to this publication, we know the contents of the Duchesse de Berry's collection, later dispersed through several sales. It provides exceptional evidence of very high quality about the tastes of one of the most expert collectors of modern painting from this period. The group included works influenced particularly by Dutch masters by such artists as C.-M. Bouton, Drolling, C. Bonnefond, Mallet, Haudebourt-Lescot, Marguerite Gérard, Duval-Le-Camus, Swebach, etc.

It appears that after 1817 Bonnemaison dedicated himself to his job as curator and restorer and no longer participated in the Salons. He died in Paris ten years later, in 1827.

At the sale of his possessions which comprised about 150 paintings, all the notable schools were represented —Italy: from the primitives to Carlo Maratta, including Correggio, Parmigianino, Raphael and Guido Reni; Spain: Murillo, Velasquez, etc.; Belgium and Holland: Jan Brueghel the Elder, Huysum, Rubens, Rembrandt, Teniers; and finally France: Le Nain, Stella, Claude Gellée (Lorrain), Lemoyne, etc. Forbin indicated to La Rochefoucauld five paintings well worth buying (Arch. nat., O³ 1417, 10 April 1827) including a *Danae* by Correggio, *Parade of Silenus* by Rubens, *Adoration of the Shepherds* by Murillo and a *Self-Portrait* by Tintoretto; unfortunately the treasury was low and nothing was purchased by the Royal Museum.

Bonnemaison's paintings are not well-known but merit detailed study. The Louvre painting and the one in Brooklyn (No. 11) will serve as the starting point for a reconstruction of his painted œuvre.

I. J.

II
Young Woman Surprised by a Storm

" Une Jeune femme s'étant avancée dans la campagne se trouve surprise par l'orage "
Plate p. 155
Canvas; 100 × 80
Salon of 1799, no. 29
New York, The Brooklyn Museum

Until very recently attributed to Pierre-Paul Prud'hon, this painting is now given to the Chevalier Féréol de Bonnemaison, whose work is practically unknown today.

The critics of the Salon of 1799, half-astonished and half-amused by the presentation of such a subject, described it in enough detail for us to confirm the attribution to its proper author. Chaussard reported in *Le Journal de la décade* (coll. Deloynes, XXI, no. 580, pp. 458-460), "She is standing, leaning against an oak, while the north wind blows... it agitates the light gauze which serves as her adornment rather than as clothing, the gauze not able to part from these ravishing forms... Her feet are nude, her arms are nude, her entire body is nude and shivers... some people find her neck too closely set on her shoulders." The author of the article on the Salon in *Le Journal de Paris* furnished us with other details (coll. Deloynes, XXI, no. 582, pp. 555-556), "However it seemed to us that the shoulders were a bit too wide and the hips too narrow. One could observe [that] the disposition of the figure near the tree trunk where she leans makes her appear attached to it.... The drapery, the folds of which are perhaps somewhat too numerous, display movement and transparency." The dimensions (3 *pieds* × 2 *pieds* 5 *pouces:* ca. 97 × 78) and the description included in the catalog of the sale after the death of the artist makes this attribution absolutely convincing: "Surprised in the middle of a field by a violent storm, frightened by the thunder roaring all around her, a young woman huddles against a tree trunk, the only shelter that she has been able to find. There, thoroughly soaked, her legs tightly pressed together, her arms crossed below her half-exposed breasts, her hair blown by the wind, trembling, and, in a word, practically as chilled by cold as by fear, she turns her anxious glance toward the sky and seems to invoke its protection."

This work was fairly well received at the Salon, because Bonnemaison knew how to combine "all the magic of painting and the thrill of a sentimental episode" (coll. Deloynes, XXI, no. 580, p. 460). All the critics unanimously praised his light but careful touch, his refined and harmonious palette, and especially appreciated the rendering of the incredibly light drapery, which qualified as a real *tour de force*. They did criticize, however, certain awkward passages, for instance: "The outline of the background is too vague" (coll. Deloynes, XXI, no. 582, p. 556).

This painting displays, on the threshold of the 19th century, a strange juxtaposition of classicizing elements *à la grecque,* such as the young woman's costume, and romantic elements, such as unbridled nature, which will be seen again in the works of artists like Girodet and Prud'hon.

PROVENANCE

"Register for work presented by the artists for entry to the Salon" (Arch. Louvre, X, Salon 1799, 18 August, no. 159); collection of the artist; included in the sale of the artist's effects, 17 April 1827, no. 88; collection of Louis B. Thomas; Brooklyn Museum, 1924.

EXHIBITION

1799, Salon, no. 29.

REFERENCES

Coll. Deloynes, v. XXI, no. 560, p. 6; no. 561, p. 74; no. 567, p. 251; no. 580, pp. 458-460; no. 582, pp. 555-556; Bellier and Auvray, v. I, 1882, p. 119; Bénézit, v. II, 1949, p. 4.

J. V. and I. J.

Étienne Bouhot

1780 Bard-les-Époisses (Côte-d'Or) - Semur-en-Auxois 1862

Third child in a large family whose father was a gendarme, Bouhot grew up in Saulieu, then in Recey-sur-Ource. Apprenticed at a young age, he ended up going to Dijon where he was recommended to Langlois, a painter-decorator who was a former pupil of Simon-Frédéric Moench. Thanks to Langlois, Bouhot participated in the decoration of the old abbey house of Cîteaux; in 1801, Langlois sent him to Moench in Paris. Under Moench's supervision Bouhot collaborated on decorative paintings for the Tuileries, Plessis-Chaumont (for Lucien Bonaparte), and at Mortefontaine (for Joseph Bonaparte). Then along with Charles-Marie Bouton, who also became a painter of interior architecture and perspective, Bouhot worked under Prévost, one of the first French painters to do panoramas, invented in London as early as 1787 and introduced in Paris in 1789. Ligeret du Cloiseau, author of an essential treatise on the painter and a friend of the artist, cited panoramas of Rome, Wagram and Tilsitt (1808-09) as those upon which Bouhot worked.

Just like L.-J.-M. Daguerre and Bouton, Bouhot preserved a sense of architectural precision, objective purity, and a fine luminosity, which effectively mark his specialization as a painter of architecture and Parisian topography. As early as 1808, his first Salon (*Place Vendôme,* now Paris, Musée Carnavalet), he attracted attention by his impeccable technique, perfect light, his "careful, but not dry polish" (Ligeret du Cloiseau). In subsequent Salons he presented similar Parisian views which quickly earned him great success: in 1810, the *Place du Châtelet* (Paris, Musée Carnavalet) and the *Pompe à feu de Chaillot,* awarded a third-class medal; in 1812, the *Courrier de la malle, effet de neige,* which undoubtedly recalled a choice dear to César Van Loo and to Louis-Claude Mallebranche, and the *Place des Innocents ;* in 1814, a *Vue des Tuileries* from the Quai d'Orsay (Paris, Musée Carnavalet, signed and dated 1813), the *Porte Saint-Denis* (undoubtedly, the painting in Camondo, Musée Nissim, signed and dated 1813), the *Pompe à feu du Gros-Caillou* (painting acquired by the Duc de Berry), the *Pompe à feu de Chaillot* (the same painting as in 1810 ?), and again a painting of a picturesque winter subject, the *Diligence.* In 1817, which certainly marks the apex of the painter's career, Bouhot painted the *Porte Saint-Martin,* the *Jardin Beaumarchais* (snowfall) and the *Intérieur d'une maison de roulage rue Saint-Denis* (the last two acquired by the Duc d'Orléans and reproduced in lithographs by Renoux and Motte in the gallery of the Duc d'Orléans—the second painting is now in Paris, Musée Carnavalet, which also has one of the replicas. Finally, there are the *Fête-Dieu à Pantin* and the *Prière pendant un orage ; vue prise dans la plaine des Vertus, près Paris.* Bouhot won a gold medal at the Salon of 1817. In addition, he received medals in exhibitions organized between 1820 and 1825 in Douai, Arras and Lille (see the interesting notice published in the *Galerie de la duchesse de Berry* and the one in the dictionary by Gabet, 1831, p. 87). In 1819, he exhibited eight paintings, including the *Cour ovale de Fontainebleau* (Lyon) and a *Vue de la Porte dorée de Fontainebleau ;* the *Vue intérieure du porche latéral de Saint-Etienne-du-Mont* (acquired by a Russian diplomat, Count Woronzov); the *Fontaine Saint-Victor* and the *Entrée de l'Hôtel Bullion* (both acquired by the Duchesse de Berry and reproduced in her *Galerie*); and lastly, and above all, the *Vue de l'escalier du Palais-Royal,* which had the greatest success and was bought by the Duc d'Orléans.

It was at the Salon of 1822 that Bouhot saw his first painting purchased by the State: the *Chapelle de la Vierge à Saint-Sulpice,* which then entered the Luxembourg museum, assuring public recognition of the artist (today the painting is in Paris, Musée Carnavalet, where it was deposited by the Louvre in 1876, INV. 2753). In the same Salon were the *Vue de la maison de M. Odiot,* the *Vue de l'entrée principale du musée royal* (undoubtedly, the painting, s.d. 1822, which entered the Musée Carnavalet in 1958 and was reproduced in the *Bulletin* of this museum, 1973, nos. 1-2, p. 35) and an *Effet de lumière dans un escalier.*

The death of his elder son in 1823 deeply affected Bouhot, but he did not exhibit a smaller number of works at the Salon of 1824 (he did not, out of sorrow, show only a single work, the *Salle des Pas-Perdus,* No. 12, as stated by Ligeret du Cloiseau). The others, which have not yet been found, were mostly related to the region of his birth: Semur, Bard-lès-Époisses, the environs of Châtillon-sur-Seine; particular mention must be made of his *Vue prise dans l'institution de Sainte-Barbe* (Paris, Musée Carnavalet), the *collège* of his elder son. Thus, the painting is a delicate allusion to familial mourning. The *Pont de Semur,* which is in the Semur museum, bears the date of 1825, which may contradict its traditional identification with the painting of the Salon of 1824. Of the paintings from the Salon of 1827, in which Bouhot won a silver medal, one has just been found (and is now in the Musée de l'Œuvre of Reims Cathedral), the *Vue intérieure de la salle gothique de l'archevêché de Reims le jour du Sacre de Charles X.* A reduced replica of this painting was already known and in the Semur museum. It is signed and dated 1825, which invalidated the identification made by Jeanne Magnin (1930, p. 9), with the painting of the Salon of 1824.

Under the July Monarchy, Bouhot continued regularly to send paintings to the Salons. His life changed beginning in 1834, the date of the death of his second son. Deeply affected, Bouhot left Paris and withdrew definitively to Semur, where he accepted the duties of director of the Municipal School of Drawing that had just been founded by the subprefect Larribe. He fulfilled his duties conscientiously and was also involved in founding a museum and securing collections for it. Little by little he slipped into oblivion, despite his submission to the Exposition Universelle in 1855, his exhibition in 1850 in Besançon and a favorable review by Tainturier in the *G.B.A.* of that year. He tended to specialize in views of the Auxois and the north of Burgundy. He also exhibited in Dijon (1837, 1840, 1849, 1858).

Among the paintings from the Salons after 1830 known today are two views of the *Château d'Aney-le-Franc* (Salons of 1831 and 1833; Auxerre); the *Porche de Saint-Germain-l'Auxerrois* (Salon of 1833, Rouen); the *Pont de la Poissonnerie à Semur après l'inondation de 1835* (Salon of 1836, Semur); the *Salle du musée des Thermes* (Salon of 1846, Dijon). One may also find his works in Cherbourg, Chalon-sur-Saône, Semur (6), in Paris at the Musée Marmottan (4), in Dijon at the Musée Magnin, Montpellier (s.d. 1840). At the Musée Carnavalet, Paris, which with the Marmottan has the best collection of Bouhot's work, are a total of 12 paintings, among which should be noted the *Entrée d'une carrière à Montmartre,* Paul Jamot bequest in 1943; and *Napoléon visitant la halle à l'Eau-de-Vie* (s.d. 1811), whose attribution has sometimes been questioned (see L. Lazard, 1901, p. 66, no. 37) but certainly wrongly so, once in the David-Weill Collection (fig. 65 in Chr. Aulanier, n.d.), etc. The catalog of the posthumous sale held in Semur on 14 October 1862, with a preface by Horsin-Déon, indicates that Bouhot was a steady worker who repeated his compositions, keeping many of them for himself. In addition to the sites already mentioned, this catalog states that Bouhot also painted views of Sens, Charonne, Autun, Dieppe, Reims, Fismes, Rouen, Alésia, Jumièges, Tonnerre, Larrey and Pizy.

In his Parisian period, Bouhot had no students, but he encouraged a friend of his elder son, Alexandre Decamps, who entered his studio in 1818 (see Horsin-Déon, introduction to the catalog of the posthumous sale of Bouhot's works, 14 October 1862, p. 9). On the contrary, in Semur, Bouhot trained many pupils, of whom Eugène Nesle is the best known.

Bouhot's works were engraved in many editions, notably by Tellier, Jazet, Denis, Laignier, J.-B. Arnout (the *Escalier du Palais-Royal*). In this regard one must mention the useful lithographs contained in the *Recueil de la galerie de la duchesse de Berry* (the *Fontaine Saint-Victor* of the Salon of 1819, the *Entrée de l'Hôtel des Ventes, rue Bullion* with figures by Xavier-Leprince) and in that of the Duc d'Orléans. It is interesting that Leprince collaborated on the figures, for Marmottan was certain that L.-L. Boilly often painted the figures in Bouhot's works, and that in exchange the Burgundian artist painted architectural backgrounds for Boilly. This point remains to be verified.

Bouhot represents the archetype of the minor master of which there were so many in the period of the Restoration—forgotten and charming, modest and engaging. They were fascinated by the Dutch and at the same time tried to work with contemporary subjects. Stylistically, Bouhot is similar to such painters as Boilly, Duval-Le-Camus, Daguerre, Bouton, Leprince, Gassies and Drolling. His Corot-like integrity rescued Bouhot from oblivion many years ago (to the point that he is now reproduced in Skira publications ! See P. Courthion, *Paris d'autrefois,* Geneva, 1959, pp. 78-79).

J. F.

12
View of the Salle des Pas-Perdus in the Palais de Justice, Paris

"Vue de la salle des Pas-Perdus, au palais de Justice" (de Paris)
Plate p. 277
Canvas; 123 × 143; s.d.l.r. *Bouhot/1824*
Salon of 1824, no. 223
Paris, Ministère de la Justice

This picture, one of the most important by the artist, is also one of his least known, as it has just been discovered. It was noticed by Jal in his account of the Salon of 1824. "In interior genre painting, M. Bouhot has acquired a reputation that none of his contemporaries can rival. He does not have Granet's firm line, or the broad, transparent effects of Bouton, but he is rather natural. He knows how to render an effect of light; and lastly, he is pleasing, and that is no small merit. This view of the *Salle des Pas-Perdus in the Palais de Justice* is very well done. Everyone must agree that to imitate life in this way one has to have real talent." The other critics, like Thiers, Landon and those of the *Moniteur,* the *Journal de Paris* and the *Revue Encyclo-*

pédique apparently considered the picture unworthy of attention, perhaps because it was genre and not in the noble category of history painting. The anonymous writer in the *Revue Critique,* who did not much like interior painting: "... a style too praised and admired these days" or "these painters who have nothing to say either to the heart or the mind," found that the works by Bouhot in the Salon were less successful than those of the preceding Salon, and even that they were "very ordinary." Though "all are distinguished by delicate, fine, precise brushwork and by their airy effect... his *Salle des Pas-Perdus* is too long!" His figures "are rarely well characterized," a comment incidentally, that seems quite inaccurate in the case of this picture, in which the familiar figures of the legal world can be clearly distinguished.

This beautiful hall is large, light and deep; its classicizing architecture had just been reinforced in 1817 by Peyre's recent restoration after Salomon de Brosses' reconstruction done after 1618, in a style that was already very austere. (It reminds one of the "purified" churches of the Netherlands and especially of the extraordinary neo-Palladian halls of the Amsterdam Town Hall, built between 1648 and 1655 and so flatteringly painted by Pieter de Hooch and Gerrit Berckheyde.) It was a favorite subject for topographical artists of Bouhot's time. Let us note for comparison the watercolor painter, Frederick Nash, author of the famous compilation, *Picturesque Views of Paris and its Environs,* published in London in 1820 with notices by John Scott (Nash's preparatory watercolor, formerly in the David-Weil Collection, is now in the Gosselin Gallery, Paris); a lithograph by Schmit (published by Engelmann in 1825) in a book by B. Sauvan on the Palais de Justice; and another by J.F. van Marcke, published by F. Noël. In this picture, as in the above documents—which show the same scene but seen from the other end of the hall—is, at the left, the staircase leading to the present Civil Courtroom. The scene is shown facing the Boulevard Saint-Michel, down the lefthand part of the hall. The famous monument to Malesherbes by François-Joseph Bosio, erected in homage to Royalist sentiment, is not visible here, since it dates from 1826; it was placed against the wall of the second section of the right aisle.

The Dutch influence, inherent both in the subject and the general trends of genre and interior painting of this period, is, not surprisingly, very evident in this picture. The light is pure and cold in the style of Jan van der Heyden; the geometry is faultless, the perspective skillful and there is great clarity—as in the church interiors of Hendrick van Vliet, Gerard Houckgeest, Anthonie Delorme or Emmanuel de Witte. The anecdotal activity, typically descriptive of daily life (as also in Louis-Léopold Boilly or Jean-Baptiste Mallet), is in the spirit of the minor northern masters of the 17th century. Nash's album explained that, as seen in the center of Bouhot's painting, "public scribes place their tables around the walls and offer their services for a modest sum to those who may have need of a talent greater than their own to help them draw up petitions, memoranda, etc." To combine successfully such a "modern" subject with the taste of 17th-century Dutch pastiche, remains a rare achievement; Bouhot, with this fine exercise in purely frontal perspective, shows himself a worthy member of the school of interior architecture painters that was so active between 1800 and 1830, with Bouton, Daguerre, Gassies, Bonnard, Cochereau, Drolling and of course Granet.

PROVENANCE
Posthumous sale of the artist, Semur, 1862, no. 19 ("major work"). At the Galerie Marcus, Paris, 1971 (came on the market with another Bouhot, of smaller dimensions, showing the Salle des Sacres at Reims during the coronation of Charles X, in 1825, which was bought by the Département des Monuments Historiques for the Musée de l'Œuvre de Notre-Dame in Reims); the Galerie Heim-Gairac, Paris. bought from the latter by the Ministère de la Justice, 1971;

EXHIBITION
1824, Salon, no. 223.

REFERENCES
A. Jal, 1824, p. 418; M..., 1825, p. 114; Paris, Arch. Nat. o³ 1420-1824: "alphabetical list of remarkably talented painters" (Bouhot is mentioned as the creator of the "most beautiful paintings, among them the Salle des Pas-Perdus"); Ligeret du Cloiseau, 1854, p. 16; J. Magnin, 1930, p. 9.

J.F.

Joseph Boze

1745 Martigues - Paris 1825

The son of a sailor, Joseph Boze studied painting at Marseille, Montpellier and finally in Paris, probably under the pastellist Maurice de La Tour. He had an inquiring, technical mind and invented not only a method for fixing pastel colors but also systems for braking and instantaneously unhitching four-horse wagons and for propelling ships. He was presented to Louis XVI by the Abbé de Vermont, confessor to the Comte de Brienne and to the Queen, and had a semi-official but active career at the Court: his account-book for the years 1783-1788 (Bibliothèque d'Art et d'Archéologie, MS. 72) shows that he spent his time painting and copying miniatures and portraits of members of the royal family which he sold to a diverse clientele. He exhibited miniatures and pastels at the Salon de la Correspondance from 1782 on (*Portrait de Vaucanson*, Académie des Sciences; *Autoportrait*, Louvre, Cabinet des Dessins); various other pastels from this period have also been preserved, mostly of oval format, some of which display a certain vigor (*Portrait de Charles*, Versailles, Bibliothèque; *Madame Campan*, 1786, Versailles), while others are rather insipid (portraits of the royal children, Louvre, Cabinet des Dessins). Since he was not an academician, he could only exhibit in the Salon beginning in 1791; severely criticized (the *Journal de Paris* published a protest against this on 6 October), he gave up exhibiting entirely, especially as the ties he had maintained with the royal family (he was compromised in the preparations for the flight to Varennes) created problems in 1793 and even caused his arrest after the Queen's trial in October. He was freed by the fall of Robespierre but was forced to emigrate for lack of work, and lived obscurely in Belgium, Holland and later in England, where he was given a pension by the future Louis XVIII. He returned to France with the rise of Napoleon, where sinister accusations were made against him by the painter Robert Lefèvre (see No. 119 and below). His loyalty to the royal family was rewarded in 1816 by the title of Count, but his career as a painter, which was probably not very active, is almost entirely unknown: of his painted works, we know practically nothing except his large *Portrait du Maréchal de Castries* (Versailles).

A. S.

13
Portrait of Mirabeau

Portrait de Mirabeau
Plate p. 119
Canvas; 214 × 126
Aix-en-Provence, Musée Granet

The famous orator and politician of the "first Revolution," who tried in vain to establish a constitutional monarchy in France and who died prematurely in April 1791, is shown here in front of the statues of France and Liberty. The bas-reliefs, according to the *Moniteur* of 22 October 1790, show "Minerva dictating the Rights of Man to the legislators" and "Truth delivering from their dungeons the victims of despotism."

Boze's works in oil, including this example from Aix, gave rise to a curious polemic. On 25 Frimaire, Year IX a letter signed "Durand, amateur" appeared in the *Journal des Arts, des Sciences et de la Littérature* implying that Boze claimed authorship of a picture done by Robert Lefèvre (see No. 119) showing *Bonaparte et Berthier à Marengo*, which Boze had bought and exhibited in London. In the month of Thermidor, Robert Lefèvre made an open accusation in the *Journal des Arts* and the *Moniteur*: Boze, he said, was incapable of painting a full-length figure in oils. After a weak reply by Madame Boze, Robert Lefèvre detailed his accusations and claimed that he had been the painter of the big portrait of Mirabeau as well as of that of the brother and sister of Louis XVI (also full-length); he said, too, that the portrait of Louis XVI was by Landon, and that Boze had only done head-and-shoulders pastels for these pictures. Since Boze did not reply, the question remains open: why did Lefèvre not protest in 1790, when the *Moniteur* announced the completion of the picture? There was practically no follow-up to this late accusation, and even Landon remained silent. Mirabeau's family only mentioned Boze's name. Louis XVIII ennobled Boze in 1816 and gave the portrait of Louis XVI to the House of Peers.

However, there is an overwhelming piece of evidence in support of Robert Lefèvre's accusation, even though it does not directly concern the picture exhibited here. Boze's own account-book, which unfortunately ends in 1788, shows that in 1785 and 1787 Boze did in fact pay large sums to "M. Lefèvre, Painter in Paris," for full-length portraits of M. Thiéry, first *valet de chambre* to the King (600 *livres*), Louis XVI (600 *livres*), Monsieur, the King's brother (744 *livres*) and for a round portrait of the King kneeling (384 *livres*). Two pages later, the full-length portrait and the round portrait of Louis XVI are billed to him at 2,400 *livres* apiece! And it appears that for the portrait of the future Louis XVIII, his wife paid 6,000 *livres*. Thus, it is not at all improbable that Robert Lefèvre helped paint the present work; the difference in execution between the head, which is painted very freely in hatchings like a pastel, and the rest of the picture suggests that Boze may only have painted the head.

PROVENANCE

Completed before 22 October 1790 *(Moniteur)*. Belonged to Mirabeau himself, who bequeathed it to his adopted son Gabriel, son of the sculptor Lucas de Montigny. The picture remained in the family and was left to the Musée Granet by Gabriel Lucas de Montigny in 1912 (INV. 12.1.1).

EXHIBITIONS

1900, Paris, Pavillon de la Ville de Paris (?) (according to A. Foulon de Vaulx, 1901 b, not catalogued); 1906, Marseille, no. 482.

REFERENCES

Moniteur, 22 October 1790 and 13 April 1791; *Moniteur Universel,* 11, 17, 18 Thermidor, Year IX; (Lucas de Montigny), v. VIII, 1835, pp. 511-512; "Notice...," 1872, p. 407; Volcy-Boze, 1873, pp. 30-31, 65-70; H. Marcel, 1901, p. 272 (ill. w. engraving); A. Foulon de Vaulx, 1901 b, v. VIII, pp. 339, 404, v. IX, p. 52; P.-A. Lemoisne, 1918, p. 12, ill. p. 14; M. Terrier, 1931, pp. 137-138; F. Boyer, 1969 b, p. 142, note 18.

RELATED WORKS

Boze drew Mirabeau for the first time bust-length using his usual pastel technique (Versailles, MV. 6032; probably no. 625 in the Salon of 1791; see also H. Marcel, 1901, p. 269). A sketch in oil for the head was given to the Musée Carnavalet, Paris, in 1931 by J. Strauss (exh. cat., Paris, 1931, no. 7; see also M. Terrier, 1931). The large canvas was engraved toward the end of 1790 by Étienne Beisson, with the indication: *"peint en 1789"*. A copy by Gilbert in Versailles (MV. 4604) was paid for in 1847. There is a small replica or copy in Bucharest (52 × 37) from the former collection of Charles I of Rumania. An inferior imitation was sold in Paris, Palais Galliera, 3 December 1969, no. 50 (ill.).

A. S.

Jacques-Raymond Brascassat

1804 Bordeaux - Paris 1867

Brascassat first worked in Bordeaux under the supervision of the landscape painter, Théodore Richard (whose works can be found in Aurillac, Bordeaux, Narbonne and Toulouse). Together, in 1823 to 1824, they visited much of the French coast, which helped Brascassat's execution of a collection of engravings published by Osterwald. In 1825, he came to Paris, where he entered the atelier of Louis Hersent. In 1825, he placed second in the Prix de Rome contest but, as a special favor, Charles X gave him a stipend, and he left for Rome, where he remained until 1830,

punctuating his stay with several trips, most notably to Naples and Sicily. He formed a strong friendship with Aurèle Robert (brother of Léopold), Léon Fleury and the Swiss landscape painter, J. Ulrich, who had a considerable influence on him. To the Salon of 1827-28, he sent four landscapes, including *Mercure et Argus, Paysage historique* (Aix), which earned him a second-class medal.

Back again in France, he exhibited six landscapes at the Salon of 1831. He won a first-class medal, and the success of his *Chèvres et moutons* (Salon no. 239) made him decide to specialize in animal paintings. This genre, "having never been done or very rarely," as he remarked (cited by Ch. Marionneau, 1872, p. 130), made him famous in his time and earned him commissions throughout all of Europe. In 1846, he became a member of the Academy of Fine Arts, replacing Jean-Joseph-Xavier Bidauld. But later, critics such as G. Planche, E. About and especially T. Thoré (who compared him to Verboeckoven, Koekkoek, Schelfout and "other foreign miniaturists") criticized his paintings as the most irritating sort of factitious realism.

The fundamental work on this artist was done in a monograph by Ch. Marionneau in 1872. All that remains is to clarify the present locations of works and to publish the Krafft donation made in 1936 to the museum in Reims.

J. L.

14
*The Hunt of Meleager**

La Chasse de Méléagre
Plate p. 281
Canvas; 113 × 145; s.d.l.l. *Brascassat 1825*
Bordeaux, Musée des Beaux-Arts

On 25 April 1825, the jury of the Academy of Fine Arts chose three subjects for the Prix de Rome historical landscape competition: *La Mort d'Hippolyte, Thésée soulevant le rocher* and *La Chasse de Méléagre*. The last subject was drawn by lot and described in the following terms to the eight candidates: "An enormous wild boar, sent by Diana, is ravaging the countryside, uprooting trees laden with fruit, etc. Meleager rallies the hunters and shepherds; Atalanta (daughter of Jasius, King of Arcadia) is their leader. Atalanta has the honor of being the first to attack the boar. The climax of the action is the moment when Meleager saves Atalanta from the rage of the wounded animal. The scene takes place at the edge of a forest; in the distance can be seen the town of Calydon in Etolia."

Brascassat won the second prize (André Giroux placed first). The report by the Department of Painting in the Academy declared that Brascassat's canvas "offers a pleasant composition, which therefore does not sufficiently express the harsh nature of the subject. The execution is fine and light, and the colors are very transparent, especially the water. However the Department would have liked to see that gradation of tone in the distance that makes a landscape look larger and indeed exalts its quality." Ch. Marionneau (1872) recalled how this judgment was contested by critics and connoisseurs (although he neglected to say that Brascassat was not alone in winning the second prize—

he shared it with Jean-Baptiste Gilbert). The Paris and Bordeaux newspapers (*Le Mémorial Bordelais* of 13 September, *L'Indicateur* of 14 September) spoke of injustice, and one has only to read the reports of the session of 1 October, when the Prix de Rome were awarded, to realize how dissatisfied was the public with the results. Duvivier said, "Young people believed they saw more talent and worth in M. Brascassat's picture... than in that of M. Giroux" and he even questioned the choice of subject: "From the point of view of inspiration, the theme was not an easy one to handle; for, after all, this is only a hunting scene, and not an historical event... it was not with these themes that painters like Salvator Rosa, Claude Lorrain and Poussin gave their masterpieces that character that distinguishes historical landscape." However this may be, thanks to the influence of the Duchesse de Berry, Brascassat's work was bought for the Bordeaux museum, and on 25 October 1825, the painter received from Charles X a scholarship to continue his studies in Italy. The minutely detailed brushwork of this picture suffices to explain the enthusiasm of the Duchesse de Berry, whose taste for the *style troubadour* is well-known. The painting also displays the influence of other painters fashionable at the time: the Dutch masters that Brascassat was so fond of copying in the Louvre, or Achille-Etna Michallon, from whom he took the model for the broken tree in the foreground.

PROVENANCE
Bought in 1825 from the artist (for 2,000 francs) by the Comte de Peyronnet (Keeper of the Seals, Minister and Secretary of State and of Justice) for the Musée de Bordeaux; (INV. No. 7025).

EXHIBITION
1947, Bordeaux, no. 142.

REFERENCES
Arch. Académie Royale des Beaux-Arts. Registre des Concours (années 1817-1827), pp. 225, 229; D., in *Journal des Débats,* 1 September 1825, pp. 1-3; D., in *Journal des Débats,* 3 October 1825, p. 4; Duvivier, 1825, v. XXI, pp. 71-73; [Anon.], in *Annales de la littérature et des arts,* 1825, v. XXI, p. 281; Lacour and Delpit, mus. cat., 1855, no. 47; Beulé, 1867, p. 2; L. Cabat, 1868, p. 3; Saint-Santin, June 1868, pp. 567-568; Ch. Marionneau, 1872, pp. 54-69, 276; Em. Vallet, mus. cat., 1881, no. 392; P. Foucart, 1887, p. 15; H. de la Ville de Mirmont, mus. cat., 1899, pp. 470-482; Alaux, mus. cat., 1910, no. 340; Geffroy, 1910, v. IV, p. 541; Ricaud, 1938, pp. 51, 61, 68; J. Vergnet-Ruiz and M. Laclotte, 1962, p. 228; F.-G. Pariset, 1969, v. VI, p. 543.

RELATED WORK
A sketch that belonged to Mlle Louise Arnal in 1872 (niece of T. Richard), who lived in Toulouse at that time.

J. L.

Nicolas-Guy Brenet

1728 Paris 1792

The early years of Brenet, son of a Parisian medal engraver, are rather obscure. The artist is traditionally said to have frequented the studies of Charles Coypel and, more especially, François Boucher. At the École des Élèves Protégés, he took lessons from Carle Van Loo and M.-F. Dandré-Bardon. In 1756, he went to Rome where he worked on a copy (now lost), of Caravaggio's *Entombment,* and on an *Endymion,* an academic study, signed and dated 1756 (Worcester Art Museum; cf. Wenfraf Catalog, London, Spring 1972, no. 3), which strongly reflects the influence of Boucher. Having returned from Rome, Brenet painted an *Assomption* for Notre-Dame de Versailles (1761, in situ) and, in the same year, two canvases with subjects drawn from Ovid—*Latone et les paysans de Lycie, Clythie transformée en tournesol,* recently bought by the Béziers museum.

Brenet exhibited at the Salon for the first time in 1763, with *Saint Denis priant pour l'établissement de la foi dans les Gaules* (Saint-Denis d'Argenteuil), which received a great deal of attention. In 1768, he painted a *Gloire d'anges* for the Chapelle du Sacré-Cœur in the church of Saint-Pierre in Douai. Following that, he continued to work in Douai for the Main Hall of Parliament, today the Palais de Justice, on an extensive ensemble of six large allegories: *La Vérité, L'Étude* (exhibited in the Salon of 1769), *La Foi, La Prudence, La Tempérance, La Force,* all done in an extremely high vertical format.

It was in 1769 that the artist's talent was officially recognized. He was received into the Academy with *Thésée recevant les armes de son père* ("the know-how of a master," Paris, École des Beaux-Arts); Diderot saw in his paintings "a technique very close to that of a master." Brenet exhibited, thereafter, regularly at the Salons and continued to work on church commissions, such as the *Fuite en Egypte* (Cathedral of Bayonne, sketch at the Salon of 1769); *Assomption* (1774); *Saint Pierre et Saint Paul* (both in the Salon of 1775; these two in the church of Saint-Jacques de Compiègne); *Résurrection* (Salon of 1775; in the church of Saint-Symphorien, Montreuil-lés-Versailles).

Brenet acquired a wide reputation and D'Angiviller, as well as Jean-Baptiste Pierre, thought highly of him. He was given the honor of painting a large canvas for the chapel of the École Militaire, Paris, the *Saint Louis recevant les ambassadeurs* (Salon of 1773) and two large commissions for the Salon of 1777, *Death of Duguesclin* (No. 15) and *L'Agriculteur romain* (Toulouse; sketch in Paris, private collection), both within the framework of D'Angiviller's program for the revival of history painting.

Subsequently, he did *Metellus sauvé par son fils* (1779, Nîmes; sketch in Metz); *Combat des Grecs et des Troyens* (1781, Nîmes); *Virginius prêt à poignarder sa fille* (1783, Nantes); *La Générosité des dames romaines* (1785, Fontainebleau); *Saint Louis rendant la justice* (1785, Hôtel-Dieu de Compiègne); *Le Fils de Scipion rendu à son père par Antiochus* (1787, Nantes; sketch in Montargis); *La Continence de Scipion* (1787, Strasbourg; re-exhibited in 1792); *Henri III décorant le vicomte de Taravannes* (1789, Versailles).

Other works by Brenet include: *Tête d'oriental,* Dijon, Musée Magnin; *Bas-reliefs feints,* 1774, Grasse; *Mort de Saint Joseph,* 1773, Grenoble; *Christ aux Oliviers* (oil on paper), 1774, Orléans; *Tête d'apôtre,* 1761 (?), *Mars et Minerve,* 1781, Poitiers; *Gloire d'Henri IV,* 1776, *Offrande à la patrie,* 1784, *Louis XVI prêtant serment,* all three in Quimper; *Jésus parmi les docteurs,* Autun Cathedral (pointed out by Sylvain Laveissière); and a group of paintings at the church of Pont-de-Vaux (Ain).

A serious and ambitious, often austere painter, Brenet occupied a central position in the revival of history painting, concerned as much with ancient as with "national" subjects, as set forth by D'Angiviller. His style, always recognizable, evolved from a fluid and clear manner done with a rich palette and very animated surface, still adhering to the style of François Boucher and Gabriel-François Doyen, to a more controlled art, static and monumental. His formation was complicated; it owed as much to what he had learned from Boucher, and through him, some long-lasting Rubensian characteristics, such as his taste for rather heavy models, rich modeling, and greatly animated figures and drapery, as it did to the study of the Bolognese school, with its careful and stable compositions, and close study of the live model. The reconstruction of an historical event, both setting and costume, was of paramount importance to him, as was the rendering of noble and virtuous subjects.   J.-P. C.

15
Death of Du Guesclin

"Honneurs rendus au Connétable Du Guesclin par la ville de Randon" also called *La Mort de Du Guesclin*
Plate p. 51
Canvas; 383 × 264; s.d.l.r. *Brenet 1777*
Salon of 1777, no. 18
Versailles, Musée National

Exhibited at the Salon of 1777 at the same time as the *Continence of Bayard* by Louis-Jacques Durameau (No. 55), this painting represents one of the very first attempts to portray a "national" subject in French painting. These paintings were part of the large commission of 1776 planned by the Comte d'Angiviller, Director General of Royal Buildings in collaboration with Pierre, First Painter to the King, with the aim to restore honor to history painting, in order to "revive virtue and patriotic feelings" (see J. Locquin, 1912, pp. 48-51). The commission consisted of six subjects drawn from ancient history, given to Louis-Jacques Durameau, Jean-Jacques Lagrenée, Noël Hallé, Jean-Louis Lagrenée, Nicholas-Bernard Lépicié and Brenet himself, and two subjects based on French history, both included in this exhibition (Nos. 15 and 55). The *Death of Du Guesclin* is listed in the commission under the significant title, *"Trait de Respect pour la vertu; Honneurs rendus au Connétable Du Guesclin par la ville de Randon."*

The other painting commissioned from Brenet, *Agriculteur romain ("Trait d'encouragement au travail chez les Romains"),* which also appeared at the Salon of 1777, like all the other paintings in the series, is located today in Toulouse. The two canvases were painted in 1776 and 1777; Brenet received 6,000 *livres* for *Agriculteur romain,* and only 3,000 *livres* for the *Du Guesclin* (F. Engerand, 1901, p. 65).

The Salon catalog devoted a great deal of space to an explanation of this painting's subject, based on the *Histoire de France* by Villaret, XI, Paris, 1763). In 1380, during the siege of Châteauneuf-de-Randon, a stronghold in the center of France held by the English, Du Guesclin fell ill and died: "The enemies themselves, admirers of his courage, could not resist expressing their respect for his memory. The besieged English had promised to surrender to the Constable if they had not received aid by a certain specified date; although he was dead, they did not consider themselves exempted from their vow to him. The enemy commandor, followed by his garrison, went to the dead man's tent; there, prostrating himself at the foot of the bed, he laid down the keys to the stronghold" (*Explications...*, 1777, p. 7). Oliver Clisson, companion in arms, standing in the center, gestures toward his dead friend; behind him, we can see Marshal De Sancerre, the new commandant of the French troops.

R. Rosenblum (1967 a, pp. 32-34) has stressed the importance of this painting, placing it among those works dealing with the theme of the death of the hero, so important in the neo-classical period, no matter whether it had to do with ancient or national history. *Du Guesclin* is one of the first examples in France of this type. The seminal place held by English painters in this realm is, of course, well-known; for example, Gavin Hamilton's *Andromache* was engraved as early as 1764.

These themes of hommage rendered to courage and virtue represented for painting, at that time, an entirely new direction, in direct opposition to the gracious and gallant style of François Boucher. This restoration of grand subjects, in lineal descent from Poussin and Le Sueur, was "a kind of anti-rococo catharsis" (Rosenblum, *op. cit.*, p. 28). The *Death of Du Guesclin* is most representative of this effort, and displays a new conception of the treatment of history painting. The artist strove to recreate the scene with utmost fidelity in matters of setting, costume and accessories; in this painting, the fortified stronghold in the background, the armor, the arms and the pennons constitute a new medieval archaeology (although still quite approximate; Lanson, 1926, p. 44, could criticize the page's costume). In fact, this work displays the elaboration of a new language, served by precise and effective descriptive means, intended to produce strong, yet exalted emotions in the viewer. It is a language that was to remain valid for history painting until the end of the 19th century.

The robust and chivalrous figure of Du Guesclin was very popular in France at about this time; an *Histoire de Bertrand Du Guesclin* by Guyard de Berville appeared in Paris in 1767 and was re-issued in 1772 (*ibid.*, p. 33, no. 104). Some engraved portraits popularized the hero's rather unpleasant features: e.g., the engraving by Alexis Loir based on a drawing by Hallé, with a medallion surrounded by trophies, and the engraving by N. Thomas, dated 1777, the very year of Brenet's painting. The theme of the death of Du Guesclin was painted some years later by P.-A.-A. Vafflard, shown at the Salon of 1806 (for the theme, see Rosenblum, *op. cit.*, p. 32, no. 100).

It seems that the reactions of the critics to Brenet's painting and to the entire series commissioned by D'Angiviller were excellent. The critic for *Mercure de France* congratulated the artist for his realization of the subject, the faithful observation of the dress of Du Guesclin's century and the variations in the personalities of the characters (coll. Deloynes, X, no. 191, pp. 1084-1085); the critic of the *Journal Encyclopédique* expressed only one reservation, stating that the one page who is in the foreground, dressed in a slashed casaque made of multi-color materials, was too harsh to the view and somewhat interrupted the coloristic harmony (coll. Deloynes, XLIX, no. 1334, pp. 850-851). It was also with respect to the artist's palette that others criticized the painting—the reporter for *Lettres Pittoresques* would have preferred a stronger and less subdued palette (coll. Deloynes, X. no. 190, p. 1031); and according to the judgment of a 14-year-old girl, Brenet showed a marked preference for purple, which might have prompted some to mistake the work for a monochrome painting done in that color! (coll. Deloynes, X, no. 178, p. 868).

Brenet's style appears here in all its complexity—the language of the work, as purified and "modern" as it could be, still retained something of the technique of Boucher and Pierre: rich and supple modeling; large often rather heavy-set figures; a theatrical and animated conception of composition with an abundance of wrinkled and "painterly" drapery made to catch the light; a pyramidal composition of the group set up on a slight rise seen slightly from below; a light and luminous range of colors. L.-J. Durameau's canvas (No. 55), in contrast, seems elegant and almost light-hearted. We must learn to consider the *Death of Du Guesclin* for what it was at the time of its creation. Beyond its ressemblance to an illustration in a history textbook, it was something profoundly new.

PROVENANCE

Commissioned by the Comte d'Angiviller for Louis XVI; collection of Louis XVI; the painting, assessed at 3,000 *livres*, was paid for in four installments to the artist, 1777-78 (cf. Arch. Louvre, *Bâtiment du Roi, registre des paiements de 1762 à 1785*, MS. p. 231, 238, 244, 262). Louvre (INV. no. 2860); installed in the Musée d'Histoire de France at Versailles under Louis-Philippe, the canvas which originally measured approximately 317 × 224, was enlarged at that time with a prominent strip (66) across the top, and two strips along the sides (each c. 20 wide); this appreciably changed the composition, which in its original format was much more compact and concentrated.

EXHIBITION
1777, Salon, no. 18.

REFERENCES
Explication des peintures... 1777, no. 18, p. 7; coll. Deloynes, v. X, no. 191, pp. 1084-1085; no. 190, p. 1031; no. 178, p. 868; v. XLIX, no. 1334, p. 850-851; H. Delaborde, 1856, p. 777; Bellier and Auvray, 1882, v. I, p. 162; F. Engerand, 1901, p. 65; Thieme and Becker, v. IV, 1907, p. 579; J. Locquin, 1912, pp. 50-51, 164, 210, 282, 285; R. Lanson, 1926, p. 44, ill. 26; L. Réau, 1926, v. II, p. 15; L. Gillet, 1935, p. 266; M. Sandoz, 1960, pp. 42-43; R. Rosenblum, 1967 a, pp. 32-34, notes 99-101, p. 32, note 104, p. 33.

RELATED WORKS
Paintings. Replica on a smaller scale (canvas; 55 × 71.5; s.d.l.r. *Brenet 1778*), Dunkerque (Sandoz, 1960, p. 43, no. 2; R. Rosenblum, 1967, p. 32, no. 100, ill. 29). Engrav-ed by Henriquez (*Honneurs rendus au Connétable Du Guesclin... Dédié à Nosseigneurs les États de Bretagne*).
Two sketches (?) lost, cited by Sandoz (1960, p. 42, no. 7), on in a sale aftert he artist's death (no. 13), the other attribut-ed to Lebrun, "placed on the market from 1778."
Painted study for the bust of the young squire in the fore-ground (canvas; 46 × 38, with incorrect date, 1760, Versailles, M⁰ Blache, 20 December 1966, "*Portrait de jeune garçon ;*" see *Connaissance des Arts,* no. 183, May 1967, p. 137, ill. 4.
Tapestries. Two examples woven at Gobelins, 1789-91, and from 1791, in the series "*Tenture de l'Histoire de France*" (cf. M. Fenaille, IV, 1907, pp. 368-369, 372-375); Fenaille noted in 1907, p. 375, that one tapestry, with border, was in the Medical School, Paris, and the other, without a border, in the Ministry of Foreign Affairs.
Engraving. By Geille, in *Galerie historique de Versailles,* no. 61: "*dessiné par Sandoz, gravé par Geille.*"

J.-P. C.

Jean Broc

1771 Montignac (Dordogne) - Poland 1850

Recent research by George Levitine has disclosed Broc's correct date of birth as 16 December 1771 (formerly given as c. 1780) at Montignac in Dordogne, and has called attention to the importance of his immense (315 × 480) painting, *L'École d'Apelle* (Salon of 1800, Louvre), as one of the few extant works that reflect fully the ideas of the Primitifs, a group of rebellious students in David's atelier who were led by the fervent Maurice Quaï. Broc's picture clearly demonstrates how he and other students of David wilfully archaized the master's style by purifying contours, simplifying compositional rhythms, and dulling colors; This direction was generally inspired by the art of Perugino and the early Raphael, as well as by the planar and linear clarity of Greek vase painting. Broc's next Salon entries of 1801, *Death of Hyacinth* (No. 16) and the *Naufrage de Virginie* (untraced but known through an Antoine Monsaldy sketch), add a morbid pathos to this abstract formal primitivism. Broc's youthful innovations, however, were soon adapted to more public demands, as in his *Mort du Général Desaix* (Versailles) at the Salon of 1806, which complies with conventional standards of Napoleonic history painting. Although he continued to exhibit at the Salon until 1833, Broc's later career is virtually unknown and needs study.

R. R.

16
Death of Hyacinth

"*La Mort d'Hyacinthe*"
Plate p. 180
Canvas; 175 × 120;
Salon of 1801, no. 45
Poitiers, Musée

The best known version of the myth of the death of Hyacinth is that told in Ovid's *Metamorphoses* (X, 162-219). Apollo was in love with the young Hyacinth and while playing discus with him, accidentally slew him. The fatal discus was directed by the wind, Zephyr who, also in love with Hyacinth, was jealous. From Hyacinth's blood, the flower that bears his name sprang from the ground. Despite its famous appearance among other mythological floral origins in Poussin's *Triomphe de Flore,* the subject is relatively rare in French art before Broc. Benjamin West exhibited a *Death of Hyacinthus* at the Royal Academy in 1772 (Swarthmore College Collection, Swarthmore, Pa.). In France, its only Salon appearance was in a painting by Antoine Boizot (Salon of 1745, no. 133).

Broc's interpretation of the theme is characteristic in form and emotion of a major current that emerged among the younger Davidians around 1800. It was a current that combined erotic fantasies of a new, heightened pathos with formal fantasies that took bizarre liberties with David's figural canon. Thus, Broc transforms the Apollo Belvedere into a waxen, yet marmoreal creature whose draperies, like his limbs, seem to waft with the malevolent Zephyr, responsible for the youth's death. The expiring Hyacinth, in turn, is even more limp, as his torso and limbs sag poignantly to the earth while Apollo tries desperately to sustain him in a last embrace. It is hardly surprising that in 1899, when Mme Demarçay proposed to give Broc's painting to the Musée de Poitiers, she gave as her reason the unsuitability of such a work to a home where her young granddaughters were growing up.

In going far beyond the purifying trends in David's own work around 1800 (as in the *Sabines*), Broc's painting conforms to tendencies in the work of many young artists of his own generation. Most conspicuously François Gérard's famous *Psyché et l'Amour* at the Salon of 1798 (Louvre) offers a precedent for the curiously, glacial, yet pliant treatment of smoothly chiseled flesh and for the growing liberty to attenuate anatomy in fluent, abstract contours. Moreover, the pairing of an amorous couple, mesmerized in the magic of love's revelation against a low, softly luminous landscape of idyllic cast, was an idea that Broc would also explore. The crystalline effect of Broc's lighting, whereby contours are suddenly illuminated in contrast to the rest of the body, which is largely shadowed, is yet another formal device employed by younger Davidians, especially by Antoine-Jean Gros in his *Sappho* (No. 87) and Anne-Louis Girodet in his *Ossian* (No. 80). The strong silhouettes that emerge from this curious luminary effect emphasize the planar disposition of figures in a manner that corresponds to the growing taste around 1800 for Greek vases and Italian primitive painting.

It was a taste, in fact, that became the esthetic rallying point for that group of refractory students in David's atelier who, led by Maurice Quaï, called themselves the Primitifs, and with whom Broc was closely associated. As George Levitine has shown (1972, p. 286), Broc was not born, as usually stated, about 1780, like most of his fellow Primitifs, but rather in 1771. This seniority may account for the acceptance of his enormous painting, the *École d'Apelle* (Louvre) at the Salon of 1800, a painting which today is the most important of the few extant works of this group. Critics accused the *École d'Apelle* of resembling too closely the dull surfaces and faded color of an old fresco, a criticism which is even more apt for the *Death of Hyacinth,* whose pallid hues and flat brushwork evoke a quattrocento panel painting. When the *Death of Hyacinth* appeared at the Salon of 1801, together with Broc's lost *Naufrage de Virginie* (no. 44 in the Salon catalog), its individuality was sufficiently noticed to warrant an honorable mention. Nevertheless, there were many complaints about what the *Moniteur universel* referred to as its being "more bizarre than original." Thus, though it was conceded that the figures were svelte and graceful, the strange, flattening light, the muted color and the abstract linearity were generally considered the odd results of youthful eccentricity.

Such willful archaisms, however, were common to this younger generation of Davidians and were soon to be developed into richer and more perverse extremes by the young Ingres. In addition, the erotic intensity of Broc's painting is typical of the more complex explorations of sexual feeling that emerge in the late 18th century and that, in this exhibition, are further exemplified in Taillasson's *Hero and Leander* (No. 172) and Gros' *Sappho* (No. 87), also exhibited at the Salon of 1801. Broc's composition was closely paraphrased by Jean-Pierre Granger in his treatment of another Ovidian homoerotic theme, *La Mort de Cyparisse,* at the Salon of 1817 (C.-P. Landon, *Salon de 1817,* Paris, 1831, pl. 17), a subject also treated by Claude-Marie Dubufe at the Salon of 1822 (No. 53). The legend of Hyacinth, with its morbid fusion of love and death, was, in fact, to grow in popularity in the early 19th century, and was even referred to in John Keats' *Endymion* (1818). In French art, the myth was to be illustrated soon after Broc in a painting by Merry-Joseph Blondel (undated; Gray) and in one attributed to Girodet (Angoulême), as well as in sculptures by Charles-Antoine Callamard (Salons of 1812 and 1814; Louvre) and François-Joseph Bosio (Salon of 1817; Louvre).

PROVENANCE
Purchased by Baron Demaray and given by his wife to the Musée de Poitiers in 1899; no. 374 in original register, no 376 in inventory, *"Section des Beaux-Arts."*

EXHIBITIONS
1801, Salon, no. 45; 1814, Salon, perhaps re-exhibited as *Hyacinthe blessé,* no. 155.

REFERENCES
Coll. Deloynes, v. XXVI, no. 687, p. 269; no. 683, pp. 572-575; no. 695, pp. 727-731; *Examen des ouvrages modernes...,* 1801, pp. 24-25; C.-P. Landon, 1802, v. II, pp. 103-104, ill. 52; J. Renouvier, 1863, p. 480; F. Benoit, 1897, p. 311, ill. 30; H. Perrault, 1930, p. 29, no. 376; G. Levitine, 1972, p. 292, ill. 7.

RELATED WORK
Engraving by Normand, in Landon, 1802, p. 52.

R. R.

Antoine-François Callet

1741 Paris 1823

In 1764, Callet received the Prix de Rome for his painting *Cléobis et Biton conduisant le char de leur mère au temple de Junon,* and was appointed history painter to the Royal Academy in 1777, the same year that Jean-Simon Berthélemy, François-Guillaume Ménageot and François-André Vincent were appointed. Callet contributed to the development of a taste for the antique. In this vein is his painting *Le Printemps* or *Zéphire et Flore couronnant de fleurs Cybèle* (Louvre, panel in the ceiling of the Galerie d'Apollon), which Callet presented as his acceptance piece at the Academy in 1780 and then exhibited at the Salon of 1781; it is one of his most successful compositions. While on a trip to Genoa, Callet painted a ceiling in Palazzo Spinola illustrating the *Apothéose d'Ambroise Spinola.* After his return to France, he painted portraits, notably one of the King in coronation dress—the first copy was commissioned from him in 1778, and for this he used Louis-Michel Van Loo's pose for Louis XV. He also did large compositions of antique subjects: *Achille traînant le corps d'Hector devant les murs de Troie* (Salon of 1785, Saint-Omer). For the Gobelins manufactory, he executed *Quatre Saisons: L'Hiver* or the *Saturnales* (Salon of 1783, Louvre); *L'Automne* or the *Fêtes de Bacchus* (Salon of 1787, Louvre); *L'Eté* or the *Fêtes de Cérès* (much admired at the Salon of 1789, now at Amiens); *Le Printemps* or *Hommage des dames romaines à Junon Lucine* (Salon of 1791, also at Amiens).

Callet devoted himself mainly to illustrating glorious moments in the career of Napoleon Bonaparte. At the Salon of 1800, he exhibited sketches for two alle-gorical compositions, *Le 18 Brumaire*—the final painting, shown at the Salon of 1801, was executed for the ceiling of the Salle du Sacre at Versailles—and *La Bataille de Marengo.* This last composition, also at Versailles, was in the Salle de Réunion of the Conservative branch of the Senate at the Luxembourg until the end of the Empire. Still in the east gallery of the first floor (library annex) of the Senate is a ceiling painting, the *Lever de l'Aurore,* painted by Callet to complete the decoration of the gallery of the Musée du Luxembourg where, in 1803, Jordaens' *Signes du Zodiaque* had just been installed. Of particular note are Callet's later renditions of the *Bataille d'Austerlitz* or the *Reddition d'Ulm* (Salon of 1812), both at Versailles. In 1815, Callet called attention to the fact that he had been the "painter to the King and to the King's brother" and managed to receive a few more commissions. Callet did not abandon antique subjects entirely—for example, *Vénus blessée par Diomède* (Salon of 1785, Louvre)—and such subjects appear sporadically in his work until the Salon of 1817.

On 9 October 1823, *La Pandore* published a harsh obituary: "M. Callet's talent echoed the style of the old school; lack of style and a weakness in the handling of color were the major faults of this academic painter, who came to us by way of a school which had recreated an artistic tradition of the reign of Louis XV. Endowed with all the virtues of an honest man, M. Callet had many friends; it is entirely natural to assume that he will be sadly missed...."

G. L.

17
Portrait of Louis XVI

"*Portrait du Roi*" *(Louis XVI)*
Plate p. 99
Canvas; 246 × 192
Salon of 1789, no. 63 (?)
Clermont-Ferrand, Musée Bargoin

It is difficult to isolate and to identify this painting from the many versions of the portrait of Louis XVI in coronation dress that Callet painted. He executed his first commission for the portrait in 1778-79 and, like Duplessis a few years before, was able to obtain a loan of the Royal coronation garb from the treasury of the Royal Abbey of Saint-Denis on 10 September 1778. The portrait, which was destined for the Hôtel de la Guerre, was completed in August 1779 and the coronation regalia were then handed over to the painter, François Guérin, who in turn had been commissioned to do a portrait for the office of the King's secretaries. Callet was subsequently instructed by the Comte de Vergennes to paint a new portrait which would "serve as a model for those to be sent to foreign courts." In a letter of 5 October 1779, the Minister of Foreign Affairs asked the Comte d'Angiviller that the artist be allowed a few posing sessions with the King. And finally, the Salon catalog of 1789 announced that Callet would exhibit no. 63, *Portrait du Roi,* and no. 64, *Portrait de Monsieur, Frère du Roi,* specifying that "these two paintings, ten *pieds* high and seven *pieds* wide, would not appear in the first days of the exhibition." The *Portrait de Monsieur* was mentioned several times by the critics (coll. Deloynes, XVI, no. 412), and rather nastily at that. "I advise him not to do any more portraits," concluded the "*admirateur*" (no. 412). They never, however, referred to the portrait of the King, which must have been exhibited quite late.

By 1785, on the other hand, negotiations were under way to commission an engraving from Charles-Clément Bervic; he was to use as a model the painting which was in the possession of the Comte de Vergennes. But Bervic did the engraving independently and on 6 August 1785 placed the following notice in the *Mercure:* "M. Bervic requested and was granted the honor of reproducing by engraving the full-length portrait of the King painted by M. Callet. It will be completed in the course of 1787." Actually, the announcement of availability for sale did not appear until 2 September 1790 in the *Journal de Paris* and the engraving was then shown at the Salon of 1791. It bore the following caption : *Louis seize, Roi des Français, restaurateur de la Liberté « Présenté au Roi et à l'Assemblée nationale, Par l'Auteur. Peint par Callet, peintre du Roi, gravé en 1790 par Bervic, graveur du Roi.* The phrase "*présenté au Roi et à l'Assemblée nationale*" referred, it would seem, to the engraving, and not, as Engerand would have it, to the Salon portrait.

What has become of the different versions painted by Callet ? Only the painting in Grenoble is dated to 1788. Dimensions do not offer much help, since in the inventories of 1832 and of Villot they do not correspond; they must have been altered in the course of restorations. If one believes the Salon catalog of 1789, Callet planned to exhibit and had not yet finished (hence the Grenoble painting is not in question here) a work measuring—with frame, no doubt—"ten *pieds* high by seven wide" (334 × 227). None of these paintings is now that size; the one that went to Clermont-Ferrand measured 305 × 200 at the time of the Second Empire, which would leave room for a frame of about 15 cm. on each side. In its present state, it corresponds in width to the ensemble of Bervic's composition excluding a balustrade on the left, but is significantly smaller in the upper portion. Louis Gonse, referring to the painting in 1903, explained that it "had disappeared almost entirely under a layer of terrible yellow varnish" and that it was restored before going to Clermont-Ferrand. He added, "it was wonderful to see a painting of such brilliance and truly exceptional refinement emerge." And Gonse stated, "we have before us, without a doubt, the full-length portrait which appeared at the Salon of 1789." This claim is entirely possible, if one accepts that a modification in the dimensions occurred at the time of restoration, and that the remarkable technical quality of the portrait (most of the other versions are dryer in execution) might be due to the fact that the artist did not completely finish it to his satisfaction.

An exchange between Callet and the "*administration des Musées*" (Arch. Nat. o³1389), although difficult to interpret, tells us something about the painter's concerns. On 24 June 1814 Callet wrote, "M. Denon has notified me that the *Portrait de Louis XVI* which was at the Sallon (sic) has just been taken at your orders to the Château de St. Cloud, Sallon des Princes (sic). This painting is a copy of the one I did for the King; since the colors are weak, I have begged M. le Directeur du Musée to make it possible for me to make the painting worthy of the great pains that were taken with the original...." On 1 July 1814, a report to Denon specified, "M. Callet requests permission to retouch the painting of Louis XVI which he once painted. I beg you to discuss this with M. C. [Callet] to ascertain whether this retouching is absolutely necessary...." Denon replied on 6 July, "With regard to the portrait of Louis XVI which is at Saint-Cloud and which M. Callet would like to retouch, I have convinced him to do nothing, as everyone agrees that it is a strong likeness...." But on 22 July, Callet insisted again, "In an earlier statement which I had the honor of addressing to Your Excellency, I begged you to be kind enough to make it possible for me to retouch the portrait of Louis XVI (a notion I value highly) which is at Saint-Cloud, this being a copy which is generally thought to be my original. As I have been informed that this copy is going to be taken to the Gobelins, I beg Your Excellency once again to be kind enough to entrust it to me for three weeks at the most, so that I may endow it with the vigor of the original." The favor was refused.

From these texts it is clear that the Salon painting was in Callet's eyes merely a copy of his original, either the version of 1778 or that of 1779, but that the administration considered the painting entirely acceptable and moreover a "likeness." Vivant Denon, who firmly rejected the artist's petition, doubtless realized that in resuming work on his painting Callet risked spoiling it. What has become of the painting discussed in this correspondence? It is tempting, but only hypothetical, to identify it with the painting from Clermont-Ferrand, if one supposes that later repaintings disfigured it. That would explain why it was no longer attributed to the author at the time of the Second Empire but was instead classified among the copies.

PROVENANCE
Collection of Louis XVI; taken into the national collections during the Revolution; listed in the Inventory B of the Royal Museums in 1832 under no. B. 475, measuring 260 × 190, as an original by Callet; listed in Villot's recapitulative inventory under the Second Empire as no. INV. 3120, measuring 305 × 200, as a work after Callet; deposited at the Clermont-Ferrand museum in 1872 (INV. 2398-875-1045-1).

EXHIBITION
1789, Salon, no. 63 (?).

REFERENCES
J.-B. Bouillet, mus. cat., 1875, nos. 1-190; R. Portalis and H. Béraldi, 1880, V. I, p. 181; F. Engerand, 1901, pp. 180-183; L. Gonse, 1903, pp. 367-368, ill. 369; M. Audallent, mus. cat., 1908, p. 14, ill. 5; Ch. Maumené and L. d'Harcourt, 1931, pp. 481-482; M. Roux, 1933, v. II, p. 473; J. Vergnet-Ruiz and M. Laclotte, 1962, p. 229.

RELATED WORKS
Engraving. By Bervic after Callet (69 × 52) exhibited at the Salon of 1791, no. 434; full-length portrait; engraving in the *manière noire* by Johann-Peter Pichler (oval, 48 × 33), c. 1790, showing the King in half-length after Callet.
Full-length portraits. By Callet (or after Callet), notably: 278 × 196, INV. B. 476, INV. 3111, MV. 3890, Versailles; 226 × 159, signed and dated 1788, INV. du Louvre, no. INV. 3110, deposited in the Musée de Grenoble in 1872; 280 × 195 (?), INV. du Louvre no. MR. 1305, INV. 3113, deposited in the Musée de Saumur in 1872; another example is preserved in Valenciennes; C. Maumené and L. d'Harcourt pointed out several others (1931, p. 482) at the Belvedere in Vienna, at the Prado in Madrid (gift of Louis XVI to the Conde d'Aranda in 1783), at the Château de Vatimesnil (Eure; gift of Louis XVI to M. de Vatimesnil in 1785), at the Hôtel-de-Ville in Geneva (gift of Louis XVI to the Republic of Geneva).
Half-length portraits. By Callet (or after Callet): two examples at Versailles (INV. no. INV. 3114, MV. 7547 and INV. no. MV. 218), each measuring 65 × 57; an example offered at public sale, Paris (Palais Galliéra), 23 March 1964, no. 25 (60 × 95).
Finally the Louvre inventory of 1832 refers to another painting (150 × 117), INV. no. B. 488, granted to the Comte de Vergennes by decision of 1 June 1818 (present location unknown; the absence of a description makes it impossible to know if this is Callet's model or the one by Duplessis with which it was sometimes confused during the 19th century); a half-length portrait (165 × 131) was recently on the New York market.

G. L.

Armand Caraffe

1762 Paris 1818 or 1822 ?

The life of this forgotten artist remains obscure, having interested only Bellier de la Chavignerie and especially J. Renouvier (1863, pp. 122-125). According to J.-L.-J. David (1880), he was a pupil of David, but Louis Lagrenée is his only known teacher; he recommended Caraffe in February 1780 (*Correspondance des Directeurs...*) and he is mentioned as his teacher in the 1799 Salon catalog. Caraffe won a minor prize at the Academy in 1780 and in 1783 began to exhibit at the Salon de la Correspondance, showing *Le Retour du fils prodigue* and *La Résurrection du fils de la veuve de Naïm*. In 1784 and 1785, he entered the preliminary competition for the Prix de Rome. He then traveled to Rome at his own expense; but when Jean-Germain Drouais died, he took his place at the French Academy in Rome from April to September 1788 (*Correspondance des Directeurs..., XV*). He was then working on a large canvas representing *Le Temps, l'Amour et l'Amitié*. François Menageot had already mentioned his "wild and barbaric taste," which he considered "an abuse of style." Caraffe then went to Naples, and from there, to Calabria, Sicily, Greece and Constantinople. He was back in France in the summer of 1790. In 1791, he exhibited in Lebrun's rooms on the rue de Clichy his academic figure *La Vigilance d'Alexandre,* which may have been the painting he sent to Paris in 1788 that was severely criticized by an Academy Committee ("an abuse of the antique... an elephantine approach," *Procès-verbaux... IX*, p. 387; see also *Correspondance des Directeurs...*); it aroused interest and discussion, but once again was thought too visionary (coll. Deloynes, XVII).

Caraffe exhibited regularly at the Salon from 1793 to 1802, mostly drawings with themes from ancient history, but also allegorical pictures like *l'Innocence sous la garde de la fidélité* (Salon of 1796, known by the engraving made by Perrée, 1797), *L'Amour abandonné de la jeunesse et des grâces se console dans le sein de l'Amitié des outrages du Temps* (destroyed in the Tuileries in 1871, engraved by Normand in the *Annales du Musée,* I, 1801) or *Le Destin règle le cours de la vie ; de vains songes en font le charme* (also engraved by Normand in Landon, III, 1802). His entry in the Salon of 1795 was noticed by the critics, who were surprised by the black background of his *Allégorie sur l'extrémité de la vie* and his "brilliant colors," like those in *Marius at Minturnae*. In 1799, Caraffe showed (*L'Etude ramenant aux hommes la santé sous la figure d'Egya),* which was intended for the ceiling of the École Clinique, rue des Saints-Pères. Travel provided the inspiration for some drawings with oriental subjects that he exhibited at the Salons of 1796 and 1799; they were intended to illustrate a work that never appeared (a *Bataille en Egypte,* s.d. 1801, which is preserved in the Bibliothèque Nationale, Paris, Cabinet des Estampes, Hennin Collection). Caraffe remained a Jacobin after the fall of Robespierre and spent time in prison for partly political and partly private reasons (he was accused of being the lover of the wife of the engraver Pierre Audouin), but the dates given, particularly by J. Renouvier, for this period in prison (1794-1797) are not correct; Caraffe's home address is listed in the catalog for the Salon of 1795 and 1796. Caraffe made some engravings after his own works (*Le Remords ou le Criminel vis-à-vis de lui-même*) and began a *Cours Historique et élémentaire de peinture* (starting with the Egyptians), which was completed and published from 1802 on by A.-M. Filhol and Lavallée under the title *Galerie Complète du Museum Central*. Caraffe left for Russia about this time and stayed there some ten years; only two of his pictures are now known to be located there. Besides the *Oath of the Horatii,* there is a *Metellus arrêtant ses guerriers* at the Hermitage. We know nothing of the end of his life.

A. S.

18
The Oath of the Horatii*

Le Serment des Horaces
Plate p. 125
Canvas; 88 × 114; s.d.m.l., *A. C. Caraffe, | Anno | MDCCXCI*
Arkhangelski, Museum

This canvas has little more than its subject in common with the famous work by David (1785, Louvre). Not only are the figures placed differently (without the separation of men and women which is so characteristic of David), but in particular, the draughtsmanship and colors are quite dissimilar. Caraffe appears here as a "primitive", ignoring realism and reducing his characters to the level of one-dimensional puppets. But this abstract aspect is in strong contrast to the fresh colors and smooth surfaces that Caraffe probably inherited from Lagrenée. As with Peyron, Caraffe's reaction to the Rococo did not necessarily banish all ornamentation (although Peyron's work is more polished). In such medium-sized history paintings, despite the difference of subject-matter, we are in fact closer to genre artists like Louis-Léopold Boilly, who were influenced by the Dutch, than to the large-scale compositions of David and his imitators.

PROVENANCE
This canvas, accompanied by a drawing of the same subject, was shown by Lebrun, at the rue de Cléry, from 30 June to 15 July 1791 (coll. Deloynes, XVII). It was either taken by Caraffe himself to Russia or bought directly by Prince Youssoupoff; it was in the Youssoupoff Collection at Archangelski Castle near Moscow, where it still is today (INV. 96-G).

REFERENCES
Arkhangelski Gallery, 1827, v. I, p. 187, no. 6; G. Le Cointe de Laveau, 1828, p. 284; *(idem)*, 1835, v. II, p. 282; L. Dussieux, 1852, 1876 ed., p. 581; J. Renouvier, 1863, p. 122; Bellier and Auvray, 1882; A. Praksov, 1907, pp. 210, 224, 225; Thieme and Becker, 1911, v. V, p. 565; S. Ernst, 1924, p. XX; N.-T. Ounaniantz, 1970, p. 48, ill.; N. Volle, 1974-1975, no. 11.

RELATED WORKS
Engraved by L. Laurence (Paignon-Dijonval catalog, 1810, no. 9628). Two drawings without significant variations are known: one is in a private collection at Göttingen (28 × 37), and the other (29 × 39) was recently acquired by Rennes at a sale in Paris, Hôtel Drouot, room 10, 30 January 1974, no. 9, as "school of David."   A. S.

Constance Charpentier, née Blondelu

1767 Paris 1849

According to 19th-century encyclopedias, Mme Charpentier was trained under Wilk (possibly a typographical error for J.-G. Wille), David, Lafitte, Gérard and Bouillon, and received a *Prix d'Encouragement* in 1788. Judging from *La Mélancolie* (No. 19), her style was strongly influenced by David. She exhibited frequently at the Salon between 1795 and 1819; and, characteristically for the many women artists of the period (e.g., Jeanne-Élisabeth Chaudet, Henriette Lorimier, Marguerite Gérard), she specialized in sentimental genre scenes, often of her own complex invention

(Salon of 1806, *Un aveugle entouré de ses enfants est consolé de la perte de la vue par les jouissances des quatre autres sens*), and portraits, particularly of women and children. She apparently received, three times a week, young artists who wished to hear her advice on painting and drawing; and in 1819, the year of her last Salon, she was awarded the gold medal by the Royal Museum.

Mme Charpentier's fame became international in 1951 when Charles Sterling proposed that a portrait of Mlle Charlotte du Val d'Ognes (New York, Metropolitan Museum), traditionally attributed to David, might in fact be by her. The new attribution was based primarily on the appearance of the painting in a print of the Salon of 1801 (year IX), and the probable identification of the work as one of a group of portraits exhibited at that Salon by Mme Charpentier as no. 60. This suggestion, however, must remain tentative, especially since the contemporary Salon descriptions of Mme Charpentier's exhibited portraits are extremely imprecise and since the only known works by her available for comparison are *La Mélancolie* (No. 19) and a portrait drawing (Dijon, Musée Magnin), which resemble each other far more closely than they do the New York portrait. Current research on the growingly popular subject of women artists should bring to light new information about Mme Charpentier that may pertain to this attribution.

R. R.

19
Melancholy

"La Mélancolie"
Plate p. 179
Canvas; 130 × 165; s.l.r. *CM Blondelu* |*f. Charpentier*
Salon of 1801, no. 58
Amiens, Musée de Picardie

The subject and mood of Mme Charpentier's painting are summed up in a poem it inspired in a contemporary Salon critique:

A l'ombre d'un saule pleureur,
Sur le bord d'une onde limpide
Cette femme nous peint son cœur
Dans un regard doux et timide,
On a du plaisir à rêver
Près d'une femme si jolie
Et ce tableau nous fait trouver
Du charme à la mélancolie.

(*Arlequin chassé...*, p. 22)

Such female figures—their seated bodies limp and passive, their facial expressions inward and dejected—are ubiquitous in late 18th-century painting and tomb sculpture, but are usually associated with a specific narrative context that identifies the deceased. The romantic exploration of the pleasures of sensibility, however, began to permit the depiction of isolated melancholic figures which, unlike the emblematic figures of melancholy in, for example, Ripa's *Iconologia,* provoke imaginative conjecture about the cause of their dejection. Already in the late 18th century, individual figures of melancholy had been excerpted from larger compositions—as in Louis Lagrenée the Elder's painted study of a mourning woman (*La Mélancolie ;* Louvre) and from his *Mort de la Femme de Darius* (Salon of 1785;

Louvre). At the Salon of 1798, which included many works by Mme Charpentier, Benjamin Devouge exhibited a drawing, *La Mélancolie* (no. 123 in the Salon catalog); and Étienne Pallière exhibited a painting, *Une Jeune Femme assise sur un morceau de rocher et se livrant à la mélancolie* (no. 325 in the Salon catalog). At the Salon of 1801, there appeared not only Mme Charpentier's version of this subject, but one by François-André Vincent (Catalog no. 368), a painting as yet untraced but in which, according to the Salon critiques, an anonymous weeping woman is seated next to the tomb of her father as night falls.

Although the ultimate sources for Mme Charpentier's figure and her attributes may range widely from emblem books and literary illustrations to such famous artists' interpretations of the theme as Dürer's engraving of *Melencolia* or Poussin's figure of Agrippina in *La Mort de Germanicus,* the immediate source is closer at hand in the work of one of Mme Charpentier's own teachers, the figure of Camilla in David's *Serment des Horaces.* In effect, Mme Charpentier has isolated David's grieving figure and relocated her in a landscape setting that includes the frequent attributes of melancholy, a weeping willow and a body of water. Her talent was recognized by one anonymous critic as another promising artist in that "group of women distinguished by their talent," although he complained that there was "little subtlety in the contours" (*Examen des ouvrages...*, p. 57).

Internationally speaking, the traditions of a melancholic figure isolated in a landscape are long and complex, especially in England, where late 18th-century art and literature newly explored this mood of loneliness and sorrow (see F. Cummings, "Boothby, Rousseau, and the Romantic Malady," *The Burlington Magazine*, CX, Dec. 1968, pp. 659-666). In fact, Mme Charpentier's painting, in its juxtaposition of a neo-classical figure, viewed in profile, with a highly emotive romantic landscape, finds its closest analogies in British painting, whether in such predecessors as Joseph Wright of Derby's *Indian Widow* (1785; Derby Museum and Art Gallery) or successors as Francis Danby's *Disappointed Love* (1821; London, Victoria and Albert Museum). For French contemporaries, these personifications of melancholy evoked a characteristically romantic fusion of pleasure and pain, a combination evident not only in the responses of Salon critics to the paintings of Mme Charpentier and Vincent at the Salon of 1801 *("Volupté dur malheur! douce Mélancolie!")*, but one that constantly informed the writings of such authors as Jean-Jacques Rousseau and the Abbé Delille.

PROVENANCE
Acquired in 1801 by the Musée Napoléon as a *prix d'encouragement*; 13 October 1864, sent to Amiens, Musée de Picardie (INV. 3213).

EXHIBITIONS
1801, Salon, no. 58; 1969, Amiens, no. 8; 1969, Dunkerque, no. 8; 1973, Paris, Musée des Arts Décoratifs, n. no.

REFERENCES
Coll. Deloynes, v. XXVI, no. 682, pp. 128-129; no. 690, p. 326; v. XXVII, no. 710, p. 449; F. Benoit, 1897, p. 339; mus. cat., 1911, p. 19, no. 83; Ch. Sterling, 1951, pp. 129-130; Ch. Sterling, 1951, p. 127; J. Foucart, 1970, p. 76.

R. R.

Jeanne-Élisabeth Chaudet

1767 Paris 1832

In 1793, Jeanne-Élisabeth Gabiou married Antoine-Denis Chaudet (1763-1810), a sculptor and painter with whom she had studied. From 1798 to 1817, she exhibited at the Salon and was, especially in the first years of the period, a great success with the public. In 1808, Charles Landon described her as following: "A modest artist, skilled in choosing or rather in creating subjects for her paintings, Mme Chaudet seems to adopt only those which she knows to be suitable to her talents and commensurate with her abilities; to this she adds the virtue of doing only compositions that are gentle, unaffected, graceful and always new" (Landon, 1808, v. II, p. 16).

Mme Chaudet did many paintings of girls, children and animals, and often composed them in the manner of antique bas-reliefs with the figures in profile. She became famous at the Salon of 1799 with her painting *Une petite fille voulant apprendre à lire à son chien*, which the critics discussed at some length and which François Godefroy engraved.

L'enfant endormi dans un berceau sous la garde d'un chien courageux from the Salon of 1801 is moving for its dramatic subject (it was for many years exhibited at the Musée du Luxembourg, now the Musée de Rochefort). *La jeune fille donnant à manger à des poulets*, which Landon published as a work from the Salon of 1802 (v. I, 1832, fig. 17) was acquired by Josephine (now at the Musée d'Arenenberg). The Empress also commissioned the *"Jeune fille à genoux devant la statue de Minerve lui fait le sacrifice des dons de l'Amour"* exhibited at the Salon of 1808 (also now at Arenenberg). Only once did Mme Chaudet attempt an antique subject, *Dibutade* (Salon of 1810, shown again in 1814, destroyed at the Musée d'Arras), and this she handled in her usual pleasant and graceful manner. The same qualities reappear in her portraits, where the models always have some anecdotal attribute, as for instance in the *Portrait d'enfant portant le sabre de son père* (Salon of 1819, now in a private collection).

Mme Chaudet received a *prix d'encouragement* in 1812 and in the same year married an archivist, Pierre-Arsène-Denis Husson. Her husband died in 1843, leaving a number of works to the museum in Arras, his native town: in addition to a portrait of M. Husson, several genre scenes which had been exhibited at the Salons from 1806 to 1817. The fact that these paintings had remained in the artist's studio indicates that her success declined under the Empire (with the exception of painting exhibited here, No. 20, all these works were destroyed in Arras during World War I). It is odd to find that by 1808 Lebreton in his *Rapport sur les Beaux* *Arts* already referred to Mme Chaudet in the past tense; he pointed out, as if composing an epitaph, "Mme Chaudet often appealed to us with the charm of her ideas and the grace of her paintbrush."

G.L.

20

Young Girl Mourning the Death of her Pigeon

" Jeune fille pleurant son pigeon mort"
Plate p. 199
Canvas; 130 × 97; s.l.c. *Eli.*th *Chaudet*
Salonof 1808, no. 122
Arras, Musée

The Salon of 1808 was a *"Salon de dames,"* noted the *Moniteur* of 21 December 1808. Among the 410 participants, 50 were women. Mme Chaudet, who was one of the most famous, exhibited several compositions, one of which belonged to the Empress. In the words of *Le Journal de l'Empire,* "Mme Chaudet distinguished herself as usual with her pretty easel paintings."

Although her sentimental subjects are varied, it is true that they are handled in a fairly uniform manner. A girl, seated or kneeling, appears at the center of the composition in a setting composed entirely of vertical and horizontal architectural elements; a little vegetation adorns the severity of this rigid geometrical scheme and in the background is a conventional green landscape beneath a vast open sky; one's attention focuses on the feelings expressed. *L'Observateur au Museum* commented, "This figure is so gentle and her expression so touching that one feels encouraged to share her suffering. It is one of Mme Chaudet's best works, and the pink color is less dominant than in the other paintings by this capable artist."

It was in her use of color that Mme Chaudet failed to satisfy her contemporaries. Landon, who reproduced many of her compositions, accompanied an engraving of the Arras painting with the following ironical comments: "Mme Chaudet's colors leave a little vigor and warmth to be desired, but they are not without delicacy. Paintings in which color is handled as it is in the one of which we show the sketch retain their freshness longer than those that are entirely finished on leaving the studio; with time the hues ripen and become harmonious. But Mme Chaudet's are so near the point where one would like to see them that it would be a mistake for her to leave to time alone the task of finishing them."

PROVENANCE
Gift of M. Husson, the artist's second husband, to the Musée d'Arras, 1843.

EXHIBITIONS
1808, Salon, no. 122; 1973, Paris, Musée des Arts Décoratifs.

REFERENCES
Coll. Deloynes, v. XVIII, pp. 628-629; v. XLIV, p. 585; v. XLV, p. 420; C.-P. Landon, 1808, v. II, p. 16, ill. 9; mus. cat., 1866, no. 58; *ibid.*, 1880, no. 93; *ibid.*, 1907, no. 199; F. Mathey, 1973, p. 13., ill.

RELATED WORKS
Outline engraving by Devilliers the Elder for Landon (see References).

G.L.

Pierre-Athanase Chauvin

1774 Paris - Rome 1832

A student of Valenciennes, Chauvin at first specialized in landscapes, both historical and actual. Dussieux (1876, pp. 502-504), author of a precious document about Chauvin written with the aid of information obtained from the artist's son, pointed out that several of Chauvin's historical landscapes were in the possession of Mme David, widow of the French consul to Smyrna.

The artist first exhibited at the Salon in 1793, with three landscapes, one with a rock and figures, one with a fountain, the last with a waterfall and figures; in 1796, he showed *Soleil couchant* and *Soleil levant* (the figures were painted by Antoine Fleury who owned the paintings); *Vue des environs de Rheingravenschten* in the Palatinate, owned by the artist at the time of exhibition; and *Les Salines de Creutzenach dans le Palatinat,* owned by Merlin de Thionville, representative of the people.

In the Salon of 1801, he exhibited the *Berger effrayé à la vue d'un serpent qu'un chien découvre,* a very popular subject (cf. the painting by Frédéric-Jean Schall in Strasbourg). Italian subjects did not seem to appear in Chauvin's work until the *Vue des cascades de Tivoli,* Salon of 1802, the year in which he made a trip to Italy, where he was, in fact, to spend the rest of his life; he settled permanently in Rome in 1804.

A very interesting letter from Talleyrand to Chauvin from 1806 (cited in P. Marmottan, 1889, p. 127) informs us that the painter already had a patron named Morin, whom Talleyrand succeeded (Chauvin's father, a rich Parisian butcher, had been ruined by the Revolution). For Chauvin, this meant an annual pension in exchange for some paintings (Dussieux was more precise—the exchange involved two paintings per year). His paintings in the Salon of 1810 attest to the actuality of the arrangement with Talleyrand, since two of the paintings shown belonged to the Prince of Benevento, *Vue de Bénévent* and *Vue de la Cava,* in the kingdom of Naples.

Talleyrand's patronage lasted a long time; the collection of letters in the possession of Chauvin's son, consulted by Marmottan, contained many from Talleyrand to the artist, dating notably from 1815, 1817, 1819 and 1832 (P. Marmottan, *op. cit.,* p. 128). In 1814, he again exhibited an Italian subject, *Vue extérieure de la grotte de Pouzzoles,* a Neapolitan site greatly favored by painters.

In Rome itself, Chauvin became highly esteemed for his landscapes; Dussieux mentioned examples in the possession of the Duchessa of Dino, in 1855; of Bodinier in Angers, which accounts for their presence in the museum of this city; of Mme Jourdan in Paris, *Vue de Rome au soleil couchant,* also entitled *Pins de la Ruffinella* (cf. No. 21). In 1819, he even painted a view of Villa Medici for Metternich, the renowned statesman. In the same year, he sent to the Salon in Paris a *Fourches*

caudines, then in the collection of the Comte d'Ormesson d'Eaubonne; and, in particular, *Entrée de Charles VIII à Acquapendente,* commissioned in 1817 for the Galerie de Diane at Fontainebleau, placed in Amboise by the Louvre in 1876, and today in the Hôtel de Ville. Louis-Philippe had a copy of it made by Édouard Hostein (1837) for his historical museum at the Château de Versailles. This was later engraved by Lejeune for *Galeries historiques de Versailles* by Gavard, 1833-45 (cf. exh. cat., 1971, Bourg-en-Bresse, no. 145, fig. 18). After this Salon, Louis XVIII awarded the artist with the gold medal in 1820.

In the Salon of 1824 were two paintings from Talleyrand's collection, *Vue des environs de Tivoli* and *Vue de Rome depuis le Monte Pincio ; Chartreuse dans le royaume de Naples,* belonging to Principe Aldobrandini Borghese; two landscapes from the collection of the Marshal De Lauriston, *Jardin des Capucins de Genzano, Couvent de Grotta Ferrata ;* and finally a *Vue du lac de Varèse.*

Many of his landscapes in the Salon of 1827 were just as favored by high society: *Vallée de Narni,* owned by the Duke of Fitz-James ; *Villa de Mécène à Tivoli, Vue du Pausilippe, Aqueduc de Molini près de la Cava ;* by the Duc de Noailles ; *Vue de Bénévent,* by M. Schickler; *Vue de Saint-Pierre de Rome au couchant, Vue du pont Lupo à Tivoli,* by Talleyrand; *Site de la Pouille,* by P. Perrey. The last Salon in which Chauvin participated was in 1831, with a *Site d'Italie.*

In addition to works mentioned in the entry of Thieme and Becker, (v. VI, pp. 442-443), let us cite: *Vue du Vésuve,* s.d. 1811 (Montpellier) ; *Villa d'Este, Villa Falconieri, Grotta Ferrata* from the Thorwaldsen estate and now in Copenhagen; others in Oslo, Moulins, Nantes. Among his works in Parisian private collections is a beautiful Italian vista in refined mauve tones, s.d. Rome 1809; in the Bibliothèque Marmottan, Boulogne-Billancourt: *Bords de l'Aniene près de Rome ; Pavillon forestier au bord de l'étang, 1822,* Dijon, Musée Magnin; from Talleyrand's collection, *Vue d'un monastère près du lac de Côme,* Château de Valençay; two small *tondi* landscapes, Leningrad, the Hermitage, one of which is reproduced in color by V. Bérézina, 1972, p. 75. Chauvin was, in fact, greatly appreciated by Russian collectors.

By 1813, Chauvin had gained such fame that he was named a member of the Academy of Saint Luke, Rome, and decorated in 1814 by Louis XVIII with the Royal Order of the Fleur de Lys. In 1825, Charles X commissioned the work shown in this exhibit; in 1827, the artist was named a corresponding member of the

Institute and, in 1828, a knight of the Legion of Honor.

Held in high regard by French and foreign artists in Rome, such as Ingres, Wicar, Auvray, Guillaume Bodinier and Lorimier; Vogel von Vogelstein even made a portrait of him for his collection of famous contemporary men (drawing in Dresden).

In 1812, Chauvin had married a Parisian woman in Rome, Albertine-Suzanne Hayard; they are the subjects of two famous pencil drawings by Ingres done in 1814, in the Musée Bonnat, Bayonne. The couple had one son, Charles Chauvin (1820-1864), who was a student of Jacques-Félix Duban, and became a painter of scenery and architecture. It was he who copied the *loggie* of Raphael, in the École des Beaux-Arts, Paris.

Chauvin's works are distinguished by a smooth finish, a rather warm and sensitive palette like that of Jean-Joseph-Xavier Bidauld; a correct and wise drawing, a Bertin-like handling, "slick brushwork"... [and]... perspectives of an exquisite soft handling. The sites chosen by Chauvin on Italian soil rarely had a more faithful and talented interpreter" (P. Marmottan, 1889, p. 126).
J. F.

21
La Ruffinella, near Rome

Vue de la Ruffinella
Plate p. 282
Canvas; 82 × 106; s.l.l. *Chauvin Roma*
Paris, Musée des Arts Décoratifs

According to a reasonable suggestion by M. Pierre Lamicq, an expert on Michallon, the title of Ruffinella (which must be kept since it comes from old inventories and, therefore, very likely from the artist himself) might designate some prominence situated in the Monti Ruffi, in the region of Tivoli-Subiaco, although the name does not appear on maps of Italy. We know, interestingly enough, that another painting by Chauvin, *Vue de Rome au Soleil couchant* also bore the title *Pins de la Ruffinella* in the 19th century (Mme Jourdan Collection; see L. Dussieux, 1876, p. 503).

Combining in this painting academic stylization with a taste for the *style troubadour,* Chauvin already displayed the somber Romanticism made popular by Chateaubriand and Senancour (see J. Magnin, 1928). The gothic element (which is seen in the use of only one bright color—blue) is brought out by the armed knights who ascend the hill in the foreground, where there is a small chapel; we know that Hippolyte Lecomte exhibited a *Soleil couchant* at the Salon of 1804, no. 283, with the same details. Similarly based on a mixture of genres was the large canvas Chauvin painted in 1819 for the Galerie de Diane at Fontainebleau, and today at Amboise, the *Entrée de Charles VIII à Acquapendente, 1494,* where the traditional Italianate landscape is more prominent than the other component, historical anecdote, which is reduced to a simple use of figures in *troubadour* fashion.

The only unexpected note in our painting is the group of trees silhouetted against the light. It produces a dominant graphic effect, anticipating the composition of Caruelle d'Aligny, and lends a timely and strangely poetic Romanticism to what otherwise would have been a simple Italian view. The latter was especially suited to neo-classical taste, treated here in a manner that tends, toward a clear, yet harsh palette; a smooth but precise harmony (simultaneously refined and clearcut) and an enveloping luminosity that nevertheless had to be legible throughout, as in the works of J.-V. Bertin, A.-H. Dunouy or J.-F.-X. Bidauld.

PROVENANCE

Acquired for 1,500 francs for the collection of Charles X in 1825 (INV. no. C 20 from register 2 DD 11 on deposit in the Archives du Louvre); sent to the Musée du Luxembourg, then to the Château de Saint-Cloud in 1827 (cf. the entry of 1847 which indicates that the canvas was in the apartments of H.R.H. Mgr. the Prince de Joinville); placed in the Château of La Motte-Beuvron from 1856 to 1872, then in the Élysée Palace from 1875; returned to the Louvre in 1907, and placed in the Musée des Arts Décoratifs in 1928 (registered in 1930 as coming from the Château of Saint-Germain). (INV. no. 3226).

EXHIBITIONS

1925, Paris, no. 215; 1957, Amsterdam, no. 260 (not in. cat.).

REFERENCES

Notice des peintures... placées dans les appartements... du palais de Saint-Cloud, 1847, no. 251; L. Dussieux, 1876, p. 503 (at Saint-Cloud); J. Magnin, 1928, p. 202; mus. cat., 1938, p. 192 (*"Paysage avec deux Croisés"*); B. Lossky, 1961, p. 165.

J. F.

Jean-Baptiste Corot

1796 Paris 1875

"I went to school in Rouen until I was 18 years old. Then for eight years I worked in business. Because I couldn't resist the inclination, I became a landscape painter and at the beginning followed the advice of [Achille-Etna] Michallon. After this, I entered the studio of Victor Bertin. Eventually, I took up the study of nature all on my own. And that's where I am now...." These words, recorded by Geoffroy, sum up perfectly Corot's life until about the year 1830, after his return from his first visit to Italy (1825-26). Since Corot had chosen to be a landscape painter, it was natural, at this moment, that he be encouraged to go to Italy, first by Michallon and then by Bertin. Inhabited by the circle of Valenciennes, Hue, Boguet, Taunay, Fabre, etc., Rome had been at the end of the 18th century the setting for the rebirth of classical landscape, which was then referred to as *paysage historique* and is now called *paysage composé.* This genre had been a great success among artists who were receptive to nature, the *beau idéal,* and the lessons of antiquity, as well as to the teachings of 17th-century landscape painters. The genre came into its own in France in 1817 with the creation of the Grand Prix for historical landscape, a prize which was justly awarded to Michallon.

Around 1820 to 1825, there emerged a second generation of landscape artists, formulated under Pierre-Henri de Valenciennes, Jean-Joseph-Xavier Bidauld and Bertin. These artists adhered to the rules laid down by Valenciennes and yet, at the same time, recognized the esthetic value of natural landscape, the role of light and the importance of the sky and of color in rendering the effects they had perceived. The influence of J.-B. Deperthes, whose *Théorie du paysage* appeared in 1818, and that of the English and Dutch schools thus began to appear along with the classical tradition formed in Italy.

Thus, when Corot reached Rome in 1825, he discovered an artistic milieu in the process of change. At the Villa Medici he found J.-Ch.-J. Rémond, winner of the historical landscape prize in 1821, and A. Giroux, who had won it in 1825. But Corot formed his closest ties with Léopold Robert, Schnetz, Bodinier, Lapito, Édouard Bertin and particularly with Aligny, who like himself was working independently in Rome outside of the academic framework. Even though these artists are not accorded the same importance in the history of art, the charm of their extremely free oil sketches —in the same vein as Valenciennes—is often close to what one sees in Corot's work.

In Rome, the *castelli romani,* the Sabine hills and the gulf of Naples, Corot and his friends discovered a rocky landscape, blunt in form under a brilliant sun, softened by vegetation, and modeled in planes of shadow and light. Their direct and brutal vision was expressed in an extremely free technique, in which thick strokes of paint contrast with dry scumble, in a manner so characteristic of Corot's oil sketches.

The artist also brought back drawings which are by contrast more analytical and greatly influenced by Aligny. This exercise in technique had some influence on Corot's paintings. The last views of Rome dating from his first stay there—the *Forum,* the *Trinité des Monts* (Louvre)—show the artist once again using tonalities and glazes.

This vision which Corot expressed with such immediacy was gradually subjected to a desire to show at the Salon only those works which adhered to principles still current at the time—Quatremère de Quincy's *L'Essai sur l'Idéal* was published in 1837. Nevertheless, the artist did remain faithful to his earlier vision— especially during his subsequent trips to Italy and Provence.

The elements of directness in Corot's work eventually won out and were further enriched by the mood of subjectivity and lyricism which appeared in his painting around 1850. Contemporary criticism was aware of the liberties that Corot took: "He doesn't imitate anything, not even nature" or "Corot paints not so much nature as his love for it" (E. About, 1855, p. 217).

His last works—*Le Beffroi de Douai* or the *Cathédrale de Sens* (Louvre)—demonstrate Corot's importance for the evolution of landscape painting during the 19th century.

J.-F. M.

22

Bridge of Narni, near Rome

"Vue prise à Narni" also called *Le Pont de Narni*
Plate p. 294
Canvas; 68 × 93; estate mark l.l.
Salon of 1827-1828, no. 221
Ottawa, The National Gallery of Canada

Represented here are the ruins of the bridge where the Via Flaminia crossed the Nera River, tributary of the Tiber, below the little village of Narni. During August and September 1826, Corot and his friend Behr stayed at Papigno and Narni, where the artist also drew a *Vue panoramique* (L. Robaut, 1905, IV, no. 2491). There Corot painted directly from nature the famous sketch (Louvre) which he gave to his friend Lapito. It was very bold in execution and color, and remains to this day vibrant with the emotion that the artist felt confronted by the brilliant, sunny landscape.

On the other hand, in the landscape exhibited here, which was painted during the winter of 1826-27, Corot recomposed the view. The left-hand portion, with its typically Italian umbrella pines—a naturally hard and rugged landscape—is in Corot's painting flattened to include shepherds, a young girl spinning wool, and the flock. More characteristic is the opening up of the landscape toward a distant horizon which, behind the ruins of the bridge, makes way for a line of hills.

In his search for an equilibrium and a distant perspective between two masses, an effect which was borrowed from the theater, Corot is reminiscent of Claude Lorrain. But since he hardly ever went to museums, we are not concerned here with a direct influence, but rather with a lesson which Corot learned from the work of his comrades.

In this painting, the artist turned away from his more spontaneous vision (described so often as "impressionist"); here he chose instead to return to an image that conforms to a pre-established order. But when Corot gradually gave up this method of recomposing his subjects—"never lose hold of the first impression that strikes you," Corot's own words as quoted by Venturi (1941, p. 140)—he proved to be one of the significant teachers of the 19th century.

PROVENANCE

Painted in Rome in 1827; kept by Corot until his death, then included in the atelier sale in Paris, 26 May-4 June 1875, no. 21; collection of Lemaistre, the artist's nephew; Charles André Collection; offered for sale in Paris, Hôtel Drouot, 17 May 1893, no. 3 (ill.); Desfossés Collection, sold in Paris, Hôtel Drouot, 26 April 1899, no. 16, ill.; Bernheim Jeune Collection; acquired by the National Gallery of Canada, Ottawa, in 1940 (INV. 4526).

EXHIBITIONS

1827-1828, no. 221; 1895, Paris, no. 116; 1940, Toronto, no. 89; 1942, Montreal, no. 54; 1942, New York, no. 9; 1946, Philadelphia, no. 6, ill.; 1947, Saint Louis, no. 8, ill.; 1949, Toronto, no. 129; 1950, Philadelphia, no. 56, ill.; 1952, Venice, no. 2, ill.; 1954, Toronto, no. 46, ill.; 1954, Fort Worth, no. 14; 1960, Bern, no. 17; 1965, Edinburgh, no. 17, ill. 10; 1969, New York, no. 9.

REFERENCES

L. Roger-Milès, 1895, p. 25; A. Michel, 1896, p. 919; G. Geoffroy, 1902-1903, p. 4; A. Robaut, 1955, v. I, p. 46 and v. II, p. 70; no. 199, ill. p. 71; M. Hamel, 1905, ill. I; E. Moreau-Nélaton, 1924, p. 22, ill. 31; M. Lafargue, 1925, p. 25; F. Fosca, 1930, p. 34, ill. 9; René-Jean, 1931, p. 13; G. Bazin, 1942, p. 37; G. Geoffroy, 1946, pp. 39-40; L. Venturi, 1941, p. 143, ill. 88; *idem*, 1946, p. 141; A. Malraux, v. I, 1947, p. 67, ill. p. 68; R. Huyghe, 1955, p. 213, ill. 197; D. Baud-Bovy, 1957, p. 79; mus. cat. 1959, v. II, p. 12, no. 4526; G. Bazin, 1973, p. 30, ill. p. 31.

RELATED WORKS

A drawing preserved in the National Gallery of Canada, Ottawa (not in Robaut's catalog; cf. E. Popham and K.-M. Fenwick: *European Drawing... in the Collection of the National Gallery of Canada*, Toronto, 1965, pp. 166-168, no. 240, ill. p. 169); painted sketch preserved in the Louvre (R.F. 1613).

J.-F. M.

23
La Cervara

"La Cervara, campagne de Rome"
Plate p. 297
Canvas; 68 × 95; s.l.r. *Corot*
Salon of 1831, no. 399
Zurich, Kunsthaus

In the hills halfway between Tivoli and Subiaco, the village of La Cervara dominates the Roman countryside. Moreau-Nélaton and Robaut (1905, pp. 40-41) mentioned that Corot made a trip to this region during the summer of 1827, accompanied by Antoine Guindrand from Lyon and Jules Boilly from Paris and also by three architects. The date of 1827 for the sketch in the Louvre confirms this fact. But the painting exhibited here was done in Paris probably not until after 1828. And yet Baud-Bovy (1957, p. 81), without mentioning the painting, was certain that Corot, Aligny and Edouard Bertin went to La Cervara in the fall of 1826 and that they then went as far as the Adriatic. And indeed, at the same Salon of 1831, which included this painting and other works by Corot, the artist exhibited the *Couvent sur les bords de l'Adriatique* (Salon no. 398).

There is, however, no localized and dated work to prove such a trip. It is known only that Aligny did three views in ink of this site, dating from 1834, which were recently offered at public sale in Paris (Hôtel Drouot, 30 June 1972), as M.-M. Aubrun has pointed out. One of these works was engraved (see Bibliothèque Nationale, Cabinet des Estampes, 91 b 232, Gr. in-fol.). As for Bertin, his work, *Les Carrières de la Cervara dans la campagne de Rome,* was exhibited at the Salon of 1839 (no. 153).

The views of the Roman countryside which Corot, Aligny and Bertin painted, and the site of La Cervara in particular, inspired the young Théophile Gautier in 1839 to write a poem, *"Trois paysagistes,"* which is part of the *Premiers Poèmes:*

Ainsi nous vous voyons, austères solitudes,
Où l'âme endort sa peine et ses inquiétudes !
Grottes de Cervara, que d'un pinceau certain
Creusa profondément le sévère Bertin...
Plus loin c'est Aligny, qui, le crayon en main

Comme Ingres le ferait pour un profil humain,
Recherche l'Idéal...
Mais voici que le soir du haut des monts descend
L'ombre devient plus grise et va s'élargissant...
A peine reste-t-il assez de jour pour voir,
Corot, ton nom modeste luit dans un coin noir.

The preceding lines suggest a landscape composed in the classical mode. Corot's *La Cervara* is, on the other hand, an atmospheric study, with elements of Romanticism. The cart being drawn home, the setting sun, the onset of evening as the mists rise, point to the influence of Dutch landscape and perhaps also (independently or by way of Dutch art) to the influence of the English landscape painters who had such a tremendous success in Paris between 1820 and 1830. In the years just preceding his departure for Italy, Corot had been able to see works by Bonington, Constable and the Fieldings. When he returned, he saw the results of their influence on a new generation of landscape painters.

PROVENANCE

Collection of Mme Corot, the artist's mother; bequeathed to the artist's grandson, Georges Lemaistre; Charles André Collection, sold in Paris, Hôtel Drouot, 17 May 1893, no. 4; Bernheim Jeune Collection; Emile Hahnloser Collection; gift to the Zurich Kunstmuseum in 1942 in memory of E. Hahnloser.

EXHIBITIONS

1831, Salon, no. 399; 1934, Zurich, no. 39; 1938, Paris, no. 21; 1943, Zurich, no. 55; 1959, Paris, no. 25; 1960, Bern, no. 14; 1960, Chicago, no. 60, ill.; 1963, London, no. 4, ill. p. 44.

REFERENCES

A. Robaut, 1905, v. II, p. 70, no. 200; W. Gensel, 1906, pl. 4; E. Moreau-Nélaton, 1924, v. I, p. 29, ill. 41; V. Gilardoni, 1952, ill. 2, 25; mus. cat., 1959, ill. 73; M. Vaughan, 1961, p. 69, ill. 41.

J.-F. M.

Louis-Philippe Crépin

1772 Paris 1851

According to the dictionary of Bellier and Auvray, Crépin studied with Joseph Vernet, Jean-Baptiste Regnault and Hubert Robert, and exhibited his work on a regular basis at the Salon from 1796 to 1835. Modern studies of this artist, who was famous in his own time, are very rare. In 1923, the article by J. Vivielle appeared; however, particularly important is the 1964 article by Claude-Gérard Marcus, which provides a catalog of works by Crépin in French museums (Bagnères-de-Bigorre; Chalon-sur-Saône; Orléans; Paris, the Musée de la Marine; Tours; Versailles) and reproduces various paintings in private collections. The article also makes the interesting point that Crépin was not only the painter of the great naval battles of his time, but also an artist who, in the manner of Joseph Vernet, painted a large number of anecdotal landscapes in a style that recalls the landscape painters of the end of the 18th century (by painters also not particularly well-known, for example J.-M. Lantara or Lazare Bruandet).

J. L.

24
*Harbor of Cherbourg**

"La Rade de Cherbourg"
Plate p. 266
Canvas; 170 × 258; s.d.l.m. *L.P. Crépin F.ᵗ 1822*
Salon of 1822, no. 271
Paris, Musée de la Marine

The following description of the painting appeared in the Salon catalog: "Ships, vessels at anchor and under sail practice maneuvers and canon drill." Crépin's painting is not as unsophisticated as it appears. The simple procession of people watching the maneuvers seems artless—perhaps because it reminds us of some early motion photography of the last century—but in fact dissimulates a real knowledge of perspective, which the artist may have achieved with the help of an optical instrument (as in J.-F. Hümmel's painting of *The Granite Fountain of the Lustgarten in Berlin,* 1832, Berlin, Staatliche Museen). Crepin's work also records a famous historical event, the French intervention in Spain. The lighthouse on the island of Pelée (see M. Parlange, 1962, p. 43) which one sees in the foreground was not put back into service under the Restoration until this occasion. The special interest of this site no doubt explains the large number of spectators.

One should point out that contemporary critics did not take notice of this painting at the Salon, although they had in 1817 discussed at length an historical scene by the same artist, *Louis XVI visitant le port de Cherbourg.* Thus Crépin's talent for anecdotal illustration appears to have been ignored at the time. And yet for us, by contrast, this painting is particularly interesting as an unusual example of an art which, while neglected in France, developed successfully in northern countries—in Germany and especially in Denmark.

PROVENANCE
The painting was listed in the inventory of the Musée de la Marine in 1962.

EXHIBITION
1822, Salon, no. 271.

REFERENCES
P. Schommer, 1962, ill. 21; M. Parlange, 1962, p. 43, ill.

RELATED WORKS
At the Salon of 1814, Crépin exhibited several sketches of views of the port of Cherbourg.

J. L.

Louis-Jacques-Mandé Daguerre

1787 Cormeilles-en-Parisis - Bry-sur-Marne 1851

Inevitably overshadowed by his eminence in the history of photography, Daguerre's career as a painter is also important. In 1804, he was apprenticed in Paris to a stage designer, Ignace-Eugène Degotti; and from c. 1807-15, he was the assistant to Pierre Prévost, a painter of panoramas. Between 1816 and 1822, he designed sets for both the Théâtre de l'Ambigu-Comique and l'Opéra; and on 11 July 1822, together with Charles-Marie Bouton, also a painter, he opened the Paris Diorama, whose immense success prompted the opening in the following year (29 September 1823) of another Diorama in London. In 1830, Daguerre and Bouton dissolved their partnership, Bouton then taking charge of the London Diorama, Daguerre remaining in Paris. The Paris Diorama burned down in 1839, shortly after the invention of the daguerréotype was officially announced to the Académie des Sciences. By then, Daguerre's career as a painter was virtually at an end.

Trained as a stage designer, Daguerre fully reflects the arts of the theater in his paintings and drawings. His professional status as a painter permitted him, as it had his collaborator Bouton, to exhibit at the Salon, where he first showed, in 1814, the *Intérieur d'une chapelle de l'Église des Feuillants à Paris* (Louvre), whose complex luminary effects and deep perspectives reveal his close connections with the theater. Daguerre's later paintings and drawings are most often related directly to his diorama presentations, recording awesome spectacles of light, landscape, and architecture that would appeal to a popular audience increasingly aware of Romantic tourism. His *Ruines de la Chapelle de Holyrood* (Liverpool, Walker Art Gallery), exhibited at the Salon of 1824 and probably executed after, not before, his successful diorama of this subject (1823-24), is characteristic in its choice of gothic architecture, a mysterious moonlit sky, and an historically evocative setting (the Scottish royal tombs), as it also is in its almost photographic rendering of a building seen in deep perspective and dramatically silhouetted by theatrical light. Like Bouton, Daguerre's preferred subject was medieval architecture, although his repertory also included city views (*Vue de Montmartre*, Paris, Musée Carnavalet) and such imaginary subjects as *Le Temple de Solomon* and *Le Commencement du Déluge*. His taste for the accurate recording of historic monuments made him a frequent contributor to the long-lived series of lithographs edited by Baron Taylor and Charles Nodier, *Voyages pittoresques et romantiques en l'ancienne France*, which first appeared in 1820. Broadly speaking, Daguerre's pictorial art is associated both with the modest topographical records of medieval architecture painted by Corot in the 1820's and 1830's and with the taste for spectacular paintings of architectural wonders, both real and fantastic, exemplified not only by such French traveler-artists as the Comte de Forbin and later Adrien Dauzats, but by such an English painter as John Martin, who was immensely popular in France in the 1820's.

R. R.

25
People Visiting a Romanesque Ruin

Personnages visitant une ruine médiévale
Plate p. 289
Canvas; 102 x 154; s.d.u.l. : *Daguerre 1826*
On the back of the canvas, a monochrome landscape sketch
Paris, Gérard Lévy Collection

The exact identification of this painting, undoubtedly related to a stage set or a diorama, remains uncertain. The inscribed date, 1826, suggests that it closely relates to the paintings Daguerre exhibited at the Salon of 1824 (no. 400, *Ruines de la Chapelle de Holyrood,* Liverpool, Walker Art Gallery; no. 401, *Esquisse de l'intérieur de l'abbaye de Roslyn à sept milles d'Edimbourg,* untraced); and the architectural style of the ruins further suggests that the setting is meant to evoke Scotland or northern England. The hilly landscape, viewed through the arcade, and the kilts worn by the gesticulating visitor confirm this. The choice of Scotland would be characteristic of the period not only in terms of the strong Royalist associations with the Stuart dynasty that were stressed by the Restoration (and by Daguerre's own diorama of Holyrood Chapel), but in terms of literary taste, whether in the novels of Sir Walter Scott or in the dramas and operas derived from his plots and from related episodes in Scottish history.

The building itself, despite its being rendered with almost photographic precision, appears to be a pastiche invented by the artist from motifs in Romanesque architecture of the late 12th century, although the stairs visible at the left suggest a later date.

Formerly entitled *Personnages visitant un cloître,* the painting has been re-titled because the ruined medieval building does not, in fact, conform to any any known cloister type. It is conceivable that the painting is related to Daguerre's diorama of 1825-26, *Effet de brouillard et de neige vu à travers une colonnade gothique en ruine ;* for the early 19th century would still have categorized Romanesque architecture as Gothic, and the vista through the ruined arcade is indeed of snow-covered hills blanketed with fog. In any case, the painting closely resembles Daguerre's other works, not only in its choice of medieval ruins dramatically silhouetted against a mysterious light in a strange landscape, but in its deep perspectives and meticulously literal description of detail.

It should be noted that the figure in the top hat, next to the man in kilts, wears the red emblem of the Legion of Honor. Like the inscription, *Daguerre 1826,* embedded in the medieval masonry, this may also be a reference to the artist himself, for Daguerre received this award from Charles X in January 1825, at the closing of the Salon of 1824.

PROVENANCE
Vicomte Vigier Collection; sale, Paris, Hôtel Drouot, 1972.

EXHIBITION
1962, Turin, n. n. (entitled *Personaggi che visitano un chiostro*).

R. R.

Henri-Pierre Danloux

1753 Paris 1809

Born in Paris in 1753 and a student of N.-B. Lépicié, Henri-Pierre Danloux exhibited at the 1771 *Exposition de la Jeunesse* an *Ivrogne auprès d'une table.* A close friend of Vien, whose portrait he painted in 1775 (formerly in the R. Portalis Collection), Danloux with him traveled to Rome, where Vien had just been appointed head of the French Academy.

Danloux remained in Rome until 1780, after which he settled in Lyon, where he specialized in portraiture and genre scenes. He married Marie-Antoinette de Saint-Redan in 1785 in Paris, and they traveled together in Italy for more than a year and a half before settling down once more in Lyon and finally in Paris.

The Revolution forced Danloux out of France in 1791, when he settled in London, where he spent the next ten years as a successful portraitist. He returned to Paris in 1800, exhibited in the Salon of 1802 without much notice and died in 1809, embittered by the small recognition accorded to his last works.

During his exile, Danloux had written a very interesting *Journal,* most of which was published by R. Portalis (1910), the artist's principal biographer. Above all, an elegant portrait-painter, "distinguished and sincere," Danloux was less open than the other artists of his time to the new political and artistic ideas of his generation. His influence, however, on English artists of his epoch is not to be ignored. His own painting was affected by contact with the English. In London, he had met Reynolds, Russel, West, Beechey, Hoppner, Northcote and Romney, whom he especially admired. He even wrote, "I have become very English."

When Danloux returned to France after the Peace of Amiens, he could give to his French colleagues a first-hand report on English painting, still relatively unknown on the continent at that time.

P. R.

26
The Deluge *

"*Episode du Déluge*"
Plate p. 184
Canvas; 202 × 174; s.l.m. *H. Danloux. ft*
Salon of 1802, no. 965
Saint-Germain-en-Laye, Musée Municipal

Danloux exhibited three works at the Salon of 1802: *The Deluge, Supplice d'une Vestale* (a drawing and study for the head are reproduced in R. Portalis, 1910, pp. 409, 411) and the *Portrait de Mme J... anglaise*. All three were done in England before Danloux's return to France in 1800.

On 15 July of that year, he wrote in his *Journal*: "M. Odell, who had come to lunch with me, allowed himself to be used as a model for the male head in my *Deluge*. I worked like a dog, until I was bathed in sweat and ready to drop with exhaustion. After four hours of work, I still had not succeeded and I erased what I had done... Miss Fairfield having come..., I asked her if she would model for the neck of the woman in *The Deluge* and she agreed." On 29 July he wrote, "the female model brought me a sick woman, in order to do the skin-color of the dying woman in my *Deluge*."

The three paintings presented at the Salon—the first works which Danloux exhibited publicly after his return from England—were not a great success. The author of a *Revue du Salon de l'An X* said that the canvas was "painted in a course manner." The editor of the review in the *Journal des Arts* (coll. Deloynes, no. 780, p. 168) was especially harsh: "The same artist exhibited a scene of a shipwreck or a flood. We are not so tasteless as to find it beautiful. The use of color is a *lazzi* which may please some artists, but seems glaireous to us. It exhibits a lack of dignity, sloppy brushwork, a false color which would never occur in nature, excessive and distasteful foreshortenings... one is, after all, permitted to be critical when one has in mind

Monsieur Hue's version of the subject." A century later, Portalis's evaluation, "The work adds nothing to his glory," was hardly more gentle. The severity of these critiques explains how the Saint-Germain painting came to be totally ignored.

These criticisms, it seems, ought to be modified. Danloux was an agreeable and piquant portraitist, at times excellent, although his models never possess the assurance or calm presence of the subjects of Joseph-Siffred Duplessis or Alexandre Roslin. And yet, we preferred to include *The Deluge* in our exhibition because it is one of the painter's most ambitious works—not only because of its daring color (the vivid red spot of the coat and the white of the robe, set against the green sea), but above all because of its theme. This theme appeared in the works of many other artists: J. Gamelin's painting of 1779 (No. 63), J.-B. Regnault's of 1789 (No. 149), and A.-L. Girodet's somewhat later and famous painting in the Louvre (about this painting, see James Rubin's important iconographic study published in 1972). One should also look at to the work of P.-M. Delafontaine (Salon of 1798, no. 106; Musée de Gray; see mus. cat., n.d. by A.-P. de Mirimonde), of P.-B. Duvivier (Besançon), J.-F. Hue (the specialist in this genre; cf. *Marine pendant la Tempête,* Salon of 1802, no. 131) and finally M.-H. Bounieu (brought to our attention by G. Levitine, who is preparing an important study on the theme of natural catastrophes). Under the influence of Poussin's great example, French painters of this period seem to have been inspired by the Deluge of the Bible, rather than the one described by Salomon

Gessner (1730-1788). According to Portalis, (*op. cit.*, p. 455), Danloux "knew [the painting] was an undertaking beyond his capabilities," but wanted nonetheless to work as a history painter and did not wish to limit himself to the "minor" genre of portrait painting. Danloux attempted, with some success, to "arouse compassion, not to inspire disgust, but to inspire terror," a "terror that should never be exaggerated," to adopt the language used in the critique of Girodet's painting at the Salon of 1806.

The Saint-Germain painting is interesting in yet another respect. Painted in England, it should reflect what a gifted painter in his prime, visiting London, could assimilate from the various artistic creations of the time. It seems that Danloux was inspired by Henry Fuseli (the painting in the Milton Gallery, 1796-1799; a modified version is in Winterthur), Benjamin West, and most of all by Van Loutherbourg's (R. Rosenblum directed our attention to Loutherbourg's *Déluge*, in the Victoria and Albert Museum, painted in 1789-1790, engraved by Thomas Milton in 1797 for Thomas Macklin's famous *Bible*). Thus, Danloux drew his inspiration from the work of three "foreigners" who had come to live in Great Britain, and not from those English portraitists and landscape painters who less than 30 years later were to be admired by Géricault, Delacroix and so many of the "modern" painters of the new generation.

PROVENANCE
Given to the Musée de Saint-Germain-en-Laye (in 1869 ?) by the descendants of the artist's son, Jules Danloux.

EXHIBITION
1802, Salon, no. 965.

REFERENCES
Coll. Deloynes, v. XVIII, no. 769, p. 202; v. XXIX, no. 782, pp. 168-169; Bellier and Auvray, 1882, v. I, p. 336; R. Portalis, 1910, pp. 7, 430, 434, 441, 455; C. de Monicault, 1974, pp. 56-58.

RELATED WORKS
Portalis (1910, p. 434) reproduced a drawing which was then part of General Danloux's sketchbook and could be a study (reversed) for the child in the foreground.

P. R.

Jacques-Louis David

1784 Paris - Brussels 1825

Jacques-Louis David was born in Paris on 30 August 1748; his father was a haberdasher, and his mother came from a family of masons and building contractors. After his father was killed in a duel when the young David was only nine, he was cared for by his mother's family, and especially by his uncles Buron and Desmaisons, whose portraits have been preserved. He did reasonably well in school and then began to study painting under Joseph-Marie Vien, at that time the most famous history painter and teacher, to whom he had been recommended by François Boucher, a distant relation by marriage. Despite some stormy scenes during the Revolution, David always remained fond of his master. He regularly attended classes at the Academy, but was not a precocious pupil, since he only obtained a minor prize in 1769. His first known picture, *Jupiter et Antiope,* is in Sens. In 1770, he was allowed to compete for the Prix de Rome, but was unsuccessful. In 1771, he reached the final stage, for which he painted, like his fellow candidates, *Le Combat de Mars et de Minerve* (Louvre). The prize was rightfully awarded to Suvée (whose picture is at Lille), since David's version is rather insignificant and unfortunate in its color harmony. He failed again the following year with his *Apollon et Diane qui percent de leurs flèches les enfants de Niobé* (formerly in the Hérouville Collection); his third failure occurred in 1773 with *La Mort de Sénèque* (Petit Palais)—the prize was won by Peyron. From all these negative experiences, David retained enormous bitterness. He was finally successful in 1774 with his *Erasistrate découvrant la cause de la maladie d'Antiochus* (Paris, École des Beaux-Arts), even though the colors remain garish and the execution rather weak.

David's personality began to mature after laborious effort during his first stay in Rome (1775-1780). The few sketchbooks that have been preserved (Berlin, Louvre, Fogg Museum of Art, etc.) show that he studied the art of the 16th century (Veronese) and especially that of the 17th (the Bolognese school and Caravaggio and his followers—he copied Valentin's *La Cène*); he was also interested in landscape and became increasingly absorbed with ancient art: at about the time of his return to Paris, he did outline tracings from the antique (see J. Adhémar, 1953, and C. Coggins, 1968). He sent back to Paris from Rome some fine academic studies (Cherbourg and Montpellier), his *Funeral of Patroclus* (No. 27), and a *Saint Jerome* (1780, Quebec Cathedral). These latter pictures, like his *Moïse et le serpent d'airain* (Ruffey) show the influence of 17th-century painting which, as it had been for his master Vien, was an early form of escape from the style of Boucher and his imitators. The same influence still appears in his *Saint Roch* (No. 28), although some of his sketches show he was already capable of drawing *à l'antique*. Before leaving Rome (July 1780), David made studies for a large portrait of Count Potocki on horseback (No. 29), which he was to paint in Paris along with his *Belisarius* (No. 30), probably his first "Davidian" picture. This work created a sensation at the Salon of 1781, and from then on young artists like Fabre, Hennequin, Wicar, Girodet and Drouais began to frequent his atelier, which was to become the most popular studio in Europe for more than 30 years. In the next few years, David was admitted as a full member of the Academy, thanks to his *Hector and Andromache* (No. 31), painted his last religious picture *(Christ en croix*, 1782, recently rediscovered in the Mâcon Cathedral), and did a number of portraits whose stark decor and energetic execution were probably influenced by Greuze (portraits of Desmaisons, Buffalo; Dr. Leroy, Montpellier; the Pécouls, Louvre). A commission by the King to do a history painting precipitated his decision to work in Rome, where he lived in 1784 and 1785; here he painted his *Serment des Horaces* (Louvre). After his return to Paris, he painted *The Death of Socrates* (No. 32), *Pâris et Hélène*, Louvre (for the Comte d'Artois —the first of his pictures inspired by Anacreon); the portrait of the Lavoisiers (No. 33) and his *Brutus* (Louvre). During the Revolution, he played an important part in French artistic life, first by leading the attack on the Academy, which was abolished in 1793; after being elected a deputy to the Convention in 1792, his role became even greater, and he was soon the most

influential member of the Committee for Public Instruction and the principal organizer of the Revolutionary festivals. He voted for the death of the King and was a Montagnard and close associate of Robespierre; he was made a member of the Committee for Public Safety and, as such, signed a number of orders for arrest. His political activity and the rapid chain of events prevented his completing the *Serment du Jeu de Paume*, which was to have been a grandiose commemoration of a contemporary event in the antique style and for which a number of drawings have been preserved, as well as the portraits of *Mme Trudaine* (Louvre), *Mme de Pastoret* (No. 34) and a picture of the young Joseph Barra dying (Avignon). However, he did complete the *Mort de Marat* (Brussels), and a work that may be his masterpiece, the *Mort de Le Peletier de Saint-Fargeau,* which has unfortunately been lost. He was imprisoned for a short time after the fall of Robespierre but was soon painting again; he divided his time between portraiture (the Sériziats, Blauw, Meyer) and work on his *Sabines* (Louvre), which he completed in 1799.

A founding member of the Institute in 1795, he was an early supporter of Bonaparte, whom he greatly admired and painted frequently: in works ranging from that stupendous heroic allegory, *Le Passage du Grand-Saint-Bernard* (1801, best example in Berlin, the Charlottenburg Museum and at Malmaison) to a simple portrait of Napoleon in his study (No. 36 bis; another in the Prince Napoléon Collection). David was commissioned to paint enormous canvases commemorating the great festivals of the Empire, but he only completed the *Couronnement* (1806-1807, Louvre) and the *Distribution des Aigles* (1810, Versailles), in which a wealth of realistic detail is subordinated to the grandiose vision. He did not abandon antiquity, however, and in 1814 he finished *Léonidas aux Thermopyles* (Louvre), which he had begun 15 years earlier as a pendant to *Sabines*. Going from Rome to Greece, David attempted to reach the purest sources of antiquity, as much from the point of view of drawing and execution as from that of moral content. He remained faithful to Napoleon (during the Hundred Days, he signed the *Actes Additionnels*), and went into exile on the return of the Bourbons: he took up residence in Brussels at the beginning of 1816, where he eventually died. His late portraits, of which there seem to have been a large number, have not yet been accurately catalogued; but some are of splendid quality, like that of Sieyès (1817, Fogg Art Museum, Cambridge, Mass.) or those of the

Comte de Turenne (Copenhagen and private collection). His mythological pictures, however, have never been very popular. In these, David again attempted what he had tried to accomplish in his *Sappho and Phaon* (No. 36), which was to reconcile drawing with color. The extreme boldness of his palette and the incursion into the ideal of realistic detail, so striking in his *L'Amour et Psyché* (1817, Cleveland Museum of Art) and his

Mars Disarmed by Venus (No. 38) of 1821-24, his last great picture (he died on 29 December 1825) have always threatened the over-simplified image that has been created of David, who is supposed to have required the moral tension of the great subjects of antiquity or the reality of daily life to be himself. This seems to be the moment to revise this judgment.

A. S.

27
Funeral of Patroclus

"Les Funérailles de Patrocle"
Plates p. 54
Canvas; 94 × 218; s.d.l.l. *J. L. David f./roma 1779*
Salon of 1781, suppl. no. 314
Dublin, National Gallery of Ireland

David's painting illustrates that passage in the *Iliad* which describes the funeral of Patroclus (Book XXIII, vv. 110 ff.). In the center, at the top of a flight of steps, Achilles mourns the dead Patroclus. Behind them is a huge funeral pyre of logs, constructed on Agamemnon's orders. In the right foreground, the corpse of Hector is attached to a chariot to be drawn by two rearing horses. At the left, 12 Trojan princes are being killed as sacrifices to be added to Patroclus' funeral pyre. At the right, a funeral procession leads sacrificial animals to the pyre. On the horizon at the left, ships are illuminated by the sun.

The *Funeral of Patroclus* is the most ambitious product of David's Roman sojourn (4 November 1775 to 17 July 1780), and a pivotal work in the formation of his mature style of the 1780's. Pursuing the new enthusiasm for tragic Homeric illustrations that was codified in Paris in the Prix de Rome subject of 1769 *(Achille, après avoir traîné le cadavre d'Hector le dépose aux pieds du lit où repose le corps mort de Patrocle)*, David in Rome projected an enormous painting that expanded this theme. In the earlier of two extant preparatory drawings (Louvre, R.F. 4004), David included the Homeric narrative of the airborne deities, Apollo and Venus, who preside over the funeral; but in the later drawing (Honfleur, Musée Eugène-Boudin), he eliminated them, in keeping with his newer, earthbound style. The Honfleur drawing (of which only the right two-thirds is preserved), in fact, offers only minor differences from the painting.

David may have begun work on this project as early as 1777, after completing the large related drawing, *La Colère de Diomède* (Vienna, Albertina) in 1776, and he seems to have considered it the first painting in which he would demonstrate his mastery (J.-L. J. David, 1882, I, p. 12). It was exhibited in Rome in 1778 and then sent to Paris for judgment by the Academy, which reported on it on 10 April 1779 *(Procès verbaux de l'Académie*, IX, p. 421). The date on the painted inscription is probably to be read as 1779 rather than 1778 (the last cipher is blurred), which suggests that David may have waited until 1779 to retouch it and sign it before sending it to Paris for scrutiny by the Academy jury. It was then exhibited at David's Salon debut of 1781, as an *"esquisse,"* a year after the artist's own return to Paris. Critics understood that it was a painted project for an even larger and more ambitious canvas (*Année littéraire*, 1781), but David apparently realized that by comparison with his newer works at the Salon—*Belisarius* (No. 30), *Saint Roch Interceding for the Plague Stricken* (No. 26), *Portrait of Count Potocki* (No. 29)—the *Funeral of Patroclus* was stylistically retardataire. Indeed, he seems to have esteemed it so little that he was not only willing to use the painting as a table top for lunch in the winter of 1781-82 (see J.-L.-J. David, *op. cit.*, pp. 22-23), but soon after, on 12 March 1782, sold it to M. Fontanel of the Montpellier Academy of Fine Arts for 2,400 livres, a transaction for which there is an extant autograph receipt in the collection of Prof. Maurice Bloch (J. de

Caso, 1972, p. 686, no. 9). It was undoubtedly in Montpellier that Gamelin made a drawing after the painting (see Related Works). For the painting's 19th-century history, see Provenance. It had always been considered a lost work until its rediscovery in 1972 and subsequent acquisition by the National Gallery of Ireland.

As both the academic jury of 1779 and the Salon critics of 1781 were aware, the *Funeral of Patroclus* is a startling work in which David's genius emerges for the first time on so grandiose a scale. In both dramatic and stylistic terms, it marks a pivotal point in David's evolution. On the one hand, it looks back to the agitation of figural movement, brushwork and light of David's late rococo style of the 1770s; on the other, it introduces a new narrative and formal clarity of focused drama, earthbound processions and slower, more frieze-like rhythms. In this regard, the drawing in Sacramento, probably of 1778 (see Related Works), may offer a more consistently classicizing statement of this Homeric theme, by comparison with which the painting was already retardataire. And by 1780-81, David's own paintings, as well as his drawings, had so thoroughly assimilated this new style that the *Funeral of Patroclus* must have seemed compromised in its lingering allegiance to the rococo. It is exactly this dual aspect of the *Funeral of Patroclus* which renders it so historically crucial in the formation of David's mature style and which also makes it so visually fascinating as a transitional work between the rococo and neo-classicism.

PROVENANCE

12 March 1782, sold by David to M. Fontanel of the Montpellier Academy of Fine Arts; Naples, collections of the Acton family; before 1840, in Naples collection of Serra Duca di Cardinale family; 1973, purchased by the National Gallery of Ireland from Heim Gallery, London.

EXHIBITIONS

1778, Rome; 1781, Salon, suppl., no. 314.

REFERENCES

(Anon.), *Le Pourquoi* 1781, p. 25; *Année littéraire*, 1781, pp. 80-81; (Anon.), *Exposition des ouvrages...*, 1781, p. 436; Bachaumont, 1783, v. XIX, pp. 341-342; *Notice sur la vie...*, 1824, p. 26; A. Thomé, 1826, pp. 14, 161; P.-A. Coupin, 1827, p. 52; J.-L. David, 1851-52, pp. 340-342; *Notice sur le Marat...*, 1867, pp. 32, 40; J.-L.-J. David, 1880, pp. 12, 22-23, 632; A. Montaiglon and J. Guiffrey, 1904, v. XIII, p. 421; "L'Exposition centennale...," 1912, p. 187; H. Vollmer, 1913, p. 459; H. Lapauze, 1924, v. I, p. 367; R. Cantinelli, 1930, p. 13; K. Holma, 1940, pp. 33-34, 125; Paris, Orangerie, 1948, M.-O. 88; L. Hautecœur, 1954, pp. 41-42; J. Seznec, 1967, pp. 351, 378; P. Rosenberg, 1970, p. 36, no. 20; Paris, Louvre, Cabinet des dessins, 1972, p. 18, no. 31; J. de Caso, 1972, p. 686; London, The Arts Council of Great Britain, 1972, p. 327, no. 550; P. Rosenberg, 1972, no. 39; P. Rosenberg, 1973, pp. 78-79; D. and G. Wildenstein, 1973; p. 8; R. Verbraeken, 1973, p. 49; R. Rosenblum, 1973, pp. 567-576; J. Lacambre, 1973, p. 303.

RELATED WORKS

Three drawings by David: Louvre, 33 × 75 (R.F. 4004); Honfleur, 33 cm. high; Sacramento, E.B. Crocker Art Gallery, 26 × 153. Drawing by Gamelin, Narbonne, 58 × 112 (see Lacambre, 1973, p. 303).

R. R.

28
Saint Roch Interceding for the Plague-Stricken

" Saint Roch intercédant la Vierge pour la guérison des pestiférés "
Plate p. 61
Canvas; 260 × 195; s.d.l.l. *L. David faciebat/Romae. 1780.*
Salon of 1781, no. 312
Marseille, Musée des Beaux-Arts

The plague of 1720, which caused thousands of deaths in Marseille, left exceptionally lasting memories. Even in 1837, according to Stendhal "they never stop talking about it in Marseille; here, for the first time, I have learned the meaning of the proverb *Boring as*

the Plague" (*Mémoires d'un Touriste,* ed. 1929, III, p. 178). In fact, even in Stendhal's time, Paulin Guérin was still representing the *Dévouement du chevalier Roze* (1826-1833) and François Gérard's *Mgr de Belzunce distribuant du pain aux malheureux* (1835) as subjects; the latter was also painted by Nicolas-André Monsiau in 1819 (no. 133). This was the final stage of a long pictorial tradition, which was started by J.-F. de Troy and Michel Serre. The Marseille museum has two views of the city during the plague by Serre, who was an active eye-witness to the drama. But while the other painters portrayed actual events, mainly the courage of the Chevalier Roze and of Mgr de Belzunce, David used the traditional iconography of the story of Saint Roch, himself stricken with the plague, who was always invoked as an intercessor since his lifetime in the 14th century. David was careful to show the saint with his pilgrim's staff and knapsack, a sore visible on one bare leg, and accompanied by the dog that saved him. In the Musée Magnin in Dijon is a small sketch, very dark and of dubious quality, which may be by David, but is conceivably by some other artist influenced by David's painting. If it is indeed by David, as the large number of variations suggests (and it is accepted as such by J.-L.-J. David, 1880, in his description of it in the Sosthène Moreau Collection), the artist had already worked out the general lines of his composition and positioned the three principal figures; but the group of the Virgin and Child is quite different, and more clearly inspired by 17th-century Italian painting, especially Guercino (whose influence is also felt in David's *Saint Jérôme,* painted in 1780 and now in the Quebec cathedral). The strong lighting contrasts of this sketch are also very Italian, but more Caravaggesque whereas the big canvas is lit more evenly, and in grayish tones that were not to Stendhal's taste. However, David's most spectacular invention is the large figure of a plague-victim that occupies the whole lower portion of the picture. The names of Géricault and Gros are often cited in connection with this figure, but its origin is in fact to be found in the art of Charles Le Brun; the first clear influence of Le Brun on the work of David is the *Moïse et le serpent d'airain* at Ruffey (published by R. Rosenblum, 1963), in which there is also a recumbent man in the foreground. The admirable head of David's figure seems to have been inspired by one in Poussin's *Peste d'Asdod* (Louvre); as early as 1780, Vien said of it: "the expression is so moving that one can hardly bear to look at it" *(Correspondance des Directeurs...).* This head was copied by Ingres (drawing at Montauban, J. Momméja, 1905, no. 2615,) and is also known from an often-exhibited pen drawing in Paris, École des Beaux-Arts (no. 12002, gift of E. Gatteaux). It bears two inscriptions in David's handwriting: "study for the head of the plague-victim in my painting of

Saint Roch which is at Marseille," and, at the bottom: "done at Ferrara by David upon his return from his first journey to Rome in 1780 and given to his friend [the name is crossed out] on 7 Germinal, Year VIII of the French Republic." The drawing is almost identical to the painted head, except that the head is vertical in the drawing and there is a variation in the turban. Although the inscription is 20 years later than the drawing, its accuracy is such that one must suppose that the immediate success of the painted head, attested by Vien, led David to repeat it from memory. Finally, J. Adhémar (1953, pl. 251, drawing no. 42) has published a tracing that reproduces the outlines of this drawing; it supports the explanation suggested in 1968 by Cl. Coggins for the large number of tracings, published in part by J. Adhémar, that many of them were done from drawings by David himself, retaining only the outlines.

PROVENANCE

To commemorate once again the plague that ravaged Marseille in 1720, the Public Health Office of the city in 1779 asked Joseph-Marie Vien, director of the French Academy in Rome, to suggest the name of a pupil to do a painting for the Chapelle du Lazaret, for the approximate sum of 50 *sequins* (550 *livres*). In the fall, Vien picked David, who completed the picture by 10 May 1780. The work was considered so successful in Rome that David brought it back to Paris and tried, unsuccessfully, to become an *agréé* at the Academy with it; however, he exhibited it successfully at the Salon of 1781. Throughout that year David was engaged in difficult negotiations with the Public Health Office in Marseille to obtain a higher price, which was finally granted (900 *livres*). The picture was at last sent to Marseille at the end of January or in February of 1782; it was hung not in the Chapelle du Lazaret but in the Public Health Office. It stayed with the Health Administration until it entered the museum in 1944.

EXHIBITIONS

1781, Salon, no. 312; 1948, Paris, M.O., no. 7 (never exhibited); 1959, London, no. 104, ill. 6; 1961, Bordeaux, no. 145.

REFERENCES

Correspondance des Directeurs..., v. XIV, p. 20 (10 May 1780) [file of reports on the difficulties with Marseille in J. Guiffrey and L. Gonse, 1874-1875, pp. 379-394]; coll. Deloynes, v. XII, no. 260, pp. 181-182; no. 263, p. 281; no. 264, p. 332; no. 267, p. 382; no. 268, p. 412; no. 270, p. 470; Bachaumont, v. XIX, pp. 340-341; Diderot, 1781, ed. J. Seznec, v. IV, 1967, p. 377, ill. 156; [P. Chaussard], 1806, ed. 1808, pp. 148-150; *Notice...,* 1824, pp. 17-18; A. Th., 1826, pp. 21-22 and 232; P.-A. Coupin, 1827, pp. 11-13, 52; Stendhal (1838), ed. 1930, pp. 274-275; Ch. Blanc, 1845, p. 208; Miette de Villars, 1850, pp. 72-73; E.-J. Delécluze, 1855, p. 115; J. Du Seigneur, 1863, p. 360; J.-L.-J. David, 1880, pp. 16-17, 21,

633, ill. 1882; Ch. Saunier (1904), pp. 20-21; L. Rosenthal (1905), pp. 24-25, 167; J. Locquin, 1912, pp. 219-220, 274; A. Humbert, 1936, p. 35; K. Holma, 1940, pp. 36-38 and no. 21, p. 125; J. Maret, 1943, p. 8; A. Maurois, 1948; J. Adhémar, 1953, pp. 34-36; L. Hautecœur, 1954, pp. 49-50; J. Billioud and P. Ripert, 1956, ill.; A. Brookner, 1958, p. 71; J. Lindsay, 1960, p. 36, ill. 4; R. Rosenblum, 1963, p. 558, ill. 44; mus. notice, 1964, ill. 33; R. Verbraeken, 1973, pp. 24, 244, ill. 9; D. and G. Wildenstein, 1973, nos. 73, 75, 78, 84, 85, 88, 95, 96, 99, 102, 106, 1368, 1810, 1838 (no. 7), 2041 (no. 34).

RELATED WORKS

A sketch in Dijon, Musée Magnin, and a drawing in Paris, École des Beaux-Arts (see above). Freely interpreted in a lithograph by Langlumé. A copy drawn by François Gérard belonged to the Baronne Meunier in 1860 (E. Cantaloube, 1860).

A. S.

29
Portrait of Count Stanislas Potocki

"Portrait du Comte Stanislas Potocki"
Plate p. 62
Canvas; 304 × 218; s.d.l.l. *L. David 1781*
Salon of 1781, supplement, no. 313
Warsaw, National Museum

Stanislas Potocki (1757-1821) at the time of this portrait was making his "grand tour." He was to become an important statesman at the time of Napoleon and later under the new kingdom of Poland. A connoisseur of art and literature, he translated Winckelmann into Polish. Despite the recent studies by A. Ryszkiewicz, little is known of the origins of this famous portrait. At least it is clear that the anecdote related by J.-L.-J. David in 1880, which all the historians have accepted, is without foundation. According to him, the artist saw the Count break in a supposedly untameable horse during the course of a hunting party given by Ferdinand IV in Naples. Polish sources (catalogue of Wilanow Castle, 1834) stated that "the portrait was completed in Paris after a sketch made from life in the Naples riding School." A. Ryszkiewicz has demonstrated that Potocki, who had arrived in Rome in December of 1779, was in Naples only in February 1780, whereas David's visit there took place the preceding summer. Thus, it was probably in Rome that the artist met the great Polish nobleman. The setting does seem to be a stable, judging from the straw underneath the horse's hooves, but the stately architecture in the background suggests an imaginary scene. Once again, David shows his interest in 17th-century painting, but this time it is Flemish, rather than French or Italian. The composition recalls Van Dyck's equestrian portraits, especially that of *Prince Thomas of Savoy* (Turin, Galleria Sabauda), which David sketched (Louvre, INV. 26157 ter, Guiffrey-Marcel 3364). And the horse's forequarters correspond to a tapestry fragment of Decius Mus, after Rubens, of which there is also a study by David in the Louvre (INV. 26112, Guiffrey-Marcel 3269). As Diderot remarked, here David used a light palette, in contrast to the history paintings executed at about the same time. Freed from the rigors involved in history painting, he achieved an admirable portrait, whose life and brilliance were without parallel in the art of his time.

PROVENANCE

In the Potocki Collection; said to have been in Warsaw in the studios of the painters Tokarsky and later Smuglewicz, before being deposited in the castle of Wilanow, acquired by the Potocki family in 1799. The castle, together with the collection, passed into the hands of the Branickis in 1892. Seized by the Germans in the Second World War, and afterwards by the Russians; returned to Poland in 1956 and placed in the Warsaw Museum.

EXHIBITIONS

1781, Salon, no. 313; 1913, Paris, no. 16; 1923, Warsaw; 1932, London, no. 397; 1937, Paris, no. 292, ill. XXIII; 1956, Moscow and Warsaw; 1958, Paris, no. 9, ill. XXIII; 1959, Rome, no. 185; London, no. 105, ill. VII; 1961, Bordeaux, no. 145; 1966-1967, Chicago, no. 79; 1968, London, no. 176, ill. 337.

REFERENCES

Mercure de France, October 1781, pp. 17-18, 38; Diderot, 1781, ed. J. Seznec, v. IV, 1967, p. 381; Bachaumont, v. XVIII, pp. 74-75; *Explication... coll.* Deloynes, v. XII, p. 59; *Journal de Paris,* 23 September 1783, pp. 1098-1099; *Notice...,* 1824, p. 17; A. Th., 1826, p. 20; P.-A. Coupin, 1827, p. 53; (Chaussard) 1806; ed. 1808, p. 153 (as a portrait of Prince Poniatowski); Ch. Blanc, 1845, p. 208; Miette de Villars, 1850, p. 72; J. Du Seigneur, 1863, p. 360; J.-L.-J. David, 1880, pp. 13, 21, 634, ill. 1882; Ch. Saunier (1904), p. 23; L. Rosenthal (1905), pp. 27, 28, 170; *(ibid.),* 1913, pp. 339-340, ill.; Ch. Saunier, 1913, p. 274, ill. p. 277; R. Cantinelli, 1930, pp. 31 et 102, ill. VII; K.-E. Simon, 1936, p. 150,

A. Humbert, 1936, p. 46; K. Holma, 1940, pp. 36, 41 et cat. 33, p. 126; J. Maret, 1943, ill. 35; A. Maurois, 1948; ill. 6; W. Tomkiewicz, English ed., 1950, no. 38; W. Friedlaender, 1952, p. 33; J. Adhémar, 1953, p. 33; L. Hautecœur, 1954, pp. 46-47, 58; J. Bialostocki and M. Walicki, 1955, no. 405; A. Ryszkiewicz, 1963, pp. 77-95; *(ibid.),* 1964, pp. 31-54 (with a French summary and preceding Polish bibliography); *Grands peintres,* 1966-1967, no. II, ill.; mus. cat. *(Foreign Schools),* 1969, no. 285, ill.; R. Verbraeken, 1973, pp. 24, 33, 39, 52, 182-183, ill. 11; D. and G. Wildenstein, 1973, nos. 80, 88, 1810, 1938 (no. 8).

A. S.

30
Belisarius

"Bélisaire, reconnu par un soldat qui avait servi sous lui au moment qu'une femme lui fait l'aumône"
Plate p. 66
Canvas; 288 × 312; s.d.l.l. L. *David faciebat anno 1781. Lutetiae* (illegible)
Salon of 1781, supplement, no. 311
Lille, Musée des Beaux-Arts

Belisarius was a general under Justinian who won victories on battlefields all over the ancient world, in Africa, Italy, against the Bulgars and in Persia, but was accused of conspiracy and disgraced. His story was immensely popular in the second half of the 18th century following the publication in 1767 of Marmontel's *Bélisaire.* This author revived the doubtful tradition according to which the unfortunate Belisarius even had his eyes put out before being reduced to begging. The touching nature of the subject—the fluctuations of fortune and the ingratitude of great men—was made all the more poignant by a recent historical event: in 1766, Lally-Tollendal, the hero of Fontenoy, was accused of treason after his defeats in India and beheaded. His reputation was restored in 1781. Several important paintings were dedicated to this theme in France before David's: by Louis-Jacques Durameau (1775, for d'Angiviller; picture sold at Versailles in 1970), by François-André Vincent (1776-77, No. 199), and especially by Jean-François Peyron (No. 139). This last painting, for which preparatory work was started in 1778, was painted in 1779 for Cardinal de Bernis in Rome, before David's very eyes. It is significantly quite different from David's version, showing Belisarius being welcomed by a peasant family, while David depicts the central character

holding his young guide on his knees. This theme had already appeared in David's œuvre in 1779 in an important signed and dated drawing which was seized in 1793 with the collection of the émigré Clermont d'Amboise (of whom David painted a portrait that is now lost), and is presently in Paris, at the École Polytechnique (G. Pinet, 1910, pl. VII; the better-known sheet in the Dijon museum from the His de la Salle Collection is only a repetition).

Mme Biosse-Duplan has kindly drawn our attention to a possible source for this Belisarius: in an album of engravings (*Icônes et segmenta,* B.N. Rés. J 1245, no. 49), attributed to Perrin, with interleaved drawings from the end of the 17th century. Included is a drawing that represents the Louvre Crysippus, then in the Giustiniani Palace, which is identified as Belisarius by an inscription below the drawing. The figure by the fluted column has some similarity with the Belisarius in the 1779 drawing.

Before returning to France, David painted a small picture (66 × 79) showing Belisarius and the child in half-length. It belonged to Coutan (in the Coutan-Hauguet sale, 16-17 December 1889, no. 4, engraved by J. David in 1882) and subsequently to Henri Rouart (sale on 9-11 December 1912, no. 13); it might be the painting, with a questionable signature, from a private collection, shown in the Orangerie in 1948 (no. 8; 60 × 73); another version, belonging to Wildenstein, which was exhibited as the original in Toulouse and Montauban in 1955 (no. 34; 70 × 80), appears, from the reproduction, to be a copy.

For his submission for Academy membership in 1781, David did not return to this composition but to his 1779 drawing, changing the shape (the earlier work was vertical), the costume of the woman and various details. A drawing in Lille (pl. 1193) probably represents this stage: the soldier in the middle ground is naked and his arms are raised to the position they assumed in the final work (they were lower in the 1779 drawing and were to be different again in the repetition of 1784). However, the attribution to David of the sketch, made without variations (a gift of Armand Cambon to the Montauban museum in 1885) is questionable. This did not, as is usually stated (most recently by D. Ternois in 1965), come from the collection of the émigré Noailles, in which there was only the well-known copy signed and dated 1784 (now in the Louvre), even though it was largely painted by the young François-Xavier Fabre (the seizure inventory, published by M. Furcy-Raynaud, 1912, p. 308, states, "Two small pictures painted on wood"—a careless mistake on the part of the copyist, who clearly repeated the previous entry; the original documents, Arch. Nat. F17 1267, items 18 and 36, are quite clear).

The *Belisarius* caused a sensation upon its exhibition at the Salon of 1781 ("I see it every day, and each time I think I am seeing it for the first time," wrote Diderot, paraphrasing Racine). This picture does in fact mark a turning-point in David's work, the importance of which has always been recognized. As in his *Saint Roch*, the example of David's 17th-century predecessors, especially of Poussin, is visible here. But now the artist went further, binding together the small number of characters, each amply draped and modeled with a new firmness of line, by a regular architectural pattern. The importance of the 1779 drawing is thus evident, since it was the basis for a painting that can be described as David's first "neo-classical" work. Critics have felt, not without reason, that David went too far in his "anti-rococo" reaction by his refusal to use color to lighten the picture, which has been considered too dull and dark. According to A. Lenoir, 1835, the influence of Vien is partly responsible: he is supposed to have advised David to make the drapery of the woman white instead of red.

PROVENANCE
Having learned toward the end of 1780 that only a painting done in Paris (and not his *Saint Roch*) could be accepted as submission for his Academy membership, David painted this *Belisarius,* which he successfully presented to the Academy on 24 August 1781. The canvas was subsequently bought by Duke Albert of Saxe-Teschen, brother of the Elector of Trier, who was to become Governor of the Netherlands. It was abandoned in his Brussels home at the time of the French invasion and sold in March 1793. Its purchaser, Louis Vollant, was guillotined for embezzlement on 1 Messidor, Year VII. The picture was stored in the Rue de Beaune and returned to its heirs in 1796; it was sold in Paris in Germinal, Year VII (L. Hautecœur, 1954) and not, as is always stated, in the Tolozan sale of February 1801. In the Lucien Bonaparte Collection; then the Northwick Collection; in the sale of John Rushout, Baron Northwick at Thirlestone House, 26 July-30 August 1859, no. 457 (bought for £ 110 by Meffre); in the Meffre sale, 9-10 March 1863, no. 15, withdrawn at 7,150 francs and sold to the Lille museum.

EXHIBITIONS
1781, Salon, no. 311; 1860, Paris; 1913, Paris, no. 15; 1972, London, no. 60.

REFERENCES
Procès-verbaux de l'Académie... 1781, ed. 1889, v. IX, pp. 76-77; Diderot, 1781, ed. J. Seznec, v. IV, 1967, pp. 351, 377, ill. 140; coll. Deloynes, v. L, no. 1341, pp. 188-189; v. XII, no. 267, p. 382; no. 268, p. 412; no. 259, p. 147; no. 270, p. 460; T.-C. Bruun-Neergaard, 1801, pp. 83-87, 96; (P. Chaussard), 1806, ed. 1808, pp. 150-151; *Notice...,* 1824, pp. 18-19; A. Th., 1826, pp. 24 et 232; P.-A. Coupin, 1827, p. 13; A. Lenoir, 1835, pp. 3-4; Ch. Blanc, 1845, pp. 163, 207; Miette de Villars, 1850, p. 75; E.-J. Delécluze, 1855, p. 116; W. Burger, 1860, p. 358; J. du Seigneur, 1863, p. 360; J.-L.-J. David, 1880, pp. 19-20, 634 (ill. II, 1882); F. Sauerhering, 1893, pp. 291-292; Ch. Saunier (1904), p. 24; L. Rosenthal (1905), pp. 26-27, 167, ill.; Fr. Benoît, 1909, v. III, pp. 443-445, ill. 118; G. Pinet, 1910, pp. 23-24, ill.; J. Locquin, 1912, pp. 220-221, 252, 253, 257; L. Rosenthal, 1913, p. 339; M. Furcy-Raynaud, 1915-1917, pp. 115-123; R. Cantinelli, 1930, cat. no. 30, p. 101, ill. VI; A. Humbert, 1936, p. 47; K. Holma, 1940, pp. 40-41 and no. 32, p. 126; J. Maret, 1943, ill. 33; W. Friedlaender, 1952, p. 14, ill. 3; L. Hautecœur, 1954, pp. 55-61; J. Seznec, 1957, p. 101, ill. 68; J. Lindsay, 1960, pp. 37-38; D. Ternois, 1965, under no. 98; H. Honour, 1968, pp. 33-34, 71, 143, 194, ill. 7; R. Verbraeken, 1973, pp. 22, 24, 29, 46, 146, 149, 167, 174, 221; D. and G. Wildenstein, 1973, nos. 86-89, 273, 1153, 1280, 1810, 1938.

RELATED WORKS
Apart from the works mentioned above (Louvre, Montauban, private collection, drawings in the École Polytechnique, at Lille and Dijon), a sketch in pencil and pen figured as no. 46 in the sale after David's death in April 1826. The picture was engraved by Morel in 1799. In Tours, there is a poor and quite different drawing showing Belisarius; despite its inscription, *David 1803,* it cannot be attributed to the artist.

A. S.

31
Hector and Andromache

"La Douleur et les regrets d'Andromaque sur le corps d'Hector son mari"
Plate p. 69
Canvas; 275 × 203; s.d.l.l. *L. David. 1783.*
Salon of 1783, no. 162
Paris, École des Beaux-Arts

David's composition, based on a famous passage in the *Iliad,* recalls, apart from the general theme of the Pietà and the recumbent figures in old paintings, a number of precedents with which the artist may have been familiar, and which have often been listed: the *Mort de Germanicus* (Minneapolis Institute of Arts) and the *Testament d'Eudamidas* by Nicolas Poussin, Pompeo Batoni's *Atalante et Méléagre,* Gavin Hamilton's *Andromache* (engraved in 1764), the *Dame de Charité* (1775, Lyon) and the *Fils puni* (1777-78, Louvre) by J.-B. Greuze, etc.

Using an antique sarcophagus as a model, David himself interpreted the theme of woman's sorrow in two long, horizontal drawings (one in the Louvre, Inv. 26158, the other a tracing published by J. Adhémar, 1953, fig. 280, no. 424). We know of at least three important works which were used in the preparation for this picture: a drawing in the former Dumont Collection, engraved by J.-L.-J. David, 1882, in which one sees the young Astyanax crying in his mother's arms; a drawing in the Petit Palais, s.d. 1782; and lastly a sketch in the Pushkin Museum in Moscow, s.d. 1783 (58 × 43). These last two works are close to the picture in design, and have in common some variations (the shape of Andromache's chair, the "pillow" under Hector's head, the position of the slings holding the sword). In the Petit Palais drawing (reproduced by A. Brookner, 1968, and in the exh. cat., 1972, London, no. 552, fig. 84), the background is entirely filled with architecture, decorated with a horizontal lance and a shield. This drawing does not have the big candelabra supporting an incense burner which, however, does appear in the painted sketch, though with different decoration from that in the final picture.

"Nothing is closer to the beautiful antique," wrote the anonymous author of *Messieurs, ami de tout le monde* (coll. Deloynes, no. 295) at the Salon. His detailed criticism on the anatomy of Hector and the left hand of the young Astyanax is close to that made by David

himself in 1803; other critics compared the picture, also quite rightly, to the work of Poussin. The most obvious qualities of this memorable painting are the archeological detail and especially the strict simplicity of the composition, the admirable execution of the draperies, the contained expression of sorrow and the resulting moral lesson. This, after the *Christ en croix* painted the preceding year and recently rediscovered in the cathedral of Mâcon, is David's last "somber" painting. For his *Oath of the Horatii,* which he was to paint in 1784-1785, David conceded to the repeated criticism and lightened his palette.

PROVENANCE

David presented the sketch for his picture to the Academy on 29 March 1783. The final picture, which gained him membership by unanimous vote, was presented by J.-M. Vien on 22 August and immediately exhibited in the Salon. It remained in the Academy's rooms at the Louvre not, as has been said, until 1793 (date of the abolition of the Academy), or until 1801 (A. Fontaine, 1910), but right up to the end of 1803. Vivant Denon suggested to David on 6 December of that year (Arch. Louvre, AA5) that the picture be hung in the Musée Spécial de l'École Française at Versailles. On 12 December, David accepted (letter published by J.-L.-J. David, 1880, p. 415, and later by D. and G. Wildenstein, 1973, no. 1409), on condition that he be allowed to retouch certain parts (draperies over Andromache's breast, Hector's ribs, etc.). Denon agreed, but David then kept the picture, trusting it to Antoine-Jean Gros during his exile, despite protests by the Direction des Musées in 1816 and 1818 (Arch. Nat. O³ 1390). In the David sales in Paris on 17 April 1826 and 11 March 1835, no. 2. Taken back by the heirs, and bought back from the other heirs by Jules David in 1860, given to the École des Beaux-Arts in 1886. Deposited at the Louvre in 1969.

EXHIBITIONS

1783, Salon, no. 162; 1826, Paris, no. 39; 1913, Paris, no. 18; 1934, Paris, École des Beaux-Arts, no. 18; 1936, Paris, no. 203; 1948, Paris, M.O. 11; 1952-1953, Hamburg, Munich, no. 12; 1964-1965, Munich.

REFERENCES

Coll. Deloynes, v. XIII, no. 285, pp. 165-166; no. 287,

pp. 207-208; no. 291, p. 333; no. 292, p. 407; no. 295, pp. 477-478; no. 298, pp. 597-588; no. 299, pp. 618-619; no. 305, pp. 814-817; no. 310, p. 927; no. 311, pp. 952-953; no. 316, p. 1034; Bachaumont, v. XXIV, pp. 22-23; Bruun-Neergaard, 1801, p. 95; P. Chaussard, 1806, ed. 1808, p. 153; *Notice...,* 1824, pp. 24-25; A. Th., 1826, p. 162; P.-A. Coupin, 1827, pp. 14 and 53; A. Lenoir, 1835, p. 3; Ch. Blanc, 1845, p. 208; Miette de Villars, 1850, pp. 82-83, 90; E.-J. Delécluze, 1855, p. 116; J. Du Seigneur, 1863, p. 361; J.-L.-J. David, 1880, pp. 24-25, 415, 581, 634, ill. 1882; E. Müntz, 1897, ill.; H. Jouin, 1904; Ch. Saunier (1904), p. 24; L. Rosenthal (1905), p. 31; A. Fontaine, 1910, pp. 93, 198, ill. VI; J. Locquin, 1912, pp. 157, 161, 221, 242-243, ill. XXVIII; Ch. Saunier, 1913, p. 273; R. Cantinelli, 1930, no. 34, p. 102; A. Humbert, 1936, pp. 51-52; K. Holma, 1940, pp. 42-43 and no. 36, p. 126; J. Maret, 1943, p. 8, ill. 36; A. Maurois, 1948, ill. 7; J. Adhémar, 1953, p. 37; L. Hautecœur, 1954, pp. 65-66; R. Zeitler, 1954, pp. 53-56, 64, ill. 6; A. Brookner, 1958, p. 71, ill. IX; J. Lindsay, 1960, pp. 40-41; A. Brookner, 1964 (1967), p. 187; S. Howard, 1964 (1967), p. 221; R. Rosenblum, 1967a, pp. 19, 41, 82-83, ill. 37; H. Honour, 1968, pp. 66, 150, ill. 80, p. 151; P. Rosen-

berg and N. Butor, 1973, p. 59, ill. 94; R. Verbraeken, 1973, pp. 24, 29, 53, 88, 93, 104, ill. 12; D. and G. Wildenstein, 1973, nos. 114, 116, 1409, 1759, 1760, 1765, 1810, 1877, 1890, 1938 (no. 43), 2043 (no. 84), 2062 (no. 2), 2063, 2069, 2077 (no. 8), 2087 (no. 2).

RELATED WORKS

In addition to those discussed above (drawing formerly in the Dumont Collection, drawing at the Petit Palais, sketch in Moscow), a sketch was sold during David's lifetime (Choiseul-Praslin sale, 1808, 16 × 13 *pouces*, about 43 × 34—sold for 1,220 francs). M. Florisoone (exh. cat., 1948, Paris), mentioned several drawings of this subject in sale catalogs. The "sketch" he refers to in the former collection of King Charles I of Rumania (most of which has come to the Bucharest museum), has nothing to do with David. Similarly it is not certain whether there is any connection between the Aulard sketch, which is the same as the one belonging to Wildenstein, and the picture exhibited here.

A. S.

32
Death of Socrates

"Socrate au moment de prendre la ciguë"
Plate p. 82
Canvas; 130 × 196; s.l.r. *L. David;*
d.l.l. *MDCCLXXXVII* and on a block s. *L.D.*
Salon of 1787, no. 119
New York, The Metropolitan Museum of Art, Wolfe Fund

David based his work freely on Plato's *Phaedo* and on advice from the Oratorian father Adry (E. Bonnardet, 1938). Since the middle of the 18th-century, the subject had been fashionable, rich as it was in moral lessons (see J. Locquin, 1910). In 1758, Diderot, in his *Traité de la Poésie Dramatique,* commended the subject to artists, and Sauvigny brought it to the stage as early as 1763. At the same time, painters were using it as a theme: Dandré-Bardon in 1753; Challe in 1761: Sané, in 1762 (his picture became famous and was engraved in 1786, the year David commenced his own). The subject was treated often outside France. Peyron exhibited a work devoted to the theme in this same Salon of 1787; it had been commissioned from him as early as in 1780 by the Comte d'Angiviller, and it is today in a private collection

in Denmark. According to Plato, there were 15 or so disciples present, but David reduced this number, more so even than Peyron, to better unify his composition. Several attempts have been made to identify the characters, without much success (see, especially, A. Salmon, 1962), except perhaps for Crito, seated on a stool, and Plato, whom David included following Adry's advice, even though he was not actually present. He is represented as an old man, seated at the foot of the bed. In the background, Xanthippe leaves the prison, escorted by the servants of Crito (she had in fact already left in the morning). In Lille is a drawing (INV. 2181), which shows David's earliest ideas: quite different from the final picture, there are about 15 people, all nude, including Xanthippe, who is shown fainting. As soon as it appeared in the Salon of 1787, the picture was hailed as a masterpiece, especially by the painter Reynolds, who saw in it "the greatest effort of art since the Sistine Chapel and the Raphael rooms in the Vatican" (from an article now lost; see J.-L.-J. David, 1880, pp. 46-48, and E. Wind, 1943); according to Delécluze, it was "perhaps the most perfect composition that David ever created." Chaussard, who was equally admiring, relates that David based his pose for the grief-stricken Crito on the position assumed by Uncle Harlowe during the reading of Clarissa's will in Richardson's famous novel, *Clarissa Harlowe*.

The stark décor of the prison, entirely in stone, the noble heads, inspired from antique models, the predominant red color scheme, and the moral lesson to be read in Socrates' pose—all these features combine to make David's picture, coming as it does between his *Horatii* and his *Brutus,* one of the most striking productions of the first completely neo-classical generation of painting.

PROVENANCE

Commissioned before April of 1786 by Charles-Michel Trudaine de la Sablière (C. Sterling, 1955, confirmed by Arch. Nat. F^{17} 1267 [190]), and not, as was believed, by his elder brother Charles-Louis Trudaine de Montigny. The two brothers were guillotined in 1794; even though their pictures were "reserved for the Nation" (inventory drawn up by Lebrun, 2 Frimaire, Year III, Arch. Nat. F^{17} 1267 [95]), Mme Trudaine de Montigny managed to keep the David, which after her death in 1802 went to her brother Micault de Courbeton, from whom Napoleon is said to have tried in vain to buy it (*Notice...* 1824). It subsequently belonged to the Marquis de Vérac, and afterwards to his son-in-law the Comte de Rougé, who lent it for a time to the Luxembourg museum; in the latter's sale (8 April 1872, no. 1, for 17,600 francs), it was bought by Marius Bianchi, husband of Mathilde, née Jeannin, great-granddaughter of David. The picture was inherited by their son-in-law, the Marquis de Ludre, and was bought in 1931 by the Metropolitan Museum (INV. 31-45, Wolfe Fund).

EXHIBITIONS

1787, Salon, no. 119; 1791, Salon, no. 299; 1820-1823, Musée du Luxembourg; 1826, Paris, no. 37; 1846, Paris, no. 7; 1874, Paris, no. 761; 1913, Paris, no. 23; 1948, Paris, M.O., no. 21; 1970, Boston, p. 72; 1972, London, no. 63, ill. 2.

REFERENCES

Coll. Deloynes, v. XV, no. 384, pp. 524-525; no. 385, pp. 547-562; no. 378, pp. 319-322; no. 379, pp. 374-376; no. 394, pp. 765-767; no. 395, pp. 836-838; no. 397, pp. 863-865; no. 402, pp. 957-959; Bruun-Neergaard, 1801, p. 89; C.-P. Landon, v. III, 1802; (P. Chaussard), 1806, ed. 1808, pp. 155-156; C.-P. Landon, 1823, 12th ed.; *Notice...,* 1824, pp. 32-34; A. Th., 1826, pp. 45-46, 187-188, 234; P.-A. Coupin, 1827, pp. 19, 53; Ch. Blanc, 1845, pp. 171-172, 209; Ch. Baudelaire, 1846, ed. 1971, v. I, p. 131; Miette de Villars, 1850, pp. 100, 189, 232; E.-J. Delécluze, 1855, pp. 119, 348, 399; A. Cantaloube, 1860, p. 291; J. Du Seigneur, 1863, p. 366; P. Mantz, 1874, pp. 200-202; J.-L.-J. David, 1880, pp. 46-51, 637, ill. 1882; Ch. Saunier (1904), p. 35; L. Rosenthal (1905), pp. 33, 37, 44, ill.; L. Hautecœur, 1912, p. 194, ill.; Ch. Saunier, 1913, pp. 273, 280; L. Rosenthal, 1913, p. 339; R. Cantinelli, 1930, p. 24, no. 52, p. 104, ill. XVIII; B. Burroughs, 1931, pp. 140-144; A. Bonnardet, 1938; K. Holma, 1940, pp. 50-51, ill. 9, p. 55, cat. 57, p. 126; J. Maret, 1943, ill. 41; E. Wind, 1943, pp. 223-224; G. Brière, 1945-1946, p. 179; W. Friedlaender, 1952, p. 17, ill. 4; J. Adhémar, 1953, pp. 42-43; L. Hautecœur, 1954, pp. 90-94; Ch. Sterling, in mus. cat. *(French Paintings),* 1955, pp. 192-196; J. Seznec, 1957, p. 20, ill. 9; J. Lindsay, 1960, pp. 55-56, ill. 2; A. Salmon, 1962, pp. 190-211; A. Brookner, 1964 (1967), p. 189, ill.; R. Rosenblum, 1967 a, pp. 73-76, 81, 103, 125, ill. 74; R. Verbraeken, 1973, pp. 24, 28-30, 33, 46, 54-55, 80, 82, 85, 87-88, 94, 106, 108, 149-150, ill. 21; D. and G. Wildenstein, 1973, nos. 162, 180, 188, 189, 191, 192, 195, 303, 327, 352, 1165, 1167, 1543, 1810, 1929, 1938 (26).

RELATED WORKS

Drawings. An important drawing in the Lille museum (INV. 2181) represents David's first thoughts for this picture (see above). He seems to have reused several studies of heads drawn from the antique in Rome (see especially J. Adhémar, 1953, ill. 12-13), and to have taken the gesture of Socrates, which is incidentally very close to that in Peyron's picture, from a study in the album in the Berlin Kunstbibliothek (no. 23). There are some admirable studies for the isolated figures, in black charcoal heightened with chalk and squared off (similar preparatory studies also exist for the *Horatii* and *Brutus*), in Dijon (Musée Magnin), New York (Metropolitan Museum of Art), in Tours, and especially in Bayonne (three). Trudaine, who commissioned the picture, also owned a sketch of 11 by 18 *pouces* (Arch. Nat. F^{17} 1267 [190] no. 13). A number of drawings are mentioned in old sales catalogues; for instance no. 68 in the Révil sale 29 March-2 April 1842), and nos. 90 and 91 in the Coutan-Hauget sale (16-17 December 1889). A "very finished wash drawing" is mentioned by M. Florisoone in the 1948, Paris, exh. cat. as belonging to the Vicomtesse de Fleury.

Engravings. The picture was engraved by Massard (see D. and G. Wildenstein, 1973, no. 192: the contract was signed on 20 September 1787, but the engraving was only begun in 1795, see nos. 1165, 1167); line engraving by Ch. Normand, in C.-P. Landon, III, 1802, pl. 170 (Landon states again that Massard was in the process of engraving the picture).

A. S.

33
Portrait of Lavoisier and his Wife

Lavoisier et sa femme
Plate p. 87
Canvas; 286 × 224; s.d.l.l. *L. David* [*faciebat* illegible] *Parisiis Anno 1788*
New York, The Rockefeller University, Gift of John D. Rockefeller, Jr.

Antoine-Laurent Lavoisier (1743-1794), a rich farmer-general (a position which led him to the guillotine) and a famous chemist, was elected to the Academy of Science in 1768. He studied oxygen and respiration, demonstrated the mechanics of combustion in 1775, discovered the chemical composition of water in 1784, formulated in collaboration with Guyton de Morveau a new chemical nomenclature, and published his theories in the *Traité élémentaire de chimie* in 1789. Lavoisier's interests encompassed also the applied sciences, agriculture and government administration (he wrote reports on the lighting system and the water supply of Paris). He was one of the first directors of the administration of gunpowder, a department which he had advised Turgot to set up in 1775, and thus was appointed to his post at the Arsenal.

In 1771, Lavoisier had married Marie-Anne-Pierrette Paulze (1758-1836), the very young daughter of a farmer-general, who is believed to have studied with David and who assisted her husband in his work. She translated Richard Kirwan's *Essay on Phlogiston and the Constitution of Acids*; after Lavoisier's death in 1794, published a portion of his papers in 1805 *(Mémoires de chimie)*. At this time she married her second husband, the English scholar Count Rumford. By 1809, they were separated. One of her preparatory drawings for the *Traité élémentaire de chimie* (ill. in É. Grimaux, 1888, p. 119) shows her sitting at a table recording the results of an experiment.

The portrait which David painted in 1788 was supposed to be exhibited at the Salon of 1789. However, on 6 August, Lavoisier, who had arranged to obtain musket powder from Essonne, had the Arsenal stocked and loaded up with gunpowder. This action caused a riot in which Lavoisier was very nearly killed. As a result, the Administration of Royal Buildings decided that it would be wiser not to exhibit the portrait at the Salon, which was to open in a few days. On the other hand, David exhibited the *Pâris et Hélène* (Louvre), which he had painted for the Comte d'Artois. The pose of the couple, that of Paris in particular, is not unlike the portrait of the Lavoisiers. The talents of Mme Lavoisier, who is represented as a kind of Muse inspiring her husband, are evoked by the portfolio that lies on the chair. The admirable still-life on the floor and the table refer to the experiments of Lavoisier. The effect of grandness in the painting is accentuated by its size, as is the case with the *Portrait of Count Potocki* (No. 29), and by the background—simple, as always in David's work, yet noble with its decoration of fluted pilasters. Only in his portraits of Napoleon (No. 36 *bis*) did David so successfully combine formality with the qualities of everyday life.

PROVENANCE
The large sum of 7,000 *livres* was paid to David on 16 December 1788. Bequest of Mme Lavoisier (d. 1836) to the Comtesse de Chazelles. Chazelles Collection, Château de la Canière, near Aigueperse. Sold in 1924, acquired by John D. Rockefeller in 1925, placed in the Rockefeller Institute for Medical Research in New York in 1927.

EXHIBITIONS
1889, Paris, no. 234; 1913, Paris, no. 20; 1948, Paris, M.O. 23 (ill.) (cat. by M. Florisoone).

REFERENCES
Correspondance de M. d'Angiviller avec Pierre, ed. 1905-1906, v. II, pp. 264-265 (10 Aug. 1789); (Chaussard), 1806, ed. 1808, pp. 156-157; *Notice...*, 1824, p. 43; A. Th., 1826, pp. 151, 240 (as two portraits); P.-A. Coupin, 1827, p. 54; Ch. Blanc, 1845, p. 209; Miette de Villars, 1850, p. 100; E.-J. Delécluze, 1855 p. 137; J. Du Seigneur, 1863, p. 366; J.-L.-J. David, 1880, pp. 53, 637, ill. 1882; E. Grimaux, 1888, pp. VI, 364-365, frontispiece ill.; Ch. Saunier (1904), p. 17, ill. and 124; L. Rosenthal (1905), p. 165; P. Dorbec, 1907, pp. 310-311, 321, ill.; G. Capon (1924); R. Cantinelli, 1930, no. 55, p. 104, ill. XIX; D.-S. MacColl, 1938, pp. 264, 268, ill.; K. Holma, 1940, p. 53, no. 61, p. 126, ill. XVII; J. Maret, 1943, ill. 38; L. Hautecœur, 1954, pp. 105, 107; J. Lindsay, 1960, p. 60; *Grands peintres,* 1966-1967, no XVII, back cover ill.; H. Honour, 1968, pp. 72, 198, ill. 28; R.-L. Herbert, 1972, pp. 58-59 and notes 44-47, ill. 29; R. Verbraeken, 1973, pp. 14, 28, 30, 32, 147, ill. 22; D. and G. Wildenstein, 1973, nos. 205, 1810, 1938 (17).

RELATED WORKS
Engraving by Latteur and J.-J.-F. Wassaert showing Lavoisier alone; another in half-length by J. Levasseur. A. S.

34
*Portrait of the Marquise de Pastoret***

Madame de Pastoret
Plate p. 129 and color pl. p. 19
Canvas; 133 × 100
The Art Institute of Chicago

The exact date of this delightful portrait is not known, but can be placed toward the beginning of 1792. In fact, Amédée-David de Pastoret, seen in the cradle next to his mother, was born in 1791 (see the entry on his portrait by Ingres, No. 111). On the other hand, since Claude de Pastoret emigrated after 10 August 1792, circumstances could scarcely have permitted his young wife, who stayed in Paris and was imprisoned during the Reign of Terror, the leisure to have her portrait painted, especially by an artist as politically tainted as David. It is probably this political atmosphere which explains the incomplete state of the portrait (on this point, see No. 35).

Adélaïde-Louise Piscatory, born in Marseille in 1765, married on 14 July 1789 Claude de Pastoret, future Chancellor of France, whose portrait by Paul Delaroche is exhibited here (No. 43); she probably received painting lessons from David. Under the Consulate, she worked on charitable projects and later presided over a very popular and elite salon. She died in 1843.

Along with the other incomplete portraits of the Revolutionary period, the *Portrait of the Marquise de Pastoret* forms the most immediately appealing part of David's œuvre, thanks to the charm of the model and the intimate setting, the spots of color on an essentially gray background, with its simultaneously neutral and vibrant quality, and, in general, to its unfinished state which appeals so much to modern sensibilities.

PROVENANCE

Left in David's atelier, transported from Brussels to Paris after his death (inventoried at rue Cadet on 27 February); sold 17 April 1826, no. 16 (for 400 francs to M. Révil); Pastoret Collection; sale of the Marquise du Plessis-Bellière, née Pastoret, Paris, 10-11 May 1897, no. 21; P.-A. Chéramy Collection, sale 7-8 May 1908, no. 44, ill. (41,000 francs to G. Petit); Joachim Murat Collection, and then Vicomte de Fleury; bought by the Chicago Art Institute in 1967 from Wildenstein and Co. (Clyde M. Carr Fund and Major Acquisitions Fund).

EXHIBITIONS

1909, Paris, no. 48, ill.; 1913, Paris, no. 39; 1926, Amsterdam, no. 35.

REFERENCES

P.-A. Coupin, 1827, p. 55; A. Lenoir, 1835, p. 9; J. Du Seigneur, 1863, p. 367; J.-L.-J. David, 1880, p. 644; E. Delignières, 1890, pp. 491-493, ill. XIX; P. Dorbec, 1907, p. 314, ill. p. 328; L. Rouart, 1907, p. 17, cover ill.; J. Meier-Graefe and E. Klossowski, 1958, no. 75, ill.; Ch. Saunier, 1913, p. 274; R. Cantinelli, 1930, cat. no. 193, p. 118; K. Holma, 1940, p. 65 and cat. no. 206, p. 130; J. Maret, p. 314, ill. p. 328; L. Rouart, 1907, p. 17, ill. couverture; J. Meier-Graefe and E. Klossowski, 1958, no. 75, ill.; Ch. Saunier, 1913, p. 274; R. Cantinelli, 1930, cat. no. 193, p. 118; K. Holma, 1940, p. 65 and cat. no. 206, p. 130; J. Maret, 1943, ill. 71; L. Hautecœur, 1954, pp. 105-106, 187, 281; J. Maxon, 1968, p. 65, ill.; *ibid.,* 1970, p. 279, ill.; R. Verbraeken, 1973, p. 102, ill. 47; D. and G. Wildenstein, 1973, nos. 2042 (80), 2062 (16), 2420.

A. S.

35
*Portrait of a Youth**

Portrait de jeune homme
Plate p. 134
Canvas; 72 × 58; s.d. l. *L. David f. 1793*
Paris, Private Collection

This handsome portrait, not well known, is the only work by David left purposely in a rough-sketch state, although signed and dated; the date and signature seem incontestable. This, then, forces us to consider, briefly, at least, the question of David's unfinished portraits. Given their quality and relative abundance, we might be tempted to believe that the artist considered them to be finished, like this painting, especially since he has also left the scumbling clearly exposed in the backgrounds and less important parts of several finished paintings (*Autoportrait,* Louvre, *Sériziat,* Ottawa, *Madame de Verninac, Mademoiselle Tallard,* Louvre; *Mort de Marat,* Brussels, etc.) In fact, we know, at least, the history of the *Portrait de Madame Récamier,* undeniably unfinished and left in the artist's studio until his death. Not even counting studies of heads done with a more important work in mind, or canvases barely begun (such as the *Serment du Jeu de Paume*), the case is the same for several other paintings, although the sources do not reveal the reason. Listed clearly as unfinished in the catalog of the sale after his death, are *Apelles and Campaspe* (No. 37), which all the sources identify as un finished; *Mort du jeune Barra,* Avignon; *Madame de Pastoret* (No. 34); *Madame Trudaine,* Louvre; *M. de Joubert,* Montpellier; *M. Estève,* a canvas which cannot be confused with either of the two portraits in the *David* exhibition, 1948, Paris. One could add the obviously unfinished portraits of the artist's daughters (San Francisco, De Young Memorial Museum and Winterthur, Reinhard Collection). None of these paintings, any more than this portrait of a young man, is included in the lists of paintings compiled by David himself (D. and G. Wildenstein, 1973, nos. 1810 and 1939), since the *Portrait de M. Estève,* which is included

in it, is probably different from the one left in the studio. Why are there so many unfinished works? While they do not explain everything, two reasons are evident: the painter's slowness, which must have been what made Mme Récamier impatient and forced her to appeal to Gérard in order to have her portrait (we should remember that David resumed work on his *Léonidas* and finished it nearly 15 years after it was begun); and the acceleration of time in the Revolutionary period, which at least explains the abandonment not only of *Serment du Jeu de Paume,* but also of *Barra,* and the portraits of the *Marquise de Pastoret* (whose husband emigrated) and *Mme Trudaine* (whose husband was guillotined).

As for our *Portrait of a Youth,* it does not appear to be a commissioned work, but rather the likeness of an acquaintance, possibly a student, executed rapidly, at the moment when David was the most involved in his political activities. Its monochromatic palette heightened by touches of pink make the painting one of David's most poetic creations. Its vague grace recalls the *Barra* in Avignon, even if, contrary to what has been suggested, the model does not seem to be the same.

PROVENANCE
It might have come from the region of Aix-en-Provence.

EXHIBITION
1956, Paris, no. 31, ill. V.

A. S.

36

*Sappho and Phaon*****

Sapho, Phaon et l'Amour
Plate p. 203
Canvas; 222 × 260; s.d.l.l. *David 1809*
Leningrad, The Hermitage Museum

Prince Youssoupoff was one of the greatest art lovers of his time; after the Revolution, his collection (studied by S. Ernst, 1924) was divided between the Arkhangelski Palace, where the nucleous remains today, the Moscow museum and the Hermitage. This collection was particularly rich in contemporary French

works: P.-N. Guérin, L.-L. Boilly, N.-A. Taunay, etc. The equestrian portrait of the Prince's son, also painted in 1809, by Antoine-Jean Gros, is at the Hermitage. The subject represented here by David is derived from the history of the poetess Sappho, whose translations were generally edited with the works of Anacreon and were numerous from the end of the 17th century (Mme Dacier, Longepierre, Poinsinet de Sivry), were very popular at this time. (Girodet illustrated them in drawings, the engraved edition of which appeared in 1829.) Sappho, surprised by her lover Phaon, lets go of her lyre; Eros seizes it and sings to Venus the hymn which Sappho composed. Later Sappho, betrayed and abandoned by Phaon, threw herself into the sea (this subject was painted by Antoine-Jean Gros in 1801, see No. 87).

David appears to have executed this painting quickly, with minimal preparatory studies. As a matter of fact, in a letter to Prince Youssoupoff of 31 May 1814 (S. Ernst, *op. cit.,* p. 269), the painter wrote: "If I may venture to ask a small favor, my Prince, would you have drawn for me a small sketch of the painting which I made for you, as I have no trace of it in Paris." This is the first painting by David which referred back to the inspiration of Anacreon from the period of *Pâris et Hélène* (1788); he executed many others after 1815. David strove to give an everyday face to mythological heroes, somewhat in the manner of the young Caravaggio, whose influence is felt here in the figure of Phaon, as well as that of Eros in the painting *Psyché et l'Amour* (1817, Cleveland).

This painting has almost always been judged harshly. The most faithful admirers of David had a fixed idea of the painter of the *Horaces, Sabines* and *Léonidas,* which they could not reconcile with the mythological paintings or those derived from Anacreon. G. Le Cointe de Laveau was astonished "that the entire composition is a failure... [and Sappho] absolutely lacks nobility." L. Viardot dared "hardly to indicate, out of respect for the author... a deplorable composition of *Sappho and Phaon,* signed Louis David, 1809." The only admirer of this painting, A. Lenoir, in fact almost unknown to Frenchmen, noted "the tender and perfect expression of Sappho," the unusual skill with which the painter let her face be seen through Phaon's fingers, and that the color "bears a very close ressemblance to that of the *Pâris et Hélène.*" The 20th century, forgetting the *Pâris et Hélène* and ignoring the *Sappho and Phaon,* has too readily dismissed the Anacreon-inspired paintings as the decadent production of a senile David. Even A. Humbert characterized these paintings as unworthy of the revolutionary David and attributed them to his submission to the base instincts of his clients, seeing in the *Sappho and Phaon* a "lamentable and tasteless finicalness... [and a] slightly senile affectation of the erotic and mundane detail." She considered it a "work

typical of class painting, which is an accurate reflection of the preoccupations of the client." (On the same page, the author also condemned cubist painting, as intended for a "small elite of indifferent and useless bourgeois intellectuals.") More recently (1957), Charles Sterling wrote, "All the faces are affected, all the gestures are lifeless and insignificant... With a classical pretext, this painting is in reality irritatingly mannerist... David appears to have surrendered untroubled to the over-refined graces of the 18th century..." However, David did remain faithful here to his deep-rooted practices—strict and stable construction of the composition, impeccable clarity of drawing, regard for archaeology, to which he added an incomparable palette of brilliant colors. From this point of view, this painting is important as it dates well before his exile in Brussels, which all agree, after David himself, is when David's interest in color began. As he himself said, "Did I not take it in my head to aim at the color, and I too want to get involved in it, but in truth, it is too late. If I had the good fortune to come to this country sooner, I believe that I would have become a colorist" (letter to A.-J. Gros, 13 September 1817).

PROVENANCE

Commissioned by Prince Youssoupoff, who resided in Paris from 1808 until 1811. Confiscated during the Russian Revolution with the Youssoupoff Collection and placed in the Moscow museum. At the Hermitage since 1925, following an exchange.

REFERENCES

Notice..., 1824, p. 44; A. Th., 1826, pp. 152-153, 236; P.-A. Coupin, 1827, p. 55; G. Le Cointe de Laveau, 1828, pp. 281-282; *ibid.,* ed. 1835, v. II, p. 278; J.-H. Schnitzler, 1834, p. 60; A. Lenoir, 1835, p. 5; mus. cat. of Prince Youssoupoff, 1839, no. 217; Ch. Blanc, 1845, p. 215 (dated 1799); Miette de Villars, 1850, p. 156; L. Dussieux, 1852, ed. 1876, p. 561; L. Viardot, ed. 1855, p. 315; J. Du Seigneur, 1863, p. 364; J.-L.-J. David, 1880, p. 390 (dated c. 1800), 579, 646 (exact. date); Ch. Saunier [1904], p. 84 (dated c. 1799); L. Rosenthal [1905], p. 170; S. Ernst, 1924, p. 162, ill., 268-269; L. Réau, 1929, p. 23, no. 59; R. Cantinelli, 1930, p. 93, cat. no. 119, p. 112, ill. LXIX; A. Humbert, 1936, pp. 144-145, 173; K. Holma, 1940, p. 80, cat. no. 126, p. 128; W. Friedlaender, 1952, pp. 31-32; L. Hautecœur, 1954, p. 226; Ch. Sterling, 1957, pp. 68-69; mus. cat., 1958, v. I, p. 375, ill. (see also album opp. p. 142); F. Haskell, 1972, pp. 21-22, ill. 23; H. Honour, 1972, p. 316; R. Verbraeken, 1973, p. 189 (note 273); D. and G. Wildenstein, 1973, nos. 1563, 1632, 1810, 1938; V. Berezina, 1972, pp. 14-15 (color).

A. S.

36 bis
Napoleon in his Study

Napoléon dans son cabinet de travail
Plate p. 216
Canvas; 205 × 125; s.d.l.l. *Lud. David opus/1812*
Washington, D.C., National Gallery, Samuel H. Kress Collection

This painting was commissioned by Alexander Douglas (1767-1852), heir of an illustrious Scotch family (he was not, as is sometimes said, the son of Lord William Hamilton, the celebrated antiquarian and husband of the no less famous Emma Lyon, but a cousin). After having grown up in Italy, where he became involved with art and began to collect, he returned in 1801 to England, becoming a member of Parliament in 1803 and ambassador to Russia from 1806 to 1807. In 1810, he married a cousin, daughter of William Beckford, the author of *Vathek* and also a collector. If the political career of Alexander Douglas (who in 1819 became Duke of Hamilton) was modest, his collection was both fabulous and eclectic: rich in ancient Italian painting, it also included furniture which had belonged to Marie-Antoinette and Chinese porcelain; some 2,200 lots from the 1882 sale produced about £400,000.

His request for a portrait of Napoleon, coming right in the middle of a war between France and England, may be surprising (according to Suau, it was transmitted by the Chevalier de Bonnemaison, himself a painter (see No. 11), who had emigrated to England during the Revolution. A certain Scotch patriotism on the part of the noble Duke, who claimed to be the legitimate heir of the most ancient kings of Scotland, may partially explain the surprising request, but one must not forget that nationalism had at this time scarcely begun to ravage European civilization. Alexander Douglas' admiration and connections with the Bonaparte family is attested by other works of art in his collection: a bust of Napoleon by Berthel Thorvaldsen, offered by Pauline Bonaparte (no. 542 of the sale); a miniature representing the First Consul (no. 1484); Sèvres vases with paintings of the sisters of Napoleon by Charles-Étienne Le Guay (no. 1700); an intaglio of Napoleon crowned with laurel, set in a ring (no. 2128).

David, himself a great admirer of Napoleon, to whom he remained faithful during The 100 Days, often represented his "hero," but not without having difficulties with his model. Although the painting of Bonaparte crossing the Grand-Saint-Bernard (1800-01) is famous and distinguished, David was able to paint the head only from a former portrait (Louvre). He had scarcely more luck with a full-length portrait in imperial robes destined for the city of Genoa (sketch dated 1805, in Lille); it was rejected by Napoleon in 1806 and again in 1811, when David proposed to resume the work. David presented in the Salon of 1808 (no. 145) a similar portrait, destined for the brother of the Emperor, King Jerome of Westphalia.

Recently-discovered correspondence (P. Mesplé, 1969) of P.-Th. Suau, a student of David between 1810 and 1813, is precise about the date of the Washington painting and its repetition. On 4 February 1812, he wrote, "M. David has almost finished"; in fact, on 4 March, "he has still to finish the background and some accessories." On 28 March, Suau saw the completed painting, which he described precisely, including the "the clock which says 4:15." Suau then noted on 19 April that David had begun a second version, on which he was still working on 19 July. A. Lenoir (1835), who hailed the Lord Douglas painting as a masterpiece and considered it "the best likeness which has been done of the Emperor," reports the comment which David himself made to him: Napoleon spent the night composing the Napoleonic Code (in fact, promulgated since 1804); he glimpsed the break of day only by the dying candles and by the clock, which had just chimed 4:00 in the morning. He got up from his desk in order to buckle on his sword and review his troops. David then chose to represent here the image not of the legendary hero, as in 1800-01, but of the tireless worker, who devotes his nights to the welfare of his subjects. The preparatory drawing in Besançon, missing both candle and clock, also proves that the painter had not yet conceived of this ingeniously flattering political emblem, but that he added it to a composition in which the principal dispositions underwent no other change.

The realism of the effigy, which translates without complaisance the slightly puffy face, the thinning hair and the fleshy silhouette of the sovereign, is accentuated by the detailed rendering of the blue uniform of a colonel of the Grenadiers of the Foot-Guard, and especially by that of the decor, which is in contrats with the customary style of David's portraits. The artist does not seem to have faithfully depicted the actual decor (N. Hubert, 1969, observed that the arm-chair was in fact situated not in the study, but in the Grand Cabinet des Tuileries [A. Gonzalez-Palacios, 1973b, has located it in Palazzo Caserta]; the inventory of the Cabinet de Travail, published by C. and G. Ledoux-Lebard, 1952, bears no trace of the clock) but to have recomposed it in order to establish an element for a sort of allegory of the Legislator. The careful adjustment of the decor, with the armchair placed obliquely to break the vertical hierarchism of the composition, the Dutch-derived opening to another room (map room), the admirable details of the torch, the plaque of the Legion of Honor, or the detail, worthy of the most beautiful portraits of Ingres, of the key on the side of the clock, make this portrait, in which the intellectual program of the artist is embodied so well in a superb bit of painting, one of the most astonishing of the century.

PROVENANCE

Painted for Alexander Douglas (1767-1852), who in 1819 became the tenth Duke of Hamilton; Hamilton Collection, Hamilton Palace, near Glasgow. Twelfth Duke of Hamilton sale, London, 17 June-20 July 1882, no. 1108 (8 July, bought for £ 378 by F. Davis); Lord Rosebery Collection; acquired in 1954 by the Samuel H. Kress Foundation (K. 2046) and placed in the National Gallery, Washington, D.C. (INV. 1374).

EXHIBITIONS

1948-1949, London-Manchester, no. 23 (cover ill.); 1956, Paris, Orangerie, no. 17 (ill. 1).

REFERENCES

P.-Th. Suau, 1812, in P. Mesplé, 1969 pp. 100-101; Notice..., 1824, p. 72; A. Th., 1826, p. 184, 236; P.-A. Coupin, 1827, p. 56; A. Lenoir, 1835, p. 10; Ch. Blanc, 1845, p. 211; G.F. Waagen, 1854, v. III, p. 298; E.-J. Delécluze, 1855, pp. 346-347; J. Du Seigneur, 1863, p. 365; J.-L.-J. David, 1880, pp. 487, 647; A. Dayot, 1895, pp. 259-263; R. Cantinelli, 1930, no. 123, p. 112; K. Holma, 1941, pp. 79-80, no. 129, p. 128; G. and C. Ledoux-Lebard, 1952, p. 192; L. Hautecœur, 1954, p. 200; Time Magazine, 30 Aug. 1954 (color ill.); mus. cat. (Kress Collection), 1956, no. 22, pp. 64-66 (ill.); J. Walker, G. Emerson, Ch. Seymour Jr., 1961, pp. 193-194 (ill. 184, color); F. Markham, 1964, p. 190 (color cover); A. Gonzalez-Palacios, 1967, p. 14, ill. V; N. Hubert, in exh. cat., 1969, Grand Palais, in no. 158; P. Mesplé, 1969, pp. 100-101; R. Verbraeken, 1973, p. 11, 28, ill. 53; D. and G. Wildenstein, 1973, nos. 1642, 1645, 1648, 1651, 1938 (49).

RELATED WORKS

An important preparatory drawing (in which the clock is not shown) in the Besançon museum (D 1979, from the Gigoux Collection; ill. J. Maret, 1943, p. 17). Since 1824 (Notice..., p. 72), it has been stated often that David did four copies of this painting, but this statement is the product of a confusion with the equestrian portrait of 1800-01; in fact, David only did one repetition of this painting, destined for a certain Huibans, but which he must have kept in his studio until almost 1824 (Notice..., 1824). This repetition, also signed and dated 1812 (see above), entered the collection of Napoleon III, and today belongs to Prince Napoleon (exh. cat. 1969, Paris, Grand Palais, no. 158, ill.). It is this second example, where Napoleon is represented in the green uniform of the Chasseurs à cheval de la Garde and where the clock shows exactly 4:00, which was engraved by Jean-Nicolas Laugier and by J.-L.-J. David (1882). Laugier must have worked from a drawing by Michel-Ghislain Stapleaux, probably the one which belonged to David himself (posthumous inventory, no. 31, in D. and G. Wildenstein, 1973, no. 2041). A small painted copy, attributed to Moina de Savigny, is in the Museo Napoleonico, Rome.

A. S.

37
*Apelles and Campaspe**

Apelle peignant Campaspe devant Alexandre
Plate p. 225
Panel; 96 × 136
Lille, Musée des Beaux-Arts

According to the legend related by Pliny the Elder (*Natural History,* XXXV, 10), Apelles fell in love with Alexander's mistress while he was painting her portrait, and Alexander then abandoned her to the painter.

This subject, so flattering to artists, has been depicted very often since the Renaissance; some artists, like Louis Lagrenée, for example, even used it as the allegory of painting. The popularity of this theme, which may seem typically rococo, continued during and after the Revolution: for example, Demoustier's play staged at the Opéra in 1798, or the canvases by Langlois (1819, Toulouse) and Charles Meynier (sale after the artist's death), which were painted after the unfinished work by David.

Although most of David's uncompleted paintings date from the heady years of the Revolution, this one was done about 1814: the drawing David gave to Gros is dated 1813 (see Related Works); but A. Th. in 1824 and E. J. Delécluze in 1855 state that the work was retouched in Brussels, therefore after 1816. Like all David's "pleasant" subjects, this one had little success with the critics (according to Jean Adhémar, 1953, the picture is "close to ridiculous"), despite the charm of its unfinished state.

Carrying on the tradition that David had launched in 1788 with *Pâris et Hélène* (Louvre), and especially with his *Sappho and Phaon* (No. 36), *Apelles and Campaspe* announces his late paintings, which are multiple variations on the traditional theme of the couple in love: *Amour et Psyché* (Cleveland Museum of Art); *Télémaque et Eucharis* (private collection), *Mars and Venus* (No. 38). The use of panel, unique as far as we know in David's painting, reveals his growing interest in a smooth finish, even if he did not completely realize his intention.

PROVENANCE

Remained in David's studio in Brussels; taken to Paris in March 1826. In the David sale, 17 April 1826, no. 3, withdrawn; in the second David sale, 11 March 1835, no. 3; in 1874 bought back from the Meunier family by Jules David, who donated it to the Lille museum in 1885 (catalogued in 1893 as no. 1098).

EXHIBITIONS

1913, Paris, no. 51; 1948, Paris, M.O. 66; 1964, Berlin-Charlottenburg, no. 10; 1967, Montauban, no. 209.

REFERENCES

A. Th., 1826, pp. 215-216 and 238; P.-A. Coupin, 1827, p. 57; Ch. Blanc, 1845, p. 213; Miette de Villars, 1850, p. 210; E.-J. Delécluze, 1855, pp. 354 and 368; J. Du Seigneur, 1863, p. 366; J.-L.-J. David, 1880, pp. 569, 648, ill. 1882; Ch. Saunier (1904), p. 111; L. Rosenthal (1905), p. 167; *ibid.*, 1913, p. 341; R. Cantinelli, 1930, no. 130, p. 113; K. Holma, 1940, pp. 8, 87, ill. and cat. 136, p. 129; L. Adhémar, 1953, p. 54; L. Hautecœur, 1954, p. 226; A. Brookner, 1958, p. 71; R. Verbraeken, 1973, pp. 22, 29, 30, 104, ill. 58; D. and G. Wildenstein, 1973, nos. 2052 (96), 2062 (3), 2077 (17), 2087 (3).

RELATED WORKS

A preparatory drawing given by David to Gros in 1820 (J. David, 1880, p. 564; see also D. and G. Wildenstein, 1973, nos. 1868, 1869, 1877). In Jules David's time, this drawing, bearing the date 1813, belonged to Mlle Duseuil. A rough sketch of the composition, no. 95 in the April 1826 sale after David's death. Among the other drawings mentioned by J. David, there was one in the Coutan-Hauguet sale, Paris, 15-17 December 1889, no. 94.

A. S.

38
Mars Disarmed by Venus and the Three Graces

Mars désarmé par Vénus et les Grâces
Plate p. 279
Canvas; 308 × 262; s.d.l.m. *L. David Brux. 1824.*
Brussels, Musées Royaux des Beaux-Arts de Belgique

David must have begun work on the painting in 1821, since Gros was able to see a rough version in oil when he was in Brussels at the end of that year. The oil sketch was modified in 1822 (according to a letter of 30 October from Mme David to A.-J. Gros; Paris, École des Beaux-Arts, MS. 317). David had Dupavillon and then Michael-Ghislain Stapleaux do the

under-painting and the accessories. In December 1823, when Gros returned to Brussels, only the foreground clouds had not yet been painted (J.-L.-J. David, 1880, p. 589). The painting was probably finished and signed in February 1824, exhibited in Brussels at a benefit for the poor, and then in Paris at 115, rue de Richelieu, starting on 26 May. It was hung in a room with green walls, along with most of the works which David still had in his possession.

The original idea for the painting, preserved today in a drawing at the Fogg Art Museum (1963-62), was a composition of two figures—similar to the *Amour et Psyché* of 1817 (Cleveland Museum of Art)—in which Venus, appearing almost full-face, takes off Mars' helmet. The vacant portion of the painting at the right was subsequently occupied by the Graces, as in a drawing in Besançon (D. 1999), and the result is close to the finished work. Venus finally appears with her back turned, a long, smooth nude, almost as stylized as an Ingres. How, indeed, can one fail to think of the figure of the *Grande Odalisque* in the Louvre (1814), who, it has been pointed out, was herself reminiscent of the *Portrait de Mme Récamier* (D. Ternois, Paris, 1967-1968, exh. cat.).

The exhibition in the rue de Richelieu was quite a success. There were nearly 10,000 visitors, most of them during the first month. David's students and friends wrote to him expressing their admiration (Paris, École des Beaux-Arts, MS. 318). Gros, the most loyal of all, was no doubt also the most sensitive to this work, whose creation he had followed so closely. The influence of the painting is apparent in Gros' late works, like the *Acis et Galathée* (New York, Walter P. Chrysler, Jr. Collection). But the truth of the matter is also revealed in the failure of the posthumous sales of 1826 and 1835, where the most important paintings had to be withdrawn. In 1824, attention was focused on the Salon of which the historical importance is well-known. "We are on the verge of a Revolution in the Fine Arts," wrote Stendhal in his critiques, referring in particular to David. It was indeed in 1824 that the "romantics," Delacroix, Sigalon, Delaroche, A. Scheffer, had, despite Géricault's premature death, their first successes (Géricault's *Radeau de la Méduse* was acquired by the Louvre in the same year). It was not so much the arabesque element in *Mars Disarmed by Venus and the Three Graces,* the severe stability of the composition or strict frontality of the temple in the clouds (which Ingres no doubt remembered when he began the *Apothéose d'Homère* in 1826), but rather the intensity of the colors that startled and puzzled the viewers. Jal found in this work "the whole of David, David in his prime and in all the perfection of his genius." But Thiers, in a balanced criticism of the painting, regretted the "jarring colors," the "affected transparency," the "glassiness," and yet admired the execution: "Never, if one may be permitted to use the word, has a fabric of color, composed of a mixture and a controlled succession of a multitude of different tones, been so perfect, so finely done." As far as modern criticism is concerned, it has, as we know, rejected the entire late work of David. Thus, W. Friedlaender considered that David, working in the absence of that moral tension inherent in his historical paintings, and without the sustaining force of contemporary events, was incapable of creating a genuine late style. One may or may not admire the late style, but one can hardly deny its existence.

PROVENANCE

Taken to Paris in 1824; offered without success at the posthumous sales of April 1826 and May 1835 (no. 1); kept by the painter's children; bought in 1860 by Jules David-Chassagnolle, who then gave it to the Brussels museum in 1881, along with the *Marat*.

EXHIBITIONS

1824, Brussels, then Paris; 1926, Brussels; 1957, Charleroi, no. 13; 1972, Antwerp, no. 11.

REFERENCES

(Anon.), *Courrier Français,* 31 May 1824; (Anon.), *Revue encyclopédique,* June 1824, pp. 769-773; A. Jal, 1824; A. Thiers, 1824; *Un mot sur le dernier tableau de M. David, par un amateur* (1824); *Notice...,* 1824, p. 71; A. Th., 1826, pp. 214, 215, 238; P.-A. Coupin, 1827, pp. 42, 57; Ch. Blanc, 1845, pp. 199, 213; Miette de Villars, 1850, p. 223; E.-J. Delécluze, 1855, pp. 368, 370-371; J. Du Seigneur, 1863, p. 366; J.-L.-J. David, 1880, pp. 578, 583, 587-590, 651, ill. 1882; L. Rosenthal, 1900, p. 100; J. Guiffrey, 1903, pp. 205-208, ill.; Ch. Saunier (1904), pp. 115-116; L. Rosenthal (1905), pp. 151-152, 169, ill.; Fierens-Gevaert, 1926, p. 170; R. Cantinelli, 1930, p. 94 and no. 159, p. 116, ill. LXXXVIII; A. Humbert, 1936, pp. 157-158; K. Holma, 1940, pp. 97-98, no. 165, p. 129, ill.; M. Praz, 1940, ed. 1972, p. 79; R. Huyghe, 1948, p. 28; A. Maurois, 1948, ill. 37; W. Friedlaender, 1952, p. 32; J. Adhémar, 1953, p. 54; L. Hautecœur, 1954, pp. 270-275; J. Billioud and P. Ripert, 1956, pp. 31-33, ill.; J. Lindsay, 1960, p. 144; R. Rosenblum, 1967a, p. 102; R. Verbraeken, 1973, pp. 58, 104-105, 184; ill. X; D. and G. Wildenstein, 1973, nos. 1934, 1936, 1945, 1947, 1950, 1955, 1956, 1959 - 1962, 1965, 1967, 1971, 1972, 1974, 1978, 1979, 1985, 2042 (81), 2049 (42), 2062 (1), 2063, 2077 (7), 2087 (1).

RELATED WORKS

In addition to the previously mentioned drawings in the Fogg Museum (1963-62) and in Besançon (D.1999), there is another sheet at the Besançon museum (D. 1998), a study of three different poses for the Grace who pours the wine (the pose on the right was finally used); the drawing bears the inscription: *Mme D. est partie de Bruxelles pour Paris le 27 juin 1823.* In the sketchbook preserved in the Musée de Lille (no. 1214 v.) is a study for the head of Venus. A study for Mars exists on the recto side of a drawing in the Montauban museum (1955, Toulouse-Montauban, exh. cat., no. 69). A "small book" of sketches was included in the David sale, April 1826, no. 82. The painting was engraved by Chazal and Martiné. There is a colored lithograph parody by Langlumé.

A. S.

Eugène Delacroix

1798 Charenton-Saint-Maurice - Paris 1863

Eugène Delacroix lost his parents at an early age. In November 1805, after the death of his father, Prefect in Bordeaux, the family returned to Paris to live. When his mother died in 1814, Delacroix was taken in by his sister, Mme de Verninac. When he came of age he established his own household. Delacroix had entered the studio of Pierre-Narcisse Guérin in 1815 and in the following year was admitted to the École des Beaux-Arts. In 1819, he painted, in the spirit of the Raphaels that he copied at the Louvre, the *Vierge des moissons* for the church at Orcemont. Following this, he began work on the *Vierge du Sacré-Cœur* (Cathedral of Ajaccio), a commission that Géricault had declined. Delacroix finished the painting just as the Salon of 1822 opened.

At the Salon of 1822, he exhibited for the first time and showed only one work, *Dante et Virgile...* (Louvre). The painting brought him immediate recognition. It was acquired for the Musées Royaux and exhibited immediately at the Musée du Luxembourg. The criticism was rather fierce, but Adolphe Thiers was enthusiastic and wrote in *Le Constitutionnel* of 11 May 1822: "I believe I make no mistake when I say that M. de Lacroix is a genius." Delacroix was congratulated by Antoine-Jean Gros—"whose talent he idolized"—and invited to visit the artist's studio where he was able to see Gros paintings and sketches from the time of the First Empire which could not be shown at this time. But Delacroix did not become Gros' pupil and indeed disappointed him in 1824 with his painting the *Massacre de Scio* (Louvre), inspired by the Greek war of Independence. The painting won him a second class medal and was acquired by the Musée du Luxembourg. Géricault had just died and Delacroix thus appeared to stand at the head of the romantic school. Later on he was to remark, "I imagine that it was with the *Massacre de Scio* that I began to be an object of antipathy and a sort of monster for the school... Most of those who took my side and made me into a kind of rallying point were really only trying to defend themselves and their own ideas, insofar as they had any. For better or worse they enlisted me on the side of the romantics" (cited by P. Courthion, 1944, pp. 44-45).

As a romantic, in 1825 Delacroix visited England rather than Italy, and began to dream of seeing the East. In London he found Richard Bonington, became interested in English literature, Shakespeare, Byron, Walter Scott, and admired the work of John Constable. At the Salon of 1827 the *Mort de Sardanapale* (Louvre) was considered shocking, but Delacroix also exhibited several small paintings and two Commissional works: one by the city of Paris, the *Christ in the Garden of Olives* (No. 40); the other commissioned by the Minister of the Interior for the Conseil d'État, *L'Empereur Justinien composant ses lois* (destroyed in 1871). In a letter to his friend Soulier on 26 April 1828, Delacroix remarked, "I have a special sort of genius which does not even allow me to live as peacefully as a poor little clerk... I cannot expect either work or encouragement. All those who are most favorably inclined think of me as an interesting madman, but one whom it would be dangerous to encourage in his vagaries and bizarre ways." He lived with difficulty, doing lithographs for Goethe's *Faust* or portraits of students from the Institution Saint-Victor. In 1830, under the impact of recent events, he painted *Liberty Leading the People* (No. 41) which he showed at the Salon of 1831. At the same Salon, he exhibited *Cardinal Richelieu dans sa chapelle du Palais Royal,* commissioned in 1828 by the Duc d'Orléans (destroyed in 1848 in the Palais Royal), as well as a few portraits and romantic compositions.

During this early part of his life, known to us through his correspondence and the *Journal* which he kept between September 1822 and October 1824—and did not resume until 1847—Delacroix seems to have been very much as he described himself on 9 May 1824: "I have no taste for reasonable painting; I know that my unmethodical mind needs to become active, to tear things apart, to try a hundred ways before reaching my goal, the need for which drives me in everything I do." For each of his compositions, Delacroix increased his draw-ings and sketches in a baroque manner—the 1963 centennial exhibition and the *Mémorial* published on this occasion by Maurice Sérullaz show this very clearly. Then in the final work, Delacroix sought to achieve a deliberate and classical geometry. Delacroix' trip to Morocco in 1832 taught him much more about color than he had previously learned from his study of the works of Rubens and Gros. G. L.

39
*Greece on the Ruins of Missolonghi***

La Grèce sur les ruines de Missolonghi
Plate p. 287
Canvas; 213 × 142; s.l.l. *Eug. Delacroix*
Bordeaux, Musée des Beaux-Arts

First, one should restore to this celebrated painting the title that Delacroix gave it when it was shown at the Galerie Lebrun in 1826—"to benefit the Greeks." Boutard, the critic of the *Journal des Débats*, referred to the title in his review of 2 September 1826. Many years later, on the occasion of the exhibition of the painting in Bordeaux in 1851 and then again when it was acquired by the city of Bordeaux, it was called *La Grèce sur les ruines de Missolonghi*. This is what Delacroix called it in his correspondence with Dauzats in October 1851 when he referred to the sale price (2,500 francs), and again in a letter of thanks to the mayor on 31 March 1852 (the letter is preserved in the Bordeaux museum; see M. Sérullaz, 1963, p. 74). The word *"expirant"* was incorrectly added to the title at a later date and could confuse the interpretation of this *"allégorie"* (to use Delacroix's term for it in his letter of October 1851 to Dauzats). And yet André Michel, in his article about the centennial exhibition of 1900, made a point of saying that the painting represented *La Grèce encore debout sur les ruines de Missolonghi*. But elsewhere, the same author echoed the dictionary of Bellier and Auvray (1882). In its listing of the works shown at the Salon of 1827, the dictionary had replaced the catalog title for no. 299, *Scène de la guerre actuelle des Grecs et des Turcs* with the title *La Grèce sur les ruines de Missolonghi* (Bordeaux

museum). Following the dictionary, A. Michel thus attempted to affirm that the painting exhibited here was shown at the Salon of 1827-1828 along with the *Apothéose d'Homère*. But for our painting to have been at this Salon is quite impossible, since it was already on exhibit in London before the close of the Salon in March 1828. The Salon records, published by Lee Johnson in 1966 (p. 220), were quite precise in this regard: no. 299 measured only 96 × 121 (A. Robaut, 1885, no. 206; in 1966, in the collection of the late O. Reinhardt, Winterthur).

Delacroix referred to the *Greece...* of "the year 1827" in a list which he sent on 18 January 1836 to the critic Théophile Thoré. Nevertheless, one can be certain that the painting was executed in 1826, before Boutard's remarks could echo the public's very unenthusiastic reaction. A. Michel, in 1900, in citing Boutard, noted that "at the time everybody thought the author had gone completely astray." In effect, Boutard wrote: "One can see in it a talent competing in a strange way with the artist's systematic eccentricity and disorderly technique, exactly in the way that one may see glimmers of reason, sometimes even flashes of genius, lamentably pierce through in the talk of a madman." Even though Boutard recognized in the painting "the beautiful expression of a suffering incapable of tears," he went on to say, "It is of course a great pity that the creator of such a painting was not born 20 years sooner, in the time of the wise and knowing school of David."

About the genesis of the work, Delacroix provided us with no precise information, either in his correspondence or in his *Journal*. It seems clear, however, that he used the same model, Laura, who appears in the *Femme au perroquet* (1827, Lyon). Also, in the book of drawings preserved in the Louvre are several very free sketches which show a more theatrical conception of the subject. The drawing of fol. 12 v° has the word "découragement" above the weeping figure of Greece, shown with several dead at her feet. Other pages from the same sketchbook give further details: "the main figure helmeted—a 12-year-old child wearing a shirt" (fol. 86), "the patriarch on his knees, dying—devouring vultures and dogs—flaming debris thrown on the shore" (fol. 16; described by M. Sérullaz, 1963, no. 112). In the final composition, the foreground figures disappear, the figure of Greece holds herself more erect, her face expressing "both anguish and the will to live" (Sérullaz, *op. cit.*); she rests her knee on the fallen stones —from which a hand emerges—evoking the explosion in which, on 23 April 1826, the last members of the resistance died with their families. In the Greek War of Independence, which began in 1820, Missolonghi became sadly celebrated for the many sieges that took place there, in 1822, 1823, 1824 (the one in which Lord Byron died on 9 April), and finally 1825.

It is not surprising that Delacroix, who had already painted the *Massacres de Scio* (Salon of 1824, Louvre), should have chosen an episode connected with the illustrious memory of the poet, Byron, whose works Delacroix had been reading since 1824, and in which he found many subjects for his paintings. Delacroix' choice was that of a Romantic and was destined to be misunderstood in a time that preferred the narrative representation of events. The painting in fact remained in the artist's possession for 25 years, even though it was exhibited repeatedly. Delacroix deliberately chose as simple an allegory as possible: a Turkish soldier, proudly erect, haunting the ruins, and, turning her back on him, the young woman personifying Greece, ready to fight on in spite of the calamities of war. Delacroix's allegory becomes dramatic through an entirely new use (that is, in relation to Neo-Classicism) of color, which here becomes the real vehicle for expressing "the passions of the soul, the poor and suffering soul of modern man" (A. Michel). In the sketches, as in the final painting, there are elements which prepare the way for the later painting, *Liberty Leading the People* (No. 41).

One should emphasize that subjects touching on the Greek war of Independence were rare; the Salons of the Restoration included scarcely 20 such examples. The French government tried to observe strict neutrality. In addition to the works that Delacroix showed on many occasions, one can also cite paintings by artists like J.-D. Odevaere (*Lord Byron à Missolonghi,* Amsterdam, and the *Mort de Lord Byron,* Bruges) or by Pierre Roch Vigneron (*Prise de Missolonghi,* unfinished, Bagnères-de-Bigorre).

PROVENANCE

Acquired from the artist by the city of Bordeaux in February 1852, for the sum of 2,000 francs; INV. of the Bordeaux museum: INV. Anc. 439.

EXHIBITIONS

1826, Paris, Galerie Lebrun, h. c.; 1828, London, Hobday's Gallery of Modern Art; 1829, Paris, Musée Colbert, no. 8; 1830, Paris, *idem,* no. 90, then no. 195; 1851, Bordeaux, no. 142; 1900, Paris, Grand Palais, no. 214; 1921, Basel, no. 65; 1928, Paris, no. 6; 1930, Paris, no. 38, ill. album, p. 23; 1938, Amsterdam, no. 118; 1939, Belgrade; 1940-1942, San Francisco, no. 34; 1947, Bordeaux, no. 128; 1950, Bristol, no. 14; 1952, London, no. 11; 1953, Brussels, no. 85; 1961, Recklinghausen-Amsterdam, no. D. 91; 1963, Paris, no. 108, ill.; 1963-1964, Bern, no. 21; 1964, Bremen, no. 17, ill. p. 97; 1964, Bordeaux, no. 115, ill. 35; 1964-1965, Munich, no. 92, ill. p. 223; 1965, Moscow-Leningrad, no. 14; 1967, Montreal, no. 114; 1970, Ghent, Laren, no. 45; 1973, Paris, Atelier Delacroix, no cat.; 1974, London, no. S. 68, ill. 88.

REFERENCES

Boutard, in the *Journal des Débats,* 2 September 1826; P. Lacour and J. Delpit, mus. cat., 1855, pp. 37, 96, no. 106; L. de Pesquidoux, 1857, p. 130; L. Clément de Ris, 1860, p. 32; P. Lacour, J. Delpit and O. Gué, mus. cat., 1862, no. 120; L. Clément de Ris, 1872, p. 99; E. Vallet, mus. cat., 1881, no. 440; Th. Guédy, s.d., p. 103; A. Moreau, 1873, p. 199; A. Robaut, 1885, p. 61, no. 205; M. Tourneux, 1886, pp. 135-136; E. Vallet, mus. cat., 1894, p. 151, no. 497; A. Michel, 1900, pp. 290-292, ill. p. 191; P. Galibert, 1906, no. 22, ill. 22; D. Alaux, mus. cat., 1910, p. 75, no. 393; E. Moreau-Nélaton, 1916, v. I, p. 91, ill. 75; Ch. Saunier, 1925, p. 121, ill. p. 119; R. Escholier, v. I, 1926, pp. 213-214, ill. opp. p. 212, v. III, 1929, p. 173; L. Hourticq, 1930, ill. p. 23; Ch. Manciet, mus. cat., 1933, p. 65, no. 234, ill. p. 140; T. Ricaud, 1935, p. 64; A. Joubin, 1936, p. 355, ill. p. 349; A. Joubin, v. I, 1936, p. 407, v. III, 1937, pp. 84, 107, 112, v. IV, 1938, p. 59; T. Ricaud, 1938, pp. 9, 10, 15, 18, 19, 21; ill. opp. p. 16; L. Rudrauf, 1942, p. 40; J. Cassou, 1947, no. 8, ill.; J. Lassaigne, 1950, p. 11, ill. 13; J. Leymarie, 1962, p. 76; J. Vergnet-Ruiz and M. Laclotte, 1962, pp. 129, 233, ill. p. 127; Ph. Jullian, 1963, pp. 51, 88; R. Escholier, 1963, pp. 40, 64, 126, ill.

p. 41; R. Huyghe, 1963, pp. 178, 181, 183, 199, 282, 302, ill. V, p. 73, ill. 214 (detail); M. Sérullaz, 1963, no. 111, ill.; L. Johnson, 1964, p. 261; R. Huyghe, 1964, pp. 178, 181, 184, 199, 285, 302, ill. V, p. 73 and ill. 214 (detail); G. Martin-Méry, 1970, color cover ill.; M. Sérullaz, 1971, pp. 14, 86, ill. color p. 87; G. Martin-Méry, 1972, p. 48, ill. pp. 49-50; S. Tominaga, 1972, p. 127, no. 31 color ill. 31; M. Rheims, 1973, p. 236, ill. p. 237.

RELATED WORKS
Book of drawings by Delacroix; the first 16 pages comprise studies for this painting (Louvre, Cabinet des Dessins, R.F. 9145).
Oil sketch by Delacroix (A. Robaut, 1885, no. 206), in 1963 in O. Reinhardt Collection, Winterthur.
A copy by Odilon Redon (Paris, Ari Redon Collection).

G. L.

40
Christ in the Garden of Olives

"Le Christ au Jardin des Oliviers"
Plate p. 290
Canvas; 294 × 362
Salon of 1827-1828, no. 293
Paris, Église Saint-Paul-Saint-Louis

By January 1824, when Delacroix did his first sketch for this painting, he had already attracted attention at the Salon of 1822. His two earlier religious paintings were, however, not known to the public (see Biography above).

From his *Journal* of the spring of 1824, we know that Delacroix was working on the commission from the Prefect of the Seine. He did not find the task easy, and the watercolors show that Delacroix made important modifications in the composition. On 30 April, he wrote, "In my painting of Christ, the sad and severe angels heralding His death turn on Him their melancholy gaze," then on 3 May, "Imagining, as I did, my angels for the Prefect, those beautiful and mystical figures of women, one of them carrying her breasts on a platter." M. Sérullaz has rightly suggested that Delacroix used Zurburan's *Saint Agatha,* then in the Soult Collection (now in Montpellier). Interestingly enough, when the finished work appeared at the Salon of 1827-28, the critics made many references to the angels but apparently did not make any connection with the Spanish model. On 24 November 1827, the reporter of the *Journal de Paris* remarked that the group of "three angels, borne on a sort of mattress in the guise of a cloud, calls to mind, in more ways than one, English vignettes." A. Béraud took up the same idea: "Ought one not say that they are copied from some English vignette or engraving and are placed in the painting just as they were in the original?" But he went on to question the iconography: "But why three angels? The Scriptures mention only one. A history painter... should be faithful to history, all the more so when it is a question of an event which concerns our religious beliefs" (1827, p. 74).

Other critics, like L. V. (Louis Vitet) in *Le Globe* of 10 November 1827, approved of Delacroix's invention: "There is in these three figures an undefinable sort of poetry: there is real inspiration here. What M. Delacroix also does, and it brings new life to this worn subject, is to endow his angels with a character less southern than the Italian painters, yet without giving them the heavy and massive quality that most of the Flemish painters do: these three figures are almost Ossianic, or rather they are altogether heavenly." A. Jal was especially enthusiastic: "The group of three angels appearing to Jesus is delightful in expression, sentiment and style. A revelation is made to us here; it is the Christian heaven which opens up to us. What sorrow there is in this message of solace..." (1828, p. 114). Like most of the critics, Jal found that "the figure of Christ is less successful" *(ibid.).* Jal was less harsh than the *Journal de Paris* on 8 November 1827, which asked: "Is this really Christ himself? But this earthy, African color is more for a dead man than an immortal being" but he still did not like the flesh-tones. And he found further faults which made it impossible for him to accept the painting as "a masterpiece of Romanticism" (1828, p. 115). The anonymous author of the *Visite au musée du Louvre* explained that here Delacroix, in rejecting the academic mode, "was trying to show something real" and "thought that he could suddenly show on canvas all the coarseness of a subject; he painted nature not as Winckelmann and Lessing understood and prescribed it, but as the common people like to see it..." (1828, p. 15).

And yet, with the perspective of time, Charles Baudelaire saw the painting as an important stage in the career of the romantic artist whom he admired. In 1859, he defined the painting as follows: "One of the paintings of his youth, the *Christ in the Garden of Olives* ("My Father, if it be possible, let this chalice pass from me") exudes feminine tenderness and poetic fluidity" (ed. 1961, pp. 1048-1049).

PROVENANCE

Commissioned by the Comte de Chabrol, Prefect of the Seine, in early 1824; in 1827, the sum of 2,400 francs was paid (see J.-A. Grégoire, 1837, p. 42) and the painting placed in the Église Saint-Paul-Saint-Louis in Paris, where it decorated the left arm of the transept, next to Bra's two statues, *Saint Pierre* and *Saint Paul*.

EXHIBITIONS

1827-1828, Salon, no. 293; 1855, Paris, no. 2908; 1864, Paris, no. 13; 1878, Paris, Champ de Mars, no. 151; 1885, Paris, no. 25; 1930, Paris, no. 30, ill. album p. 17; 1963, Paris, no. 86, ill.

REFERENCES

Journal de Paris, 8 and 24 November 1827; L. V., in *Le Globe,* 10 November and 22 December 1827; *Courrier des Théâtres,* 25 November 1827, p. 3; E.-J. Delécluze, in *Journal des Débats:* 20 December 1827; A.-D. Vergnaud, 1827, pp. 9-10; A. Béraud, 1827, pp. 70-75, ill. 30; (Anon.), 1828, pp. 15-16; A. Jal, 1828, pp. 113-115; J.-A. Grégoire, 1837, pp. 42-43; P. Pétroz in *La Presse,* 5 June 1855; E. Gebauer, 1855, p. 33; A. Moreau, 1873, pp. 124, 168, 187, 220-221; A. Robaut and E. Chesneau, 1885, no. 176; M. Tourneux, 1886, pp. 47-54, 94-98; *Inventaire général des Richesses d'art de la France: Paris, monuments religieux,* 1901, v. III, p. 203; E. Moreau-Nélaton, 1916, v. I, pp. 77-78, 84, ill. 51; R. Escholier, 1926, v. I, pp. 170, 172, ill. p. 171; L. Hourticq, 1930, ill. p. 17; E. Delacroix, éd. 1932, v. I, pp. 44-45, 61, 89-91, v. II, pp. 321-322; A. Joubin, 1936, v. I, pp. 407, 426, v. II, p. 411, 1937, v. III, pp. 248-249, 252, 1938, v. V, pp. 194-195; L. Rudrauf, 1942, p. 173; R. Escholier, 1963, pp. 24, 33, 131, 183; M. Sérullaz, 1963, no. 89, ill.; R. Huyghe, 1963, pp. 20, 25, 103, 174, 185, 259; Ch. Baudelaire, ed. 1961, pp. 894, 898, 970, 1048-1049, 1123; L. Johnson, 1966, p. 220.

RELATED WORKS

Several watercolors by Delacroix; one, representing the figure of Christ alone (Louvre, Cabinet des Dessins, R.F. 23325), was etched by Villot around 1846 (see M. Sérullaz, 1963, nos. 90, 91, ill.).
Lithograph by Hippolyte Poterlet (published by A. Jal, 1828, opp. p. 113).
The theme was taken up again by Delacroix, notably in a pastel executed for Mme Roche in 1847 and in a canvas dating from 1851 (Amsterdam, Rijksmuseum).

G. L.

41
Liberty Leading the People

"Le 28 juillet: La Liberté guidant le peuple"
Plate p. 302 and cover (detail)
Canvas; 259 × 325; s.d.m.r. *Eug. Delacroix | 1830.*
Salon of 1831, no. 511
Paris, Musée du Louvre

The four decrees signed at Saint-Cloud on 25 July 1830 and published in *Le Moniteur* on the 26th suppressed the freedom of the press, dissolved the newly elected Chamber, reorganized the electoral system and increased the tax rate for the industrial and commercial bourgeoisie. The decrees also precipitated the fall of the government of Charles X, which in turn caused the outbreak of three days of revolution in Paris, the *"trois glorieuses,"* as they were called. The fighting began on Tuesday, 27 July, and reached its peak between the night of the 27th and the 28th. On Wednesday the 28th, the Marshal Marmont made a fruitless attempt to quash the people's assault around the Hôtel de Ville. By noon on the 29th, he had evacuated Paris, taking with him the loyal Royalist troops. After a brief period during which it was hoped that a new Republic might be formed, the Constitutional Monarchy was established.

The events of these few days inspired many, even some like Delacroix—if one is to believe Dumas—who had not participated directly. There were many artists who illustrated heroic, dramatic or sentimental episodes in the Revolution. For an exhibition arranged in September 1830 at Moyon's, rue de l'Université, as a benefit for widows and orphans, Delacroix did a drawing, the *Prise du pont de la Grève* (Cambridge, Mass., Fogg Art Museum), illustrating the heroic attack led by the young d'Arcole on the morning of 28 July. Then the artist continued to experiment with his allegorical figure of Liberty for the painting which he was preparing for the next Salon. Meanwhile, there opened on 14 October at the Musée du Luxembourg an exhibition to benefit the wounded of 27, 28 and 29 July 1830, and included among more than 300 works were 11 with subjects relating to the recent events. Delacroix wrote in a letter to his brother the general of 18 October 1830: "I have undertaken a modern subject, a barricade... and if I have not fought and won for my country at least I can paint for her..." (published by M. Sérullaz in Delacroix exh. cat., 1963, Paris, under no. 122, p. 49). On 6 December he told his friend Guillemardet, "I have finished, or very nearly finished, my painting" (A. Joubin, I, 1936, p. 262).

Delacroix exhibited the painting at the Salon of 1831, which included 23 paintings inspired by the Revolution of 1830. Delacroix' huge painting, which had been awaited with considerable anticipation, shocked the public and aroused diverse reactions among the critics. The most malicious among them, like A. Tardieu, would not accept the painting's realism. For him, the people presented "the repugnant appearance that vice and crime imprint on the sullied brows of those of like conviction" (1831, p. 44), and he accused the artist of "having found his models among the rabble rather than among the true people" (*ibid.*, p. 46). As for the figure of Liberty, she "is no more than a soiled and shameless woman of the streets" (*ibid.*, p. 44). The painting had, however, a few admirers who dis-

cussed it at length. Gustave Planche, a steady defender of the artist, pointed out that the painting was not suitably displayed during the first month, and asked whether it might be "understood by the public" if it could be better seen. He considered it "simply the most beautiful painting at the Salon; it is a work which should last" (1813, p. 111), and concluded, "Gros, Géricault and Delacroix, these are the three great names which our century will give to the history of painting." Jal, describing the painting at length, remarked: "There is in M. Delacroix' talent something which moves [and] surprises me; it is a new poetry, a vigorous expression of fresh and bold thoughts, a use of color which I might call cruel; a kind of deviltry, if you like, as in Hugo and Paganini..." (1831, p. 42). In Charles Lenormant's fine description of the painting, we find all the elements necessary to a good understanding of the subject:

He was not attempting to reproduce a barricade on any particular crossroads, in which case one might have expected him to account for each detail of the pavement or a forgotten bullet hole. An open scene, a cloud of smoke through which the towers of Notre-Dame are glimpsed in the distance —all evoke, in a general sense, the city where the great Revolution took place and dispel the need for all topographical explanation; the actors in the drama are the same ones whom we have seen everywhere and yet are not certain of having seen anywhere. The fighting is drawing to a close: a Swiss [and] a cuirassier, touching victims of a misunderstood honor, lie at the base of the smoking barricade.... But the blood of the assailants is mixed with the blood of the defeated.... Who then are the victors? Some children and at the center a young woman—strong, striking, dressed like the people, but startling in a strange light, made bizarre by the nudity of her shoulders, the cap that crowns her head, the standard that waves in her hands. This woman, whom many will think they have seen somewhere, so much is she a part of the time and place, this woman is none other than the Liberty of the people. Some may cry out against the apparition of this allegory; but I found her so alive, so real, so much a part of the subject which she poetically sums up, that I could not prevent myself from giving M. Delacroix his due (1833, pp. 195-197).

For a brief time the *Liberty* was in the Musée du Luxembourg, but was then completely ostracized under the July Monarchy. During the Second Republic,

Jeanron seems to had difficulty in getting the cooperation of Villot, who had once been Delacroix' friend (it has even been suggested that Villot is the young man in the tall hat; Ladoue proposed instead to identify this figure as Étienne Arago). For a long time, the Second Empire was reluctant to accept the painting and the Comte de Nieuwerkerke was horrified in 1855 at the idea of exhibiting a work which "represented Liberty in a red bonnet at the top of a barricade with French soldiers piled at the feet of the rabble rouser" (in a letter to M. Varcollier, 11 April 1855, Arch. Louvre, p. 30). Once the Emperor's authorization was obtained, the *Liberty* was favorably received. "But the official critic, Maxime du Camp, was instructed to make a savage attack, which weighed heavily on the painting and rendered it inoffensive" (H. Adhémar, 1954, p. 91). Finally, with the advent of the Commune and the Third Republic, the painting became once again an important work. It was at this time that it entered the Louvre.

With the exception of Delécluze, who in 1831 suggested Delacroix's relation to Jouvenet, 19th-century criticism paid little attention to Delacroix' technique. It is only in recent times that an interest in the sources for the painting has developed. S. Ringbom points out the influence of Pierre-Narcisse Guérin's teaching and sees in Delacroix the development of a neo-classical formula that was used by his teacher in *Iris and Morpheus* (No. 94) or *Aurore et Céphale*. J. Vergnet-Ruiz has suggested as a possible model Jean-Jacque Lebarbier's *Jeanne Hachette,* which was in Beauvais at the time (the painting was destroyed in 1940) and was also known through an engraving. With more certainty, one might point to a painting of the same sort as *Greece on the Ruins of Missolonghi* (No. 39) that resulted from the intense kind of experimentation that we see in the many preparatory sketches for the painting. For the *Liberty* exhibited here, Delacroix rejected a picturesque representation of a moment in the *"Journées de Juillet."* Inspired by the strong emotions that had been sparked by events, he created instead an allegory of Liberty, a work of universal significance, which disturbs or arouses according to the times.

PROVENANCE

Acquired for 3,000 francs by the Minister of the Interior after the Salon of 1831; exhibited at the Musée du Luxembourg in 1832, then taken down by order of Royer-Collard, Director of Fine Arts; in 1839, returned to the artist, thanks to Cavé, successor to Royer-Collard and friend of Delacroix, just at the moment in which it had been decided to dismantle and roll up the paintings inspired by the Revolution of 1830; in Frépillon in 1842, in the possession of Mme Riesener, a relative of the artist; in March 1848, after Delacroix had approached Garraud, temporary Director of Fine Arts, Jeanron wrote to the Minister of the Interior: "This beautiful thing, which has no destination, is still in the artist's studio... I suggest that you reclaim it and give it a place at the Luxembourg or elsewhere" (cited by A. Joubin, 1936, II, p. 345); in April 1848, Delacroix went to see Villot about the "destination of my painting of the *Barricades*" (*ibid,* p. 360; date corrected by H. Adhémar, 1954, p. 90): we know that nothing was done at this time, since Delacroix was able to offer the painting—on behalf of Alphonse Jame, friend of Charles Blanc, then Director of Fine Arts—for an exhibition in Lyon which never took place (cf. E. Delacroix, 1932, v. I, pp. 252-254). We also know that the work was handed over to the Administration of the National Museums at the beginning of 1849, since Jeanron, Director of the Museums wrote to Villot, Curator of Paintings: "I ask you to go to the Musée du Luxembourg to consider a way to hang M. Eug. Delacroix's painting which we have had here for some time. The public should no longer be deprived of this important painting" (Arch. Louvre, p. 30). On 28 May, Villot proposed hanging the painting "in the place of a Blondel and under an Aligny" (H. Adhémar, 1954, p. 91) and on 30 May, Jeanron again wrote to Villot: "I have arranged a meeting for four o'clock tomorrow with M. Naigeon in order to finalize the placement of M. Delacroix's *Liberté*. I hope you will agree to this request unless there is some major impediment" (Arch. Louvre, p. 30). We can thus conclude that the painting was exhibited at the Luxembourg for a few months starting on 31 May 1849, when Jeanron was still director (until 1850); the painting does not appear in any of the catalogs of the Musée du Luxembourg from this time, but the 1849 edition gives the state of the museum only on the eve of 1848, and the 1852 edition is too late. The painting was again put into storage and in 1855 Delacroix requested that it be loaned to the Exposition Universelle; the Comte de Nieuwerkerke arranged for the painting to be taken to the Tuileries (letter of 11 April 1855, Arch. Louvre, p. 30) to obtain the authorization of the Emperor; following the exhibition the painting was returned to storage until the arrival of Ph. de Chennevières as curator at the Musée du Luxembourg in 1861. The painting was exhibited at the Luxembourg until November 1874, then transferred to the Louvre and listed in the Inventory of Paintings as a gift of the Administration of Fine Arts (INV. no. R.F. 129).

EXHIBITIONS

1831, Salon, no. 511; 1855, Paris, no. 2926; 1864, Paris, no. 37; 1889, Paris, no. 258; 1930, Paris, no. 53, album ill. 29; 1948, Paris, no. 566; 1956, Warsaw, Moscow, Leningrad, no. 38, ill.; 1963, Paris, no. 122, ill.

REFERENCES

Le Courrier français, 2 May 1831; E.-J. Delécluze, in *Journal des Débats,* 7 May 1831; *Moniteur des Arts,* 9 May 1831; L.-P. (Peisse). in *Le National,* 30 May 1831; *Le Constitutionnel:* 4 June 1831; *L'Observateur aux Salons de 1831,* 1831, 3rd ed., p. 3, 9; G. Planche, 1831, pp. 107-111, ill. p. 106; A. Tardieu, 1831, pp. 44-46; V. Schoelcher, in *L'Artiste,* 1831, p. 226; *Journal des Artistes:* 1831, v. I, p. 433; mus.

cat., Luxembourg, 1832, no. 160 (supplement); H. Heine, 1833, pp. 299-302; Ch. Lenormant, 1833, pp. 27, 195-197; G. Planche, 1855, pp. 61-65; P. Petroz, in *La Presse,* 5 June 1855; Ch. Perrier, in *L'Artiste,* 10 June 1855, p. 174; E. About, 1855, p. 179; E. Gebauer, 1855, p. 35; M. du Camp, 1855, p. 95; E. de Mirecourt, 1856, p. 74; E. Chesneau, 1862, reed. 1864, p. 333; E. Chesneau, 1864, pp. 347-348; mus. cat. Luxembourg, 1863 (no. 56) to 1874 (no. 67); A. Cantaloube, 1864, pp. 25-26; *L'Artiste,* 11 October 1864, p. 149; A. Moreau, 1873, pp. 123, 142, 170, 190, 205; P. Petroz, 1875, pp. 48-49; Tauzia, mus. cat. Louvre, 1878, no. 755; A. Robaut and E. Chesneau, 1885, no. 326; Ph. de Chennevières, 1885, p. 35; M. Tourneux, 1886, pp. 54-55, 94-98; E. Morgau-Nélaton, 1916, v. I, pp. 113, 118-120, ill. 81; J. Meier-Graefe, 1922, ill. p. III; G. Brière, mus. cat., 1924, no. 209, ill.; R. Escholier, 1926, v. I, pp. 266-276, ill. opp. pp. 266, 268, 270 (details); H. Focillon, 1927, p. 218; P. Jamot, 1928, pp. 118-119; ill. XVIII; P. Jamot, 1929, 2nd part, p. 17, ill. 23 (detail) and 24; L. Hourticq, 1930, ill. p. 33 and 34 (details); E. Delacroix, 1932, v. I, pp. 252-254, 273; A. Joubin, 1936, pp. 345-360; A. Joubin, *B.S.H.A.F.,* 1936, pp. 135-136; A. Joubin, 1936, v. I, pp. 262, 282, 408, 426, v. II, pp. 345, 346, 360, 1937, v. III, p. 343; L. Rudrauf, 1937, v. II, pp. 500-505; A. Joubin, 1938, p. 64; R. Escholier, 1943, v. II, pp. 62, 64, ill. p. 65; P. Ladoué, 1948, p. 196; C. Aulanier, 1953, p. 59; H. Adhémar, 1954, pp. 83-92, ill.; G.-H. Hamilton, 1954, pp. 55-66; Ch. Sterling and H. Adhémar, mus. cat., 1959, no. 669, ill. 235; L. Johnson, 1963, pp. 38-39, ill. 19; Ph. Jullian, 1963, pp. 51, 69, 99-103, 105, 119, 126, 194; R. Escholier, 1963, pp. 19, 58, 62, 64, 66, 100, 126, 158, 160, 167, 183, ill. pp. 59, 60, 61 (details); R. Huyghe, 1963, pp. 21-26, 153, 154, 174, 181, ill. XII; M. Sérullaz, 1963, no. 124, ill.; P. Gaudibert, 1963, pp. 4-21; Th. Reff, 1964, p. 55; R. Houyoux et S. Sulzberger, 1964, pp. 183-184; A. Chastel, 1964, pp. 333-334; H. Lüdecke, 1965, pp. 6-18, ill. p. 7; L. Johnson, 1966, p. 220; S. Ringbom, 1968, pp. 270-271; H. Bessis, 1968, p. 196; H. Kogina, 1969, pp. 186-208, ill. p. 198, 199, 200; M. Laclotte, 1970, p. 51, color ill.; J. Vergnet-Ruiz, 1971, pp. 84-85, ill. p. 85; M. and A. Sérullaz, 1971, pp. 57-62, ill. p. 58; mus. cat., 1972, p. 128; T.-J. Clark, 1973, p. 126, 129, 140-141.

RELATED WORKS

Sketch painted by Delacroix (no. 142 in the Inventory after his death; cf. H. Bessis, 1968, p. 213).
Preparatory drawings in the Louvre, Cabinet des Dessins (R.F. 4522-4523, R.F. 9236-9237), in the Bremen Museum, in the Detroit Institute of Arts (the head of the figure of Liberty), and in a private collection (17 sheets published by M. and A. Sérullaz, 1971, pp. 57-62 with 19 ill.).
Woodcut signed by Porret and executed in collaboration with Tony Johannot (in G. Planche, 1831, p. 106); woodcut for posters and frontispiece of Louis Blanc's *Histoire de dix ans,* published in 1840; lithograph by A. Mouilleron, around 1848; etching by Émile-Frédéric Salmon. A copy by Paul Cézanne done in 1868 (cf. T. Reff, 1964, p. 555).

G. L.

Pierre-Maximilien Delafontaine

1774 Paris 1860

Descended from an unusual family of sculptors who worked in bronze, Pierre-Maximilien Delafontaine is not be confused (as in Vergnet-Ruiz and Laclotte, 1962, p. 233) with the neo-Dutch church painter, Pierre Delafontaine, who has a work in Laon. Delafontaine first turned to painting and studied in Jacques-Louis David's studio. He was to remain loyal to his teacher even through difficult political circumstances. When David was arrested in 1794, Delafontaine insisted on accompanying him to the prison door; he and 16 colleagues signed a document that was sent to the Convention demanding David's freedom. Delécluze often quotes this devoted student in his book on David and his school (1855), and Delafontaine's own manuscripts, donated to the Institute library in 1855, constitute one of the most precious sources about David's life and his entourage. They were utilized by L. Hautecœur in his biography on David (1954).

Delafontaine's first known paintings were exhibited at the Salon of 1798, where he presented three canvases: *Déluge* (Salon no. 106, signed and dated *An VI* [1798], praised by Landon in *Le Journal de Paris* 6 vendémiaire, year VII [September 27, 1798] and located in Gray; A. P. de Mirimonde, 1956, fig. 1, p. 31), the *Portrait of Andrieu* (No. 42) and a lost portrait of a woman (Salon no. 108).

At the Salon of 1799 (Salon no. 68) he exhibited the full-length portrait of Lenoir, signed and dated year VIII of the Republic. It was bequeathed to the Louvre in 1921 by Lenoir's descendants (R.F. 2304) and sent to the Château of Versailles shortly afterwards (A.-P. de Mirimonde, 1956, fig. 3).

In 1801, Delafontaine presented to the Salon a *"tableau de famille"* (Salon no. 8) and in 1802 *Jupiter endormi sur le mont Ida* (Salon no. 70). Both of these have been lost. From that time on he stopped sending works to the Salon, as this was the beginning of a difficult period for artists. He seems to have renounced painting and took over the direction of the family atelier. He became a well-known bronze caster and often collaborated with Jacob Desmalter, the cabinet-maker. But since most of Delafontaine's work was unsigned, it remains anonymous. However, Delafontaine is credited by Mirimonde with the gilded bronze ornaments of the tabernacle of the Chapelle de la Trinité, Fontainebleau and the bronze casts of *Aristée* and *l'Eurydice* from models by François Rude at Dijon. Delafontaine maintained contact with painting circles, however, since in 1832 his younger daughter, Louise-Amélie, married the neo-classical painter Merry-Joseph Blondel.

In 1840, he left his business to his son Auguste-Maximilien (who cast the doors of the Panthéon and the bronzes of the chapel in Dreux); he, in turn, left the family business to the painter's grandson, Henri-Maximilien.

Among the other known paintings by Delafontaine, we must mention a chef-d'œuvre in the style of David, a youthful *Autoportrait* in a white shirt, on permanent loan from the Musée des Arts Décoratifs, Paris, to Gray (A.-P. de Mirimonde, *ibid.* fig. 5). In Gray, there is also a good copy by Delafontaine of the left panel of Rubens' triptych *The Doubting Saint Thomas* (Antwerp), showing the burgomaster Rockox praying in the orant position (*ibid.*, fig. 4), a work that demonstrates the deep interest of David's followers in Rubens. A final important work is the *Portrait de Bichat* (s.d. 1799), which was rediscovered and donated by D. Wildenstein to Versailles (*Revue du Louvre*, 1973, p. 131, fig. 3).

The name of Pierre-Maximilien Delafontaine has remained a part of the history of painting through the many excellent works in his private collection repurchased by his family in Paris on 6 February 1861 and finally willed in 1932 to the Musée des Arts Décoratifs, Paris, and to the Gray Museum (a collection supplemented by numerous loans from the Musée des Arts Décoratifs). Included in this group are the well-known small landscape by Ingres illustrating the *Casino de Raphaël à Rome* (Paris, Musée des Arts Décoratifs), drawings by David, Granet and Nicolle, paintings by Blondel, Revoil and Turpin de Crissé—all of which assure the posterity of Delafontaine, a very modest but talented painter who deliberately remained in the background of the art scene of his time.

J. F.

42
Portrait of Andrieu

"Un Portrait d'homme patinant" also called *Le Patineur*.
Portrait du graveur en médailles Bertrand Andrieu
Plate p. 149
Canvas; 179 × 130; s.d.l.r. *P.M. Delafontaine.*/*1798*
Salon of 1798, no. 107
Paris, Hôtel de la Monnaie

In the Salon catalog, this picture was simply described as a man skating, which classified it more as a genre picture than as a portrait. But according to the family tradition of its donors, it in fact represents the medal engraver Bertrand Andrieu (1763 Bordeaux - Paris 1822). He was one of the leading medallists of the Revolutionary and Imperial periods; among his best-known creations were the medal struck for the anniversary of the taking of the Bastille and that for the birth of the Duc de Bordeaux. The charming naturalness of the model's posture—it is a portrait in action—does indeed imply friendship, or at least familiarity, between him and the painter. In fact, as Mirimonde points out, Andrieu had business connections with Delafontaine's father, Jean-Baptiste, who was a medal engraver and gilder (and, moreover, from 1787 on, spokesman for the association of founders, gilders and engravers); according to the *Mercure* of 23 October 1790, the sale of the medals cast by Andrieu in honor of the taking of the Bastille and the arrival of Louis XVI in Paris took place in his atelier.

Mirimonde rightly emphasizes the traditional character of this picture, very much within late 18th-century taste. Its charm, grace and the attractive, silky colors link it much more to the the works of Elisabeth Vigée-Lebrun or Henri-Pierre Danloux than to Delafontaine's teacher, David. The painting's theme (at this date, skaters were rarely painted alone and life-size), its concept as a genre portrait, the action, and the relationship between the figure and the landscape background, compare to the almost contemporary portrait of a skater by Sir Henry Raeburn (although, of course, neither influenced the other) in the Edinburgh National Gallery, or again to Gilbert Stuart's masterpiece in the National Gallery, Washington. Also to be noted is the admirable snow landscape in the background, which is almost as good as the best of César Van Loo.

Although obviously successful, this picture seems to have attracted little critical attention (there is nothing about it in the coll. Deloynes in the Bibliothèque Nationale, Paris). In the same Salon (no. 108), Delafontaine exhibited a *Portrait de Femme*, since lost; it is impossible to say whether this was a pendant to the present picture.

PROVENANCE
In the collection of Dr. Dewulf, a descendant of Andrieu; placed in the Musée de la Monnaie in February 1897 and donated in May 1897 by the subject's great-grandchildren, Mmes Charles Chappoteau-Dewulf and Aubrun-Dewulf, and M. Louis Chappoteau (see the correspondence exchanged in May and June 1897 between M. de Foville, then director of the Musée de la Monnaie, and M. L. Chappoteau, preserved at the Administration des Monnaies et Médailles, Paris).

EXHIBITION
1798, Salon, no. 107.

REFERENCES
(A. de Foville), anonymous note on the gift of the painting in the *Journal des Débats*, 28 June 1897; Ch. Saunier, 1913, p. 285 (regretting its exclusion from the exhibition *David et ses élèves*); A.-P. de Mirimonde, 1956, p. 33, ill. 2, p. 32.
J. F.

Hippolyte (called Paul) Delaroche

1797 Paris 1856

Although closely identified with the reign of Louis-Philippe, Delaroche first came to prominence toward the end of the Restoration. In 1816, he entered the École des Beaux-Arts and, planning on a career as a landscape painter, joined the studio of Louis-Étienne Watelet. In 1817, he competed unsuccessfully for the first Prix de Rome in landscape painting. Yet, history painting was his true calling. Entering Gros' studio in 1818, he made his debut four years later at the Salon with a *Christ descendu de la croix* (c. 1820, Chantilly), an awkward but ambitious work indebted to the Italian grand manner as well as late 18th century French classicism; *Joas dérobé au milieu des morts par Josabeth, sa tante* (1822; formerly in Troyes), a Guérin-like interpretation of an horrific theme from Racine's *Athalie* ; and *Une Tête d'étude*. These paintings were little noticed by the critics, but the first entered the collection of the Duchesse d'Orléans and the second was acquired by the government. Moving into the newly popular field of modern history, Delaroche showed at the Salon of 1824 a *Filippo Lippi devient amoureux de la religieuse qui lui servait de modèle* (1822; Dijon, Musée Magnin), a small and entertaining essay in the *style troubadour* ; *Saint Vincent de Paul prêchant... devant la cour de Louis XIII* (1823), a sober, journalistic picture commissioned by the Duchesse de Berry; and *Jeanne d'Arc malade est interrogée dans sa prison par le cardinal de Winchester* (1824; Paris, private collection). This is a large, imposing work in which Delaroche first achieved that combination of appealing sentimentality, historical accuracy and pictorial realism which would soon become all but synonymous with his name. The Salon critics praised these paintings, especially the latter two, for their captivating themes, winning sentiment and archaeological verisimilitude. Well aware of Delaroche's insistence on restraint and discipline, an insistence which seemed to contrast sharply with, say, Delacroix' taste for violence and startling effects, the reviewers likewise recognized in 1824 that Delaroche, if a romantic, was a romantic of a far more conservative and, to many, acceptable, order than a good number of his contemporaries. At the Salon of 1827-28, Delaroche showed six history paintings and several small portraits. The portraits were largely ignored. And the critics were not impressed with Delaroche's *Le jeune Caumont de La Force, sauvé par un marqueur du jeu de paume de Verdelet* (c. 1825; formerly in Konigsberg museum), and *Suite d'un duel* (c. 1826). But they responded warmly to his *Miss Macdonald* (c. 1825) and gave a great deal of attention to his *Prise du Trocadéro* (1827; Versailles), a notable State commission; *Mort du président Duranti* (1827; destroyed in 1871), another important State commission, in this case for the Louvre's Conseil d'État; and *Mort d'Élisabeth* (1828; Louvre). Delaroche was named to the Legion of Honor in 1828 and in the last years of the Restoration was offered several new official commissions. Of these, however, only two came to fruition, one for a portrait of the Duc d'Angoulême and the other for a portrait of the Prince de Carignan (both paintings, 1828; Versailles). At the Salon of 1831, Delaroche, while encountering his first implacable critic, Gustave Planche, nevertheless solidified his position as one of France's foremost artists. His *Cardinal de Richelieu* (1829; London, Wallace Collection) and *Cardinal Mazarin mourant* (1830; London, Wallace Collection) were greeted with extraordinary enthusiasm; his portrait of *Mademoiselle Sontag* (1830; destroyed in 1945) earned modest praise; *The Children of Edward IV* (No. 44) was a large success; and his *Cromwell et Charles Ier* (1831; Nîmes), if controversial, was recognized as a major offering by a major artist. And while it was obvious in 1831 that Delaroche did not fit the description of a true romantic, it had become no less clear that he was one of the leaders of the *juste milieu,* the newly-prominent middle current in French painting. Delaroche continued to exhibit at the Salon until 1837, meeting increasing critical resistance but scoring memorable public triumphs with his *Jane Grey* (1834; London, National Gallery), shown at the Salon of 1834, and *Duc de Guise assassiné au château de Blois* (1834; Chantilly), which appeared at the Salon of 1835. In 1841, Delaroche completed work at the École des Beaux-Arts on the *Hémicycle,* a large and scholarly statement on the history of art and one of the most revealing and influential monumental paintings of the period. In his post-Salon years, Delaroche also devoted much of his time to portraiture, religious painting and the tapping of new thematic and stylistic veins. After his death in 1856, though long out of the public light, he received the tribute of a major retrospective exhibition at the École des Beaux-Arts.

N. Z.

43
Portrait of the Marquis de Pastoret

Portrait du marquis de Pastoret
Plate p. 298
Canvas; 155 × 121; s.l.l. *P. Delaroche*
Inscribed upper right (now barely visible):
CLAUDE EMMANUEL JOSEPH PIERRE / MARQUIS DE PASTORET / CHANCELIER DE FRANCE /
TUTEUR DES ENFANS / DE FRANCE
Boston, Museum of Fine Arts, Susan Cornelia Warren Fund

Between the Revolutions of 1789 and 1830, Claude-Emmanuel-Joseph-Pierre Pastoret (1756-1840) played an active and prominent role in French political and intellectual life. In 1791, as *Procureur général syndic de la Seine,* he initiated the proposal which led to the transformation of Sainte-Geneviève into the Panthéon. Under Napoleon, he taught law at the Collège de France and philosophy at the Sorbonne. He was made a Count in 1808. During the Restoration, he became successively a Peer, a Marquis in 1817, a member of the French Academy, Minister of State and, in 1829, Chancellor of France. In Delaroche's portrait, which dates from 1829, Pastoret wears the black, purple and wine-red robes of the chancellor's office with the insignia of a Grand Officer of the Order of Saint-Esprit. The upper medal is the Saint Andrew's cross with the blue ribbon of a Knight of the Order of the Holy Ghost, and the lower medal is the large cross of the Legion of Honor with its red shoulder sash.

The portrait may demonstrate Delaroche's customary allegiance to reality, showing, for example, no attempt to improve on Pastoret's rugged and unattractive face, but otherwise it is an exceptionally fascinating and elaborate picture. Besides being painterly, it is characterized by a richness and profusion of silk, satin and lace, and would seem to be modeled on similar 17th and 18th-century court portraits. Delaroche was able to work in a variety of styles, and he doubtless believed that this was the most appropriate manner to represent a high official in the Bourbon government. In the late 1820s, Delaroche's art passed briefly through a phase of heightened drama and pictorial elaboration, a "romantic" phase to which the portrait of Pastoret belongs. He depicted Pastoret as an old, wise and astute man of recent nobility, thirsty for ambition, having served all the regimes, not long before as a *"progressiste"* and at that moment, *"ultra."* He exhibits a formality, a lambent eloquence and an unreadable expression, as Barras noted. He was described as having "a mind of a fox in a head of a calf" by Rabbe, combining the judgments of Mirabeau and Talleyrand (who added, "the calf dominates !"). But Pastoret profited from the extreme charm and lively intelligence of his wife, whose salon reputedly attracted many (see No. 34; concerning Pastoret, see F. Bassan, 1969, p. 7 ff., who recorded the correspondence of the Pastorets preserved in the Pierpont Morgan Library, New York, and who published amusing biographical and bibliographical details).

Although Delaroche never showed a major portrait at the Salon, probably to protect his reputation as a history painter, he did hope to exhibit this portrait at the first Salon after its completion (undated letter, Delaroche to the Marquis' son, Comte Amédée-David de Pastoret), but this became impossible or inadvisable when Pastoret refused allegiance to Louis-Philippe and was forced to retire from public life in 1830. In 1834, he became tutor to the royal family because of his relationship with Charles X.

The change in political climate might also explain why the Pastoret coat of arms, to be seen in the upper left in an oil sketch for the portrait (Bayonne), was removed from the final picture, and why a similar attempt was made to eliminate the inscription in the portrait's upper right-hand corner. Neither the coat of arms nor the inscription appear in Henriquel-Dupont's 1838 engraving of the portrait. In the David Daniels Collection (New York) is a highly finished, squared-for-transfer pencil drawing, which was certainly a Henriquel-Dupont study for the engraving. Delaroche apparently did not produce such preparatory drawings for his portraits. This drawing lacks both the coat of arms and inscription and has approximately the same measurements as the engraving. In a letter of 8 June 1830 to the Comte de Pastoret, Delaroche mentioned that Henriquel-Dupont wanted to make a small drawing of his father's portrait.

In contemporary letters to the Count, Delaroche also speaks of a history painting which the Pastorets had commissioned him to execute. We do not know the theme, but it was perhaps *Saint Georges terrassant le Dragon.* Delaroche had produced a small sculpted *modello* of this subject in anticipation of a painting he was going to do, and the Comte de Pastoret tried to arrange to have Delaroche supply a monumental version of the sculpture for placement along the Champs-Élysées. The project came to an end with the Revolution of 1830.

Delaroche was the third major artist to paint a member of the Pastoret family. David painted Mme Pastoret (No. 34) and Ingres, their son (No. 111). Degas acquired Ingres' portrait, and he is said to have also briefly owned the one by Delaroche (J.G., 1911, p. 47).

PROVENANCE
Collection of the Marquis de Pastoret; the Marquise du Plessis-Bellière (née de Pastoret) sale, 10-11 May 1897, no. 25, ill.; Pierre Decourcelle sale, 29-30 May 1911, no. 11, ill. (30,000 francs); to Boston Museum of Fine Arts (Picture Fund, 1911, 11.1449).

EXHIBITION
1900, Paris, Grand Palais, no. 230.

REFERENCES
H. Delaborde and J. Goddé, 1858, p. 25; R. Pinset and J. d'Auriac, 1884, p. 220, ill. p. 219; A. de Lostalot, 1892, p. 186, ill. p. 179; G. Larroumet, 1904, p. 125; H. Marcel [1905], p. 1130; *Correspondance de Paul Delaroche avec le comte de Pastoret, B.S.H.A.F.,* 1911, pp. 438-440; J. G., 1911, pp. 46-48, ill. p. 49; L. Rosenthal, 1914, p. 214, 225; mus. cat., 1921, p. 95, no. 244; F. Bassan, 1969, ill. 1 (after the engraving); W. Muir Whitehill, 1970, p. 311, ill. p. 312; A. Boime, 1971, p. 103, ill. 54.

RELATED WORKS
Sketch by Delaroche (Bayonne): portrait drawing of Pastoret père by J.-F. Heim (s.d. 1827; Louvre, Cabinet des Dessins; Guiffrey and Marcel, no. 4710).
Engraved by Henriquel-Dupont in 1838. Study for engraving in David Daniels Collection, New York (see above).

N. Z.

44
The Children of Edward IV

"Édouard V, roi mineur d'Angleterre, et Richard, duc d'York, son frère puîné" also called *Les Enfants d'Édouard*
Plate p. 301
Canvas; 181 × 215; s.d.l.l.: *Paul Delaroche. 1830*
Salon of 1831, no 522
Paris, Musée du Louvre

The infamous Tower of London provides the setting for the painting. The year is 1483, and in moments King Edward V and his brother, the Duke of York, will be smothered by men sent by the youngsters' ruthlessly ambitious uncle, the Duke of Gloucester, soon to be Richard III. At this point, while the Duke of York and family dog are alert to danger on the other side of the door, King Edward, ill and leaning on his brother's shoulder, remains lost in private thoughts. He sits on an elaborately carved wooden canopy bed. His brother cradles an illustrated prayer book in his lap. With this pictorial drama, Delaroche obviously hoped to stimulate great fear and pity to titillate the emotional palette of each and every Salon-goer. Just as important, however, he also wished to suggest historical truth and compelling, close-up realism. Thus, he labored conscientiously to discover the exact furnishings and costumes required for his subject. And if he painted his findings in a no less painstakingly photographic manner, he also placed his life-size protagonists in the foreground of his painting in a space that almost seems continuous with ours. In comparison with the *Portrait of Marquis de Pastoret* (No. 43), this cool and immaculately finished painting betrays little sign of brushwork or baroque rhetoric and confirms the end of Delaroche's "romantic" phase of the late 1820s.

At the Salon, the painting drew generally favorable reviews. Delécluze, typically, wrote: "This intriguing, very dramatic scene, was executed with much skill by M. Delaroche, and it is difficult not to experience strong emotion in regarding the painting, whose author drew upon all the resources of his talent in order to give it the conviction of a scene copied faithfully from life." Delaroche, he observed, conceived and executed his work in a manner "that would convince us that his work was made in the presence of the characters themselves and in the time in which they lived... the latest work marks the place in history of what is called the new school." The painting, he added, sheds more light on the classic/romantic issue than 20 volumes of criticism on the subject. Musset and Gros liked the picture, and Ingres considered it the best historical composition of the period. In *Lutèce,* Heine described the work as perhaps the most pleasing Delaroche had painted. And much later, Henry James would describe a youthful appreciation of the painting in *A Small Boy and Others:* "Yet, *Les Enfants d'Edouard* thrilled me to a different tune, and I couldn't doubt that the long-drawn face of the elder prince, sad and sure and sick, with his wide crimped side-locks of fair hair and his violet legs marked by the Garter and dangling from the bed, was a reconstitution of far-off history of the subtlest and most 'last word' modern or psychological kind. I had never heard of psychology in art or anywhere else—scarcely anyone then had; but I truly felt the nameless force at play." The painting inspired Casimir Delavigne's popular play *Les Enfants d'Edouard* (1833), which bore a dedication to Delaroche, and the picture's success prompted many other artists in France and abroad to treat the same theme (e.g., Hildebrandt, 1835; P. Miglioretti, 1869; J. E. Millais, 1878).

From the first, however, the painting also had its detractors. Speaking of Delaroche's penchant for inventing heads which were too melodramatic, Jal commented in his review of the Salon of 1831: "It is above all in the painting of the *Children of Edward IV* that I notice this fault; remarkable enough in the face of the Duke of York, it is all the more so in that of his elder brother." Of the new slickness which had taken control of Delaroche's art, he complained: "Could he not relinquish this care to render everything in the same way: curtains, bedframe, skin and velvet?" Planche was even harsher. "As for *Edward V,*" he wrote in his review of the Salon of 1831, "we must admit that the two heads lack life, that it is impossible to detect any blood under these violet complexions; everything is discouragingly new: furniture, clothing, the faces themselves are new and have never lived....

The great failing of M. Delaroche's picture is, in effect, to be so clean, to be so close to painting that aims at prettiness and neatness above all."

This was one of the many subjects Delaroche depicted from British history. It was familiar from Shakespeare's *Richard III* (Act IV, scene iii). But Delaroche, who wished to be thought of as a high-minded painter of documented history rather than as simply a book illustrator, did not give Shakespeare's play as his source in the Salon catalog; indeed, he gave no source at all. The subject had been treated by James Northcote (engraved 1791) for Boydell's Shakespeare Gallery and by Thomas Stothard (engraved 1795) for Bowyer's Historic Gallery. A version by Henri Decaisne was shown at the Salon of 1824. In 1830, C. R. Leslie painted a *Children of Edward IV Praying in the Tower*. Delaroche's subject concerns an instance of a rightful ruler challenged by a usurper. Delaroche often dealt with themes of this sort, so much so that Heine could justifiably describe him as "the court-painter to all decapitated sovereigns." Following the installation of Louis-Philippe, a usurper, the theme of usurpation took on fresh relevance in France; and when Delavigne's *Les Enfants d'Edouard* first opened at the Théâtre-Français, it was briefly closed down by worried government officials who saw in the Duke of Gloucester a reference to France's new king.

Delaroche's painting was not intended as an allusion to Louis-Philippe. Already in 1828, Delaroche had produced a small plaster model of the painting's two principals. The picture was finished before the July Revolution. And, soon after, it was acquired by the State for 6,000 francs. In 1831, Delaroche produced a small replica of the painting (London, Wallace Collection). In probably the same year he executed a small related lithograph, the *Dernière prière des enfants d'Edouard*.

Delaroche rarely returned to an old subject, but owing to a strange and painful twist of fate, he would make a significant exception here. In 1852, as an aging widower deeply concerned about the future of his own two young sons, he would discover personal application in this theme, and paint a *Dernière prière des enfants d'Édouard* (see Related Works).

PROVENANCE
Acquired by the Musées Royaux from the Salon of 1831 for 6,000 francs. Exhibited at the Musée de Luxembourg. Transferred to the Louvre in 1874 (INV. 3834).

EXHIBITIONS
1831, Salon, no. 522; 1857, Edinburgh, no. 247.

REFERENCES
[D.] *Journal des débats*, 7 May 1831; *Le Courrier français*, 10 May 1831; [D.] *Journal des Débats*, 12 May 1831; [L.P.] *Le National ;* 12 May 1831; F. Pillet, 1831, p. 968; M. Raoul 1831, p. 17; H. de Viel-Castel, 1831, v. I, p. 187; *L'Artiste*, 1831, v. I, p. 146; *L'Artiste*, v. I, p. 174; A. Jal, 1831, pp. 53, 125, 278-279; C.-P. Landon, 1831, pp. 17-18, ill. 8; G. Planche, 1831, pp. 40-43; Ch. Lenormant, 1833, v. I, pp. 27, 146-148; Saint-C., 1833, p. 213; H. Heine, 1855, p. 225; *ibid.*, 1857, p. 372; E. de la Bédollière, 1856, n.p.; E. de Mirecourt, 1856, pp. 31-32; A. de Calonne, 1857, pp. 499-502; L. Ulbach, 1857, p. 365; H. Delaborde and J. Goddé, 1858, pp. 8-9, 15, ill. 14; Ch. Perrier, 1863, pp. 63, 65-66; M.-C.-H., 1864, pp. 278-279; Ch. Blanc, 1865, v. III, pp. 9, 14, 18, ill. p. 1; H. Delaborde, 1870, p. 72; J. Tripier le Franc, 1880, pp. 510-511; J. Breton, 1889, pp. 86-87; L. Rosenthal, 1900, pp. 229, 290; G. Larroumet, 1904, pp. 125-126; H. Marcel, 1905, p. 113; A. Soubies, 1906, pp. 170, 172; H. Delaroche-Vernet, 1910, p. 517; H. James, 1913, p. 358; L. Rosenthal, 1914, pp. 212-215, L. Benoist, 1928, p. 92; S. Giraud, 1932, p. 357; L. Hautecœur, 1942, pp. 41, 54, ill. VII; Ch. Sterling and H. Adhémar, v. II, 1959, p. 18, no. 718, ill. 256; Fr. Saint-Pierre, 1970, p. 11, n. 1; G.B.A., 1971, January, p. 17, ill. 32.

RELATED WORKS
Replica (canvas; 44 × 52, s.d.l.l. *Paul de la Roche 1831*, London, Wallace Collection). Lithograph by Delaroche (1831 ?), *Dernière Prière des Enfants d'Édouard*. Engraved by Ambroise Tardien in C.-P. Landon, 1831, pl. 8. Another version painted by Delaroche, 1852, *Dernière prière des enfants d'Édouard* (location unknown; version in Moscow, Pushkin Museum).
Lithographed by L. Noël for *L'Artiste*, I, 1831, after p. 187. Engraved by H. Prudhomme. Two lithographs after the heads by A. Béranger. Engraved by A.-H. Cabasson and J. Quartley.

N. Z.

Pierre-Claude-François Delorme

1783 Paris 1859

A student of Girodet, he made his first appearance at the Salon of 1810 with *La mort d'Abel* (Montpellier), and continued to exhibit mostly paintings with mythological or religious subjects until 1851. From the State, he secured several commissions for paintings, among them the *Descente de Jésus-Christ dans les limbes* (1819, for the Cathedral of Notre-Dame in Paris), *Cephalus and Aurora* (No. 45), *Hector adressant des reproches à Pâris* (1824, Amiens), *Sapho et Phaon* (1833, for the city of Elbeuf), *La Vierge* (1834, Compiègne) and *Fondation du Collège Royal par François Ier* (1847, Versailles). He executed numerous decorations in churches, for example, in Saint-Eustache, the cupola of Notre-Dame-de-Lorette.

Few references can be cited in connection with this artist, except for accounts in dictionaries and above all Châlon-d'Argé's study, which appeared in *La Revue des Beaux-Arts* in 1859 (pp. 466-468). The cited works reveal the influence of Davidian esthetics, but transformed by the imagination of a style which aims only for effect.

J. L.

45
*Cephalus and Aurora**

"*Céphale enlevé par l'Aurore*"
Plate p. 265
Canvas; 220 × 158; s.d.l.r. *Delorme/1822*
Salon of 1822, no. 325
Sens, Musée Municipal

The Salon catalog gave an incorrect title to this painting. Actually, the scene represents Aurora carrying off Cephalus. Cephalus, son of Mercury and Herse and husband of Procris, was carried off in his sleep by Aurora. Aurora grew furious at Cephalus' indifference to her, and finally let him return to his wife, whom he ardently loved. On his return, Procris gave him a gift of a javelin and a hunting dog. Later, Cephalus, while out hunting, threw his javelin at what he thought was a wild beast; it turned out that he had killed Procris who had hidden herself behind a bush, in order to spy on him, because her jealousy had been aroused. Recognizing his grave mistake, Cephalus killed himself in despair.

The work was fairly well received at the Salon. The editor of the *Journal de Paris* judged that "M. Delorme has gracefully depicted the ravishment of Cephalus." Doubtlessly remembering Anne-Louis Girodet's painting exhibited in 1810, and his other works in Compiègne, C.P. Landon wrote that, "the painting, with its pleasing composition and correct drawing, displays refinement in its characters, a careful technique, and recalls the sensibility of the school in which Delorme's talent had been formed; one can tell that the artist was a student of Girodet." In a parenthetical but nonetheless relevant way, Landon expressed some regret "that the figures in the painting were not done on a larger scale, because they seem to be close to miniatures, not producing much of an impression since the painting itself is so large;

the artist's palette is rather bright and the sharpness of the contours borders on dryness."

To these remarks, which reflect the bias of a partisan of the neo-classical doctrine, should be added this observation, by Delécluze, who affirmed an evident analogy with a painting of Joseph-Ferdinand Lancrenon (today in Montargis): "Despite the merits of "*Céphale enlevé par l'Amour*" [sic], M. Delorme is able to perceive the effect that satisfactorily rendered forms can produce on us when a subject does not speak to our passions or depend on popular beliefs. What I say about Delorme's picture applies equally well to Lancrenon's *Borée enlevant Orytie*."

Thus—and it was important to emphasize it at the time of this exhibition—the components of academic art were defined from that moment on; subjects which aroused less and less interest were done in a school-like technique, that is, indifferent to the subject being treated. Foreseeing the growing popularity of this type of painting, Landon wrote in his *Salon of 1822:* "The paintings *à effet* would soon be the only ones to gain any sort of success. A thoughtfully composed piece, sustained by an ample palette, yet simple and natural, would be nothing more than an insipid work to the eyes of a number of connoisseurs whose appreciation could lead any artist to fame and fortune."

PROVENANCE
Acquired by the Musées Royaux at the Salon of 1822 for

3,000 francs; exhibited at the Musée du Luxembourg until its transfer to the Louvre in March-April 1854; placed in Sens in 1872 (INV. L 3840 and INV. 3856).

EXHIBITION
1822, Salon, no. 325.

REFERENCES
(Anon.) in *Journal de Paris*, 25 April 1822; E.-J. Delécluze, 18 May 1822, p. 734; (Anon.) in *Journal de Paris*, 22 June 1822; C.-P. Landon, v. II, 1822, p. 71, pl. 18; mus. cat. Luxembourg, 1822, no. 30; mus. cat., Luxembourg, 1852,

no. 47; Châlons d'Argé, 1859, v. X, p. 467; H. Vollmer, 1913, p. 34; mus. cat. 1891, no. 83.

RELATED WORKS
Four drawings for this painting are in Sens: one study for the entire painting, three studies of details.
A replica by the artist (canvas; 130 × 98), s.d. *Delorme 1851*, bequeathed by J.-B. Renaud in 1875 to the Troyes museum; today it is in the town hall of Troyes. (These facts were kindly communicated to us by M. Sainte-Marie, curator of the museum in Troyes.)

J. L.

Jean-Louis Demarne (or de Marne)

1752 ? Brussels - Batignolles (near Paris) 1829

According to the Comte de Nape (see below), the date of Demarne's baptism is 1754 and the date of 1744, which is often given, is clearly erroneous. He came to Paris at the age of 12. He learned painting in the studio of Gabriel Briard, a history painter who had taught Élisabeth Vigée-Lebrun. At first, Demarne wanted to enter this field and remained with Briard for eight years. But after failing to receive the Prix de Rome in 1772 and 1774 (competing against David and also César Van Loo and Jean-Joseph-Xavier Bidauld), he concentrated on genre and landscape. Here he was indirectly influenced by the very skillful and witty pastiches by Dutch painters, ranging from Claes Berchem to Karel Dujardin and Adriaen Van de Velde and from Albert Cuyp to the Van Ostades, which were in great vogue at that time. According to the Comte de Nape, a great admirer of Demarne (see Ch. Blanc, 1865, p. 6) and the editor of a valuable small biography of Demarne, based on the artist's own testimony, published in the *Annales encyclopédiques* of 1817, Demarne is supposed to have returned rather soon to Flanders during a youthful escapade. Moreover, the Dujardin works in the famous Randon de Boisset Collection, which he might have seen either before or in 1777, the date this collection was sold, could have made a vivid impression on him. Finally, De Nape noted that before being accepted at the Academy in 1783 on Pierre-Antoine Demachy's recommendation (the same year that Demarne received the King's permission to go to Brussels for three months; is it possible that he then went as far as Salm in the Vosges ?), Demarne travel-

ed for the first time to Switzerland with several artists, among them, Taunay, to make studies from nature. Furthermore, he resided there a second time for two years (De Nape did not specify if this was after 1784). These trips to Switzerland are important, for they testify to the great curiosity for the exotic and picturesque which Switzerland attracted by virtue of its Alps, its simple and rustic customs, its having been Rousseau's homeland and Voltaire's refuge. Demarne's sojourns there influenced his choice of subject matter. "Swiss"—Alpine or Valaisian—sites are illustrated by many paintings exhibited at the Salons of 1783 (a view of Lac Morat among others), 1785 (a landscape with Mont Blanc and several *Vues de Suisse*), 1787 (for example, a *Vue du Valais* with the waterfall of Pisse-Vache), 1789, and so on.

At the same time, Demarne must have sojourned alternately or simultaneously with his Swiss trips to the Franche-Comté, especially to Saint-Hippolyte; this supposition alone explains the extremely precise names for a number of his Salon paintings. He may also have visited the coast of Normandy, since his wife was a native of Dieppe and several of his paintings carry Norman titles (Salons of 1796; 1799; 1812; 1814, with the exact title, *Bords de la mer aux environs de Bayeux*, 1817; 1824). But if the work *Sables de la Normandie* (Salon of 1796; see Watelin, 1962, no. 385, fig. 47) preserves a rather accurate memory of the cliffs of Normandy (near Étretat rather than Caen), how many other seacoasts enlivened with fishermen, fishmongers or idlers are merely neo-Dutch adaptations of Adriaen

Van de Velde, Peeter Bout, Jacob Van Ruisdael or Philip Wouwerman? Demarne especially liked this ambiguity between the painting of his time and that of the past, and it is rather senseless to deny, as Watelin tried, Demarne's attraction to Dutch art in order to make him appear as a minor French painter of daily life. The same is true of his evocations of Parisian suburbs (thus, he often painted *routes* with implied fantasy, for example, in the Salon of 1812, a *Monument gothique au bord de la grande route de Saint-Denis...*) or of the Fontainebleau forest (Salon of 1824). It is certain, however, that although enjoying the use of a studio at the Sorbonne, as did many artists during the Empire, he often withdrew during the summer to his property of Bois-Ramard, near Charny, in the region of Auxerre. During the Revolution, Demarne was conspicuous in his non-involvement; but for lack of better resources, he had to work for a long time for the Sèvres and Dihl manufacturies. This activity does not account for his polished, clean, somewhat porcelain-like workmanship, which actually derives from his admiration for the Dutch. Although often commended by official recognition, at the Salons (1795, 1799, 1806, 1819), by Vivant Denon (commission for the Tuileries in 1806, the *Entrevue de Napoléon et de Pie VII à Fontainebleau*; the landscape is by Alexandre-Hyacinthe Dunouy, Salon of 1808, now at Versailles), nominated as a member of the Antwerp Academy in 1808, Demarne did not care for honors and never wanted to advance beyond the position of *agréé* at the Academy. He was unable, unwilling or lacking in conviction to seek support for a post at the Institute in 1815. Antoine-Jean Gros, Pierre-Narcisse Guérin and later Charles Meynier were elected instead. Still, he was fervently sought after by his admirers: Didot; De Nape, who had 31 Demarnes in his collection in 1817; Camus; M. de Joubert, the treasurer of the States of Languedoc who had himself painted by David; the Marquis de Cossé; Gallot de l'Ormerie (a gentleman of the Comte d'Artois); Dubois de Lyon; Prince Giustiniani; Prince Youssoupoff, admirer of Demarne as were many other Russian aristocrats; and Carle Vernet, who had seven pictures in his own collection. Empress Josephine owned four Demarnes, among them a *Foire* with a gothic monument which, because of its Leuchtenberg provenance, might tally with the painting sold in Paris (25-26 March 1936, no. 82, ill.) and the *Procession de la Fête-Dieu*, undoubtedly the painting sold on 3 May 1913 (no. 33, ill.). Yet, it was not until the late date of 1815 that Demarne's work was included in the Royal Museum with the *Route* and *Foire* of the Salon of 1814 (Louvre). His unexpected award of the Order of the Legion of Honor at the Salon of 1828 had the appearance of a tardy redress in his twilight years.

Demarne's production was considerable, "The protean Demarne produces paintings as La Fontaine produces fables," the connoisseur Henry wrote in the Didot sale catalog in 1817. Watelin estimated his œuvre at a thousand paintings or so, but they are difficult to trace through innumerable sales (Watelin's book is insufficient in his respect, in comparison with Hofstede de Groot's method for tracing the Dutch 17th-century masters). From 1783 to 1827, Demarne was strongly represented at the Salons, but the laconic titles, arbitrary pedigrees, even the abundance of works by this very "commercial" painter make the identification of the pictures presented to the Salons very hazardous. Before 1783 and concurrently with the great official Salons held at the Louvre, Demarne had also participated in the Exposition de la Jeunesse with a painting in the style of Dujardin (a significant choice), and in the Exposition de la Correspondance in 1783 with two *Vues des Pays-Bas avec figures et animaux*; in 1785, with a *Vue de forge à Salm* (an interesting subject to note); in 1786, with a *Paysage* from the collection of Basan, the period's most famous Dutch print dealer, who had reissued many copper plates by Rembrandt (another sensible contact for Demarne). From the first Salons, his repertory was fixed and scarcely varied: rustic subjects where figures and animals are intermingled in imitation of the Italianized Dutch style of Berchem and Potter, just like Delerive's work in Switzerland or Nicolas-Henri Fassin's, Jean-Baptiste Berré's or Balthasar Paul Ommeganck's work in Flanders.

The *Foires* that were to be so important for his reputation appeared as early as the Salon of 1785. The *Marines* began in 1796. Demarne was so fond of his *Routes*—rectilinear perspectives like those in the period of Louis-Jacques-Mandé Daguerre, Charles-Marie Bouton and the painters of *Panoramas,* which appeared from the Salon of 1799—that he ran the risk of dryness. As in Taunay's work, *grand genre* appeared, at times (*Retour de Cincinnatus,* Salons of 1795 and 1796; *Intérieur de Sparte,* Salon of 1795), or *troubadours* (*Naissance d'Henri IV,* Salon of 1789; *Le Petit Poucet,* Salon of 1798, sold in Paris, Hôtel Drouot, 26 March 1962, no. 9, ill.; *Le Départ du Chevalier,* sold in Paris, Hôtel Drouot, 14 June 1954, no. 11, ill., etc.). But in Demarne, the *troubadour gothique* is interrupted by the insertion of fantastic monuments with no connection to the depicted scene. There are also purely decorative, historically retrospective exercices, such as the *Corps de garde* in the style of Anthony Palamedes (London, Wallace Collection) or the *Marines* in the style of Peeter Bout (at Dieppe, for example). The workmanship is simultaneously lively and neat, alert and detailed; the foliage well-executed, the skies clean and clear; there are many affinities with Jacques-François Swebach and Michel-Hamon Duplessis. All of Demarne's contemporaries have observed that his late paintings (i.e. after 1820) seemed dry because of their mechanical execution; he enjoyed his best years during the Revolution and Empire.

Watelin pointed out that Demarne frequently collaborated with other painters, as did the 17th-century Dutch artists. Thus, figures by Demarne can be found in landscapes by Bruandet, Lantara, Georges Michel, Turpin de Crissé (No. 177), Lallemand, Van der Burch, César Van Loo, Senave, Victor Bertin; other collaborators included the artists Millin du Perreux (*Vue du Château de Pau après la bataille de Coutras*, coll. Empress Josephine, today at Arenenberg), Swebach, Xavier Leprince, Boilly (who definitely portrayed Demarne in the *Atelier d'Isabey,* in the Louvre, beside his friends Taunay, Swebach and Carle Vernet). Students like Jean-François Robert (the painter of the Sèvres manufactory) Dieterle, Caroline Demarne (the artist's daughter) and the animal painter Georges Diebolt copied the master. And Demarne's influence was extensive on such lesser followers as Pierre-Alexandre Pau de Saint-Martin, Budelot, Langlacé and Demay. Finally, Demarne's innumerable engravings (among his own engravers, the prolific Devisnes must be cited) and drawings (an important collection of drawings has recently appeared in Paris at Prouté, cat. 52, Fall 1970) must be mentioned.

Demarne's work is well-represented in French museums. Watelin's list included, in Paris: Louvre, Petit Palais, Musée Marmottan, as well as Besançon, Versailles, Aix, Amiens, Bordeaux, Châteauroux, Cherbourg, Dieppe, Dijon (four, not three), Dôle, Dunkerque, Grenoble (*Saltimbanques,* Salon of 1824), La Fère, Lyon, Montpellier (six, not three), Orléans, Quimper (among others, the portrait of Caroline Demarne). Additional museums mentioned by Vergnet-Ruiz and Laclotte are: Chaalis, Gray, Le Havre, Rouen, Toulouse, Valenciennes and Valence. To be noted in passing is the beautiful drawing of a road at Boulogne-Billancourt. In museums outside France, Demarne can be found especially in Brussels, Amsterdam, London (Wallace Coll.), Turin, Basel, Washington, D.C., and especially in Russia (perhaps because Demarne's sister married and lived in "Red Russia" or Ruthenia). Even during Demarne's lifetime, such Russian admirers as Demidoff or Youssoupoff were enchanted by his beautifully executed anecdotal paintings, to the extent that after 1815 Demarne painted especially "Russian" subjects (the *Foire de Makarieff,* for example, in the famous Demidoff Collection, sold in Paris, 15 June 1945; Watelin, fig. 34). To be noted are the Demarnes in the Hermitage (cf. on this subject V. Berezina, 1972, figs. pp. 63, 65, especially an astonishing and large *Gué*), ten Demarnes in the Youssoupoff Collection, many of which are now in the Moscow museum (five in the catalog of 1961), those of Tsarskoe-Selo, etc. Even the artist's contemporaries, with Gabet in the forefront (1831, p. 199), deplored the fact that so many beautiful paintings of the master were leaving France for Russia.

J. F.

46
Hay Pitchers' Lunch

"Un goûter de faneurs dans une prairie"
Plate p. 227
Canvas; 29 × 44
Salon of 1814, no. 286
Cherbourg, Musée Thomas-Henry

Bellier and Auvray's dictionary is the first to identify the Cherbourg *Hay Pitchers' Lunch* with the painting of the same subject displayed in the Salon of 1814.

Clément de Ris had suggested it but unfortunately assigned to it the date of 1804. This indication by Bellier and Auvray represents an important reference which is not cited again, either by the museum catalogs or even Watelin, author of the only monograph on the artist.   But it seems quite possible, more so in any case than Watelin's proposal (made without critical discussion) to identify the painting from the Salon of 1814 with a *Collation champêtre* sold in Paris in 1958 (Galerie Charpentier, 2 June 1958, ill., and Watelin, no. 614, fig. 52).   In the latter painting, the hay pitchers' tools are hardly visible and the scene takes place at the edge of a stream: the Salon catalog speaks explicitly of a meadow.   This type of subject is evidently connected with numerous memories of Switzerland, Franche-Comté or the Vosges Mountains as the Salon catalogs or old sales catalogs demonstrate: Salon of 1785, *Une foire de Franche-Comté*, *Ruines du Château de Bermont,* in Franche-Comté and especially a *Vue des environs de Saint-Hippolyte en Franche-Comté: on aperçoit dans le lointain l'entrée de la caverne appelée le château de de la Roche ;* Salon of 1787, *Une foire de Franche-Comté ;* Salon of 1796, *Vue prise dans les Vosges ;* Salon of 1806, *Intérieur d'une ferme de Franche-Comté ;* Salon of 1817, a *Foire de Franche-Comté* and a *Vue de Franche-Comté ;* Salon of 1824, *Une forge, vue prise dans les Vosges près d'Épinal.*   Certainly none of these landscapes were based on the observation of nature or done for their own sake (Demarne was too fond of small, active figures and first and foremost a passionate lover of rustic and "Flemish" genre).   Nevertheless, they display a freshness of vision, an undisputed feel for nature to which the background testifies (a landscape of the Jura Mountains, actually including the cavern of Saint-Hippolyte in the background ?) and a calm, pure and insistent luminosity that is very effective.   Never did Demarne show more markedly than in these pictures his desire to be a landscapist and his capability in that mode.   The anecdotal is clearly constrained by the calmness, the almost total absence of animals, the minimum of description (remarkable for Demarne, who was generally fond of busy and animated compositions) and a joyous green nature bathed in a crystalline light, as in works by Karel Dujardin, Gerrit Berckheyde or Adriaen Van de Velde.   The result is that Demarne can complete with these painters, as well as with Jean-Joseph-Xavier Bidauld and Jean-Victor Bertin, the painter of the Ile-de-France; or the outstanding painting by Turpin de Crissé in the Musée Marmottan (No. 177), with its same coarse freshness and direct vision, a picture in fact in which Demarne painted the figures.

Without slipping into the obligatory Dutch pastoral pastiche, he was able to remain "modern" and local (here the region of Franche-Comté ?).   The immediate result can be ascertained in comparing the *Hay Pitchers' Lunch* with a painting by Demarne of the same subject, sold in London (Sotheby's, 14 November 1973, ill.).   Entitled *Groupe de paysans buvant*, it depicts a group of peasants seated on a meadow in the shade of a tree; cows and horses dot the scene in the free and decorative style of Berchem or Adriaen Van de Velde.   The soft and conventional lighting; the mountains, distant, vague and unidentifiable; the thistles in the foreground— all are in the manner of Abraham-Jansz Begeyn or Marseus van Schrieck, an arrangement of motifs selected and combined in one stroke.   In contrast, the quality of the Cherbourg painting seems so outstanding that attributing it to Demarne would be difficult were it not for the characteristic and exceedingly witty presence of the distinct, playful little figures, carefully modeled, everywhere engaged in the light jokes characteristic of 18th-century taste and quite close to those of Nicolas-Antoine Taunay and Jean-Baptiste Mallet.

PROVENANCE

Comte de Nape Collection, 1817 (not De Narp, 1820, as stated by Watelin who, moreover, does not list his sources); but, in Millin's *Annales encyclopédiques*, published in 1817, 31 paintings by Demarne in De Nape's collection ar edescribed following an anonymous review on Demarne, undoubtedly written by Comte de Nape. The Cherbourg painting appears on pp. 68-69 (v. I): "*Faneurs*... width 16 *pouces ;* height 10 1/2 *pouces*." The great significance of these documents of 1817 did not escape P.L. (Paul Lacroix), who republished them in his *Revue universelle des Arts* in 1865 (pp. 269-299), a basic reference which was reissued by A. Wauters in his useful account of Demarne in the (Belgian) *Bibliographie nationale*, v. 13, 1894, cols. 768-772, but not included by Watelin.   Comte de Nape was one of Demarne's most zealous promoters; his biographical account of the artist is incredibly hyperbolic, reflecting in its praise the immense popularity of Demarne at the beginning of the 19th century: "M. Demarne is to his art what Voltaire is to literature" (1817, p. 44; 1865, p. 282).
Henry probably acquired his painting from the congenial De Nape himself; the 1817 description clearly appears to be a text written for publicity; but as part of his role as an art expert, Henry could have bought it in a sale.
Donation by Thomas Henry.   Thomas Henry (1766 Cherbourg - Paris 1836), art expert for the Royal Museums, dealer in paintings and excellent art connoisseur, gave to his hometown museum from 1831 to 1835 (the opening date of the institution) 183 paintings, as well as two from his own hand; these constitute the core of the Cherbourg museum. The special value of this collection, enriched by the work of other good and even great painters, is that it includes a large number of works by minor French and Flemish masters from the end of the 18th century and the beginning of the 19th, collected by Henry at the time they were painted and thus with well-established attributions.   These include

works by Berré, Verboeckhoven, Ommeganck, Swebach, Mallet, Richard, Boilly, Bouhot, Vallin, Taunay, Bertin, Bidauld, César Van Loo, Rioult, Révoil, Lecomte, Garneray. The documentary value of a collection that so well represents the taste of the period 1800-20 is immeasurable. It must be mentioned that Thomas Henry offered Cherbourg two other small paintings by Demarne. His particular taste for this painter is at least established by the fact that five of the Demarnes exhibited in the Salon of 1804 belonged to him, and in the posthumous sale of his collection in 1836 there was still another Demarne (Watelin, 1962, no. 313: *"Les petits amusements"*).

EXHIBITIONS
1814, Salon, no. 286; 1962, Sceaux, no. 193; 1971, Paris, no. 981, ill. p. 17.

REFERENCES
Nape, 1817, pp. 68-69; *ibid.*, 1865, p. 294, no. 24 (numbers

added by P. Lacroix); mus. cat. 1835, 1912, no. 104 (to entitled *"Le déjeuner des faneurs"*); L. Clément de Ris, 1865, p. 207 (Salon de 1804 instead of 1814, certainly, a printer's error),; Bellier and Auvray, v. II, 1885, p. 405; J. Watelin, 1962, no. 616, pp. 143, 199, ill. 17.

RELATED WORKS
Paris, sale of 21 March 1828; according to Watelin, a painting of the same subject with somewhat different dimensions; 24 × 32. Were there really two different paintings or rather a slight error of measurement or printing?
Paris, Camus sale, 20 January 1831; Watelin mentions this sale afterwards without any explanation. Is this the same painting or a different copy, or even the Cherbourg painting bought by Henry. The pedigrees were too summarily indicated by Watelin to be believable or useful.

J. F.

Jean-Baptiste-François Desoria

1758 Paris - Cambrai 1832

A student of Jean-Bernard Restout, he exhibited at the Salon from 1791 to 1822. He went to Italy at the end of the 1780s, taught painting at the secondary schools of Évreux, Rouen and Metz, and in the year of his death was named director of the Academy of Cambrai to replace Jean-François Ducis.

Few biographical details are known about Desoria.

We know that he exhibited portraits: *Ch. L.F. Letourneur,* Salon of 1798 (Versailles); *Portrait d'Homme,* 1804 (Rouen); *Fauchard de Grandmesnil dans le rôle d'Harpagon,* Salon of 1817 (Paris, Musée de la Comédie-Française); and that he did history paintings of mediocre quality: *Achille délivrant Iphigénie,* Salon of 1798 (Bayeux); *Pierre Corneille dans son cabinet,* Salon of 1819 (Rouen).   J. V.

47
Portrait of Élisabeth Dunoyer

Madame Élisabeth Dunoyer
Plate p. 146
Canvas; 130 × 98; s.d.l.l. *Desoria/1797. an V*
The Art Institute of Chicago

The portrait of the sister of Marshal Brune is probably an exception in the work of Desoria, which is often of mediocre quality. The Davidianism of the painting is striking because of its similarity to David's *Portrait de Madame Hamelin* (Washington, National Gallery) and especially his *Portrait de Madame de Ver-*

ninac of 1799 (Louvre). The pose is the same in both pictures, although the model is depicted before a monochromatic background; in the painting in Chicago, the model is placed in front of a landscape. In any case, the *Portrait of Élisabeth Dunoyer* should be considered as the direct source of David's *Madame de Verninac*.

PROVENANCE
Collection of Jacques Doucet, Paris; acquired in 1939 by
The Art Institute of Chicago, Simeon B. Williams Fund
(INV. 39.533).

EXHIBITIONS
1942, San Francisco, no. 23; 1950, Detroit, no. 6, pl. 13.

REFERENCE
Mus. cat., 1968, p. 126.

RELATED WORKS
A preparatory drawing with slight differences in the Art
Institute of Chicago (INV. 60-855; pen, charcoal and white
highlights, 16.3 × 12.9).   J. V.

Eugène-François-Marie-Joseph Devéria

1805 Paris - Pau 1865

Eugène Devéria's training was supervised by his older brother, Achille (1800-1857), with whom his art and life were closely associated until 1838, when Eugène left Paris for Avignon. He also studied under Girodet and Lethière, but he quickly rejected the classicizing traditions of David in favor of a style that depended heavily upon the painting of Venice and of Rubens and in favor of subjects culled mainly from national history and picturesque genre. He made his debut at the Salon of 1824, and rose rapidly to prominence at the next Salon (1827), with the *Naissance de Henri IV* (Louvre; replica, Pau; sketches, Montpellier and Quimper), an enormous picture whose opulent color, agitated composition and historical pageantry were considered a triumphant manifesto of the new romantic painting exemplified at the same Salon by Louis Boulanger's *Supplice de Mazeppa,* Eugène Delacroix's *Mort de Sardanapale,* and Edouard Delaroche's *Mort de la reine Élisabeth.* On the basis of the success of this work, which was even copied by Richard Bonington, Devéria was considered to be the successor of Veronese himself, and the leader of an anti-classical current that had its social counterpart in the salons held at the home (Rue de l'Ouest) of Eugène and his brother where, in addition to artists (Delacroix, Boulanger, David d'Angers), literary figures and musicians (Hugo, Dumas, Vigny, Musset, Gautier, Liszt) also met.

Under Louis-Philippe, Devéria's early fame soon earned him official commissions for Versailles *(Serment du roi à la chambre des Députés, le 9 août 1830,* sketch at Salon of 1831; and such military scenes as the *Bataille de Marseille, le 4 octobre 1793,* Salon of 1838) and for a ceiling in the Louvre *(Puget présentant le groupe de Milon de Crotone à Louis XIV,* 1832), which was criticized for its historical innacuracies. His reputation, however, rapidly declined, although he continued to receive commissions, especially for religious paintings, of which the most important are the badly damaged frescoes in the Notre-Dame des Dôms, Avignon, begun in 1838, after Devéria left Paris. Despite personal misfortunes (failing health, the destruction of his home by a flood of the Rhône in 1840), he was able to perpetuate until the end of his life the kind of style and subject with which he had made his reputation in 1827. Thus, his early interest in narratives from late medieval and renaissance history and literature continued to mark his Salon entries from 1831 (*La mort de Jeanne d'Arc,* Angers) and 1847 (*La Mort de Jane Seymour le lendemain de la naissance d'Édouard VI,* Valence) to 1859 (*Une scène de l'Henri VIII de Shakespeare,* Le Havre) and 1861 (*Réception de Christophe Colomb par Ferdinand et Isabelle,* Clermont-Ferrand), all paintings which repeat closely the formulas of the *Naissance de Henri IV.* Devéria's particular interest in British history, characteristic of the 1825, may have been kept alive during his later career by his frequent sojourns (three between 1849 and 1854) in England and Scotland, where his uncle (a convert, like him, to Protestantism) was living.

In addition to these ambitious history paintings, Devéria constantly produced a wide range of more modest works, including many genre scenes. He was especially attracted to the documentation of colorful costumes other than those necessary for the accuracy of his history paintings. These small studies—paintings, watercolors, drawings, prints—ranging from those after elegant Parisian women in romantic costumes of the 1820s to the picturesque record of the folkloric costumes found in the Pyrénées and in Pau, where he settled in 1841. During a visit to Paris in 1845, he was even inspired, like Delacroix, by the American Indians presented in person and in paintings by the American artist George Catlin at the Galerie Indienne and made six drawings of them in native costume. He was also a prolific portraitist, often painting his friends and immediate family with an intimacy and warmth characteristic of much romantic portrai-ture of his generation (*Portrait d'Eugène et Achille Devéria*, 1836, Versailles; *Portrait de Céleste Devéria*, 1837, Pau).

R. R.

48
*Young Women Asleep**

Jeunes femmes assises
Plate p.291
Canvas; 33 × 41; s.d.l.l. *E. Devéria/1827*
Paris, Musée du Louvre

Young Women Asleep serves as model for the intimate genre scenes of which Devéria was so fond, even as early as this period (cf. *Femmes et enfants,* 1825, Béziers). This painting evokes the Romanticism that had penetrated life and customs by this time and is representative of a style related to illustration. The artist was probably inspired by the models used by his older brother, Achille, under whose direction he was working at the time. Moreover, an engraving by Achille, dated 8 October 1827, depicts a young woman similar to the sleeping woman in the foreground, and who represents Céleste Motte (the lithographer's daughter), whom Achille later married (cf. the portrait by Eugène Devéria recently acquired by the Pau museum).

PROVENANCE
In the Viefville Collection; bequest of Mlle Viefville in 1961 (INV. R.F. 1961-15).

REFERENCE
Mus. cat., 1972, p. 141.

RELATED WORK
A watercolor sketch was sold in Paris, Palais Galliera, 6-7 December 1965, no. 22.

J. L.

Martin Drolling

1752 Oberhergheim, near Colmar - Paris 1817

Trained by studying 17th-century Dutch masters, Drolling specialized in portraiture and genre painting. He and Louis-Léopold Boilly are the best examples of that intimate, bourgeois art which appeared quite early in total contrast to the historical and neo-classical school of David and his pupils (Drolling exhibited from 1793 on). Even when Drolling applied himself to historical subjects, he treated them like a bourgeois scene: a detailed study of the objects takes precedence over the story: for example, *Une jeune femme* [Queen Hortense] *portant secours à une famille qui a éprouvé des malheurs* (Caen). His neat and careful style is directly inherited from the Dutch genre scenes, as are his portraits, where he used a Gérard Dou device of placing the characters in a window frame: for instance, *Portrait de sa fille Adéone* (Strasbourg). While Drolling may be compared with Boilly, he is sometimes more obscure and his themes more banal; he also has affinities with certain German, Dutch or Scandinavian painters (W. Bendz, J. Jelgerhuis, G.F. Kersting, C.G. Carus) who were also interested in scenes from domestic life and painted them with the same precise care.

J. V.

49
Self-Portrait*

Portrait de l'artiste par lui-même
Plate p. 122
Panel; 75 × 54
Orléans, Musée des Beaux-Arts

In 1785, Drolling married his second wife, Louise-Élisabeth Belot, who became the mother of his three children, Marius, Louise-Adéone and the painter Michel-Martin Drolling. The Musée d'Orléans, in addition to this *Self-Portrait,* possesses an important series of portraits of the Belot family; the *Portrait de Madame Drolling* was acquired in 1905; the portraits of *Michel Belot,* father-in-law of the artist, and of *Mademoiselle Belot,* his sister-in-law, were bequeathed in 1872. Since the *Portrait de Michel Belot* is signed and dated 1791, it is probable that the *Self-Portrait* exhibited here dates from the same period. To be noted in this rather monumental picture is the artist's aristocratic pose and the absence of the palette and brushes, which custom-arily accompany all portraits of painters. This unusual omission must be explained by the fact that this is an intimate work, destined for the artist's immediate family.

PROVENANCE
Collection of the Belot family, coming from the painter's second wife; acquired by the museum in 1901.

EXHIBITIONS
1933, Paris, no. 24; 1952-1953, Hamburg and Munich, no. 17; 1973, Pau, p. 30.

REFERENCES
P. Ratouis de Limay, 1920, p. 100; P. Vitry, 1922, p. 17, ill. p. 43; J. Pruvost-Auzas, 1958, ill.; D. Ojalvo, 1969, ill. p. 12.

J. V.

50
Interior of a Dining Room

Intérieur d'une salle à manger
Plate p. 250
Canvas; 64 × 81; s.d.l.l. *Drolling 1816*
Salon of 1817, no. 254
Paris, Private Collection

Designed as a pair, these two works have been separated since 1817, and are brought together here for the first time. They are perfect examples of Drolling's penchant and great gift for trompe-l'œil, for which he was admired. "The two pictures by M. Drolling, which must be paired, are a model of perfection in the imitation of inanimate nature; the space has depth, the furniture stands out, all the objects fall into place distinctly and without confusion; the illusion caused by these pictures is not diminished by lengthy contemplation; the more the eye studies them, the more it is deceived; each of these *Interiors* creates the effect of panorama" (M..., 1817, p. 170). L. Eitner (1955,

51
Interior of a Kitchen*

Intérieur d'une cuisine
Plate p. 249
Canvas; 65 × 81; s.d.l.l. *Drolling pt 1815*
Salon of 1817, no. 253
Paris, Musée du Louvre

p. 283) compares the Louvre *Interior* with certain works of Cochereau, but also with Caspar David Friedrich's *Woman at her Window* (Berlin, Nationalgalerie). However, while in Friedrich's work there is always an underlying and often hidden symbolism, to quote H. Borsch-Supan's analysis, Drolling concerns himself only with reality of detail in an objective manner: "This jewel ravishes the eye; one can almost pick up the pots. Each brick on the floor could practically be counted" (Champfleury, 1847, p. 34). Drolling's sense of detail leads him to be compared with Boilly who, in fact, made two copies of the pictures exhibited here, which were in the Boilly sale on 31 January 1845, no. 32.

No. 50

PROVENANCE

In the collection of the Duchesse de Berry, included in her sale in Paris on 22 February 1836, no. 46; subsequently in the collections of Delessert, Baron R. Hottinguer, Vernes and De Margerie.

EXHIBITIONS

1817, Salon, no. 254; 1923, Paris, no. 154.

REFERENCES

M..., 1817, pp. 168-170; C.-P. Landon, 1817, p. 95; T., 1817, p. 486; Filhol and J. Lavallée, v. XI, 1828, pp. 4-6; Ch. Gabet, 1831, p. 224; A. Jal, 1867, p. 506; Bellier and Auvray, v. I, 1882, p. 447; P. Marmottan, 1886, p. 259; C. Mauclair, 1923, ill. p. 268.

RELATED WORKS

Engraved by Philibert-Louis Debucourt, together with its pendant, *Interior of a Kitchen* (No. 51). Engraved by Leroy and by Piringer.

No. 51

PROVENANCE

Acquired in 1817 by the Musée of Michel-Martin Drolling, the artist's son, for the sum of 4,000 francs (Archives des Musées Nationaux, AA 13, p. 116, 6 September 1817 Arch. Nat. O³ 1395 and 1398), (INV. 4097).

EXHIBITIONS

1817, Salon, no. 253; 1948, Strasbourg, suppl.; 1968-1969, Paris, no. 140.

REFERENCES

M..., 1817, pp. 168-170; *Journal de Paris,* 9 May 1817; C.-P. Landon, 1817, p. 95; T., 1817, p. 486; E. Delécluze, 1825, 1948, re-ed., p. 277; Filhol and J. Lavallée, v. XI, 1828, pp. 4-6, ill. 63; Ch. Gabet, 1831, p. 224; Champfleury, 1844, p. 212; Ch. Baudelaire, 1845, see *idem,* 1961, pp. 328 and 848; Champfleury, 1847, pp. 33-34; F. Villot, mus. cat., 1855, no. 186; A. Jal, 1867, p. 508; Bellier and Auvray, v. I, 1882, p. 447; P. Marmottan, 1886, p. 259; F. Benoit, 1897, p. 436; Thieme and Becker, v. IX, 1913, p. 570; G. Brière, mus. cat., 1924, no. 261; L. Eitner, 1955, p. 283, ill. 1; Ch. Sterling and H. Adhémar, mus. cat., v. II, 1959, no. 787, pl. 277; R. Lindon, 1961, pp. 371, 372, ill. 2; mus. cat., 1972, p. 145; G. and J. Lacambre, 1973, pp. 45-46, pl. opp. p. 56.

RELATED WORKS

A preparatory drawing, with numerous variations, in the Louvre, Cabinet des Dessins (INV. R.F. 34.523).
Engraved by Coupé in Filhol (Filhol and J. Lavallée, XI, 1828, fig. 63). Engraved by Philibert-Louis Debucourt with its pendant, *Interior of a Dining-Room* (No. 50); engraved by Leroy, Piringer and Roemhild.
A sketched copy is in the Wallraf-Richartzmuseum, Cologne (28 × 33; see mus. cat. 1973, p. 36, no. 2461). A finished copy, with some variations (especially is in the floor) in Saint Gall (65 × 81).

J. V.

Jean-Germain Drouais

1763 Paris - Rome 1788

After studying under his father, the portraitist François-Hubert Drouais, Jean-Germain entered the atelier of Nicolas-Guy Brenet, and then, around 1780, worked with David, who soon showed an almost paternal affection for him, calling him "the first in time, and perhaps, alas !, the first in everything" (D. and G. Wildenstein, 1973, no. 1368, p. 157). In 1782, he presented his first work, the *Retour du fils prodigue* (Paris, église Saint-Roch) and after failing in 1783 with his *Résurrection du fils de la veuve de Naïm,* recently acquired by the Le Mans museum, he won the Grand Prix de Rome with his *Christ et la Cananéenne* (Louvre) in the following year (along with Louis Gauffier); his painting was saluted as being worthy of Le Sueur and Poussin. This first Grand Prix was such a great triumph for the artist that C.-P. Landon wrote: "He astonished the entire Academy. Never had a student presented to the contest a work of such powerful conception and execution; and the most fervent wish that his teachers expressed was that such a prodigious talent could be sustained to the same degree of perfection. The enthusiasm that it generated was universal" (1832, I, p. 75). Shortly afterwards, he left for Rome in the company of J.-B. Wicar and David, with whom he had formed a lasting friendship: "I [David] decided to accompany him to Italy, for the sake of my art as well as for him. I could no longer do without him; I myself profited from giving him lessons, and the questions he addressed to me will be life-long lessons" (E. Delécluze, 1855, p. 250).

Arriving in Rome when Louis Lagrenée the Elder was director of the French Academy, David finished his preparations and began to execute his *Serment des Horaces* (Louvre). According to J.-L.-J. David (1880, pp. 26-27), he was helped by Drouais, who is supposed to have painted the arm of the third brother and the yellow garment of Sabina. Returning to Paris the following year, David left Drouais in Rome and the latter kept up a correspondance with him, which included many requests for advice.

In Rome, Drouais painted *Marius at Minturnae* (No. 52), *Philoctète à Lemnos,* 1788 (Chartres), and another *Résurrection du fils de la veuve de Naïm,* 1788 (Aix). Exhausted by work and ill with smallpox, Drouais died in Rome on 13 February 1788; thus, one of the most, if not the most, gifted Davidians passed away. In David's view, he could even have become his master's rival: "He alone could trouble my sleep" (Miette de Villars, 1850, p. 86).

Jean-Germain was part of the arising severe neo-classic current which grew out of the tradition of Poussin. His calm and noble compositions, as well as his precise drawing made him, along with Jean-François Peyron, the best representative of neo-Poussinism in the 1780s. In the *Résurrection du fils de la veuve de Naïm* his occasionally acidic colors are close to Poussin's color in the *Aveugles de Jéricho* (Louvre). Drouais' death and the fact that Peyron stopped exhibiting, in effect, at the Salon of 1791; removed two lights of the new school, leaving David alone as the uncontested master of French Neo-Classicism.

J. V.

52
Marius at Minturnae

Marius prisonnier à Minturnes
Plate p. 78 and color pl. p. 18
Canvas; 271 × 365
Paris, Musée du Louvre

The subject is taken from Plutarch's *Life of Marius*. After defeating the Cimbrians, Marius came into conflict with the Roman Senate; in 89 A.D., following the victory of Sylla, he took refuge in the marshes of Minturnae, in the Campagna (a drawing of this subject attributed to Pierre-Narcisse Guérin is in Bayonne, Musée Bonnat). He was captured, tried, condemned to death and a Cimbrian soldier was sent to kill him. Marius asked him: "Fellow, darest thou kill Gaius Marius?" and the Cimbrian soldier fled, crying, "I will never be able to kill Marius." This subject was revived in 1791 in a tragedy by M.-A.-V. Arnault, who depicted the scene as follows:

The Cimbrian: Cimbrian, Gauls, Teutons, slaughtered by his hand, dear, lamentable Spirits, now you will be avenged! Let us hurry.
Marius (awaking): Who comes to me?
The Cimbrian: Death.
Marius: What are you?
The Cimbrian: Tremble!
Cimbrian, I avenge Rome and the Cimbrians together.
Think of the sea of blood shed by your arm; Think of...

Marius: Will you, Cimbrian, dare to slaughter Marius"?
The Cimbrian: What a voice! what a look and what a terrifying appearance!
What arm places an invincible object before mine?
Fear has overtaken my bewildered senses.
I will never be able to kill Marius (he drops the weapon with which he is armed).

Let us note that Peyron had decided to do a *Marius at Minturnae* in 1783 and that this subject was subsequently painted by Gautherot (Salon of 1796, no. 188), by Gros (exh. cat., 1936, Paris, no. 7), by Fabre (Montpellier, Musée Fabre; INV. 837-1-400 and 401), by Lethière (Musée Fabre; INV. 837-1-850), and by Gamelin (Carcassonne, INV. 892-52-381).

Drouais arrived in Rome on 7 October 1784, and David on the 8th. The latter immediately set to work completeing the *Serment des Horaces,* which he sent to the Salon of 1785; he was then 38 years old. As for Drouais, he began his *Marius at Minturnae* which he completed in the summer of 1786; he was then 23 years old.

Seven drawings presently exist for this painting;

they permit us to follow its genesis very easily. The first of these drawings, in Lille (INV. 2483), differs significantly from the final composition, especially in the poses of Marius and the Cimbrian, as well as in the details of the bed and helmet. We should note, however, that Marius is depicted with a nude torso, as in the Louvre picture. This study precedes two general drawings which are pratically identical: one in the same museum (H. Pluchart, mus. cat., 1889, no. 1322), the other in Lyon, Musée des Arts Décoratifs. They present the final stage of the painting, with a few variations in the Cimbrian soldier's drapery, which is flung back, and in the table depicted at the right, which is set in both cases on lion paws. We should also mention that Marius is dressed in a tunic. A study in Besançon reproduces exactly this pose of the Cimbrian soldier. Another drawing in Lille (H. Pluchart, op. cit., 1889, no. 1323) indicates the final positions of the Cimbrian soldier and Marius (still dressed in a tunic), as well as the form of the table; an inscription by David above the figure of Marius, "Change nothing, it's good" proves, if it were necessary, the specific influence of the master on his pupil. We can therefore conclude that at the end of 1785, which was the time of David's return to Paris, the placement of the figures and the choice of practically all the details had already been made. This drawing probably slightly preceded another in Lille (H. Pluchart, op. cit., 1889, no. 1324), which is squared; it indicates measurements and presents the final stage, except, as always, for the figure of Marius, dressed in a cuirass. A drawing at the École des Beaux-Arts repeats the figure of the Cimbrian soldier, with more detail in the scabbard, making it perfectly identical to the figure in the Louvre's picture. At this point, a painted sketch (?) could be mentioned, which should in no case be confused with the two studies cited below. In fact, a letter from Louis Lagrenée the Elder to d'Angiviller of 3 May 1786 notes: "I have seen the sketch of this painting, which promises a very fine work. It represents *Marius qui dit au soldat: "Oses-tu bien tuer Marius?"* (A. Lecoy de La Marche, 1872, p. 413).

In any case, the painting was completed in August 1786 and was exhibited at Palazzo Mancini, and Lagrenée wrote: "Never before has such a chorus of praise been heard at either the Royal Academy or Palazzo Mancini; his painting is superb " (*Correspondance des Directeurs...*, ed. 1906, XV, p. 96, 23 August 1786). On 11 October, the painting was sent to Paris and favorably judged in a report of the Academy on 24 August 1787. Finally, to be noted is its subsequent exhibition at the house of Mme Drouais, the painter's mother, where, according to David himself, "People could not stop admiring it; they were forced to place guards at his mother's door to prevent a disturbance" (D. and G. Wildenstein, 1973, p. 158, no. 1368).

A comparison with David's *Serment des Horaces* (canvas; 330 × 425) becomes essential: first of all, in the ambitious format of the two paintings, then in the subjects demonstrating exceptional character traits: in the *Horaces,* patriotic self-denial, in the *Marius,* the reaction of an enemy (the Cimbrian soldier) facing the force of character of his conqueror, on whom he has the opportunity to wreak vengeance.

From a more formal point of view, we should note that, except for the initial sketch in Lille (INV. 2483), all the other known drawings present the figure of Marius in the same manner, seated, with the right arm extended. The influence of David is obvious in this noble gesture, which recalls the stance of the three Horatii and of the elder Horatius. Also noteworthy is the accentuated profile of Marius' head, perhaps inspired by an antique medal, which echoes the virile heads in the *Serment des Horaces.* But, whereas David adopts a light tone of delicate color in his picture, especially in the feminine group at the right, Drouais presents a somber composition, brightened only by the striking red of the drapery covering Marius, which might recall the red of the elder Horatius' mantle.

This comparison between the two painters was chiefly made by their contemporaries; both of them were, at that time, placed on an equal level; Drouais' death was to remove one of the few artists who could have rivaled David.

It is unnecessary to mention all the citations concerning *Marius at Minturnae*; nearly all are summarized by the lines that Chaussard devoted to the painting: "Admirable are the boldness of the composition, the good taste and the skill of the drawing, the realism and harmony of the color in general, especially the powerful and fine expression of the head of Marius and the brillant effect of this principal figure, which, in forcefully attracting the viewer's attention, seems to be the focus of the light that illuminates this composition" (1808, pp. 341-342).

Also noteworthy are two letters from Pierre-Paul Prud'hon to his friend Fauconnier, addressed from Rome, probably in 1786-1787, in which he severely condemned Drouais' work: "M. Drouais is the most distinguished, he follows the manner of M. David, in avoiding everything that might fascinate and dazzle the eyes of those who lack fine and delicate sensitivity. The violent desire to cause an uproar and the ambition for glory and applause are the guides they prefer; but my friend, ambition is often a bad guide, it disturbs the tranquility of the soul necessary to work soundly and accurately. A degree of affectation, a certain enjoyment taken in creating rather than in things created, and the pleasure to be gained if one succeeds, attract the genius more readily and incite the ambitious urge. M. Drouais combines all that I first said above with a great facility in painting, and he lacks, as do the others, all that I said subsequently" (see C. Clément, 1870, pp. 154-155).

The difficult character of Drouais, who avoided everyone except David, is well-known; yet Prud'hon's criticisms sound strangely partial, even petty. They are the only comments that categorically condemn Drouais' *Marius at Minturnae ;* we prefer to conclude with the phrase of Delécluze, who was more skillful in judging what is one of the masterpieces of French Neo-Classicism: "In comparing the material execution of Drouais' picture with that of the *Horaces,* one finds so little difference; the superiority of the master manifests itself especially in the boldness of the attitudes and the grandeur of the design. This precocity in the practice of painting is undoubtedly a remarkable thing, and it explains the extraordinary admiration which Drouais' *Marius* generated in Paris" (1855, p. 251).

PROVENANCE
Painted in 1786; collection of Mme Drouais, the artist's mother; offered to the museum in 1795; acquired by the Louvre in 1816 from Mlle Marie-Jeanne Doré, the artist's aunt (INV. 4143). (See Arch. Nat. O³ 1390, 25 September 1815; 3, 8, 18 January 1816, 12, 20, 26 February 1816).

EXHIBITIONS
August 1786, exhibited at Palazzo Mancini, Rome, on Saint Louis' day (see Arch. Nat. O³ 1390, 29 August 1786; A. Lecoy de la Marche, 1872, p. 413); 1788, exhibited at the home of Mme Drouais, the painter's mother (see E. Vigée-Lebrun, 1869, v. I, p. 154; Arch. Nat. O³ 1390, 18 January 1816; D. and G. Wildenstein, 1973, p. 158, no. 1368).

REFERENCES
Correspondance des Directeurs..., ed. 1906, v. XV, p. 89 (3 May 1786), p. 92 (5 June 1786), p. 96 (23 August 1786), pp. 112-113 (11 October 1786), p. 124 (24 August 1787), p. 368; *Procès-Verbaux,* ed. 1889, v. IX, p. 334 (27 January 1787); T.-C. Bruun-Neergaard, 1801, pp. 102-103; C.-P. Landon, 1803, v. V, ill. 70, pp. 147-148; J.-D. Fiorillo, 1805, v. III, pp. 466-467; J.-B. Suard, 1806, p. 278; P.-M. Gault de Saint-Germain, 1808, p. 262; P.-J.-B. Chaussard, 1808, pp. 341-342; Filhol and J. Lavallée, v. XI, 1828, pp. 1-3, ill. 37; C.-P. Lan-

don, 1832, v. I, ill. 35, pp. 79-80; E. Miel, 1836, p. 58; E. Delécluze, 1855, pp. 249-251; F. Villot, mus. cat., 1855, no. 189; A. de Montaiglon, 1857-1858, pp. 164, 168-170; F. de Villars, 1859, p. 313; Ch. Coligny, 1862, p. 100; J. Du Seigneur, 1862, p. 50; J. Renouvier, 1863, p. 222; Ch. Blanc, 1865, v. III, pp. 3-5, 8, ill.; A. Jal, 1867, p. 509; E. Vigée-Lebrun, 1869, v. I, p. 154; Ch. Clément, 1872, pp. 152-156; A. Lecoy de La Marche, 1872, p. 413; A. Lecoy de La Marche, 1874, p. 343; Bellier and Auvray, v. I, 1882, p. 449; C. Gabillot, 1906, pp. 257-258; Thieme and Becker, 1913, v. IX, p. 579; G. Brière, mus. cat., 1924, no. 270; H. Lapauze, 1924, v. I, p. 411; J.-P. Alaux, 1933, v. I., p. 200; L. Hautecœur, 1954, p. 95; mus. cat. 1972, p. 147; D. and G. Wildenstein, 1973, p. 22, no. 168, p. 158, no. 1368; mus. cat., 1974, p. 113, ill. 238; J. Vilain, 1974, p. 400.

RELATED WORKS
Drawings. A study in watercolor, 33.5 × 46, s. *Drouais fecit Roma,* sold 23 June 1930, Paris, Hôtel Drouot (L. Dimier, 1930, p. 21). An initial sketch significantly different from the final composition in Lille (INV. 2483), charcoal, 24.7 × 36.3; see J. Vilain in exh. cat. 1974-1975, Paris and Copenhagen. A complete study in Lille (H. Pluchart, mus. cat., 1889, no. 1322), pen and gray wash, 18.5 × 25.6. *Idem,* in Lyon, Musée des Arts Décoratifs (INV. 696-a), pen and gray wash, 20.5 × 27.5. In relation to the final composition, these two drawings offer several variations in the Cimbrian soldier's drapery, thrown backwards, and in the table placed at the right, which in both cases is sitting on lion paws.
A study for the Cimbrian soldier in Besançon (D. 2003). A study of several details in Lille (H. Pluchart, *op. cit.,* 1889, no. 1323), pencil, pen and gray wash, 15.5 × 28. Next to the figure of Marius, a note in David's handwriting: "Change nothing, it's good." A complete drawing, sqared off, in Lille (H. Pluchart, mus. cat., 1889, no. 1324), lead pencil and ink, 21 × 17. A study for the figure of the Cimbrian soldier, identical to the same figure in the final composition, in Paris, École des Beaux-Arts (E.B.A. 861). Two drawings in Dijon, one at the Musée des Beaux-Arts (mus. cat., 1883, no. 855), the other at the Musée Magnin (J. Magnin, mus. cat., 1938, no. 305), both similar to the Louvre painting; the dry and precise technique leads to the conclusion that they are probably copies from the engraving (see exh. cat., 1974, Dijon, no. 67).
Painted Studies. A painted sketch; canvas, c. 35 × 46 (Paris, private collection). We have only been able to see a poor photograph; according to a note written by M. Florisoone, 25 September 1950 (Louvre, Département des Peintures, S.E.D.), it could be a copy.
A painted sketch; canvas, 34.5 × 46 (Paris, private collection); inscribed on the frame: *"Germain Drouais inv. fecit— Marius à Minturne."* Identical to the engraving by Louis Darcis; the technique is dry, again, it is probably a copy.
Engravings. Engraved by Louis Darcis in 1796 (print exhibited at the Salon of 1796, no. 807); see J. Renouvier, 1863, p. 222. Engraved by Normand in 1803 (C.-P. Landon, 1803, I, pl. 35). Engraved by Pigeot *père* in Filhol (Filhol and J. Lavallée, 1828, XI, fig. 37).
Copies. Drawn by Wicar (see Salon of 1793, no. 549). Drawn by G. Schick c. 1798-1800 in an album a now in Stuttgart (see W. Becker, 1971, p. 349).

J. V.

Claude-Marie Dubufe

1790 Paris - La Celle-Saint-Cloud 1864

A pupil of David, Dubufe first did mythological and religious paintings. He made his debut at the Salon of 1810 with *Un Romain se laisse mourir de faim avec sa famille plutôt que de toucher un dépôt d'argent qui lui a été confié*; in 1812, he presented *Achille prend sous sa protection Iphigénie*; in 1819, *Jésus-Christ apaisant la tempête* (destined for the musuem in Riom; now lost); in 1822, *Apollo and Cyparissus* (No. 53) and *Psyché rapportant à Vénus la boîte de beauté*; in 1827, *La Délivrance de saint Pierre* (Saint-Pierre de Chaillot). That same year he painted *Les Souvenirs* and *Les Regrets,* and these works of a sentimental nature were very successful, as were *Le Nid* and *La Mésange* in 1831.

Exhibiting regularly up to his death, Dubufe later specialized in portraits, and it became fashionable to be painted by him. The anonymous author of his obituary notice in the *Chronique des Arts et de la Curiosité* remarked on 14 May 1864: "The portraits by Dubufe enjoyed a great vogue." These paintings have most often remained within the families of the sitters, which makes it difficult to evaluate the work of this artist. It must be stressed that Dubufe, unlike many artists of his time, did not hesitate to change his mode (and abandon history painting) in order to respond to the demands of bourgeois society.

J. L.

53
Apollo and Cyparissus

"*Apollon et Cyparisse*"
Plate p. 264
Canvas; 188 × 228; s.d.l.l. *Dubufe. 1821.*
Salon of 1822, no. 388
Avignon, Musée Calvet

The 1822 catalog of the Musée du Luxembourg explained: "Cyparissus, having inadvertently killed a young stag which he had raised with great care, felt so sorry that he wanted to kill himself. Apollo, touched by the young man's sorrow, had pity on him and changed him into a cypress."

Presented at a time when the Davidian esthetic was being questioned, despite the efforts of the Administration of the Museum, this work represents a curious return to a form of Neo-Classicism even more radical than that of the Primitifs. Indeed, the painting relates to their work through its artificial subject, its elementary composition and its acidic color. However, the refinement of details creates at the same time a totally different impression: that of a mannerist, if not mannered work, which is not unrelated to art *bellifontain*. In the last analysis, this ambiguity reveals very well the contra-

dictions of a style which was to evolve toward academicism.

At the Salon, the work was not very well received. Delecluze wrote: "One cannot imagine the quantity of works exhibited that glitter with commendable qualities, but which give neither glory to their creators nor pleasure to the public. The *Apollo and Cyparissus* by M. Dubufe is precisely in this class. However, this work is not inferior in its execution to the *Psyché* by the same artist, which is very successful." For the *Observateur et Arlequin aux Salons*: "*Apollo and Cyparissus* by M. Dubufe is a hackneyed subject which one sees at every exhibition and which, this time, could have been dispensed with for more than one reason."

Among the critics, apparently only Landon showed his approval: "This painting, one of the most pleasant at the exhibition, is distinguished by the elegance of the forms, especially in the figure of Cyparissus, by the suavity of the colors and by the lightness of the brushwork. This figure, endowed with a noble and gracious character, is modeled with finesse; that of Apollo is less successful and the drapery which covers part of the nudes, is an obstacle to the development of the contours. In both heads, the skull is not given enough fullness. This fault, which would have been easy to remedy, detracts from the grace of the profiles and makes the facial features too powerful. The effect of the painting is simple, luminous, unpretentious; the execution is in good taste and is equally distant from both the negligent manner which certain artists affect and from the precious, yet cold and polished finish which, although defective, is the sole merit of several other works we could cite."

PROVENANCE
Acquired by the Musées Royaux at the Salon of 1822 (3,000 francs); exhibited at the Musée du Luxembourg until its transfer to the Louvre in March-April 1854; deposited at Avignon in 1872 (INV.: L 3842 and INV. 4250).

EXHIBITION
1822, Salon, no. 388.

REFERENCES
E.-J. D(elécluze), 18 May 1822, p. 374; C.-P. Landon, 1822, v. 1, p. 48, ill. 28; *L'Observateur et Arlequin aux Salons*, 1822, pp. 10-11; mus. cat. of Luxembourg, 1822, no. 34; mus. cat. of Luxembourg, 1853, no. 54; J. Girard, mus. cat., 1909, no. 149.

RELATED WORK
Outline engraving by Étienne-Achille Réveil.

J. L.

Joseph-Siffred (or Siffrein) Duplessis

1725 Carpentras - Versailles 1802

Son of a surgeon from Carpentras and locally educated, Duplessis traveled to Rome in 1745, where he became acquainted with Pierre-Hubert Subleyras, whom he copied (and whose role as a portrait painter has been overlooked—he considerably influenced Sir Henry Raeburn, for example). He returned to Carpentras in 1749 and went to Paris in 1752, but only became famous after the Salon of the Academy of Saint-Luke in 1764.

An associate member of the Academy in 1769, he was made an academician in 1774 and from that time became a fashionable portrait painter and the official painter of Louis XVI (*Mme Lenoir*, 1764, Louvre; *Marie-Antoinette*, 1771; *Allegrain*, 1774, Louvre; *Vien*, 1784, Louvre; *Le Comte d'Angiviller,* private collection, Denmark; *Le Docteur Lassone*, 1785, Avignon and the Faculté de Médecine; *M. de Chabanon*, 1785, Orléans). Appointed director of the galleries of Versailles, he fell into disfavor during the Revolution and practically abandoned painting. From 1792 to 1796, he remained in Carpentras, where he compiled the inventory of works seized during the Revolution and was named Curator of the Musée de Versailles in 1796, together with Louis-Jacques Durameau (who, at his death, was replaced by Esprit-Antoine Gibelin), Philippe-Laurent-Roland and J.-D. Le Roy. He died, in 1802, destitute and forgotten.

The principal portrait painter of his generation, recognized as such by the King's painter, Jean-Baptiste-Marie Pierre, and universally by contemporary critics, Duplessis had only one rival, Alexandre Roslin. "If Roslin only painted flesh-tones like Duplessis, and Duplessis only painted textures like Roslin," wrote a critic of the Salon of 1783 (cited by J. Belleudy, 1913, p. 250).

The painter liked encircling his forms, avoiding hazy and imprecise outlines. His models, their social class clearly defined, present themselves to us, a smile on their lips. No artifice or false elegance, but rather a finesse and a taste for "truthfulness" characterize the art of Duplessis, marked by a reserve and distance from the model, whom he only wished to serve.

Duplessis has never been entirely forgotten: the French know his official portrait of *Louis XVI* (1775, best-known version at Versailles, cf. No. 17). His portrait of *Franklin* is popular in America (it was in the Salon of 1779) and musicians all know his *Portrait de Gluck* (1775; Vienna, Kunsthistorisches Museum). But, with the exception of the excellent monograph by Belleudy in 1913, there as been little study of his work, which deserves fresh attention.

P. R.

54
Portrait of André Dupré de Billy (?)

Portrait dit d'André Dupré de Billy
Plate p. 63
Canvas; 147 × 114
San Francisco, California Palace of the Legion of Honor
H.K.S. Williams Fund Purchase

This portrait poses certain problems. First, there is the identity of the model. Belleudy (1913), who had seen the canvas, because he gives details of the colors, says the subject is "unknown." In 1920, Wildenstein thought it represented the Marquis de Chillon. Since 1931, the sitter has been described as a certain André Dupré de Billy, whose identity we have been unable to establish. Second, there is the date of the work. It is difficult to identify this picture among the portraits Duplessis regularly exhibited, listed under the same number, at the Salon. But it may be compared, both from the point of view of the model's pose and costume—not to mention the armchairs, mirrors and wall brackets — with the famous *Portrait de Necker,* s.d. 1781, which was in the Salon of 1783 and is today in the château of Coppet in Switzerland.

In 1779, the City Council of Valenciennes, desiring to honor Gabriel Senac de Meilhan, Intendant of the province of Hainault, by having his portrait painted, asked the Secretary of the Academy, Cochin, to recommend an artist. He answered, "The two best portrait painters we have are M. Rollin [*sic*] and M. Duplessis. I believe M. Duplessis to be the more excellent of the two..." (Belleudy, *op. cit.* p. 130). This is perhaps a somewhat hasty judgment; but when we look at David's early portraits, we realize how much he owes to artists like the ones mentioned by Cochin.

PROVENANCE
According to its former owner, this picture came from the collection of a Comte d'Arjuzon (see No. 59), but did not appear in the sale of 2-4 March 1852. From 1913, it belonged to M. Wildenstein; in the United States since 1920. Bought by the museum from Wildenstein, 1966.

EXHIBITIONS
1920, San Francisco, no. 94, ill. p. 41; 1923, New York, no. V, pl. V; 1931, New York, no. 13; 1948, New York, no. 12, pl. XII.

REFERENCES
J. Belleudy, 1913, pp. 340-341; G. Bazin, 1965, p. 187, ill. p. 186; *G.B.A.*, suppl., February 1967, p. 91, no. 323, ill.

P. R.

Louis-Jacques Durameau

1733 Paris 1796

Louis-Jacques Durameau was born in Paris on 5 October 1733. His father, a master-printer in copper-plate engraving, intended him to take up engraving but the young artist, against his family's wishes, chose the painter's trade. He earned his living as a youth while pursuing his studies under the sculptor Jean-Baptiste Defernex. Before coming of age he joined the studio of Jean-Baptiste-Marie Pierre and became a student at the Academy. As early as 1754 he was allowed to compete for the Grand Prix, which he won only three years later with the painting *Elie ressuscitant le fils de la Sunamite* (Paris, École des Beaux-Arts). After three years of study at the Ecole des Elèves Protégés (October 1757 to May 1760), under the direction of Carle Van Loo, he was sent to the French Academy in Rome, directed at that time by Charles-Joseph Natoire. During his residence (May 1761 to October 1764), he copied particularly the frescos by Dominichino at Saint

Sylvestro with Jean-Bernard Restout and, for Mariette, "the most famous paintings of various great masters who are not yet known by any print... Luti, Trevisani, Imperiali, Passeri, Mola." He traveled to Naples and Herculaneum, where he designed 16 bronze plates which were engraved by P.-A. Martini and C.-F.-A. Macret in *Le Voyage pittoresque... de Naples et de la Sicile* (Abbé de Saint-Non, 1781). Upon his return to Paris, he pursued the traditional career of a history painter: he was made *agréé* in 1766, academician in 1774, associate professor in 1776, professor in 1781 and had the honor of being named painter of the King in 1778. Despite leaving few students of renown (Étienne Garnier and Jean-Charles-Nicaise Perrin), his function as professor at the École des Elèves Entretenus from 1776 to 1784 should also be mentioned. At this time, he replaced Etienne Jeaurat in the Superintendence of Buildings at Versailles as Guard of the King's Paintings. In this important office, he prepared a complete inventory of the King's collections. Revolutionary disturbances caused him to lose his position in 1794, but the Commission Temporaire des Arts, recognizing him to be the best expert on Versailles, reinstated him. Named curator at the Musée Spécial de l'École Française in July 1795, he died slightly more than a year later, on 3 September 1796.

Durameau was fortunate in having exceptional benefactors during his entire career; particularly Cochin, Pierre and, later, d'Angiviller. With their help, he inaugurated after 1769 a career as the most brilliant decorator of the second half of the century. His first commission was the ceiling of the Opera at Versailles on the theme of *Apollon couronnant les Arts*. Later, he did two ceilings for the Opera of the Palais Royal (1770; destroyed by fire in 1781); *Eté,* a partition of the ceiling for the Galerie d'Apollon (1775; Louvre); a ceiling for the Hôtel de Nivernais (1784; destroyed in the 19th century) and another for the Chancellerie d'Orléans (today at Asnières, depot of the Banque de France). Although his contemporaries admired his great decoration, they knew less about his talent as a history painter. Outstanding among the works of the *grand genre* that the artist exhibited at the Salons between 1769 and 1789 are *Le martyr de saint Cyr et de sainte Juliette* and *La mort de saint François de Sales* (1767; Paris, Saint-Nicolas-du-Chardonnet), both belonging to the great revival of religious painting; in 1775 and 1779, two works from ancient history: a *Bélisaire* (lost) and a *Cléobis et Biton* (Mont-de-Marsan, Marie); and finally, two episodes of national history: in 1773, *Saint-Louis lavant les pieds aux pauvres* (Paris, Chapelle de l'École Militaire) and in 1777, *Continence of Bayard* (No. 55), Durameau was forgotten soon after his death. It was not until 1854 that the Goncourt brothers' purchase of *La Partie de Cartes aux bougies* (Louvre, Cabinet des Dessins) renewed his popularity as a draughtsman, which had already been established by numerous drawings by him in the best collections of the period (Mariette, Trouard, Watelet, the Duc de Chabot). At the end of the century, Philippe and Henri de Chennevières devoted themselves to reviving his reputation as a decorator. But true recognition occurred thanks to J. Locquin (1912) who, basing his argument on the artist's *Entelle et Darès* (Riom), was the first to emphasize the pre-Romanticism of the painter. In 1963, M. Sandoz published his study of the artist.

Honored as a painter of history at the Salon of 1767, Durameau developed after 1775 in growing opposition to the taste of his time. His efforts to express a certain realism, his rejection of color remained misunderstood during his time. Representative of a transitional generation between Boucher and David, Durameau illustrates well the diversity of temperaments that faced the ascendancy of Neo-Classicism.

A. L.

55

Continence of Bayard

"La Continence de Bayard"
Plate p. 50
Canvas; 323 × 227
Salon of 1777, no. 22
Grenoble, Musée de Peinture et de Sculpture

In 1775, Durameau received from d'Angiviller "the proposal of a series of paintings, the subjects of which are drawn from the History of France, to be executed at Gobelins." The artist, for lack of time, could only undertake one of the four subjects initially proposed: "*Le Chevalier Bayard sauve l'honneur de sa prisonnière; il la remet à sa mère et la dote*" (Arch. Nat., O¹ 1913 [1] f⁰ 122, letter from d'Angiviller to Pierre, 27 June 1775).

The Salon catalog devoted a long description to the painting: "At Grenoble in the midst of his family, Bayard, after a long illness, the result of his wounds and his military efforts, had a temptation from which heroes are not exempt. One day he ordered his valet to find him company for the following night. Upon his return home in the evening after one of those parties which he attended or gave for the ladies of the city, his valet presented him with a young lady of exceptional beauty. He was struck by her loveliness, but noticing that her eyes were red from weeping, he asked her, 'What is the matter, my lovely child?' 'My virtue and my birth,' she cried, falling to her knees and bursting into tears again. 'Poverty, which is killing my mother, puts me today in your hands. May death prevent my dishonor!' Touched, Bayard helped her rise and said, 'Reassure yourself; I cannot oppose such beautiful sentiments; I have always respected virtue and nobility; you have endowed both with beauty; I want to give you security both from my self and from suspicion. I shall take you for the night to a relative who lives nearby.' He immediately took a lamp and accompanied her there himself. The next day he sent for her mother, whom he strongly reproached and asked if no husband had bidden for her hand. Upon her assurance that one of her neighbors would have taken her with a dowry of 600 florins, he had the money brought and had 1,200 florins counted out to her, enough for a dowry and a trousseau. Three days later, the wedding took place. The artist has chosen the moment when Bayard dowers the girl."

The critics of the time were unanimous in judging the moment chosen by the artist as uninteresting. The *Mercure de France,* while praising the simplicity of the purely domestic scene, regretted that the good chevalier was not painted during a more noble action than that depicting him as "coldly holding up a purse"!

For Bachaumont, the subject's true interest resided in "the hero's response upon weighing his love and his virtue. There is no longer any sign of combat on Bayard's face, which reflects a Spanish sense of gravity."

The critics also bore down on the style. Bachaumont reproached Durameau for the manner in which he painted Bayard: "The entire figure is dry and stiff, particularly one arm, which is repulsive at first glance." For him, the women lacked grace and gentleness, "those sensitive touches which their situation demanded." Moreover, since both women seem to be more or less the same age, it is not clear which one is the mother and which the daughter. This ambiguity confused *Le Journal de Paris,* which identified the woman with the gold chain as the mother but criticized her for being too luxuriously dressed and much too young. Daniel Ternois has suggested that the figure in white is the young woman, who with her left hand tells her mother to rise.

La Prophétesse scolded the artist: "Ah, my dear Monsieur du Rameau, you had a lovely subject to treat in such a man as Bayard, but you did nothing worthwhile. I am afraid you have a heavy manner of drawing, an improper coloring for the fresh appearance of the lovely women." A real controversy ensued in the press of the time (four successive articles in *Le Journal de Paris*) which precipitated the decline of the artist, who had already been attacked by the criticiques of the Salon of 1775: "M. Durameau, misled like many others by too much interest in costumes, has not neglected them. He has even shown the scruple of placing Bayard's florins in a purse with playing counters. But in good faith, should the genre of history consist of these miserable accessories? It was in the depiction of passions and the movements of the heart that a Raphael, a Poussin, a Le Sueur and a Le Brun sought to excel."

It is paradoxical to see a work judged so harshly, when it would appear to correspond to the criteria of the new taste in its exaltation of national subject matter made fashionable by literature. We need only recall, according to R. Rosenblum (1967 a), the literary vogue of the theme of the Chevalier Bayard (1473-1524) and its precocious use by the English (Edward Penny, *Generous Behavior of Chevalier Bayard*, 1768). If Durameau's contemporaries did not like the painting, it was perhaps because the artist gave this historical scene an intimate touch and thus played on two different levels. What enchants us the most today, in contrast with the chroniclers of the Salon, is precisely the care which Durameau devoted to placing this episode in the framework of its period: the visible beams, the tapestries with floral designs, the door panel with its pointed arches are an attempt to recreate the atmosphere of a secular gothic room. The costumes are those of the French stage between 1760 and 1780, used in plays with medieval subjects (e.g. *Gaston et Bayard* by Buirette de Belloy, 1771): the women wear bouffant sleeves and fussy ruffs despite their hoop skirts; Bayard is dressed in armor covered by a 15th-century "tabard." Even the arms emblazoned on the shield are scrupulously accurate ("azure with a silver chief charged with a lion opening its mouth with gold thread in bands crowning everything").

Thus we are transported, a half-century before anyone else, into the *troubadour* world of a Fleury Richard, Paul Delaroche or Ary Scheffer. But the technique remains unquestionably 18th-century. The impasto is characteristic of the artist, who excels here in the rendition of various textures; let us note especially the thick layer of paint in the mother's white dress and the delicate detail of the purse which Bayard holds. Durameau showed himself here a vigorous and subtle colorist; he enhanced his normally dull colors and boldly extended his color scale. If the effect appears a bit showy, the unity is maintained by a repetition of golds, skillfully dispersed in the details of the decor and the costumes.

Together with Jacques-Antoine Beaufort and Brenet, Durameau was among the first to pursue a concern for archeological accuracy. As co-workers on a commission for the chapel of the École Militaire beginning

in 1773, they each painted an episode from the *Vie de Saint Louis* in the same historicizing spirit. The part played by the work of these artists in the neo-gothic movement indicates an attractive and modern element. But their vision for the fantasy of the medieval past did not have time to develop and was unable to counter the triumphant taste for antiquity.

PROVENANCE
Durameau was selected on 27 June 1775 to paint four canvases, because "the Gobelin manufacturing firm needed some new paintings to use for the production of its tapestries." Commissioned of Durameau for the King on 20 March 1776, the painting (for subject, see Entry above) was detained for the Salon of 1777 and estimated to be worth 3,000 *livres* (Arch. Nat. O¹ 1921 A and O¹ 1925 B 11); four payments were made to the artist between 1777 and 1778 (cf. Arch. Louvre, Bâtiments du Roi, register of payments of 1762 to 1785, Ms. pp. 231, 238, 245, 262). Kept at the Gobelin firm since 1777 for its rendition as a tapestry, the painting was part of the "Tapestry of the History of France" (cf. Guiffrey, 1886, p. 455). In September 1794, the judges for the classification of patterns for Gobelins rejected the painting "with respect to the art." In 1810, it was included in the inventory of Napoleon as no. 1284 and was wrongly attributed to Nicolas-Guy Brenet (cf. Arch. Louvre, 1 DD 19, p. 520: *Générosité de Bayard* executed by the Gobelin firm, approximately 1,000 francs). Durameau's painting was confused with the Brenet exhibited at the Salon of 1783, *Une Courtoisie de Bayard*. Until 1876 it remained at the Louvre, still as a Brenet. It was then sent to Grenoble to be stored (cf. Arch. Louvre, P.¹⁴, 1876, 15 March, no. 1284, *Magnificence de Bayard*, by Brenet). It was deposited by the Grenoble museum at the old City Hall, remodeled into a court house.

EXHIBITION
1777, Salon, no. 22.

REFERENCES
Coll. Deloynes, v. X, no. 178, p. 868; no. 180, pp. 892-893; no. 189, p. 963; no. 190, p. 1032; v. XLIX, no. 1333, pp. 775-780; no. 1334, pp. 851-853; *Mercure de France*, October 1777, pp. 169-170; *Journal de Paris,* September and October 1777, no. 272, p. 1; no. 276, pp. 2-3; no. 278, p. 1; no. 280, p. 2; Bachaumont, 1777, v. XI, letter I, p. 14, ed. 1784-1789; M.-F. Pidansat de Mairobert, 1777 (ed. 1865, *Revue Universelle des Arts,* p. 223; Du Pont de Nemours, 1777 (cf. *A.A.F.,* 1908, II, pp. 52-53); *Revue Universelle des Arts,* 1865, v. XXII, p. 223; *I.G.R.A.F., Province, Monuments Civils,* 1876-1907, v. VI, p. 14; M. Reymond, 1879, pp. 24, 204; Bellier and Auvray, 1882, v. I, p. 493; F. Engerand, 1901, pp. 185-186; *N.A.A.F.,* 1903-1906, v. XXI, no. 50; *A.A.F.* 1908, new series, II, pp. 52-53; J. Locquin, 1912, p. 51, 164 (n. 4), 170, 283; Thieme and Becker, v. X, 1914, p. 197; R. Lanson, 1926, pp. 43-44; J.-S. de Sacy, 1953, pp. 97, 107, 109, 110, 115; M. Sandoz, 1960, p. 47; J. Vergnet-Ruiz and M. Laclotte, 1962, p. 104, 235; M. Sandoz, 1963, pp. 105-106, 116, ill. I (p. 112); R. Rosenblum, 1967 a, p. 32, note 101, p. 58, notes 27-30, 59, ill. 56.

RELATED WORKS

Tapestries

Part of the "Tapestry of the History of France" (cf. M. Fenaille, 1903-1933, v. III, v. II, pp. 368, 369, 372-375); woven twice by the studio of Cozett père. One, 1788-1790, was donated to the Metropolitan Museum of Art, New York; another (1788-1791) in Paris, Mobilier National; on deposit since 1897 at the French Embassy, Bern.

Drawings

Preparatory pen drawing at Besançon, Bibliothèque Municipale (in a factitious album of P.-A. Paris; coll. 453), the painting was drawn twice by Gabriel de Saint-Aubin in the left margin of his copy of the guide to the Salon of 1777 (drawings published by E. Dacier, 1909-19, II, IV, p. 44). Sketches (canvas; 39 × 29); at Grenoble and exhibited in Brou in 1971 (no. 29).   A. L.

François-Xavier Fabre

1766 Montpellier 1837

The name François-Xavier Fabre evokes the museum in Montpellier that bears his name, because of his noteworthy donations of 1825 and 1837; but this artist also had a long and, at times, brilliant career as a painter of historical subjects, portraits and landscapes. After several years at the art academy in his native town, he became a member of Jacques-Louis David's studio and entered the school of the Royal Academy of Paris in 1783, thanks to a recommendation from Joseph-Marie Vien and the generous help of the collector Ph.-L. de Joubert, Treasurer of the States of Languedoc. In 1787, Fabre was the second of David's pupils to win the Grand Prix de Rome. Fabre fulfilled his duties conscientiously by painting the four required works for the Academy: *Un soldat romain au repos* (1788), *Saint Sébastien expirant* (1789), *La Mort d'Abel* (1790)—all in the Musée Fabre—and a *Milon de Crotone* (1790-1791) for Lord Bristol, which has since disappeared. His *Abel,* which was a great success at the Salon of 1791, reminds us of the graceful forms of Jean-Baptiste Regnault, but with *La Prédication de saint Jean-Baptiste* (sketches in the Musée Fabre; a fragment in Arles, Musée Réattu), a large work commissioned in 1790 by Joubert for a church in Montpellier and unfortunately abandoned, Fabre returned to David's style of the 1780s. Since Fabre was reserved and disinterested in politics, he did not share the enthusiasm of the French artists in Rome for republican ideas and in January 1793 he took refuge in Florence from the dangerous atmosphere in Rome. In Florence he became a portrait painter for foreign tourists. He immediately became friendly with the poet Count Vittorio Alfieri and his mistress, the Countess of Albany; several portraits resulted from this friendship —in Montpellier, Florence (Galleria degli Uffizi), Asti—

and in 1803 he painted his *Saul* for the Countess (No. 56). During his first years in Florence, Lord Holland was one of his patrons. He commissioned several portraits (London, the National Portrait Gallery; Eton; Melbury, Dorset, the Lady Agnew Collection), as well as two history paintings, *Marius et le Gaulois* (1796); which is very similar to Drouais' painting of the same subject, No. 52, and *Ariane et Thésée* (1797), both currently in the Lady Agnew Collection at Melbury. Other pictures from this early Florentine period, which show the influence of Poussin as well as that of David, include *La Charité Romaine* (1798; Dijon, Musée Magnin); the same subject (1800, Dayton Institute of Art); *Néoptoleme et Ulysse enlèvent à Philoctète les flèches d'Hercule,* painted for Lord Bristol (1800; Louvre, lent to the French Embassy at the Vatican); *Sainte Famille au Repos* (1801, Montpellier); *Socrate buvant la ciguë* (1801, former Diodati-Le Fort Collection, Geneva); and several portraits, including *Lord Wycombe* (1793), *Marshal Malachowski* (1794, Cracow), and the minister *Carletti* (1797, Montepulciano). The French occupation and Fabre's relations with the Court of Elisa encouraged him to return to Paris. Demonstrating a new interest in landscapes, he exhibited at the Salon of 1806 a *Madeleine Pénitente* (Montpellier), and in 1808 a *Jugement de Paris*, which was bought by his friend Bertin the Elder and has since disappeared. He was given an official commission to do the *Portrait du général Clarke, duc de Feltre* (Nantes) for Compiègne, and also painted *Mme Clarke et ses enfants* (Paris, Musée Marmottan), both exhibited at the Salon of 1810. After 1808, Fabre painted mostly portraits, many simple half-lenght figures in a neo-classical style, but psychologically occasionally romantic. These include *Lucien Bonaparte* (1808; Rome, the Napoleon

Museum, and the Lady Agnew Collection); *Ugo Foscolo* (1813, Florence, the Bibliothèca Nazionale, and the Mario Praz Collection, Rome). Other paintings with a landscape background recall Louis Gauffier (*Elizabeth Skotnicka,* 1807, Cracow; *Amalia Oginska,* 1808, Kovno). Until the end of this life, Fabre was chiefly interested in enlarging his art collection. In 1825, after the death of the Countess of Albany, he returned to Montpellier and assumed the management of the museum and the new

École des Beaux-Arts. Several portraits date from this period: in Toulouse, the *Marquis de Nattes* (1832); and in Montpellier, *Creuzé de Lesser, Gache* (1832) and an *Autoportrait* (1835). The latter shows a man disappointed with his life after the collapse of the monarchy. By temperament, a man of the 18th century and an orthodox classicist, Fabre nevertheless often displayed in his work a variety of interests and unusual effects.

L. P. and Ph. B.

56
Saul Crazed by his Remorse

Saül, agité par ses remords, croit voir l'ombre du grand-prêtre Achimelech, qu'il a fait périr
Plate p. 185
Canvas; 151 × 214; s.d.l.l. *F. X. Fabre f. Flor/*1803; inscription: *Saul Atto V.*
Montpellier, Musée Fabre

It is surprising that Fabre only undertook a history painting for Alfieri and the Countess of Albany after ten years of close, mutual friendship. On 21 May 1803, the Countess wrote to a friend in Siena: "He has several history paintings to complete, including two for me, which two years ago I commissioned for my drawing room; but there are always other works that prevent him from finishing." In his autobiography, Alfieri wrote that of all his characters, Saul was his favorite, and he played this role many times between 1793 and 1796. This preference clearly explains the choice of this theme for the canvas commissioned by the Countess. The painting was probably completed before Alfieri's death on 8 October 1803 which, as the Countess mentioned, affected Fabre profoundly. Alfieri's tragedy *Saül,* published in 1784, was freely inspired by the First Book of Samuel in the Bible. In the last act, Saul is haunted by two dreadful visions as his daughter Micol, David's wife, tries to calm his tears. One vision is that of Samuel, the great priest who had chosen him to be King of Israel and who condemned him for straying from the ways of the Lord; the other, on the right, shows Achimelech, the priest whom Saul put to death along with his children for having helped his rival David. They predict Saul's future: he will soon die by his own hand. The very romantic character of Saul inspired several painters of this period who used the Bible as their source; Fabre was unique in his use of the text of Alfieri. In this work, the visions are only suggested; but Fabre used a realistic representation.

Unlike Girodet, Fabre was reluctant to portray anything immaterial.

Fabre's emphasis on dramatic gesture and facial expression, to show the feelings of his characters, indicates the profound influence of Poussin, whose engraved works he enthusiastically collected. But his exceptionally careful brushwork and attention to minute detail recall David's *Death of Socrates* (No. 32), the last painting by David that Fabre had seen. The night-time atmosphere and muted colors are in perfect harmony with the tragic nature of the subject; this is one of the rare works of Fabre in which he indulged the taste for *chiaroscuro* that we find so often in his drawings and engravings. Alfieri's art, with its inspiration derived from antiquity and its romantic expressiveness, was echoed with remarkable fidelity in Fabre's *Saul.*

PROVENANCE
Painted for the Countess of Albany, who bequeathed it to Fabre in 1824; Fabre Donation, 1825.

REFERENCES
F.-X. Fabre, 1828, p. 25; J.-B. Prier and D. Soulas, 1855, pp. 32-33; L.-G. Pélissier, 1904, 1st series, p. 434; L.-G. Pélissier, 1912, 2nd series, p. 86; F. Boyer, 1969, pp. 26-27.

RELATED WORKS
Two preparatory drawings with interesting variations in the right-hand group, in Montpellier (INV. 837-1-337, 837-1-338). See N. Volle in exh. cat., 1974-1975, Paris and Copenhagen.

L. P. and Ph. B.

Alexandre-Evariste Fragonard

1780 Grasse - Paris 1850

Son of the illustrious Fragonard and himself the father of the romantic genre painter Théophile Fragonard (who painted the *Visite à la malade,* Grasse; *Jeune femme de profil,* Dijon, Musée Magnin), Alexandre-Evariste Fragonard was influenced both by his father and David, with whom he studied. Thus in his work neo-classical features are combined with the taste for moving pictorial effects and beams of light, inherited from his father as well as from northern painters, to create a "flamboyant" style, as Jal stated so well (quoted by A. Ananoff in *B.S.H.A.F.,* 1961, p. 156). His Neo-Classicism was all the more pronounced by the fact that Alexandre-Evariste was also a sculptor and designed many ornamental patterns for Sèvres. A charming example of his sculptural design is *Le jeune Pyrrhus chez Glaucias* of 1814 at the Louvre (1972, Paris, exh. cat., no. 99, pl. XIII). Very precocious, he made his first appearance at the Salon of 1793 at the age of 13 with a drawing, *Timoléon immolant son frère,* followed by other drawings with historical or mythological subjects (Salons of 1796 to 1800). He also exhibited drawn portraits (Salons of 1799, 1800, 1802, 1808), as well as works depicting contemporary politics: *Triomphe de l'Empereur* at the Salon of 1808, *Napoléon visitant le tombeau de Frédéric, Austerlitz, Présentation au corps législatif des tableaux pris aux Espagnols,* drawings for the sculptured friezes for the Palais du Corps Législatif. Moreover, Fragonard worked a good deal in the current Palais Bourbon; in 1927, some of his grisaille paintings executed in 1810 under Napoleon (cf. *B.S.H.A.F.,* 1928, pp. 39-41) were rediscovered, but his sculptured frontal disappeared in the Revolution of 1830 and was replaced by one by Jean-Pierre Cortot.

After exhibiting nothing between 1812 and 1819, Alexandre-Évariste Fragonard began to send to the Salons from 1819 on innumerable paintings with *gothique troubadour* subjects, which he treated with an undeniable pictorial verve, while retaining the sound pictorial traditions inherited from the 18th century: *François Ier armé chevalier par Bayard,* Salon of 1819 (the ceiling of one of the rooms in the Louvre, where it is still in the galleries of ancient ceramics; a smaller copy exists at Versailles and a sketch at the Louvre); *L'Entrée de Jeanne d'Arc à Orléans,* commissioned in 1821, exhibited at the Salon of 1822 and sent to Orléans (destroyed in the war); *Les Bourgeois de Calais,* at the same Salon, deposited by the Louvre in Arras; *Marie-Thérèse présentant son fils aux Hongrois,* at the same Salon, deposited by the Louvre at the Préfecture of Nice in 1867 and transferred to the Grasse museum in 1974. At the Salon of 1824, there appeared a painting with an equally "Royalist" subject: *Les Derniers moments du duc de Berry* (a lovely grisaille sketch is at Bayonne) and *La Reine Blanche délivrant les prisonniers de Châtenay* (Blois); in 1827, *Jean Le Mennuyer, évêque de Lisieux* (Saint-Étienne).

At the Salon of 1827, he exhibited another large ceiling, painted for the rooms of the Louvre: *François Ier et le Primatice,* of which a sketch still remains at the Louvre and a repetition or copy of the sketch at Morez (see 1971, Brou, exh. cat., no. 31 and the placement by J.-P. Cuzin, 1974, p. 78, who also mentions another sketch, of better quality, in a private coll., fig. 3). Participating then in the famous competition for the decoration of the Chambre des Députés (very washed-out sketches of *Mirabeau et Dreux-Brézé* and *Boissy d'Anglas saluant la tête du député Féraud à la Convention* sold in Paris, Galliera, 6 December 1966, nos. 27-28, ill.), Fragonard again exhibited at the Salons of 1831, 1833 and 1842. Faithful to his taste for the picturesque, he produced three compositions, among them a large *Bataille de Marignan* (1836) with a fine decorative sense, for the historical museum at Versailles. Much appreciated by the authorities, Fragonard received many commissions for religious paintings (*Fuite en Egypte,* Strasbourg Cathedral; *Assomption de la Vierge* commissioned in 1828 for the church of Sainte-Geneviève, today at the Panthéon, etc.). Moreover, Thieme and Becker mention several Parisian churches decorated by Fragonard paintings: Saint-Laurent, Saint-Jacques-du-Haut-Pas, Saint-Étienne-du-Mont. Fragonard is well-represented in French museums; to the lists of Vergnet-Ruiz and Laclotte—Arras, Bayonne, Dijon (Musée Magnin), Grasse, Morez, Orléans, Saint-Étienne, Sens, Strasbourg (No. 58), Valence—we could add Blois (cited above), Vire (*Ostension du Saint-Sacrement,* bought in 1973), Bagnères-de-Bigorre (*Angelo tyran de Padoue,* sketch), Saint-Malo *(Mme Récamier en Sapho)*, Amiens *(Baptême de Clovis,* commissioned in 1826), Quimper *(Wasa donnant des lois à la Suède,* sketch; *Scène de massacre* bought in 1973 in a sale at Drouot, 19 October 1973, no. 27), Saint-Quentin (No. 57), Angoulême *(S.A.R. la duchesse d'Angoulême remet l'acte de propriété de la maison où fut nourri Henri IV à la famille du père nourricier ;* this is the painting mentioned by Bellier and Auvray at the château of Villeneuve-l'Étang; it was acquired in 1973), Montpellier *(Portrait de J.-B. de Joly, architecte du corps législatif,* Salon of 1831). To be noted also are *L'Autoportrait* in Paris, Musée des Arts Décoratifs, drawings at Narbonne *(Œdipe)* and at Dijon, Musée Magnin *(Visite dans l'atelier)* a good copy of the portrait of Lagrenée by Dumont (Paris, École des Beaux-Arts), two important albums of draw-ings at Grasse, briefly mentioned by A. Ananoff (B.S.H.A.F., 1961, pp. 155-157) and recently published by G. Vindry *(Revue du Louvre,* 1974). But whether paintings or drawings, the most beautiful and represent-ative collection of works by Fragonard *fils,* remaining practically unknown, is that for the Sèvres Manufactory. Finally, it would be fitting to resort to the testimony of his engravings (the list of engravers in Thieme and Becker) in order to give this unappreciated artist proper recognition. Fragonard himself frequently furnished lithographs (for the *Voyages* by Baron Taylor from 1824 on, for example) and textual illustrations. His work as a sculptor *(Pichegru,* Versailles) and architect (fountain in the Carmelite Market, the obelisk on the Pont-Neuf, a Napoleonic project not completed) should also be mentioned.   J. F.

57
Vivant Denon Returning the Bones of El Cid to his Tomb

Vivant Denon replaçant dans son tombeau les ossements du Cid
(Campagne d'Espagne)
Plate p. 218
Gouache on paper laid down on canvas; 40 × 34.5; s.l.l. *A. Fragonard*
On the reverse, a label with a no. 668 and the above title in French
Saint-Quentin, Musée A. Lécuyer

Discovered by Pierre Rosenberg in storage at the Saint-Quentin museum, this painting (or, really, gouache, although the effect of this highly finished technique is similar to oil) has been reproduced with an attribution to Adolphe Roehn (1780-1867) by the author of the most recent biography on Vivant Denon. For, in his catalog of the Denon sale in 1826 (no. 220, sold for 220 francs to Billaudel), Pérignon did, in fact, ascribe to Roehn a picture that corresponds exactly to the Saint-Quentin gouache, both in the subject (includ-ing Zix, the scene set in a "gothic" chapel, etc.) and in dimensions (20 *pouces* × 16 *pouces*). Admittedly, Péri-gnon spoke of a canvas, whereas this picture is in fact painted on paper, laid down on canvas; but a minor error like this is understandable.

There remains the unmistakable signature, *A. Fra-gonard,* which is not mentioned in the catalog cited above. Are we to conclude that the expert for the sale, which took place less than a year after Denon's death in 1825, made a mistake in his description ? This seems difficult to believe; Pérignon was, in fact, a conscientious and highly regarded connoisseur, and he was cataloguing items in the sale of one of the most famous collections of the period, given the reputation of the man who had assembled it. Moreover, Roehn's style, as we know it from the paintings of Napoleonic subjects in Versailles—stiff and dark, often with deep contrasting shadows—could hardly be confused with the much freer and more subtle manner of Alexandre-Évariste Fragonard. On the contrary, the fine Rembrandtesque diagonal lighting, which was probably much to the taste of connoisseurs of this period, is not unusual in Fragonard's work; for example, the sketch of *Mirabeau répondant à Dreux-Brézé,* painted in 1830 for the competition of the decor-ation of the Chambre des Députés, sold in Paris, Palais Galliera, 6 December 1966, no. 28, ill.). The lively, nimble technique, the witty treatment of an apparently shy Spanish spectator, the picturesque *gothique troubadour* style—all these are typical of Fragonard. We must therefore conclude that Roehn's picture, which Pérignon incidentally described as having only three figures, has been lost, and that Alexandre-Évariste Fragonard used the same subject-matter at the same period (possibly for Zix). Either he copied Roehn's subject and even his composition, or else he was the originator, and his work later inspired a lesser artist like Roehn. The latter explanation seems preferable, especially as in the Saint-Quentin work, Fragonard used a gray-brown camaieu technique, a very special treatment generally confined to sketches made for engravings and preparatory studies; Pérignon would surely have mentioned the use of grisaille in his description of the Roehn work. And there is no better preparation for another picture than this monochrome technique.

However this may be, the curious ceremony shown here seems indeed to have a basis in fact. For, following Ulrich Richard-Desaix, who wrote a short work entitled *La Relique de Molière du Cabinet Vivant Denon* (Paris, 1880), J. Châtelain has recently drawn attention to Denon's bizarre taste as a collector (was he serious or cynical?) and mentions in the catalog of his sale in 1826 (no. 676) a surprising gilded-copper reliquary containing among other objects "Fragments of the bones of the Cid and Ximena, found in their tomb at Burgos," fragments of the bones of Héloïse and Abélard, locks of the hair of Agnès Sorel, Inés de Castro and Général Desaix, some bones of La Fontaine, half of one of Voltaire's teeth and part of the moustache of Henri IV, discovered when he was exhumed at Saint-Denis, Napoleonic relics, etc. The reliquary, sold in 1826, reappeared in the Pourtalès sale in Paris in 1865; it was then bought by Comte Desaix, great-nephew of the general of the same name who distinguished himself at the battle of Marengo. Ulrich Richard-Desaix, without knowing the Saint-Quentin picture, also mentioned Roehn's canvas from the same Denon collection and assumed that Denon must have acquired the remains of the Cid and Ximena at the time of the sack of Burgos by French troops in November 1808. In fact, as illustrated in Roehn's and Fragonard's pictures, the Strasbourg painter Zix, an enthusiastic draughtsman of the Napoleonic campaigns and frequent traveling companion of Denon (in Fragonard's picture, he can be identified with certainty as the figure on the left) did accompany him to Spain; they left France together in October 1808 and came back in February of 1809 (see Zix' letters, published by Ferdinand Dellinger in *Archives alsaciennes d'histoire de l'art*, II, 1923, pp. 193-220; see also the useful biographical notice for the Zix exhibition in Strasbourg in 1961-62 by Paul Martin, p. 22). Moreover, Zix

did in fact choose as a subject the Cid's tomb at Burgos (cf. the engraving of his drawing by Millet in the *Voyage Pittoresque et Historique de l'Espagne* by Alexandre de Laborde, Paris, 1820, II, part 2—i.e. Vol. IV, pl. XV, under the name Zix). Unfortunately, as P. Martin notes, Zix' Spanish drawings are very rare (only half a dozen are known), while large numbers exist of other campaigns like that of Prussia (Versailles). Martin also mentioned (*op. cit.,* p. 23) that one of Zix' drawings of Wagram (1809) was copied as a painting by Roehn (the latter is at Versailles), which may explain the connection between the Saint-Quentin camaieu and the Roehn in the 1826 sale.

The Zix engraving, brought to our attention by Katrin Simons, who is currently writing an article on the Saint-Quentin picture, shows the Cid's tomb rather differently—which incidentally is not at Burgos itself but some miles away in the monastery of San Pedro de Cardena. The Cid, we may recall, was a semi-legendary hero who is supposed to have died in 1099 and whose exploits became immensely popular with the *Reconquista*. As early as 1272, Alfonso IX had a stone coffin executed for him alongside the altar at San Pedro de Cardena; it was moved in 1447, but replaced in 1541 by order of Charles V. This tomb gradually became a veritable place of pilgrimage, and subsequently Philip II was even to ask for his canonization which was, needless to say, refused. The gothic chapel evoked by Zix is quite similar to the one in Fragonard's picture, but the magnificent dramatic concentration of light is Fragonard's; Zix' approach is that of a topographer, depicting exactly a much larger space amply lit by a window and laden with architectural and sculptural detail that distracts the eye. It is possible that this drawing, shown to Fragonard by Denon, was used by him as a working reference to set the scene (just as Denon probably supplied Gros, Meynier and all the other entrants for the painting competition to portray the battle of Eylau with a sketch of the scene by Baron Lejeune, Berthier's aide-de-camp; see Martin, *op. cit.,* p. 22).

To understand the picture properly, we must refer, as does Katrin Simons, to the *Mémoires* of Général Baron Thiébault, at the time governor of Old Castille (Paris, 1895, IV, pp. 295-296). He explained that the remains of the Cid were in his charge since, during the campaign of 1808 and the terrible siege of Burgos, soldiers from a French regiment of dragoons had destroyed the Cid's tomb at San Pedro de Cardena in the hope of finding gold and jewels; and that he had resolved "to make amends by French hands for this act of vandalism committed by Frenchmen." This led to the construction of a new monument to the Cid, but this time at Burgos itself—differing greatly from what is shown in the Saint-Quentin picture. This monument was to survive until 1842. When Denon visited Burgos, no doubt in view of his official position as director of Museums and of his collector's passion, Thiébault gave to him and only to him fragments of the bones of the Cid, but at Cardena there was only an empty tomb for him to visit.

Thus, the Saint-Quentin gouache illustrates a very revealing hoax on the part of Vivant Denon, both an act of enlightened propaganda (implying a generous Napoleonic gesture—the encyclopedic, humanist spirit of the 18th century in the service of the Emperor of France) and also an amusing mystery of a great state official and clever author (he wrote fiction) who delighted in fantasy: in 1811, Zix drew him, pen in hand, in a veritable imaginary cave of masterpieces from the Musée Napoléon, as if he were the trustee and vigilant guardian of all the artistic wonders of the world (cf. the drawing in the Louvre, which became well-known through the engraving by Reinhold executed about 1812—no. 182 and ill. in the Zix exh. cat. mentioned above). Perhaps Fragonard's picture was painted at the same date with the same purpose in view.

"Denon's intense contemplation of the Cid's skull, the spiritual dialogue between him and this 11thcentury, chivalrous hero; the almost mystical atmosphere created by this fascinating encounter between death and life; the quasi-supernatural light that plays on the scene: all of this is in fact nothing but fiction. But it is fiction offered to the eyes of history, in the original setting, intended as a strong suggestion that the rediscovery of the Cid was the work of Vivant Denon" (Katrin Simons, written commentary).

PROVENANCE
Old holdings of the museum.

REFERENCE
J. Châtelain, 1973, ill. opp. p. 193 (as Roehn).   J. F.

58
Don Juan and the Commander's Statue

Dom Juan et la statue du commandeur
Plate p. 269
Canvas; 38.5 × 32
Strasbourg, Musée des Beaux-Arts

The theme of Don Juan, famous in itself, could only experience a renewal of favor in the 19th century with Mozart's famous opera, first played in Prague in 1787 and long known in France through a highly modified version (text by Thuring and Baillot, music by Kalkbrenner, opening in Paris in 1805) competing against the more faithful version by Castil-Blaze. But even the renown of the plays of Molière (1665; first printed edition, 1682) and Corneille (1667; it was this "corrected" edition which was usually presented instead of Molière's original text until 1841) taking up the famous theme invented by Tirso de Molina (1630) would have sufficed to give Fragonard the idea of a subject so well suited to the fantastic light effects and sculptural illusion that he liked. The person lying on the ground is Don Juan's amusing valet—Leporello in Mozart's opera, Sganarelle in Molière. We should note that the last terrifying scene in Molière's play (Act V, scene vi) does not show Sganarelle taken aback with fear; he claims his wages as Don Juan falls into Hell with an ultimate threat to God and the Commander. Above all, the free-thinking hero does not try to escape (as he does here) the statue of the Commander (a tangible and almost unfortunate attenuation of a tragic climax) but, on the contrary, gives him his hand, as the Commander orders. Actually, Fragonard was very interested in Molière and the theater, as his series of lithographs appearing in an *Album dramatique* of about 1829 (the date given in the Fragonard section of the Cabinet des Estampes, Bib. Nat., Paris) shows. The series does not include any lithographs on the subject of Don Juan but does have various depictions of scenes from the *Malade imaginaire,* the *École des Maris, Sganarelle,* as well as Beaumarchais' *Barbier de Séville, Mariage de Figaro* and Goethe's *Faust—Apparition de Marguerite, Marguerite et Méphisto.* To be noted, even in 1835, is an engraving by Swebach based on Alexandre-Évariste Fragonard's *Étourderie de Dom Juan.* But his facile and somewhat "bourgeois" anecdotism, in the Gavarni manner of the taste of the 1830s, differs completely from the fairy-tale atmosphere of the present painting. On the contrary, the latter's vertical shape and its special lighting effects bring it closer to the lithographs of 1829 devoted to the Faust story. The strange and artificial lighting recur as a constant in Fragonard's art: among his compositions known only by lithographs: the *Orage* of 1826, the *Enfant trouvé* of 1827, the *Belle Arsène* of 1825, and a *Scène de l'Orage* in *Le Barbier de Séville*. There are just as many subjects borrowed from the theater: the *Songe,* the *Signal, François Ier chez l'avocat Féron,* etc. This taste for contrasts of light, luminous clouds and surprising effects, as well as for the *troubadour gothique* (an interest that often extended to the Renaissance) and that included "old" costumes, the vividness of the coloring, the joyous rhythm of forms or that amusing nuance that contradicts the deeply tragic atmosphere of the subject (Don Juan's final impenitence), prevents Fragonard from being an entirely serious and profound painter, but makes him all the more charming. Everything here speaks in favor of the traditional attribution to Fragonard, even though the picture is neither signed nor dated, and a date before 1830, in the midst of *troubadour* Romanticism.

PROVENANCE
Acquired in 1929 by the Society of the Friends of the Arts of Strasbourg (founded in 1832), who gave the museum the painting in the same year.

REFERENCE
H. Haug, mus. cat., 1955, no. 603.

J. F.

Jean-Honoré Fragonard

1732 Grasse - Paris 1806

In 1774, Fragonard was 42 years old; since 5 December of the preceding year he had been in Rome, for the second time in his life. Born in Grasse in 1732, he won the Grand Prix de Rome in 1752, and he departed for Palazzo Mancini at the end of 1755, after three years at the École des Élèves Protégés under the direction of Carle Van Loo. Fragonard remained in Italy until 1761. On his return, he exhibited his *Corésus et Callirhoe* (Louvre) at the Salon of 1765. His *Figures de Fantaisie* (eight of which are in the Louvre) date from 1769, and the *Progrès de l'Amour* series commissioned by Mme du Barry for Louveciennes (now in New York, the Frick Collection) date from 1771-73.

Although numerous details are known concerning the remaining 32 years of Fragonard's life (he was named, thanks to David, curator of the Museum of Arts in 1793), little is known about the works he executed during this period. Thus, Wildenstein (1960), who catalogued c. 450 paintings before 1776, counted scarcely more than 100 executed between 1777 and the death of the painter in 1806. At this point, the problem of the chronology of his work, far from being resolved at the present time, remains complex. In addition, the painter's young sister-in-law, Marguerite Gérard, took up residence in 1775 with Fragonard and collaborated on a still undetermined portion of her brother-in-law's works (see Nos. 71, 72). Also his son, Alexandre-Évariste, born in 1780, was already a celebrated painter during his father's lifetime. Fragonard exhibited at the Salon only irregularly, that is to say, he worked only for a private clientele, and he practically never dated or signed his paintings. Also, from the time of the painter's rediscovery in the middle of the 19th century, any work the least bit loose or licentious in inspiration has carried the name of the painter from Grasse. Thus, the art historian faces great difficulties in attempting to give Fragonard his proper place in the transformation which French art experienced in the last quarter of the 18th century. Did Fragonard try to adapt himself to a new pictorial vision which hardly conformed to his vigorous "southern baroque" temperament, or, on the contrary, did he play an eminent role in the elaboration of the new esthetic, before the widely recognized triumph of David at the Salon of 1785 ? It is too early to give a clear reply to this question. Paintings such as *The Lock* (No. 59) or *The Kiss* (No. 60) should, nevertheless, help resolve the problem.

P. R.

59
The Lock

Le Verrou
Plate p. 57 and color pl. p. 17
Canvas; 73 × 93
Paris, Musée du Louvre

The Lock, which reappeared very recently and was acquired by the Louvre, was one of the great successes of Fragonard's maturity. Painted for the Marquis de Véri, under his very eyes no doubt, the painting was admired in the 18th century and then disappeared. But the engravings that were made from it and unflaggingly repeated assured that it would always remain one of the artist's most popular compositions.

The subject seems clear. A young man clasps a girl, who attempts to reject him, while closing her eyes in an expression of dreamy consent. But the question is complicated by the existence of a pendant of a completely different, and at first glance, rather surprising subject—*L'Adoration des Bergers* (Wildenstein Gallery). Not only were the two works sold together at the sale of 1785, and closely associated in the accounts of the connoisseur, Paillet, but above all, Alexandre Lenoir informs us in a text on Fragonard, which appeared in 1816 (*Biographie Universelle,* attributed to Michaud, XV; XIV in the 1854 ed., p. 601), and therefore during the lifetimes of Fragonard's widow and Marguerite Gérard, that Fragonard "painted a picture for the Marquis de Véri in the manner of Rembrandt, representing *L'Adoration des Bergers,* and since the connoisseur asked him for a second work to serve as a pendant to the first, the artist, wishing to give proof of his genius, by a bizarre contrast, made a painting for him called *The Lock,* which is free and filled with passion."

The polemic between the Abbé de Fontenai and M. de Saint-Félix in the *Affiches, Annonces et Avis divers* in 1784, at the time of the publication of Maurice Blot's engraving, shows clearly that Fragonard's painting was not merely one of the naughty scenes so beloved in that epoch. If Fragonard's canvas was for the former, by virtue of its subject, an example of *genre inférieur,* it was above all, for the latter, the creation of a *peintre d'histoire.* This interpretation is confirmed by several details, not in the least gratuitous; we need mention only one, the apple, which is very evident on the table at the left. It is a clear allusion to Original Sin, and a testimony to the

ambitions of a painter who had not renounced the *grand genre,* to the extent, in any case, we have always thought.

The date of the work is far from being certain. In any case, *The Lock* dates before 1784—the year in which Blot's engraving appeared—and after 1777, the date in which a preparatory drawing for the painting appeared in the Varanchan de Saint-Geniès sale. It was, no doubt, a little before 1780 that Fragonard executed his work, a few years, in any case, after his second trip to Italy in 1773-1774.

This voyage, in the company of Pierre-Nolasque Bergeret, was undoubtedly very important for the artist. Fragonard had just completed the series of canvases of the *Progrès de l'Amour* (New York, Frick Collection) commissioned by Mme du Barry. She had preferred to the works of Fragonard four compositions by Joseph-Marie Vien, which could only have mortified the painter from Grasse. His trip put him once again in contact with the masterpieces of Italian art. He wished, on his return, to prove to the new generation that he was not old-fashioned and did know how to adapt himself to the new esthetic honored by Jean-Baptiste-Marie Pierre, successor to François Boucher as First Painter to the King. Although, in the utilization of a warm *chiaroscuro,* he paid homage to Rembrandt, he also used it to simplify, construct and reduce the composition to a great diagonal which links the bolt to the apple, and lightly touches the faces, and strips the composition of all superfluous detail. Although Fragonard forgot neither Rubens nor Boucher, and although the artist retained his own vitality and spirit, he also attempted to make his artistic conception more profound, and to give to this creation a gravity, a seriousness, a poetry and an emotion which are totally unexpected. One must wait for the Salon of 1785 and David's *Serment des Horaces* to encounter a more novel picture in French painting.

PROVENANCE
Painted for the Marquis de Véri; sold after his death, 12 December 1785, no. 37 (3,950 *livres*); acquired by the connoisseur

Lebrun, husband of Mme Vigée-Lebrun; collection of Grimod de La Reynière (1734-1793); Grimod de la Reynière sale, Paris, November 1792 (in actual fact 3 April 1793), no. 28 (3,010 *livres*); acquired once again by Lebrun. The painting was perhaps proposed as a purchase for the Louvre in 1817 by "M. d'Arjuzon." Collection of the Marquis A. de Bailleul in 1887 (in the Château de Rouville, Alizay [Eure]); collection of Mme de La Potterie (d. 1921), daughter of the Marquis de Bailleul. Proposed as a purchase for the Louvre in 1922 by the connoisseur G. Sortais. André Vincent Collection; Vincent sale, Paris, Galerie Charpentier, 26 May 1933, no. 21; X sale..., Paris, Galliera, 21 March 1969, no. 166. Acquired by the Louvre in 1974, through a subsidy from the Minister of the Economy and Finance (R.F. 1974-2).

EXHIBITION
1974, Paris, no. 22.

REFERENCES
P. Rosenberg and I. Compin, 1974, pp. 263-278 with color ill. (All the authors who have worked on Fragonard discussed the painting without knowing the original, which was considered lost until 1974.)

RELATED WORKS
(See P. Rosenberg and I. Compin, 1974.)
Paintings. A painted sketch: panel, 26 × 33. Seized during the Revolution at the house of the émigré Duc de Coigny, Maréchal de France; Jourdan Collection, B.-G. Sage, Abel Rémusat, B. [ertrand], A. Fauchier-Magnan, Barbara Hutton. Sale, 24 June 1964 at Sotheby's (£ 27,000). Private collection.
Drawings. One of the two most celebrated drawings was in the sale of Varanchan de Saint-Geniès (1777), and of the Fiquet and Edmond de Rothschild collections (in 1889); and the other was in the sales of Tondu, Walferdin, Josse, Beurdeley, Féral, Édouard Kann, Albert Meyer and Cotnareanu. For other drawings, some mentioned as early as 1789, see, besides P. Rosenberg at I. Compin: A. Ananoff, 1970, IV, nos. 2002-2007.
Engravings. If the picture has remained one of Fragonard's most famous, it is because of the great number of engravings that popularized the work. The most famous is that by Maurice Blot, which appeared in 1784.
As for the pendant, *L'Adoration des Bergers,* slightly earlier than *The Lock,* in the Wildenstein Gallery, see above.

P. R.

60
*The Kiss**

Le Baiser à la dérobée
Plate p. 86
Canvas; 45 × 55
Leningrad, The Hermitage Museum

The success achieved by Nicolas-François Regnault's engraving of *The Lock* (No. 59) prompted the engraver in 1788 to do a pendant; he chose to engrave a composition by Fragonard of a totally different inspiration, *The Kiss:* a young man chastely embraces a girl; he delicately holds her hand as she goes to get her shawl. In the background at the right, behind a half-open door, two card players are noticeable in another room.

How can we explain the immense difference in style, technique and spirit between this painting and *The Lock,* which could not, however, have been painted more than ten years before the former. *The Lock* is a passionate and lyric work, as profane and pantheistic as the *The Kiss* is sober and bourgeois. "In the painting, *The Kiss,* Fragonard has imitated Terborch with much skill and elegance" (L. Dimier, 1913). Did the evolution of Fragonard truly lead him to this "finished manner" and

to these "effects borrowed from the minutely precise Dutch masters ?" (J. Thuillier). "This [is an example of] the displeasing and cold style of this time, in which the imitation of the minor Dutch masters became so popular at the end of the century, in [our] impoverished school. Here are the coats trimmed with ermine of Metsu and the white satin dress of Terborch; the ever-present costume which soon everyone would come to fight over... one no longer knows who signed it: Fragonard or Boilly" (E. and J. Goncourt, 1909 ed., III, p. 272).

Are not a good number of these late paintings, while conceived by Fragonard indebted to the brush of Marguerite Gérard ? It is very difficult, considering the present state of research, to resolve the problem. It must be pointed out, nevertheless, that Ananoff catalogued no drawing whatsoever related to *The Kiss. The First*

Step (No. 71), engraved in 1786 by J. Vidal, is in our opinion, a collaborative effort between Fragonard and Marguerite Gérard. Its presence in the exhibition should advance the debate to a slight extent, especially when it is compared to a painting in the Hermitage, *Les Premiers Pas,* signed only by Marguerite Gérard, and one of her first works (see V. Bérézina, 1972, pp. 60-61, with ill.).

"The Kiss leads to Boilly, but this new sensibility... which half opens the door upon a delicate, soft interior... is not this reminiscent of the great master, Chardin?" (J. Thuillier). Does this painting indicate the completely new orientation of an artist much less confined to a single manner than we have long believed, and who knew how to adapt himself to a new clientele with a taste for bourgeois scenes, painted in a polished manner, with a minute and porcelain-like execution; or is this the abdication of a prematurely old artist (in 1788, Fragonard was not even 60 years old!), who agreed to see his name at the bottom of an engraving that reproduced a painting which he had only designed? In considering the refinement of color, the simple intelligence of composition, the powdery quality, present here but missing even in the best works of Marguerite Gérard, we cautiously lean toward the first of these two hypotheses.

PROVENANCE

Formerly collection of the King of Poland, Stanislas-Augustus Poniatowski (1732-1798), (valued at 200 ducats in the catalog manuscript of the collection; see L. Réau, 1957). In the Lazienki Summer Palace at Warsaw, in 1851, on the second floor, in the Cabinet du Roi. Entered the Hermitage in exchange for the *Polonaise* by (?) Watteau in 1895.

EXHIBITIONS

1937, Paris, no. 165, pl. 61; 1955-1956, Moscow-Leningrad, p. 60; 1965, Bordeaux, no. 21, ill.; 1965-1966, Paris, no. 19, ill.; 1969, Budapest, no. 10; 1972, Dresden, no. 15, pl. 34.

REFERENCES (SUMMARY)

(Anon.) "Catalogue des tableaux du Palais de Lazienki à Varsovie," in *Revue Universelle des Arts,* 1856, v. III, p. 58; L. Dussieux, 1878, p. 533; R. Portalis, 1889, pp. 27, 72; L. Dimier, 1913, p. 32; L. Réau, 1929, p. 188, no. 102; L. Réau, 1957, p. 157, pl. 59; Ch. Sterling, 1957, p. 52, with color pl.; mus. cat., 1958, v. I, p. 346, pl. 277; G. Wildenstein, 1960, p. 320, no. 523, pl. 124; W.-F. Lewinson-Lessing, 1963, no. 82, color ill.; J. Thuillier, 1967, pp. 12, 54, 72, with color pl., pp. 73, 74; D. Wildenstein and G. Mandel, 1972, no. 546, ill.; P. Rosenberg and I. Compin, 1974, p. 274, ill. p. 275.

RELATED WORKS

Engraved by Nicolas-François Regnault in 1788 (see R. Portalis, 1889, p. 322); in a medallion of 1790 by J.-Ch. Charpentier, the central group alone is reproduced, as a pendant to *The Lock* (No. 59).

P. R.

Jean-Pierre Franque

1774 Le Buis (Drôme) - Paris 1860

The twin brother of Joseph, Jean-Pierre Franque pursued a common career with his brother for a long time. They became the concern of the National Assembly, which in a decree of 15 January 1792 agreed to supplement their feeble financial support and assign them as apprentices to David, who accepted by sending a letter of the most beautiful "Revolutionary" élan (cf. E.-J. Delécluze, 1855, pp. 139-140). In 1796, when Delécluze visited David's studio for the first time, he saw Jean-Pierre Franque help David sketch his *Sabines* and heard him praising already the "primitivist" system of Maurice Quaï (*op. cit.,* pp. 187-188). J.-P. Franque's originality, or at least his independence from David, was certainly confirmed by the theme of his first Salon painting (1806), *Songe d'amour causé par*

la puissance de l'Harmonie. It was deposited by the Louvre at Valence in 1872 and disappeared in the fire at the museum in 1969 without ever having been photographed. In 1807, the artist participated in the *Eylau* competition (sketch no. 25 was registered as the work of Pierre Franque in the documents of the Arch. Louvre, cf. Y. Cantarel, 1973, p. 111). The very strange *Allegory of the Condition of France* (No. 61) dates from the Salon of 1810. It was one of the most "Ossianic" paintings of the period because of its style, which is an even more interesting adherence than a simple conformity of subject matter.

The collaboration of the two brothers was proclaimed clearly at the Salon of 1812 with the *Bataille de Zurich.* The painting still belongs to the Masséna family which had commissioned it at that time. This collaboration continued in the Salon of 1814 with a *Hercule arrachant Alceste aux Enfers,* which must be distinguished from a painting with the same subject signed by Joseph Franque and exhibited in 1806. Beginning in 1814, the careers of the two brothers separated. Joseph became professor at the Academy of Fine Arts in Naples (after having been named professor of drawing at the Academy of Carrara in 1813 as the successor of Frédéric-Jean-Baptiste Desmarais). Jean-Pierre continued to exhibit large paintings of religious or mythological history, done in a rather emphatic style, such as *Josabeth dérobant Joas aux fureurs d'Athalie* (Salon of 1817, Nîmes); the *Conversion de Saint Paul* (Salon of 1819, Dijon), which served as a pattern for a tapestry at the Gobelin firm; *Jupiter endormi dans les bras de Junon sur le mont Ida* (Salon of 1822, Montauban); *Angélique et Médor* (Salon of 1822, Angers). Besides those works shown at the Salons, we should mention a *Bergère fuyant l'orage* from the year 1821 (Dijon, Musée Magnin); the *Monument à Clotilde de France, Reine de Sardaigne* [† 1802] *érigé à Naples,* acquired by Louis XVIII in 1818 and sent by the Louvre to Mâcon in 1872; the *Justice veillant sur le repos du monde,* painted in collaboration with Jean Alaux in 1827 (decoration of the former Conseil d'État at the Louvre) and deposited at Quimper; *Saint Jean-Baptiste reprochant à Hérode son adultère* (1828, Paris, Église Saint-Jean-Saint-François), a simple transposition of Pierre-Narcisse Guérin's *Hippolyte,* as L. Rosenthal observed (1900, p. 257).

After 1830, while continuing to exhibit several religious paintings in the Salons (1844, 1851 to 1853), Franque became involved with the restoration of the Versailles museum and painted innumerable, insipid historical portraits that did little for the artist's image. The Versailles museum has more than 60! Others can be seen at Saint-Malo *(Duguay-Trouin),* Valenciennes *(Louise de Bourbon),* Dreux *(Louis-Philippe),* Metz *(Marquis de Marbois),* etc. The *Nodier* at Besançon, mentioned by Thieme and Becker, has disappeared from the museum. J.-P. Franque also worked in the Galerie des Batailles, often with Alaux.

His style is difficult to define, but at its best represents an attempt at strange light effects, a taste for eloquent academic poses, a use of glossy color, a clear overstepping of Davidian correctness. His approach is close to that of François Gérard, a brilliant and polished history painter, who carried over from his Ossianic experience a certain attraction for obscure and mysterious effects. Also to be noted is the fact that in 1832 Jean-Pierre Franque was selected to enlarge Gérard's *Bataille d'Austerlitz* (Versailles) under his direction (cf. Y. Cantarel, 1973, p. 112).

Not to be ignored is Jean-Pierre's brother, Joseph (1774 Le Buis-Naples 1833), related to his brother by style and structure as well as by blood. He, too, made his first appearance at the Salon of 1806 with a *Hercule arrachant Alceste des Enfers,* sent by the Louvre to Meudon (?) during the 19th century. His *Daphnis enseignant à jouer de la flûte à Chloé,* engraved by Landon and sent by the Louvre to La Réunion in 1872 (still there?) appeared in the Salon of 1808. Since the Salon catalog of 1810 did not give first names and since Joseph seems to have been a good portraitist, the *Portrait d'Asker-Kan, ambassadeur de Perse,* praised by the critics of the time, was probably his work. In any case, his well-known painting at the Salon of 1812, *Marie-Louise contemplant le Roi de Rome dans son berceau* (Versailles) stands out among the portraits and genre scenes. A *Portrait équestre de Murat en costume de Garde du corps du royaume de Naples* can be seen at Malmaison. The Marmottan library and museum have a number of his portraits of the Imperial family, especially portraits of the Bacciochi family. Even at Naples (Accademia), there is a lovely portrait of the Duc de Berry, rich in the effects of romantic lighting (cf. *Arte francese a Napoli,* exh. cat., Naples, 1967, no. 33, pl. XXXVIII). Finally, there was a recent, fortunate discovery of Joseph Franque's last Salon painting, the *Scène de l'éruption du Vésuve* (1827) acquired by the Philadelphia Museum of Art after an exhibition of neo-classical paintings at the Heim Gallery, London (1972, no. 21, ill.), a large work with bright colors and strong, touching movement.

J. F.

61
Allegory of the Condition of France Before the Return from Egypt

"Allégorie sur l'État de la France avant le retour de l'Égypte"
Plate p. 208 and color pl. p. 26
Canvas; 261 × 326; s.l.l. *Franque* (initial illegible)
Salon of 1810, no. 342
Paris, Musée du Louvre

The attribution of this painting presents some difficulties, since it is signed with the single name of Franque, and neither the Salon catalog nor Landon specified a first name (nor, for that matter, did Forbin's list of 1824). However, the twin brothers Jean-Pierre and Joseph sometimes worked together; there is evidence for this in the case of the *Bataille de Zurich,* which was in the Salon of 1812 (see the *Journal de l'Empire* of 23 December, quoted by Y. Cantarel, 1973, p. 113: "Messrs Pierre and Joseph Franque have jointly produced a *Bataille de Zuric* [sic], which is better executed than the allegory that one of them, I do not know which, exhibited at the last Salon"). It was the same for the *Hercule et Alceste* in the Salon of 1814. However, Villot's inventory (c. 1850) and previously the MR inventory during the Restoration attributed this work to Jean-Pierre. This should have been taken seriously, since the MR inventory was drawn up during Franque's own life-time, and less than 15 years after the Salon of 1810. Bellier and Auvray, on the other hand, followed by Benoît and all later authors, have peremptorily assigned this picture to Joseph Franque. There is, however, in the archives of the Musées Nationaux Français a document from 1819 concerning the purchase of the picture, in which the name Franque is quite definitely preceded by the initial P., which would seem to settle the matter and confirm the attribution of the old inventories.

Landon explained "the meaning of an ingenious allegory, which is in fact perfectly clear" as follows: the entreating figure stretching out her arm to Bonaparte is France, appearing to him in a dream (which accounts for the misty area of clouds that fills the left-hand part of the picture, in contrast to the only clearly defined form, the figure of Bonaparte); "the hero, awakened by the power of this illusion, arises to speed to her aid." France is surrounded by evil deities (including Crime, holding a dagger and the flame of dissension, and blind Fury), while Plenty (with her cornucopia) is shown overturned, as is the Altar of Law. The latter's inscription is fully readable: "France, suffering under an unhappy government, summons from the bosom of Egypt the hero on whom her destiny depends." Pyramids and palm trees are the only direct allusions to the Egyptian campaign. A similar explanation is given in the MR inventory.

Landon spoke highly of the picture. "Its technique reveals an extraordinary talent." He praised especially its skillful lighting that separated the two areas of the composition (the allegorical and symbolic from the historical reality), while at the same time linking them strongly and distinguished the allegorical figures, all the more unreal for being in full light, from that of Bonaparte, in a foreground shadow, and vigorously silhouetted.

Not without justification, Landon's only criticism was for the awkward drawing of the figure of France "whose posture could have been more successfully developed." Gueffier, in his provocative dialogues, *Un Peintre, un Poète et un Compilateur,* was much more critical, to the point of incomprehension: "this mass of fluid, in which I seem to see ghosts" and "the idea is poetic, but it needed a great master to paint it; after Messrs Gérard and Girodet's airborne Caledonians [note this appropriate allusion to pictures of Ossianic subjects], how is one to tolerate this group of shadows, not at all enveloped in mist, and that glides over the canvas instead of swimming in the atmosphere !... For my part, I can hardly comprehend the position of the Emperor. If this apparition is a dream, why is he not asleep ? And if it is real, why does he remain seated ? The first movement of the hero is to arise when his fatherland calls him.... This painting then is badly put together; M. Franque would do very well to content himself with portraits; that of the Persian ambassador is very fine."

In fact, this is one of those rare and important attempts at imaginary painting in the Ossianic tradition;

moreover, neither Gérard nor Girodet would have dared undertake a picture in this wispy, magical style, with its intensified lighting effects, particularly in such ambitious, monumental dimensions. For Landon, curiously, "the author [of this picture] is to be praised all the more for not seeming to follow in the footsteps of any other artist and listening only to his own inspiration." He sold short the importance of the Ossianic tradition to which Gueffier had alluded (see above) and which Jean-Pierre Franque had directly interpreted in his picture for the Salon of 1806, *Le Songe d'Ossian causé par la puissance de l'Harmonie* (placed in Valence in 1872, but destroyed in a fire on 20 May 1969), a fact that can only confirm the often controversial attribution of this picture to Jean-Pierre rather than Joseph.

The recent renewal of interest in pictures with Ossianic subjects could only benefit from this unusual painting, which for many years has been in storage in the Louvre (it had never been catalogued until 1972 !) and was doomed to oblivion. We must admit that the interesting promise of this painting was not fulfilled by the rest of Franque's work, which consists mainly of nondescript historical portraits commissioned for Louis-Philippe's châteaux.

PROVENANCE
Purchased for 2,000 francs at the Salon of 1810 (Arch. Louvre: P⁶ 5 January 1811); appears on the list compiled by Forbin in 1824 of the 132 pictures with Napoleonic subjects that were stored at the Louvre during the Restoration, and of which an exhibition had been planned in the middle of the last century either at the Invalides or at Versailles (see F. Boyer, 1966, p. 278); deposited at the Château de Malmaison in January 1922; returned to the Louvre at an unknown date (INV. MR 1710; INV. 4560).

EXHIBITION
1810, Salon, no. 342.

REFERENCES
C.-P. Landon, 1810, pp. 78-79, ill. 54 (outline engraving by C. Normand); "*Beaux-Arts, Exposition de 1810. Sixième article,*" *Le Moniteur Universel,* 16 January 1811; Gueffier, 1811, p. 96; *Journal de l'Empire,* 23 December 1812; Luxembourg mus. cat., 1831, no. 43 (with no first name); in all subsequent editions the title became *Vision de Napoléon en Égypte (allégorie).* The name of Pierre Franque was finally listed in the 1846 edition (no. 56); Bellier and Auvray, 1882, v. I, p. 586; F. Benoît, 1897, ill., p. 403 (after the engraving published in Landon and as Joseph Franque); F. Boyer, 1966, p. 278; J. Foucart, 1970, p. 76, note 1, ill. I, p. 77 (as Joseph Franque); D. Ternois, 1972, pp. 12-13, ill. 4, p. 12 (as Joseph Franque); summary cat. 1972, p. 167 (as Joseph Franque; the initial *J.* mentioned here seems to have been invented); Y. Cantarel, 1973, p. 116 (as Joseph Franque).   J. F.

Bénigne Gagneraux

1756 Dijon - Florence 1795

In his early youth, Bénigne Gagneraux was a pupil at the drawing school in Dijon founded by François Devosge in 1767. Fascinated by Italy, the young Gagneraux secretly departed for Rome, but insufficient funds forced him to start back to Dijon (1774). During his return journey, he stopped for some time in Marseille, where he won the first prize in a contest conducted by the city's Academy of Painting. In 1775, a competition prize was instituted which granted two scholarships for residence in Rome every four years, one for a painter and one for a sculptor. Gagneraux won the prize the first year, in 1776, with the subject *Marcus Curtius refusant les présents des Samnites,* and he finally realized his stay in Rome, arriving at the end of the year. The young painter lived in the city with Claude Renaud, who had won the sculpture prize. The prize's meager financial assistance immediately forced him to earn

money by painting fans. He also made copies: *Le Triomphe de l'amour* after Baroccio (1779, Dijon) and *L'Ecole d'Athènes* after Raphael (1780), created as a decoration for a room in the Palais des États de Bourgogne.

In 1784, he executed, as an exercise, some large sketches in charcoal and white chalk on the walls of a room in a Carthusian convent (the convent of Sainte-Marie-des-Anges, at the Baths of Diocletian). These improvisations on bacchanal themes and the feast of the gods were admired by many, including: King Gustave III, made him famous in Rome and his future was assured. The King of Sweden admired these works and visited the artist's studio in the company of Cardinal de Bernis, buying an *Œdipe aveugle qui recommande sa famille aux dieux* (Stockholm); he commissioned a pendant to this painting, a *Calypse* (lost), and more importantly, the *Visite de Gustave III au musée du Vatican* (Stockholm), which was a canvas Pope Pius VI liked very much. The Pontif commissioned Gagneraux to paint a replica of this composition (1786), which is today in Prague.

The Swedish King also requested Gagneraux to make a replica of an *Education d'Achille* (1787, Castle of Lofstad), painted the preceding year for Cardinal de Bernis. Negotiations for these commissions were carried out by Francesco Piranesi, who had been assigned to buying works of art for the King in Rome and by Baron Évert Taube, Prime Minister of Gustave III. Baron Taube also bought paintings from Gagneraux for his own collection: *Amour qui a dompté la Force* (1787), *Ariane et Bacchus* (1785), *Hébé qui verse à boire à l'Aigle* (1792), *Psyché transportée dans les airs par les Zéphirs* (1792). These canvases are still in Sweden in the Castle of Lofstad. The artist executed two replicas of this last picture, one for Duke Charles of Sudermania, the brother of Gustave III, and the other for Count Armfelt. It was in 1784, at the moment when Gustave III was traveling in Italy, that Gagneraux made the acquaintance of the sculptor Johan Tobias Sergel, the artistic counselor of the King; the two artists carried on a correspondence, and Sergel owned several works by Gagneraux (two drawings in the Stockholm museum came from his collection).

From 1788 to 1790, Gagneraux painted two large battles glorifying the great Condé for the *Palais des Etats de Bourgogne: Le Passage du Rhin* and *La Bataille de Senef* (now in Dijon; a study, dated 1787, for Condé's horse in the second picture is in Dijon, Musée Magnin). In 1792, Gagneraux painted *Seranus et Servilie* (Dijon) for Mmes Victoire and Adélaïde, daughters of Louis XV, émigrés in Rome. After the assassination of Gustave III (1792), Gagneraux continued to work for the Swedish court; for Duke Charles, he painted the *Nid d'amours* (1792), as well as a replica of his *Psyché*.

Wounded in the uprising of the Romans against the French Republicans in January 1793, Gagneraux had to leave Rome. He went to Florence, where he was well received by the Grand Duke of Tuscany, Ferdinando III, who made him a professor at the city's Academy; he executed his own portrait for the *Gallery of Self-Portraits* in the Uffizi (still hanging there; a copy is in Dijon). The relations of the artist with Sweden became closer; in May 1794, he was named official painter to the Court *("Peintre en Histoire de sa Majesté")*, thanks, it seems, to the protection he received from Baron Reuterholm, counselor of Duke Charles (for whom he also worked), and he planned a trip to Germany to study the painting collections. He proposed to paint a series of pictures illustrating glorious episodes from Swedish history, but his death in August 1795 in Florence prevented this enterprise from being realized. The cause of his death was reported as an accidental fall from the window of his residence; probably, his distress and instability drove him to suicide.

Gagneraux was soon acclaimed a great artist: his *Seranus et Servilie* of 1792 was triumphantly exhibited in 1798 at the Academy of Paris, in hommage to its creator. The importance of Gagneraux, who is at present known chiefly in his native province and in Sweden, should be stressed. His series of 15 line engravings (1792) anticipate those of John Flaxman (R. Rosenblum, 1967a, pp. 179-180, no. 124). His painting, simultaneously icy and sensual, willfully linear and influenced by the study of classical antiquity, is not indebted to the milieu of the Academy of Paris but rather to the international Roman circle of Anton Raphael Mengs and Sergel. His art would influence that of his compatriot, Pierre-Paul Prud'hon.　　　　　　　　　　　　J.-P. C.

62
The Spirit of Peace Halting the Horses of Mars

Le Génie de la Paix arrêtant les chevaux de Mars
Plate p. 136
Canvas; 69 × 93; s.d.l.r. *B. Gagneraux, 1794.*
Geneva, Musée d'Art et d'Histoire

The theme of this allegory is clear: a winged and laurel-crowned spirit holds back the four savage horses of Mars with tethers as thin as threads and prevents them from trampling the grains of wheat, symbols of peace and prosperity. In the foreground, to the right, an inverted torch and broken arms symbolize the end of war. The Geneva painting is mentioned in the *Catalogue des principaux ouvrages de Bénigne Gagne-*

raux, drawn up from now-lost manuscripts of the painter (A. Baudot, 1889). It appears among the pictures painted in Florence during 1793: "Spirit of Peace, 2 *pieds,* 8 *pouces* × 2 *pieds,* 3 *pouces* for the Comte de Sellon" (Baudot, 1889, p. IX). The same catalog mentions an earlier version, in the year 1792, among the pictures executed in Rome: "No. 32, *Le Génie de la Paix,* 1 *pied* 8 *pouces* by 1 *pied* 4 *pouces,* for the Princess of Sweden" (Sophie-Albertine, sister of Gustave III). This painting seems to be lost (B. Sandstrom, 1972, p. 77). Moreover, the Mâcon museum has recently bought a version of the *Spirit of Peace* on panel, of small dimensions and admirable quality, which differs in some respects from the painting in Geneva: absence of the white horse to the extreme left, drapery of the young man, different grouping of the emblazoned arms, absence of mountains in the background. An inscription on the back dates the picture 1791. Consequently, Sandstrom (*ibid.* p. 77) proposes that *The Spirit of Peace* was executed in three versions : the one in Mâcon (1791); the one lost, owned by Princess Sophie-Albertine (1792); and finally, the one owned by the Comte de Sellon, which is exhibited here (1793-94).

But the present author's proposal, in 1972, that the Princess' painting was actually the one in Mâcon, is not entirely impossible. The dimensions are approximately the same (about 43 × 54 and 41 × 59; the dimensions of the picture in Geneva also do not exactly agree with those of the painter's catalog). A more troubling fact is that the picture in Mâcon possesses a pendant, *Phaéton effrayé par le signe du lion* (showing a quadriga seen frontally, in a cloudy sky). In fact, Gagneraux painted a pendant to the *Spirit of Peace* in Florence in 1794, for Princess Sophie-Albertine, and there is some ground to believe that it depicted a *Phaéton* (Sandstrom, *ibid.,* p. 78); is this the painting with the same subject mentioned in no. 43 of the painter's catalog for the year 1794 ("1 *pied* 8 *pouces* by 1 *pied* 4 *pouces,* for M. XXX"), or is it another version? The problem is complicated even further by the date on the back of the second picture in Mâcon—1790; but it could be wrong, since it appears evident that the two little canvases were pendants executed at the same time. We tend to believe that the two paintings at Mâcon were those of the Princess of Sweden; Brigitta Sandstrom now inclines toward this solution, as she has indicated to us (written communication).

Moreover, the set of *Dix-huit estampes au trait, composées et gravées à Rome, par Gagneraux* includes a line engraving of *The Spirit of Peace* dated 1792 (no. 15), which differs from the Mâcon picture only in tiny details (the head of a fourth horse appears between the heads of the two chargers to the right); this engraving seems to be of Princess Sophie-Albertine's painting, as Baudot suggested (1889, p. 43).

We know that the Swiss philanthropist, the Comte Jean-Jacques de Sellon (1782-1839), to whom the painting belonged, traveled at the age of 12 to Rome, where he was greatly affected by the massacre of the French; he then went to Tuscany, where the death penalty had been abolished. He later committed himself to humanitarian concerns, founding a *Société de la Paix* in 1830. Because of its subject, the picture by Gagneraux must have appealed to him. There is reason to believe that it was bought in Florence in 1794, probably by the parents of this young boy. The painter worked on several projects for the De Sellon family: a *Portrait des deux filles du comte de Sellon* (lost), engraved in the set already cited (no. 1; Baudot, *ibid.,* p. 48), which probably depicted the sisters of J.-J. de Sellon; two paintings of 1794, *Des amours qui jouent avec un lion* and *Les vestales qui reçoivent des mains de Metellus le palladium,* which in Gagneraux' catalog are mentioned as belonging to the Comte de Sellon (Baudot, *ibid.,* nos. 40 and 41, p. 45).

A line drawing in Dijon (see Related Works), entitled *Apollon sur son char* shows only minimal differences with the painting in Geneva; the pen lines, purposefully dry and anonymous, make judgment difficult. Is it a drawing by Gagneraux redoing his composition one last time, or is it a pupil's exercise following the painter's composition?

The Spirit of Peace appears to be one of the Burgundian expatriate's masterpieces. Strangely delicate, it offers an example of a purified and neo-classicism based on the study of antique reliefs and vase paintings. Gagneraux' chiseled and suave art deserves to be better known.

PROVENANCE
Geneva, Jean-Jacques de Sellon Collection (MS. cat. no. 75); given to the Musée de Genève by J.-J. de Sellon in 1837.

REFERENCES
A. Baudot, 1889, p. 45; A. Chabeuf, 1913, p. 78; Thieme and Becker, v. XIII, p. 67; L. Hautecœur, mus. cat., 1948, p. 29; B. Sandström, 1972, p. 77; J.-P. Cuzin, 1972, p. 465.

RELATED WORKS
Same subject (canvas; 41 × 59); inscription on back: *Gagneraux 1791,* Meindorff Cresse Collection. Acquired by the Musée de Mâcon in 1969 (Cuzin, 1972, p. 465, n. 12, fig. 4).

Same subject (canvas; "1 *pied* 8 *pouces* by 1 *pied* 4 *pouces,* for the Princess of Sweden," painted in Rome in 1792 (Baudot, 1847, no. 32, p. 46). The same as the preceding work ?
Same subject line engraving, signed *B Gagneraux inv. sculp.*

Romae 1792 (no. 15 of the set *Dix-huit estampes au trait, composées et gravées à Rome par Bénigne Gagneraux.*
Same subject, line drawing (pen; 246 × 325); Dijon (Joliet Bequest, 1928).

J.-P. C.

Jacques Gamelin

1738 Carcassonne 1803

Gamelin was one of the very rare French painters of the 18th century endowed with a strong personality who did not make his career in Paris. Coming from a family of drapers that had originated in the Loire and settled in Carcassonne, he was at an early age put under the protection of the Baron de Puymaurin, one of the principal art connoisseurs in southwestern France, who was among the founders of the Academy of Toulouse, afterwards the Society of Fine Arts of Montpellier. Thanks to him, Gamelin was able to study in Toulouse under the direction of Chevalier Rivalz, and then in Paris (1764). Although he failed to win the Grand Prix, his protector sent him to Rome, where he spent ten years. He attained there a position so brilliant that he was named professor of the Academy of Saint Luke in 1771, and he worked for Pope Clement XIV. Upon the death in 1775 of his father, who left him a small inheritance, he returned to France and settled in Toulouse. He worked for a long time on his *Nouveau recueil d'ostéologie et de myologie dessiné d'après nature,* published in Toulouse in 1779, which was a financial failure. His reputation extended, nevertheless, over the entire southwest of France. He accepted the direction of the schools of the Society of Fine Arts of Montpellier (1780-83). The enterprise being unsound, he settled in Narbonne. There, he played a certain role during the Revolution,

among the *sans-culottes.* After having been painter of the army at the camp of Boulou, he settled in Carcassonne in 1796 as a drawing professor at the Ecole Centrale de l'Aude and as organizer of the museum.

His work, restored to its proper place by the exhibition at Carcassonne in 1898, numerous articles by Julien Yché published from 1901 to 1909, and the important exhibition at Carcassonne in 1938, is easy to distinguish; its willfully caricaturing approach often comes close to that of the younger Goya, through his particular figural style and his intense and often bizarre color. His œuvre is abundant and varied, and well represented in the museums of Carcassonne, Béziers and Montpellier. To be noted especially are the genre paintings (often on panel and of small dimensions, which take up the Dutch tradition with a biting and naïve humor), the battle scenes (as captivating as they are original), and the large drawings also of combats (often on blue paper and in the form of a frieze)—all of which illustrate the originality of an artist who cannot be classified. Gamelin was more at ease with small formats (with certain exceptions) than he was with the numerous large religious pictures he did for the churches of Carcassonne and Narbonne, where the compositions are at times a bit awkward.

A.S.

63
The Deluge

Le Déluge
Plate p. 53
Canvas; 230 × 217; s.d. l.m. *Jacques Gamelin pinx.* 1779
Carcassonne, Église Saint-Vincent

We still know very little about this painting discovered in 1961-62 by M.-P.-M. Auzas and Canon Gabriel

Sarraute, who has kindly furnished the following information. It seems to be part of a series of seven canvases of analogous dimensions, three of which are in the church of Saint-Vincent and four in the treasury of the cathedral of Saint-Michel, most of which illustrate the mystery of the cross. The Deluge is a theme often treated by painters at the end of the 18th and early 19th centuries—cf. the canvases by Jean-Baptiste Regnault, No. 149; Henri-Pierre Danloux, No. 26; and the slightly later version by Anne-Louis Girodet (Louvre). In these, the theme was treated not as a biblical subject but rather as a recollection of the loves of Phanon and Sémire in the celebrated poem by Salomon Gessner—

love triumphing over death and the unleashed elements of nature.

PROVENANCE
Unknown.

REFERENCES
G. Sarraute, 1963-1967 (1971), p. 187; *ibid.*, 1968-1970 (1972), p. 129.

RELATED WORK
A drawing of the same subject in the Musée Fabre, Montpellier (INV. 837-1-1140, see J. Claparède, 1952).

A. S.

Étienne-Barthélemy Garnier

1759 Paris 1849

Étienne-Barthélémy Garnier was the student of Louis-Jacques Durameau, Gabriel-François Doyen and Joseph-Marie Vien. His first years remain obscure. In 1787, he won a second prize (*Mort de Sédécius,* Le Mans); in 1788, he beat Girodet to win first Grand Prix (*Mort de Tatius,* Paris, École des Beaux-Arts). As a *pensionnaire* in Rome the work he sent to Paris each year attracted attention: in 1790, a *Saint Jérôme,* an academic study (painting recently purchased by the Musée de Troyes, dated 1791?); *Phèdre et Hippolyte* and *L'Empereur Maurice mis à mort par les licteurs,* sketch purchased by the Society of Friends of the Arts and won by Louis XVI in the lottery organized by the Society. In 1791, Garnier sent an *Ajax ;* a copy of Carracci's *Descent from the Cross,* donated by the government to the city of Lyon; an *Alcibiade et Socrate,* a small painting which was very successful and to which the artist, upon his return to Paris, was to add a pendant—*Anacréon avec sa maîtresse et le jeune Bathylle.* In 1792, he sent a *Dédale et Icare* which Lucien Bonaparte bought in 1804. Garnier had been working for a long time on his large sketch of the *Consternation of Priam* (No. 64).

The uprising against the French in January 1793 forced the artist, who had just returned from Naples, to flee to Florence, then to return to France; he arrived in Paris in March. He exhibited regularly at the Salon beginning in 1795.

Commissioned by the government in 1801 to do a painting, Garnier chose to paint *Une jeune femme allaitant sa mère condamnée à mourir de faim en prison.* Napoleon

offered this picture to Comte Mollien, Minister of the Treasury (the picture was deposited by the Louvre in the Pont-de-Vaux museum in 1872). The painter was commissioned, together with Pierre-Paul Prud'hon and Mérimée, to decorate the ceiling of the Salle de Diane (or the Salle du Candélabre) in the Louvre; there in a tympanum he created *Hercule obtenant de Diane la biche aux cornes d'or.* He was also asked, along with Antoine-Jean Gros, Charles Meynier and others, to do a picture for the new sacristy of Saint-Denis, for which he completed an *Enterrement de Dagobert Ier.* His *Portrait de Napoléon Ier dans son cabinet de travail* (1808), commissioned by Denon for a room of the Château de Versailles was greatly admired, but the work was never put in place. Garnier exhibited *Eponine et Sabinus* in the Salon of 1810; exhibited again in 1814, the picture was purchased then by Louis XVIII and is presently in Angers. In 1810, Garnier worked on his huge *Cortège nuptial de Napoléon et de Marie-Louise dans le jardin des Tuileries,* crowded with anecdotal details. Shown at the Salons of 1810 and 1846, it is today at Versailles. After the fall of the Empire, the painter continued to receive commissions: e.g. in 1816, for a *Henri IV visitant les travaux de la Grande Galerie du Louvre* for above the door at the Tuileries (today at Versailles; preparatory drawing in the Cabinet des Dessins), exhibited in 1818. The Salon of 1828 included three huge canvases by Garnier: a *Vierge de douleur,* commissioned for the altar of the Virgin in the church de la Madeleine in Paris, later given to the Cathedral of Nantes; an *Arbitrage solennel de*

Saint Louis ; and a *Rencontre du duc et de la duchesse d'An-goulême à Chartres* (Chartres). The painter created his *Procession expiatoire à Milan* in 1827 for the church of Saint-Germain-en-Laye, then *Le sourd-muet guéri par Jésus-Christ,* completed in 1833, for the Institution of Deaf-Mutes, rue Saint-Jacques in Paris.

He delivered a *Dévotion aux âmes du Purgatoire* for a church of the diocese of Saint-Pol-de-Léon (commissioned in 1834), a *Vierge avec l'Enfant et saint Jean* for the church of Corbeil (stolen, according to legend, by an unscrupulous priest), a *Saint Vincent de Paul et Richelieu* for the main altar of the Seminary of Cambrai. Garnier

also did portraits, among them, *Cardinal Maury* (Avignon).

In 1816, the painter joined the Institute; in 1829, Horace Vernet was selected over Garnier for the position of Director of the Academy in Rome. The painter was to live 20 more years; he died in 1849, somewhat forgotten.

One of the important artists of his time, Garnier is almost unknown today; two recent purchases by French provincial museums (the *Saint Jérôme* of Troyes and the *Consternation of Priam,* (No. 64) have fortunately thrown new light on him.   J.-P. C.

64
Consternation of Priam and his Family

"*Consternation de Priam et de sa famille après le combat d'Achille et d'Hector*"
Plate p. 130
Varnished gouache on canvas; 74 × 100; s.d.l.m. *Steph. Barth. Garnier Fac./Romae. 1792.*
Salon of 1795, no. 217
Mâcon, Musée des Ursulines

The *Consternation of Priam* was the largest project undertaken by Garnier, a fine artist who has been nearly forgotten. The painting exhibited here is the *modello* produced by the artist in Rome at the end of his residence at the French Academy for a gigantic picture painted upon his return to Paris which took years to complete and was finally exhibited at the Salon of 1800 (now at Angoulême).

For the completion of the large canvas, the artist was awarded a *prix d'encouragement*—a sum corresponding to 10,000 francs and a studio in the Louvre. Garnier had prepared a canvas eight meters long, but since the studio placed at his disposal was no larger than six meters in its largest dimension, the artist was forced to change his composition slightly in condensing it and bringing the different groups closer together (Raoul-Rochette, 1850, pp. 62-63).

But the differences between the sketch and the large composition at Angoulême (see Related Works) are minimal and are confined to certain details in the draperies, weapons and landscape.

The entries for the picture at the Salons of 1795 and 1800 describe the composition in detail and explain its subject, drawn from Canto XXII of the *Aeneid.* Hector's family, gathered on the ramparts of Troy, watch

the hero's defeat and see his body dragged by Achilles' chariot. Hecuba, Hector's mother, is placed on the left; her daughter Laodice embraces her; Polyxena, her youngest daughter sits at her feet. On the extreme left, Paris, responsible for the war, turns away and covers his eyes. In the center, in the middle plane, Andromache has fainted, surrounded by Astyanax, her servants and warriors. The main group consists of Priam, who wants to go reclaim his son's body from the Greeks; at his feet is Panthous, the priest of Apollo, who restrains him by pulling on his cloak; his daughter Cassandra kneels at his knees; and at his left, Antenor explains to him the folly of his plan. Polydamas and another Trojan chief kneel before him.

The sketch was generally admired by the critics of the Salon. "Polyscope" (coll. Deloynes, XVIII, no. 473, pp. 561-562) criticized the composition's lack of unity because of its three groups: "Here are three pronounced areas of activity; thus, there is no longer any unity; our attention is divided between the different groups," but he concluded that "the subject is treated with grandeur and feeling" and added that "Priam's head is of a fine quality; the color of the entire picture is well arranged." Another critic found fault with the color, granting the painter a "sure and light" hand but condemning the picture for having "a bit of those coarse tones that are exaggerations of a fresh palette to which it is dangerous to succumb" and finding in it "the weakness of those whose figures are too many and whose light and shadow are not distributed with grandeur and wisdom" (*Explications...*, coll. Deloynes, XVIII, p. 409).

The commentaries on the large painting of the Salon of 1800 were numerous and verbose. As they had with the sketch, several deplored its lack of unity. Thus, the critic of the *Coup d'Œil sur le Salon de l'an VIII* mentioned this fault, but affirmed, "To copy Homer exactly is to demonstrate the ability to invent" (coll. Deloynes, XXII, no. 623, pp. 295-318). The review appearing in *La Vérité du Museum* (coll. Deloynes, XXII, no. 623, p. 305) considered it the best painting in the exhibition. "It brightens the hope of people of good taste by demonstrating that the art of painting is not yet lost in France, despite the outrages of vandalism," while the review in the *Journal des Débats* (coll. Deloynes, XXII, no. 632) denounced the mercantile spirit in painters of small pictures and praised Garnier for having chosen a gigantic canvas as a counteraction. Otherwise, his painting was derided by *Jocrisse dans le Museum des Arts,* who found that "the artist Garnier cannot boast that he has composed a pretty family" (coll. Deloynes, no. 622, p. 286), and by the *Arlequin au Museum* who sang:

> Hector je plains ton triste sort
> Et ta bizarre destinée;
> Dans Homère on pleure ta mort,
> Mais elle fait rire au Musée.
> (Coll. Deloynes, XXII, no. 629, p. 486).

Pierre Rosenberg has identified an important preparatory drawing for the complete composition in Quimper, most probably done in Rome immediately before the Mâcon sketch, from which it differs in several respects; the result, no doubt, of numerous, highly polished drawn studies, the sheet reveals a magnificent draughtsman, still almost unknown.

The canvas certainly constituted a bit of bravura and affirmed the young painter's ambition to achieve *the* masterpiece which could establish his reputation: the painting of the Salon of 1800 was one of the largest shown in Paris for a long time. The presentation of the different groups in planes by the use of a complex interplay of levels and steps evokes a theatrical mise-en-scene. The clever and supple modeling of the figures, following a principle of elongation, the bright and iridescent colors indicate an elegant and discreet art, if a bit precious and trifling. It was the complete opposite of the art—tense, strange and violent—of Philippe-Auguste Hennequin, as seen in *Les remords d'Oreste,* also a very large painting exhibited in 1800, which the critics readily compared to the *Family of Priam* and radically opposed to David's art, which was sober, vigorously realistic and intensely dramatic.

PROVENANCE
Acquired in Paris in 1971.

EXHIBITION
1795, Salon, no. 217.

REFERENCES
Coll. Deloynes, v. XVIII, no 469, p. 409; no. 470, p. 530; no. 473, pp. 561-562; no. 476, p. 595; *Notice...,* 1843, p. 10; R. Rochette, 1849, p. 2; R. Rochette, 1850, p. 62; J.-P. Cuzin, 1972, pp. 465-466, ill. 6.

RELATED WORKS
Same subject. Canvas; 420 × 596; Salon of 1800, no. 159, exhibited again in 1814, no. 417. Deposited by the Louvre (INV. 4679) in Angoulême in 1872, where it is rolled up and impossible to see; it can be studied through an engraving by Louis-Yves Queverdo.
Preparatory drawing. Quimper, wash; 57 × 67; Silguy bequest, 1864. See J.-P. Cuzin, 1972, p. 466 and ill. 7; exhibited London, 1972, no. 605. See exh. cat., 1974-1975, Paris and Copenhagen (J. Lacambre) .

J.-P. C.

Louis Gauffier

1762 Rochefort - Leghorn 1801

The competition for the Grand Prix in 1784 on the subject of the *Chananéenne aux pieds du Christ* saw two painters share first place: Jean-Germaine Drouais, a student of David who at that time was painting the *Serment des Horaces* in Rome, and Louis Gauffier, the student of Jean-Hugues Taraval, whom Diderot considered a late disciple of François Boucher. The award to these two painters would appear to symbolize the opposing movements which then animated artistic life in Paris. But a comparison of the two works, both at the École des Beaux-Arts, Paris, demonstrates that both works totally belong to the new esthetic.

Although Gauffier was part of the generation now classified too broadly as neo-classical, he distanced himself rather soon from its esthetic, less by the choice of his subjects than by the form he gave them. After his departure for Rome in 1784 as a pensionary at the French Academy, events caused him to spend the rest of his life in Italy, first in Rome until 1793, then in Florence until 1801, with the exception of a brief return to Paris in 1789.

Although he was evaluated by Lagrenée the Elder, then Director of the Academy in Rome, as being "unaccustomed to painting nobly" (*Correspondance des Directeurs,* XV, p. 49), Gauffier, emulating his companions at the Academy, restricted himself at first to history painting. His composition especially reflected the influence of the antique. Thus, Conrad Gessner, in a letter to his father, author of the *Idyllen* and a *Brief über die Landschaftsmalerei,* wrote concernnig Gauffier's *Jacob et Rachel* (painted in 1787, exhibited in Paris at the Salon of 1789): "[this painting] is remarkable for its beautiful arrangement, a beautiful composition and very good taste" (quoted by P. Marmottan, 1926, p. 285). But J.-G. Drouais wrote to David about this same work: "Gauffier has exhibited a small painting which is charming and above all amazing for its rendition; it is like a miniature" (J.-L.-J. David, 1880, I, p. 42).

These two opinions defined very well Gauffier's entries in the Salons of 1789 and 1791. *Alexandre et Ephestion* (Florence, Palazzo Pitti) revealed a somewhat Hellenistic grace suggested also by the title, *Auguste et Cléopâtre après Actium* (a painting now lost). The subjects he drew from Roman history all exalted the feminine virtues: *Cornélie* (Fontainebleau) or the *Générosité des femmes romaines* (Poitiers). Despite their execution, which displays a concern for rigor and severity, these works tend toward the sentimental in attitude and expression, a taste for "polish" and a technique a bit precious in its love of detail.

One of Gauffier's most characteristic features was his fondness for placing his subjects into a landscape. The reason for this preference was his contact in Rome with a group of artists including Nicolas-Didier Boguet, Jean-Joseph-Xavier Bidauld, François-Xavier Fabre and northern and British artists.

Forced to leave Rome in January 1793, after reprisals against the French were undertaken as a result of the news of the execution of Louis XVI, Gauffier and his wife, his former student, Pauline Châtillon, fled to Florence. There, in a very cosmopolitan and cultured circle of Englishmen and Russians, he gathered a group of patrons attracted by the genre he adopted. He painted society in the form of individual portraits, often in a landscape, or groups in a room inspired by English portraitists and "conversation pieces." His very exacting but elegant execution and the accuracy in evoking the environment of Rome, Florence or the Tuscan countryside were extremely successful, measured not only by the originals we have today but also by a kind of *liber veritatis,* in the form of tiny copies which the artist made as reminders.

During these years, he brought back from his travels in the Apennines very sensitive and delicate views which presaged the best of the landscapists of the following generation. Condemned as a "traitor" by the Convention for having consorted with "the enemies of the Fatherland," Gauffier was nevertheless able to renew contact with his country as soon as the French arrived in Tuscany, and afterwards he did a portrait of Lucien Bonaparte and his entourage. Recalled to Paris in 1801, he died at Leghorn just as he was about to embark. His death interrupted a career which might have been that of portraitist for the Empire, leaving the field open to François Gérard and Robert Lefèvre.

J.-F. M.

65

Convent of Vallombrosa and the Arno Valley seen from Paradisino

Le Couvent de Vallombrosa et le val d'Arno vus du Paradisino
Plate p. 141
Canvas; 28 × 40
Montpellier, Musée Fabre

The Camaldules monastery, retreat of Saint Jean Gualbert, rebuilt in 1697 by D. Everard Nicolini, is located in the Apennines, close to the source of the Arno. Antoine-Laurent Castellan, a companion of Fabre (who accompanied himhere in 1798) and of Gauffier, described this location: "This wild spot, which was first named Aqua Bella, was called Vallombrosa. Indeed, the thick and black foliage of the beeches and pines, the steepness of the cliffs which only allows the sun to reach the base of the valley long after sunrise, the clouds and fog which often cover it give it a wild, somber and melancholy character which is well—suited to contemplation and religious meditation" (*Lettres sur l'Italie,* 1819, III, p. 316).

The features of this scene, which also inspired Lamartine, along with the coolness of the water and the forest, made it a favorite spot foreigners: Englishmen and exiled Frenchmen residing in Florence.

At least one stay here by Gauffier is precisely dated. The Musée Fabre in Montpellier owns a very large drawing by the artist, done with black chalk, which copied this view exactly. On the back the date 8 August 1796 is inscribed. This squared drawing (Inv. 837. I. 837), gives the indications of tones and nuances.

Fabre owned at least four views of Vallombrosa painted by Gauffier (see Related Works), one of them (INV. 825. I. 114), nearly identical to another painting, s. d. 1799, owned by the Musée Marmottan in Paris, reproduces the same view with the addition of several people on the terrace.

The sincerity of vision, the accuracy of the luminous accents lead us to believe that this view was painted directly on location, like the one at Montpellier (INV. 825. I. 113), as Fabre noted himself on the back. The ordering of the planes is due less to an abstract spirit of order and clarity than to the construction of nature herself. Outside of the academic restraints still weighing on this genre (it was in 1800 that Valenciennes, the creator also of many spontaneous studies that can be seen in large number at the Louvre, published his *Éléments de perspective*), this delicate vision is a perfect testimony of the moment of transition which these years represented for landscape painting in Italy. It preceded by a third of a century the direct vision which Jean-Victor Bertin's students and especially Jean-Baptiste Corot would express in Rome.

PROVENANCE
F.-X. Fabre Collection; gift to the Montpellier Museum in 1825 (INV. 825-I-115).

REFERENCES
Mus. cat., 1859, no. 220; E. Michel, mus. cat., 1879, no. 493; *ibid.* 1890, no. 191; G. d'Albenas, mus. cat., 1904, no. 258; *ibid.* 1910, no. 258; *ibid.* 1914, no. 258; A. Joubin, mus. cat. 1926, no. 554; P. Marmottan, 1926, p. 297; R. Crozet, 1941-1944, p. 111.

RELATED WORKS
A drawing showing an almost identical view, three drawings and three oil paintings showing the same spot owned by Montpellier, Musée Fabre (INV. 837-I-837 to 840 and INV. 825-I-112-114). Another view of the same site, almost identical to one of those at Montpellier, is owned by the Musée Marmottan in Paris. The painting for which this was a careful study just appeared at a sale at Christie's, London, 13 December 1974, no. 80 (82.5 × 114).

J.-F. M.

66

Portrait of Doctor Penrose

Portrait du docteur Penrose
Plate p. 147 and color pl. p. 20
Canvas; 69 × 53; s.d.l.r. *L. Gauffier, / Flor. 1798*
Minneapolis Institute of Arts, The John R. Van Derlip Fund

One of the most successful of the numerous portraits painted by Gauffier in Florence after 1793, this painting portrays Thomas Penrose (1769-1851), son of the poet of the same name.

Combining his talents as a portrait and landscape painter, the artist has placed his model on one of the terraces of the Boboli Gardens, while unfolding in the fine Tuscan light the panorama over Florence and the hills of Fiesole.

Thomas Penrose, then 29 years old, was not an artist, as the sketchbook and pencils might lead us to believe. After publishing *A Sketch of the Lives and Writings of Dante and Petrarch* in 1790, he had left England in 1792 and had gone to Florence, where in 1794 he had become secretary to W.F. Wyndham, Ambassador of the United Kingdom to the Grand Duke of Tuscany. He was active in English circles and became particularly close to Lord Holland and his friend and future wife, Lady Webster, whom Gauffier also portrayed (England, private collection; sketch or smaller copy in Montpellier, Musée Fabre; see J.-F. Méjanès, 1974, no. 6). Penrose probably met Gauffier through them and asked him to do his portrait. On 6 March 1798, he wrote to the recently remarried Lady Holland, "Gauffier has just finished my Phiz and made a good picture" (British Museum, Dept. of Manuscripts, Holland papers, MS. 51650, fol. 37; published by Philip Bordes, 1974).

The portrait had been preceded by a drawing now at the National Museum of Ancient Art in Lisbon (INV. no. 1059). The squaring technique and the quick application of the wash confirm that the purpose of the drawing was to position the figure and was perhaps done for his patron. This perhaps unique example of a preparatory drawing raises the problem of the purpose of the miniscule versions of numerous portraits painted at that time by Gauffier, painted (Montpellier, Versailles, Poitiers, etc.) and more infrequently drawn (*Portrait d'un officier de l'armée cisalpine*, Poitiers). Were they intended as outlines for his patrons or as a sort of *liber veritatis* which the artist had put together as souvenirs of his work that scattered throughout Europe when his models returned to their native countries?

Upon his return to England in 1800, Penrose spent the rest of his life as a village pastor. On this subject, we will quote the appropriate conclusion of Philip Bordes (1974), to whom we are indebted for a very complete study of this work: "Through the monotonous years in an English country village, the portrait hung on the walls of the house, brought back from Italy, a vivid memory of a brilliant and elegant world of diplomats, artists and art-lovers with which he had been in close contact during his youth."

PROVENANCE
Sold in London, Sotheby's, 4 April 1962, no. 56; London, Wildenstein & Co.; acquired by Minneapolis (The John R. Van Derlip Fund, 66-20).

EXHIBITION
1965, Palm Beach, no. 106, ill.

REFERENCES
The Minneapolis Institute of Arts Bulletin, 1966, p. 59, ill. p. 72; *The Art Quarterly*, 1967, p. 294, ill. p. 309; *G.B.A.*, 1967, p. 93, ill. no. 330; *The Connoisseur*, 1967, p. 109, ill. no. 7; [Mrs. Shissler] 1971, p. 178, no. 93, ill. no. 93, Ph. Bordes, 1974, pp. 72-75.

RELATED WORK
A preparatory drawing owned by the Lisbon National Museum of Ancient Art (INV. no. 1059).

J.-F. M.

Baron François Gérard

1770 Rome - Paris 1837

Gérard spent the early years of his childhood in Rome, where his father, married to an Italian woman, was attached to the household of Cardinal de Bernis, the French ambassador to the Holy See. The family returned to France in 1780; and through M. de Breteuil, a minister of the Royal household, for whom his father worked from that time on, François Gérard was admitted to the Pension du Roi, a small establishment founded by M. de Marigny to receive 12 young artists. Gérard studied next in the studio of the sculptor J.-B. Pajou and later in that of the painter Nicolas-Guy Brenet, before entering David's studio in 1786. He won second place in the Prix de Rome of 1789 with *Joseph se faisant reconnaître par ses frères* (Angers)—Anne-Louis Girodet placed first—but had to give up participation in the competition the following year because of his father's death. In April 1791 (as his correspondence with Girodet attests), Gérard was on his way to Italy with his mother and brothers. On his return to Paris in 1793, he obtained lodgings and an atelier in the Louvre and, thanks to David, avoided military duty by serving as juror for the Revolutionary tribunal where, under the pretext of poor health, he sat only twice. He had already shown at the Salons of 1791 and 1793, but he attracted attention at the Salon of 1795 with *Bélisaire,* painted in only 18 days. It was first acquired by M. Meyer, the ambassador from Holland and later formed part of the Leuchtenberg Gallery in Munich. Gérard illustrated editions of Virgil and Racine for Didot, and began to be known as a portraitist with the *Portrait d'Isabey, peintre* (Louvre) at the Salon of 1796 and that of *La Comtesse Regnault de Saint-Jean-d'Angély* (Louvre), which was much admired at the Salon of 1799. The *Psyché et l'Amour* (Louvre) was an enormous success at the Salon of 1798, and the painter's fame was securely established when, in 1800, he received commissions from Bonaparte: official portraits and the Ossian decoration for Malmaison (No. 68). Altogether, the portraits of members of the imperial family, of dignitaries of the Consulate and the Empire, and of European nobles left him little time to develop new compositions. Nevertheless, he exhibited the *Bataille d'Austerlitz* (Versailles) in 1810. From 1814 on, he worked in the service of the Restoration (thanks to Talleyrand) and exhibited a *Portrait en pied du roi Louis XVIII* (Versailles). He received the commission for the *Entrée d'Henri IV à Paris* (Versailles; reduced version at Chartres), a monumental canvas for which Thibault drew the perspective lines and which was presented at the Salon of 1817. In 1819, Gérard painted *Corinne au Cap Misène* (Lyon) for Augustus of Prussia, and later did a replica of this work at the request of Louis XVIII for Mme du Cayla (Salon of 1822). In 1824, he exhibited *Daphnis et Chloé* (Louvre). In 1827, the Salon catalog announced the *Sacre de Charles X* —a vast composition which was not to be completed until 1829 (Versailles; reduced version in Reims, Musée du Sacre). The artist exhibited his *Sainte Thérèse* (No. 70) for only a few days, his immense renown allowing him this privilege. He received every honor: Knight of the Legion of Honor from the time of the establishment of the order in 1802 (he became an officer in 1824), first painter to the Empress Josephine in 1806, professor at the École des Beaux-Arts in 1811, member of the Institute from 1812, Knight of the Order of Saint Michael in 1816, first painter to the King in 1817, Baron in 1819, and was a member of most of the academies of Europe. In addtion, A. Jal was able in 1829 to publish in *Le Peuple au Sacre* (p. 31) a canticle in honor of the painter with the refrain: "Glory be to Gérard, who is a Baron and the first painter to the King! What matter that he is a Baron? he is Gérard! What matter that he is the first painter to the King? He is the King of first painters." Under the July Monarchy, Gérard painted a portrait of Louis-Philippe in 1831. He executed some colossal figures for the history gallery of Versailles: *Le Courage guerrier, La Clémence, Le Génie, La Constance* in 1832. About the same time he again took up the decoration of the four pendentives of the cupola of the Panthéon, which had been commissioned in 1820, begun in 1829 and iconographically modified with the advent of the new regime. This work was not completed until 1836. Throughout his career, Gérard required the assistance in his manifold works of artists such as Charles-Auguste Steuben, Paulin Guérin, and Mlle Godefroid, who entered his atelier in 1812. He left some 30 history paintings, innumerable half-length or bust portraits, 87 full-length portraits, not only known through engravings, but also through the invaluable series of reduced versions acquired at his death by the Musées Royaux (Versailles). No comprehensive study of his œuvre has been made during this century; his portraits are the subject of a thesis by M. Alain Latreille, École du Louvre, 1973.

G. L.

67
Portrait of Larevellière-Lépeaux, Member of the Directory

Portrait de Larevellière-Lépeaux, membre du Directoire
Plate p. 143
Canvas; 160 × 112; s. at the right on the stone *Fᵒ Gerard*
Angers, Musées

Louis-Marie de Larevellière de Lépeaux was born in Montaigu in 1753 and died in Paris in 1824. His parents added the second name, that of a small family property, to distinguish him from his elder brother. His childhood health was poor, and it is reported that the blows he received from his first teacher, an irascible priest, caused the deformation of his backbone that so definitely marked his silhouette. He studied law at Angers, worked for some time in Paris for an attorney, and then returned to Anjou, where he married in 1781. His wife imparted to him a taste for natural history, which he began to study. In 1787, while teaching a botany class at Angers, he was noticed for his talented oratory; this led to his election to the Third-Estate of the *Sénéchaussée* of Angers. At this time, he began to call himself Larevellière-Lépeaux. He participated successively in the work of the Constituent Assembly, the Legislative Assembly and the Convention, but as a Girondin and a combatant against the Montagnards, he had to flee for some time and only returned to the Convention after 9 Thermidor. From the beginning of the Directory, he was one of the five Directors, an office he retained until he was forced to resign on 30 Prairial, Year VII (18 June 1799), following the intrigues of Barras and Bonaparte. During his Parisian residence, he continued to pursue his interest in botany and often spent his evenings in the botanical gardens, at the house of the Thouin. As early as the period of the Convention, he had acquired a small country house at Andilly, in the valley of Montmorency, where he resided for more than a year after leaving his post as Director.

In his *Mémoires,* he recounts his life during the Directory and, notably, "In the *décadi* [a holiday celebrating the last day of a decade in the calendar of the First French Republic] we gathered our friends from the Jardin des Plantes, our good friend Gérard van Spaendonck... Méhul... In the summer, our friends came to pass the *décadi* with us at Andilly" (1895, II, p. 412). It was at this site in the valley of Montmorency that Gérard was to portray him. In the *Introduction* which he wrote for his father's *Mémoires*, Ossian Larevellière-Lépeaux reported under what circumstances the portrait was executed: "François Gérard had not, I believe, been back from Italy for very long, when he insisted on painting a full-length portrait of Larevellière, who certainly hardly dreamed of having one done at a time when, as president of the Directory, he was overburdened with the very critical circumstances of the French government. Gérard achieved a masterpiece in which another friend of my father, Van Spaen-

donck, wished to join by painting the flowers which Gérard had placed in his hand. The affection of the great painter for his model was long-lasting and courageous. It was never altered...." In accordance with this evidence, it is permissible to affirm that it was Gérard van Spaendonck, professor of the Jardin des Plantes during the Revolution, who painted the flowers, and not Corneille van Spaendonck, as is stated in the exhibition catalog, 1878, Paris, *Portraits nationaux*; since that time, no one has bothered to correct the identity of the flower painter. The same uncertainty lies in trying to specify the date when the portrait was completed. The year 1795 was proposed in the lists published in 1852-53 as a supplement to the first volume of *L'Œuvre...* and in 1886, following the edition of the *Lettres...,* and was repeated recently by A. Latreille. This date seems improbable, because Larevellière-Lépeaux only became Director on 26 October and because a summer landscape is depicted. In 1847, Lenormand indicated the date of 1796; the smaller version in the Musée de Versailles has been assigned the date of 1797 since the time of the sale after the artist's death; finally, the engraving by Pierre Adam in *L'Œuvre...* (see Related Works) carries the date 1798 in its margin, and it seems likely that it was executed during Gérard's lifetime and under his supervision. On the other hand, Ossian Larevellière-Lépeaux precisely stated that at the time his father was president of the Directory, an office which the five Directors successively held for three-month periods. Larevellière-Lépeaux, a fervent Republican, reports in his *Mémoires* the role which he played in the anti-Royalist coup d'état of 18 Fructidor (4 September 1797) and explains it by the fact that he was president at the time: "My capacity as president and my discourses in the public meeting of 10 Fructidor had succeeded in showing me to the public as the principal promoter of that day" (1895, II, p. 130). Was this period of the summer of 1797 not the time of "these very critical circumstances" of which his son speaks? The painting never appeared at a Salon; also, the earliest known account is that of a friend of both painter and model—the poet, Jean-François Ducis. He paid a visit to Larevellière-Lépeaux at his retreat in La Rousselière in Sologne, and wrote at the time to Népomucène Lemercier, on 12 June 1805, regarding his host: "His portrait by our common friend, Correggio, is here. He painted him seated, tranquil, dreaming like a botanist about a little flower which his wife gave him. The flower, small and charming, has a German name which means: forget me not. In this family

I have before my eyes the morality of Isaac and Jacob, or one of Plutarch's lives." In this work, which is considered to be one of his most remarkable portraits, Gérard was able to convey the penchant for a modest and retired life of this man, whom Bonaparte nastily described in his *Mémorial de Sainte-Hélène* as "small, hunch-backed, having the most unpleasant appearance one could imagine," recognizing, however, that "he was an honest man, and an upright, learned citizen" (cited by H. Janeau, 1953, pp. 48, 64).

PROVENANCE
Coll. of the sitter; then of his son Ossian; given to the Musée d'Angers in 1843 (INV. no. 66. J. 1881).

EXHIBITIONS
1878, Paris, no. 443; 1932, London, p. 253.

REFERENCES
Ch. Lenormant, 1847, p. 182; *Œuvre du baron François Gérard*, v. I, 1852-1853, ill.; A. Viollet-le-Duc, in H. Gérard, 1867, p. 11; H. Jouin, mus. cat., 1881, no. 66; *Lettres adressées au baron François Gérard*, 1886, v. I, p. 9, v. II, p. 404; E. Regnard, 1889, v. XXIX, p. 591; *Mémoires de Larevellière-Lépeaux,* 1895, v. I, frontispiece ill., pp. XXIV-XXVI; L. Gonse, 1900, p. 43-44, ill.; A. Pérate, 1909, p. 5; mus. cat., 1928, p. 48, ill.; G. Robison, 1938, pp. 197, 289, ill. opp. p. 197; H. de Morant, mus. cat., 1968, no. 68, ill.; A. Latreille, 1973, no. 5.

RELATED WORKS
Reduced version (26 × 19) by Gérard in the collection of 84 painted sketches "done after full-length portraits representing the most celebrated individuals painted by Baron Gérard between 1796 and 1836" (see Ch.-O. Zieseniss, 1961, p. 171), acquired for 10,000 francs by a decree of the Royal Museums on 30 April 1837 (part of no. 26 of the sale of the artist at his house in Paris, 27-29 April 1837), now at Versailles (INV.: LP. 3057, INV. 4774, MV. 4854). The sales catalog and the Inventory of the Paintings of the Royal Museums under Louis-Philippe (L.P.) give the date of 1797 to this version.
A pen drawing by Prud'hon (15 × 12) has at times been identified as a caricature of Larevellière-Lépeaux (see J. Guiffrey, 1924; no. 556; and the Prud'hon exhibition, 1958, Paris, no. 105).
Etching by Pierre Adam, including in the lower margin: *F. Gérard, pinx.* 1798 *Pre Adam sculpt.,* executed around 1825-28, from the drawing by Eugène Devéria, which itself was executed from the smaller version owned by Gérard, and published in *L'Œuvre...,* I, 1852-53.

G. L.

68
Ossian

Ossian évoque les fantômes au son de la harpe sur les bords du Lora
Plate p. 182
Canvas; 184.5 × 194.5
Hamburg, Kunsthalle

According to the testimony of Gérard's first biographers and recent studies, notably the fundamental work of G. Hubert (1967, pp. 243-248), of the various versions of *Ossian* which he painted, it seems almost definite that it was about 1810 that the original version, painted in 1801, was sent to Sweden, and was lost en route in a shipwreck. The present picture, commissioned in 1800 by Percier and Fontaine to decorate the *"Salon doré"* at Malmaison, was finished in the autumn of 1801. It was installed later (Girodet's decoration had not yet been finished) after a trip to England, where it was shown and possibly engraved, and before 1806, when we know, through C.-P. Landon (1806, XII, p. 74), that it was then "placed in one of the rooms at Malmaison." No document instructs us as to when and why it was taken down (it could have been the moment of Napoleon's separation from Josephine, 15 December 1809) and then sold or given to Bernadotte on the occasion of his designation by the Swedish Diet as heir to their throne on 21 August 1810 (he was to succeed Charles XIII in 1818). Bernadotte's concern that he offer "to his future subjects a famous painting which evokes the Scandinavian pseudolegends" (as G. Hubert suggests, *op. cit.,* among other hypotheses) explains persistent efforts to obtain a replica of the lost work. If we are to believe his earliest biographers, the copy was executed in 1809 or 1810 by Gérard himself, and was indicated in 1821 as at the royal castle of Rosersberg, and identifiable with the Hamburg version.

It is important that Bernadotte himself was certainly an admirer of Macpherson's poems, since he named his son Oscar after one of Ossian's heroes, the husband of Malvina and son of the Caledonian bard. In the same vein, Larevellière-Lépeaux (see No. 67) named his son (b. 1797) Ossian. The popularity of Ossianic names is only one of the aspects of the immense vogue the poem enjoyed in France during the time of the Revolution and Empire. The poet Ducis was asked in 1801 to produce a play "with a simulated Ossianic flavor" (cf. N. Schlenoff, 1956, p. 74). Both were friends of Gérard, who not surprisingly was ready to conceive and execute this composition quickly: "An impassioned sketch escaped his hand in less than 40 days," according to the *Journal des Spectacles* (23 November 1801, no. 1, pp. 3-4, cited notably by H. Toussaint, 1974, p. 80). The painting was praised by the critics of the time and endorsed, it seems, by David himself. A critique of the Salon of 1801, which appeared in the *Journal de la Décade* (coll. Deloynes, XXVI, no. 694, pp. 648-652) dealt with this subject:

Although this painting of Ossian by Gérard should not be exhibited publicly until it has been seen at the Salon, it belongs too much to the glory of the school not to publicize it.... It is not an action or a character of Ossian that the painter has captured, as the arts are accustomed to doing, but rather a whole system of the poetry and mythology of the Caledonian bard. One knows how original and poignant is this mythology! It allows the belief that death does not break the ties of love and friendship, that one is near to and understood by the beings one most cherishes... after death, those who are valiant and virtuous will inhabit the aerial palaces of their ancestors.... Here now is the subject of the picture. Ossian, old and blind, having lost his son and his companions in arms, appears to be alone in the world, singing of the heroes of his life and of his grief. His harp comes alive at his touch, the cherished shades of Fingal and Roscrana [his parents, on the right], of Oscar and Malvina [his son and daughter-in-law, embracing, on the left], the bard Ullin and various warriors are brought together on the clouds and grouped around him; the Lora runs at his feet; one sees in the background the aerial Palace of Selma; the moon illuminates this melancholy scene; a wild nature, a Hyperborean and humid sky, phantoms and reflections almost as magical as the moon; such is the painting. As to the execution, the artist does not seem to be concerned. One would say it is as much a game of his brush as of the imagination. Its effect, however, is perfect. One divines the subjects at first glance and the whole poetic system presents itself to the spirit, at the same time as the bard catches the interest of the soul.... We do not believe

that ever before have poetic ideas been so happily expressed on canvas.

The Hamburg version, with some significant variations that make it possibly even more nostalgic (H. Toussaint, 1974, p. 80 rightly notes the somber scarf here attached sadly to Ossian's harp, while it floats on the wind in the Malmaison version or in the Godefroy engraving, and the ruined towers of Selma, while in the original version they have a proud bearing), restores rather faithfully, it would seem, through its equally light and sketchy technique, one of the signal works of nascent Romanticism. We know, principally from Jean-Baptiste Isabey's watercolor—the frontispiece in the edition of Ossian's poems which Napoleon owned—that furthermore it had the approval of the master of France. From 1797 on, Napoleon's taste for Ossian was known (cf. P. Van Thieghem, 1918, and D. Ternois, 1969). He had contributed to the emergence of a veritable vogue and had given these poems a role comparable, for his image as a conqueror, to that of the epics of Homer and Virgil, respectively, for Alexander and Augustus (his illustrious models). Napoleon was to remain faithful to his choice, because even though he lost Malmaison and its decorations (these being the compositions of Gérard and Girodet and also those of Forbin, dating to 1806), the preparation for him, in Rome, of a new Ossianic decoraton was soon conceived, that is, the ceiling for Palazzo del Quirinal which was given to Ingres in 1811 (completed in 1813; Musée Montauban) and was inspired, precisely, by the composition of Gérard.

PROVENANCE
Collection of Bernadotte (?) heir apparent, later King of Sweden as Charles XIV—John; later collection of his descendents (indicated in 1821 as at the royal castle of Rosersberg, in Sweden); Goteborg, Robert Dickson Collection, 1908; gift of Ludwig Hansing to the Hamburg Kunsthalle, 1910 (INV. 1060).

EXHIBITIONS
1974, Paris, no. 74, ill.; 1974, Hamburg, no. 83, ill.

REFERENCES
Coll. Deloynes, v. XXVI, no. 694, pp. 648-652; Ch. Lenormant, 1847, pp. 51, 180; *Œuvre du baron Gérard*, v. II, 1856 (the work is dated 1810 and placed in Stockholm, but the engraving is of another version); A. Viollet-le-Duc, in H. Gérard, 1867, p. 16; *Lettres adressées au baron Gérard*, 1886, v. II, p. 396; P. Van Thieghem, 1918, pp. 61-62; K. von Baudissin, 1924, p. 60; mus. cat., 1926, p. 71; G. Hubert, 1967, pp. 243-244, ill. 4; H. Okun, 1967, p. 348; D. Ternois, 1969, pp. 195-197; E.-M. Krafft and C.-W. Schumann, mus. cat., 1969, pp. 94-95 ill.; H. Toussaint, 1974, pp. 78-80; P. Vaisse, 1974, p. 82; P. Joannides and C. Sells, 1974, p. 361.

RELATED WORKS
Paintings. Of the four versions painted by Gérard, two were destroyed, the original in 1801, lost at sea with the ship carrying it to Stockholm (A. Viollet-le-Duc in H. Gérard, 1867, p. 16) and the version acquired from Gérard in 1832 by the King of Prussia, Frederick William III, destroyed during the bombing of Potsdam in 1945; the copy painted for Prince Eugène is presumably that which entered the Musée National du Château de Malmaison in 1967.
Drawings. Graphite by Gérard (18 × 20), squared, with the overall initial composition (Louvre, Cabinet des Dessins, R.F. 35641). Preparatory studies by Gérard: one representing *Ossian chantant* (Louvre, Cabinet des Dessins, R.F. 35642), and the other, a *Guerrier calédonien, idem,* R.F. 35616).

Engravings. By Jean Godefroy (Salon of 1804, no. 843), by Charles Normand (appeared in C.-P. Landon, 1806, XII, pl. 33 and 1832, I, pl. 50), by Édouard Rosotte (appearing in the *Œuvre du baron Gérard,* II, 1856, with the inscription: *F. Gérard pinxit 1810* and the location: *Stockholm*).
Watercolor. By Jean-Baptiste Isabey (1805), reproducing, with some variations, Gérard's composition, as frontispiece of the volume of the French edition of the poems of *Ossian,* translated by Letourneur, 1777, which belonged to Napoleon (Paris, Bibliothèque Nationale, Réserve des Imprimés, INV. no. Yn4).
For other artists' representations of Ossian, see here No. 80 and exh. cat., 1974, Paris and Hamburg.

G. L.

69
Portrait of the Comte de Fries and his Family*

Le comte et la comtesse de Fries, famille noble de Vienne
Plate p. 187
Canvas; 223 × 163; s.l.l. F° GERARD
Vienna, Kunsthistorisches Museum

With the exception of Charles Lenormant, who assigns an undetermined date after 1802 and before 1805, all authors agree on dating this portrait 1804. In that year, Moriz, the son of the Viennese banker, the Comte Moriz Fries (1777-1826) and his wife, Marie-Thérèse, whose maiden name was Princess Hohenlohe-Waldenburg-Schillingfürst (d. 1829), was born in Paris. This work testifies to François Gérard's growing fame as a portraitist; as Lebreton recalls in 1808, it could be said that "the foremost merit of M. Gérard's portraits is that they customarily recall the spirit, character and usual mental state of the people" (1808, p. 80). Following a technique dear to the artist, the young couple faces the viewer in a domestic setting, the Count in a cavalier's dress with his riding whip in his hand and the Countess seated near her child, who lies naked in his cradle. However, the infant's position more closely resembles the presentation of the heir than a mere anecdotal episode. Gérard painted naked young children several times and thus endowed his portraits with a certain allegorical dimension, notably in 1801 in *Caroline Murat,* accompanied by two children, one in a cradle, as well as in the *Comtesse Zamoïska et ses deux enfants* (1805, Salon of 1808). Here the decor intervenes largely to give the collective portrait nobility and elegance; the portico in the center, recalling in a way the one in the portrait of *Madame Récamier* (Paris, Musée Carnavalet); the wall to the left and the folding-screen on the right restrict a somewhat shallow space in a highly neo-classical manner, despite the opening toward the sky and large trees.

The contrast between the artificial decor, based on the same principle as the background used in photographs, and the reality of the characters create in this portrait an image of durability, the presence of which is as forceful as that of Davidian portraits, although in a completely different style.

PROVENANCE
Remained in the family until 1909; coll. of the banker Rudolf von Güttmann; acquisition of this collection by the Austrian National Museums, 1938; became part of the Kunsthistorisches Museum in Vienna in 1953 (INV. no. 3386).

EXHIBITIONS
1896, Vienna, no. 1933; 1965, Vienna, R. XVI, no. 2.

REFERENCES
J. Lebreton, 1808, p. 79; Ch. Lenormant, 1847, p. 182; *Œuvre du baron François Gérard,* v. I, 1852-1853, ill.; *Lettres adressées au baron François Gérard,* 1866, v. II, p. 404; E. Leisching, 1898, ill. 13; A. Fries, 1903, p. 82; A. Pératé, October 1909, p. 7; K. Blauensteiner, 1940, p. 121; A. Latreille (1973), no. 21.

RELATED WORKS
Etching by Pierre Adam, bearing in above margin the inscription: "*1825 Pre Adam, exécutée d'après le dessin de Devéria, exécutée lui-même d'après la version réduite que conservait Gérard*" and edited in the *Œuvre* (see above) in 1852-53.
Smaller version (32 × 24) by Gérard in the collection of 84 painted sketches (for the origin of these paintings, see

No. 67) presently at Versailles (INV. LP. 3138; INV. 4855; M.V. 4864). The catalog of the Gérard sale (under no. 26) and the Inventory of the paintings of the Royal Museums from the reign of Louis-Philippe (L.P.) give the date of 1804.

G. L.

70
Saint Theresa

Sainte Thérèse
Plate p. 293
Canvas; 172 × 96
Salon of 1827-1828, not listed in catalog
Paris, Infirmerie Marie-Thérèse

Gérard completed this composition early in 1828 for the main altar of the chapel of the *Infirmerie de Marie-Thérèse,* rue d'Enfer, which was an institution founded in 1819 by Mme de Chateaubriand to shelter aged and infirm priests and noble ladies ruined by the misfortunes of the time; this charitable institution carried the name of Marie-Thérèse, daughter of Louis XVI, and wife of his first cousin, the Duc d'Angoulême, Dauphin, son of Charles X. It was, therefore, quite natural to consider decorating the chapel with an image of Saint Theresa of Avila, patron saint of the Princess.

The appearance of this painting of *Saint Theresa* in the Spring of 1828 was such a great event that the press commented at great length. The discourses by Jal give us some insight into the circumstances surrounding its execution: "Mme Récamier wanted the painter of *Austerlitz* to decorate a chapel founded by Mme de Chateaubriand; M. Gérard showed great eagerness to oblige his honorable friends." The close relationship between Gérard and Mme Récamier was of long standing, since he had executed her portrait in 1805 (Paris, Musée Carnavalet), and since she had intervened with him on behalf of Augustus of Saxony's commission for *Corinne au Cap Misène,* which appeared at the Salon of 1819.

She received the work as a gift from the prince and subsequently bequeathed it to the Lyon museum. In addition to Mme Récamier, whom Chateaubriand had known since 1817 and who was also an intimate friend of Mme de Chateaubriand, the writer was also acquainted with the Duchesse de Duras. Gérard executed for her around 1823 a painting illustrating an episode from the novella entitled *Ourika,* which she had published in 1820. In this picture, engraved by Alfred Johannot *(Œuvre du baron Gérard,* II, 1856), the heroine, a black nun, recounts the misfortunes of her existence, while seated on a bench; and her expression as well as her costume prefigures *Saint Theresa.*

At what date did Mme Récamier intervene to obtain from Gérard a gift for the charity so dear to Mme de Chateaubriand through the donation of this painting? As early as 1823, perhaps, if one believes the date given by Charles Lenormant, nephew by marriage of Mme Récamier, in his biography of Gérard. The same date appears in the margin of the etching of 1855 by Charles Bazin, who had made a drawing from the painting during Gérard's lifetime (see Related Works). Perhaps it was the fact that on 30 July 1826, Chateaubriand and his wife settled in the pavilion next to the Infirmerie that induced Gérard to carry through his project. He must have been working on it when Chateaubriand wrote to him on 28 April 1827: "Since you very kindly permit it, Monsieur, Mme de Chateaubriand and I will come next Monday at 2 o'clock to admire your masterpieces and to bring you our sincere thanks. Great talents are charitable. Raphael painted several pictures for poor villages, the price for which could only be paid by glory."

The genesis of the work otherwise remains surrounded by circumspection and, according to Jal, "M. Gérard composed and executed his *Saint Theresa* without telling any confidant the secret of his work; no person spoke of it before it was finished. Mme A... herself, who, they say, lent her pretty hands and feet to the artist, and who could have taken pride in being part of her relative's masterpiece, kept a heroic silence that she alone perhaps was capable of not breaking."

However, Guizot noted in *Le Globe* of 5 March 1828: "A new painting by M. Gérard has been discussed for some time... the painting is to go without an intermediary stop from M. Gérard's studio to the hospital's chapel. We have seen it in the studio, and we regret even more deeply that the Salon is deprived of it. Surely nothing could have given the friends of the arts and the entire public a more exciting and sweet pleasure." Immediately thereafter, L.-V. stated precisely in *Le Globe* of 8 March: "We have seen in our last issue that M. Gérard has finished a *Saint Theresa,* which is admired by everyone fortunate enough to be admitted to his studio. Is it really true that this beautiful painting will not appear in the last days of the Salon? We still hope that M. Gérard will not thus refuse the wish of the public and his friends."

As a matter of fact, Jal reported that after Guizot's article, "For an entire day the distress was great in all the salons of the capital," but, because of Gérard's timidity, "M. de Forbin, whose only desire was the glory of his Salon, fought this repugnance; he reiterated the entreaties to the artist and requested Mme de Chateaubriand to consent to nationalize her private property for several days. M. Gérard... was obliged to yield. *Saint Theresa* was taken to the Louvre, and every distinguished person in Paris rushed to see it."

Guizot had enticed the public with a long and astounding description in *Le Globe,* where he analyzed "poetically the choice morsel which we are not allowed to enjoy"; (Jal): "Saint Theresa, after praying for a long time in the church, perhaps that of the Carmelites of the Incarnation at Avila, has risen to leave. She has been walking slowly, profoundly meditative, preoccupied with the spirit, her heart moved by her pious and tender meditations. Suddenly, as she was passing before a column, the divine object of her ardent hope appeared to her; she raises her eyes and she sees the sky open; she sees there the God whom she has invoked, whom she adores with so much love. A celestial joy floods her soul; suddenly, involuntarily, her body sags; she leans against the column and rests one knee on the ground; her hands are clasped, her head raised, her gaze is fixed upon the blissful vision; she is calm and yet beside herself, enraptured with joy and yet seized by a saintly terror; she has attained the goal of all her wishes; long did she know and search for what she now sees; and yet the vision astonishes her, intimidates her, as does a happiness too great, too strong; it was as unexpected as it was desired. It is Paradise which a thunderbolt opens and toward which her soul leaps, still troubled by a moment of fright. We would speak lengthily if we wished to describe everything expressed by the sublime ecstasy of this charming face...."

"Admirable power of inspiration! The saint does not know all that she experiences, nor does the artist know all that he has caused her to experience. Never, perhaps, has anyone represented so well the alliance of self-communion and contemplation. One feels that a few minutes before the soul of Saint Theresa was closed, concentrated within herself, that she looked only inwardly, seeing nothing of what surrounded her. Then suddenly, at the vision which struck her, her soul leaps out, crosses the immensity of space; mounts, rises and aspires still higher, to unite with the one she contemplates. The intimate meditation has not ceased entirely, a trace of it is still visible; but already the saint is very far from herself, already she is in heaven. And this depth of sentiment and expression bursts forth amidst a perfect beauty and in the most youthful, graceful and pure of forms. The execution is in M. Gérard's best manner, rich in harmony, finesse and suavity. The saint's clothes are ordered with much grace, without any appearance of artificial arrangement. The artist took care to give the church the character of Spanish churches, where the style called moorish is allied with that called gothic without distinguishing the true origins or the precise contributions of either of them. M. de Chateaubriand is going to receive a beautiful present, and it is surely one of the most charming and complete works that M. Gérard has yet given to our school, to which he has already given so much."

Thus it is not surprising to learn that from the time of its appearance at the Salon, *Saint Theresa* achieved "a very brilliant success," according to A. Béraud, who also mentioned that Gérard did not exhibit the *Sacre de Charles X,* which was listed in the Salon catalog (no. 446, "this painting will not be finished until near the end of the exhibition"). For Jal, this was explained by the fact that Gérard "dislikes the stately picture; he never succeeds so well as with his poetic pictures." A. Béraud was ecstatic and saw here the illustration of a passage on religious passion from the *Génie du Christianisme:* "What enraptured reverie this illustrious master has thus inspired! Has his genius alone created these enchanting features? What suavity of brushwork! What exquisite sentiment in the melancholy expression of this adorable face! Such a creation is above all praise; the effect of this angelic head is so powerful that it rivets the eyes of the most severe critics, so that they no longer consider the imperfections which they noted at first in the pose and drawing of the other parts of the figure." Nevertheless, Jal made a long catalog of the picture's faults: "Yes, I could have wished for more austerity in the general tone of the picture, more severity in the arrangement of the drapery, greater elevation with more naturalism in the pose and character of the saintly daughter of Avila; I would have liked to see the passionate eyes of the virgin in ecstasy made a little less dry; M. Gérard, in painting the eyeballs could have employed the successful device which Sir Thomas Lawrence used to enliven the eyes of Little Master Lambton... I could have wished for some disorder in the coiffure of the beautiful Carmelite, who resembles too much the young nuns of the Order of the Visitation painted by the author of *Vert-Vert*. Finally I would have liked to see the charming composition made less stylish." He recognized, however, that "the picture's conception is very ingenious: never perhaps has M. Gérard, who has always infused his compositions with so much spirit, put as much in as he does here. The expression of the young saint is delightful... how pretty she is, this girl who loves with all the might of her Spanish soul ! Here is certainly the mistress of the poet's dreams; but the saint ?..." With this doubt, concerning the interpretation of the subject, he added in an almost ironic manner: "The hands are charming and justify all the praise given to the painting; their movement, their drawing and their color are admirable." He admired Gérard's "brush... caressing and... tender," and compared the effect of the light on the face, contrasted with the shadow of the church, to that which appears in David's *Portrait de Le Peletier de Saint-Fargeau,* on which Gérard could have worked.

Chateaubriand found the painting "incomparable" and informs us, in a letter to Gérard of 20 April 1828 that "*Saint Theresa* is more beautiful than ever" in her solitude, that is, in the chapel of the *Infirmerie,* where she was placed after the close of the Salon. He added: "A crowd is assailing us and we will be obliged to announce fixed days, pending the solemn day of the unveiling. I await that day with impatience, so that I will have the opportunity to manifest to the public my high admiration for your latest masterpiece. But, as I have already told you, I do not overly regret your labor, seeing that it adds to your glory."

The unveiling was set for Tuesday, 3 June 1828. Its reception was not disappointing, as is explained in a letter from Mme de Chateaubriand addressed to the artist on 10 June: "If M. Gérard does not wish to enjoy his triumph, he must a least come and partake of ours; does he believe that we are not conscious of the price and that we are not proud of the honors paid to a master-piece which we owe to his charity, and which the saints and the laity admire equally ? Our good archbishop, who is to officiate Tuesday, came yesterday to spend an hour in front of *Saint Theresa,* to avoid, he told us, the inevitable distractions on the day of the ceremony." The enthusiasm elicited by this work leads to the affirmation that in this work Gérard created a composition which best corresponds to the religious ideal of the Royalists of the "Faubourg Saint-Germain" (written by Bertin the Elder to Fabre; (cf. Pélissier).

In its extremely polished technique, it is still part of the Davidian school, whereas the gesture and the glance evoke the expressive figures of Greuze's manner, continued at the time by Claude-Marie Dubufe. The conception, based on past examples, exists in the last analysis, in total contrast to a work by Eugène Delacroix, who exhibited at the same time *Greece on the Ruins of Missolonghi* (No. 39), another unforgettable yet modern and romantic figure.

PROVENANCE
Executed by Gérard for the chapel of the Infirmerie de Marie-Thérèse, rue d'Enfer (now 92, avenue Denfert-Rochereau, Paris 14e), and given by the artist for this purpose to Mme de Chateaubriand; placed on the main altar of the chapel at the end of April 1828, and unveiled Tuesday, 3 June 1828; it remained in place when Chateaubriand ceded the Infirmerie to the archdiocese of Paris, in 1838.

EXHIBITION
1827-28, Salon, h. c.

REFERENCES
A. Béraud, 1827, pp. 137-138, ill. 61; F.G. in *Le Globe,* 5 March 1828, p. 247; L.V. in *Le Globe,* 8 March 1828, p. 253; A. Jal, 1828, pp. 372-388; Ch. Lenormant, 1847, p. 51, p. 180; *Œuvre du baron François Gérard,* v. II, 1856, ill.; A. Viollet-le-Duc, in H. Gérard, 1867, p. 21; H. Gérard, 1867, pp. 368-370; *Lettres adressées au baron F. Gérard,* 1886, v. II, pp. 315-318; M. Brunet, December 1948, pp. 299-301; Chateaubriand, ed. 1951, v. II, p. 623; L.-G. Pélissier, 1896, p. 73.

RELATED WORKS
A sepia drawing faintly highlighted with white by Bazin (sale of M. le baron Gérard, Paris, at his residence, rue Saint-Germain-des-Prés, 27-29 April 1837, no. 59).
Engravings by Normand (in outline), Jean-Marie Leroux and Charles Bazin in *Œuvre du baron Gérard,* II, 1856 (in the lower margin: "*F. Gérard pt 1823, et Ch. Bazin sc. 1855*").
A copy on porcelain executed at the request of Alexandre Brongniart, director of the Royal Manufactory of Sèvres, by Mme Ducluzeau; begun in November 1828, redone in March 1829 and finished 30 November 1829, it was exhibited 1 January 1830, with the creations of the Royal Manufactory in the Louvre (no. 3); at first kept at the Manufactory of Sèvres, it was lodged in 1875 in the Musée National de Céramique de Sèvres.

G. L.

Marguerite Gérard

1761 Grasse - Paris 1837

Marguerite Gérard personified the typical woman artist of her period who was almost invariably the wife, daughter, sister or in-law of an established artist. The daughter of a perfume distiller, Claude Gérard, she was born in Grasse in Provence on 28 January 1761, but moved to Paris about 1775 to join her sister Marie-Anne, her senior by 11 years and the wife of Jean-Honoré Fragonard. Under her brother-in-law's instruction, she rapidly developed her artistic talents, signing in 1778 her first significant creation, an engraving after a lost work by Fragonard entitled *Le Chat emmailloté.* Several other engravings after Fragonard followed the same year, including *La Première leçon d'équitation, Au Génie de Franklin* and *M. Fanfan jouant avec M. Polichinelle,* the last jointly signed by student and master.

The degree of collaboration between Gérard and her illustrious mentor during the decade of the 1780s is unclear, since no paintings with a joint signature are known today, although in 1786 the engraver Gérard Vidal issued two pendant prints, *L'Enfant chéri* and *Le Premier pas de l'Enfance,* with the legend *"peint par M. Fragonard et Mlle Gérard"* and in 1793 the engraver Nicolas Ponce exhibited two unidentified prints *"après Fragonard et la Citoyenne Gérard"* in the Salon (no. 403; see also No. 71). On the basis of these prints, stylistic evidence and the notoriously close relationship between pupil and teacher, scholars and connoisseurs have discerned collaboration in works attributed to both artists, including Fragonard's *The Kiss* (No. 60) and Gérard's *La Liseuse.* If the themes of courtship, motherhood and domesticity attracted both artists, by the mid-1780s, Marguerite Gérard seems to have evolved an original genre style inspired by the Dutch 17th-century masters, a style distinguished by its quiet intimacy and charming verism.

Although Mlle Gérard was prohibited election to the Royal Academy due to the 1770 resolution restricting the number of female members to four (the number reached in 1783 with the election of Mmes Vigée-Lebrun and Labille-Guiard, who retained their places until the Academy's dissolution in 1793), the artist had established a considerable reputation by the late 1780s. In his report of 1808 on the fine arts, J. Le Breton remarked that in 1789, Mmes Labille-Guiard, Le Brun, Vallayer-Coster, and Mlle Gérard were the only widely respected women artists. Despite her brother-in-law's royal connections, Marguerite Gérard survived the turmoil of the Revolution, presenting her valuables with other women artists to the National Assembly on 7 September 1789, and continued to enhance her renown through regular contributions to the Salon exhibitions from 1799 to 1824. The proliferation of prints after her paintings by Gérard Vidal, Antoine de Launay and her brother Henri Gérard popularized her work with the general public, which appreciated the anecdotal quality of her genre scenes.

By the late 1790s, Mlle Gérard had modified her Metsu-Terborch manner, incorporating classical types and a languid coolness into her disarmingly sentimental characterizations. Her illustrations for the 1796 and 1798 editions of the *Liaisons dangereuses* and the *Amours de Faublas* reflect this admiration for the neo-classicists and for David himself, who later acknowledged to Fragonard the talent of Mme Gérard. In the Salon of 1801, her second, Gérard received a *prix d'encouragement ;* in 1804, a gold medal; and, in 1808, was honored by the Emperor's purchase of her only recorded contemporary history painting, *La Clémence de Napoléon à Berlin.* During the Empire and the Restoration, Marguerite Gérard's individual blend of ingratiating sentimentality, meticulous realism and neat order appealed to both the critics and the prosperous bourgeoisie which purchased her small-scale canvases and panels, so well-suited to hanging in the home. A prolific painter, Gérard exhibited 42 works in 11 Salons until 1824, when severe criticism of the repetitious, passé nature of the artist's works seems to have precipitated her retirement. However, she continued to live comfortably in Paris until her death on 19 May 1837, at the age of seventy-six.

Since Marguerite Gérard never married, Fragonard biographers have delighted in romantic interpretations of her supposedly illicit relationship with her brother-in-law, while her critics have analyzed her preoccupation with domestic subjects as a reflection of thwarted maternal desires. Although several extremely affectionate letters from Mlle Gérard to Fragonard have been preserved, they seem to date from about 1803, when

Gérard was at the height of her fame and her mentor in retirement at the age of seventy-one. It seems much more reasonable to assume that rather than fitting the stereotype of the frustrated, faithful lover, Marguerite Gérard chose to immerse herself in her art. It is reveal-ing that from a very early age she demonstrated her independence from her master by creating an individual genre style to which she remained loyal throughout her highly productive, successful career.

S.R.

71
The First Step

Le Premier pas de l'enfance
Plate p. 59
Canvas; 44 × 55
Cambridge, Mass., Fogg Art Museum, Gift of
Charles E. Dunlap

If the radical change in the concept of the family in the 18th century may be attributed primarily to the theories expounded by such enlightenment thinkers as Rousseau, Diderot and Buffon, the new sentimental attitudes towards marriage and childhood were popularized through prints after paintings inspired by the cult of motherhood and domestic bliss. Rather than a mere legal contract based on material interests, marriage was to foster personal happiness through the natural, harmonious relationships between spouses and between parent and child. Rather than delegating their offspring to wet nurses, servants and boarding schools, parents were encouraged to savor the delights of child-raising themselves, to be affectionate parents responsible for the development of their children's characters. Such efforts would be amply rewarded by their children's love, virtue and achievements.

The nucleus of the enlightenment family was the ideal mother whose own emotional fulfillment would be realized through the happiness of her husband and children. The joys of maternity were duly celebrated by Greuze, Boucher, Aubry and Fragonard during the 1760s and 1770s, but it was Marguerite Gérard who perpetuated this theme in the style of her master, Fragonard, establishing herself as the preeminent painter of maternal genre scenes from 1785-1825. *The First Step*, dating from the first decade of Mlle Gérard's remarkable career, testifies to the artist's early technical proficiency, her debt to her brother-in-law Fragonard and her predilection for sentimental genre scenes. In addition to this painting's pendant, *L'Enfant Chéri* (Cambridge, Mass., Fogg Art Museum), three works of the same period and style survive: *L'Élan de la Nature* (Leningrad, Hermitage), *Le Baiser de l'Innocence* (private collection), and *L'Enfance de Paul et Virginie* (New York, Wildenstein & Co.). In every painting, a pudgy, blond baby is the center of worshipful, female attention in a leafy sylvan setting. Since lush, outdoor settings are exceptional in Gérard's œuvre, the allusions to the fecundity and purity of Nature uncorrupted by civilization would seem to be deliberate in these images of maternity and innocence. Such a conclusion is confirmed by the title of the Hermitage canvas and by the treatment of a scene from the contemporary romance, Bernardin de Saint Pierre's *Paul et Virginie*, published in 1787. The formula for Gérard's rendition of the infancy of Paul and Virginie had been well established in the four paintings, *The First Step* and *L'Enfant Chéri* engraved by Gérard Vidal and Regnault in 1786 and *L'Élan de la Nature* and *Le Baiser de l'Innocence* engraved by Henri Gérard, the artist's brother, in 1788.

The First Step and its pendant *L'Enfant Chéri* are unsigned and undated but have traditionally been attributed to both Marguerite Gérard and her more illustrious master, Fragonard. The legend *"Peint par M. Fragonard et Mlle Gérard,"* which appears on the 1786 prints by Regnault and Vidal after these paintings, has been interpreted as proof of collaboration between master and pupil in the creation and execution of many canvases. Although the young Marguerite Gérard would have emulated her master, on occasion even borrowing compositional motifs and figure types, it seems highly unlikely that pupil and teacher actually worked on such small-scale canvases together. There are no extant paintings signed by both artists. It is noteworthy that Henri Gérard, also Fragonard's pupil and a member of the family atelier in the Louvre, in his 1788 engravings of *L'Élan de la Nature* and *Le Baiser de l'Innocence,* credits his sister alone for the original paintings which are so similar to *The First Step.* One is tempted to surmise that Regnault and Vidal shrewdly decided to safeguard their commercial interests by introducing the charming domestic scenes of the fledgling artist under the protective wing of the famous Fragonard. In numerous subsequent prints, Vidal cites Marguerite Gérard alone, never again suggesting collaboration with her brother-in-law. With the exception of two lost engravings by Ponce exhibited in the Salon of 1793 (no. 403), whose subjects remain unknown, there is no other contemporary documentation of collaboration between pupil and teacher. Although stylistic evidence may be used to demonstrate Marguerite Gérard's early dependence on her master for inspiration, in certain instances, it offers little proof of active collaboration.

In *The First Step,* Gérard's lifelong preference for elegant, aristocratic or bourgeois mothers, always exquisitely gowned and coiffed, asserts itself in opposition to Fragonard's taste for earthy maternal heroines. The simplicity of the composition, the frozen exclamatory poses, and the porcelain perfection of the mothre and nursemaid typify Gérard's static, controlled style. However, the more dynamic quality of the tottering baby, the casual pose of the wrinkled old woman and of the child slumped on the ground, as well as the heavy foliage, all indicate the influence of Fragonard. In fact, it is clear that the motif of the old woman leaning over the cradle is derived from a detail of a drawing attributed to Fragonard (A. Ananoff, 1963, IV, no. 628). The baby's extended arms might also be compared to Fragonard's *Le Petit Prédicateur,* although they are actually much closer to the pose of the babies practicing walking in *L'Élan de la Nature.* It would seem unlikely that the master would repeat random details from his earlier works, inserting them in pastiche fashion into another painting, but Marguerite Gérard's paintings are full of direct borrowings from Fragonard and Greuze, from Metsu and Terborch, and from many other artists she admired as well.

The possibility of distinguishing between the brush of the master and the pupil in *The First Step* as evidence of collaboration must be considered. A study of this canvas and its pendant under the Infra-Red Vidicon System at the Fogg Museum of Art provided no confirmation of collaboration by two artists: the texture of the pigment and the brushwork are homogeneous on every level; there are no brusque transitions between different areas of the composition and there are no corrections visible over a previously executed area. Due to the mystery surrounding Fragonard's limited production during the 1780s and the incredible transformation of his exuberant, painterly style into a smooth, tight technique, it is also extremely difficult to attempt to discern the master's hand on a stylistic basis with the naked eye on a canvas executed in Gérard's own meticulous manner.

During the years 1780-1785, Marguerite Gérard was acquiring her renowned ability to rival the Dutch 17th-century masters in the careful reproduction of reality and had succeeded in creating an intimate genre style, her "Metsu" manner, by 1785, the date appearing on the signed painting, *La Leçon de Musique* (New York, Schickman Gallery). The similar *décolleté* satin gowns of the mothers in *La Leçon de musique* and *The First Step* are painted in a cool, analytical way which contrasts with the energetic, vibrating folds of satin in the gown of the heroine of Fragonard's *The Lock* (No. 59). It is revealing that the figure of the mother in *The First Step* reappears in reverse in the same pose and gown in another canvas of the 1780s by Mlle Gérard, *Je les relis avec plaisir* (private collection).

It is crucial to understand that Marguerite Gérard was also capable of painting in a freer, broader style while employing a warmer palette, notably in the series of extraordinary portraits dating from the 1780s through 1800. For example, in the portraits of the architect Ledoux (Paris, Musée Cognacq-Jay), M. Luce (Grasse), M. Gretry (private collection), and Mme Gérard (Grasse), the golden tones, the tracks of the brush, the shorthand treatment of detail, the honest representation of the sitters' physical imperfections, all demonstrate the artist's ability to imitate her master's sketchy style. Thus, one must be cautious in attributing the old woman on the left of our painting or the children to the master himself. Not only did Gérard emulate Fragonard's freer style in her portraits, she occasionally combined her cool "Metsu Manner" with her Fragonardesque style in a single genre scene, such as *La Leçon de Danse* and *Je m'occupais de vous* (private collections). Indeed, in these two works of the same decade as the Fogg canvas, the artist altered her tight brushwork to depict the ravages of time in the faces of the complacent chaperones, descendants of the wrinkled, smiling crone in *The First Step.*

Although Mlle Gérard preferred interior settings, she remained capable of producing a Watteau-like background when necessary, as in *Les Regrets* (Salon of 1802, private collection) and *Le Souvenir d'Amour* (c. 1810, private collection). Thus, one might conclude that in spite of her reliance on the example of her brother-in-law, there is no definitive indication in *The First Step* to support the theory that Gérard and Fragonard created this work together. Since there is nothing exceptional about this painting which does not appear in other canvases known to be by Gérard's hand alone, and since technical analysis suggests that only one artist executed this canvas, it seems highly probable that both *The First Step* and its pendant were executed solely by Marguerite Gérard in the early 1780s under the benevolent eye of her mentor, Fragonard.

PROVENANCE

O... sale, 16-17 December 1839, no. 89; De Rigny sale, 2 June 1857, no. 40; Pillot sale, 6-8 December 1858, no. 43; Lord Roseberry Collection, Mintmoor, England; Wilden-stein & Co., New York; Charles E. Dunlap Collection, Saint Louis, 1952; entered Fogg Art Museum 1961 (INV. 1961.166). In all the aforementioned sales and collections, it appeared with its pendant, *L'Enfant Chéri* (Cambridge, Mass., Fogg Art Museum; canvas, 44 × 55; INV. 1961.165).

EXHIBITIONS

1967, Buffalo, New York; 1967, New Haven.

REFERENCES

J. Doin, 1912, p. 432; G. Wildenstein, 1960, p. 323, no. 540, ill. 234; mus. cat., 1962, p. 8; *ibid.*, 1963, p. 128; P. Rosenberg and I. Compin, 1974, p. 276 (note 59), ill. 24.

RELATED WORKS

Oil sketch, lost, 24 × 35; Van Leyden sale, 10 September 1804, no. 131 (with its pendant).
Engraving by Regnault and Vidal, 1786; with legend: *Peint par M. Fragonard et Mlle Gérard; Retouché par Regnault et par G. Vidal; Dédié aux bonnes mères.*
Les Premiers Pas, De La Roncière sale, 28 March 1859, no. 25; attributed to Fragonard in the catalog of this sale; could it be the Fogg painting?

S. R.

72
Bad News

" Une dame assise devant sa toilette " or *La Mauvaise nouvelle*
Plate p. 188
Canvas; 63.5 × 50.5
Salon of 1804, no. 201
Paris, Musée du Louvre

Marguerite Gérard's mature style, a discrete fusion of cool neo-classical idealism, 18th-century sentimentality and 17th-century Dutch literalism, is epitomized in one of her most successful paintings, *Bad News*. Exhibited in the Salon of 1804, this canvas was acclaimed by critics who reported that it was one of the most admired works of the exhibition and was chiefly responsible for the selection of Mlle Gérard as a recipient of the coveted gold metal. It was purchased with its pendant, *La Toilette,* by a Monsieur Livry prior to its appearance in the Salon and a copy of it on panel was commissioned by another collector.

In 1804, Marguerite Gérard had been working independently from her celebrated brother-in-law, Fragonard, for nearly 20 years. Although maintaining close family ties, and exchanging affectionate letters until the master's death in 1806, Marguerite Gérard had established her own lodgings and studio independent from that of her sister and former teacher. If her preoccupation with the theme of the love letter may be traced to her period of apprenticeship with Fragonard, her non-erotic, sentimental renditions of the subject seem remote from her teacher's *billet doux* paintings. The nature of Fragonard's early influence is revealed in a comparison of Gérard's 1787 representation of Geneviève de Brabant, letter in hand, lamenting dramatically over the news of her husband's betrayal and the 1804 painting in this exhibition, an image of a fashionable lady reacting to tragic news in a more passively theatrical manner. The agitated line and spontaneity of the early work contrast markedly with the controlled linearism and restraint in the artist's reinterpretation of the same theme nearly 20 years later.

The inspiration for Mlle Gérard's genre scenes which revolve around the perusal of a letter from a loved one may be discovered in the works of such Dutch 17th-century masters as Terborch and Metsu, whose paintings were highly valued by royal and aristocratic collectors. Indeed J.-B. Descamps, the 18th-century historian of Dutch painting, advised genre painters to adopt Metsu as their model. Marguerite Gérard would have enjoyed an entrée to the private and royal collections containing many paintings by these *petits maîtres,* and the motives of the brass chandelier, oriental rug, gold pitcher, convex mirror, spotted spaniel and wall map familiar in Dutch genre reappear in their trompe-l'œil perfection in innumerable Gérard interiors. She also emulated the calm compositional simplicity and limited dimensions of canvases by Terborch and Metsu, placing her few figures close to the foreground plane in front of a chimney or screen and beside a table decorated with a printed cloth and personalized accessories. However, the most striking parallel between the Dutch masters and Mlle Gérard is their superbly tactile reproduction of the effects of light passing over various fabrics and textures. In *Bad News* the artist skillfully depicts the plush patterns of the Persian carpet, the flocking on the chairback, the glass sphere with its reflection of a silhouette against a window, the stiff envelope on the floor and the curly coat of the spaniel. The contrast of the shimmering satin gown of the blond lady with the softer flowing muslin dress of her friend, as well as that of the hard strand of pearls lying against the heroine's transluscent skin demonstrates that Gérard's technical ability matched her obsession with capturing reality in minute detail. Nevertheless, she succeeded in uniting the myriad of meticulously rendered details into a satisfactory whole through the subtle tonal harmonies, polished surfaces and delicate play of light and shadow.

During her artistic career, Marguerite Gérard contributed eight paintings to Salon exhibitions which explored emotional responses to the reading of a letter, and at least eleven more works devoted to the same subject have been documented. Indeed, nearly ten percent of her œuvre deals with this sentimental theme.

Despite its dramatic content, the precise meaning of *Bad News* is ambiguous. Its pendant (Salon no. 200), presents the same leading characters at a lighter moment in another interior reading a letter with obvious delight. It might appropriately be entitled *La Bonne Nouvelle.* Although the before and after contrast of the two scenes may enhance their impact, the pendant also fails to elucidate the exact details of this two-part drama. Contemporary critics did not agree on the interpretation of the heroine's plight, but several were fascinated by the artist's success in suggesting the parallel between fainting and death in the moment of loss of consciousness. *Bad News* might be considered not merely as an image reflective of the hyper-sensitivity cultivated by fashionable women of the day, but also as an example of the preoccupation with death and the sublime, pervading both neo-classical and romantic tendencies at the turn of the century. A spiritual, translucent light does seem to infuse the pale skin of the heroine and to envelop her hair and gown, supernaturally isolating her from her companions and setting.

Although Marguerite Gérard's modest genre paintings might seem removed from the heroic neo-classical mainstream, like her academically trained contemporaries, she rejected the painterly exuberance of the rococo for a style characterized by smooth surfaces, precise anonymous brushwork, and over-all order. She was aware of the Davidian revolution in painting, although as a woman without the right to study from the nude or attend the Academy classes she could hardly attempt large-scale history paintings. Several of her female contemporaries such as Mmes Chaudet, Auzou, Lemire and Servières might transport their genre scenes to antiquity, but Gérard was content to modify her style by flattening her spaces and forms to create more frieze-like compositions. The linearism inherent in her hyper-real technique asserted itself under the influence of David, Girodet and later Ingres, whose own historical genre scenes seem surprising related to Gérard's "Metsu" manner. Despite the continual evolution of her style through four decades, Mlle Gérard's work is distinctive. One would never confuse it with that of her two leading competitors, Léopold-Louis Boilly and Martin Drolling, whose genre scenes present a more picturesque vision of the entire social strata.

As the first woman genre painter to win the respect of her colleagues, the critics and the public, Marguerite Gérard provided a precedent for aspiring women artists of the following generation. During the Empire and the Restoration, the number of female exhibitors in the Salon multiplied; and these artists ventured into the fields of historical and journalistic genre, and even large-scale history painting, all areas previously reserved for men.

PROVENANCE
Included with its pendant in the Livry sale; 16-17 April 1810, no. 71, but withdrawn. Appeared again with its pendant in Livry sale, 2 February 1814, no. 180. Office des Biens Privés, 1950. Louvre MNR. 140.

EXHIBITIONS
1804, Salon, no. 201; 1958, Bordeaux, no. 179.

REFERENCES

Coll. Deloynes, v. XXXI, no. 866, p. 404; no. 876, p. 657; v. XXXII, no. 884, p. 37; no. 883, p. 253; no. 889, p. 496; R. Monsaldy, 1804, no. 201; Bellier and Auvray, 1882, v. I, p. 638; P. Marmottan, 1886, p. 275; J. Doin, 1912, p. 437; ill. 8; M. Quenot, 1964, p. 37; G. Levitine, 1968, p. 26, ill. p. 27; mus. cat. 1972, p. 178.

RELATED WORKS

Copy on panel; 45 × 38; Godefroy sale, 14 December 1813, no. 55.

Pendant, *La Bonne Nouvelle (La Toilette* or *La Lecture de la Lettre),* Salon of 1804, no. 200; canvas; 62 × 51; Livry sale of 2 February, 1814, no. 179; Fitz-James sale, 15-18 December 1902, no. 16; sale X, Paris, Hôtel Drouot, 12 March 1948, no. 12.

Copy of pendant on panel; s.l.l.; 64 × 53; Muhlbacher sale, 13-15 May 1907, no. 28, ill.; sale X, Paris, Galerie Charpentier, 10 June 1954, no. 28, pl. VII.

S. R.

Théodore Géricault

1791 Rouen - Paris 1824

Géricault belonged to that "passionate and nervous generation" (Musset) which was deeply marked by the glory and downfall "of the greatest man who had appeared in the world since Caesar" (Stendhal, *Vie de Napoléon,* Paris, 1845 ?). He was born in 1791, at the height of Revolutionary turmoil, into a well-to-do middle-class family of Rouen. He went to Paris at an early age (his father had obtained an important post in the tobacco administration), and was a poor student at the Imperial *lycée,* more attracted to horses than humanities. Upon leaving the *lycée* in 1808, thanks to a goodly inheritance from his mother and the help of his uncle Caruel de Saint-Martin, he was able to join the extremely popular studio of Carle Vernet, the painter of elegant and pure-bred horses. He stayed with the master for two years and began a friendship with his son, Horace, which was to last the rest of his life. He became aware of the limitations of Carle Vernet's teaching and associated himself with the studio of Pierre-Narcisse Guérin, the last great master under whose tutelage the romantic generation would be formed: Champmartin, Léon Cogniet, Henriquel-Dupont, Paul Huet, the Scheffers, Riesner and Delacroix. But the greatest school for him was the Musée Napoléon, at the time really a "world museum," where victory upon victory brought antiques like those from the Borghese Collection (1808) and especially the paintings of the most illustrious artists. In a frenzy, Géricault copied the canvases of these glorious predecessors; Clément (1879, pp. 31-34, 319-323) accounts for 32 studies, but he must have done many more (see L. Eitner, 1959, p. 120). His taste led him to copy colorists like Titian, Van Dyck, Velasquez or luminarists like Caravaggio, Rembrandt, Ribera or Jean Jouvenet. He was fascinated by the baroque grandeur of Rubens, and his companions at the studio jokingly nicknamed him "Rubens' cook."

He first participated in the Salon of 1812 with the *Portrait équestre d'un officier de chasseurs à cheval* (Louvre). The critics received it quite well and he won a gold medal. Through its daring movement, solid composition and luminous effects, this gigantic picture of an imperial soldier expressed in a flashing epitome the glory of these years of conquest. The rhythm of history quickened; at the following Salon, it was downfall, defeat and agony that he depicted with the *Wounded Cuirassier* (No. 74). Like Vigny and Lamartine, Géricault joined the Red Musketeers of the King and escorted the sovereign to Ghent during The Hundred Days, then quickly returned to civilian life.

Clément mentioned a complete cessation of work from the end of 1815 to the middle of 1816 (*op. cit.,* pp. 67, 70, 75, 77), due to a tumultuous affair with a married woman. To escape this passion, he left for Italy, visited Florence and Rome, where he was confronted by the powerful work of Michelangelo that helped him discover his own limits. Eagerly he also studied ancient sarcophagi, Raphael, Giulio Romano, as well as contemporary life, as his numerous sketches of street scenes attest. In the spring of 1817, he attended the Roman carnival, where he discovered the *Riderless Horse Race* (No. 76). Fascinated by this theme, he planned a large painting which he prepared with a series of studies in which he reached epic dimensions. Although he had friendly relations with French artists in Rome—Schnetz, Ingres, Monsieur Auguste—he missed his friends Dedreux and Lebrun; he therefore decided to return home in the fall of 1817.

In Paris, he set up a studio very close to Horace Vernet's on the rue des Martyrs, in the "New Athens," and associated with liberal circles. He was one of the first in France to take up that new means of expression, the lithograph. In two years he produced some twenty prints, among which seven portray the poignant disorder of the vanquished army which Alfred de Vigny would evoke in *Servitude et grandeur militaires* (1835). The six sculptures cited by Clément (*op. cit.*, pp. 325-326), of which only two survive (Rouen and Buffalo), also certainly date from this period. For 16 months, from the spring of 1818 to 25 August 1819, the opening date of the Salon, Géricault devoted all his time to a daring project: to illustrate the resounding news story of the shipwreck of the *Méduse* through the suffering of the survivors. This immense painting (491 × 715) produced a scandal; the liberals were delighted, while the Royalists decried it. The artist received a medal and a commission from the State for a religious painting which did not inspire him and which he left to his young friend Eugène Delacroix. Tired by his superhuman effort, disillusioned and discouraged by his comparative failure, Géricault left Paris with Charlet for England, which was attracting as many artists as Rome at that

moment. In the spring of 1820, he was in London where he became acquainted with G. G. Bullock who exhibited the *Radeau de la Méduse* from city to city. He met Sir Thomas Lawrence and Sir David Wilkie and was enthusiastic about John Constable. His trip to the other side of the Channel enlarged his vision of the world considerably. He produced his great series of lithographs, some watercolors and painted the *Course de chevaux à Epsom* (Louvre), where for the first time a painter tried to reproduce an instantaneous vision. On his way back, he passed through Brussels to salute the great master in exile, David.

A few months after his return to Paris, he had a bad fall from a horse and never regained his health. He worked on his last paintings, the portraits of the insane (No. 77) and the *Four à plâtre* (Louvre), a work whose accuracy, ease and fullness have never been equaled. He spent the year 1823 in bed; his illness gave him short moments of respite, during which he projected two huge paintings, the *Traite des noirs* and the *Ouverture des portes de l'Inquisition*. He died at 32 years of age, as did Giorgione and Seurat. He knew that he had only been able to complete a small portion of the immense work he had envisioned. As with all true geniuses, he escapes rigid classification; he was simultaneously classical and romantic, realistic and poetic.   I. J.

73
Portrait of a Carabinier

Portrait d'un officier de carabiniers
Plate p. 217
Canvas; 64 × 54
Rouen, Musée des Beaux-Arts

Géricault began his career as a painter of the military glories of the Empire. He first exhibited at the Salon of 1812 and offered *L'officier de chasseurs à cheval de la garde impériale chargeant* (Louvre) to the votes of admirers; perhaps, this *Portrait of a Carabinier* dates from the same period. Géricault demonstrated great psychological penetration here; the tragic look of this proud soldier seems to defy the world. But it is 1812, the turning point, the end of the Imperial epic. The carabinier's massive face, with its powerful bone

structure, is suggested by sculptural and dense modeling and contrasts of light and shade. The tragedy about to occur can be guessed from his dramatic pose and immobility. The restrained ardor of his horse, symbol of force and drive and indispensible instrument of his exploits and his glory, the stormy sky are already very romantic components. The firmness of the drawing and the subtleties of the completely harmonious colors are a testimony to the power and mastery of this young artist. This moving portrait fascinated the young

Delacroix at the time of his visit to the dying Géricault on 30 December 1823 (see Delacroix' *Journal,* 30 December 1823, ed. 1893, p. 47).

PROVENANCE

Bought for 7,000 francs by the Rouen museum at the Vollon sale, 20-23 March 1901, no. 156.

EXHIBITIONS

1924, Paris, no. 24; 1937, Paris, no. 332; 1937, Paris, Galerie Bernheim, no. 26.

REFERENCES

E. Delacroix, 1893, p. 47; L. Rosenthal, 1905, p. 167; R. Régamey, 1924, ill. face p. 64; *ibid.,* 1926, p. 61, ill. 7; G. Oprescu, 1927, p. 44; E. de Trévise, 1927, ill. p. 184; L. Eitner, 1954, p. 258; J. Vergnet-Ruiz and M. Laclotte, 1962, p. 237, ill. 138; A. del Guercio, 1963, pp. 18, 140, ill. 9; P. du Colombier, 1963, n.p., color cover ill.; F.-H. Lem, 1963, pp. 13-14; mus. cat., 1967, p. 51; K. Berger, 1968, p. 165, ill. 15.

RELATED WORKS

Portrait d'un carabinier (canvas; 100 × 85), Louvre, INV. 4887; the same model posed for both paintings. Drawing for the carabinier (17 × 22) in the album of drawings preserved in Chicago, fol. 34 r⁰ and 51 v⁰.

I. J.

74
Wounded Cuirassier

"Cuirassier blessé, quittant le feu"
Plate p. 229
Canvas; 358 × 294
Salon of 1814, no. 435
Paris, Musée du Louvre

The *Wounded Cuirassier* is one of three canvases presented by Géricault to the Salon. He had exhibited a *Carabinier chargeant* (Louvre) for the first time in 1812 and he did not exhibit there again until he showed the *Radeau de la Méduse* (Louvre) in 1819. According to Clément, the present painting was conceived and completed by Géricault in two weeks (1879, p. 64) as an answer to the pleas of his father, who forced him to participate again in the Salon, after the success he had had in the preceding Salon. But René Huyghe (1931, p. 65) has shown that this was only a legend. The artist carefully thought out his composition and executed it meticulously (see Related Works). He searched for the moment that best rendered the drama of the episode and as a student of the Davidian, Pierre-Narcisse Guérin, he studied his model first nude, then clothed.

The canvas did not please the small number of critics who mentioned it. Landon lamented the fact that the "drawing [was] incorrect and done with a heavy and choppy touch" (1814, p. 106). N.B.F., the author of the article on the Salon for the *Journal de Paris,* also reproached him for his abrupt style: "I am certainly far from liking fussy painting, especially in historical pictures. On the contrary, I admire a touch that is masculine, daring and even a bit abrupt; but here, I am forced to state, the boldness of the brush is far too powerful and the brush strokes are felt far too strongly. One can really only consider this composition a sort of study, a rough sketch which entertains the hope of being a lovely painting. I hope that in his final attempt, the artist will shorten by a good half a head the enormous height of his soldier; that he will give more fullness to his thighs, which scarcely stand out, and especially that he will take care to smooth out those uneven strokes on the horse's body which have the effect of a coarse mosaic."

The monumental format Géricault gave this subject surprised his contemporaries, who considered this episode as a simple subject for a genre painting. The motif of the massive figure restraining a fiery horse was not new in Géricault's work; it was adapted from the *Enseigne du maréchal-ferrant* (Zurich, Kunsthaus). In a powerfully constructed composition, the artist gave the forms a sculptural solidity, and he used light and shade contrasts to amplify the physical presence of the bodies. Géricault did not like this work; he said that "the eye did not stay in its socket" and that it was "a calf's head with a big, stupid eye." His *Cuirassier* bothered him, and Clément reports that he begged his friends to get rid of it for him at any price and even asked Jamar to cover it with white paint (Clément, 1879, p. 70).

There are many for whom the painting summarizes the fall of the Empire in the figure of an anonymous soldier in distress. It is an image which expresses the collapse of the ideals of an entire generation which, like Géricault, had come of age around 1810. With poignant force, the work renders their uncertainties and anguish: "His cuirassier is not a symbol for him. But a man. Man. The tragic destiny of man. At the end of everything there is only defeat" (L. Aragon, 1958, p. 94.)

PROVENANCE

Painted for presentation at the Salon of 1814, sold after the artist's death, 2-3 November, 1824, no. 3, p. 1 (cited by L. Eitner, 1959, p. 117); bought for 2,005 francs by the Duc d'Orléans; Duc d'Orléans Collection; sale by Louis-Philippe, Paris, 29 April 1851, no. 339, bought by the Louvre; (INV. 4886).

EXHIBITIONS

1814, Salon, no. 435; 1848, Paris, no. 38; 1936, Paris, no.270.

REFERENCES

N.B.F., *Journal de Paris,* 28 November 1814; C.-P. Landon, 1814, p. 106; Fr. Villot, mus. cat. 1878, v. III, p. 152; Ch. Clément, 1879, pp. 64-70, 289, no. 52, ill. III; H. Houssaye, 1879, pp. 380-382, 385; L. Both de Tauzia, mus. cat., 1881, p. 152; A. Etex, 1885, p. 6; Bellier and Auvray, 1882, v. I, p. 640; W.-C. Brownell, 1901, p. 45; L. Rosenthal, 1905, p. 386; G. Brière, mus. cat., 1924, v. I, p. 112, no. 341; R. Rey, 1924, pp. 258-259, 263; L. Rosenthal, 1924, p. 9, note 1; *ibid.,* 1924, p. 54; *ibid., R.A.A.M.* 1924, p. 230; R. Régamey, 1924, pp. 27-28; L. Dimier, 1926, p. 52; R. Régamey, 1926; pp. 21-24, ill. 5; E. de Trévise, 1927, p. 185; G. Oprescu, 1927, pp. 38-39, 196; R. Rey, 1928, p. 86; J. Guiffrey, 1929, p. 56, ill. 69; R. Huyghe, 1931, p. 65; M. Gauthier, 1935, p. 26, ill. 23; F. Antal, 1940, v. II, p. 73; W. Pach, 1945, p. 235; K. Berger, 1946, pp. 52-53; P. Courthion and P. Callier, 1947, pp. 151, 154-157; W. Friedlaender, 1952, p. 95, ill. 51; *ibid.,* 1952, p. 262; L. Eitner, 1954, pp. 237-241; K. Berger, 1955, pp. 11, 35, 47, 71, ill. 8; L. Johnson, 1955, pp. 78-81; D. Aimé-Azam, 1956, pp. 91-92, 96-98; L. Aragon, 1958, pp. 94-95; L. Eitner, 1959, pp. 117, 121; R. Lebel, 1960, pp. 331-333; Ch. Sterling and H. Adhémar, 1960, v. II, p. 36, ill. 333; V.-N. Prokofiev, 1963, pp. 77-81, ill.; A. del Guercio, 1963, pp. 16-17; F. Lem, 1963, pp. 69-70; K. Berger, 1968, pp. 25-26, 164-165, ill. 12; D. Aimé-Azam, 1970, pp. 97-109; mus. cat., 1972, p. 179; G. Hopp, 1973, p. 316, ill. 8; L. Eitner, re-issue of Ch. Clément, 1879, pp. 64-70, 289, no. 52, p. 449.

RELATED WORKS

Oil Sketches. Canvas (46 × 38), gift of His de la Salle in 1878 to the Louvre, R.F. 211; the cuirassier leans against a knoll; a second sketch (canvas; 55 × 46), New York, the Brooklyn Museum: the definitive conception has already been found.
Drawings. Zoubalov notebook of drawings given to the Louvre in 1924, R.F. 6072 (19 × 12), fol. nos. 90, 92. *Cuirassier étendu sur un rocher,* pen, sepia and watercolor (19 × 12), Louvre, R.F. 4619 r⁰. *Soldat assis tenant un enfant et une figure masculine accroupie,* pen, Louvre, R.F. 4619 v⁰; *Cuirassier assis sur un tertre,* pen, brown ink (20 × 16), Paris, private collection.
Lithograph. By Volmar, *Galerie du Palais-Royal,* I.

I. J.

75
*Landscape with a Roman Tomb : Morning**

Grand Paysage d'Italie par temps d'orage, also called *Paysage classique: matin*
Plate p. 247
Canvas; 250 × 219
Paris, Musée du Petit Palais

Among the discoveries at the Winterthur exhibition, the greatest, without a doubt, was that of the two great landscapes: *Landscape with a Roman Tomb* and its pendant *Paysage d'Italie au coucher du soleil.* Lorenz Eitner, who in 1954 was the first to publish them, thinks that they were painted along with a third picture, *Grand Paysage d'Italie au petit jour,* to decorate the home of one of Géricault's friends who lived in Villers-Cotterêts. The first two can only really be traced since 1953, while the third appeared in the 1960s in the New York Huntington Hartford Collection and can, unfortunately, no longer be located today. Each one illustrates a particular moment in the day and subtly renders its individual atmosphere.

Even though the background of his paintings are usually summarily painted, Géricault constructed these three paintings very carefully and infused them with a fine poetic and emotional quality. The painting from the Petit Palais is a composed landscape in the tradition of the heroic landscapes of Gaspard Dughet and Claude Lorrain. But the influence of Giambattista Piranesi's engravings (tomb of Cecila Metella, wife of Crasus the Younger, for whom a vast tomb was erected on the Appian Way) can also be discerned. Painted no doubt around 1815, before Géricault visited Italy, the composition does not have the density of the paintings created after the artist had been confronted with Michelangelo's work. Although Clément described in his catalog the only landscape that he had seen as done "in the manner of Guaspre" (C. Clément, 1879, p. 230), the influence of Claude Lorrain is felt more strongly here than that of Dughet. Even the layout of the landscape, the relationship of the people and their surroundings, the poetic subject matter, the melancholy side and the restrained lyricism all recall Claude. Nevertheless, details like the gallows with a leg and an arm are a curious foretaste of the anatomical studies made for the *Méduse*.

According to Lorenz Eitner, the *Italian Landscape* could have been painted after the *Soir ;* there is more spontaneity in the former. While the *Soir* is bathed in a golden light quite reminiscent of the 18th century, in the manner of Pierre-Henri de Valenciennes, Jean-Joseph-Xavier Bidauld or Jean-Victor Bertin, the *Italian Landscape* offers original and subtle colors. This painting already gives the impression of a fully romantic heaviness, anguish and oppressiveness.

PROVENANCE

Coll. H. Brame and C. de Hauke, according to the catalog of the exhibition at Winterthur, where the painting appeared for the first time, no. 71; New York, Walter P. Chrysler Collection; 30 June 1970 sold at Christies, London, no. 2, color ill. p. 20; acquired by the Musée du Petit Palais with the aid of the Dutuit fund (INV. Dut. 1170).

EXHIBITIONS

1953, Winterthur, no. 71; 1956-1957, Portland, etc., no. 73; 1958, New York; 1971-1972, Los Angeles, etc., no. 32, ill.

REFERENCES

Ch. Clément, 1879, p. 230, no. 16; L. Eitner, 1954, pp. 131-142, ill. 1; M. Hüggler, 1954, pp. 234-237, ill. 1; D. Aimé-Azam, 1956, p. 126; R. Lebel, 1960, pp. 328-330; F.-H. Lem, 1963, p. 66; A. del Guercio, 1963, pp. 26, 33-34, 142.

I. J.

76
Riderless Horse Race

Course de chevaux libres à Rome
Plate p. 253
Paper on canvas; 45 × 60
Paris, Musée du Louvre

The carnival in Rome was undoubtedly the culminating point of the social season, with all its celebrations the week before Ash Wednesday. The Barbary horse race deeply impressed those who witnessed it, from Goethe to Berlioz. Impressed by this spectacle, Goethe gave an enthusiastic description of it in his second voyage to Italy (February 1788, published in 1825, 1962 ed., pp. 495-518). The artists who depicted the event included David Allan (before 1780, pen drawing, 21 × 37, Windsor Castle), Carle Vernet (No. 185), Horace Vernet (No. 186) and Géricault.

This contest was the chief attraction of popular entertainment: 15 to 20 small half-wild horses of Arabian stock (hence their name, *barberi*) raced riderless along the Corso. The winner was then given the *palio,* a square of gold cloth, symbol of victory. The contest took place between the Piazza del Popolo and the Piazza del Palazzo de Venezia, the promenade area of Roman high society. Each evening during the preceding week, the grooms would lead their horses over the race track. On the prescribed day, a tumultuous crowd would press into the stands to watch the match.

Géricault, struck by this struggle between man and horse—a passionate, fiery animal—began studies for a huge 30-foot canvas in February 1817.

He hesitated at first, not knowing what scene to choose: the start, the finish or the race itself. He finally decided for the moment when the struggle was at its climax, when the grooms curbed the horses only with the utmost difficulty and when the frenzy of men and horses was at its height. Starting with a genre scene (the sketch in Baltimore, Walters Art Gallery), a simple realistic and direct description, he developed an increasingly organized subject, constructed according to the classical rules of bas-relief. The horses were shorn of their harnesses, the costumes of the robust Roman peasants were simplified, the surroundings were made vague and the architectural decor was hardly suggested. Géricault eliminated details in order to emphasize only the formal conception and to endow the spectacle with a more abstract feeling. Géricault demonstrated here a monumental approach; he accentuated masses and set them into opposition with contrasts of values and beautiful accents of color. He attained a rhythmic purity close to the Parthenon friezes, which he knew through casts (the friezes had been brought to London by Lord Elgin in 1803 and were first exhibited in 1806). The composition is divided into three independent groups as in an ancient bas-relief (cf. the Louvre sarcophagus 261); the center group is reminiscent of one of the *Chevaux de Marly* by the 17th-century sculptor, Guillaume Coustou.

This series of sketches of the *barberi* horses constitutes the pictorial zenith of Géricault's Roman sojourn; in them he combined the eternal beauty of figural and animal forms with the commonplace. Ch. Clément considered the horse race at the Louvre to be "of the greatest beauty; it is very advanced and seems to us to be the last one that Géricault produced. It can be regarded as the finished and definitive version of the painting that he contemplated" (1879, p. 297). It renders powerfully and poetically the romantic theme of man's eternal struggle with wild nature.

PROVENANCE
Sold after Géricault's death, 2-3 Nov. 1824, no. 13 (?)

(cited by L. Eitner, 1959, pp. 119, 121); Camille Marcille Coll., sold 6-7 March 1876, no. 31; Jean Dolfus Coll., sold 2 March 1912, no. 38; acquired with the funds of the Maurice Audéoud bequest by the Louvre, R.F. 2042.

EXHIBITIONS
1885, Paris, no. 216; 1924, Paris, no. 103; 1928, Copenhagen, Oslo, Stockholm, no. 82; 1931, Rome; 1934, New York; 1936, Paris, no. 270; 1956, Warsaw, no. 49, ill. 18; 1956, Moscow, Leningrad, no. 70; 1958, Agen, Grenoble, Nancy, no. 26, cover ill.; 1961, Rome-Turin, no. 155; 1963, Bordeaux, no. 283; 1968, Mexico City, no. cat.

REFERENCES
Ch. Clément, 1879, pp. 93, 96, 297, no. 85, ill. IV; H. Houssaye, 1879, p. 375; A. Etex, 1885, p. 15; L. Rosenthal, 1905, pp. 68-74; R. Régamey, 1924, p. 41; G. Brière, 1924, mus. cat., v. I, p. 114, no. 3089; R. Régamey, 1926, pp. 24-25, ill. 10; E. de Trévise, 1927, p. 187, ill. p. 188; G. Bazin, 1932, pp. 46-53, ill. 50; F. Antal, 1940, v. II, p. 79; D. Aimé-Azam, 1954, p. 142, 144; L. Eitner, 1959, pp. 119, 121; Ch. Sterling and H. Adhémar, 1959, v. II, p. 36; no. 939, ill. 335; V.-N. Prokofiev, 1963, pp. 86, 99, 104, 112, 115-117, ill. p. 113, details pp. 114-115; A. del Guercio, 1963, pp. 37, 42-43, 136, ill. XII; H. Kogina, 1969, ill. p. 39; mus. cat., 1972, p. 181; L. Eitner, 1972, pp. 17-18, ill.; L. Eitner, 1973, re-issue of Ch. Clément, 1879, pp. 93, 96, 297, no. 85, ill. IV, p. 452.

RELATED WORKS
Paintings. According to Clément, Géricault painted at least 20 different studies on this theme (Ch. Clément, 1878, p. 100) and he catalogued the following:
Clément 82: (42 × 59), Baltimore, Walters Art Gallery; Clément 83: (45 × 60) disappeared; Clément 84: (31 × 43) disappeared; Clément 86: (44 × 59) New York, V. Spark Collection; Clément 87: (47 × 60) Rouen; Clément 88: (33 × 23) Winterthur, Hans Buehler Collection, Clément 89: (32 × 40) Paris; Clément 90: (21 × 21) not located. In addition to these sketches, another (45 × 60) is presently at Lille; and a final, larger one probably remained in Italy (61 × 89), Parma, private collection.
Drawings. Clément also cites 16 drawings related to these sketches, nos. 58 to 73 in his catalog of drawings.
Lithograph. By Eugène Le Roux.   I. J.

77
Portrait of an Insane Man ("Kleptomaniac")

Le Fou assassin, also called *La Monomanie du vol*
Plate p. 268
Canvas; 61 × 50
Ghent, Museum voor Schone Kunsten

The limits of consciousness and reason as well as the boundaries of life and death particularly concerned the artists and writers at the beginning of the 19th century. It is not known how Géricault became acquainted with one of the youngest and most eminent psychiatrists of his time, Étienne Georget (1795-1828).

Their meeting occurred perhaps through Savigny, the doctor who survived the shipwreck of the *Méduse*. After the completion of this huge canvas, Géricault suffered extreme fatigue, close to a depression and Georget might have treated him (D. Aimé-Azam, 1956, p. 216).

Humanitarian ideas developed at the end of the 18th century brought about a great change in methods of treating the insane. Together with his teachers Pinel and Esquirol, Georget was the founder of French psychiatry. Philippe Pinel, named immediately after the Revolution chief doctor at Bicêtre, the section of the Hôpital Général set aside for the indigent and incurably insane, profoundly changed the therapy applied to the mentally ill. He freed them from their chains and regarded them as simply sick people. At the age of 22, Georget, the student of Esquirol, the doctor at Salpêtrière, the section for insane women at the Hôpital Général, was made instructor of the first clinical course concerning the mentally ill. Applying Pinel's theories, Georget felt that there were connections between thought and facial features and that one could read from facial features the repercussion of cerebral changes. According to Clément (1879, p. 317), Géricault created ten portraits of the insane for this doctor, but only five are known today: *La Monomanie du commandement militaire* (Winterthur, Reinhart Collection, Ch. Clément, no. 155a), *La Monomanie du vol des enfants* (Springfield, Mass., Museum of Fine Arts, Clément, no. 156b), the Ghent *Kleptomaniac, La Monomanie du jeu* (Louvre Clément, no. 158d) and *La Monomanie de l'envie* (Lyon, Clément, no. 159e). It has been stated that these portraits of the insane were created to illustrate a new edition of Georget's work, *De la folie* (1820), but none of the insane painted by Géricault corresponds to those analyzed by the psychiatrist. Klaus Berger (1968, p. 188) feels that if these portraits had been conceived to illustrate a book, the artist would have done lithographs rather than paintings. He thinks that they were a sort of demonstration material which allowed the doctor to give pathology lectures with more precision and freedom than in the presence of the patients.

This series of portraits was executed between the return from England in December 1821 and the beginning of the illness which was to overpower the artist. Biographers have tried to date the series as precisely as possible (Clément, *op. cit.,* p. 317; G. Oprescu, 1927, p. 162; R. Régamey, 1926, p. 46; L. Eitner, in 1973, Los Angeles, exh. cat., p. 171) and concur that the portraits were probably painted during the fall of 1822 and the spring of 1823.

Géricault broke with the tradition of the portrayal of the insane, who were regarded until then as being possessed by demons and grotesque fools. For him, they were normal portraits of disturbed individuals. He conveys with lucidity the signs of physical and moral decomposition. He renders this mental shipwreck with sobriety; he uses no anecdote, no symbol, only those pictorial means that permit him to transcribe the wandering consciousness; this confers a visible grandeur and monumentality upon these faces. The sober harmony of colors (green and brown), restrained and solid technique, free touch, and impasto make this portrait a document of an admirable pictorial quality. Along with certain of Goya's *Caprices,* Géricault's insane are the most extraordinary psychological paintings from the beginning of the 19th century; through their realistic sincerity, they pave the way for some of the most powerful works of Courbet, Degas and Manet.

PROVENANCE

Created by the artist for his friend, Dr. Georget; collection of Dr. Lachèze, Baden-Baden until 1868; Charles Jacques Collection, sold 1878; Chéramy Collection, sold 7 May 1908, no. 108; acquired by the friends of the museum of Ghent who donated it to the museum (INV. 1908. F).

EXHIBITIONS

1924, Paris, no. 263; 1939-1940, Buenos Aires, Rio de Janeiro, no. 48; Montevideo, p. 11, n.n.; 1940, Chicago; 1941, Washington; 1947, Paris, atelier Delacroix, no cat.; 1948, Brussels, etc., no. 37; 1953, Winterthur, no. 107, ill. 27; 1953, Brussels, no. 54, ill.; 1955, Rome, Milan, no. 50, ill. 20; 1959, London, no. 178; 1964-1965, Munich, no. 123; 1969, Minneapolis, no. 41; 1971-1972, Los Angeles, etc., no. 123, ill.

REFERENCES

Ch. Clément, 1879, p. 317; no. 157 c; M. Hamal, 1887, p. 257; L. Rosenthal, 1905, p. 142; J. Meier-Graefe and E. Klossowski, 1908, p. 79, no. 108, ill. 108; M.-G. [1920], no. 20; R. Régamey, 1926, ill. 27; G. Oprescu, 1927, p. 162; mus. cat., 1930, p. 64; M. Gauthier, 1935, ill. 50; [Anon.] *L'Amour de l'art, Prométhée,* 1939, p. 18, ill.; M. Miller, 1940-1941, pp. 151-163, ill. 136 c; G. Bazin, 1946, p. 44; P. Courthion and P. Cailler, 1947, pp. 250, 341; G. Chabot, 1951, p. 14, ill. 36; K. Berger, 1952, pp. 39-40, ill. 91; D. Aimé-Azam, 1956, p. 231; A. del Guercio, 1963, pp. 91, 152, ill. 99; F.-H. Lem, 1963, pp. 98-100, 101-102, ill. IX; K. Berger, 1968 (French ed.), pp. 187-188, ill. 95; D. Aimé-Azam, 1970, pp. 248, 364; L. Eitner, 1973, re-issue of Ch. Clément, 1879, p. 317, no. 157c, p. 457.

I. J.

Anne-Louis Girodet-Trioson

1767 Montargis - Paris 1824

After his father's death in 1784 (he was adopted by Dr. Trioson in 1806), he joined David's studio. He failed in the competition for the Prix de Rome in 1787 with *Nabuchodonosor fait tuer les enfants de Sédécias* (Le Mans), won second prize the following year with *La Mort de Titus* (Angers) and finally first prize in 1789 with *Joseph reconnu par ses frères* (Paris, École des Beaux-Arts). A *Deposition* (No. 78), an amazing prefiguration of a kind of religious Romanticism, dates from the same year. He left for the Villa Medici in 1790, painted *Le Sommeil d'Endymion* (1791; Louvre), which was to have an astounding success both in Rome and in Paris at the Salon of 1793, then in 1792, *Hippocrate refusant les présents d'Artaxerxès* (Paris, Faculté de Médecine). Because of political events, he left Rome, first for Naples and then Venice. In 1795, he returned to Paris. To earn a living he drew illustrations for Didot publications and did a number of portraits, as did F. Gérard and P.-P. Prud'hon. In the Salon of 1799, the *Portrait de Mlle Lange en Danaé* (Minneapolis; sketch at Montargis) caused a scandal. In 1801, Napoleon commissioned him to do *Ossian* (No. 80) for the Château de la Malmaison. This work and his *Scène de Déluge* (1806, Louvre) placed him "in the top rank among the masters of the new school" (*Athenaeum,* no. 12, December 1806).

Next, he dealt with subjects as varied as the *Funérailles d'Atala* (1808, Louvre), *Napoléon recevant les clefs de Vienne* (1808, Versailles), *La Révolte du Caire* (1810, Versailles) and in 1809, undertook the decoration of the apartments of the Emperor and Empress at Compiègne. At the Salon of 1814, he showed 15 paintings which constituted a real retrospective of his work. In 1815, he became a member of the Academy of Fine Arts. His last compositions were uneven. *Pygmalion et Galatée* (1819, Château de Dampierre) was a failure, notwithstanding what the critics and public of his time thought of it, while the portraits of *Général Bonchamp* and *Cathelineau* (both in Cholet), exhibited in 1824, were certainly more successful; the high quality of the latter distinguishes it from other very mediocre portraits of Vendean chiefs which were commissioned during the Restoration (with the exception of Guérin's painting of *Henri de La Rochejacquelein,* No. 95).

Like Pierre-Henri de Valenciennes and Jean-Joseph Taillasson, Girodet was also a writer and a theorist. The complete edition of his writings appeared as a posthumous anthology in two volumes, published by P.-A. Coupin; it contains mainly poems (*Le Peintre, Les Veillées*), as well as his correspondence, his speeches at the Institute, etc.

Revealed to the modern public by an exhibition organized in 1967 at Montargis by Jacqueline Pruvost-Auzas, Girodet now appears as one of the greatest painters of his generation. His contemporaries were not mistaken when they preferred *Le Déluge* to David's painting *Les Sabines* during the decennial competition of 1810.

There are many thorough studies on Girodet: e.g. the *Notice historique* of P.-A. Coupin (1829), the thesis by G. Levitine, submitted to Harvard in 1952 and certainly, the catalog of the 1967 exhibition. Several basic texts should also be mentioned: first Girodet's correspondence with several contemporary artists edited by Pélissier (1864) in *La Revue encyclopédique ;* then the articles published by J. Adhémar in the *B.S.H.A.F.* (1934), by G. Levitine (*The Burlington Magazine,* October 1953; *The Art Bulletin,* 1954, no. 1; *G.B.A.,* April 1965) and by Jacqueline Pruvost-Auzas in the *Revue du Louvre:* "Musée Girodet, à Montargis. Récentes acquisitions" (1968, no. 6, pp. 355-358); "Girodet et le thème de Danaé" (1970, no. 6, pp. 377-382); in collaboration with D. Ternois, 1973, and in the *B.S.H.A.F.,* "Les Peintures de Girodet au Palais de Compiègne" (1971, pp. 93-106). It is also profitable to read H. Focillon's sensitive analysis of Girodet's position with regard to Romanticism (*Histoire de l'Art,* 1927, pp. 49-51). In his preface to the Montargis exhibition, Michel Laclotte has accurately shown how the originality of Girodet's art, affectations, mannerism, even the graphicness are so well-suited to modern taste, charmed as we are by Art Nouveau. Also to be read are the accounts of the 1967 exhibition by Jacques de Caso (1969) and by P. Ward-Jackson (1967). R. Rosenblum (*Revue de l'Art,* 1969) recalls how Girodet's art moved rapidly toward extravagance of form, feeling and subject, leading him to break with David's teachings.

J. L.

78
*Deposition****

La Déposition de Croix
Plate p. 90
Canvas; 335 × 235; Inscription near the shroud on the right, in five lines; *A. L. Girodet De Roussy facit Parisus An 1789 aetatis Suae 22.*
Montesquieu-Volvestre (Haute-Garonne), Église de la Paroisse

Religious paintings were rare during the reign of Louis XVI; for obvious political reasons, they were even more so during the Revolution, the period when, almost alone, the Royalist François-Xavier Fabre treated this type of subject. Locquin (1912, pp. 272-275) has recalled the disfavor in which sacred painting was held from 1774 to 1785; let us add that of the 634 works presented at the Salons of 1785, 1787 and 1789, only 42 paintings or drawings were inspired by religious history. There was an essential contradiction between idealistic art inspired by antiquity, whose domination was gradual, and the Christian spirit. One is forced to state, in fact, that the emotion and mystery inspired by religion were incompatible with the neo-classical esthetic, if not because of its style, then at least because of its spirit. During the Restoration, some artists did attempt to apply David's lessons to religious subjects. However, it was Romanticism which espoused religiosity. A few years later, Chateaubriand was to write in the *Génie du Christianisme* (part III, book II, chap. III, cited by L. Rosenthal, 1900, p. 39): "Religion has provided the arts with subjects more beautiful, more rich, more romantic and more touching than mythological subjects." And Jacqueline Pruvost-Auzas was right to emphasize this in her entry on *Les Funérailles d'Atala* in the Girodet exhibition catalog in 1967. The components of both are the same. Ph. Ward-Jackson (1967, p. 663) has suggested that Girodet was inspired by the *Deposition* of Sebastiano del Piombo. More likely, the precise source might have been the often-copied engraving of the *Entombment* by Parmigianino (eg. Germain Pillon's altar screen for Saint-Germain l'Auxerrois). In any case, the powerful expression here of death and sorrow, the obscurity of the forms, the setting of the cave—all combine to create a work whose modernity is striking.

PROVENANCE

Painted for a Capuchin monastery, this picture was thought to have been destroyed (this was affirmed by Coupin in 1829) until it was sorted out by *Monuments Historiques* in 1953 and revealed to the public at the Montargis exhibition in 1967. It was in the church of Montesquieu-Volvestre in 1865, as is indicated by the church's inventory at that date. The inventory of the possessions of the church vestry of 24 January 1906 mentions a painting signed *Girodet*, but gives no indication at all of its origin.
J. Adhémar (1933, p. 281) has cited the postscript of a letter of 1789 by Girodet to his friend Gérard from Tours, where he wrote: "By the way, do not forget to ask Garnier if he has packed my picture of Christ, if he has included the large removable frame and the smaller model, as well as the bottle of varnish..." (see Pruvost-Auzas, 1967, no. 7).

EXHIBITION
1967, Montargis, no. 7.

REFERENCES
P.-A. Coupin, 1829, v. I, p. LV; J. Adhémar, 1933, p. 281; J. Pruvost-Auzas, 1967, no. 7; P. Ward-Jackson, 1967, pp. 660-663; J. de Caso, 1969, p. 85; R. Rosenblum, 1969, pp. 100-101.

RELATED WORKS
A sketch for this painting (paper on canvas, 45 × 37) is in Montpellier, Musée Fabre. It had been noticed by Bruun-Neergaard (1801, p. 157), who wrote: "The Virgin seen here is a beautiful as Van Dyck's." Given by Girodet to his friend Chenard. Valedeau bought it for 1,300 francs at the Chenard sale and gave it to the museum in 1836. A *Pietà* attributed to Girodet was sold in Milan, 15 December 1955 (no. 21); by Regnault?

J. L.

79
*Portrait of Bourgeon**

"*Portrait du Citoyen B...*"
Plate p. 157
Canvas; 92 × 72; s.d.l.l. *ALG/1800*
Salon of 1800, no. 167
Saint-Omer, Musée de l'Hôtel Sandelin

Jean-François de Bourgeon (b. 12 May 1757) was mayor of Boissy-le-Sec and one of the painter's best friends (alluded to by the book in his hand: Cicero's treatise, *De Amicitia*).

It is important to stress that on the occasion of this Salon, the critics deplored the immense number of portraits exhibited. Jacques Lebrun, in the *Moniteur Universel*, spoke of the "sterile abundance of portraits" and the critic of the *Journal des Débats* remarked that "out of the 380 paintings as well as drawings which cover this Salon, we count up to 250 portraits." Guipava sang in *Les Tableaux du Muséum en vaudevilles:* "Aujourd'hui frères, papas, mamans, / Cousins, voisins, créanciers ou chalans / Vieilles femmes et siècles ambulans, / Voilà les portraits à la mode," and he mocked: "Portrait du citoyen N. / Portrait de Madame D. / Puis portrait de Madame M. / Portrait du citoyen C. / Portrait du citoyen P. / Portrait du citoyen B. / Ces portraits (ter) sont-ils bien vrais ? Sont-ils bien vrais ? (bis)." The anonymity also intrigued the author of the *Dernières observations sur cette exposition:* "I wonder why we see so many of these individuals who desire to be seen in public but do not consider it at all appropriate to be recognized by this same public, so that the catalog number which indicates their portraits most often does not indicate their names...." In another connection, this author gives some incidental information which permits us to appreciate the difficult situation of the artists of the time working without State commissions and who, in order to live, were obliged to attract a private (bourgeois) clientele totally concerned with its image. "Vanity was often the only reason why so many had themselves painted, and the only useful aspect of this conduct is its advantage to painters, who attempt in this way to recoup from the few opportunities they find of exercizing their talent and bringing it to light."

The critics were disturbed to see the best painters abandoning the genre of history painting. "One ex-periences, no doubt, a painful surprise," the *Mercure de France* stated, "when, at the head of the artists who have exhibited only portraits, one finds two men, who are still young and have made their mark among our best history painters through successes as brilliant as they were precocious. The reader recognizes in these characteristics Gérard and Girodet." More particularly, concerning Girodet, the editor of the *Journal du Bulletin Universel* complained: "I only know one fault of this artist; it is to have rendered this portrait with so much art and truth that it seems to have cost him a great deal of time. The time wasted perfecting a suit of clothes could have been employed in perfecting a masterpiece of history painting."

Nevertheless, the work was generally well liked. Bruun-Neergaard declared it a "fine portrait." The critic of the *Mercure de France* admired "the particular finesse combined with a profound knowledge of all the resources of art"; and the critic of the *Journal des Débats* wrote: "We reproach the personage of no. 167, who is reading Cicero, with looking too much as if he is being painted: people who know Monsieur C. B... are nevertheless persistent in maintaining that this portrait is a perfect resemblance in all ways. It is, besides, a very good painting. We admire the bold color of the coat, the drawing of the head and hands. We should correctly observe that the artist has, despite his intentions, made the hair white instead of powdered; it is a very slight fault."

Finally, Landon, summing up the many portraits exhibited by Girodet, noted in *Le Journal des Arts:* "They are correctly drawn and executed with a precise brush."

PROVENANCE
Bought at a sale on 3 March 1873 for 1,550 francs; collection of Teil-Chaix d'Est-Ange; gift of the Baronne Joseph du Teil-Chaix d'Est-Ange in 1921 in memory of her husband.

EXHIBITIONS
1800, Salon, no. 167; 1967, Montargis, no. 24.

REFERENCES

Coll. Deloynes, v. XXII, no. 630, p. 538; no. 632, pp. 689-690; no. 633, pp. 730, 735; *ibid.* v. XXIII, no. 634, pp. 29-30; no. 635, pp. 153-154; no. 638, p. 214; no. 644, pp. 493-495; T.-C. Bruun-Neergaard, (1801), p. 40; P.-A. Coupin, 1829, p. LIX (indicates the date of 1798); J. du Teil, July 1907, no. 67, ill.; A. Dezarrois, Féral and Mannheim, 1925, no. 13; J. Vergnet-Ruiz and M. Laclotte, 1962, p. 237; G. Wildenstein, 1963, p. 17; J. Pruvost-Auzas, 1967, no. 24; Ph. G. Chabert, February 1971, ill.

RELATED WORKS

The catalog of the collection of J. du Teil (1926) and the catalog of the exhibition *Girodet* at Montargis (1967, no. 24) mention a replica of this portrait. In April 1883, at the time of the *Première Exposition des Portraits du siècle*, Paris (no. 108), it belonged to M. Féral; then, in 1889, to the collection of Marie Rothan, at the time of the *Exposition Centennale* in Paris (no. 390); it was in the Rothan sale, Paris, Galerie Georges Petit, 29-31 May 1890, no. 152 (1,400 francs); it was sold in Paris, Hôtel Drouot, room 1, 20-21 April 1932 (no. 48) and again in Paris, Galerie Charpentier, 25 June 1937. These catalogs indicate that the replica is dated 1806. Jacqueline Pruvost-Auzas (1967) has stressed that it seems likely that only one replica existed, with the same dimensions as the original.

J. L.

80
Ossian Receiving Napoleonic Officers

"Hommage offert à Napoléon Bonaparte, par A.-L. Girodet, du Tableau dans lequel il a représenté l'Apothéose des Héros français morts pour la patrie pendant la guerre de la Liberté"

Plate p. 183

Canvas; 92.5 × 184

Salon of 1802, no. 907 (3rd supplement)

Rueil-Malmaison, Musée National du Château

For the decoration of Malmaison, Girodet intended to execute an allegorical composition with subject matter "derived from the event of 3 Nivôse (24 December 1800)," the assassination attempt from which Bonaparte had escaped; Coupin provided a description of the sketch painted in 1801: "The first consul is represented with the features of a Hercules, crushing a monster which breathes fire" (1829, I, p. LXX). Discouraged from carrying out this project by the architect Percier, he agreed to draw his inspiration from Ossian, but without renouncing the idea of evoking some glorious event from the history of the Republic. He was acquainted with the *Ossian* of François Gérard (No. 68) and adopted a composition with balanced areas of light and shadow, and figures of similar proportions. A certain rivalry seems to have existed between the two artists at this time. Girodet explains his intentions to Bonaparte in a letter of 6 Messidor, Year X (25 June 1802): "I have tried to trace the *apothéose des héros* for whom France mourns.... In this work, the fruit of long and arduous toil, the importance of my theme has caused me to forget that I have only been charged with executing a pleasant painting for Malmaison.... " Somewhat apprehensive, he proposed "to paint another, simpler in effect and thought, which will achieve this end"; he invited Bonaparte to view it "in the very atelier where it was conceived and perfected." Bonaparte saw the painting and said: "You have had a great idea: the figures in your painting are genuine ghosts; I believe I have seen those of generals whom I have known" (letter from Girodet to Bernardin de Saint-Pierre, in Coupin, 1829, II, p. 28). Among the numerous persons who thronged to the artist's studio at the Louvre that summer, his master Jacques-Louis David was a surprised visitor. Girodet relates in the same letter: "David let slip, on seeing it, that this production did not resemble any master or any school, that he had never seen a comparable painting and that it will get its just recognition after my death. He perhaps owed me redress for what he had said about it, as I have been told, at court" (*ibid.*, p. 278). According to Delécluze, on leaving the painter's studio, David exclaimed: "Now then! Girodet is a lunatic !... Either he is insane or I no longer understand the art of painting. He has created persons of crystal for us there... What a pity ! With his fine talent, he will create nothing but follies..." (Delécluze, 1855, p. 266). By order of the first Consul, this painting was finally presented to the Salon, with a large explanatory note in the catalog; it aroused more criticism than praise and was taken down before the exhibition ended. Meanwhile, Mme de Vandeul shrewdly noted: "A painting by Girodet attracted general attention. It was talked about with so much enthusiasm and criticism that this work must have carried the seal of a superior talent"; as for herself, she expressed some disapproval: "I do not find enough space there for so many people and things" (in M. Tourneux, 1912, p. 126). If Landon abandoned the idea of executing a line engraving of this painting, owing to the excessive number of figures, he tried to justify the decisions of this artist whom he admired: "Some objections which could be raised to citizen Girodet concern the intricacy of ideas and the wealth of objects which embellish his canvas; it is a fact that it was conceived in this manner, because the subject of this painting belongs completely to the realm of the imagination and he had been authorized not to recognize any other rule except that of thei magination whose prerogatives are boundless...." The artist's imagination was, in fact, subservient to a profound sense of allegory, carefully organized to reflect the historical events of the time, as G. Levitine pointed out. The political undertones appeared to L. Aragon as secretly anti-Bonaparte (based on a description of the painting published by Coupin in 1829; Aragon was hesitant about the interpretation of the eagle, which is not mentioned in this text; he believed the eagle is the "bird of Napoleon," even when Girodet stated precisely in the catalog of the Salon, that Cafarelli-Dufalga "ascribes to the French army a marvelous vision, the eagle surrendering dominion over the sky to the cock, an unquestionable omen of an approaching and glorious peace..."). Girodet wrote a flattering letter to Bonaparte: "In straying from ordinary fiction to create a mythology... your preference for Ossian has revealed the secret to me..." (A.-P. Coupin, 1829, II, p. 295). Nevertheless Girodet remained faithful to traditional heraldic symbolism by including the Gallic cock, the Austrian eagle, the dove of peace. Suggesting a battle just finished—the feathers are still flying—and the loss of the eagle, who puts to flight a "Victory representing France" (as Mme de Vandeul understood it, see M. Tourneux, op. cit.), he made reference to the Continental peace after the Treaty of Lunéville in 1801, a period still agitated by England's hostility, suppressed slightly later by the Treaty of Amiens (25 March 1802). This general peace must have occurred just as the artist was finishing the composition, which required 12 to 15 months work.

Under these role-defining emblems, appear several groups of characters: to the right, "the phantoms of the French heroes who have died for the fatherland,"

among whom can be recognized (from left to right) Joubert, Dugommier, Hoche, Marceau, Desaix, Dampierre, Kléber, Championnet, Caffarelli-Dufalga and La Tour d'Auvergne. They have come to meet Ossian, the old bard of Morven, surrounded by his warriors and ancestors. "All these heroes admire the French heroes." With young female musicians or offering bearers, they participate with the Austrians in a feast of peace which the warriors of Lochlin, in the background and at the lower left, would like to upset. Their chieftan, the ferocious Starno, stabs a young French dragoon "with a sabre of honor which the first Consul awarded him." Fingal's enemies play the part of the English. It is not certain (the critics remain silent on this point) whether all the cryptic references, which had become a little anachronistic by the end of 1802, were obvious to the spectators. The public was outraged above all by Girodet's sense of fantasy, which was deliberately opposed to Neo-Classicism and already romantic. He wished to justify this in a letter to Bernardin de Saint-Pierre, in which, with regard to form, grayish color and lighting effects, he insistently repeats the word "creation" and, with regard to the ideas—the personification of Victory, the old warlike phantoms, the young girls who celebrate the heroic deeds—he confesses: "These ideas, or at least their application are, I dare to believe, new and poetic" (Coupin, op. cit., pp. 278-279). G. Levitine has correctly noted the obvious analogy with Rubens' *Arrival of Marie de' Medici* (Louvre). Should we not point out that Girodet already had the idea of a composition with two groups approaching one another, as evidenced in the sketch in Paris, École des Beaux-Arts, the sketch of the *Serment des sept chefs devant Thèbes* (Paris, École des Beaux-Arts; see exh. cat. 1967, Montargis, no. 89, ill.), which Jacqueline Pruvost-Auzas has shown was influenced by a composition of John Flaxman.

To this we should add the Davidian influences: a pose inspired by the *Serment des Horaces* (but reversed) seen in the preparatory sketch of Angers; or the crowd in the *Serment du Jeu de Paume* (drawing, 1790-1791, Louvre). While Girodet allowed less space above, he did not regret the "proportions used" and, as he wrote to P..., "with one more foot of space, filled only with clouds, I would have given this painting an effect which would have totally confused my critics" (Coupin, op. cit., p. 342). Finally, more than David's *Distribution des aigles* (Versailles), it is perhaps Ingres' *Napoleon au pont de Kiel* (drawing, Montauban) which retains, some years later, a recollection of one of the innumerable iconographic inventions of Girodet: the Victory bearing trophies. This composition was so overladen with ideas that it became incomprehensible, largely because of the eagle, as early as two years after its presentation to the Salon. It remains isolated in the artist's œuvre, as well as in the painting of the time. H. Toussaint saw in it an indication "of the style of many of the mural decorations of the years 1880-1900" (1974, p. 86). Was the impetus of another Republic necessary for it to inspire the *Rêve* of Édouard Detaille (Musée de l'Armée)?

PROVENANCE
Commissioned in 1800 by the architects Charles Percier and Pierre-François Fontaine for the decoration of the Salon Doré of Malmaison, for 12,000 francs (see Coupin, *op. cit.*, II, p. 296); according to the *Journal des Débats* of 17 October 1802, it was then located in the Salle du Conseil of Malmaison in preparation for transferal to Saint-Cloud or to the Tuileries (H. Toussaint, *op. cit.*, p. 86); passed, at an unknown date, into the collection of Prince Eugène de Beauharnais, future Duke of Leuchtenberg; remained after his death in 1824 and until 1929, in the possession of his descendants (located there in 1834, during the visit of Charles Lenormant [1847, p. 84], and in 1838, according to the Muxel catalog, in the Leuchtenberg Gallery, Munich); acquired by the Musées Nationaux on the Swiss market, at Vevey, in 1931.

EXHIBITIONS
1802, Salon, no. 907 (3rd supplement); 1936, Paris, no. 317; 1967, Montauban, no. 256; 1967, Montargis, no. 26, ill.; 1968-69, Moscow-Leningrad, no. 64; 1974, Paris, no. 79, ill.; 1974, Hamburg, no. 88, color ill.

REFERENCES
C.-P. Landon, 1801, pp. 233-238; C.-P. Landon, 1802, pp. 65-67; A.-L. in *Journal des Arts, des Sciences et de littérature,* 19 June 1802, pp. 410-412; *Journal des Débats,* 3 June 1802, 1 and 17 October 1802; *Revue du Salon de l'An X...,* 1802, pp. 183-184; coll. Deloynes, v. XXVI, no. 698, pp. 861-863 and v. XXVIII, nos. 761-762, pp. 301-321, no. 769, pp. 183-184, no. 778, pp. 748-755; P.-A. Coupin,
1829, v. I, pp. XV-XVI, LVII, 152, v. II, pp. 277-282, 287-297, 341-342; E. Miel, 1843, p. 292; Ch. Lenormant, 1847, p. 84; E.-J. Delécluze, 1855, pp. 260, 263-266; M. de Lescure, 1867, p. 252; M. Tourneux, 1912, pp. 126-127; H. Lemonnier, 1913, pp. 48, 51-54; P. van Thieghem, 1917, v. II, pp. 8, 142, 145-152; P. van Thieghem, 1918, pp. 61-63; Kl. von Baudissin, 1924, p. 60; P. van Thieghem, 1924, p. 255; L. Hautecœur, 1928, p. 16; J. Bourguignon, 1931, pp. 214-216, ill.; J. Adhémar, 1933, pp. 271-272; F. Antal, 1936, p. 137, pl. II; R. Escholier, 1941, v. I, pp. 78-80; E.-J. Delécluze, 1948, pp. 65-67; L. Aragon, 1949, pp. 201-209; G. Levitine, 1952, pp. 108, 173, 195; W. Friedländer, 1952, pp. 42-43; L. Hautecœur, 1954, pp. 227-228, 291; G. Levitine, 1956, pp. 39-56, ill.; J. Billiet, mus. cat., 1956, pp. 31-32; N. Schlenoff, 1956, pp. 75-76, 83, 87-88; G. Levitine, 1962, p. 214; J. Lacassagne, 1965, p. 216; G. Levitine, 1965, p. 231; H. Okun, 1967, pp. 348-351, ill. 40d; G. Hubert, 1967, pp. 241, 245; Ph. Ward-Jackson, 1967, p. 663; H. Honour, 1968, pp. 186-187; R. Rosenblum, 1967a, p. 47; R. Rosenblum, 1969, p. 100; D. Ternois, 1969, pp. 193, 197-201, ill. 15; J. de Caso, 1969, p. 86; J. Pruvost-Auzas and D. Ternois, 1973, pp. 262-263, ill. p. 263; P. Vaisse, 1974, pp. 83-84; P. Joannides and C. Sells, 1974, p. 361; G. Levitine, 1974, pp. 319-323, ill. p. 320 (detail).

RELATED WORKS
Paintings. Smaller version (panel; 34 × 29) painted by Girodet (Louvre, R.F. 2359): his iconography, notably the rabbit in the eagle's claws, contained an element of humor for Aragon (1949, p. 209); H. Toussaint (*op. cit.,* pp. 87-89) described it as a satirical replica, whereas it was traditionally regarded as a sketch (an interpretation that P. Vaisse, P. Joannides and C. Sells prefer to retain).
Drawings. An *Étude de guerriers* (charcoal; 25 × 28), Angers, Musée Turpin de Crissé.
Girodet made numerous drawings on the theme of Ossian (see *Ossian* exh. cat., 1974, Hamburg and Paris) which are not, for the most part, direct studies for this painting.
A drawing of the entire composition (98 × 84), by Charles Châtillon was acquired at the Girodet sale, 2 April 1825, no. 367, by Antoine-Claude Pannetier (see Coupin, *op. cit.* I, p. LXXIX).
Lithographs. Some of the principal heads were executed in 1821 by Hyacinthe-Louis Aubry-Lecomte under the direction of Girodet and appeared in two albums in 1822.

G. L.

81
Portrait of an Indian

Un Indien
Plate p. 196 and color pl. p. 21
Canvas; 145 × 113
Montargis, Musée Girodet

This painting remained unpublished until its acquisition in 1973 by the Montargis museum.

It can easily be attributed to Girodet because of the manuscript annotations in the catalog of the Girodet sale in the Bibliothèque du Louvre, annotations which, in other respects, are highly revelatory of the attitudes of a contemporary admirer. "The complexion is that of an African, but the features are extremely regular. A slight mustache accompanies the full and very black side whiskers. The turban in various shades of red. His varied yellow dress is trimmed in green. Through its opening can be seen another white dress tied with a bright red scarf. Another scarf, whose ends are ornamented with elaborate palmettes, rests on his right shoulder; one end falls in front of him; the other behind the left shoulder after having passed across the chest. His left hand holds the hilt of his sabre; the right arm falls its full length at his side, the hand, half-closed or slightly contracted. His face stands out against the light background with a remarkably powerful effect. The eyes look at the spectator—large as life."

The description confirms the identification of the painting with the one which appears under no. 2 in the Girodet sale and which, according to Coupin (1829, p. LXVI), dates from 1807. It seems that the work was never exhibited at the Salon. We do not know for whom, or why was it painted. It is even questionable whether it was really finished. Usually, in fact, Girodet presented his models (J.-B. Belley, Chateaubriand, Cathelineau or Bonchamps, for example) in a setting which accented their character, a method followed also by Ingres. Here, on the contrary, the landscape, without precise reference, except for the palm tree, is reduced to a simple indication of a mountain chain, vaguely sketched at the right. However, as the anonymous author of the annotations in the sale catalog remarked, it is precisely this light background that gives the painting such remarkable power. Thus, this effect might very well have been voluntary.

In any case, this portrait pays tribute once again to the painter's fascination with exotic types (as evidenced also by the many descriptions of portraits of Turks, Odalisks, Mamelukes and Greeks in the *Notice historique* by Coupin). His fascination is communicated to the spectator by a presentation close to the picture plane, which strongly attracts the viewer. The simplicity of the composition accentuates even more the personality of the subject. Girodet explained this in his advice to painters *(Quatrième Veillée)*:

La simplicité noble encadre mieux la gloire.
Voyez donc Titien, Vandick et Raphaël,
Exemples du vrai simple et du beau naturel;
Qu'ils vous guident toujours; sur ces doctes modèles
Grandissez vos modèles....

PROVENANCE
Sold by Girodet, Paris, 11 April 1825, no. 2; Becquerel-Despréaux Collection; bought in 1973 for the Montargis museum.

REFERENCES
Pérignon, 1825, no. 2; P.-A. Coupin, 1829, v. I, p. LXVI.

J. L.

François-Marius Granet

1775 Aix-en-Provence 1849

Son of a mason from Aix-en-Provence, François-Marius Granet discovered his vocation at an early age. He was the pupil of Constantin at the free drawing academy, founded in 1771, and directed by Arnulphy. His early sketchbooks (Aix, Musée Granet and Bibliothèque Méjanes) show his interest in ruins and cloisters. Granet was already linked with the Forbin family before the Revolution; Auguste de Forbin, a painter and future national museum director, two years younger than Granet, was to be his friend and patron throughout his life. After an interval at the siege of Toulon (1793), where he was employed as a draughtsman, Granet joined Forbin in Paris and attended David's atelier. According to E.-J. Delécluze (1855), he worked in the Capuchin monastery on the Rue Saint-Honoré with Ingres, Bartolini and Girodet, but Granet's memoirs only mention the Feuillants monastery, which inspired a painting. He began exhibiting at the Salon in 1799 *(Intérieur d'un Cloître)* and journeyed to Rome in 1802 with Forbin. Granet became a protégé of Cacault, the French *chargé d'affaires,* and also of Cardinal Fesch; and was admitted to the Academy of Saint Luke in 1813. He returned to France permanently in 1819. His successes at the Salon (*Le Chœur des Capucins à Rome,* 1819, Hermitage, and *Le Couvent de Saint-François d'Assise,* 1822, Louvre) earned him the Cross of the Legion of Honor and the ribbon of the Order of Saint Michael. Forbin had him appointed a curator at the Louvre in 1826 and at Versailles in 1830. From then on, he only devoted part of his time to painting, but he did some contemporary history paintings for Louis-Philippe (Versailles) and also some admirable watercolors (Louvre and Aix). The outbreak of the Revolution of 1848 precipitated his retirement to his hometown, to which he donated his studio and collection, in particular his famous portrait painted by Ingres in 1807. Granet's souvenirs, the manuscript of which is in Aix at the Musée Arbaud, were published in *Le Temps* (28 September to 28 October 1872).

Granet's œuvre is somewhat repetitious; it originated in a school that has fallen into oblivion but which flourished from the beginning of the Revolution: views of monasteries, church interiors, and ruins with romantic or pre-romantic sensibility, to which Granet added a sincere and compelling religious inspiration. In his work, the sensation of the weight of history and the passage of time are combined with a picturesque evocation of the past: Granet adopted the *style troubadour* (he was a friend of Pierre-Henri Révoil and Fleury Richard), although he did not favor the smooth finish and wood base of which Richard or Jean-Baptiste

Mallet were so fond. His art owes more to the study of the old Dutch and Flemish painters, Teniers in particular, than to David, with whom Granet did not stay long, and even to visiting Lenoir's Musée des Monuments Français. In his souvenirs, he wrote that Flemish engravings had helped him see nature. An interesting passage in Fleury Richard's memoirs (brought to our attention by M.-Cl. Chaudonneret), which like those of Granet, were written a little earlier than 1850, sums up well the origins and aims of the *genre anecdotique.* "One may perhaps recall the brilliant success obtained some 40 years ago by certain genre painters, which so stirred the admiration of their contemporaries that since that time, genre painters have become very numerous. However, though the encouragement they were given at the time led to some progress in the use of color, through the study of nature in the manner of the Dutch artists neglected until then, why should one not paint, as they did, pictures whose subjects capture our attention much more than does the charm of their color, such as Stella painting a Virgin on the prison wall or Valentina of Milan mourning the death of her husband the Duc d'Orléans, Mademoiselle de La Vallière in her Carmelite cell cultivating a lily, the ring of Charles V, and many others that offer historical interest and that create an ideal beauty without which painting is no longer an art, and the artist is no more than a craftsman."

A.S.

82
*The Painter Stella in Prison**

"*Le peintre Stella en prison*"
Plate p. 207
Canvas; 195 × 144; s.d.l.r. *Granet* / *Roma* / *1810.*
Salon of 1810, no. 387
Moscow, Pushkin Museum of Fine Arts

Francis Haskell (1971) has studied the fashion current between the end of the 18th and the mid-19th century of taking subject matter from painters lives; this may be extended moreover to writers, since Granet was to exhibit at the Salon of 1820 a picture of *Montaigne dans la Prison de Tasse* (today in Montpellier). Most popular were themes of honors rendered to great painters as they were dying: *La Mort de Raphaël* (Pierre-Nolasque Bergeret, Salon of 1806), *Poussin reçoit les*

soins du cardinal Massimo et les secours de la religion (Granet, Salon of 1834, formerly in the Demidoff Collection, first version in Aix). The subject chosen here, also painted by the Lyon artist Michel-Philibert Génod (Tarbes, now on loan to Angers), is more unusual, since it shows a time of misfortune—but misfortune accepted in good spirit—providing an opportunity to demonstrate the spiritual strength of the painter, busy drawing a Virgin and Child on the prison wall, to the wonder of a group of fellow-prisoners and a good-natured jailer.

In his Souvenirs (see above), Granet recalled at length the history of this picture, the first large-scale work he had undertaken. Visiting the old prisons of the Capitol in Rome (the *Tabulario* of the ancient Romans), he was attracted by their picturesque architecture and especially by the greenish color of the stone *(peperino)*; he particularly noticed a gallery about 50 feet long, lit by high windows, in which there were "pilasters in *peperino* stone bearing fine brick arches." Searching for "a subject for this remarkable site," he thought of the story of Stella, which he had just recently read. In fact, Félibien (*Entretiens,* 1688 ed., II, pp. 654-655) described how the painter Jacques de Stella (1596-1657), who had been falsely accused around 1633, shortly before his return to France, of "carrying on certain love affairs in a family," was arrested, along with his brother and his servants. "To divert himself during the short time he was in prison, he made a drawing in charcoal on a chamber wall of the Virgin holding her Son, which was declared so beautiful that Cardinal François Barberin went there expressly to see it. Not long ago, it was still in the same place, with a lighted lamp before it; the prisoners go there to say their prayers."

Granet hastened to buy a large canvas and painted his picture on the spot; Canova and Camuccini are said to have admired it. He offered the painting to Cardinal Fesch, who tactfully refused it but sent it instead to the Salon. "This was in 1812," added Granet, mistakenly; he went on to say that through the good offices of the Abbé Payard, curator of the Fesch Collection, the picture was bought for 2,400 francs by Du Fresne de Saint-Léon, who subsequently resold it to the Empress Josephine. Although it is not mentioned in the catalog of Josephine's collection published in 1811 (which, however, lists two pictures by Stella), the work does appear in the inventory of the Empress's possessions (published by S. Grandjean, 1964) after her death on 29 May 1814. We may thus speculate whether Granet in fact made a copy of the picture which Guizot had much admired at the Salon of 1810 ("Never was

a scene more felicitously conceived, better disposed and executed... the brushwork is broad and firm, yet it is well finished"), since he presented the same subject at the Salon of 1814, which did not open until November. Admittedly, Granet made no mention of such a repetition in his Souvenirs, whereas he did in the case of those he made of the *Chœur des Capucins.*

PROVENANCE

Bought at the end of the Salon by Du Fresne de Saint-Léon, who sold it after 1811 to the Empress Josephine. After her death in 1814, it was part of her legacy to Prince Eugène, who became the Prince of Leuchtenberg and took up residence in Munich. When he died in 1824, the painting went to his son Maximilian, whose widow, the Grand Duchess Marie, daughter of the Czar Nicolas I, moved the collection to Saint Petersburg sometime between 1852 and 1855. After 1884, the picture was deposited in the Academy of Fine Arts (cat. no. 224, p. 47); and in 1890 returned to the Nicolas of Leuchtenberg Collection. It became property of the State with the Revolution, was taken to Moscow and placed in the Rumiantsev Museum (1919-1924) and subsequently in the Pushkin Museum (INV. no. 816).

EXHIBITIONS

1810, Salon, no. 387; 1814, Salon, no. 464 (?); 1955, Moscow, p. 28.

REFERENCES

Guizot, 1810, 1852 ed., pp. 74-76; Inventory after the death of Josephine, 1814, see S. Grandjean, 1964, no. 1230 (... *un Intérieur de prison...* 600 francs); Cat. of Paintings... Leuchtenberg... at Munich, 1833, II, no. 101; *ibid.,* 1841, I, no. 39; F.-M. Granet, in *Le Temps,* 10 and 15 October 1872; A. de la Fizelière (1850), p. 6; J.-N. Muxel, 1851, no. 245; L. Dussieux, 1852, 1856 ed., pp. 324, 443-444; P. Silbert, 1862, pp. 23-24; Ch. Blanc, 1863, Granet entry, pp. 4, 8; Bellier and Auvray, 1882, v. I, p. 688; Leuchtenberg Gallery cat., Saint-Petersburg, 1886, no. 224; F. Benoît, 1897, p. 360; L. Réau, 1929, p. 80, no. 535; E. Ripert, 1937, pp. 59-60; mus. cat., 1957, p. 42; H. du Rivau, in cat. exh. *Granet,* Louvre, Cabinet des Dessins, 1960, p. 111; F. Haskell, 1971, p. 69, ill. 18, p. 77, note 85; M.-Cl. Chaudonneret, 1972, pp. 171, 174.

RELATED WORKS

A line engraving by J.-N. Muxel in the album of the Leuchtenberg Gallery (2nd ed., 1851). A preparatory drawing in the Louvre (INV. 26.934, from the Granet bequest; Guiffrey-Marcel, no. 4392, ill.).

A. S.

Jean-Baptiste Greuze

1725 Tournus - Paris 1805

In 1774, Greuze was at the height of his glory. Certainly, he had severely felt the disappointment of his unsuccessful *Caracalla* (Louvre), which had brought him admission to the Academy, not, as he had hoped, as a history painter, but as a genre painter. Nevertheless, his pictures, which he knew how to exhibit effectively in his atelier, earned him the support of the enlightened minds of the day—in Russia as well as in France—and Diderot was insistent in his praise of these works. Greuze had just finished painting the *Cruche cassée* (1773; Louvre) and was about to produce some of his most popular portraits of Russian models, *Paul Stroganov* (1778), the Youssoupov family (all in the Hermitage), and also *Franklin* (1778), and above all some of his best moralizing pictures (*Le Gâteau des rois*, 1774, Montpellier; *La Dame de charité*, 1775, Lyon; *La Malédiction paternelle*, 1777, *Le Fils puni*, 1778, both in the Louvre). From 1780 on his work evolved little, (although it was somewhat influenced by Prud'hon), and it was no longer fashionable. Yet, Greuze was visited by his English contemporary, Sir Joshua Reynolds, and by George Romney, both of whom also sought out David (Romney in 1790, Reynolds on his last visit to France in 1787). At this time, Greuze was still painting large moralizing compositions (*Le Premier sillon*, Moscow; the *Innocence entraînée par les Amours et suivie du Repentir*, Louvre), and above all portraits—*Bonaparte* (Versailles), *Fabre d'Églantine* (Louvre), the *Citoyen Dubard* (San Francisco, California Palace of the Legion of Honor), *Édouard-François Bertin* (Louvre)—which lost in technical virtuosity what they gained in emotion and sincerity.

Since the 18th century, Greuze has been neglected. Despite the courageous writings of Louis Hautecœur as early as 1913, the excellent works of Edgar Munhall, and the recent monograph of Anita Brookner, the artist has not regained with the general public that place which he deservedly held in his lifetime. Like Poussin, whom he understood more intimately than did any other artist of his generation, he wished to elevate the soul. He hoped, in his pictures, to introduce the lessons of the Bible into modern life. His attempt preceded by 20 years that of David, who was entirely directed toward the moral examples of the Greco-Roman world and who proceeded with diametrically opposed technical means to attain the same exalted goal.

P. R.

83
Distributor of Rosaries

L'Ermite or *Le Donneur de chapelets*
Plate p. 58
Canvas; 111 × 117
Montclair Art Museum, Gift of Mrs. Charles C. Griswold

The 18th century has accustomed us to representations of the theme of the Hermit which have a completely different nature from that of this work. From Subleyras (1732; Louvre) to François Boucher (1742; Moscow) and Hubert Robert (Leningrad), it was the famous and somewhat licentious tale of La Fontaine which inspired the majority of French painters of the time. Greuze broached the scene in an entirely different vein and one certainly colored by moral intentions. A hermit presents to a girl, who with her companions has come to bring him offerings, a rosary taken from a box held out to him by a young monk who kneels at his side. The scene, which takes place at the entrance to a grotto (open-air scenes are rare with Greuze), is dominated by a cross, which confirms the religious character of the work. The painter played on the contrast between the severe face of the bearded hermit and the playful or curious expressions of the girls, among whom only the oldest show any respect in front of the holy man.

Painted about 1780—according to E. Munhall (whom we would like to thank for his help regarding the paintings by Greuze exhibited here) and to A. Brookner—or in any case before 1785 (the date of the Véri sale in which it was included), this painting marks a step in the evolution of the painter's art. Greuze represents an essential link in the history of French painting between Chardin and Prud'hon. From the former he took scenes from everyday life, glorifying the domestic virtues of the working classes; and he foreshadowed the latter's perverse innocence or sensualism. But that which was fundamental to him is the constant concern to be a moralist, to elevate the spirit by setting an example. This quality, despite differing technical means and diametrically opposed themes, curiously brings his work very close to that of David.

Beyond the genre aspect, there is, in the *Distributor,* a juxtaposition of contrasts—the happiness of innocent childhood and the simple joys of adolescence with the harsh wisdom of age—which transcends the simple anecdote.

PROVENANCE
Marquis de Véri Collection (for information regarding the Marquis and his collection see here Nos. 59 and 85); sale after his death, 12 December 1785, no. 21 (4,200 *livres* to Paillet); Marquis de Montesquiou Collection; sale of 9 December 1788, no. 255 (2,590 *livres*); according to Martin and Masson "at a sale in 1790, it brought 5,000 *livres*; at that of 1819, 14,000 francs"; Paris, Gilbert Collection, 1864 (according to Martin and Masson); Count Koucheleff-Besborodko sale, 5 June 1869, no. 14 (55,000 francs; for this collector see R. Ménard, 1869). Probably was acquired by the Empress Eugénie (L. Réau, 1920). Countess Koucheleff of Saint Petersburg, sale 18-19 March 1875,

no. 15 (24,500 francs); Comtesse de la Ferronnays (to whom the painting belonged from 1885), sale 12 April 1897, no. 9. Baron de Précours in 1907. Durand-Ruel, Paris (apparently had belonged to J. Pierpont Morgan). Comtesse de Navarro Collection. Sale London, Sotheby, 27 May 1961, no. 15. Given to Montclair by Mrs. Charles C. Griswold in 1963.

EXHIBITIONS
1885, Paris, no. 240; 1968, London, no. 314.

REFERENCES
Smith, v. VII, 1837, no. 149; R. Ménard, 1869, v. I, p. 484; J. Martin and Ch. Masson in C. Mauclair, n.d. (1907), p. 11, no. 140; E. and J. de Goncourt, 1909, v. II, p. 88; L. Réau, 1920, p. 286; E. Munhall, 1964, p. 19, note 6 and ill. 13; *Gazette des Beaux-Arts, Supplément,* February 1964, no. 204, ill.; A. Brookner, 1972, pp. 116, 123-124 and p. 171, note 4, ill. 64.

RELATED WORKS
Paintings. An excellent and very faithful copy was on the art market in Paris around 1955. (Is it the Gilbert picture cited in Paris in 1864 by Martin and Masson?)
Either a study painted for or a copy after the central group of the two oldest girls, from the Mailly-Nesle Collection was sold in Paris, Palais Galliera, 14 March 1970 (no. 12, ill.; panel; 28.7 × 22.9).
Drawings. Drawing for the principal figure of the painting, in the Louvre (INV. 26.994; *cf.* Guiffrey and Marcel, VI, 1911, no. 4564, ill; on the verso, another study for the same figure). A drawing for the two little girls behind the major protagonist of the scene, formerly part of the J. Masson Collection (sold 7-8 May 1923, no. 90, ill.) and recently sold again (26 November 1969, no. 13, ill.). The Tournus drawing (no. 28), which according to Martin and Masson (no. 14), came from a Tinardon sale in 1827 (according to the curator of the museum in 1897, neither appears in Lugt's *Répertoire*) bears no direct relation to this painting. Martin and Masson (n.d. [1907]) still mention in connection with *The Distributor,* "under the title of *Une Rosière,* a drawing on panel *attributed to Greuze,* sold at the Failly sale, April 1859, no. 152."
Engraving. By Henri Marais, of 1788 (*Mercure de France,* September 1788, p. 95) dedicated to the Abbot Véri, "*ancien auditeur de Rote, abbé de Troarn et de Saint-Satur.*"

P. R.

84
*A Widow and her Priest**

La Veuve et son curé
Plate p. 72
Canvas; 126 × 160
Leningrad, The Hermitage Museum

"This subject involves a group of various characters with whom I have already dealt. [It] represents a priest who goes to help a widow and her children, of his counseling and instructions in virtue to them"

(Greuze in his *Lettre à MM. les Curés,* "guardians of Religion and morals," which appeared 5 December 1786 in the *Journal de Paris,* on the occasion of the publication of Charles Levasseur's engraving, four years after the acquisition of the picture by the Grand Duke Paul of Russia on his visit to Paris in 1782. See also Bachaumont's account: "Here is how the painter himself tells the story of his composition...").

Greuze achieved here a simplicity of composition, a kind of low relief of rhythmic motion created with masterful ease, a legibility that permits the eye to interpret a different expression for each face according to the age of the model and a sobriety of the coloring—creamy whites, blacks that are animated solely by touches of pink, pale lilac and royal blue—that place this work among the last masterpieces of Greuze. It was painted on the eve of the death of Diderot (1784)—one of those critics, rare even today, who passionately admired and profoundly understood the artist.

There is nothing sentimental or moralizing in this everyday scene, rather it is a very simple description of a priest's morning visit "to the country." The mother, in morning *déshabillé,* "smiles with a tender and modest look"; the eldest daughter "listens with a rather respectful or embarrassed mien, her right hand on her breast." Each of the three other children, from the young boy "hiding behind his sister" to the "spoiled child" and "younger sister" who is the victim of her "elder sister's privileges," genuinely participates in the scene.

We know that after 1769, when he was affronted by the academicians for his presentation to them of the *Caracalla,* Greuze did not exhibit at the Salon. In order to make his works like *A Widow and Priest* known,

he, of course, still had recourse to engraving, but the artist also never hesitated to receive distinguished visitors in his atelier: Gustaf III of Sweden in 1771, Joseph II in 1777, as well as distinguished artists like the Englishmen Sir Joshua Reynolds and George Romney (see biography above). It was in this way that this painting was sold to Grand Duke Paul Petrovitch, the future Paul II (see Provenance below).

PROVENANCE
Purchased from Greuze by Grand Duke Paul Petrovitch, the "Comte du Nord," heir to the throne of Russia, during his trip to France in June 1782, according to Mme de Valory in 1813 (cited by A. Brookner, 1956). In Pavlosk during the 19th century. Transferred to the Hermitage at the time of the Russian Revolution.

EXHIBITION
1956, Leningrad, p. 8.

REFERENCES
Greuze, *Journal de Paris,* 5 December 1786, pp. 1412-1413; Bachaumont, v. XXXIII (3 December 1786), pp. 231-233; Mme de Valory, 1813; Smith, v. VII, 1837, no. 143; J. Martin and Ch. Masson in C. Mauclair, n.d. (1907), p. 17, no. 220; E. and J. de Goncourt, ed. 1909, v. II, p. 90; L. Hautecœur, 1913, p. 85; L. Réau, 1920, p. 282; L. Réau, 1929, p. 191, no. 127; A. Brookner, 1956, p. 196; mus. cat., 1958, I, p. 281, no. 7521; A. Brookner, 1972, pp. 79-80 and notes 30 and 31, p. 169, pp. 99, 116-117, 126-128, and note 13, p. 171, ill. 74.

RELATED WORKS
Drawings. Drawing, from the Vivant Denon Collection, for the principal female figures (British Museum 1860. 4.14.2; ill. by E. Munhall, 1961, II, p. 240, ill. 4, "ca. 1786"). According to Martin, "a first version in sanguine was engraved by an anonymous artist (29 × 35)." Again according to the same author, another sanguine drawing for this painting was sold on 8 January 1819.
Engraved in 1786 by Charles Levasseur.   P. R.

85
Return of a Drunkard

L'Ivrogne chez lui or *Le Retour du cabaret*
Plate p. 68
Canvas; 72 × 91
The Portland Art Museum

This work comes from the collection of the Marquis de Véri, a great connoisseur of modern painting who owned, in addition to the *The Lock* of J.-H. Fragonard (no. 59), a dozen signal works of Greuze. Among them

are the *Fils ingrat* and the *Fils puni* (Louvre) and the *Distributor of Rosaries* (No. 83). A drunkard returns home and is greeted by his wife and barefoot children, in whose faces one reads pity, stupor and chagrin, anger, distress and incomprehension. "Greuze was not the painter of the people, but the popular poet," wrote the editor of the 1835 Huard sale catalog. "This worn commode, this half-broken cradle, this sad group, this dog with drooping ears who also seems hungry, contrast marvelously with the fleeting happiness that drunkenness affords the unfortunate head of the family. From this admirable picture all classes may learn a lesson in morality." And, eulogized M. Mefre, author of the Duval sale notice 11 years later, "Such moral suffering [is communicated] in her gaze upon the degraded man whom she has loved, on the father of these two hungry children whom she brings before him; Greuze has infused his soul in the scene, entirely through his own brush."

Later called "bourgeois drama" and "comedy for those who think, tragedy for those who feel," the *Return of a Drunkard*—coming as it did at a decisive moment in the artist's career, no doubt shortly after 1780 or, at least, before 1785—is also a testimony not only to the painter's ambitions, but also to the esthetic changes and spiritual transformations of the painting of the time—to which Greuze contributed so much.

We notice from the first the bareness of the room where the scene takes place. This starkness of course alludes to the misery to which the drunkard has reduced his family, but it is also no doubt—and a number of writers from H. Honour to A. Brookner have insisted on this point—a reflection of the influence on the elder painter of David's works, especially of the *Belisarius* (No. 30) of 1781. One notes primarily the importance of the play of hands which in both works assists in making the scene more meaningful and comprehensible. Reduced to four figures (excluding the dog, whom we have already seen in *A Widow and her Priest*, No. 84) who stand out against a monochrome wall, the composition is indeed simple. Greuze knew, at this moment in his career, how to eliminate detail, avoid the picturesque, and lead the viewer's eye toward that which is essential. What is particularly striking, however, is the power and truth of the moral lesson. Greuze ceased to be an isolated figure when French painting, in reaction to the easy virtuosity of Boucher and his disciples, turned to a serious art with the intention of setting an example, of educating and of elevating the soul.

PROVENANCE

Collection of the Marquis de Véri; sale at his death, 12 December 1785, no. 22 (6,501 *livres* to Paillet; on Véri, see also Nos. 59 and 83). De La Reynière Collection; his sale which took place 3 April 1793, no. 27 (505 *livres*). Mme Huard sale, wife of the painter, 6 April 1835, no. 245. Duval sale, Geneva, 12-13 May 1846, no. 109 (9,975 francs); posthumous sale of the Comte d'Arjuzon, 2-4 March 1852, no. 10 (8,200 francs); "in 1858, at La Terrade sale, it came down to 1,108 francs"; Pillot sale, 6-8 December 1858, no. 48 (1,050 francs); belonged in 1860 to Baron James de Rothschild; Mrs. Lyne Stephens sale, London, Christie's, 9 May 1895, no. 356; Wildenstein Gallery from 1923, sold for $15,000 "to a collector from Portland" (R. Gimpel). Mrs. Bowles, Portland; Mrs. Marion Bowles Hollis; given by the latter to the Portland Museum in 1959.

EXHIBITIONS

1860, Paris, no. 173; 1920, San Francisco, no. 93; 1954, Pittsburgh, no. 59, ill.; 1961, Los Angeles, ill. p. 27; 1964-1965, San Francisco, no. 189; 1972, London, no. 120 (J. Vilain).

REFERENCES

J. Martin and Ch. Masson in C. Mauclair, n.d. [1907], p. 12, no. 158; E. and J. de Goncourt, ed. 1909, v. II, p. 92; L. Hautecœur, 1913, p. 93; A. Brookner, 1956, p. 195, ill. 7; R. Gimpel, 1966, p. 231, ill. 33; H. Honour, 1968, pp. 143-144, 199; E. Haverkamp-Begemann and A.-M.-S. Logan, 1970, v. I, pp. 31-32, ill. 4; mus. cat., 1971, ill. p. 105; A. Brookner, 1972, pp. 116, 120, 124, 127, ill. 65.

RELATED WORKS

A copy, from the bequest of Alexandre Leleux (1873), "attributed to Mlle Ledoux," according to J. Martin and C. Masson, belonging to Lille (mus. cat., 1893, no. 359). "At the sale of 23 March 1872, the same subject (73 × 91) was attributed to Greuze by the expert Féral under the title: *Le Père désabusé.*" Several other copies are known: at Narbonne (mus. cat., 1923, no. 129); in a sale: London, Christie's, 10 June 1932, no. 93; and in German collections (photographs of three different paintings at the Courtauld Institute, London).
Drawings. A drawing for the main figure is in London, British Museum (see exh. cat., 1968, London, no. 320, ill. 238); its counterproof in the Louvre (INV. 26989; Guiffrey and Marcel, VI, 1911, no. 4562, ill., on verso a counterproof for the figure of the woman in the same painting). INV. 26960 (Louvre) is a study for the female figure in the same work. INV. 26971 (Louvre) is a counterproof of a different study for the same figure. In conclusion, there is a study for one of the drunkard's hands at Yale University, New Haven (E. Haverkamp-Begemann and A.-M.-S. Logan, 1970, II, ill. 38).

P. R.

86
*Self-Portrait**

Autoportrait
Plate p. 74
Canvas; 73 × 59 (inscribed in an oval)
Paris, Musée du Louvre

Greuze, like Rembrandt, whom he so admired, was fond of portraying himself. The Louvre painting poses above all a problem in dating. If we rule out the hypothesis recently set forth (*Connaissance des Arts*, July 1955, p. 14) that the other *Autoportrait* in the Louvre (MI 1071) is a study for the one shown here, since in fact, it is slightly earlier than our picture, it becomes as equally difficult to accept the date of 1775 advanced by Smith (1837), as to accept that of 1777-1778 suggested by Anita Brookner (written communication). The painting should be dated considerably later, c. 1785. It proudly depicts a man in his sixties dressed in studio attire, wearing a loosely knotted white tie, a grayish vest and a blue coat with a turned-down collar. The sad but dignified glance has a moving clarity, but the face does not yet display that pathetic and poignant look of sincerity which makes the *Autoportrait* in Marseille so unforgettable (see Related Works). Greuze scrutinizes his face, trying to render a faithful image of his features, but does not hesitate over details. He does not aspire to a clear description or sharpness of line, as do Joseph-Siffred Duplessis (No. 54) and Alexandre Roslin (No. 161) at a similar date. With the help of soft brushwork, by nuance and degree, he seeks not to evoke pity, but rather to move by showing his heart and soul, an approach characteristic of his more ambitious works and with parallels to Rousseau.

PROVENANCE
Acquired for the collection of Louis XVIII in 1820 (2,000 francs) from M. Spontini. (It is not, as has often been said—e.g. in J. Seznec and J. Adhémar, ed., *Diderot*, I, 1957, p. 98—the painting from the Salon of 1761, which is, on the other hand, undoubtedly that of the La Live de Jully sale of 1770, no. 108) INV. 5034.

REFERENCES
Smith, 1837, v. VIII, no. 2; mus. cat. (Villot), 1855, no. 264; J. Martin and Ch. Masson in C. Mauclair, n.d. [1907], p. 70, no. 1133; E. and J. Goncourt, ed. 1909, v. II, p. 75; L. Hautecœur, 1913, p. 39, pl. I; mus. cat. (Brière), 1924, no. 381; mus. cat., 1972, p. 188; mus. cat., 1974, no. 327, ill.

RELATED WORKS
A copy in Tournus (see also Martin and Masson [1907], nos 1133-1146. Lithograph by Desbordes (Salon of 1824, no. 210; see G. Wildenstein, 1963, I, p. 36). Engraved numerous times during the 19th century (Bordes, ill. in in C. Normand [n.d.], Belliard, Desmarets, Nesle and Adolphe, and by Hesse in 1823).
Greuze was fond of portraying himself. The following are famous self-portraits: Tournus (early; A. Brookner, 1972, ill. 1), Louvre (MI 1071, on panel, formerly Cypierre and La Caze Collection, cat. 1974, no. 317, ill.) and Marseille, where the artist depicted himself with his chalk in hand (Salon of 1804, no. 221; A. Brookner, *op. cit.*, ill. 96).
In addition there are the Hermitage canvas (no. 5644), the picture from the Salon of 1761, no. 98 (that of the La Live de Jully sale, 5 March 1770, no. 108 ?); a so-called *Autoportrait* in pastel, attributed to Greuze, sold in London, Sotheby's, 9 July 1968, no. 5, ill. Finally there is the handsome *Portrait de Greuze* attributed to Jeanne-Philiberte Ledoux in Dijon, from the Joliet Collection (cat. 1968, no. 263), a copy—inasmuch as it is a copy—not of the present work, but rather of MI 1071, Louvre.

P. R.

Baron Antoine-Jean Gros

1771 Paris - Meudon 1835

As the son of miniaturists, Antoine-Jean Gros was able to meet artists like Mme Vigée-Lebrun very early in his life and to develop his gifts freely. He was scarcely 15 when he entered David's studio at the end of 1785. Two years later, he was admitted to the Academy of Painting. He competed unsuccessfully for the Prix de Rome in 1792 with the subject *Antiochus voulant contraindre Eléazar à manger d'un mets impur* (Saint-Lô; sketch in Dijon, Musée Magnin).

In 1793, he received a passport to Italy, visiting the south of France, Genoa and Florence before settling in Genoa, where in 1796 he met Josephine, who brought him to Milan to introduce him to Bonaparte. Through Bonaparte, Gros became a member of the committee responsible for searching out works of art in Italy. Later, he was named *inspecteur aux revues*. In 1799, he had to leave Milan and take refuge in Genoa, before returning to France via Marseille. During this lengthy Italian period, during which he only briefly visited Rome, unlike other artists, Gros studied Rubens and the colorists of the 16th-century. He painted portraits, notably in Milan, that of *Bonaparte à Arcole* (1796, Salon of 1801; Versailles; study in Louvre), and attempted antique subjects and even romantic ones by illustrating Young and Ossian or depicting *Sappho at Leucadia* (No. 87). He had experienced military life and was prepared to interpret realistically the glorious events of the Consulate and the Empire. Shortly after his return to Paris in October 1800, he won the competition for the *Combat of Nazareth* (No. 88). By order of Bonaparte, the great canvas was not completed, but he later commissioned the *Pestiférés de Jaffa* (Louvre; sketch, New Orleans), the huge canvas which was triumphantly hailed at the Salon of 1804. Without abandoning portraiture, he continued in the following years to produce large compositions "with subjects uplifting for the national character," of which Napoleon dreamed. These are the *Bataille d'Aboukir* (Salon of 1806, Versailles; sketch, Detroit), the *Champ de bataille d'Eylau* (Salon of 1808, Louvre), the *Prise de Madrid* and the *Bataille des Pyramides* (Salon of 1810, Versailles). In 1811, he received the commission for the cupola of the Pantheon. This vast work was not completed until 1824, as its iconography had to be modified in 1814-15 to the advantage of Louis XVIII. From 1814 on, Gros was the official portraitist to the King. In 1815, he entered the Academy of Fine Arts and in 1816 was named professor at the École des Beaux-Arts in place of the exiled David. In almost 20 years, Gros had hundreds of pupils, among whom were J.-B. Delestre (his first biographer), Court, Larivière, Roqueplan, Eugène Lami, Delaroche, Charlet, Riesener, etc.

Delacroix, in his notable article in the *Revue des deux mondes* (1 September 1848, p. 663), summarized the principle behind Gros' teaching: "He made it a point of vanity to continue all the traditions of David in his lessons." Although he continued to paint modern subjects (*Louis XVIII quittant les Tuileries dans la nuit du 20 mars,* Salon of 1817, Versailles; or the *Duchesse d'Angoulême s'embarquant à Pauillac,* Salon of 1819, Bordeaux), he tried, against his own temperament, to deal with antique themes or with allegories, which the press criticized heatedly during the Salon of 1822, where he exhibited the *Ariane et Bacchus*. He decorated three ceilings for the Charles X Museum in the Louvre and was made a Baron by Charles X at the same time as his work began to decline. He increased his criticism of the new school and spoke out against Ingres' influence in the École des Beaux-Arts. After 1831, the discouragement of the artist became more pronounced. Finally, when a last attempt for a classical triumph, *Hercule et Diomède* (Toulouse), was poorly received at the Salon of 1835, he chose suicide and drowned himself in the Seine.

He was deeply admired by Géricault and Delacroix, who wrote, "Gros has idealized modern subjects; he could paint the costumes, customs and passions of his time without falling into paltriness or triviality, the usual pitfalls of this type of subject" (*op. cit.,* p. 649). For the 19th century, he remained the painter who understood "how to introduce into the creation of paintings two new elements frequently neglected by the entire school: color and movement" (L. Viardot, *Merveilles de la peinture,* Paris, 1877, p. 327). In conclusion, E.-J. Delécluze recalled: "It is beyond doubt that, after David, Gros is the painter who exerted the greatest influence on the doctrines and practice of those artists who were his contemporaries" (1855, p. 292).

G. L.

87
Sappho at Leucadia

"Sapho à Leucate"
Plate p. 181
Canvas; 122 × 100; s.d. on the rock *Gros. 1801*
Salon of 1801, no. 164
Bayeux, Musée Baron-Gérard

The *Journal des Débats* explained this painting precisely: "Abandoned by her lover Phaon, Sappho, whose feet still touch the point of the promontory of Leucadia, holds her lyre tightly in her arms, against her breast. She throws her head back and closes her eyes, as if to hide from view the abyss into which she soon will leap. Behind her and on a point further removed from the rock, we see an altar; the fire still burns; close by the altar are some overturned vases, which have served, no doubt, in the sacrifice that the muse of Lesbos offered either to Venus or Apollo (for the experts are not in agreement)."

The work attracted much attention at the Salon (*La Décade philosophique* tells us, moreover, that it was placed at the entrance of the exhibition) and was sufficiently appreciated by numerous critics, among them the *Moniteur Universel, L'Observateur au Muséum,* the *Journal de Paris* and Charles Landon (1801, p. 27). But as the historians have noted (Blanc, Delécluze, Delestre, Benoit), its "discordant" coloring generally shocked the people of the time. "Oh! Dear me, it's so green," exclaimed the *Arlequin au Muséum.* "I find this a bit too blue," said *Rubens au Muséum* (1801, p. 21). The critic of the *Moniteur Universel* regretted that "the greenish blue tone which predominates in this painting destroys a part of its effect," while that of *L'Année littéraire* asked: "How is it that Antoine Gros does not know that moonlight is not green?" *L'Examen des ouvrages modernes par une société d'artistes* (year IX, p. 55) concluded that "the greenish tone and unnaturalness of the lights and reflections do much damage to this painting." Finally, P. Ch., in the *Journal des Arts, des Sciences et de Littérature* (no. 156, p. 426) explained: "This is not the way that Vernet, that great magician expressed moonlight."

Curiously, it was in the name of a certain sort of realism that they judged the work. For the *Journal de Paris,* "There is more poetry than truth in this painting—the scene is romantic, the color ideal. The subject could be presented to the imagination in this manner, but never to one's sight." They reproached the painter for not having respected historical verisimilitude. The critic of the *Journal des Arts, des Sciences et de Littérature* remarked: "Sappho, according to the testimony of antiquity was a small brunette. Beauty gains in this new portrait, but truth loses out." In the *Mercure de France,* it was explained that "the handling of paint in this picture is spiritual; the arrangement is in good taste; but the head of Phaon's lover resembles an Egyptian rather than a Greek." At any rate, Roussel recalled: "This action must have taken place during the day with its accompanying magnificence." As a matter of fact, *Arlequin au Muséum* added: "The leap from Leucadia, this terrible trial which several unhappy lovers tried in order to seek the end of their pain, was a ceremony, almost a festival, done with pomp, in plain daylight and in view of an immense crowd which stood on the shore. Why is Sappho represented to us here alone and in the middle of the night?"

Thus, Gros' interpretation was astonishing. "The carrying out of this depiction of despair was one of the first departures from the principles of Greek art," remarked Charles Blanc in 1845. Never, Rosenblum has noted (1967 a, p. 21), had such a Wertherian peak been reached. Let us underline in this connection that in that epoch, they more easily accepted romanticism in literature than in the plastic arts (see also no. 178). And let us add that his audacious interpretation (of color, no doubt, but also of composition) was upsetting.

Important to mention are an evocative description of the *Moniteur Universel* ("the moon is disappearing... the lover of Phaon, her head thrown back... is standing on the edge of a rock. Her body advances on the precipice, giving way to despair; her knees bend; she no longer touches the ground, except by the tips of her feet; she is about to fall into the waves"), a remark of *Mme Angot au Muséum* ("One could say that Sappho wants to make a *jeté-battu*"), and an especially revealing critique in the *Journal des Débats:* "Sappho is about to fall; she as already lost her balance, and we believe this moment is badly chosen. It seems to us... that the movement, properly so, is not at all within the bounds of painting. In order to fix upon canvas any lively action whatsoever, the painter must seize an instant of tranquillity, and the imagination does not conceive of this instant in a body which falls. Whatever the artist would do, whatever the catalog would say, a Sappho who falls would only be a woman suspended, holding onto nothing, between rock and the water: that is equally contrary to good taste and good sense."

These diverse commentaries show well how his contemporaries disapproved of such a representation of movement (and no doubt preferred a painting such as that by Jean-Joseph Taillasson, recently acquired by the Musée de Brest, which was well received at the Salon of 1792). Moreover, Gros had accentuated the effect of falling through the staggered disposition of the essential elements of the composition. This pre-occupation brings to our mind the pursuits of the Futurists, and more contemporarily recalls the different variations on this subject by Gustave Moreau.

PROVENANCE

Commissioned by General Dessoles, whom Gros had met in Milan; Dessoles collection; collection of his daughter, Mme de La Rochefoucauld, Duchesse d'Estissac; sale of the collection of Mme de La Rochefoucauld, Paris, Hôtel Drouot, 25 March 1865 (510 francs); given to the museum by Baron Henri-Alexandre Gérard in 1898.

EXHIBITIONS

1801, Salon, no. 164; 1936, Paris, Petit Palais, no. 20; 1972, London, no. 124, ill. 15; 1972-1973, Antwerp, no. 17.

REFERENCES

Deloynes, v. XXVI, no. 690, p. 330; no. 693, p. 353; *(L'Amateur),* 30 Fructidor, year IX, p. 2168; [Anon], 30 Fructidor year IX, no. 36, pp. 556-557; [Anon.], in *Le Mercure de France,* Frimaire year X, p. 348; [Anon.], *Examen des ouvrages modernes,* an IX, p. 55; [Anon.], *L'Observateur au Museum,* year IX, p. 16; [Anon.], *Rubens au Museum,* year IX, pp. 20-21; P. Ch., 30 Fructidor, year IX, p. 426; Landon, 1801, p. 27; Roussel, 19 Vendémiaire, year X, p. 73; J.-B. Delestre, 1835, p. 4; Ch. Blanc, 1845, p. 330; E. Delacroix, 1 September 1848, p. 656; E.-J. Delécluze, 1855, p. 290; E. Chesneau, 1861, p. 11; J.-B. Delestre, 1867, p. 60; Tripier-Le-Franc, 1880, pp. 185-189; E. Chesneau, 1883, p. 78; G. Dargenty, 1887, p. 80, pl. 6, p. 17; F. Benoît, 1897, p. 350; A. Michel, 1900, p. 157; L. Rosenthal, 1900, p. 28; H. Mireur, 1911, v. III, p. 372; R. Graul, 1922, p. 91; H. Focillon, 1927, v. I, p. 42; H. Lemonnier (n.d.), p. 24; R. Escholier, 1936, pp. 7-8; L. Hautecœur, 1953, p. 96; N. Schlenoff, 1954, p. 58; J. Lindsay, 1960, p. 119; J. Vergnet-Ruiz and M. Laclotte, 1962, p. 120; R. Rosenblum, 1967a, pp. 21-22, fig. 18.

RELATED WORKS

Engraved by Jean-Nicolas Laugier. Lithograph by Mme Renaudin. Blanc (1845) and Delestre (1867) mention a sketch (formerly Mme Carbonnet Collection). A copy is at Arenenberg.

J. L.

88
Battle of Nazareth

Le Combat de Nazareth
Plate p. 176
Canvas; 135 × 195; s.d.l.r. *Gros, AN IX.*
Nantes, Musée des Beaux-Arts

This painting depicts the victory of General Junot, commander of the advance guard of the army of Kléber. Before retreating to Cana, Junot, leading 500 men, held out against 6,000 Turks and Arabs at Nazareth, on the slopes of Mount Tabord, on 19 Germinal, Year VII (8 April 1799), from ten o'clock in the morning to three in the afternoon.

As a sign of his satisfaction, Bonaparte decided on 2 Floréal, Year VII (25 April 1799), outside the city of Saint-John-of-Acre, that a contest should be instituted to commemorate this victory. In Ventôse, Year IX (March 1801), the conditions of the contest had been established. And on 19 Vendémiaire, Year X (11 October 1801), a statement from the Minister of the Interior fixed the number and quality of the jury. Composed of 15 members, five being designated by the contestants (Vien, Moitte, Vincent, Chaudet, David), five by the Institute, and five by the Minister of the Interior (among whom was General Junot), the jury met on 17 Frimaire, Year X (8 December 1801) to examine the sketches presented by 20 artists. The judges unanimously declared Gros the winner and commissioned him to complete the painting, which was to be at least 25 feet long (ca. 8.11 meters).

The moment Gros chose to represent is the end of the combat, during the rout of the Mamelukes, who, being desperate, throw themselves on their bayonets. Junot is shown killing two Mamelukes, who have attacked him. The Sergeant at Arms of the Third Dragoon carries away the Turkish flag. One of the sons of the former Pasha of Acre, allied with the French, is thrown down by General Junot, at a short distance from his troops. Close to Junot, Desnoyers, head of the Second Brigade of Light Infantry, is mounted on a bay horse. General Duvivier, head of the Brigade of the 14th Dragoon, is seen the background, mounted on a black horse.

The announcement of the result of the contest fostered a dispute, echoes of which appeared in various reviews—most notably *Le Journal des Bâtiments Civils, des Monuments et des Arts* and *Le Journal des Arts, des Sciences et de Littérature*. In the first of these journals, no. 109, the painter Chéry did not hesitate to declare: "On the day of the judgment of this contest... General Junot arrived and with saber in hand, declared that the prize had to be awarded to Citizen Gros. The jury, very astonished by this new method of judging, was obliged to yield." This assertion was repeated by someone named René who, in no. 135 of the same journal, wrote: "One can say that the prize of the contest was won, saber in hand. The jury members were terrified." Moreover, on 30 Frimaire, Year X (21 December 1801), the critic who signed himself as Xixixius in *Le Journal des Arts, des Sciences...*, no. 174, asserted: "For the last three months we have been hearing predictions about the injustice which has just come to pass." As Landon recalled, the public had distinguished four principal sketches, "the creators of which were C.-C. Hennequin, Taunay [see Related Works], Gros and Caraffe... We can indeed say that all of the sketches have a distinctive character. Actually, the first is remarkable for the movement and the warmth of the composition; the second, for its agreeable distribution of masses and harmonious colors; the third, for its vivacity of brushwork and the faithfulness to local color; the fourth, for its astonishing truth of character and costume." There was an identical comment by an anonymous critic in the *Moniteur Universel* of 6 Vendémiaire, Year X, and by Détournelle, who remarked on 30 Frimaire: "Of the many sketches, four were worthy of note; four with more or less different kinds of beauty among them," and he added that "David had intended to vote for the completion of all four paintings." But because this could not be realized, the artists prepared to defend their work themselves. Caraffe had a letter published in no. 174 of the *Journal des Arts, des Sciences....* As for Hennequin, who seemed to have won the support of the public and a good part of the press, he decided, as soon as the winner was announced, to execute his painting in large format at his own expense; he made his intention known in a letter of 20 Frimaire, Year X (11 December 1801), addressed to the editors of *Le Journal des Bâtiments civils....* Hennequin's composition is unknown. What is there to conclude? Must we believe that the result of the contest was secured in advance?

Nevertheless, this hypothesis is plausible for two reasons. The first is the amicable relationship between Gros and Junot. The second relates to the political situation at the time. Bonaparte in fact had forbidden Gros to complete his picture (half of the canvas was used for *Les Pestiférés de Jaffa,* and the other half for *La Bataille d'Aboukir,* where Junot is the hero). Moreover, the critics, belonging to a press which still seemed Republican, preferred Hennequin's sketch precisely because in that work, the role of General Junot (a Republican) appeared decisive. For Chéry, in *Le Journal des Bâtiments civils...* of 23 Frimaire, Year X: "There is no doubt, the sketch by Citizen Hennequin was the best conceived. In it, General Junot marched like a hero, everyone bowed and fled before him." And in *Le Journal des Arts* of 30 Frimaire, Détournelle wrote: "The main action of the General, which struck me in the Hennequin, creates a sensation found nowhere else." We must conclude then, that in order not run counter to Bonaparte, Junot had preferred, finally, that Gros' sketch be designated winner; according to Chéry, in Gros' work, Junot "appears as an officer bringing up the rear, a corporal placed behind his men, concentrating solely on defending himself against two attackers."

Nevertheless Gros' painting was not unprovocative. It is important to recall that among his detractors, as well as his admirers, there was confusion at the time concerning his style. For René, "it seems at this moment that a destructive genius is trying to resuscitate the erroneous systems of the Van Loos and the Bouchers," and for Rozet Saint-Genest: "What eye, however inexperienced, has not immediately seen how close this very witty sketch is to our great masters of this genre: it has the rich and varied composition of Joseph Parrocel; the expression, warmth and truth of his son Charles Parrocel; the piquancy of effect and the correct drawing of Ignace Parrocel, Cozette and Cazanova: in a word, one would have to be blind or dishonest to deny the immense talent of Citizen Gros.... As for me, I was captivated from the first glance; I thought I was dreaming and still at the Opera, in that fairyland temple, where Noverre used to enchant us in the chivalric ballet of Adèle de Ponthieu."

In fact, the modernity of the work was obviously clear. How could it be otherwise, when the first generation of romantic painters was not mistaken (a fact R. Rey forgot when he spoke of the "technique of the 18th century")? Géricault paid 1,000 francs in order to copy it, and Delacroix, in an article which appeared in 1848, studied this "admirable sketch at length." The technical basis for its modernism was succinctly and brillantly analyzed by Kl. Lankheit in 1965: "Gros is certainly within the tradition of battle painting in Western art, but even in relation to Rubens' *The Conquest of Tunis by Charles V,* his composition and color is infinitely more free and supple: instead of a single focal point it offers several centers of interest. The artist definitively distanced himself from academic principles.... At a time when Classicism maintained a static construction even in depictions of battles—for example, David's *Enlèvement des Sabines*—everything is subservient here to the dynamism of the conception."

PROVENANCE
Bought for 2,000 francs from the artist by an *amateur* (Bizet?); sale of the collection of M. B(izet), 21-22 May 1828, rue de Cléry Paris "reduced" to 20,000 francs; Urvoy de Saint-Bedan Collection; gift of Saint-Bedan to the Musée de Nantes in 1854.

EXHIBITIONS
1826, Paris, no. 99; 1900, Paris, no. 339.

REFERENCES
Arch. Nat., F²¹ 2 (26 sheets); Arch. of the Nantes museum (part of the Egyptian correspondence: letter of Gros, battle plan of Nazareth, certified by Junot; authorization by Chaptal, minister of the Interior, to the artist to execute the painting in the Jeu de Paume at Versailles; geometric and perspective battle plans); coll. Deloynes, v. XXVI, no. 693, pp. 426-436; v. LVI, nos. 1766-1773; (Anon.), in *Le Moniteur Universel,* 6 Vendémiaire, year X, pp. 21-22; Hennequin, in *Le Journal des Bâtiments civils...,* 20 Frimaire year X, no. 133, pp. 392-393; C(her)y. *ibid.,* 23 Frimaire year X, no. 133, pp. 375-393; (Anon.), in *La Clef du Cabinet,* 26 Frimaire year X, pp. 25-26; René, in *Le Journal des Bâtiments civils...,* 29 Frimaire year X, no. 135, pp. 430-431; Détournelle, in *Le Journal des Arts...,* 30 Frimaire year X, no. 173, pp. 391-397; Hennequin, *ibid.,* pp. 397-398; Xixixius, *ibid.,* 30 Frimaire year X, no. 174, pp. 412-414; Caraffe, *ibid.,* pp. 414-416; Détournelle, *ibid.,* 5 Nivôse year X, no. 175, p. 9; Cl. Rozet Saint-Genest, *ibid.,* 10 Nivôse year X, no. 176, pp. 25-28; Mecoenas, *ibid.,* pp. 28-30; (Anon.), in *Le Journal des Bâtiments civils...,* 13 Nivôse year X, pp. 61-62; Landon, 1801, pp. 6, 33-34; J.-B. Delestre, 1835, p. 4; (Anon.), in *L'Artiste,* 1835, v. IX, p. 265; (Anon.), in *Le Journal des Artistes,* 12 July 1835, pp. 6-25; Ch. Blanc, 1845, pp. 333-335, 389-391; E. Delacroix, 1 September 1848, pp. 656-657; E.-J. Delécluze, 1855, p. 291; J.-B. Delestre, 1867, pp. 66-78; E. Delacroix, September 1872, pp. 8-12; J. Tripier-Le-Franc, 1880, pp. 189-199; E. Chesneau, 1883, pp. 80-82; G. Dargenty, 1887, pp. 16-22; A. Alexandre, 1889, pp. 136-139; F. Benoit, 1897, pp. 350-351; L. Rosenthal, 1900, pp. 30, 102; M. Nicolle, mus. cat., 1913, no. 1005; Roger-Marx, 1914, pp. 85-86; R. Graul, XV, 1922, p. 91; H. Lemonnier (n.d.), pp. 28-31; H. Focillon, 1927, v. I, p. 44; R. Rey, 1928, p. 80; P. Balagny, 1936; R. Escholier, 1936, p. 9, pl. 3; P. Lelièvre, 1936, p. 289; R. Escholier, 1949, I., pp. 46-47, ill. p. 38; W. Friedlaender, 1952, p. 62; L. Benoist, mus. cat., 1953, no. 1005; L. Hautecœur, 1953, p. 96; H.-S. Francis, 1955-1956, p. 8; J. Vergnet-Ruiz and M. Laclotte, 1962, p. 120, repr. 131; K. Lankheit, 1966, pp. 118-120, ill. p. 119; A. Gonzalez-Palacios, 1967, p. 18, ill. XXXIV; P. Granville, 1968, no. 3, p. 144, ill. 6.

RELATED WORKS
Engraved by Jazet père. Copied by Pierre-François Lehoux (this is the copy presented by Horace Vernet to the Avignon museum in 1836: see Ch. Clément, 1868, note p. 228 and P. Granville, 1968, no. 3, p. 144).
Many drawn studies for the composition are known. Sold in the Gros sale, some belonged to the Delestre Collection. The sketch by Taunay (canvas; 92 × 139) is at Versailles.

J. L.

89
Portrait of Bonaparte, First Consul

Portrait de Bonaparte Premier Consul
Plate p. 175
Canvas; 205 × 127; s.d.l.r. on base of pilaster, *Gros. à Paris an 10.*
Paris, Musée National de la Légion d'Honneur et des Ordres de Chevalerie

Upon his return from Italy, Gros exhibited at the Salon of 1801 the *Portrait du général Bonaparte à Arcole* (Versailles; sketch, Louvre), which was well received.

He knew Bonaparte well, since he had been present at the Battle of Arcole, 17 November 1796, and then had obtained a few sittings, arranged by Josephine, in Milan.

It was, therefore, not surprising that Gros was asked to do the portraits of the First Consul. He did several of the same type, though not exactly identical. There are, for example, differences in the costume (coat with open collar in the portrait belonging to the Duc de Mouchy), in the gesture of the right hand, or in the texts inscribed on the papers lying on the table, attuned to the destined recipient. This portrait, dated Year X (that is, before 22 September 1802), was completed after the electoral meeting of Lyon, 26 January, and the Peace of Amiens, 25 March of the same year. Apparently, Gros had not obtained any further sittings and therefore used his own observations in Italy for the face. Although he shortened and subdued the hair style, he repeated precisely the pose of his *Bonaparte à Arcole,* which gave the First Consul the juvenile expression of the general who was victorious over the Italian army. Contemporary portraits, however, show that in 1802 his cheeks were already fuller.

It is difficult to know how many versions of this portrait Gros produced: perhaps four or five, excluding the smaller version owned by Denon. We cannot, in fact, support the hypothesis that Gros painted only three full-length portraits, a theory proposed by Mme Ducourtial (exh. cat., 1969, Paris, no. 113) based on a letter to Denon in 1805, now in the archives of the Musée de la Légion d'Honneur, in which Gros alluded only to the execution of three portraits of the First Consul. He was, in fact, referring to those which Denon discussed in a letter of 28 Ventôse, Year XI (19 March 1803) to the Minister of the Interior:

The First Consul has ordered three portraits to be painted by Citizen Gros. I have the honor of presenting you with the sketches for these portraits: the first one for the city of Lyon, the seat of the Electoral Meeting, the second for the city of Rouen, in conjunction with his trip, and the third for the Court of Appeals in Paris. He has agreed with the artist that the price of the three portraits altogether will be fixed at 9,000 francs, to be paid in three parts: 3,000 francs at the beginning, 3,000 francs when the work is half done, and 3,000 francs at the delivery of the last portrait. Citizen Gros has already made all necessary preparations for this enterprise and even is ready to deliver the first portrait in a month. I beg of you, Citizen Minister, to agree to the terms of the agreement made with him and to have delivered to him an ordonnance for the sum of 3,000 francs, the amount of the first third....

On 23 Germinal, Year XI (13 April 1803), Gros was advised of the payment. His work proceeded quickly and on 15 Fructidor, Year XI (2 September 1803), Vivant Denon was able to ask the Minister of the Interior for the remaining payment of 6,000 francs, since "the three portraits of the First Consul, commissioned from Citizen Gros, painter, are completed..." (National Archives, F²¹2). These three portraits were, therefore, finished between March and August of 1803, one year after the one which was given to Cambacérès. Their eventual fate is not known, and they seem to have disappeared. We should be able to recognize at least one of them, but neither the portrait in Lyon, where according to Tripier le Franc (1880, p. 183), Bonaparte is seated, nor the one in Rouen, on account of its inscription, locating it in the collection of the Duc de Mouchy and dating it to Year XI, seem to correspond. In conclusion, we must note that the 3,000-franc price for the painting is the same as that stipulated in July 1803 for a portrait of Bonaparte which was commissioned from Ingres for the city of Liège.

For this series of official portraits, Gros furnished the prototype, since Ingres repeated the same posture, but with a noticeably different costume, while Greuze, at the same time, portrayed Bonaparte (Versailles) in a coat similar to the one which Gros used here in its bright red, which contrasts with the muted green tones of the background and the rug on the table. The gilt embroidery adds the pomp of a glorious effigy to this austere portrait. Mme Ducourtial noticed that Bonaparte carries at his left side "the sword, on which the Régent shines" supported by a red cross-belt embellished with gold; he "exhibited for the first time this jewel which was added to his escutcheon in 1800, at the anniversary ceremony of 18 Brumaire" (exh. cat., 1969, Paris, no. 113). Judging from its quality, this portrait, which served as a model for the engraving, was apparently the first version done by Gros.

PROVENANCE
As indicated by the rectangular cartouche, placed at the top of the (original) frame, which bears the inscription: DONNÉ PAR LE PREMIER CONSUL AU SECOND CONSUL, the picture was given by Bonaparte to Cambacérès; Cambacérès Collection; Gaboriaud Collection; acquired by the Musée de la Légion d'Honneur in 1949 (INV. no. 04378, painting; no. 04379, frame).

EXHIBITIONS
1938, Paris, no. 138; 1968, Paris, no. 42; 1969, Paris, no. 113, color cover ill.

REFERENCES
J. Tripier-le-Franc, 1880, pp. 183-184; H. Torre and Cl. Ducourtial, mus. cat., 1963, p. 51, color cover ill.; Ch.-O. Zieseniss, 1968, pp. 21-26.

RELATED WORKS
Paintings. On panel (43 × 31) by Gros, owned by Denon

(collection of Prince Napoleon); it is dated 1802 and on one of the papers lying on the table we read: "*Traité d'Amiens, Paix générale.*" On canvas (200 × 150) by Gros (*cf.* 1936, Paris, no. 27, collection of the Duc de Mouchy); it is dated Year XI; Bonaparte is shown about to sign a paper (on the table), where we read: "*Réunion des 4 départements de la rive gauche du Rhin.*"
Engraving. By William Dickinson, with the inscription: "*Le Premier Consul au Second Consul.*"

G. L.

90
Portrait of Second-Lieutenant Legrand

"*Portrait du fils du général Legrand*"
Plate p. 212
Canvas; 250 × 175; s.l.l. *Gros.*
Salon of 1810, no. 393
Los Angeles County Museum of Art

The Salon catalog does not indicate whether or not this is a posthumous portrait. Charles Legrand, however, a second lieutenant in the 13th provisory regiment of cuirassiers, died in Madrid at the age of 19 during the 2 May 1808 Revolution—the subject of Goya's well-known masterpiece in the Prado, Madrid. Are we to see here an effort to minimize for the general public the horror of a day of war? The painting was exhibited at the same time as another portrait with the same dimensions, which was no doubt intended as a pendant and which portrays the subject's father, the division general Claude-Just-Alexandre-Louis Legrand (1762 Le Plessier-sur-Saint-Just, Oise-Paris 1815, buried in the Panthéon), who was made a count precisely in 1808. A few years later, Gros was to paint the portrait (Salon, 1814) of Comtesse Legrand, the general's second wife, on a canvas of similar dimensions. The two latter portraits were given by Mlle Legrand to Versailles in 1913. In *Gros et ses ouvrages,* J.-B. Delestre (pp. 160-161), on the basis of Gros' own words, alluded to the fact that the artist had not painted the portrait of the youth from the model:

The young Legrand presses a helmet, somewhat too heavy for his brow, against his thigh with his left hand; the appearance of the rest of the body seems to belong to a person of an age different from that suggested by the face. Gros himself admitted this discrepancy, but having taken great pains in painting the face from memory, he pre-

ferred to sacrifice his artistic vanity to the family's desire that he do nothing to change the highly accurate facial features... [At the Salon] he was justly reproached for this lack of harmony between the character of the head and the more mature appearance of the rest of the figure. The critics were not in the artist's confidence and they were, in any case, correct. The artist was later in the position of reconciling the wishes of his friends with the severity of his critics.

In 1880, Tripier-le-Franc was also unaware of the patrons' wishes and, although he noted correctly that the picture was shown in the Salon of 1810, rather than in that of 1808 as Delestre indicated. Having no knowledge of the biography of General Legrand's son, he incorrectly maintained that the landscape "showing trees, water, a fortified castle, and a small chapel... surely represented one of the family's estates." It is no doubt on account of this text that James B. Byrnes (1951) surmised the setting to be Le Plessier-sur-Saint-Just, in Oise. The theory of Tripier-le-Franc is purely imaginary, however; most likely, Gros wanted to evoke some mountainous landscape of Spain, where the last journey of the young second-lieutenant had taken place. It is difficult to identify the site, since the landscape is probably a pastiche. Perhaps Gros wanted to impart a Moorish quality to the medieval castle; we see a fortified terrace of characteristic Moslem influence being used as an arsenal, but the various elements of the landscape recall above all the numerous castles, mountains and waterfalls Gros had observed in Italy and recorded in his sketchbooks (Louvre, Cabinet des Dessins, RF. 29955 and RF. 29956), executed about 1794-1796 (as attested by Genoese addresses at the beginning of the first of the books). Most significant are the landscapes of fols. 30 verso and 32 verso of the first book and fols. 44 verso and 45 recto of the second. Some are closer to the landscape shown in the Saint-Étienne sketch, others to the landscape of the final picture. In the sketch there is neither a castle in the background nor a chapel at the left. There are also other variations, notably in the position of the horse's head. Altogether it appears that Gros had another blond (although mustached) youth pose for him in the attire of a cuirassier. This further explains the lack of harmony between the figure and the face which Delestre had noted.

Finally, in a progression similar to that seen in comparing the posthumous portrait of *Christine Boyer,* the first wife of Lucien Bonaparte (Louvre), with the sketch (Lefuel Collection), Gros added a number of elements to the final work to evoke the concept of death. The cascade is a symbol of a short life and the chapel, here with a Virgin and a cross, recalls the sacrifice of Christ and "emphasizes the votive character of the work" (K. Lankheit, 1966, p. 122). Compared with the portraits of Général Legrand and Comtesse Legrand, treated in the style of Gérard, the posthumous portrait is already a romantic work. The element which contemporaries criticized contributes to its character. "In the contrast between the almost childlike face and the heavy metallic cuirass lies the gripping tension of the work. It bespeaks a very real

tragedy to which we, in the 20th century, are particularly sensitive" *(ibid.).* To attain this effect, Gros used a dazzling technique, somewhat reminiscent of that of Van Dyck or of the English 18th-century portraitists. In order to make a moving statement in what could only be a parade portrait, he brings into play all his artistic capacity as a colorist and as a painter of horses, qualities admired by Géricault and Delacroix.

PROVENANCE
Legrand family; Pierre Paulet Collection, 1935; collection of the Duc de Trévise, 1936; gift of the California Charities Foundation to the museum, 1949 (INV. no. 49-41).

EXHIBITIONS
1810, Salon, no. 393; 1935, Paris, no. 976; 1936, Paris, no. 54; 1937, Paris, no. 343, ill. 69; 1938-1939, New York, etc. no. 8, ill. 8; 1939, San Francisco, no. 7; 1939, San Francisco, no. 119, ill.; 1939-1940, San Francisco, no. 128; 1939-1940, New York, no. 231; 1950, Detroit, no. 9; 1952, Minneapolis, 1954, Santa Barbara, etc., no. 19; 1959, Raleigh, no. LXI, ill.; 1969, Kansas City, no. 28, ill.

REFERENCES
J.-B. Delestre, n.d., pp. 159-161; *ibid.,* 1867, p. 127; J. Tripier-le-Franc, 1880, pp. 286-287, p. 674; G. Brière, 1913, p. 71; G. Huismans, 1937, v. I, ill. 181; A. Frankfurter, 1938, pp. 8-10, ill.; J.-J. Sweeney, 1938, pp. 12-14; R. Goldwater, 1939, pp. 37-39; H. Comstock, 1939, pp. 28-33, ill.; W.-R. Valentiner, 1950, pp. 35-37, ill.; J.-B. Byrnes, 1951, p. 14; mus. cat., 1953, v. I, p. 70, ill. 72; H. Comstock, 1955, p. 216; G. Wildenstein, 1963, p. 42; H. Francis, 1964, p. 201; mus. cat., 1965, ill.; K. Lankheit, 1966, pp. 122-123, color ill. p. 121.

RELATED WORKS
Sketch by Gros of composition with some variations painted on paper mounted on canvas (46 × 38), Saint-Étienne (entered the museum in 1893 with the Bancel bequest, attributed to Géricault).

G. L.

91
Portrait of the Comte Chaptal

"Portrait de M. le comte Chaptal, pair de France"
Plate p. 275
Canvas; 136 × 114; s.d.l.l. *Gros / 1823*
Salon of 1824, no. 820
The Cleveland Museum of Art, Purchase, Leonard C. Hanna Jr. Bequest

In this traditionally conceived portrait, which evokes the sumptuous parade portraits of Nicholas de Largillière in the drapery and inclusion of curtains, Gros has depicted one of the most prestigious person-

alities of his time, Jean-Antoine Chaptal (1756 Nogaret, Lozère-Paris 1832), at the age of 68. The sitter wears the sash of the Order of Saint-Michael, which he had been granted on the eve of the Revolution (12 May

1788, when he was also made a Count), through the efforts of Loménie de Brienne. He was already well-known as a chemist. As an adherent of Lavoisier's new theory (see No. 33) and, from 1781, a professor of chemistry at the École de Médecine in Montpellier, he studied the utilitarian application of chemistry to various branches of industry and art. He adopted the ideas of the Revolution, sided with the Girondists and established himself in Paris in 1797. It was during the Consulate that the Count made his greatest contribution to the administration of France, primarily while he was Minister of the Interior. The files seen piled on his desk in Gros' portrait indicate his most significant activities: to the right of Chaptal, *Achèvement du Louvre, Assainissement des hôpitaux et prisons;* in the center, *Canal de l'Ourcq* (which provided a better water supply for Paris), *Sœurs de la Charité rétablies* (to combat the rampant confusion in the hospitals, Chaptal re-established the order of nursing sisters and opened the first national school for midwives). The portfolios on the left correspond to Chaptal's current activities in 1824: *Chimie appliquée à l'Industrie* summarizes a constant interest; *Conseils gˣ Société d'Encouragement* alludes to his activity as president of the society he had founded in 1801 and which would later commission a copy of this portrait; and finally, *Chambre des pairs* recalls his activities as a Peer of France. Because of his membership in the conservative Senate during the Empire and his having been in favor of Napoleon after his return from Elba, he was excluded for a few years from peership by Louis XVIII, but was reinstated in the Chamber of Peers in 1818, for he was indispensable to the country. Among the books lying on the desk, one is by the chemist Berthollet, one of Chaptal's colleagues at the Academy of Science, to which he had been elected in 1816. Gros had depicted Chaptal in the embroidered dress suit of the Academy which can be seen beneath the black fur-trimmed cloak. Seated at his desk, he is writing in a notebook inscribed *Mémoires*. Is this his work *Mes souvenirs sur Napoléon,* which was not published until 1893? This is the opinion of H. Francis; perhaps it would be better to see here some scientific work in progress, since the painting, surely done for Chaptal himself, appeared nevertheless at a Salon during the Restoration. It was well received, as we can read in the 28 September 1824 issue of the *Journal des Débats:* "M. Gros has only shown one work this year, but it is a remarkable one: the portrait of M. le comte Chaptal, peer of France. The learned chemist... appears to be meditating. His head and hands have a startlingly

lifelike color, his costume is done simply and boldly. The public has been eager to pay its respects to this worthy portrait." The painting was also recommended as an example for artists: "[it] could teach them how to impart life to the work by expressing forms correctly, how to paint with verve, while satisfying good taste. The head is alive and the hands are truly flesh and blood." We find the same praise in the *Moniteur Universel* of 12 October 1824. "The portrait of M. Chaptal is worthy of its creator's reputation. Brilliant color, a bold, free handling, perfect resemblance—all are found here. The drapery is especially strong, with a faithfulness of imitation that would be difficult to carry any further. Everyone knows that M. Gros is one of the best colorists of our school. One is convinced of this in seeing the hands in this portrait... they are done in an inimitable manner. The blood seems to circulate. What a pity that the drawing of the left hand is incorrect, that it gives the pose a sort of constraint and is at least an imperfection...."

PROVENANCE
Still belonged to the Chaptal family in 1936; Collection of Germain Seligmann; acquired by the Cleveland Museum with funds from the bequest of Leonard C. Hanna, Jr., 1964 (INV. 64-54).

EXHIBITIONS
1824, Salon, no. 820; 1883, Paris, no. 119; 1913, Paris, no. 174; 1936, Paris, no. 90; 1955-1956, New York, Minneapolis, Cleveland, no. 3, ill. p. 13; 1963, Cleveland, no. 72, ill.

REFERENCES
Journal des Débats, 28 September 1824; D., in *Le Moniteur Universel,* 12 October 1824; A.-Chr. Quatremère de Quincy, 1837, p. 167; J.-B. Delestre, 1867, pp. 237-239, p. 372; J. Tripier-le-Franc, 1880, pp. 383-385, p. 676; G. Dargenty, 1887, ill. p. 57; Cte Chaptal, 1893, frontispiece ill.; H. Lemonnier, n.d., p. 67, ill. p. 81; R. Escholier, 1936, p. 16, ill. 29; Wildenstein, 1963, p. 26; H. Francis, October 1964, pp. 196-205, color ill. 4, 6, 7.

RELATED WORKS
Painted copy, of similar dimensions as the original, at the Société d'Encouragement pour l'Industrie Nationale, 44, rue de Rennes, Paris; this society, founded in 1801 by Chaptal, who was its first president, had his portrait painted some time after Chaptal's death in 1832. M.-A. Haigron, Delegate General, kindly provided us with the following text, an excerpt from the memorial report of Baron de Gérandi, which was read to the general meeting of the society 22 August 1832: "Do we not owe anything to honor his memory, which is now our inheritance? Why should we not have a bust of him executed or commission a copy of the beautiful portrait which Gros painted of him?..."
Antoine-Denis Chaudet executed a marble bust of Chaptal (Tours, Musée), in 1810. G. L.

Théodore Gudin

1802 Paris - Boulogne-sur-Mer 1879

After studying briefly with Anne-Louis Girodet, Gudin enrolled in the studio of Antoine-Jean Gros. His works were exhibited at the Salon from 1822 to 1880. He received the first-class medal as early as 1824. In 1827, his *Incendie du Kent* (Paris, Musée de la Marine) had an enormous success, and he was decorated by Charles X with the Legion of Honor at the end of the Salon. Gudin was named painter to the navy and took part in the expedition to Algiers. The works he exhibited at the Salon of 1831 included the *Coup de vent du 16 juin 1830 à Sidi-el-Feruch* (Paris, Musée de la Marine) and the *Coup de vent du 7 janvier 1831 dans la rade d'Alger* (Musée de la Marine). Both critics and public were enthusiastic. Jal (1827, p. 30) was reminded of Claude and Ruisdael; Charles Lenormant (1833, p. 44) compared him to Joseph Vernet; Jules Janin curiously, but flatteringly, called him the French Fenimore Cooper.

"Friend of princes and kings," as he described himself, Gudin was famous throughout Europe. In 1836, Jal again, in an article published in *Annales maritimes*, rated him first among marine painters, along with Eugène Isabey "after the decline of Monsieur Crépin."

However, as his biographer Edmond Béraud noted in the preface for *Les Souvenirs du Baron Gudin,* published in 1921, after the end of the July Monarchy his work was scorned by the new school. He still received numerous official commissions (notably for Versailles, one for 97 paintings illustrating the noble deeds of the French navy, but in 1844, Thoré justifiably lamented: "It is true that Monsieur Gudin endeavors to undertake too many pictures at public expense to retain the painterly gifts demonstrated in his early work... Monsieur Gudin has preferred an easy fortune to a talent developed through study and reflection" *(Salon de 1844,* p. 26). In his *Salon de 1846,* Baudelaire wrote: "Mon-

sieur Gudin increasingly compromises his reputation... I now see him in the same class... as those poor singers who, we are told, are great actors or poetic painters." In 1855, on the occasion of the World's Fair, he was criticized by Gustave Planche, and Maxime Du Camp (1855, p. 259) lamented that: "Like a child who exchanges a gold piece for a few pennies and feels himself richer because he has more coins, Monsieur Gudin, who might have produced 20 commendable works, has preferred to produce 500 ignominious ones. He is irredeemably lost at this point, and I doubt whether some of his early canvases, after which he has produced such undistinguished works, are sufficient to save him from oblivion. The Versailles museum has killed him; condemned to produce the required marine scenes, dragging like a ball and chain all the naval glories of France which he was supposed to illustrate at so much a meter, he could not stand up under this slavish labor and has died in the harness. He was a man endowed, however, with wonderful talents, and we still find evidence of this in four or five works scattered among the 25 pictures with which he has burdened the exhibition."

One may well wonder about the reasons for the failure of this so auspiciously begun career. Perhaps it resulted from his facile beginnings; perhaps also because certain critics (see *Souvenirs,* p. 85) induced the painter to give up large animated paintings, the type of composition at which he excelled, for works that were much more banal.

In any case, a study of the artist remains to be done, if only to determine the influence which he must have had on the marine painters, especially Félix Ziem, at the end of the century.

J. L.

92
Devotion of Captain Desse

"Trait de dévouement du capitaine Desse, de Bordeaux, envers le 'Colombus', navire hollandais"
Pl. p. 300 and color pl. p. 28
Canvas; 210 × 295; s.l.l. *T. Gudin 1830*
Salon of 1831, no. 996
Bordeaux, Musée des Beaux-Arts

The subject is described in the catalog of the Salon of 1831:

On July 23, 1822, the *Julia,* bound from Bordeaux to Bourbon Island (Ile de La Réunion), perceived before her a vessel stripped of her main and mizzen masts, and appearing to be in the greatest distress. Despite all her efforts, the *Julia* could not get close enough to hear the cries of the misfortunate sailors aboard the wreck, but they made signs for help in the most expressive and beseeching manner. It was not until the 25th that Captain Desse was able to learn, with the help of a speaking trumpet, that the *Columbus,* in addition to its apparent damage, was foundering. He resolved not to abandon the poor unfortunates who had no other hope but him, and after five days in which both ships were exposed to the utmost danger, he succeeded in transporting the crew of the *Columbus* on board the *Julia* in half-broken boats.
The moment depicted is when a terrible wave is breaking over the stern of the *Julia,* shattering her boat hanging in davits, and when the crew of the *Columbus* imagines that their savior has been engulfed; but at each moment of agony they hear repeated this selfless cry: "Take heart: I shall perish with you rather than abandon you."

The picture attracted much attention at the Salon, but the daring presentation and colors, which remind one both of Horace Vernet, *Joseph Vernet attaché à un mât étudie les effets de la tempête* (Salon of 1822; Avignon) and Joseph Turner (whose works Gudin must have seen during his stay in England), shocked the critics. Charles Lenormant wrote, "Most of the faults in this great work *(Le Kent)* are also to be found in the *Columbus* of 1831. There is the same transparent water, so strange in the middle of a storm, and the same importance given to a wave at the expense of the main subject; and the same fantastic color deployed over the entire painting."
The *Moniteur Universel* disagreed with some aspects of this judgment. "It would be hard to decide with any certainty whether, considering the extraordinary position in which the *Julia* is shown, the passengers and sailors could stand upright on their feet, working as they are to move the cargo. We should be inclined to believe they could not; but in these extreme circumstances, that one has so rarely the occasion to see and to see clearly, what seems as probable may itself only be a misleading appearance. Let us therefore leave this question to professional seamen to decide. However this may be, we feel that the interest would have been even further enhanced if the person of Captain Dehesse [sic] were more visible, if it were easy to recognize him. This would have required, no doubt, that the scene be shown from a lesser distance; and then we should have lost, at least in part, the admirable spectacle of the rising waves in the foreground of the picture; but however great the sacrifice, M. Gudin would have been amply rewarded by the advantages of dramatic effect. In any case, this composition has had great success, which it deserves. The colors are well blended, brilliant and harmonious; the sky and the spaces of the horizon are perfectly lifelike; and lastly, we do not believe that anyone will ever surpass M. Gudin in the art of rendering the transparency of sea water."
Jal's remarks were more in accord with the painter's own thoughts. For Gudin admitted, "Carried away by the beauty of the subject, I made the picture larger than I was instructed," and he said that "he had spent endless time on the details" (letter of 17 August 1829, Arch. Nat. F21 3). And Jal wrote, "This is a sea drama full of interest. The details are reproduced with a very spiritual exactitude.... The picture's greatest failing is its size. It would have been better smaller, I believe.

A few inches less of canvas to the left and at the bottom would perhaps alter it greatly for the better."

PROVENANCE
Commissioned on 27 August 1828 for the Minister of the Interior (Martignac), who, in a letter to the Prefect of the Department of the Gironde (Baron d'Haussez), explained that "a picture whose subject is to come from the annals of French glory should be charged to expenses of the Ministry of the Interior" (Arch. Nat., F²¹ 3). The picture was completed in 1829, and the artist was paid 6,000 francs. It was subsequently sent to Bordeaux in 1832 (New INV. 5838).

EXHIBITIONS
1831, Salon, no. 996; 1946, Bordeaux, no. 223.

REFERENCES
Arch. Nat., F²¹ 3; P***, in Le Moniteur Universel, 9 May 1831, p. 939; H. Delphis, 1831, v. XXXIV, pp. 14-15; A. Jal, 1831, pp. 214-215; Ch. Lenormant, 1833, p. 47; P. Mantz, 20 November 1846, p. 52; mus. cat., 1855, no. 173; mus. cat., 1863, no. 196; [Anon.], in La Chronique des Arts et de la Curiosité, 17 April 1880, p. 128; H. Vollmer, 1922, v. XV, p. 194; J. Vivielle, June-Aug., 1929, nos. 123-124, p. 12; Th. Ricaud, Jan.-Feb., 1935, p. 53; ibid., July-Sept. 1937, p. 130; R. Mesuret, 1955, v. IV, p. 113; J. Vergnet-Ruiz and M. Laclotte, 1962, p. 238.

RELATED WORK
In 1831, Jal drew attention to a sketch belonging to a certain Delatouche.

J. L.

Pierre-Narcisse Guérin

1774 Paris - Rome 1833

Guérin, a student of Nicolas-Guy Brenet and then of Jean-Baptiste Regnault, won the Grand Prix de Rome in 1797. Two years later he exhibited the Retour de Marcus Sextus (Louvre) at the Salon. Originally conceived as the Retour de Bélisaire dans sa famille, this picture brought him immediate success, perhaps because of the interest in seeing a pupil of Regnault rival the art of David, or more likely because this allegory of return from exile was interpreted as an allusion to the return of those who had emigrated (see E.-J. Delécluze, 1855, p. 211). From that time on, Guérin was to devote himself to epic history painting, for which he drew his inspiration from the theater, particularly from the works of Racine as, for example, Phèdre et Hippolyte, Salon of 1802 (Louvre). He was allowed to leave for Rome as a student at the French Academy (Joseph-Benoît Suvée was then director) and resided there from 1803 to 1805. He made two trips to Naples, one in the spring of 1804 and the other in February 1805, where he met Mme de Staël and did Les Bergers au tombeau d'Amyntas (recently acquired by the Louvre). He exhibited this painting at the Salon of 1808, along with Bonaparte pardonnant aux révoltés du Caire (Versailles; sketch, Caen). He continued to paint works inspired by the theater: Oreste annonçant à Hermione la mort de Pyrrhus (Caen), Andromaque et Pyrrhus, Salon of 1810, Clytemnestre, Salon of 1817,

and Enée racontant à Didon les malheurs de Troie, Salon of 1817—the last three in the Louvre. In 1816, he obtained the position of director of the French Academy in Rome, but refusing to leave Paris, he was replaced by Charles Thévenin. He solicited the position a second time and obtained it in 1822. In Rome, he planned a huge canvas (435 × 630; Angers) on the theme of La Dernière nuit de Troie, for which he made a sketch (Angers) and began the execution. After his return to Paris Guérin tried to finish the work but, exhausted, he gave it up and in the company of Horace Vernet returned to Rome, where he died. As David's heir, Guérin was one of the best artists of the second neo-classical period and was instrumental in the transition to the following generation, as the teacher of Géricault, Delacroix, Sigalon, Paul Delaroche, Ary Scheffer and Victor Orsel. His earliest compositions reveal a severe but expressive classicism, and from 1805 on, we can see his slow evolution toward a more languid and pleasing style which is fully manifest in 1810 in the Aurore et Céphale (Louvre) and especially exemplified by the 1817 Enée et Didon, where the finical spirit and acid color call to mind Girodet, especially his Pygmalion et Galatée of the 1819 Salon (Château de Dampierre).

J. V.

93
Death of Cato

La Mort de Caton d'Utique
Plate p. 144
Canvas; 111 × 144
Paris, École des Beaux-Arts

Cato of Utica, the great-grandson of Cato the Elder, took Pompey's side in his struggle against Caesar. Having little faith in the survival of Republican freedom after Pompey's assassination, he secluded himself in Utica and there, after convincing himself that he could do nothing for Rome, prepared himself for death, with stoic tranquility. He embraced his son, counseled his friends to yield to Caesar's ascendancy and, having retired to his room, spent part of the night reading Plato's *Phaedo*. Then he tested the point of his sword and having placed it beside him, cried: "At last, I am my own master!" He reread Plato and decided he needed a few moments of rest before giving up his life. He slept for several hours and, at dawn, he seized his sword and plunged it into his body. Rescued, he refused all help and persisted in his will to die. Guérin's painting, taken from the *Lives* of Plutarch, illustrates the following passage: "But after Cato recovered from fainting and began to recognize his situation, he pushed away the doctor and with his own hands opened his wound and tore his entrails to pieces." This work won Guérin the first-place Grand Prix de Rome in 1797; he did not, however, leave for Italy until December 1803. Since there had not been a competition for the Prix de Rome for four years, three first Grand Prix were awarded that year, to Pierre Bouillon, Guérin, and Louis-André-Gabriel Bouchet; Louis Hersent placed second.

If we compare the three first prizes, we are struck by the similarity of the compositions (all in Paris, École des Beaux-Arts), all derived from Poussin's *Mort de Germanicus* (Minneapolis Institute of Arts). Guérin's picture is distinguished by its heightened color scheme and especially by the expressions of the figures: Cato's son, who rushes to his father, and the doctor, who is pushed aside to the right. While Bouchet painted in a noble and static style that harmonizes perfectly with the spirit of this example of stoicism, Guérin treated the subject in an emphatic, dramatic and hence still baroque manner, although he used here a characteristically neo-classical frieze-like composition.

PROVENANCE
First Grand Prix de Rome in 1797; collection of the École des Beaux-Arts, Paris.

REFERENCES
C.-P. Landon, 1805, v. X, ill. 22; p. 51; C.-P. Landon, 1832, v. I, ill. 63, pp. 131-132; A. Le Go, 1833, p. 263; A.-C. Quatremère de Quincy, 1834, p. 417; E.-J. Delécluze, 1855, p. 211; Ch. Blanc, v. III, 1865, p. 2; Bellier and Auvray, 1882, v. I, p. 715; Thieme and Becker, 1922, v. XV, p. 231; F.-G. Pariset, 1974, p. 80.

RELATED WORKS
Black chalk drawing with white heightening (Louvre, R.F. 12844), 28 x 43.5. (See A. Sérullaz in exhibition, Paris, 1972, no. 93).
Line engraving by C. Normand in C.-P. Landon, 1805, X, pl. 22, and 1832, I, pl. 63.   J. V.

94
Iris and Morpheus*

Iris et Morphée
Plate p. 215
Canvas; 251 × 178; s.d.l.r. *P. GUERIN. 1811.*
Leningrad, The Hermitage Museum

This painting, as well as its pendant, *L'Aurore et Céphale* (Leningrad, Hermitage), comes from the Prince

Youssoupoff Collection, assembled in Paris between 1808 and 1811. The Prince had a particular penchant for French painting and commissioned, for example, from David in 1809, the *Sapho et Phaon,* which is today in the Hermitage. At the Salon of 1810 (no. 396), Guérin exhibited the *Aurore et Céphale* which entered the Louvre in 1888, after being owned by Giovanni-Battista Sommariva. The idea of exhibiting two pendants must have occurred to the artist after the Salon. Thus, in 1811, Guérin produced a replica of this work, together with a pendant, the *Iris and Morpheus* shown here. Several drawings for the *Aurore et Céphale* of 1810 are in Valenciennes, and yet little remains that can be related to the *Iris and Morpheus* of 1811. A drawing in Lille of this subject is especially revealing, however, since it unites on one sheet the compositions of both the *Aurore et Céphale* and of the *Iris and Morpheus.*

The two pictures constitute an important milestone in Guérin's career, because they show a loosening of his style and a development toward a picquant eroticism, achieved through the use of a soft and delicate anatomy. They are, of course, related to some of David's works. The *Sappho and Phaon* (No. 36) or *L'Amour et Psyché,* 1817 (Cleveland Museum of Art), are

even closer to Girodet—one thinks especially of his *Endymion* of the Salon of 1793 (Louvre), which treats the theme of sleep and also depicts elongated and languid forms.

PROVENANCE
Acquired by Prince N.-B. Youssoupoff in Paris in 1811; collection of the Youssoupoff princes, Saint Petersburg, until 1918; Palace Museum of Prince Youssoupoff, Petrograd, from 1918 to 1924; since 1924, Leningrad, Hermitage (INV. 5675).

REFERENCES
Mus. cat., 1839, no. 41; mus. cat., 1920, no. 131; Thieme and Becker, 1922, v. XV, p. 231; S. Ernst, 1924, p. 232 (ill.); mus. cat., 1958, v. I, p. 368, no. 5675.

RELATED WORKS
Paintings. Its pendant, *L'Aurore et Céphale* also from the Youssoupoff Collection; 251 × 178; Leningrad, Hermitage (mus. cat., 1958, I, p. 368, no. 7242). Another version of the pendant, *Aurore et Céphale,* Louvre; 254 × 186; s.d.l.r. *P. Guérin 1810 ;* exhibited at the Salons of 1810 and 1814. *Drawings.* A drawing, not catalogued in Valenciennes. A drawing in Lille (H. Pluchart, mus. cat., 1889, no. 1437); on *recto: Aurore et Céphale ;* on *verso: Iris et Morphée.*

J. V.

95
Portrait of Henri de La Rochejaquelein

Henri de La Rochejaquelein
Plate p. 252
Canvas; 216 × 142
Salon of 1817, no. 400
Cholet, Musée Municipal

Exhibited at the Salon of 1817, along with *Clytemnestre* (no. 398) and the *Enée racontant à Didon les malheurs de Troie* (no. 399), both in the Louvre, this portrait of Henri Duverger, Comte de La Rochejaquelein (1772-1794), forms part of an important series of portraits of Vendean generals, commissioned, beginning in June 1816, by Louis XVIII for the Château de Saint-Cloud (Arch. Nat., O³ 1393; see also G. and J. Lacambre, 1972 [appeared in 1973], p. 340); this series, which came into the Louvre as a group was, with very few exceptions, allocated in 1914 to the museum in Cholet. The series brought together many artists. Guérin executed, in addition to this portrait, that of *Prince de Talmont,* commissioned in 1826 (INV. 5189). Other portraits in the series are: Robert Lefebvre's *Por-*

trait du marquis de Lescure, commissioned in 1816 and exhibited at the Salon of 1817 (INV. 4421); Paulin Guérin's *Portrait de Charette,* commissioned in 1816 and exhibited at the Salon of 1819 (INV. 5231), and a *Portrait d'Elbée,* commissioned in 1826 and exhibited at the Salon of 1827 (INV. 5232); Anne-Louis Girodet's *Portrait du marquis de Bonchamps,* commissioned in 1816 and shown at the Salon of 1824 (INV. 4964) and a *Portrait de Cathelineau,* commissioned in 1816 and exhibited at the Salon of 1824 (INV. 4965); Jean-Baptiste Mauzaisse's *Portrait de Constant de Suzannet,* commissioned in 1816 and shown at the Salon of 1817 (INV. 6580); Louise de Bouteiller's *Portrait de Louis de Frotté* commissioned in 1821 and shown at the Salon of 1822 (INV. 2830); Jean-Joseph Dassy's *Portrait de Perrin de Précy*, commissioned in 1825 (INV. 3680); Amable-Paul Coutan's *Portrait de Georges Cadoudal,* commissioned in 1826 and shown at the Salon of 1827 (INV. 3449). Baron François Gérard received the commission for a portrait of Général Moreau (Arch. Louvre, P⁶, 1816, 22 June), but it does not seem that this work was ever executed. Charles Auguste Steuben, however, painted a *Portrait du général Pichegru* (Arch. Louvre, *id.*) which is now in Versailles (INV. 7992). The 1816 commission also included a *Portrait de Louis Duverger, marquis de La Rochejaquelein* (1777-1815), the brother of Henri, assigned originally to Pierre-Louis Delaval (Arch. Nat. O³ 1390, 28 May 1817), which entered the Louvre (INV. 3847) and was later allocated to a province and has not been found. This picture had originally not proved satisfactory, for in 1817 another *Portrait de Louis de La Rochejaquelein* was commissioned. It was Pierre-Narcisse Guérin who was given the commission (Arch. Nat. O³, 1395, 18 January 1820). The painting was exhibited at the Salon of 1819 and, although not appearing in the catalog, it was described in the account of the exhibition given by the *Journal de Paris* (no. 292, 19 October 1819, 12th article). Later entering the Louvre (INV. 5188), it was allocated to Cholet in 1914.

A price of 4,000 francs was paid for each of the paintings. "This price seems sufficient. It is in the best interest of artists, in general, that no one in particular is favored, and that all receive the same amount without exception" (Arch. Louvre, P⁶, 1816, 22 June). The family of the sitter was carefully consulted as to the elaboration of each individual portrait; thus, a series of letters still exists from the Comte de Pradel (Arch. Louvre, P⁶, 1816, 7 August) giving the painters a list of very precise instructions which, for the most part, were honored.

The political significance of this commission, contemporary with David's exile in Brussels, is obvious. It is the affirmation, on the morrow of The Hundred Days, of royal authority and the glorification—in reading the critics of the time, one is tempted to say the heroization—of those who, at the price of civil war, defended the throne.

Of all the Vendean generals, Henri de La Rochejaquelein, who died at the age of 21, was one whose memory was particularly dear to the Royalists. Born 3 August 1772, of an old Vendean family, he participated, at the side of his cousin, the Marquis de Lescure, in the Vendean wars. (His brother Louis, on the other hand, had emigrated at the beginning of the Revolution.) He took part in the Battle of Fontenay (May 1793)

and, following several military disasters, was in October 1793 named General in Chief of the Vendean armies. On 22 October, he took part in the Battle of Laval and, on 6 November, that of Fougères. Defeated by Marceau on 13 December 1793 at the Battle of Mans, he was killed 4 March 1794 at Nouiallé. "Two republican soldiers were hiding in the bushes. They were seen by the victorious party which wanted to shoot them. The Vendean general objected and said to these fugitives, 'Come out; I grant you grace.' One of the soldiers who owed him his life shot the general at point-blank range. Thus La Rochejaquelein died, aged 21, the victim of his humanity and of a greatness of spirit which the fanaticism of civil wars makes even more admirable" (E. Miel, 1817 and 1818, p. 318).

Turning to the portrait itself, we see that it follows faithfully and to the smallest detail the long description provided by the family (Arch. Louvre, P⁶, 1816, 7 August). To this description was added a miniature to assist Guérin in transcribing the features of the Vendean hero.

The criticism was eulogistic; for the composition itself ("it is the royal standard which looms behind the soldier's head, an ingenious and poetic idea, characterizing the person and the action," E. Miel, *op. cit.,* p. 317), as well as for the expression and detail ("M. Guérin has, in the physiognomies of these simple and virtuous men, excellently rendered the expression of their firm, confident, steadfast courage, like that of their illustrious chief, an expression of fiery courage and fearlessness before all," *Journal des Débats,* 31 July 1817). E. Miel (*op. cit.,* p. 319) concluded, "this portrait is a history painting"—a compliment which he reinforces with another, more important in the final analysis, when one considers the polemic and political intention of the commission for the portraits of the Vendean generals: "M. Guérin has subtly hidden the picture of civil war; we see the ends of the republican bayonets, but we do not see Frenchmen fighting Frenchmen" (*op. cit.,* p. 318).

PROVENANCE
Commissioned in 1816, for 4,000 francs, by Louis XVIII for the Château de Saint-Cloud; Louvre Collection (INV. 5187); allocated to Cholet in 1914.

EXHIBITION
1817, Salon, no. 400.

REFERENCES
C.-P. Landon, 1817, p. 66; E. Miel, 1817 and 1818, pp. 317-319; Ch. Gabet, 1831, p. 337; Ch. Blanc, 1865, v. III, pp. 12-13; Bellier and Auvray, 1882, v. I, p. 715.

A replica of this portrait, intended for the La Rochejaque-lein family, was painted by P.-N. Guérin (Arch. Nat., O³, 1396, no. 1069).

A *Portrait d'Henri de La Rochejaquelein* by P.-N. Guérin (canvas, 215 × 143; Angers) comes from the collection of his pupil, the painter Guillaume Bodinier. According to the description (H. Jouin, museum cat., 1885, p. 26), this painting, which has not been traced, is not the same as the one shown here.

A *Portrait d'Henri de La Rochejaquelein* by P.-N. Guérin (canvas, 32 × 24) was sold at the Baron de Beurnonville sale, Paris, 9-16 May 1881, no. 96. According to the description, this small painting corresponds neither to the Cholet nor to the Angers version.

Z. Belliard did a lithograph after the Cholet painting in 1824. It was also the model for numerous popular engravings and lithographs where usually only the bust is shown (see Bibliothèque Nationale, Cabinet des Estampes, series N2).

J. V.

Noël Hallé

1711 Paris 1781

Noël Hallé was an actual contemporary of two other great history painters: Jean-Baptiste-Marie Pierre, his junior by three years, who upon his nomination as First Painter to the King in 1770, gave up painting in order to devote himself to his new duties, in which he exerted a considerable influence on the evolution of French artistic taste; and Joseph-Marie Vien, born in 1716, whose career acquired a completely new aspect from the Salon of 1763 on. Hallé was the son and grandson, respectively, of the painters Claude-Guy and Daniel Hallé and was related to Restout and Jouvenet; he won the Second Prix in 1734 and, two years later, the Grand Prix with his *Passage de la mer Rouge*. His first residence in Rome lasted from 1737 to 1744. In 1746 he became *agréé*. The Academy made him a member two years later on the basis of his *Dispute de Minerve et de Neptune pour donner un nom à la ville d'Athènes* (Louvre). He was made adjunct professor the same year, professor in 1775, adjunct to the rector in 1777 and rector one month before his death on 3 May 1781. Overseer of Gobelins Manufactory in 1770, he was made a Knight in the order of Saint-Michel in 1777, a rare honor for a painter at the time—as a reward for his Roman mission in 1775, where he went to reorganize the Academy, left somewhat in chaos by Charles Natoire, before Vien assumed the directorship.

Hallé exhibited regularly at the Salon from 1746 on and received important royal commissions (the *Vendanges* or the *Triomphe de Bacchus*, Salon of 1771, for the Petit Trianon). We will mention only works from 1774 and after. In 1774, he exhibited *Jésus-Christ faisant approcher de lui les petits enfants pour les bénir* (1774; Saint-Nicolas-des-Champs; sketch catalogued under the name of Guala; London, Heim Gallery, 1970, no. 33), two gouaches and a *Tête de Vieillard*. Three years later he showed the *Libéralité de Cimon l'Athénien* (Louvre). The Salon of 1779 was the last in which the artist participated (see No. 96).

Primarily a history painter (*Clémence de Trajan*, 1765, Marseille; *La Course d'Atalante*, 1765, Saint-Étienne; *Achille reconnu par Ulysse*, 1769, Limoges; *Sainte Famille*, 1748, Hermitage), Hallé nevertheless did not neglect either genre painting (*Éducation des Riches*, two versions, 1764 and 1765; *Éducation des Pauvres*, 1765, Paris, private collection; the *Colin-Maillard* under the name of Hubert Robert at Amiens; *Vieillard se chauffant*, as French, anonymous at Dijon) or portraiture.

His style is easily recognizable: he favored elongated figures, tousled heads, faces framed by hair arranged to accentuate their oval character and silhouettes slightly off balance. His colors are pale, sometimes approaching pastel and his brushstroke, broad and liberal in the sketches, becomes smooth and glossy in his large compositions.

One must ask if his last works can be described as sensitive to new ideas, or on the contrary, if they indicate no fundamental change in relation to those that established his fame. It seems, in fact, difficult to speak in terms of evolution, although Noël Hallé, like the other painters of his generation, hastened the arrival of a new style in painting.

P. R.

96
Cornelia, Mother of the Gracchi

"Cornélie, mère des Gracques..."
Plate p. 52
Canvas; 76 × 96
Salon of 1779, no. 1
Montpellier, Musée Fabre

At the Salon of 1779, the last in which he participated, Hallé exhibited two pictures: the *Cornelia, Mother of the Gracchi* and its pendant (no. 2): *"Un ami d'Agésilas, roi de Sparte, l'ayant trouvé à cheval sur un bâton, jouant avec ses enfants, lui en indiqua sa surprise ; le roi lui dit: 'Ne parlez de ce que vous voyez que lorsque vous serez père,"* also in the Musée Fabre. Although this second scene seems to have been undertaken very rarely by painters (it of course prefigures the *Henri IV jouant avec ses enfants* painted by Ingres [see no. 106], and works of a number of other artists who from this time on were more sensitive to French history than to antiquity), the theme of *Cornelia, Mother of the Gracchi* was in its turn very popular, from Peyron (Toulouse) to Suvée (No. 170) and from Gauffier (Fontainebleau) and Réattu (Arles) to Lebarbier (Salon of 1795). According to Pigler, however, no French artist had dealt with the subject before Hallé. The story, taken from Valerius Maximus (IV, 4), is well-known. A rich lady from the Roman Campagna pays a visit to Cornelia, the daughter of Scipio Africanus, and asks Cornelia to admire her necklaces and ornaments. Cornelia then brings forth her children and replies: "These are my jewels."

This painting by Hallé was variously received at the Salon of 1779: "His reputation has been established a long time and he has the right to rest on his laurels," (*Le miracle de nos jours,* coll. Deloynes, XI, p. 596). "One prefers his former work to the paintings one sees here" (*Ah ! Ah ! Encore une critique du Salon,* coll. Deloynes, XI, p. 342). What struck the commentators was the interest in childhood which Hallé had already demonstrated at the Salon of 1765 (*L'Éducation des Riches, L'Éducation des Pauvres),* but which Chardin had expressed more movingly in a different way. "This commendable artist [Hallé] appears to have enjoyed recounting the innocent pleasures and the gentle diversions with which he fills the leisure of his old age."

In this painting, Hallé played especially on the contrast between the richly adorned Campagna lady and Cornelia, very simply dressed in the antique style and surrounded by her daughter and two sons, one of whom holds an unrolled scroll on which the first verses of the *Iliad* are written. However, if one compares the canvas of Hallé with those of the same subject by Jean-François Peyron (Toulouse) barely two years later, and Joseph-Benoit Suvée (No. 170), one is struck by the slight interest Hallé paid to the moral content of the subject. He portrayed the scene with a total absence of heroism, and with a "bourgeois sentimentality like that of Greuze, but travestied by Greek and Roman dress" (as A. Joubin reproached him in 1924). As the *Coup de patte sur le Salon de 1779* (coll. Deloynes, XI, pp. 19-21) wrote: "The Roman lady appears to be saying: 'Come forward, children, pay your respects to Madame'.... It would not have been ill-advised, on this occasion, to have included some more serious people who could have witnessed the scene with that quiet and profound admiration that is inspired by a virtuous deed, which draws and penetrates the soul...."

The time was ripe for a more heroic art than that of Hallé who, while considered a refined colorist, succeeded only in beginning to open the door.

PROVENANCE
Bequest of the widowed Mme Bouisson, born Bertrand, in 1893, as "Carle Van Loo."

EXHIBITION
1779, Salon, no. 1.

REFERENCES
Coll. Deloynes, v. XI, no. 196, p. 7; no. 230, p. 753; no. 219, p. 596; no. 211, pp. 405-406; no. 209, p. 376; no. 208, p. 342: no. 207, p. 310; no. 202, pp. 183, 185; P.-J. Itier, mus. cat., 1896, no. 32 ("Carle Van Loo"); mus. cat., 1904 and 1914, no. 591 ("anonymous"); O. Estournet, 1905, p. 218, no. 131 (did not know its location); J. Locquin, 1912, pp. 188, 252; A. Joubin, 1924, pp. 212-213 (attributed to Hallé); A. Joubin, mus. cat., 1926, no. 599; A. Pigler, 1956, v. II, p. 367; R. Rosenblum, 1967a, pp. 61-69, ill. 59.

In the catalog of the sale after the death of Noël Hallé, 2 July 1781, there appeared (no. 30) a now lost sketch for the painting *(2 pieds 3 pouces × 2 pieds 9 pouces)*.

For the pendant, the sketch for which also appeared at the Hallé sale, see above.

P. R.

Fulchran-Jean Harriet

1778 Paris (according to Landon) - Rome 1805

Little is known regarding this precocious pupil of David, who was awarded the Grand Prix de Rome in 1798 for his *Combat des Horaces et des Curiaces* (Paris, École des Beaux-Arts) after he had received various *prix d'encouragement* at the Royal Academy of Painting (a third-place medal in 1789 and a second-place one in 1794). By 1793, at the age of 17 according to C.-P. Landon, *Annales du Musée...*, 2nd ed., *École française moderne,* I, 1832, p. 145, who set his birth however at 1778 and death at 1805, he had been awarded the second Grand Prix for his *Retour à Rome du cadavre de Brutus tombé dans la bataille.* Both David and Prud'hon spoke in its favor. From 1796 on, Harriet exhibited at the Salons: in 1796, *Ariane à Naxos, Deux sujets empruntés à l'histoire de Héro et Léandre,* and two drawings: *Œdipe à Colonne* and *Sapho et Anacréon ;* in 1799, a *Portrait de la citoyenne G. ... au bain ;* in 1800, the *Mort de Virgile,* a *Portrait de femme* and an allegorical drawing of the *Mort de Raphaël ;* in 1802, an *Autoportrait* and a *Portrait d'enfant.* His *Androclès et le lion* dates from about this time, as we know from Landon's remark about it in his *Annales du Musée...* (II, Year X, 1801-1802), where he pointed out that it was successfully exhibited in the Galerie d'Apollon at the Louvre along with the works of other pensioners of the French Academy in Rome. Residing at the Villa Medici from at least 1802 on, Harriet was visited by Schlegel, who expressed to Goethe his admiration for the young artist. Another German, the painter Gottlieb Schick, must have visited Harriet often. Schick was one of the best German Neo-Classicists; he lived in Paris from 1798 to 1802 and in Rome from 1802 to 1811 and took part alongside Harriet in the competition for the *Horatius Coclès* (see W. Becker, 1971, pp. 349, 405, n. 707). However, as Landon wrote in 1832 (the second edition of his *Annales du Musée,* which contains an important biographical sketch on Harriet, including his birthdate which neither Bellier and Auvray nor Thieme and Becker included): "Too rigorous a dedicat-

ion to work, added to the change of climate, proved detrimental to his already precarious health" (p. 145). Harriet died, unable to profit from the supplementary year of stipend granted him to finish a large *Horatius Coclès défendant le pont Sublicius,* which was "about 30 *pieds* long" and which was shown in a posthumous exhibition organized in 1805 at the French Academy in Rome. At the Salon of 1806 there appeared, as a last tribute to Harriet's memory, a painting of *Hylas et les nymphes,* engraved, like the *Androclès* cited above, in Landon's *Annales du Musée,* along with a drawing, *Héro et Léandre.* Among Harriet's known but unidentified works we also should mention the heightened sepia drawing of *Atala et Chactas* in the sale of the collection of the painter Pierre-Maximilien Delafontaine, Paris, 6 February 1861, no. 26.

In addition to the École des Beaux-Arts painting and the canvas of 1796 shown here, very few of Harriet's works can be traced. Among the paintings we can cite a *Portrait de Marat* at the Versailles Musée Lambinet and a lovely *Portrait d'enfant* at Orléans, which may relate to the painting of the Salon of 1802. Among the drawings are two charcoal portraits heightened with gouache in the Musée Marmottan, Paris (presumed portraits of the artist and his wife; the first s. d. 1801, the second dates from Year IX, i.e., 1800-01 ; Lefuel catalog, 1934, pp. 57-58, nos. 193-194, both shown in Paris in 1913 at the exhibition *David et ses élèves,* nos. 270 and 269); a third is in a private collection, Paris, and displays the same taste for a complex allegorical framework; a drawing of *Daphnis et Chloé* was in the collection of the Parisian antiquarian Guyot in 1967. The catalog of the Galerie Denis in November 1929, no. 1365 (ill. in the catalog) shows a preparatory watercolor for one of the engravings from the *Bon Genre* series: *"Voilà le travail à la Mode/c'était l'ancienne Méthode,"* s.d. Paris, 1803. The location is problematic in view of the fact that in 1803 Harriet was actually in Rome, but the inscription could be the engraver's rather than the artist's. Thieme and Becker, in fact, pointed out that Harriet often did work for engravers, especially for fashion plates: the *Thé parisien* engraved by Godefroy for the series *Suprême Bon Genre,* an equestrian portrait of Général Brune (Year VII, i.e., 1798-99), the *9 thermidor* and *31 mai* engraved by J.-J.-Fr. Tassaert, *Héro et Léandre* and six vignettes for Ségur's *Les Femmes,* Paris, 1803, engraved by R. Delvaux. We should further mention, as did W. Becker (1971, p. 55, fig. 210) an extraordinary engraving by A. Hubert Lefèvre, dated 1800, done after Harriet and depicting a *"Papillon simbole* [sic] *de l'âme en se fixant près d'elle annonce que son intelligence commence à se développer."* A kind of

Léon Frédéric before-the-fact, this motif of a new-born baby lying nude on its back in the grass, as if to say that man emanates from nature and is only elevated to human status through its soul, may have influenced the closely related image of Philippe-Otto Runge (*Le Matin,* Hamburg, 1808; see W. Becker, *op. cit.,* fig. 119). But this connection may be only thematic, explained by the spirit of the times (Runge was never in Paris). Harriet's work for engravers thus acquaints us with a curious theoretical and philosophical aspect of his art, and it intensifies the interest that this artist, almost unknown and too quickly relegated to oblivion, holds for us.

J. F.

97
*Œdipus at Colonus**

Œdipe à Colonne
Plate p. 145
Canvas; 156 × 133; s.d.l.r. *harriet fecit, an 6*
Paris, Private Collection

The subject is clearly identifiable as Oedipus and Antigone, a theme already dealt with by Harriet in a now lost drawing exhibited at the Salon of 1796. The painting here probably is the transposition of the drawing. Harriet approached the theme in a highly individualized manner, in that he here represented Antigone asleep on her father's knees. This conception contrasts with the whole Sophoclean tradition furthered so effectively by Ducis at the end of the 18th century with his *Œdipe chez Admète* of 1778, made into an opera by Guillard in 1785 and treated again by Ducis in 1797 *(Œdipe à Colonne).* In accordance with this tradition, Charles Thévenin, in his painting at the Salon of 1798 (today, Paris, National Assembly), shows a supplicating Antigone, her arms clutching a pathetic Oedipus, who stands, arms outstretched, as if to walk. According to Sophocles and Ducis, Antigone never becomes resigned or passive; and in the modern versions of the play (1778 and 1797), she works actively to effect a reconciliation between Oedipus and Polynices, her brother. The change that Harriet made in this dramatic situation finds its source in the theater, but it is not the opening of either the drama of Sophocles or that of Ducis. The opening scene of Ducis' *Œdipe à Colonne*

of 1797 is, in fact, close to that of his *Œdipe chez Admète* of 1778 (although the lamentation scene between Oedipus and Antigone is moved to Act II in the later version). In these plays, Antigone supports her blind father as, sighing for rest and death, he arrives at Colonus, near the temple of the Eumenides. This extremely famous opening was frequently depicted by painters. In his excellent study of this painting of 1973, J. Rubin cited examples by Joseph-François Leroy at the Salon of 1795 (a painting hypothetically identified by him as that in Bagnères-de-Bigorre), the painting by Charles Thévenin discussed above and that by Georges Rouget at the Salon of 1814, Rouen. But Harriet was probably inspired by the middle section of the play, when Antigone recounts the lugubrious resignation of Oedipus, now under protection of Theseus; Oedipus does not yield to Antigone and does not throw himself into her arms; rather:

...muet dans son ennui,
Il ne plaint plus ses maux, il ne pleure que lui...
Pour calmer ses tourments, ma voix
n'a plus de charmes.

(Ducis, 1797, Act. III, sc. 2).

The picture here could thus portray an Antigone exhausted from her efforts to console Oedipus (a scene suggested by certain lines of the play) and an Oedipus at the mercy of his lonely reflections on the release of death, which will at last put an end to his tragic existence. Harriet nevertheless remained faithful to the spirit of Sophocles' play, and he did not adhere to Ducis' cautious approach. Thus, he portrayed Oedipus dressed in rags, with his shaggy hair blowing in the wind and his blind man's staff in the foreground, as Sophocles has Polynices describe him (verses 1255 to 1260). On the other hand, the rather desolate landscape is well within the spirit of Ducis' text where, as early as 1778, he spoke of the "arid cypresses," while Sophocles described "verdant valleys" and evoked especially the dreadful temple of the avenging Eumenides. The pine, a quintessentially nordic tree, appears here as a powerful and original element of pre-Romanticism, nurtured by English and Germanic sources, of which Ducis (a great admirer of Shakespeare) was then one of the most visible champions. The ominous crow, the severe pines, the tormented sky and the rigid architecture of rectangular stone blocks—as opposed to the chaotic rock formations one sees in the other works cited above—all work to Harriet's advantage. He has certainly created here one of the noblest representations of the theme. The skillful contrast, successfully emphasized by the architecture, between the figures of Antigone and Oedipus—one limp, the other rigid—exhibits an academic perfection. The admirable arrangement of the curving lines of the drapery—converging below and floating above, according to a completely Flaxmanesque decorative system—heralds Ingres (No. 105) and is also present in his astonishing (but certain?) drawing in Compiègne, *Diane et Endymion* (J. Cassou, 1934, fig. 9). Only the awkwardness of Antigone's shoulder reveals the novice. This "damp" drapery, finely pleated and adhering to the figure in the spirit of a Greek relief rather than that of Hellenistic or Roman sculpture, is also found in P.-N. Guérin. His *Marcus Sextus* of 1799 has certain formal analogies with the painting by Harriet, as J. Rubin has observed (p. 155). Also to be compared with Harriet are the Davidian disciples, F. Gérard and A.-L. Girodet, who emerged after 1794. The obscure artist, Harriet, also belonged to their group until his premature death. The extensive stylistic restlessness and decorative inflections of the Ossianic current during the years 1795-1800 cannot be attributed to the Ossianic current. The examples of Harriet and the Oedipus theme, as

demonstrated by Rubin, show how effective a vehicle for stylistic emotions were the famous themes of Greek and Roman tragedy. The very famous picture of Philippe-Auguste Hennequin, *Les remords d'Oreste* (1800, Louvre), is equally representative of this mode.

Can we accept the almost too-compelling explanation by Rubin that Harriet's originality is bound to a political background? One must ask if the revival of paintings on the Oedipus theme from 1795 on was so remarkable that one must draw conclusions from it. Perhaps the revival of Guillard's operatic version of the Oedipus theme (not performed since 1793) it was staged on 10 Fructidor, Year IV, i.e., 20 August 1796, for the *Fête de la Vieillesse*) and the appearance in 1797 of Ducis' new play that set in motion a sudden interest among painters in the subject. However, Guillard's opera debuted only a month before the Salon opened in Vendémiaire, Year V, i.e., 22 September 1796 on. Therefore, Harriet did not necessarily have to have been motivated by the opera in order to produce his drawing and then his painting. The 1797 version of the play shows few changes in regard to that of 1778, apart from the episode of Alcestus and Admetus; for example, at the end, the sublimely moralistic pardon of Oedipus conforms completely to the ideas of Voltaire:

> J'ai prouvé, grâce au ciel, sans en être abattu,
> Qu'il n'est point de malheur où survit la vertu...
> Je tombe et je m'élève à l'immortalité.

The lines cited here are practically the same in both versions. Even a line with a possibly clear political meaning after Thermidor, like that spoken by Theseus, "Je plains plus que jamais les princes malheureux" (Ducis, 1797, Act II, sc. 5) already figured in the 1778 play.

Above all, the number of paintings relating to Oedipus in the Salons—fifteen paintings in eight Salons, each of which included hundreds of works—is not especially significant, at least no more so than the vogue for any beautiful tragic theme often dramatized in the theater and the opera and well-known to the educated world. The fifteen include repetitions made from one year to the next, as those by Joseph-François Leroy and Michel Lambert in 1795 and 1796 (perhaps the same work each time), and includes all the themes dealing with Oedipus, even those not related to the present scene, such as the discovery of the infant Oedipus, in eight Salons from 1795 to 1806. Rubin contrasted this number with the almost total absence of the theme before 1795, but there still appeared a sculptural work by

Challes in 1761; and paintings by Brenet in 1781; Peyron in 1786 (repeated in 1806); Lethière and Bidauld (together) in 1793 and, outside the Salon, Füseli and Gagneraux (Stockholm, 1784). To see *Oedipus at Colonus* as a painting of political significance, to read into this theme, in contradiction to the literary heritage of Sophocles and Ducis, the misfortune of the exile which could indeed have affected the minds of many at the time of the anti-emigration laws of Brumaire, Year IV (October 1795), is without doubt forcing the facts into the modern, but not historic, idea of a painting with a thesis. Oedipus truly represents the man of all misfortunes and the victim of fate; his legend takes on a primarily religious and sacred aura, a drama concerned with death, a word that recurs constantly in Sophocles and Ducis. Why did Ducis not further modify his play in his definitive version of 1797, which continues the same virtuous and conciliatory moralism as the earlier version? That the leaders of the Revolution constantly expressed themselves in "Greek" and "Roman" ways in their political life, using endless comparisons, did not mean that they forgot the realm and pleasure of the *literary,* that they could not make the distinction between reality and fiction, and that their exclusive interest at the theater and at the Salon was to detect hidden allusions. Here, too, as always, cultural and artistic life had its own pace, logic and demeanor, which are not necessarily those of daily and political life. Certainly, by 1814, the reappearance of the Oedipus and Antigone theme had taken on a clear political significance, borne out by the criticism of the time. *"O France heureuse ! Une auguste princesse d'Antigone est l'originale,"* wrote the *Observateur au Museum,* in 1814, in regard to a painting by Frédéric-Jean-Baptiste Desmarais (cited by Rubin, p. 154). Political overtones are also present in the 1814 dedication of Guillard's opera, when it was re-staged and dedicated to the Duchesse d'Angoulême, Louis XVI's daughter, who had returned to France (Rubin, pp. 147-148). It is easy to assume then that the appearance of the three paintings at the Salon of 1814 does go beyond a purely literary and cultural concern. But the historic commotion was generally stronger in 1814 than in 1796 or 1797, years that were not more troubled than preceding ones.

PROVENANCE
Acquired art market, Paris, 1966.

REFERENCES
J. Rubin, 1973, pp. 146, 155-156, ill. 5, p. 159.

RELATED WORKS
Drawing exhibited at the Salon of 1796, no. 202 (*"Œdipe à Colonne"*), cited by J. Rubin, 1973, p. 164, no. 5 (from the list of drawings and paintings on the Oedipus theme in the Salons between 1780 and 1817, to which we add an interesting drawing by Alexandre-Évariste Fragonard in Narbonne, unfortunately not dated).

J. F.

Antoinette-Cécile-Hortense Haudebourt-Lescot

1784 Paris 1845

At the end of the 18th century and during the first decade of the 19th century, the number of women painters grew noticeably. One of the most famous of them was Mme Haudebourt-Lescot, the only woman portrayed by François-Joseph Heim among the artists rewarded by Charles X after the Salon of 1827 (Louvre). She was born on 14 December 1784 in Paris and, at the age of seven, became a pupil of Guillaume Guillon, (Lethière), a family friend. A fashionable painter and an intimate of Lucien Bonaparte, he introduced her into social circles where she acquired the reputation for being a graceful dancer. When Lethière was named director of the French Academy in Rome, she followed her teacher despite an ensuing scandal. Antoinette Lescot was the first woman painter of her time to have such a background and her Roman sojourn determined her career. She painted genre pictures, totally void of her teacher's influence, that described the "exotic" Italian customs, that delighted the Parisian public. Mlle Lescot first participated in the Salon in 1810 by sending eight paintings from Rome. These were very favorably received by the critics and won her a second-class medal. She returned to Paris in 1816 and produced many works, now unfortunately lost, but known through engravings. Characterized by a picturesque flavor and a charming simplicity, these engravings illustrate Italian customs; for example, *Le Marchand de reliques* (1822), *La danse de Satarellot* (1824), *Le théâtre de marionnettes à Rome* (1824), and *Un capucin expliquant un bas-relief* (1827). In 1820, she married the architect Haudebourt and continued to exhibit regularly at the Salon, where she presented more than 110 paintings over 30 years, treating picturesque genre themes on small-scale canvases. In the anecdotal aspect of her work Mme Haudebourt-Lescot heralded such artists as Jean-Victor Schnetz, Claude Bonnefond, and Léopold Robert, who were also captivated by the charm of Italian life.   S. R. and I. J.

98
Self-Portrait

Portrait de l'artiste
Plate p. 273
Canvas; 74 × 60; s.l.l. *Haudebourt Lescot/1825*
Paris, Musée du Louvre

Although Mme Haudebourt-Lescot excelled in genre painting, she was also a fine portraitist. Jal, usually a severe critic, considered her portraits "remarkable" and reported that at the Salon of 1827-1828 two of her works attracted the attention of visitors, even though they flanked a history painting by François Gérard. From this date on, moreover, she exhibited only portraits, and in 1830 she was one of the artists commissioned to paint the effigies of great figures of French history for Versailles.

The face of the young Mme Haudebourt-Lescot is known from the charming drawing by Ingres in 1814, which shows her in the costume of an Italian peasant woman (lost, known from a copy done in 1814 by Jean-Alexandre Allais, a student of Ingres; Paris, private collection) and from a painting attributed to Gérard (Dijon, Musée Magnin), where she is seated at her easel. This self-portrait of 1825 shows us a 40-year-old woman whose features are faithfully rendered. The somber palette, the fluid and supple handling and the portrait's conception itself reveal the influence of the Dutch masters. Her heavy black velvet beret and her weighty chain strangely recall the self-portraits of Rembrandt. Her thoughtful expression and the mysterious atmosphere which surround her reveal that Antoinette Haudecourt-Lescot was not insensitive to romantic explorations and mark her progress since the time of her earlier self-portrait in Nancy.

PROVENANCE
Gift of Mme Buhner, née Maria Dauby, pupil of the artist, in 1867; M.I. 719.

EXHIBITION
1973, Castres, no. 12, ill. X.

REFERENCES
Tauzia, 1878, mus. cat., no. 783; A. Valabrègue, 1887, p. 104; G. Lafenestre, 1888, no. 41, p. 27; G. Brière, 1924, mus. cat., p. 128, no. 407; R. Escholier, 1941, p. 102; Ch. Sterling and H. Adhémar, 1959, v. III, no. 1053, ill. 379, p. 1; mus. cat. 1972, p. 199.
                                                S. R. and I. J.

François-Joseph Heim

1787 Belfort - Paris 1865

Heim's father, a drawing teacher, wanted his son to be a mathematician, but François-Joseph's precocious talent for drawing finally convinced his father to let him embark on an artistic career. The younger Heim left for Paris in 1803 to join François-André Vincent's studio, which ranked along with those of Jean-Baptiste Regnault and Jacques-Louis David as the three great studios of the time. In 1807 at the age of 20, Heim won the Prix de Rome for his subject *Thésée vainqueur du Minotaure* (Paris, École des Beaux-Arts). In Rome, he studied the Bolognese School and above all the work of Michelangelo. In particular, Heim made powerful drawings from the major groups of Michelangelo's *Last Judgment*. He won a first-class medal for the paintings he sent from Rome to the Salon of 1812: *Arrivée de Jacob en Mésopotamie* (Bordeaux; the same painting was apparently re-exhibited in 1817) and a *Figure d'étude*. The same year the imperial government commissioned from him the painting of the *Defense of Burgos* (Versailles, No. 99). The *Prisonnier* (Semur-en-Auxois) must also date from this period. It is a powerful academic work very close to Géricault (donated by Heim himself, it might possibly be one of the works sent from Rome which he had kept, or even more specifically the *Figure d'étude* shown at the Salon of 1812.

The commission for the *Defense of Burgos* was the first of an entire series for religious and civil buildings, which was to occupy the painter up until 1848-49. Heim, who was determined to be a history painter, worked more or less exclusively on commission, as did Alexandre-Denis-Abel de Pujol and Louis-Charles-Auguste Couder. In fact, as Chennevières remarked, he was the "habitual painter to the Bourbons." Thus, between 1815 and 1830, Forbin and Chabrol gave him commissions for churches in Paris and its environs: *Martyre de saint Cyr et de sainte Juliette sa mère* for Saint-Gervais (exhibited in the Salon of 1819), still in its original location; *Rétablissement des sépultures royales à Saint-Denis*, in 1817, for the basilica of Saint-Denis (Salon of 1822, still in its original location in the sacristy of the church, but unfortunately corroded by bitumen; but a beautiful sketch exists in Sceaux); *Martyre de saint Hippolyte* for Notre-Dame (Salon of 1822); *Sainte Adélaïde* for the funerary chapel of Dreux (Salon of 1824); *Miracle de saint Hyacinthe* for Notre-Dame (Salon of 1827). The two paintings for Notre-Dame, given to the Louvre in 1862 and then to the city of Paris, are presently misfiled in the city repositories. Heim also created works for the châteaux of royalty and the nobility: *La Valeur, La Vigilance militaire* (1817), intended for Versailles (Belfort); two paintings of the story of Titus, for the gallery of the Grand Trianon (Salon of 1819, in Belfort since 1931); *La Délivrance du roi d'Espagne* (Salon of 1824), commissioned by the Duchesse d'Angoulême for the château of Villeneuve-l'Étang near Saint-Cloud; two ceilings (1826-28) for rooms newly-restored by Fontaine, in the new museum of Charles X in the Louvre. Other important

works that should be noted are the *Robe de Joseph apportée à Jacob* (Salon of 1817), with its bold linear distortions, formerly at Lyon and since 1971 in the Louvre; the *Résurrection de Lazare* (Salon of 1819) in Angers; the *Destruction de Jérusalem* (Salon of 1824) in Paris, Musée du Louvre; *Saint Germain évêque d'Auxerre distribuant des aumônes* (Salon of 1827) in the church of La Châtre; an *Ascension* in the Strasbourg Cathedral; an *Adoration des mages* of 1831 in Avignon; a *Résurrection de Lazare* of 1820 at Autun Cathedral; and an *Adoration des mages* and *Présentation,* mural paintings of 1828 in the apse of Saint-Germain-des-Prés in Paris. The *Ptolémée Philopator* from the Salon of 1817, placed by the Louvre in Amiens and located in Doullens in 1898, seems to have disappeared during World War I; and the Heim painting cited by Bellier and Auvray as being in Strasbourg, *Berger buvant à une fontaine,* was destroyed by fire in 1870.

The works from this time, "paintings that one would say belong to a good student of the Carracci" (Chennevières, *op. cit.*), reveal a nervous and powerful draughtsman and a stormy and violent painter. Breadth of gesture and energy of drawing are assisted by nervous but solid modeling, powerful brushstrokes, vigorous tones and a firm and forthright execution. There are still a fair number of preparatory sketches in existence which vividly demonstrate his decided talent: *Martyre de saint Hippolyte* and *Miracle de saint Hyacinthe* (Paris, private collection), sketches for the two paintings formerly in Notre-Dame; *Victoire de Judas Macchabée* (Dijon, Musée Magnin); *Scène de massacre antique* (Paris, Musée Henner, unpublished attribution); sketch for the *Massacre des Juifs* (Salon of 1824), recently acquired by the Louvre; as well as projects for decorative schemes, battle sketches and portraits in Bayonne, Rouen, and Saint-Germain-en-Laye—splendid, fiery, lively, nervous canvases done with an astonishing, vigorous impasto and free brushstroke.

The truly masterful performance that insured Heim's reputation and to which he owes his lasting importance is his *Charles X distribuant les récompenses aux artistes à la suite de l'Exposition de 1824* (Salon of 1827, Louvre). The painting had the very specific purpose of reconciling portraiture (each figure retains the intimacy of a portrait), genre and history painting. (A series of preparatory drawings of silhouetted portraits, dated 1825 and 1826, in the Louvre, Cabinet des Dessins, are characterized by an energetic simplicity.) The painting had a resounding success and Heim was admitted to the Institute in 1829 (he had already been decorated with the

Legion of Honor in 1825). After the success of the *Distribution des récompenses,* the Household of the King asked Heim for three more paintings of the same type, in which he was to represent the members of the various sections of the Institute (letters, sciences, political figures). The July Revolution prevented the execution of these works, but numerous preparatory drawings (dating from the years 1827-29) were later used for other paintings.

Is it necessary to link the decline of Heim's talent to the change in regime, as did Chennevières? A convinced, long-time legitimist, he nevertheless wrote a complimentary article on the artist which appeared in 1867 under the pseudonym Saint-Santin. In any case, during the July Monarchy Heim participated less often in the Louvre exhibitions, exhibiting only three times during this 18-year period (at the Salons of 1833, 1834 and 1847). His creative activity, however, was in fact as important as always. The number of commissions did not diminish; he continued to paint for Parisian churches (a *Présentation au temple* in 1836 for the choir of Notre-Dame-de-Lorette; two mural paintings in 1845 for the Chapel of the Souls of Purgatory in Saint-Sulpice; several mural paintings in 1848 of the *Vie de la Vierge,* Chapel of Saint Anne in Saint-Severin) and for public buildings (four large scenes from the political and administrative history of France done in 1844 for the conference room in the Chambre des Députés; in 1848, the panels for above the doors at the Présidence of the Assemblée Nationale). The success of the *Distribution des récompenses* enticed Heim to depict several other meetings: in the Salon of 1833, *Le cardinal de Richelieu recevant les premiers académiciens,* destroyed by fire in the sack of the Palais-Royal in 1848, sketch in Montpellier; Salon of 1834, *Louis-Philippe recevant au Palais-Royal les députés de 1830,* Versailles; Salon of 1837, *La chambre des pairs présentant au duc d'Orléans l'acte qui lui confère la couronne ;* Salon of 1847, *Andrieux faisant une lecture au foyer de la Comédie-Française,* Versailles (painting conceived as a pendant to the *Distribution des récompenses).* At this last Salon, Heim also exhibited the *Assemblée tenue au Champ-de-Mars en 1815* (Versailles;

sketch, Louvre). Also to be cited are his battle scenes: *La bataille de Rocroy* (1840), for the Galerie des Batailles at Versailles; the huge *Défaite des Cimbres et des Teutons par Marius* (Salon of 1853, Lyon; two sketches in the Fogg Art Museum, Cambridge, Mass). These battle scenes went completely unnoticed at the Salon.

With perhaps the exception of the almost unknown, above-mentioned painting in Lyon (not on display), these large productions are weak in drawing, with insipid and chalky tones, and contributed in discrediting the artist (Chennevières: "The ceiling of the Charles X Museum is the last work truly worthy of him"; Paul Mantz, in 1847: "Though there still remain a few sparks of the sacred fire for M. Granet, the same is not true for M. Heim, whose flame seems to us to be utterly extinguished"). Mantz' notice is rather representative of the criticism which brought about Heim's complete and undeserved neglect during the reign of Louis-Philippe. However, his retrospective room at the Exposition Universelle in 1855, with 7 paintings and 16 drawings, must have earned him a belated renewal of interest. Thus was confirmed by the Salon of 1859, where Heim exhibited for the last time—64 portrait-drawings of members of the Institute: "Among the artists," wrote Baudelaire at the time, "who are content with the picturesque naturalism of the model, one must note especially... M. Heim, whom a few superficial spirits once mocked, and who this year has again, as in 1855, revealed to us, in a procession of sketches, a marvelous knowledge of the human grimace." Grouped by critics with the Primitifs, the prodigious children of the Davidian family, on account of his *Arrivée de Jacob en Mésopotamie* (Bordeaux), Heim was charged with being a romantic a century later by Focillon. These classifications demonstrate the diversity of his talent, his evolution and his many-faceted character, which still needs to be better understood. Surely this admirable, solid and realistic portraitist must not be overlooked as a determined and vigorous history painter.

A.-B. L. and J. F.

99

*Defense of Burgos**

La Défense de Burgos (octobre 1812)
Plate p. 228
Canvas; 180 × 260
Versailles, Musée National

The subject of this painting relates to Wellington's campaign against General Marmont in northwest Spain. The English general, having soundly defeated the French general at Salamanca on 22 July 1812, marched on Madrid, which King Joseph had evacuated. He then laid siege to Burgos, which Brigadier-General Dubreton's 1,600 men vigorously defended against the 35,000 English and Portuguese troops. After a fruitless 35-day siege, Wellington retreated to Portugal. Burgos was not evacuated by the French until June 1813, shortly before the decisive defeat of Vittoria (21 June). Thus, the bold defense of Burgos alone delayed the entry of the English into France by one year.

Done practically in the heat of the moment, this painting was one of the very last commissions for a work of military propagandistic intent assigned by Denon for Napoleon I. It was also the first official commission for Heim, who had just returned from Rome. Its impact was even more significant artistically, because the painting is astonishing in its dramatic vigor and its brutal shading, reminiscent of Géricault. Few paintings of this period go so far in anticipating military painting of the 1830s and the solid realism of N.T. Charlet and D.A.M. Raffet. This relationship explains the very revealing but false attribution to Charlet of a small unpublished copy of the Heim composition in Guéret. In its powerful illumination and contrasts, this *Defense of Burgos* announces the splendid blacks of Charlet's famous lithographic series on the *Siège d'Anvers* (1831-32). *of Burgos* announces the lovely blacks of Charlet's famous lithographic series on the *Siège d'Anvers* (1831-32). The painting's success, moreover, remained almost unequalled by Heim elsewhere. Apart from only one other nocturnal scene (unfortunately ruined) in the sacristy of the Cathedral of Saint-Denis (1817) which is worthy of Antoine-Jean Gros, Heim's paintings of contemporary history (notably those relating to Louis-Philippe at the Château de Versailles) are always handled in a correct and prudent style, with a subdued realism, discreet lighting and relief. In brief, this style lacked the heroic boldness and unconventional energy so prominent in the *Defense of Burgos* and which Lafond so aptly linked with Heim's fruitful study of Michelangelo in the Sistine Chapel during his residence at the Villa Medici. His Prix de Rome painting of 1807, *Thésée vainqueur du Minotaure* (Paris, École des Beaux-Arts), and the *Prisonnier* in Semur already reveal the temperament of a painter inclined to a brutal, powerful, and honest handling of light and shadow which were to culminate in *Defense of Burgos* and reappear in the large painting of the *Robe de Joseph apportée à Jacob* (1817), recently recovered by the Louvre.

In one rather exceptional passage, the illustrious Chennevières (1867, pp. 42-43, under the pseudonym of Saint-Santin—since Chennevières adored pseudonyms as much as he did writing !) made the following definitive statement:

It is through close study of the small, hand-sized figures that enliven this military scene, which represents one of the most Homeric military deeds of the imperial epic..., it is, I say, through close study of the great character of the small figures in this picture, painted in the enthusiasm of the moment, that one cannot stop thinking of the more robust works of Géricault; I mean those which Géricault did much later at the time of his own trip to Rome.... M. Heim never again repeated this simplicity of drawing, solid, courageous and naive, this utterly fresh and sober, even somewhat rough painting; and even Géricault did not surpass the *Defense of Burgos* in this feeling of loftiness and austerity. I do not know, but I can imagine that the illustrious head of the modern school looked at the painting of a young man of about his own age to whom the Rome prize had assured a certain fame; I do not even know if he was acquainted with a work which rather quickly disappeared into the state repositories; but what I contend is that the last paintings of Géricault are more closely related to the *Defense of*

Burgos than to the works of Gros and of Carle Vernet. It had real power. In his later religious compositions M. Heim again found a kind of energy, but an academic one, which never approached that first vigor of youth, the energy of his true temperament.

Chennevières, who appears to have had first-hand information, added that in order to document the material used in the siege he was to paint, Heim often visited the home of the curator of the artillery museum; and it was there that he met the first of his three wives.

PROVENANCE
Commissioned in 1813 for the sum of 4,000 francs and probably acquired in 1814; at Saint-Cloud in 1833; at Versailles in 1834, where it was shown in the museum from 1837 (INV. 5311, MV 1764).

REFERENCES
Gavard, V, p. 86, no. 1075; E. Soulié, 1860, v. II p. 29, no. 1764 (false dimensions); Saint-Santin (Chennevières), 1867, pp. 42-43; P. Lafond, 1896, pp. 443-444; Pératé and Brière, 1931, v. I, p. 121, no. 689; Ch. O. Zieseniss, 1970, p. 130; Y. Cantarel, 1973, pp. 373, 838-839.

RELATED WORKS
Smaller copy under the name Charlet and entitled *Épisode du siège du château de Vincennes* (sic !) in Guéret (canvas; 31 × 29; INV. 658; gift of Alexis Rouart, 1910).

J. F.

Louis Hersent

1777 Paris 1860

Like Guérin, Hersent was a student of Regnault's, and won second prize to Guérin's first, in the 1797 Prix de Rome competition, *La Mort de Caton d'Utique*. His early style was founded on Davidian canons, as exemplified in his first Salon entry of 1804, *Achille livrant Briséis aux hérauts d'Agamemnon ;* but he soon adapted this style to a widening range of subjects that prominently included scenes of North American Indian life, based on Chateaubriand (Salon of 1806, *Atala s'empoisonne dans les bras de Chactas, son amant,* a painting that precedes by two years Girodet's famous version of this theme); on anthropological reports (Salon of 1806, *Le Tombeau aérien, coutume américaine*); or on such historical legend as repeated in Marmontel's *Les Incas* (Salon of 1814, *Las Casas malade soigné par des sauvages,* New York, private collection). Like most of his contemporaries, Hersent also illustrated scenes of contemporary history (Salon of 1810, *Passage du pont de Landshut,* Versailles; Salon of 1817, *Mort de Xavier Bichat; médecin de l'Hôtel-Dieu de Paris,* Paris, École de Médecine,) as well as scenes from European history that, under the Bourbon Restoration, often had propagandistic political implications, as his, *Louis XVI Distributing Alms to the Poor* (No. 100) and *Gustave Vasa,* a highly praised picture destroyed during the 1848 Revolution. His repertory also included such sentimental dramas as the rescue by monks of a mother and child robbed by bandits in an Alpine pass (Salon of 1824, *Les religieux du Mont Saint-Gothard,* Mairie, Mortagne). Often honored under the Bourbon Restoration, Hersent maintained his close governmental connections under the July Monarchy, receiving commissions for history painting *(Débarquement de Christophe Colomb à San Salvador,* Beaune) and turning often to official portraits of heads of state (Salon of 1831, *Portraits en pied du roi, de la reine, du duc de Montpensier)* and of many important personalities of the period *(Casimir Périer, Delphine Gay).*

Hersent's work was widely known through prints, especially lithographs. His art reflects less an original personality than a businesslike artist who had learned through academic study a proficient technique of lucid narrative presentation and quasi-photographic description that could be used to comply with popular demands for an expanding repertory of historical events, true or legendary, and assorted picturesque anecdotes. R. R.

100
Louis XVI Distributing Alms to the Poor

"Louis XVI distribuant ses bienfaits aux pauvres pendant le rigoureux hiver de 1788"
Plate p. 254
Canvas; 171 × 227; s.d.m.r. *hersent/1817.*
Salon of 1817, no. 414
Versailles, Musée National

The scene takes place during the winter of 1788, reputedly the most severe since 1709, and illustrates an anecdote that was later to be included in P.V.J. Berthre de Bourniseaux' *L'Histoire de Louis XVI avec les anecdotes de son règne,* Paris, 1829, II, p. 359. In the background, the chateau of Versailles is seen under a foggy grey winter sky; in the foreground, the simple, snow-covered cottages of the villagers frame the narrative. Louis XVI has left his retinue in order to attend to the needs of the poor in this neighboring hamlet. He apparently has just given a gold coin to the little girl, presented to him by her mother, and is still touching the child's cheek. He now turns his attention to an older family who have emerged from the cottage at the right. He gives a purse of money to the old woman, whose aged husband—a soldier who still wears a military medallion and who salutes the king—is supported by their daughter. In the left foreground, a young peasant has set down a bundle of faggots and respectfully removes his hat while supporting himself with his hatchet. Behind, a villager climbs a ladder in order to have, like the man who waves from an attic window, a better view of the king. In the righthand corner, a snow-covered plough lies idle.

Hersent's painting is characteristic of the propagandistic image of Louis XVI conspicuous at the Salon of 1817, which included another painting of the King's kindness to peasants, the restoration of coastal property to the residents of La Guyenne in 1786 (Salon no. 55, Nicolas Berthon, *Trait de justice de S. M. Louis XVI,* Versailles). This effort to associate the Bourbon dynasty with virtuous deeds is supported by a rich tradition, composed not only of images of Greco-Roman and Christian charity, but by their modern translations into anonymous acts of generosity recorded by Greuze, or the abundant pictorial records of Napoleon's acts of mercy to both soldiers and civilians. Already in 1785, Philibert-Louis Debucourt had painted a *Trait d'humanité de Louis XVI* (Versailles), in which the King is represented giving alms to the poor.

Moreover, the presentation of a harmonious society of humble peasants perpetuated late 18th-century traditions that would venerate the goodness and simplicity of agricultural life both in the modern and the classical world and that were to reach their fullest statement in the art of Jean-François Millet.

Critics of the Salon verbally underlined the work's clearly political intentions. C. P. Landon reminded spectators that no family was more virtuous than the Bourbons; M. M*** recalled how Louis XVI would secretly leave his palace to help the poor; and Gault de Saint-Germain associated the King with the benevolence of Marcus Aurelius, Titus and Trajan. To emphasize these political continuities, Hersent seemed to stress the physical resemblance between Louis XVI and his brother, Louis XVIII.

Like the subject, Hersent's composition is rich in historical allusions, recalling not only such Raphael figure groups as the *Delivery of the Keys to Saint Peter,* but the many variations upon these groups used for Greuzian and Napoleonic narrative painting. The repertory of peasants (of which the elderly couple reminded the Salon critic M. M*** of Philemon and Baucis) is clearly indebted in costume and expression to the *dramatis personae* of Greuze and his disciples, yet another aspect of the revival of 18th-century art under the Restoration.

PROVENANCE
Commissioned in 1816 for the Galerie de Diane, Tuileries (Arch. Nat. O³ 1395-96); paid for in 1816 and 1817 (Arch. Nat. O³ 1390, 1393); collection of Louis XVIII; M. R. 3546 (INV. 5326, no. 223).

EXHIBITION
1817, Salon, no. 414.

REFERENCES
Journal des Débats, 28 May 1817; *Journal de Paris,* 30 May 1817; C.-P. Landon, 1817, pp. 53-54, ill. 35-36; Sans-Gêne and

Cadet-Buteux, 1817, p. 58; P.-M. Gault de Saint-Germain, 1817, pp. 17-18; M***, 1817, pp. 112-115; H. (O. M.), 1817, p. 45; *Galerie de... la Duchesse de Berry,* 1822, v. II, ill. 88, n.p.; Ch. Gavard, 1838, v. II, series IV, no. 453, pp. 170-171; E. Soulié, 1859, v. I, p. 55, no. 223; L. Rosenthal, 1900, p. 79; R. Rosenblum, 1967a, pp. 101-102, ill. 107. G. and J. Lacambre, 1972, p. 340, ill. p. 341.

RELATED WORKS

First idea for the picture, a painting (canvas; 64 × 80) that belonged to the Duchesse de Berry; lithographed by d'Hardiviller in *Galerie de... la Duchesse de Berry* (see References above); two engravings by Pierre Adam and Auguste Blanchard.

R. R.

Jean-Pierre-Louis-Laurent Houel

1735 Rouen - Paris 1813

A pupil in Rouen of Jean-Baptiste Descamps, Houel came to Paris in 1755 and was trained in engraving in the studio of Le Bas and Jean-Michel Moreau (the Younger). After 1764, he worked with A. Casanova and associated with the artistic and aristocratic circles of the capital. From the Duc de Choiseul he received the commission for four overdoors for the Château de Chanteloup (1769, Tours). Granted a stipend by the King, Houel was in Italy from 1769 to 1772 with the Marquis d'Havrincourt. He brought back many topographical views (two examples dated 1772 at Besançon). After his return to Paris he became *agréé* at the Academy in 1774 and left again for Sicily and southern Italy, where he remained from 1776 until 1779. Here he produced numerous gouaches (46 in the Louvre, 260 in the Hermitage purchased by Catherine II from 1781 on). These are of documentary interest as models for the 246 plates in his *Voyage pittoresque des isles de Sicile, de Malte et de Lipari...,* which appeared in four volumes between 1782 and 1787 and were contemporary with the *Voyage pittoresque ou description du royaume de Naples et de Sicile* by the Abbé de Saint-Non (1781-86). Houel exhibited at the Salons of 1775, 1781, 1789, 1791 and 1808 and did several views of Normandy: *L'ancienne Porte cauchoise, Vue de la "Chaise de Gargantua"* (gouaches, Rouen).

During and after the Revolution, his activity waned; he published in 1798 an *Histoire des éléphants de la ménagerie nationale et relation de leur voyage à Paris* and in 1803 an *Histoire naturelle des deux éléphants mâle et femelle du muséum de Paris, venus de Hollande en France, en l'an VI.* His only real title to glory lies, then, in the gouaches from Italy, where his precision in the handling of landscape and architecture warrents comparison with other minor masters such as Victor-Jean Nicolle.

J. V.

101
*View of the Entrance to a Cave**

Vue de l'entrée et de l'intérieur d'une cave taillée dans le roc servant d'entrepôt de sel à Dieppedalle près de Rouen
Plate p. 94
Canvas; 63 × 95
Rouen, Musée des Beaux-Arts

Probably executed in September 1789, during one of the artist's trips to Normandy, this painting was described by Houel himself:

I painted a curious scene there, which was destroyed a few years later in the confusion of the Revolution.

It concerned the way in which at Dieppedalle the salt storage houses of the general farm were used. At that time, these existed in very large grottoes, scooped out of the dry rock of this region, where the accumulated salt, well compressed from top to bottom, was held in reserve. Both doors and windows were thus completely filled with salt. There were many rather deep grottoes that were filled like warehouses during certain seasons, to be emptied during others. The river, near these salty caverns, was filled either with the vessels which brought this salt or with those which transported it to distant places. The river, at this point, often had the feeling of a small seaport. You may see in the painting this memory which I shall never forget. I have painted the way in which the men, having climbed up on top of the rocks of condensed salt in the grottoes, dig it, scar it and make it fall along the vertical well, where the others take it and throw it in the *tramies* (?) numbering five, which, after receiving it, drop this salt into bushels or large measures, without letting the salt accumulate. Other men take these large measures, putting them in an equal number of large sacks, after a man with a rake, brings down the surplus. The men who hold the sack fasten it, while others, as we see, are loading it on a barrow or boat and others are waiting and carrying, while still others are arriving for the same purpose. And, before leaving the grotto, the clerks give tickets or chits to the porters to certify what they have taken and to prove that as many sacks have left the storehouse as had entered it. This

operation, when it was in working order, provided for as many as hundred people in this area... (M. Vloberg, 1930, pp. 185-186).

Houel's particular affection for rupestral sites is also evident in his Sicilian gouaches, e.g. *La Grotte des eaux au théâtre de Syracuse* and *L'oreille de Denys à Syracuse* (Louvre), as well as in his views of Normandy, e.g. *Les grottes de Caumont* (two gouaches in Rouen; E. Minet, mus. cat., 1911, nos. 1032 and 1033). In the present picture, executed in particularly delicate harmonies, the topographical description is combined with a number of anecdotal details which, unusual in Houel's œuvre, bring it closer to a genre scene than to a pure landscape.

PROVENANCE
Gift of the artist in 1808 (INV. 808-1-2).

EXHIBITION
1948, Rouen, no. 67.

REFERENCES
J.-B. Descamps, mus. cat., 1809, no. 79; E. Minet, mus. cat., 1911, no. 598; M. Nicolle, n.d., p. 13; M. Vloberg, 1930, p. 126, pp. 185-186, ill. LXII; O. Popovitch, mus. cat., 1967, p. 63.

J. V.

Jean-Baptiste Huet

1745 Paris 1811

The son of an artisan painter in the service of the King, Huet was first a pupil of the animal painter Charles Dagomer, his uncle by marriage, and later studied with Jean-Baptiste Le Prince. Received into the Academy as an animal painter in 1769 with *Dogue se jetant sur des oies* (Louvre), he exhibited at the Salon for almost 20 years. He was best known for his pastoral and shepherd scenes in the taste of François Boucher. He did not meet with success as a history painter even though he presented a large *Hercule et Omphale* at the Salon of 1779. He returned to painting landscapes filled with animals and, less frequently, small-scale gallant subjects, such as *Ce qui est bon à prendre est bon à garder*, 1786 (Paris, sale, Hôtel Drouot, Room I, 18 December 1967, unnumbered, and engraved by Alexandre Chaponnier). A prolific draughtsman,

he himself engraved or had engraved numerous studies; this part of his œuvre, perhaps the most interesting, seems to have occupied him exclusively during the Revolution, since he stopped exhibiting at the Salon. In addition to these studies, he designed models for the silk industry in Jouy (some of which were exhibited at Mulhouse in 1970). He again exhibited at the Salon from 1800 to 1802 (animal paintings and landscapes), but spent the rest of his life in almost complete obscurity. Huet's historian, C. Gabillot, justifiably preferred his animal representations, in which the artist avoided the tedious imitation of François Boucher and sought the more enriching inspiration of Jean-Baptiste Oudry.

A. S.

102
Spaniel Attacking a Turkey[*]

Épagneul attaquant un dindon
Plate p. 97
Canvas; 65 × 97; s.d.u.r. *J.B. Huet, 1789*
Leningrad, The Hermitage Museum

The violent opposition between animals, a theme related to that of the hunt, was often treated by Huet in the spirit of his great predecessor Jean-Baptiste Oudry. In addition to his acceptance piece for the Academy, there is another youthful work: *Renard dans le poulailler* (1766, San Francisco; same subject at the Salon of 1769). Not without success, J.-B. Huet here attempts a new approach to the subject by ennobling his painting through the adaptation of a somewhat fantastic antique relief, as Mlle Simone Deyts has pointed out. The painting is a striking example of the classicizing mode, even in a subject which would seem to be inappropriate.

PROVENANCE
Entered the museum in 1919, confiscated with the Roudanovsky Collection, Petrograd.

REFERENCES
L. Réau, 1929, no. 133, p. 32; mus. cat., 1958, v. I, p. 351.

A. S.

Paul Huet

1803 Paris 1869

The son of a family from Rouen, Paul Huet was born in Paris, 3 October 1803, the same year as Gabriel Alexandre Decamps, Eugène Isabey and C.-J.-E. Roqueplan. Somewhat younger than J.-B. Corot, Achille-Etna Michallon, Eugène Delacroix and C.-F.-I. d'Aligny (b. 1798), he preceded an entire generation of landscape painters, who for the most part exemplify the "school of 1830," i.e., Diaz (b. 1807), Troyon (b. 1810), Dupré (b. 1811), Rousseau and Cabat (b. 1812), Millet and Ravier (b. 1814), and Daubigny (b. 1817). During his stay in Pierre-Narcisse Guérin's studio and subsequent years (1818-23) with Antoine-Jean Gros and at the École des Beaux-Arts (where he was enrolled from 1820 to 1824), he showed little enthusiasm for classical instruction; he was attracted, rather, by Rubens, Rembrandt, the Dutch, and the contemporary painters Vernet, Charlet and especially Géricault. Encounters with Richard Bonington (Gros' pupil from 1820) and Delacroix (whom he met c. 1823) proved fruitful. Delacroix was to remain his friend and protector, and Huet delivered his funeral elegy in 1863.

Also, however, from childhood, he had sought direct contact with nature, primarily during frequent sojourns with his friend the painter Lelièvre on the Ile Seguin (below Paris), whose then deserted trees and banks constituted one of the recurrent themes in Huet's œuvre.

All his life Huet traveled with increasing frequency, often motivated by his fragile health, in Normandy, the environs of Paris, in Auvergne, etc. The impressions he brought back gave birth to his principal compositions, often realized only much later. The *Vue des environs de La Fère,* the only one of his painting to be accepted in the Salon of 1827, the first in which he exhibited, has disappeared. Among the earlier works (in addition to the studies), the best known is a *Cavalier* (also called *Le retour du grognard*), which might date to 1821. In 1829, he executed two large compositions: *Vue du Château d'Arques* and *Vue générale de Rouen,* exhibited the following year at the diorama in the rue Montesquieu, under the auspices of the Duchesse de Berry (destroyed; two reduced versions, one dating to 1840 at the Orléans museum, the other, 1831, at the

Rouen museum). Sainte-Beuve, in *Le Globe,* 23 October 1830, granted these works the eulogy of one of his rare art critiques.

The remainder of Huet's career, which goes beyond the scope of the current exhibition (he died 8 January 1869), is marked by numerous trips, notably to Italy (1841; *Vue de Spolète,* Louvre), in the Pyrenees (1843-1846), where he met with Delacroix, Roqueplan, and Devéria, and finally to England (1862), and to Belgium and Holland (1864). Named drawing teacher to the Duchesse d'Orléans in 1836, he was officially ignored under the Empire and like Corot, owed only to Delacroix's support his award of a supplementary medal at the Exposition Universelle of 1855 (where he exhibited, among other works, his masterpiece: *L'Inondation à Saint-Cloud* [Louvre], the conception of which might date from 1822).

A refined and cultivated spirit—his writings and correspondence, published by his son René-Paul Huet in 1911, bear witness to a lively curiosity and clear thinking; the value of his art criticism is little recognized—Paul Huet was involved in literary circles, and

Michelet, Sainte-Beuve, and Hugo, as well as the critics Gustave Planche (who, at the Salon of 1831, mentioned Turner in relation to Huet—40 years before Monet and Pissarro claimed the connection—as well as Poussin and Claude) and Baudelaire, gave him the praise his fellow painters often denied him. An independent, he received scarcely any official encouragement and was subject to more than one refusal from the Salons. The originality of his work and the freedom of his language are striking; he has been called the "restorer of the French school of landscape painting," the "most romantic of the romantics," and also the "Delacroix of landscape painting." In addition, Paul Huet does not align himself entirely either with the Barbizon painters—as closely as he appears to do in his "forest interiors"—nor, despite, the search for a monumental equilibrium which characterizes his large views from the time of the Italian trip (1841), with the advocates of *paysage composé*. To see him as a "precursor of impressionism" would confer a now rather bankrupt honor.

S. L.

103
Guardian's House in the Forest of Compiègne

Maison de garde en forêt de Compiègne
Plate p. 283
Canvas; 116 × 148; s.d.l.r. *Paul Huet 1826*
Paris, Michel Legrand Collection

The earliest extant large landscape of Paul Huet, this painting preceded his first appearance at the Salon by one year. It shows the young artist vividly impressed by English precedents; John Constable had come to the Salon of 1824 and had had a triumphant success with his *Haywain,* which played an undeniably stimulating role in the genesis of French romantic landscape painting. But it also responds to Huet's fondest aspiration: to create a "landscape-state of the soul," of feeling (the primacy of a powerful nature, animated by a mysterious life), realizing and continuing the old Dutch tradition of Hobbema and Rembrandt. At this time (1826), such concepts could claim the merit of originality. In this work, however, the artist had not yet developed a broad and generous technique; thus, it would be misleading to compare it with the historic landscape

style then in full force and conclude that the painting prophesied a liberated and already impressionist approach. Paul Huet, who was to push further the heroic dramatization of nature (*La Grande Marée d'équinoxe,* 1861, Louvre) and the exaltation of its mystery (*Intérieur de forêt,* 1852, Louvre), demonstrated an early predilection for this rich source of inspiration. Its beginnings are evident here, but up to the end he searched for the proper language.

PROVENANCE

Engraved by the artist in 1833. Sollier Collection (a longstanding friend and one of the artist's foremost correspondents; see R.-P. Huet, 1911, p. 103) at La Flèche, in 1869 (Burty). Dr. Sollier Collection in 1911 (exh. 1911, Paris). Galerie André Watteau (1971-1972).

EXHIBITION
1911, Paris, École des Beaux-Arts, no. 6.

REFERENCES
Ph. Burty, 1869, pp. 12, 58-59, 108; G. Lafenestre, 1911, p. 840; G. Pillement, 1974, p. 117, ill. p. 116.

RELATED WORKS
La maison de garde, etching of the painting, reversed and with

some variations, 1833 (Delteil, 1911, no. 9, ill.), not to be confused with the rather similar etching with a vertical format: *Maison du garde, forêt de Compiègne* (Delteil, 1911, no. 18; cf. Burty, 1869, frontispiece and pp. 56-57). Burty (1869, p. 134, no. 270 of the "list of principal drawings") also mentions, "*Maison de garde, Compiègne ;* watercolor gone over with gouache, 1860."

S. L.

Jean-Auguste-Dominique Ingres

1780 Montauban - Paris 1867

Encouraged from an early age by his father, himself a painter, sculptor and architect in Montauban, Ingres entered the Academy of Toulouse in 1791 under the painter Guillaume-Joseph Roques, a pupil of Vien in Rome and of the sculptor Vigan. During these years, Ingres studied the violin diligently and played in the Orchestre du Capitole in Toulouse. In 1796, he was second violinist, disproving the legend that he was a simple amateur. Some early drawings after antique casts have been preserved (see P. Hattis, *Ingres' Sculptural Style,* exh. cat., Cambridge, Mass., Fogg Museum of Art, 1973).

In August 1797, Ingres, along with young Roques, the son of his first Toulouse master, left for Paris to go into the studio of David. Ingres placed second in Prix de Rome in 1800 with his version of *Antiochus et Scipion* (the first prize going to J.-P. Granger, another pupil of David) and was already showing his unique talent in a nude study, *Torse d'homme,* with rather sharp outlines, preserved at the École des Beaux-Arts in Paris. In 1801, he finally won the Prix de Rome with *Les Ambassadeurs d'Agamemnon* (Paris, École des Beaux-Arts). John Flaxman, in Paris at the time, very much admired this work. Circumstances prevented Ingres attending the Academy in Rome, which he did not join until five years later.

As compensation, he received an annual stipend and a studio in the old Capuchin monastery in Paris. He became friendly with Antoine-Jean Gros, Anne-Louis Girodet, François-Marius Granet and Lorenzo Bartolini, whose portrait he painted in 1806 (a life-interest gift to the Musée de Montauban). He had already received official commissions such as *Bonaparte à Liège,* 1803-1804 (Liège) and the *Portrait of Napoleon on his Imperial Throne* (No. 104). His provocative

originality, which his contemporaries regarded as "archaic," was as evident in this painting as it was in the three famous Rivière portraits (Louvre), which scandalized the critics of the Salon of 1806 and clearly showed his preference for gothic, unconventional and ultra-linear stylization. In September 1806, Ingres finally arrived in Rome, where he stayed until 1820, extending by about ten years his official stay at the Villa Medici under the directorship first of Joseph-Benoît Suvée and then of Charles Thévenin. Among the many graphic and pictorial works which characterize Ingres' prolific Roman period are several large decorative canvases commissioned by Napoleon for the Quirinale Palace: *Ossian* (Montauban) and *Romulus vainqueur d'Acron* (Louvre, on loan from the École des Beaux-Arts, Paris) and the paintings he sent from Rome, including his chef-d'œuvre, *Jupiter and Thetis* (No. 105). An active French colony in Rome, which included many functionaries from the Imperial administration, was the pretext for a stunning group of portraits which often have delicate landscape backgrounds (a motif he later dropped), and a striking sense of reality at once stylized and pure: *Granet* (Aix), *Cordier* and *Bochet* (Louvre), *Marcotte,* one of Ingres' great friends and correspondents (Washington, National Gallery) *Norvins* (London, National Gallery), *Devillers* (Zurich, Bührle Foundation), *Moltedo* (New York, Metropolitan Museum of Art), *Desdeban* (Besançon), *Cortot* (Algiers, currently on loan to the Louvre), *Mme Devaucay* (Chantilly). Married in 1813 and in serious financial straits brought about by the fall of the Empire and the partial withdrawal of the French from Rome, Ingres specialized after 1814 in fascinating portraits in graphite which, while done as commercial ventures, are today considered among his greatest works. The English colony, among others in Rome, provided Ingres with a number of models, such as *Lady J. Mackie,* London, Victoria and Albert Museum), *Les jeunes sœurs Montaigu* (London, private collection). Thanks to Charles Thévenin and Blacas, Ingres received official commissions: romantic themes for the throne room at Versailles first ordered in 1817 (*Roger and Angelica,* No. 107), large religious paintings for the Trinità dei Monti (No. 108) in Rome, and for the Montauban Cathedral (*Le Vœu de Louis XIII,* 1820-24). Between 1820 and 1824, Ingres was in Florence, perhaps because of the research necessitated by the Montauban Cathedral painting and because of his close friendship with the sculptor Bartolini (another portrait of him by Ingres, which is in the Louvre, dates from 1820). From the period 1815-25 date some of his most delightful explorations of the *style troubadour,* in which his vibrant and unusual color, as well as his taste for haunting and sinuous line, work wonders: *Paolo et Francesca,* 1819, Angers), *Raphaël et la Fornarina* (Baltimore, Walters Art Gallery), *Le Duc d'Albe* (Montauban), *La Chapelle Sixtine* (Louvre and Washington, National Gallery), *Death of Leonardo da Vinci* (No. 106) and *Henri IV jouant avec ses enfants* (Paris, Petit Palais).

Returning to Paris at the end of 1824, Ingres finally acknowledged his great reputation. His *Vœu de Louis XIII* triumphed at the Salon of that year, and the artist received the Legion of Honor, entered the Institute, opened a studio which was soon to flourish (and which was described by the young Amaury-Duval in a delightful book, *L'Atelier d'Ingres,* which appeared in 1878). He won official recognition with *L'Apothéose d'Homère,* commissioned in 1826 for one of the ceilings of the Musée Charles X in the Louvre (Salon of 1827) and by his being named a professor at the École des Beaux-Arts, Paris. The rest of the painter's career after 1830 belongs to another phase of the 19th century, divided between another stay in Rome (1835-41), this time as director of the Villa Medici, with periodical quarrels with the critics. Ingres always presented himself as isolated and misunderstood in the mold of his art, a *"Chinois égaré dans Athènes,"* according to the apt phrase of Préault, and a succession of chefs-d'œuvre which overwhelmingly extend beyond the framework of their era: *L'Age d'or,* 1842-49 (Château de Dampierre), *Mme Moitessier,* 1856 (London, National Gallery), *Le Bain turc,* 1859-63 (Louvre), etc.

J. F.

104
Portrait of Napoleon I on his Imperial Throne

"Sa Majesté l'Empereur sur son trône" or *Napoléon Ier sur le trône impérial*
Plate p. 193
Canvas; 260 × 163; s.d.l.l. *Ingres Pxit/Anno 1806*
Salon of 1806, no. 202
Paris, Musée de l'Armée, Hôtel des Invalides

Shortly after 1804, Ingres received the flattering commission for the official portrait of Napoleon I in imperial robes to be placed in the Corps Législatif. This was proof of his instant fame. In contrast to the Liège version, painted in 1804, which stresses the First Consul's wisdom, in this work the strong feeling for the majesty of this eternal idol, a Byzantine Pantokrator, has always been a striking element. In addition, the painting is more effective and modern, Rosenblum notes, than the portaits of King Charles X by Gérard, which were done in the traditional pictorial formula of Van Dyck, to the point that there have been doubts (most unjustified) about the signature and attribution

of the Ingres. Monod echoed this doubt in 1912 (without proving his provision), and in 1972 P. Cabanne even relates that young Georges Wildenstein, then an orderly doing his military service at the Invalides, cleaned and rediscovered the signature and the date, 1806. In fact, the painting actually had never been lost from sight (Delaborde in 1872 and Lapauze in 1911 cited it in their monographs), but the recent restoration in 1967 as well as the exhibition on the Petit Palais have fully restored its status. The Emperor is faithfully represented in coronation robes. He holds the famous imperial regalia (Louvre), the scepter of Charles V, the hand of justice and the sword said to be Charlemagne's. These *Honneurs de Charlemagne* had been wholly restored if not, in fact, completely manufactured by Biennais for the occasion of the Coronation in 1804, notably the hand which certainly seems to be an absolute forgery (see D. Gaborit-Chopin's last statement on this subject: "Faux ivoires des collections publiques [françaises]," *Revue de l'art*, no. 21, 1973, p. 99). How can one not be conscious here of the purposely archaizing content of the Napoleonic ceremony, which is deeply compatible with Ingres' basically anti-classical style? Similarly, the bees, Frankish in origin, have been revived here as modern symbols of industry and work. Rosenblum is correct in his observation concerning the failure of the same in Ingres' painting of Charles X (1829; Bayonne), king by divine right but scarcely credible as a monarch. The frontal pose of the Emperor derives, of course, from an antique source: A. Mongan (1944, p. 409) has suggested an engraved Roman gem in the *Recueil* of Caylus (1762, I, pl. XLVI), a reference work on antiquity most frequently consulted by interested persons and artists of the period. According to Caylus, this gem represents a Jupiter, derived from the famous Zeus of Phidias. Ingres took this same figure, reversed it and substituted the hand of justice for the thunderbolt. The eagle of Jupiter was transformed into this magnificent "nazi" eagle which decorates the carpet and is at the same time abstract and tactile, one of the most astonishing passages of pure painting of the Ingres' world, but where one admires also that the artist was able to slip in an oblique reference to the venerated *Madonna della Sedia* of Raphael in place of the sign of Virgo (carpet medallion at the extreme left)—never noticed until E. Camesasca's astute observation in 1967. Moreover, Ingres was in the habit of doing this: in his portrait of M. Rivière (Louvre) exhibited in the same salon, he placed on the table an engraving of the same Madonna, and he repeated it in his *Henri IV jouant avec ses enfants* (1817, Paris, Petit Palais).

Such a provocative and baffling painting could only serve to antagonize the critics: from Fabien Pillet in the *Revue Philosophique*: "Since M. Ingres wanted to cause people to talk about him, no matter how, we should not become shocked at the bizarre *manière* which he has adopted...[to win approval from the art world] required a more elegant pose and better arranged draperies; the head of the hero had to be less pale and a better likeness, and finally, the picture would have to be less harsh," to the author of the *Publiciste*: "It is difficult to paint such a disagreable picture with such an experienced and trained brush... M. Ingres... must leave this path where he is going astray"; from the *Observateur au Musée Napoléon*: "A well-painted picture, precious details, but the face is too heavy-set and the foreshortening is not good; the head is too pale and the ressemblance is not close," to the editor of the *Lettres impartiales*: "[It] seems to be painted with moonbeams... The trip to Rome and a study of the portraits of Veronese, Titian and Correggio will most likely draw the artist away from the dry, stiff style which he seems to have adopted and will warm his colors." it is a chorus of incomprehension, where some jealousy could also creep in with respect to such a gifted young artist, and this culminates in the quatrain of the *Flâneur au Salon* on M. *Bonhomme* which expresses the regret that, like Alexander the Great, Napoleon did not forbid portraits of himself. Is this to say, then, that this extraordinary deification of the sovereign achieved by Ingres was far too advanced for the state of mind of this era, which had just overthrown the old Bourbon monarchy, symbolically annihilating it by executing Louis XVI? The most famous criticism and the one which most irritated Ingres was that by Chaussard in the *Pausanias français* which called the artist "gothic" and brillantly developed this idea: "M. Ingres intends nothing less than to move art back four centuries, to take us back to the beginning, to revive the style of Jan de Bruges." This allusion to Van Eyck was to hit home with Ingres. From Rome, Ingres again wrote to M. Forestier on 23 November 1806: "I admire Van Eyck and although I would like to resemble him in many ways, he is not the painter or master whom I would like to most imitate, and I believe, therefore, that they have cited him at random." Everything considered and despite Ingres himself, there exists, a strong connection with Van Eyck and the fascinating realism of Ingres, as shown by Rosenblum (1967b, pp. 26-27, 68; *idem*, 1969, p. 101): witnessing here the tiny reflection of the window on the polished ivory globe on the arm rest on the left (as on the arm of the chair in the portrait of M. *Bertin* in the Louvre, on the handle of the cane of M. *Bochet* in the Louvre, on the vase of flowers of *Paolo et Francesca* in Angers) or even on the subtle reflection of the scorpion in the rug in the gilt socle of the throne. Ingres always liked large, smooth surfaces that reflected light: ivory, metal, pearls, mosaic; but also Van Eyckian is the "dense array of bejeweled and gilded magenta velvet and white ermine that truly rivals Van Eyck's *God the Father* for sumptuous, heavenly splendor" (Rosenblum, 1967b, p. 68) as is featured in the Ghent altarpiece itself exhibited in the Louvre from 1799 to 1815 and which could not fail to become part of the "imaginary museum" of the young Ingres, who included in his own collection a Van Eyckian primitive (*Moine*, Musée de Montauban). Thus, heterogeneous elements are combined—a Phidian Jupiter and Van Eyck's heavily draped Christian God, in a frontal pose comparable to that of Napoleon; this characterizes very well the voluntary, recurrent but still completely liberating style of Ingres: "Had Ingres attempted to paint Dagobert or any other early king of the earliest dynasty [a revealing allusion to the Frankish period, in which there was new interest] he could not have chosen more gothic ornaments, or given the figure a more coldly symmetrical pose," declared a critic of the *Mercure de France* in 1806 (cited by Rosenblum, 1967b, p. 68). D. Ternois finally underlined the "Byzantine" aspect in the archaism of Ingres by mentioning a tracing preserved in the Musée de Montauban (see Momméja, 1905, no. 38) on which Ingres reproduced the engraving of an ivory diptych where an Emperor from the Orient is seated on his throne, flanked by his two sons—a possible source of the iconography of the present portrait. A mind as cultivated and intelligent as that of Gérard had the same reaction before the painting of Ingres, if one believes the evidence presented by P.-N. Bergeret (*Lettres d'un artiste sur l'état des arts de France*, Paris, 1848, p. 73) and cited by D. Ternois (1967), and then by Rosenblum (1969, p. 102): "After the figure of Notre-Dame-de-Lorette in all her finery, that is what I found most beautiful." One knows that this famous Virgin of the Santa Casa de Loretto, supposedly sculpted by Saint Luke, and covered with gold and precious stones, her head encircled with a triple crown, and a scepter in her hand, had been brought to Paris during the Revolution and displayed since 1798 in the Cabinet des Médailles. Returned to the Pope in 1815, the statue burned in 1921 but a copy still exists in Loretto—the statue is yet another possible archaic reference to nourish the drawing of Ingres, who achieved here his most disconcerting and, in a word, most "revolutionary" powers.

PROVENANCE

Commissioned by the Corps Législatif (now the Palais Bourbon); transferred to the Louvre around 1815, held in reserve at the Louvre under the Restoration and inventoried as MR 2069—inventory of the Musées Royaux; deposited in 1832 at the Hotel Royal des Invalides and from there transferred to the present Musée de l'Armée (on deposit at the Invalides, see the letter dated 25 August 1832, signed by Forbin, director of the Musées Royaux, and approved by Louis-Philippe on 29 August (preserved in the Louvre archives: P 12 1832, 25 August; D. Ternois in Ingres, exh. cat., 1967, p. 32, published *in extenso* this important letter, which, until that time, had never been published. Restored on the occasion of the 1967 exhibition (INV. 5420).

EXHIBITIONS

1806, Salon, no. 202; 1867, Paris, no. 102; 1911, Paris, no. 9; 1912, Saint-Petersburg, no. 611; 1921, Paris, no. 10; 1939, New York, 1967; Paris, no. 17, ill.; 1972, London, no. 147.

REFERENCES

For bibliography prior to 1967, see the very complete notice of D. Ternois in the exh. cat., 1967; to this are to be added F. Monod, 1912, p. 301 (with several successful descriptions: "the colossal chryselephantine idol of the Musée de l'Armée, the sick Jupiter," "the innocent and daring appearance of that face of Caesar the very day of the coronation, already pale with passivity like the Napoleon of The 100 Days [or rather the mask of an idol, removed from time ?]," "extraordinary parade-piece, a cartoon ready-made for tapestries or stained glass"; and R. Rosenblum, 1967b, p. 68 and color ill. 7. Since 1967, M. Méras, 1969, p. 118; R. Rosenblum, 1969, pp. 101-102; D. Ternois and E. Camesasca, 1971, no. 37, color ill. XV; P. Cabanne, 1972, p. 33; H. Toussaint, 1972, no. 147, p. 98.

RELATED WORKS

Pen and ink sketch, India ink and sepia wash; s.l.r. *Ingres*, Lefuel Collection (H. Delaborde, 1870, no. 382; reproduced on the cover of *Monde illustré*, no. 3305, Saturday, 23 April 1921).
Another drawing in graphite, Paris, private collection (Paris, exh. cat., 1952, no. 153). Six detail drawings in graphite, in the Ingres bequest to Montauban (D. Ternois, 1959, figs. 149-154; studies of the hand of justice, the sceptre of Charles V, the bees of the mantle, etc.).

J. F.

105
Jupiter and Thetis

Jupiter et Thétis
Plate p. 214
Canvas; 327 × 260; s.d.l.r. on the pedestal *INGRES | Rome 1811* (with the N reversed)
Aix-en-Provence, Musée Granet

As far back as 1806, Ingres, who had just recently arrived in Rome, began to think of *Jupiter and Thetis* as subject matter for a painting for his *Envoi de Rome*. "I feel that the theme from the *Iliad* where Thetis approaches Jupiter and kisses his knee and chin on behalf of her son Achilles (first verse of the *Iliad*) would be a fine subject and worthy of all my plans. I still do not go along with you concerning the details of this divine picture which should convey the feeling of ambrosia of the place, of the beauty of the characters, of their expressions and divine forms. I leave it up to you consider. Other than that, it should have such a physiognomy of beauty that everyone, even the mad dogs that wish to devour me, would be moved. I have the picture practically composed in my head and I can visualize it..." (letter to Forestier, 25 December 1806, cited by D. Ternois, 1967, no. 51). The Musée Ingres, Montauban, still has the edition of Homer (translation by Bitaube, 1787-88) in Ingres' possession and where he underlined in pencil the passage that related to the painting (I, pp. 155-156, cited by N. Schlenoff, 1956, p. 127, and D. Ternois, 1967, no. 51, p. 76). It is evident that Ingres has faithfully followed Homer's text: "Thetis, with one hand embracing his knees and the other hand next to Jupiter's chin, implores the monarch...." One encounters the confusion already made by Homer between the goddess of the waters Thetys, who was the daughter of Cellus and Vesta, wife of the Ocean, and our Thetis, who was the daughter of Nereus and Doris, wife of Peleus the mother of Achilles, and who was so beautiful that Jupiter would have wanted to marry her. This confusion, however, had already been protested in Chompré's classical *Dictionnaire de la Fable* (first edition, 1727). In the painting, the alleged sea origin of Thetis is recalled by the fish which decorates her diadem; she is "a creature of prodigal fluidity appropriate to her watery origin," which causes her to "slither like an eel around the immobile giant" (Rosenblum, 1967b, p. 84). On the left can be seen the jealous wife of Jupiter, Juno, for once wise and resigned (?), contrary to the curious and quite animated tracing in Montauban (Rome, 1968, no. 23, ill.). Camesasca rather loosely drew a comparison and likened Juno to the charming and frail *Jeune fille aux yeux bleus* (Laure Zoega?) from a private collection in Neuilly-sur-Seine (D. Ternois-E. Camesasca, no. 74, ill.).

In this veritable recreation of mythology, numerous references to antiquity have been summarized by Ternois (1967): the *Olympian Jupiter* of Phidias, known to Ingres through reconstruction in different media (antique marbles like those in the Museo Pio-Clementino, Vatican, or the one by Clarac, either casts or engravings) which he copied (drawing in Montauban). The long-haired, bearded head of the god is borrowed from the *Jupiter Otricoli* in the Vatican; but this did not prevent Ingres from studying the torso of a living model, a simple peasant, the drawing of which is preserved in Montauban (Boyer d'Agen, 1909, p. 324). The gigantomachy on the base of the throne is a copy of a Hellenistic cameo in Naples which is famous for having been reproduced by Caylus in his *Recueil d'Antiquités* of 1752-67 and of which Ingres acquired, at an undetermined date, a cast still preserved in Montauban. The figure of Thetis might relate to a statue in the Louvre, engraved as it was in 1820 (Clarac, 1820, pl. 120) to which Ingres refers in his Cahier IV, fol. 5. But, being in Rome, did he remember this statue? The striking linearism of this figure obviously indicates the inspiration of archaic Greek vases (*cf.* an example of a *Maenad* by the painter Kleophrades, c. 500 B.C, in Munich, with the same languid stylization which unites the head, nose and neck of Thetis in a single delightfully serpentine line; reproduced by Rosenblum, 1967b, fig. 19 and p. 23) or Flaxman's line engravings for the *Iliad* and the *Odyssey*. Similarly, Flaxman's engravings on the same theme already show a supplicating Thetis on her knees and in profile (like Jupiter, who is facing her; but Flaxman elsewhere represented

Jupiter frontally). Concerning his contemporaries, Ingres may also have had in mind Anne-Louis Girodet, who also frequently practiced the same voluptuous distortion (in his *Endymion* in the Louvre, 1793, and in his *Apothéose des guerriers français*, 1801, Malmaison) notes Ternois (1967, p. 76), or also perhaps a lost drawing by his friend Bartolini (Rosenblum, 1967b, p. 84), without forgetting the curious medical observation of Dr. Laignel-Lavastine (*Aesculape*, March 1929) concerning the pathology of the misfunctioning of the thyroid glands.

The violent reactions caused by this picture are not surprising; they are one more sign of the extraordinary stylistic originality of Ingres who, from the start, was always full of ideas for dealing with the ancient or archaic in a somewhat mannered yet original style, and who always managed not to treat traditional themes in a conventional way. "Is Hingres [*sic*] making fun of the world?" wrote Martin Drolling to his son, who was living at the Villa Medici in Rome. "We have [never before] seen such caricatures as [there are] in this picture... His pictures look like bad paintings by Lagrené [*sic*]" (cited by H. Lapauze, 1911, p. 100, and then by D. Ternois, 1967, p. 78, according to an autographed letter put up for sale in 1910). Reading further in the *Procès-Verbaux* of the *Envoi de Rome* to the Institute in Paris, signed by Lebreton, secretary of the fine arts class (H. Lapauze, *op. cit.*, p. 100; G. and J. Lacambre, 1967, p. 236), we find: "This artist seems to do his utmost to bring himself close to the period of the birth of painting rather than to penetrate the fine principles which are offered by the finest works of all the great masters of art." His archaizing tendencies always brought him censure, but nothing reveals more how much his art extended beyond his time and, finally, looked to the future. The *Procès-Verbaux* continues: "This painting... in general is lacking in dynamic spirit and profundity... [but his treatment of space and his stylizing manner are *abstract*]... he has no sense of mass; his color tones are weak and too even. The blue sky is all one harsh shade." Ingres' color, a little unreal and abstract, is intentionally flat, smooth and sometimes even harsh to the point of irritation: *Jupiter and Thetis* is a perfect example, with its pinks and pale greens in absolute contrast to the deep blue which fortunately reappeared after restoration in 1967. The *Procès-Verbaux* goes on to say: "The head of Jupiter does not at all suggest the idea of nobility, or power of the master of the gods, and the torso of this figure is excessively broad on top, while below the waist it is narrow. The

head of Thetis is bent forcibly back; one cannot guess which leg is attached to the right thigh. Juno's head, resting on a small white cloud, creates a dark spot which kills the lighting of the groups; she appears to be on the same plane as the figure of Thetis, and this does not produce a very pleasant effect." This absolute lack of understanding sought to deny that Ingres' purpose—certainly not out of inability, clumsiness or stylistic naïveté—was to regenerate and strongly impose a style and a personal focus, even if he had to go to extremes. Who would ever have imagined, before Ingres, a mythological dialogue like this, which shows "the terrifying grandeur of a supreme male deity and the seductive power of a female nude?" (Rosenblum, 1967b, p. 84). Who could repeat after him his realistic style, without falling into the historical reconstructions created in modern times by certain movie-makers.? An almost ironic and humorous note exists, moreover, in Ingres and is only one more trump in this great game of linear, poetic and formal seductions: for example, the play of the right foot of Thetis, which touches the left foot of Jupiter quite discreetly, while her other foot slithers in a serpent-like fashion off to the left, a detail carefully observed by Picon and Rosenblum. It is in this totally voluntary and liberated approach—so rich in surprising formal and abstract discoveries, and psychological insights as well—that Ingres' "prophetic" modernism resides, to use the proper word selected by Rosenblum (1967b, p. 21). The begging nymph Thetis, with her dreadfully saddened profile and her exaggerated curvilinear contour, is one of Ingres' most successful monsters (as Maurice Denis said in his *Théories*, 1910, p. 101, "But it is Ingres who made monsters!"). Does one not pass effortlessly from her to the modern and terrible supplicant in Picasso's *Guernica* (Rosenblum, 1967b, p. 24, fig. 20)? In *Jupiter and Thetis*, Ingres' anti-illusionism and anti-realism create wonders; he is the originator of new forms and an autonomous pictorial order which boldly challenged the old rules of realism concerning light, space and modeling to the benefit of a poetic universe, completely abstract and timeless, which will not come to an end.

PROVENANCE
"*Envoi de Rome* to the class of Fine Arts of the Institute," 1810, the last year Ingres was to be living at the Villa Medici, but executed with a certain delay owing to the illness of the painter in 1810, and only shipped from Rome in August 1811; he was still working on the finishing touches when the others were sent, according to Guillon-Lethière, director of the Academy (G. and J. Lacambre, 1967, p. 236; complete numerous points of the traditional historical account given

by Ternois, 1967, no. 22, p. 32). The painting arrived in Paris in November and was entrusted by Ingres to Granger and Marcotte for sale (see Ingres' letter to Marcotte dated 26 May 1814—J. Momméja, 1888, p. 739). According to administrative rulings, the picture should have been considered state property. The authorities of the French Academy in Rome as well as those of the Institute were fully aware of this, as was indicated by a complaint written between 1816 and 1819 concerning "pictures which should belong to the government," provided by the Villa Medici (Archives of the Academy of Fine Arts, G. and J. Lacambre, 1967, p. 236, no. 24). Finally acquired by the State (which in fact paid for it twice !) in 1834 for 6,000 francs and placed in the museum in Aix-en-Provence at the request of Granet, a friend of Ingres in Rome who, although at the time curator of Versailles, was originally from Aix. His collection, now in the Aix museum includes three works of Ingres: the celebrated *Portrait de Granet*, as well as an *Etude de vieillard* (Paris, 1967, no. 37, the *Envoi de Rome* he owed for the year 1808), a *Portrait d'homme barbu* (c. 1808, for *Œdipe et le Sphinx ?* ; Paris, 1967, no. 59). According to Schlenoff (1956, p. 110), Ingres would have preferred that his *Jupiter and Thetis* go to Toulouse. In exchange for the Ingres, the Aix museum returned Gros' *Fuite de Louis XVIII,* which went to Versailles. Cleaned for the 1967 exhibition (as a result, the rays of light around Jupiter's head once again became visible, the blue sky is more vivid, and the colors in general more intense).

EXHIBITIONS

1812, Paris; 1861, Marseille; 1867, Paris, no. 16; 1889, Paris, no. 439; 1911, Paris, no. 15; 1937, Paris, no. 349, ill. 71; 1967, Paris, no. 51, ill. (photo before restoration); 1968, Rome, no. 22, ill. (after restoration).

REFERENCES

For bibliography prior to 1968, see J. Foucart, 1968, no. 22, which completes that by D. Ternois, exh. cat., 1967, no. 51, to which can be added: K. Berger, 1959, p. 479; R. Rosenblum, 1967b, pp. 21-24, 84, ill. 18, color ill. 15; R. Rosenblum, 1969, pp. 101-102; D. Ternois and E. Camesasca, 1971, no. 67, color pl. XXII.

RELATED WORKS
Paintings:
Tête de Jupiter ; s.d. Rome, 1810, placed in Montauban by

the Louvre in 1954 (canvas on panel, 48 × 40, Ternois and Camesasca, 1971, no. 67b, ill.). Heavily touched up and enlarged by Ingres, when he sold it in 1866 to Eugène Lecomte. The picture returned from the furthest point of the French recovery in Germany after 1945. If the 1810 date is correct, it would allow one to say that the *Jupiter and Thetis* was, in fact, further along in 1810 than Ingres and his director would have implied. Another *Tête de Jupiter,* but in profile, private collection (canvas on panel, 48 × 40, Ternois and Camesasca, 1971, no. 67c, ill.). One of the many Ingres owned by Degas. Perhaps inspired by Flaxman, who represents a Jupiter in profile in his version of this Homeric theme (see Rosenblum, 1967b, fig. 86). *Tête de Jupiter* in an American private collection, circular format (canvas, diam. 32, Ternois and Camesasca, 1971, no. 171a, ill.). While Wildenstein (1954, no. 74) placed it around 1811, it is datable to 1864 and was painted for the drawing room of the architect Hittorf, a friend of Ingres, with a complete series of mythological *tondi*; this picture is simply a repetition with certain variation of the Aix *Jupiter.*

Drawings:

Unlike his other great pictures, such as the *Saint Pierre,* the *Vœu de Louis XIII* or the Antiochus, there is relatively little graphic material relating to the *Jupiter and Thetis:* seven drawings in the Ingres bequest at Montauban, of which two are reproduced in the Rome catalog, 1968, nos. 23 and 24: no. 23 is a drawing astonishingly close to Flaxman, in which Juno appears in the foreground crazed with jealous fury, her hair blowing in the wind, and flanked by a lion; she pulls at the garment of Thetis who is kneeling on the right (this idea was later left out by Ingres); no. 24 is a very fine study of an eagle incorrectly related by Momméja to the head of a hippogriffin in the *Roger et Angélique.* On several Montauban drawings, inscriptions written by Ingres reveal his research: "The necks of goddesses, beauty is associated with youth, Thetis half-draped, with her garment thrown over her left arm..." (Momméja, 1905, nos. 108, 3022, 3023). A drawing for Jupiter in Cambridge (England). A copy drawn by Ingres in 1848, in a private collection (N. Schlenoff, 1956, pl. XV). A line engraving by A. Réveil in *Magimel,* 1951, fig. 19.

J. F.

106
Death of Leonardo da Vinci

"François Ier reçoit les derniers soupirs de Léonard de Vinci"
Plate p. 256 and color pl. p. 27
Canvas; 40 × 50.5; s.d.l.l. INGRES. Pin^t. *1818.*
Salon of 1824, no. 924
Paris, Musée du Petit Palais

In the Salon of 1824, the painting was exhibited with another composition of a similar *troubadour* monarchist

subject: *Henri IV jouant avec ses enfants* (s.d. 1812; canvas, 39×49), which also entered the Petit Palais from the

Blacas Collection (see Provenance and Related Works). These two paintings by Ingres deal with a subject that is quite typical of the period (cf. Related Works) and are probably the artist's most perfect examples of historical genre painting—closer to genre than history painting, closer to Granet than to Delacroix. Ingres wanted to abandon this mode in favor of large paintings, according to his letter to Pastoret of 9 December 1824 (H. Naef and P. Angrand, 1970, p. 8), even though he expressed himself beautifully in these *imageries,* which are so delightful in their color and handling—i.e., *L'Entrée du dauphin à Paris* painted for Pastoret (see No. 111), different versions of *Paolo et Francesca* (Angers, Chantilly, Birmingham, Bayonne), *L'Arétin chez Tintoret* and *L'Arétin et l'envoyé de Charles Quint* (Belgium, private collection), *Raphaël et la Fornarina* (Riga museum before 1940; Columbus, Ohio; Cambridge, Mass.), *Don Pedro baisant l'épée d'Henri IV* (private collections in Paris and Oslo), *Le Duc d'Albe à Sainte Gudule* (Montauban), and *Philippe V décorant le maréchal Berwick* (Madrid, Alba Collection). Between 1815 and 1825, Ingres too often attempted such fine and tasteful paintings in the Dutch style (taking from Dou, Mieris, Metsu their lively colors, their porcelain-like treatment, their charming sense of intimacy). Thus, his small historical paintings have tended to be considered almost as whimsical exercices, secondary works executed simply for commercial purposes. But this is not the first time that one sees in an artist a discrepancy between what he says and does.

Ingres' patron, the Comte de Blacas (a duke after 1821), was a man of considerable individuality. He was French Ambassador to Naples, and then Rome, signatory of the Concordat de 1817, one of the heads of the "ultra" party which, with Polignac was to lead Charles X to ruin in 1830. He was also a courageous and lucid amateur of art who was responsible for having Louis XVIII buy the famous *Roger and Angelica* (No. 107) and for Ingres winning the commission for *Jesus Giving the Keys to Saint Peter* for the Trinità dei Monti (No. 108). (Ingres also painted for Blacas in 1817 a copy of the miniature by Saint representing Louis XVIII, but this small work, without any real importance, seems to have disappeared very early—D. Ternois and E. Camesasca, 1971, no. 96). These are the most complicated of all his historical compositions, but unlike the paintings of Louis XIV at the Comédie-Française or of Philippe IV, they are neither cluttered nor ridiculous. The paintings are distinguished by a clear and natural rhythm of line and mass and by their studied color schemes (yellows and crimsons in the *Death of Leonardo da Vinci* and a fascinating play of purples and oranges in *Henri IV jouant*). The *Henri IV* painting is a kind of Vermeerian treasure, another reference to the Dutch, as is true of all the *troubadour* painters of the period from Fleury Richard to Jean-Antoine Laurent, from Hippolyte Lecomte to Pierre-Henri Révoil. The reappearance in 1968 of this pair of paintings provided an exceptional opportunity for the Petit Palais (which at that time had no painting by Ingres in its collection) to acquire the pair.

At the Salon, while two pictures were noticed (the *Death of Leonardo da Vinci* attracted more attention than *Henri IV jouant*), it was Ingres' *Vœu de Louis XIII* which the art critics found most interesting. The serious writer of the *Journal des Débats,* E.-J. Delécluze considered that these two small pictures by Ingres, "will please, I am certain, those who truly love painting and who recognize in this art other elements which both seduce and attract rather than just a brilliant coloring and a dazzling effect"—a judgment which speaks directly his to 20th-century taste, which has been uninterested in anecdotal and sentimental content and appreciative of pure painting. One of the great charms of Dutch and *troubadour* painting is its exaltation of the pictorial elements in an anecdotal context which, by a true dialectic reversal, no longer has a narrative function as such (the opposite can also occur).

The critic of the *Débats* then analyzed, in a way no longer possible today, the ardent and profoundly moving attitude of François I, resigned to the approach of death and yet "uncertain that such a great genius can be extinguished forever." In the middle of the assembled group, "the king does not see or hear anything, he is alone, he is a man, a friend near his dying friend. The expression of this head has a certain quality that is singularly moving, as a result, one forgets to pays attention to the delicacy with the entire painting is handled." A. Jal, as always, made a fair judgment: "*The Philosopher:* this figure of François I is delightful— *The Artist:* and that of Leonardo ! what fine draughtsmanship, what admirable coloring, what delicacy of intention and execution in these two characters ! This work is ravishing, it can absolve Ingres from all his slips of genius, all his systematic aberrations." But Jal lampooned the *Henri IV,* which to him appeared absurd.

Concluding a discussion of Ingres' "gothic" archaism, which he found incomprehensible, he stated: "M. Ingres seems not to be of his century, he speaks to us in the language of Ronsard, and he is shocked that we do not understand him. Let us pity his deviation...."

And yet, here he curiously excluded the *Death of Leonardo,* which he praised very highly. *La Revue critique de productions de peinture...,* deploring what he called "vignette" painting done for the Devérias, the Chasselas, the Choquets, asked, "What is meant by this need to give us paintings which seem to want to appear old from their very birth, and to ask in this way for indulgence because of the effect of time?" Finally, Stendhal was ambiguous; he was certainly full of praise for the head of François I : "...among the finest and most beautiful historical heads which can be seen in this Salon. The expression of pain is combined with a perfect likeness of François I [actually one which derives from the famous Titian portrait in the Louvre and from the Cellini medallion] which the porcelain painters will henceforth have to copy when they reproduce this anecdote, whose only fault is that of not being exact." Since Stendhal really liked only David and great history paintings, one must ask if his reference to a return to porcelain painters is really a veiled form of praise. At least, it is to Stendhal's credit that he questioned the historical accuracy of the subject by referring to a letter from Melzi, the friend of Leonardo (perhaps in the painting to be identified as the dismayed young man with a Byronic face [B. Lossky, 1970, p. 17] who gestures with both arms to Leonardo and the King), in which the disciple announced to his Florentine brother: "François I shed tears upon learning of the death of Leonardo da Vinci, that is all." It is curious that Stendhal brought this text into the discussion; it had hardly been used in the great 19th-century controversy concerning the presence of François I at the deathbed of Leonardo, as Vasari reported in his *Vite* in 1551. Vasari was followed by Mariette in the 18th century and in 1805 by a contemporary of Ingres, Amaury-Duval *père,* in the work of P.-J. Baltard, *Paris et ses monuments* (with a slight historical error: he placed Leonardo's death in 1520 at Fontainebleau, whereas the death actually took place at the Château du Clos-Lucé near Amboise on 2 May 1519, an error repeated continually after the appearance of François-Guillaume Ménageot's painting of the subject in the Salon of 1781). Thanks to archival documents from the Chancellery of François I which were signed by the King on 1 May 1519 at Saint-Germain-en-Laye (the date and signature must also be questioned), Léon de Laborde in 1850 tried to reduce the moving account of Vasari to a "pious fraud"; as early as 1833, talking about Ménageot's composition, Ch. Landon had argued as Laborde would do later on. (On the controversy between Laborde

and Aimé Champollion and the latest restatement of this question by J. Adhémar in 1952, favorable to Vasari, see B. Lossky, 1967, p. 44.)

Returning to Ingres, one is saddened that the criticism of the time did not recognize this fine painting for what it was. Let us leave to Chauvin the task of defending Ingres against those who found that François I seemed in Ingres' painting to be *suffocating* Leonardo! Everything is organized in this painting as in the drawings, around the sublime motif of the King venerating the artist—from the puffed-up sleeves of François I and the falling drapery of the dying painter, to the curved arms of the chair, and even to the clothing of the young page, a game of plastic rhymes which answer, generate, develop and connect one to another. From the Louvre drawing to the painting, the only notable change that the signs of the Christian death of the painter (the monk, the crucifix) have been transferred from behind the bed to the foreground. Ingres also added in the background a symbolic Mona Lisa which only reinforces the ironic touch of the cardinal at the right, "so much imbued with his high dignity that no emotion of human order could make him come out of his haughtiness" (B. Lossky, 1970, p. 17)—an amusing naturalistic counterpoint in this serious painting, a touch Ingres had included before, as in the small Raphael Virgin in the rug of *Napoleon* (see No. 104).

PROVENANCE
Commissioned by the Comte de Blacas, and inherited by the Marquise Félicie de Virieu, born Blacas; photographed at Bulloz; in 1954, Wildenstein called it lost; not included in the 1967-1968 Ingres exhibition, but brought to the attention of the Louvre by Mme de Virieu at that time and acquired directly from her by the Musée du Petit Palais, with the pendant *Henri IV jouant avec ses enfants* in arrears of the Dutuit bequest in February 1968 (INV. 1165).

EXHIBITIONS
1824, Salon, no. 924; 1867, Paris, no. 430; 1868, Rome, no. 133, ill.; 1968-1969, Moscow-Leningrad, no. 104; 1971, Bucharest, Cracow, Iassi, p. 92, ill.; 1971, Budapest, no. 31.

REFERENCES
Ingres, *Cahiers IX-X ; Giornale arcadico di scienze ; lettere et arti,* I, Rome, January-February 1819, p. 449; Stendhal, 1824, pp. 48-49; A. Jal, 1824, pp. 353-355; *Journal des débats politiques et littéraires,* issues of 8 and 11 September 1824; M***, *Revue critique des productions de peintures... exposées au Salon de 1824,* pp. 152-153; Chauvin, 1825, p. 101; H. Delaborde, 1870, no. 57; H. Lapauze, 1911, pp. 190, 226; G. Wildenstein, 1954, no. 118, ill. 64 (considered lost); R. Rosenblum, 1967b, p. 35; *idem,* 1969, p. 102, ill. pl. I; J. Warnod, 1968, p. 20; J. Foucart, 1968, p. 108, no. 76, pp. 133, 176; *The Great Museums of the World,* Tokoyo, II, 1969, color. p. 86; B. Lossky, 1970, pp. 11-20, ill. 4; D.

Ternois and E. Camesasca, 1971, no. 97, ill.; D. Wakefield, 1973, p. 114, pl. II.

RELATED WORKS

Paintings. Almost identifical version, but reversed, at Smith College, Northampton, Mass. (Ternois-Camesasca, 1971, no 97b, ill.; canvas, 41 × 48; its authenticity has been questioned; perhaps it was done after the engraving (which would explain the inversion) and with the collaboration of the atelier. Another version, identical to the one above, also reversed, is in a private collection in London (Ternois-Camesasca, *op. cit.,* no. 97c, ill.; canvas, 50 × 48). At the right, instead of the table with the crucifix is a kneeling monk. Because the painting features a dedication by Ingres to Alexandre de Humboldt, G. Wildenstein dated it late, about 1850, but the dedication could have been made at the time of the gift, as E. Camesasca noted. This painting, which was part of the posthumous Humboldt sale, in 1860, recently appeared in a sale in London (Sotheby's, 30 April 1969).

Drawings. One, of the total composition, in the Louvre, coming from the Coutan-Hauguet collection (Delaborde, 1870, no. 211; B. Lossky, 1970, ill. I). Another drawing, graphite heightened with watercolor, with the date 1813 (later?) in the Brussels museum (Delaborde, *op. cit.,* no. 212). Drawing dedicated to Thévenin and acquired by Clément at the Thévenin sale November 1870, no. 1869 (Delaborde, *op. cit.,* no. 213). Drawing, s.d. 1818, exhibited at the Arts-Unis in 1861 (Delaborde, *op. cit.,* no. 214 and Galichen, 1861, I, pp. 348-349); study for Leonardo in the former collection of Richomme (Delaborde, *op. cit.,* no. 57);

probably to be identified with the energetic black chalk drawing today in Bayonne (B. Lossky, *op. cit.,* ill. 2). Study for the group of Leonardo and François I in Montauban (J. Foucart, 1968, no. 76, p. 108, ill. 109; B. Lossky, *op. cit.,* ill. 3), graphite on tracing paper, 22.8 × 23.4.

Prints. Line engraving of A. Réveil, in Magimel, 1851, pl. 36; copperplate engraving by C.-F. Dien after a preparatory drawing of J.-T. Richomme.

The subject of Leonardo da Vinci dying in the arms of François I was a very popular theme in the late 17th century. The most famous example in France is the large painting by François-Guillaume Ménageot, placed by the Louvre (INV. no. 6602) in 1872 at the Hôtel de Ville in Amboise. This painting received a great deal of notice at the Salon of 1781 and was engraved in several versions (but Ingres owes nothing to Ménageot on the formal level). In 1782, in Venice, Angelica Kaufmann sold a picture of the same subject to the future czar, Paul I, but she had already exhibited a similar one in 1778 at the Royal Academy, and, therefore, much earlier than the one by Ménageot. In 1873, in Rome, Giuseppe Cades did a drawing on this same theme (Oxford, Ashmolean Museum) as well as an engraving (undated). Let us also cite the painting by R. Cosway at Truro and J. Gigoux at Blois (*Dernière Communion de Léonard,* Salon of 1835) and the poetry of Girodet cited by F. Haskell (1971, p. 58).

For its pendant, *Henri IV jouant avec ses enfants,* see J. Foucart, 1968, no. 132, p. 174, ill. p. 175 and the French edition of this catalog, p. 499.

J. F.

107
Roger and Angelica

Roger délivrant Angélique
Plate p. 258
Canvas; 147 × 190; s.d.l.r. on the rock to which Angelica is bound: *A. Ingres. Pit Roma/1819*
Salon of 1819, not in catalog
Paris, Musée du Louvre

Roger and Angelica was Ingres' first painting to enter a museum, as early as 1824. It was part of a large commission from a group of artists begun in 1817, consisting of historical paintings which were to decorate Versailles, which had been somewhat neglected since the Revolution (Salons de l'Œil-de-Bœuf, de Mars, de Mercure, the bedrooms of Louis XIV and Louis XV, and the Chambre de la Pendule). A good number of these painters have today been forgotten (Delaval, Grenier, Berthon, Rouillard, Bordier, Lafond, Guillemot). But there were also promising young artists such as Heim, Drolling, Mauzaisse, such recognized artists as Monsiau and Ansiaux, strong painters like Vafflard and decided neo-classical painters like

Abel de Pujol. This diverse group bears witness to the authentically liberal eclecticism that characterized the artistic politics of the Restoration, often more original than one would think, that could welcome at a very early stage Géricault and Delacroix, as well as of landscape and genre painters scorned by the Institute. The hostile outburst of criticism that was caused by the purchase of Ingres' *Roger and Angelica* makes it look like a great act of enlightened patronage, pointing to the future. For the throne room, the romantic episode were selected from Ariosto's *Orlando Furioso,* Roger and Angelica, or from Tasso (*Rinaldo and Armida,* an episode which takes place in freed Jerusalem). Even though these sources had been very famous since the

16th century, their selection here indicates a strong revival, for in this period, such subjects were rarely chosen for the overheads of doors, an indisputable proof of a confirmed openness to romanticism and a declaration of the official status of the *gothique troubadour* style. A document dating from 1818 published by B. Dorival (1969, p. 8) shows, moreover, that the administration had thought for a moment of going back and choosing romantic historical subjects better suited to "the majesty of the place" rather than to "allegorical and fabulous" subjects. Borrowed from *Orlando Furioso* (1532, Canto X, stanza 92ff., which Ingres summarized in his *Cahier X*), the episode of the story of Roger and Angelica is rather freely handled by Ingres: the detail of the magic shield is depicted only in the late version in Sao Paulo, the importance of the ring which renders the wearer invisible was ignored. Through its chivalrous aspect, the picture of Ingres reflects the influence of related themes like Saint George and the dragon (a theme treated later by Delacroix) or Perseus and Andromeda. In this regard, there have been lengthy discussions concerning the possibility that Ingres' treatment of the Perseus theme preceded that of Roger and Angelica, namely because of a small painting in Detroit, which has been questioned. At present, the problem seems to have been satisfactorily resolved by D. Ternois (1967, p. 152) against the Perseus and in favor of Roger and Angelica. Moreover, Ingres himself violently attacked one of his most hostile critics, Kératry, who had dared to confuse the two subjects and to call his 1819 painting *"Persée et Andromède."* One should add only that the decorative program for the throne room at Versailles would have been less homogenous with the inclusion of a mythological episode such as Perseus and Andromeda, in contrast to a romantic subject like Bergeret's *Renaud et Armide.*

The painting is striking because of its unusual colors; rose and flesh tones in strong contrast to somber, murky and leaden tones; the fantastic lighting effects—silvery-white areas of light alternating with those bathed in shadow. One must also admire the unusually strange detail of the lighthouse. The composition is held together discretely by the contrasts between the nude body of Angelica, and that of armor-clad Roger, or of the monstrous beast from hell and the no less fabulous creation of the hippogriff, fascinating by its fixed calmness and rich is exactingly realistic details (one can count his feathers). So obsessive is Ingres' descriptive sense that one can almost slide one's hands across the armor and feel the different textures of the silk of Roger's garment, the metal of the breastplate and the sharpness of the claws. Ingres' *Roger and Angelica* was obviously, like so many original creations, very much misunderstood and badly received at the time (except, however, for Delacroix, who described the painting as "charming" in his *Journal).*

From the bold question of Kératry: "Does he want to take us back to the beginnings of art?" to the judgment of Landon: "... composition of an inexplicable strangeness...," where several areas which do show, according to Landon, some sense of taste "form a most unusual incongruity in a piece whose execution takes us back to the beginnings of art," Ingres' *Roger and Angelica* received adverse criticism. Jal mocked the "purplish" coloring and found the painting "original and mannered" in the style of the "school of Cimabue," an opinion which is related to those of Gault de Saint-Germain and the reporter of the *Journal de Paris* (29 September 1819, no. 272). For the latter the painting was totally bizarre: "Waves with no transparency, poor drawing of the woman... the figure of the knight is lacking in aplomb and character." He concluded that "one likes less than ever men who seem to have taken it upon themselves to make us move backwards." This criticism reveals a state of mind totally impervious to the strange archaizing poetry of Ingres, so innovative and effective in its will toward cool design and unrelenting reality, in its network of perfect and faultless lines, in its anguished silence achieved through chiseled forms and supreme command of graphic means. As R. Rosenblum stated (1967b, p. 138), "the whole painting produces a curiously unreal, diminutive effect, as if we were watching a puppet show in which a tale of medieval chivalry is enacted." The discovery of Ingres' picture was to come a little later with Théophile Gautier and Charles Blanc, among others, although Huysmans still remained obstinately hostile to him in *Certains* (1908, p. 211): "... his human-form balloon that he calls Angelica" and the stimulating, comforting admiration from such celebrated artists as Tissot, Burne-Jones, Seurat and Degas, who were all to pay homage to this unforgettable Angelica, with her so fragile yet firm lines, her famous goitrous throat. The most Ingresque part of the picture, she characterizes the extraordinary expressive and formal genius of Ingres.

PROVENANCE
Commissioned in November 1817 for 8,000 francs as an overdoor for the throne room, as a pendant to the compo-

sition by Bergeret (see B. Dorival, 1969, pp. 6-8, who publishes the archival document without reference to *Roger and Angelica*). Contrary to what Dorival believed, the painting was indeed placed in the throne room of Versailles between 1820 and 1823 (cf. Arch. Louvre, p. 12, register of transfers of paintings, Versailles, I, 1799-1833, p. 62). Ingres' painting left 7 April 1820 with a Bergeret of equivalent dimensions, once in the Château of Compiègne, *Renaud et Armide servis par une nymphe,* which was destined for the same décor; sent back to Paris 29 April 1823 with paintings by Landon, *Dédale et Icare ;* Dubois; Roehn, *Entrée de Charlemagne ;* Coignet; Granet, *Le Colisée* all placed in the Luxembourg (*ibid.,* p. 66); exhibited there from 1824 to 1874, the date of its transfer to the Louvre (and not in 1878, as stated by Wildenstein); restored for the occasion of the exhibition 1967, Paris (INV. 5419).

EXHIBITIONS

1819, Salon (but neither in the catalog nor in the supplement; the no. 1648 given by Wildenstein perhaps alludes to the 2nd or 3rd supplement, which this author could not consult); 1855, Paris, no. 3449; 1867, Paris, no. 19; 1967, Paris, no. 107, ill.; 1968, Rome, no. 78, ill.; 1968, Moscow-Leningrad, no. 105; 1969, Minneapolis, no. 50, ill.

REFERENCES

Before 1968, see the entry by J. Foucart in the exh. cat., 1968, Rome, no. 78, which completes the fundamental entry by D. Ternois in 1967, to which should be added: K. Berger, 1959, p. 480 (with useful comparisons between the painting by Ingres and certain 16th-century mannerist works by Bronzino, Niccolo dell'Abbate, or Primaticcio); and R. Rosenblum, 1967b, pp. 138-140, ill. 121; *ibid.,* 1969, pp. 102-103; H. Kogina, 1969, p. 102, ill. 120; P. Haudibert, 1970, pp. 7, 9, 21, 22, 27, ill. 35-38; B. Dorival, 1970, pp. 6-8

(essential archival documents which had been unpublished); D. Ternois and E. Camesasca, 1971, no. 100, ill.

RELATED WORKS

The pictorial and graphic material is too abundant to be cited here in detail. One should refer to D. Ternois, 1967, no. 107 (which is less informative than the exh. cat., 1968, Rome, no. 78), and also D. Ternois-E. Camesasca, 1971, no. 100, which includes an exhaustive list of all the related works.
Same subject painted by R. Lefèvre at the Salon of 1822, no. 1103 and by Louis-Édouard Rioult at the Salon of 1824 (Louvre; R. Rosenblum, 1967b, ill. 124; actually, Rioult represents very exactly Roger leading away Angelica after having fought the monster). Copy drawn of Angelica alone, by Edgar Degas (Paris, Bibliothèque Nationale, Cabinet des Estampes, Carnets de Degas, XX, p. 53); painted copy of Angelica alone by Georges Seurat, c. 1878 (canvas; 83 × 66; see H. Dorra and J. Rewald, 1959, no. 1, ill.; England, private collection), and a copy drawn of the same subject, New York, Lipschitz collection (*ibid.,* no. 1a, ill.). Copy painted of Angelica alone by James McNeill Whistler at the University of Glasgow (canvas; 52 × 53); pastel by Odilon Redon about 1910, a free interpretation of the theme, at the Museum of Modern Art, New York. Copy painted by James Tissot (T. Reff, 1964, p. 557). Version of the same theme, visibly influenced by Ingres' painting, in the work of the "Ingriste" painter Burthe, exhibited at the Salon of 1852 and known by a cruel caricature by Bertall (G. and J. Lacambre, 1968, pp. 20-21, ill. 1). One can finally mention, with Rosenblum (1967b, p. 140), Dante-Gabriel Rossetti's enthusiastic poetry, inspired by Ingres' painting which he saw on a visit to Paris.

J. F.

108
*Jesus Delivering the Keys to Saint Peter**

Jésus remettant les clefs à saint Pierre
Plate p. 260
Canvas; 280 × 217; s.d.l.l. on a stone *J. Ingres Rom/1820*
(the painting seems to have been enlarged or at least altered on the right and on the left)
Montauban, Musée Ingres

The subject, which frequently occurs in old paintings, is taken from the Gospel of Saint Matthew (16-18-19). To the left, behind Christ, Judas voluntarily turns away; to the right of Christ behind Saint Peter stand the apostles Paul, the young Saint John the Evangelist, Philip, Matthew (C. de Carrière suggested in 1841 that this was rather Saint Thomas), and a final apostle, seen in profile but not named in commentaries about the work. Ironically, the painting, today almost

forgotten or, at least, so contrary to modern taste that the organizers of the last great Ingres retrospective (1967) did not even dare to exhibit it, was one of the works with which Ingres was most satisfied. As his letters to Gilibert of June 1819 indicate ("This is my best work"), he was determined to have it sent to France and exhibited at the Palais du Luxembourg (see also his letter of 10 December [see Provenance], as well as the favorable review in a Roman periodical of 1821 which he carefully recopied in 1834, cited in H. Lapauze, 1911, p. 202). The work was his first large official commission since the Empire and was the occasion to leave behind his enchanting little *troubadour* pictures in an effort to aspire to the loftier goals of monumental painting. Even the possibility of painting it in fresco was considered. To be noted also is the fact that of all his paintings, this was the first to be well received. Was the reason for this the reinforcement of Ingres' powerful reference here to Raphael —i.e. the tapestry treating the same subject (London, Victoria and Albert Museum); a drawing for Saint Peter directly from the tapestry is in Montauban (Momméja, 1905, no. 501)? Or was it the intrinsic accord that could be established between this painting, which today seems so insipidly "Saint-Sulpician" and the ennobling, gloriously humanistic and sentimental religiosity with which the 19th century identified itself in part? In truth, considering its date of 1820, the work is striking in its harsh intransigence and quite extraordinary. Far from conventional, Ingres, without making any concessions, here creates a very personal and provocative ideal, much as he will later do in medieval terms with his great *Jeanne d'Arc* (1854; Louvre) another victim unjustly banished from the 1967 exhibition. Once the handicap of its anti-vogue has been overcome, its merits can be appreciated: the large size Ingres selected, the persistent frontal pose which accentuates the massiveness of Christ, the supremely abstract vocabulary of the magnificent drapery, and the sometimes shocking, but original vivid and strident colors, as well as the softness of the landscape—another surprise. Is this painting merely a Raphaelesque pastiche, the quintessence of religious art, coldly sermonizing, icy, noble, attempting to be conventional, but in the end tiresome? No Italian would ever have achieved such petrification.... One should not forget either that at the stage of the Louvre drawing and the Gilibert sketch (see Related Works), Ingres did not show any less attachment for a paleo-Christian, even Byzantine approach with a frontal grouping similar to bas-relief, very tight and regular folds, an extremely massive Christ with the demeanor of a Pantokrator. This rather un-Raphaelesque idea continued to appear in large pictures: abstract backgrounds and the archaizing halo which has been retained here. Not to be overlooked is the incontestable recollection of a particularly French 17th-century tradition; the strongly purified canons of Philippe de Champaigne. In contrast to Ingres is the art of François-Edouard Picot, Abel de Pujol, and Merry-Joseph Blondel, who continued to use traditional three-dimensional modeling and correct drawing. Ingres surpasses the Germans Peter Cornelius and Johann-Friedrich Overbeck, and instills greater dignity than Tissot with his outdated "biblicist" ideal. In this picture, Ingres creates the only truly 19th-century religious painting, sincerely archaeological in its search for a sense of remoteness conveying a deeper truth, authentically realistic in its recourse to crude, ordinary types (notably Saint Matthew; this is even more pronounced in the study in the Louvre: see Related Works). The latter feature shocked C. de Carrière, as he expressed in a violent anti-Ingres diatribe written as a letter in 1848; as well as the more restrained Charles Perrier who, at least, can be given credit for having found in 1855 the description of *"petrification"*—more accurate than he probably thought—for the surprising grouping of apostles around a strongly supernatural Christ.

R. Rosenblum has aptly observed that Ingres' famous stylistic distortions, or *provocations* (there are many in *Saint Peter*: the deliberately cool, glazed treatment, the look of Jesus himself, the too obvious beauty and youthfulness of Saint John, the overly communicative gestures, the noble draperies, etc.) are unique and acceptable because of "... the sheer genius of Ingres' formal sensitivity, which creates so immutable an abstract order that the incredibility of the resulting images [can *Saint Peter* possibly be *credible* in the eyes of viewers in 1974], as judged from the standpoint of realism [or from our own personal esthetic, which alone can measure the real and acceptable] become a peripheral issue" (1967b, p. 24). Unchanging both in its *Ingrisme,* its subtle archaizing and redeeming timelessness, *Saint Peter* is a declaration of a total religious art, praiseworthy in its realism (as exemplified at least in the work of the disciples, Hippolyte Flandrin, Victor-Louis Mottez, Amaury-Duval), and too important to be relegated away from the great confrontations of art. It is time to rectify the unfortunate omission of 1967 and to reopen a case which basically Ingres has no reason to lose.

PROVENANCE

Commissioned in 1817 on the initiative of Thévenin, director of the Academy of France in Rome. He had recommended Ingres as early as 1816 for an important work which would provide him with material security: "It is the duty of the government to develop an original and most unusual talent" (see Lapauze, 1811, p. 192). The commission was to decorate the church of the French convent of the sisters of the Sacré-Cœur—la Trinità dei Monti, which the French ambassador in Rome, the Comte de Blacas (see No. 106), was then having restored at his own expense by the architect, François Mazois (at that time, a very close friend of Ingres and very much *persona gratissima* with Blacas, see Lapauze, *op. cit.*, p. 190). Originally, the picture was to have been done in fresco. Completed in 1820, at the cost of 3,000 francs, it could not be exhibited at the Salon of 1827, Ingres himself had tried to arrange this by having the Comte de Pastoret approach the French ambassador to Rome, the Duc de Montmorency-Laval. He responded negatively to Pastoret on 18 October 1827 ("because of a law in Rome prohibiting the removal of a picture exhibited in one of the chapels where Mass is celebrated"; see H. Naef and P. Angrand, 1970, p. 17). The same fruitless attempts were made by François-Marius Granet in 1830: "...you know Rome; everything given to the church is received with eagerness, but whenever anyone wants to get something from this holy mother, the law does not permit it" (unpublished correspondence from Granet to Ingres, in collection of Mme Guille and a letter in Lapauze Collection—see Lapauze, *op. cit.* pp. 203, 310-314). The picture was finally returned in 1841 to the French authorities, shortly after Ingres' departure for Paris, as a result of negotiations lead by the Comte de Latour-Maubourg, the French ambassador to Rome. Delaborde, without furnishing any proof, states that the picture had left the church of the Trinità dei Monti as early as 1837. At the suggestion of the Abbé Lacroix, the convent agreed to relinquish the picture in exchange for a copy by Jean Murat, pensioner of the Academy of France. In Rome (Lapauze, *op. cit.,* p. 203, with reference to the letters exchanged on this subject). Transferred to the Luxembourg after having been touched up (and enlarged?) by Ingres in 1842 (see letter to Gilibert of 10 December 1842: "I have just completely finished my *Saint Peter* and I can say this time to my contentment and to that of my best judges," cited in Boyer d'Agen, 1909, pp. 41-42). Transferred to the Louvre in 1874 (and not in 1878, as stated by Wildenstein: D. Ternois, 1965, p. 161, following Wildenstein). Placed in Montauban in 1959 (Louvre INV. no. R.F. 97).

EXHIBITIONS

1855, Paris, no. 3336; 1867, Paris, no. 6; 1958, Brussels, no. 98, ill. 77; 1967, Montauban, no. 67.

REFERENCES

For bibliography prior to 1965, *cf.* D. Ternois, mus. cat., 1965, no. 162, ill., adding: J. Varnier, 1841, pp. 307-308; Ch. Perrier, 1855, p. 59; E. Saglio, 1857, p. 77; L. Rosenthal, 1900, pp. 125, 127; G. Brière, 1924, no. 415 (wrongly dates the Murat copy 1837 and says the Ingres picture belonged to Louis XVIII's coll., which is also incorrect); L. Réau, 1957, p. 315. Since 1965: D. Ternois, 1967, nos. 116-117; J. Foucart, 1968, p. 15, ill. 24; P. Angrand, 1968, pp. 307, 341; R. Rosenblum, 1969, p. 101; H. Naef and P. Angrand, 1970, p. 17; D. Ternois and E. Camesasca, 1971, no. 105, ill.

RELATED WORKS

Paintings. Multiple study in a private collection, Aix-en-Provence (canvas; 26 × 19; D. Ternois and E. Camesasca,

1971, no. 105b ill.). Given by Ingres to his friend Gilibert in 1821 (see his letter dated 3 July 1821), through inheritance became part of the Montet-Noganet Collection in Montauban, from which it was bequeathed to the present owner. This sketch was first published in 1954 by G. Wildenstein (although already mentioned by Delaborde in 1870). D. Ternois (1965, no. 161 and in exh. cat., 1967, Montauban, no. 68) refuted Wildenstein's position that is a reduced version of the large picture; such a sketch already is present in the Alaux painting of Ingres studio in Rome, dated 1818 and now in Montauban (see Ternois, *op. cit.,* no. 1, ill.). In other respects, the Aix painting exhibits too many variations which, when compared with the final painting, do not seem progressive (Judas standing to the left and hidden by Christ, the absent look of Christ, the gestures of Saint Peter, the general landscape, etc.).

Reduced copy by Paul Flandrin but completely touched up by Ingres, who added two people, in the collection of E. Gatteaux, in 1871, when it is cited by Duplessis as having escaped a fire in the collector's house during the Commune. It has not reappeared since, and Wildenstein omitted it. Used for an engraving of Pradier (Ternois-Camesasca, *op. cit.,* no. 105c).

Study for the head of Christ (Paris, private collection), which once belonged to Ingres' widow (canvas; 50 × 37; Ternois-Camesasca, *op. cit.,* no. 105d, ill.). Study for the hands of Christ (Paris, private collection), coming from the family of Ingres' widow (canvas; 35 × 22; Ternois-Camesasca, *op. cit.,* no. 105e, ill.). Double study for the right foot of Christ, formerly in the Aubry collection, left France in 1971, now on the art market (canvas on panel; 20 × 25; Ternois-Camesasca, *op. cit.,* no. 105f). Not reproduced by either Wildenstein or Ternois-Camesasca. Study for the head of Saint Paul, not indexed after 1891 (canvas; 46 × 36; Ternois-Camesasca, *op. cit.,* no. 105g).

Double study of heads of Saints Peter and Philip, in Angers (canvas; 49 × 35; Ternois-Camesasca, *op. cit.,* no. 105h, ill.; J. Foucart, 1968, under no. 71; omitted by Wildenstein). Little-known picture coming from the collection of the landscape painter Guillaume Bodinier, who knew Ingres and Corot in Rome. The second head at the right appears to be that of Philip (to the left of Matthew in the large painting) and not a variation of Saint Peter, as stated by Camesasca. Study for the head of Saint Matthew in the Louvre (canvas; 55 × 46; Ternois-Camesasca, *op. cit.,* no. 105k, ill.; J. Foucart, *op. cit.,* no. 71, ill.). Study for the head of Saint John in a private collection in Paris, after having belonged to Moitessier (canvas; 38 × 25; Ternois-Camesasca, *op. cit.,* no. 105i, ill.). Study for the head of Saint Philip not indexed after 1855 (Ternois-Camesasca, *op. cit.,* 105j, not ill.).

Drawings. Sheet of watercolor studies, s.d. 1815 (sic), in the Louvre (J. Foucart, *op. cit.,* no. 65, ill.). This date often misled certain critics to believe that the artist was working on his *Saint Peter* as early as 1815, therefore well in advance of the 1817 commission, which would be difficult to explain, for there is no proof that Ingres had actually chosen the subject himself. But it is doubtful, as Ternois suggests (1967, under no. 117), that the drawing is later than the painting and that the date is the same as that of the painting. The date and inscription were visibly added afterwards by Ingres, who must have written the date down incorrectly, as he did on several occasions. There are too many variations exactly comparable to the small painted sketch formerly in the Gilibert Collection to think that after finishing the large painting in 1820, Ingres would have come back to imperfect components such as the placement of Judas, curiously haloed and rather ridiculously placed to the side turning his back on Christ. The fact that no landscape is yet shown leads one to believe that it might be an "idea" immediately preceding the Gilibert sketch, and still in the mood of a fresco wall painting, according to the initial project of 1817.

Another multiple study in Bayonne coming from the Gatteaux Collection (Gatteaux-Marville, 1875, fig. 29): sketched landscape, Judas seated behind Christ and turned toward the right, as in the large painting. Study of the drapery of the garments for Saint Peter, in Bern.

73 drawings, Ingres' bequest Montauban, of which 20 are of Christ alone; some of these drawings, notably the drapery studies, are technically excellent (very pictorial use of charcoal, e.g., nos. 67 and 68 of the 1968 Rome exhibition) and bring Ingres nearer to the great Italian draughtsmen of the past: from Leonardo and Raphael to the Carracci, Domenichino and Lanfranco, and also to great masters of luxuriance and color such as Lebrun and Vouet. Five of the finest were exhibited in Rome in 1968 (nos. 66-70, ill.). According to Momméja (quoted by Ternois, 1965, no. 161),

several of these drawings are studies done after 1837 for the drawing which was used for the engraving by James Pradier (concerning these drapery studies done from life models, see Lapauze, 1911, p. 202, who correctly contradicts Ch. Blanc's claim that Ingres had never used a live model and that he was opposed to it).

In the Gatteaux Collection (Gatteaux-Marville, 1875, fig. 30), drawing for the head of Saint Paul.

Engravings. Copperplate engraving by Pradier; line engraving by A. Réveil in *Magimel* (1851, pl. 40).

Copies. Pictures by Murat (cited above); Joseph Sivel (done for the church in Romette, Aveyron, 1851, commission); Jean-François Boisselat (church in Sébéville, Manche, 1851); Augustine-Philippe Dallemagne (church in Seyssinet, Isère, 1858); B. Gouget (church in Collonges, Ain); Clara Fournier (church in Coings, Indre, 1860); these last five copies were ordered by the Direction des Beaux-Arts (*cf.* P. Angrand, 1968, pp. 307, 341). Other copies in the church at Bagnolet, at S. Luigi dei Francesi in Rome (perhaps the work of Murat, which might have been moved from the Trinità dei Monti); In Canjac (Aveyron) by the same B. Couget in 1849 (Archives Nationales, F 21 33, 3 May 1849: 1,200 francs).

J. F.

109
*Portrait of Count Gouriev**

Portrait du Comte Nicolas Dmitrievitch Gouriev
Plate p. 263
Canvas; 107 × 86; s.d.l.l. *INGRES. Flor. 1821* (with the N reversed)
Leningrad, The Hermitage Museum

Count Gouriev (1792-1849), the son of a finance minister of Alexander I, was intended for the military from his infancy. Inducted when he was gentleman of the Chamber, Gouriev took part in the campaign against Napoleon (1812-14) by serving in the regiment of the Garde. He was decorated with the Order of Merit and the Golden Sword, but took an early retirement in 1816 and in 1818 was named aide-de-camp of His Majesty. He married Mlle M.-D. Narychkine in 1819, and in 1820-21 he began, at the age of 29, a brilliant diplomatic career as Ambassador to Rome. According to a somewhat less certain source, he also served as Ambassador to Naples (biographical data furnished by Mme Kamenskaya in the 1959 *Bulletin du Musée Ingres* and used again by D. Ternois in his 1967 commentary). Gouriev seemed interested in the artistic life of the period: the sculptor Lorenzo Bartolini (a great friend

of Ingres in Florence whom Ingres painted twice), did a bust of Gouriev's wife; the landscape-painter, Nicolas-Didier Boguet, included Gouriev among his patrons and mentioned his presence in Rome where "he had already gone to the studios and had ordered some paintings" (letter dated 15 January 1821 from Boguet to Fabre, cited in Pélissier, 1896, p. 328; see still another letter dated 11 January 1821 concerning Gouriev's purchase of one of Boguet's paintings; apparently Fabre served as intermediary, see Pélissier, *op. cit.*, pp. 321, 323). Gouriev does seem to have commissioned Ingres to do a second portrait, that is, if one believes the little-known evidence cited by Ternois (1967) in a letter from the painter Henri Lehmann to the Comtesse d'Agoult, written in Rome 18 September 1839: Ingres, then in Rome, was going to paint "this winter" (the winter of 1839-40) the portrait of Count Gouriev and "next year" a large painting for the Duc d'Orléans (undoubtedly the Chantilly *Stratonice*). But this portrait was probably never executed. As for the Leningrad portrait exhibited here, it is difficult to doubt the 1821 date, because the work is cited by Ingres himself in a letter to his friend Gilibert on 20 April 1821 (Boyer d'Agen, 1909, p. 69, cited by Ternois, 1967, p. 202) and in the list of painted works at the beginning of Ingres' stay in Florence (*Cahiers d'Ingres*, IX and X, Montauban and the Wildenstein Collection, published by H. Lapauze, 1901). There would be no questions asked about whether the landscape were Roman or Tuscan (there is that Tuscan softness and sweetness...), if the subject did not seem older than 29-years-of-age, but there are men who look mature at that age, and here aristocratic dignity seems to have modified physical appearance.

For the artistic position of such a painting, a veritable icon of 19th-century nobility, we can refer to the excellent commentary of R. Rosenblum (1967b, p. 120), who noted the possible influence of the great English aristocratic portraits of Sir Thomas Lawrence (which also influenced Delacroix, cf. the *Portrait du Baron de Schwiter*, c. 1827, London, National Gallery), where the nobility of the individual always harmonizes with a landscape background. Everyone has emphasized the extraordinary physical and moral domination of the Russian diplomat, exalted by the receding landscape and the grouping of the minuscule pines and houses. This domination is underscored by the Count's slightly squinting glance that seems to float above us and by the burgundy lining of the coat which creates an unexpected barrier and which isolates "the count in a protected, superior environment" (Rosenblum, *ibid.*) We must reemphasize the thousand subtleties of this work, in which, like the earlier *Portrait de Granet* (c. 1807, Aix-en-Provence), the subject is "inextricably fused, in both formal and psychological terms, with the panoramic setting. The stormy windswept sky reverberates in the tousled blond hair, against which the facial expression becomes all the more resolute" and in which we find an "aristocratic harmony of severity and poise" (Rosenblum, *ibid.*). The harmony of yellows that unites the superb ring, the hair and the gloves; the contrast of the hands, one naked and limp, the other gloved and firm; the symmetric opposition achieved between the unclasped white cuff and the stiffly adjusted white collar—all combine to create a chef-d'œuvre.

PROVENANCE
Gouriev Collection; Mme Alexandra Narychkine; entered the Hermitage in 1922, probably having been confiscated during the Revolution.

EXHIBITIONS
1938, Leningrad, p. 44; 1955-1956, Moscow, p. 62; 1956, Leningrad, p. 162; 1965, Bordeaux, no. 53, ill. 15; 1965-1966, Paris, no. 63; 1967-1968, Paris, no. 120, ill. p. 173.

REFERENCES
Before 1967, see the entry of D. Ternois in the exh. cat., 1967, no. 120, p. 172. To this should be added: L. Dussieux, 1876, p. 576; G. Picon, 1967, pp. 15, 73; R. Rosenblum, 1967b, p. 120, color ill. p. 121; V. Berezina, 1972, pp. 82, 84, color ill. p. 83, black and white detail p. 85.

J. F.

110
Portrait of Madame Leblanc

"Portrait de femme": Madame Leblanc
Plate p. 272
Canvas; 119 × 93; s.d.l.l. *Ingres P. flor. 1823.*
Salon of 1834, no. 999
New York, The Metropolitan Museum of Art, Wolfe Fund

Along with the Gonon-Thomegex and Pastoret families, the Leblanc family was one of Ingres' principal clients in Florence. Like so many of Ingres' other models, the Leblancs were close and longstanding friends of the artist.

In 1811, Mme Leblanc, born Françoise Poncelle (1788 Cambrai-Paris 1839), married in Florence Jacques-Louis Leblanc (1774 Versailles - Tours 1846). She was then a lady companion to the Grand Duchess of Tuscany, Elisa Bacciochi, the sister of Napoleon, whereas Leblanc, the son of a gentleman-usher to the Dauphin, was secretary to Elisa; in addition, he was governor of the principality of Piombino and also lieutenant-governor of the palace of Their Highnesses. Having acquired a rather considerable fortune, Leblanc stayed in Florence from 1815 on and did not return to France until 1832. From this marriage, there were four children: Elisa (1812-1820); Félix (1813-1886), a chemistry professor whom Ingres drew in 1823; Elisa-Léopoldine (1816-1886), married to a certain Flandin; Isaure (1818-1895), later Mme Jean-Henri Place (Ingres was a witness at her marriage and did her portrait several times; she kept the Ingres portraits of her parents up until her death).

Through his Swiss friends, the Gonins, Ingres came to know the Leblanc family in 1820-1821: a letter from the artist to his friend Gilibert speaks of Leblanc as a "very rich and also fine and generous Frenchman who has espoused our cause and practically overwhelmed us with requests for paintings, portraits, etc. I must finish for him," Ingres added, "a life-size painting of *Vénus naissante* with cupids, which I began at least 13 years ago in Rome" (still another promise not kept, as with Pastoret—see No. 111. The Leblanc commission concerned the *Vénus anadyomène* now at Chantilly, dated 1808 and 1848). "This man seems to make as much a fuss over my well-being as for interests for my glory" (cited by D. Ternois, 1967, p. 184). Other letters from Ingres to Marcotte (15 January 1822) and to Mme Ingres (Paris, 11 January 1825) speak of the Leblanc family in equally affectionate terms. As for Mme Leblanc, Ingres, in a letter to Gilibert in 1822, wrote enthusiastically about her saying that she was "the exemplary model of her sex" (D. Ternois, 1967, p. 186 with bibliographical references). H. Naef published in 1970 a very fine intimate letter from Ingres to Leblanc, dated 16 March 1825 (acquired in 1969 by the Netherlandish Institute in Paris).

At the Salon of 1834 (where Ingres exhibited only the *Portrait of Madame Leblanc*), the painting was no better received than the *Saint Symphorien:* Laviron decried its color; Vergnaud was horrified by the anatomy and described the model as "a monster whose head was cut short, whose eyes popped, whose fingers were shaped like sausages," distortions he likened to the perspectival warpings created by curved mirrors. Only Peisse knew how to do justice to this portrait, which he judged to be one of the most remarkable in the Salon; a while later, Duret, who praised its acute psychological insight, then Degas, who became its jealous possessor, fully paid homage to Ingres for this painting. This portrait and its masculine pendant

were justly put on the same plane as the famous Rivière paintings of 1805 (Louvre). The effects of stylistic research (elongation of the body, the calligraphy of the drapery) are shown with a less conspicuous insinuation, always as effectively and masterfully calculated. The pose of the woman is taken, as R. Rosenblum has noted (1967b, p. 122), from David's masterful *Mme de Verninac* (1799, Louvre), but here the effects are still richer and subtler. Where David visualizes space and nobly dramatizes relief, Ingres plays up a sort of intangible negation of depth and aims at a precarious and skillfull equilibrium between the shallowest relief and the most enchanting calligraphy: "the fabulous circuit of her golden watch chain" and "the tour de force of diaphanous black tulle that veils the indolent arms" *(ibid.)*.

Also beautifully rendered is the vase of flowers (a fragment of floral still life introduced for the first time in Ingres' portraits, it was to be richly explored by Ingres in later paintings (cf. especially, *Madame d'Haussonville,* 1845, New York, Frick Collection), "which crowns the table's rich textural sequence of marble, mahogany and gilt, and offers in its pastel bloom a visual complement to the pink softness and delicacy of Mme Leblanc's complexion" *(ibid.)*.

PROVENANCE

Upon the death of the model (1839) the painting passed to her husband, Jacques-Louis Leblanc, who was also portrayed by Ingres in 1823. Upon the death in 1846 of M. Leblanc, who had retired to Tours, the pair of portraits went to their daughter, Mme Jean-Henri Place, who died without issue, 1895. Offered without success to the Louvre in 1886, anonymous sale (in fact, the sale of Mme Place, see H. Naef, 1970, p. 183), Paris, Hôtel Drouot, 23 January 1896, sale without a catalog, in which the portraits were acquired by Degas and Bartholomé. According to Lapauze, 1918, p. 11, they were supposed to split the pair, but fortunately, nothing was done and both portraits went to Degas, the great collector of Ingres, see No. 111. Degas sale, Paris, 26-27 March 1918, no. 55 (portrait of the female), no. 54 (portrait of the male). Acquired by the Metropolitan Museum in 1918 with its pendant through the Wolfe Fund.

EXHIBITIONS

1834, Salon, no. 999 ("Portrait de femme"); 1855, Paris, no. 3368 ("Portrait de Mme L. B."); 1867, Paris, no. 98 ("Portrait de Mme Leblanc"); 1952-1953, New York, no. 140; 1967-1968, Paris, no. 128, ill.

REFERENCES

Before 1967, see the entry by D. Ternois in the exh. cat., 1967; G. Picon, 1967, pp. 6, 70; R. Rosenblum, 1967b, p. 122, color ill. p. 123; H. Naef, 1970, p. 179, ill. 1, p. 178 (Leblanc); K. Clark, 1971, p. 359, ill. 5.

RELATED WORKS

Drawings. Twelve preparatory detail drawings, Ingres bequest, Montauban museum (D. Ternois, 1959, nos. 104-115, ill.) as against only two for the husband (*ibid.,* nos. 99 and 100, ill.). These are essentially studies for the bodice, the hands and certain adjustments for the folds and draping of the dress. The same museum also has three small drawings (*ibid.,* nos. 105-107, ill.), where Momméja noted studies for a portrait of Mme Leblanc and her infant daughter Isaure, which was never executed, unless they related to the very first thought of the 1823 portrait, and this remains to be proven. Drawn copy, of the head, in Montauban, and for many years considered as an original, but certainly a work by a student of Ingres, according to D. Ternois, *op. cit., avant-texte* nos. 99-105: INV. 867-310, and J. Momméja, 1905, no. 559, ill.; considered an original by H. Lapauze, 1911, p. 227.

Line engraving by A. Réveil, published in A. Magimel, 1851, pl. 42.

The matching portrait of her husband, *M. Leblanc,* also in the Metropolitan Museum since 1918, and catalogued by D. Ternois (1967, no. 127, p. 184, ill. p. 185) is signed but not dated. Canvas; 121 × 95.

Similarly, numerous portraits drawn of the Leblanc family can also be cited. For Mme Leblanc, a full-length drawing, signed and dated Florence 1822, acquired by Léon Bonnat, with its matching pendant of M. Leblanc, also full-length, s.d. Florence, 1823. Since 1922, thanks to the Bonnat donation, these two famous drawings have been at the Louvre (see exh. cat., 1967, Paris, no. 125—the lady; and no. 126—the man). In Bayonne, another bust portrait drawn of M. Leblanc, dated 1823. In Paris, at the École des Beaux-Arts, a portrait drawn of Mme Leblanc; dedicated to Mme Leblanc; the identity of this sitter is sometimes questioned (cf. exh. cat., 1968, Rome, no. 101, ill. with a critical discussion). In Bayonne, a portrait drawn of one of the Leblanc daughters, Isaure (dated 1834) of which the painted portrait, attested to by the *Cahier X* of Ingres, has disappeared without trace (D. Ternois and E. Camesasca, 1971, no. 112). This portrait probably dated from 1823.

At the Louvre since 1945, Polignac bequest, a portrait drawn of one of the Leblanc sons, Félix, s.d. 1823 (exh. cat., 1967, Paris, no. 129, ill.).

J. F.

III
Portrait of the Comte Amédée-David de Pastoret

"Portrait d'homme": le Comte Amédée-David de Pastoret
Plate p. 288
Canvas; 100 × 82; s.d.l.l. on the back of the chair: *INGRES 1826*
Inscribed u.l. with the dedication: *A Mis DE PASTORET/*
AETAT. 32
Salon of 1827-28, no. 575
The Art Institute of Chicago

Amédée-David de Pastoret (1791 Paris 1857), first a Count and then, a Marquis upon the death of his father, had an extremely brilliant start in his political and administrative career. Encouraged by a father who was very ambitious (even though he was not well liked by Napoleon; cf. *Portrait of the Marquis de Pastoret* by Paul Delaroche, No. 43), and profiting even more from his mother's social position (she had a highly-regarded salon and had recommended her son to Molé), Amédée was named auditor of the Conseil d'État in 1809 at the age of 18. He was attached to the Administration of Bridges and Roads under the authority of Molé who appreciated him (although he had some cruel words for the Count's father: "a mixture of fox and calf, but fortunately the calf dominates"... which made Napoleon laugh, see No. 43). The son first filled several missions abroad, notably as civil adminis-

trator of White Russia in Vitebsk in 1812, where he conducted himself in a decisive manner, and then as administrator of the German countries beyond the Elbe in Silesia (1813). In Russia, Napoleon commented, "I met in Russia the Pastoret boy who is an auditor. He appears to me a young man of promise. I like his face as well as his candor" (F. Bassan, 1969). As sub-prefet of Chalon-sur-Saône in 1814, he organized a strong resistance against the enemy. As master of requests to the Conseil d'État under the first Restoration he refused to work during The 100 days, after having served the Imperial power so well and although just having recently been made a member of the nobility (the particle "de" was not a part of the Pastoret name until the Restoration). The Pastoret son became a very zealous and sincere Royalist. In 1817, he was commissioner to Louis XVIII on the Commission du

Sceau de France, a major post because he dealt with all matters of ennoblement and of verification of titles of nobility—questions of great importance in France after 1815. This new imperial nobility based on conferred titles was in theoretical conflict with the old nobility of émigrés who had simply inherited their titles and, for this reason, were in a position of relative inferiority. As a titled gentleman of the Chambre du Roi, Pastoret was commander of the Legion of Honor in 1824. In other respects, the Comte de Pastoret had been elected since March 1823 a free member of the Academy of Fine Arts (Ingres was not to become a corresponding member until December and a full-fledged member until 1825, after profiting, most likely, from Pastoret's support). Relations between Ingres and Pastoret, very much in favor in the "ultra" royalist circles, were therefore, very motivated in 1823-24, as is indicated by their correspondence (recently published by H. Naef and P. Angrand); for example, Ingres' letter to Pastoret of 9 December 1824, in which he asks for a reevaluation of his prices while at the same time conceding to the Count a favorable net price (1,000 francs, whereas he certainly would have hoped for twice that amount).

From 1825, Pastoret had been Conseiller d'État in extraordinary service, and it was during the period that Ingres painted him—between 1823, the probable date of the first studies (where the inscription appears at the top of the painting *Aetat* [*is*] *32*, which would seem to be in contradiction with the date of 1826, as explained by D. Ternois, 1967) and 1826, or even 1827. He poses in this outfit, looking more or less consciously conceited, to the great delight of Ingres: the shining sword of the Legion of Honor is a little masterpiece of ironic and insistent exactitude. A lovely letter from Ingres to Pastoret, not dated but placed in 1827 by H. Naef and P. Angrand *(op. cit.),* attests to his scrupulous realism: he asked Pastoret to send him his gloves (which occupy such a fortunate place in the painting, just the right touch of a fresh buttery yellow in a dark harmony of heavy greens and blacks). The effigy strikes the right note by its cold monumentality and a sort of concentrated and distant splendor in which R. Rosenblum saw the influence of such renaissance Florentine masters as Bronzino (he related it to the *Portrait of a Young Man,* New York, Metropolitan Museum of Art, Havemeyer Collection; see R. Rosenblum, 1967 b, fig. 49, p. 36). Concerning the power of a color scheme so restrained in its dignity and which translates itself so well into this "Florentine" vocabu-

lary, see the charming testimony of Amaury-Duval, one of the first pupils of the master: "I congratulated him for painting a costume whose embroidery work did no injustice at all to the head of the model, the costume of the Conseiller d'État being black and with black embroidery on it: 'If it had been embroidered with green or blue palms, as in certain official costumes.... He stopped me: 'I would not have done it' " (cited by D. Ternois, 1967, p. 202).

After Castellane, who noted the suggestive conceit of "this gentleman apprentice" (cited by F. Bassan, 1969), Charles de Rémusat left in his *Mémoires* a rather cruel character description of Amédée de Pastoret, six years his elder, which explains the affected dignity present in Ingres' portrait. "He has, in general, been severely judged in society. What did it to him was his excessive pretentiousness, particularly with regard to awards or honors which befit neither himself nor his time. While following a government career, he fancied himself a poet, a society figure, a gallant knight, a faithful and courageous lover, in short, the realization of a romantic *troubadour.* And while women found his complexion a bit too ruddy and his legs too fat, he did succeed as a mediocre official, a poet for the *Almanach des muses,* a man of vulgar fortune and a wheeler-dealer" (cited by H. Naef and P. Angrand, 1970, p. 16). Mérimée and Stendhal also made discreet references to his conceit, his ridiculousness, his amorous adventures. Nevertheless, Stendhal and Pastoret remained on good terms. In fact, his faults seem to have been faults of youth. Especially after 1830, he seems to have become a perfectly kindly person, who always remained very loyal, generous and obliging to his friends.

Pastoret was well-known in society. He was very friendly with Nodier and Chateaubriand, among others. But his minimal formal education made him somewhat superficial. To judge the younger Pastoret fairly, one should consult F. Bassan's well-documented book, which makes use of a first-hand source: the Pastoret family's correspondence, fortunately preserved at the J. Pierpont Morgan Library, New York (more than 2,000 letters from 1788 to 1856, which give an accurate and diversified picture of proper society and of the innumerable relations of the Pastoret family). The Revolution of 1830 was to cut short Pastoret's ardently planned career; he was dismissed from the Conseil d'État, along with 70 other counselors who had refused to swear loyalty to Louis-Philippe (at least, he was proud of his honor and loyalty, but Rémusat was too much of an Orléaniste to give him credit for it). He continued to hold his seat at the Institute, wrote poetry and historical literature, administered the assets of the Comte de Chambord and was one of the heads of the Legitimist party (even Chambord found him a bit too excited and imaginative as a Royalist). Certain dark accusations of embezzlement of royal funds and intrigues by Louis-Philippe (?) made him swing somewhat late in his life to the other camp. Termed a "Judas," Pastoret rallied to the Empire, became Senator in 1852 and Grand Officer of the Legion of Honor in 1854.

After 1830, his relations with Ingres became less frequent, Ingres showing himself to be, moreover, a zealous Orléaniste. Nevertheless, Pastoret was among the organizers—in fact the president—of the big banquet on 15 June 1841 given in honor of Ingres' return to Paris. Like all the distinguished people of the period, Pastoret of course had his own gallery of paintings, which Théophile Thoré visited in 1845. In an article in the *Constitutionnel,* Thoré gave an exact count of the paintings by Ingres which he had seen: a *Grand Odalisque en buste* (D. Ternois and E. Camesasca, 1971, no. 83g), lost after passing from the 1897 Pastoret sale to the Prosper Crabbe Collection, Brussels; the *Entrée du dauphine (futur Charles VI) à Paris salué par Pastourel,* the supposed ancestor of Pastoret, a fine example of Royalist allegiance (1821, Hartford); the *Vierge au voile bleu* (1822-1827, D. Ternois and E. Camesasca, 1971, no. 120) and its pendant which was finished only in 1834 (D. Ternois and E. Camesasca, 1971, no. 127), both at Wildenstein's in New York; and finally, the portrait of 1826 exhibited here. But Delaborde mentioned still another portrait drawn of Mme de Pastoret, s.d. Florence, 1822, which also remains unlocated. In addition, Pastoret had sought in vain to obtain from Ingres a repetition of his *Petite baigneuse* (a painting similar to the one on the Louvre from 1828), whereas the artist promised him in its place a sketch of his *Saint Symphorien,* a promise which was never kept (see Ingres' letter to Pastoret dated 15 February 1827). In addition to these many proofs of sincere interest, which certainly merited a carefully-done portrait, Pastoret gave a supplementary demonstration in 1827 by requesting the French ambassador in Rome to obtain the loan of Ingres' *Jesus Delivering the Keys to Saint Peter*

(No. 108) for the Salon of 1827-28. Finally we should mention along with H. Naef (1969) that the portrait of Pastoret was perhaps the cause of a proposed duel (aborted) between Ingres and a certain M. de Pommereux, who said one day in front of Ingres that his portrait of Pastoret was a "daub"—a farcical anecdote related by Claretie that nevertheless reveals the painter's pride in his work.

PROVENANCE
After the death of Pastoret, collection of his wife, Louise-Alphonsine (1796-1876), born Alexandre (de Neufermeil). Given to their daughter (and only surviving child) Marie (1817-1890), who in 1835 married Hervé de Rougé, Marquis de Plessis-Bellière (1809-1888), and retired to the Château de Moreuil-en-Picardie, the estate of her mother's family; sale of the collection of the Marquise de Plessis-Bellière, born Pastoret, Paris, 10-11 May 1897, no. 85, ill.; acquired in this sale by Edgar Degas (who also owned the Leblanc portraits, see No. 110) and who was passionately fond of Ingres (see H. Lapauze, 1918, pp. 9-15; in the Degas sale were 20 paintings and 33 drawings by Ingres); Degas sale Paris, 26-27 March 1918, no. 52; David-Weill Collection, Neuilly; acquired from the David-Weill family by The Art Institute of Chicago in 1971.

EXHIBITIONS
1827, Salon, no. 575; 1846, Paris; 1855, Paris, no. 3371; 1931, Paris, Galerie Paul Rosenberg, no. 46, ill.; 1934, Paris, Galerie Seligman, no. 4; 1967, Paris, no. 140, ill.

REFERENCES
Before 1967, see entry by D. Ternois in exh. cat., 1967, no. 140, p. 202; to which should be added Th. Thore, in the *Constitutionnel,* 19 August 1845, and R. Rosenblum, 1967b, p. 36 and ill. 48; F. Bassan, 1969, p. 31, ill. 4a (detail after an engraving of the Ingres painting, pp. 27, 34; biographical details); H. Naef and P. Angrand, July 1970, cover ill., and December 1970, pp. 8, 15, 17; D. Ternois and E. Camesasca, 1971, no. 119, ill.

RELATED WORKS
Drawings. Two details, Ingres bequest, Musée de Montauban (D. Ternois, 1959, no. 167, ill.—left hand of M. de Pastoret; no. 168, ill.—clothes of same). A drawing for the left arm, on mauve paper, at the exhibition of Ingres' drawings at the Salon des Arts-Unis in 1861 (E. Galichon, 1861, II, p. 43).
Line engraving of A. Réveil (published in A. Magimel, 1851, pl. 49); lithograph (bust only) by Aubert, by Belliard. Also to be mentioned is a drawing by Heim at the Degas sale (no. 181).

J. F.

Adélaïde Labille-Guiard

1749 Paris 1803

A pupil of the miniaturist François-Élie Vincent, Adélaïde married Louis-Nicolas Guiard, a minor functionary in the Department of Finance, in 1769. After having received several lessons from Maurice-Quentin de Latour, she exhibited for the first time in 1774, showing a pastel at the Academy of Saint Luke. She then entered the atelier of François-André Vincent, with whom she studied oil painting. She was to marry Vincent in 1800, after having obtained from her first husband in 1779 a legal separation. Received at the Academy at the same time as her eternal rival, Mme Vigée-Lebrun, in 1783, she thereafter exhibited regularly at the Salon and became the "Peintre des Mesdames" (portraits of *Madame Élisabeth*, *Adélaïde,* and *Victoire* at Versailles). Adélaïde Labille did not leave Paris during the Revolution, whose ideas she shared, notably in the area of women's liberation, unlike Mme Vigée-Lebrun, who was six years her junior. She exhibited for the last time at the Salon of 1800.

Working in pastels and miniatures before oil, Mme Labille-Guiard dedicated herself exclusively to portraiture (the excellent catalog compiled by Anne-Marie Passez in 1973 includes no fewer than 150), sometimes sacrificing the model to its trappings.

As A.-M. Passez concluded in her generous and convincing plea in favor of Mme Labille-Guiard, whose "sincerety, sobriety, and naturalness" she admired: "How does one explain how such a complete talent... could even now be too often misunderstood? Mme Vigée-Lebrun is perhaps partially responsible for it. She outlived her rival by nearly 40 years, and it is apparent that she did not encourage the renown of an artist to whom she had always been hostile."

P. R.

112
Portrait of Madame Labille-Guiard and her Pupils

*"Un Tableau (Portrait) de trois Figures en pied, représentant une Femme occupée à peindre et deux Élèves regardant":
Mme Labille-Guiard et ses élèves Mesdemoiselles Capet et Carreaud de Rosemond"*
Plate p. 75
Canvas; 210 × 152; s.d. at the left on the easel *Labille f.^{me} Guiard 1785.*
Salon of 1785, no. 101
New York, The Metropolitan Museum of Art, Gift of Julia A. Berwind

In the catalog of the Salon of 1785, in which the artist exhibited numerous portraits in pastel as well as in oil, the works of Mme Labille-Guiard were shown between those of Mme Vigée-Lebrun and Jacques-Louis David: this location corresponded to a complex academic hierarchy but is not without a certain truth from the artistic point of view.

Mme Labille-Guiard, 36 years of age at the time, and wearing a magnificent hat, is shown seated in front of her easel looking out at the viewer. Two students are present: Mlle Marie-Gabrielle Capet (1761-1817), to whom Count Arnaud Doria dedicated a monograph in 1934, and Mlle Carreaud de Rosemond (d. 1788) standing with her arm around the other. Mlle Capet is looking at the canvas while Mlle Carreaud de Rosemond gazes out toward the viewer. In the background is the bust by Pajou of Claude-Edme Labille, the artist's father, which was exhibited in the same Salon and is today in the Louvre.

The work received a triumphal reception and the reviews of the Salon were unanimous: "vigorous and firm touch," "fine color tone," "firmness and facility of execution," "grandly composed," "simple and true manner," are the terms most frequently encountered in the reviews, and the critics were "amazed at the progress which she (the artist) had made in two years."

Three comments merit attention. One notice, which is surprising today, considers this portrait "beautifully close to history painting." Another predictably compares Mme Labille-Guiard with Mme Vigée-Lebrun: "Her talent is more in the form of a Diana; Mme Lebrun's talent, more in the form of a Venus." Finally, another critic admires, in this woman, a "vigor" and a "force which appear to be even above her sex." "That woman is actually a man, I have heard people say," wrote the author of the *Avis Important d'une Femme sur le Salon de 1785* (Deloynes coll., XIV, no. 344), "as if my sex were eternally condemned to mediocrity and as if her works always had to carry the stamp of her weakness and ignorance." If the *Espion du Salon de peinture* criticizes the "capricious and somewhat overdone toilette" of the sitter, he does not know what to admire more, the elegance of the make-up and the richness of the coloring, or the simplicity of the composition. Nevertheless, these questions concern the most ambitious and most nearly perfect painting of a very talented and sophisticated artist.

PROVENANCE

In the collection of the artist, and then her husband and his descendants, the Griois family, until 1876. Bequeathed to the Louvre by Mme Auguste-François Griois on 8 September 1876. Refused by the Director General of the Fine Arts, Eugène Guillaume on 20 November 1878 ("The director of the national museums... has determined these canvases to be without artistic value !..." see A.-M. Passez, 1973, p. 314). Sold in 1905 by the widow of Auguste Griois to M. Gimpel and Wildenstein; Newport, R.I., collection of Edward J. Berwind and his sister Julia; bequeathed by Miss Julia A. Berwind to the Metropolitan Museum in 1953, and entered the museum's collection in 1961.

EXHIBITIONS

1785, Salon, no. 101; 1848, Paris, no. 53; 1909, Paris, no. 7; 1910, Berlin, no. 85; 1932, London, no. 284.

REFERENCES

Coll. Deloynes, v. XIV, no. 325, p. 91; no. 326, p. 121; no. 327, p. 150; no. 329, pp. 206-207; no. 334, pp. 360-361; no. 339, p. 549; no. 341, p. 614; no. 343, p. 623; no. 344, pp. 662-663; no. 345, p. 698; no. 348, pp. 757-758; no. 350, pp. 830-831 (for other reviews of the Salon of 1785 not in Deloynes, see Passez, 1973); J. Lebreton, 1803, p. 5; J. Renouvier, 1860, p. 360; S. Blondel, 1887, p. 58; G. de Léris, 1888, p. 130; H. Bouchot, 1894, v. I, p. 246; R. Portalis, 1901, v. II, p. 491; *idem,* 1902, v. I, pp. 100-101, ill.; R. Portalis, 1902, pp. 38-41, ill.; H. Bouchot, 1907, p. 62; P. de Nolhac, 1908, p. 54; A. Dayot and Cl. Phillips, 1910, p. 70, ill.; Ch. Oulmont, 1928, p. 41, ill.; G. Wildenstein, 1932, v. I, pp. 54, 76, ill. 28; A. Doria, 1934, pp. 5, 15, 88, no. 4; P. Ratouis de Limay, 1946, p. 105; M. Florisoone, 1948, p. 118, ill.; R.-L. Redmond, 1961, p. 35, ill. p. 44; E. Gardner, 1962, pp. 265-270, ill.; A.-M. Passez, 1973, pp. 156-159, no. 62, XLIX and color cover ill.

RELATED WORKS

Mme Passez catalogued a large painted study (1973, no. 61; pl. XLVIII), whose location has been unknown since 1931. Engraved by H. Valentin. Included in the engraving by Johann Georg Martini showing the Salon of 1785. For another self-portrait by Mme Labille-Guiard, see Passez, 1973, no. 28, ill.

P. R.

113
Portrait of Robespierre

"Portrait de Robespierre, député à l'Assemblée Nationale"
Plate p. 123
Canvas; 100 × 75
Private Collection

Very few unquestionable portraits of Maximilien de Robespierre (1758-1794) are known, although he was certainly one of the major personalities of the Revolution. Two pastels of him were shown at the Salon of 1791: one by Joseph Boze (no. 215; perhaps the picture today at Versailles, M.V. 7980) and one by Mme Labille-Guiard, which disappeared some time ago. The portrait exhibited here was first given to Joseph Ducreux who, in 1793, exhibited (no. 107) the portrait of the lawyer from Arras (see G. Lyon, *Joseph Ducreux,* Paris, 1958, pp. 145, 190-191), then to Henri-Pierre Danloux (it is still reproduced under this name in the 1949 edition of the *Larousse du XXᵉ siècle,* VI, pl. CXXII). Ducreux' well-known style and Danloux' profound monarchic sentiments make these hypotheses improbable.

It is quite likely that the painting shown here is the replica in oil of the pastel exhibited by Mme Labille-Guiard at the Salon of 1791, as M. Tourneux suggested as early as 1889. One of the rather eulogistic commentators of the Salon (much more severe with the pastel by Joseph Boze), went so far as to advise Mme Labille-Guiard: "Ah ! paint Robespierre in oil." The flattering and inflated letter addressed by Robespierre to the painter and offered to the British Museum by Lord Egerton (who got it from François-Élie Vincent, the teacher and future husband of Mme Labille-Guiard) as well as the opinion of the great connoisseur, Eudoxe Marcille, and the style of the work itself, all support this idea. On this last point, there is, however, one slight difference: one may wonder if, after the disappearance of the pastel, Vincent did not help his student finish the oil version of the work. The firmness of execution, the sobriety of the colors, the smooth and porcelain-like touch suggest something of the feeling of Vincent. A comparison with his *Portrait of the Actor Dazincourt,* dated 1792, exhibited here (No. 200) should permit this debate to be settled.

Whatever the case, the contrast between the simplicity of the costume and "a certain affectation of elegance" (A.-M. Passez, from whom we have borrowed the basic information in this commentary), the face at the same time enigmatic and quick in its smile, the fine elegant hands which stand out against the black costume of the *députés du Tiers,* make this portrait a striking image of the *"Incorruptible"* at the dawn of his power.

PROVENANCE
François Marcille Collection ("bought for 250 francs, no. 6 ?" according to an inscription on the verso); Eudoxe Marcille Collection; Chevrier-Marcille Collection. For another inscription attributing the work to Danloux, see see R. Portalis, 1910.

EXHIBITIONS
1860, Paris, no. 117 (attr. to Danloux); 1878, Paris, no. 431 (H. Jouin:"Adélaïde Labille-Guiard"); 1889, Paris, no. 1071 ("Portrait of Robespierre, before the Révolution" !); 1931, Paris, no. 57.

REFERENCES
M. Tourneux, 1889, v. I, pp. 411-412; Ph. de Chennevières, 1890, t. II, p. 307; R. Portalis, 1902, v. I, p. 341, ill.; R. Portalis, 1902, p. 75, ill.; P. Dorbec, 1907, v. XXI, pp. 45,52, ill.; R. Portalis, 1910, pp. 43-44; G. Brunon-Gardia, 1931, no. III, p. 18, ill.; J. Massin, 1956, ill. p. 104; E. Berl, 1965, ill.; A.-M. Passez, 1973, p. 248, no. 121, ill.

RELATED WORKS
At the Salon of 1791 (no. 34), Mme Labille-Guiard exhibited a portrait of Robespierre in pastel, which is now lost (*cf.* A.-M. Passez, 1973, no. 120). The work was copied by Pierre-Roch Vigneron (Versailles, M.V. 6653) and engraved by Pajeut.

P. R.

Jean-Jacques Lagrenée (called Lagrenée the Younger)

1739 Paris 1821

Lagrenée the Younger was a student of his older brother, Louis J.-F. Lagrenée, with whom his work has often been confused, until M. Sandoz' recent studies (1962). Although he won only second prize, he was awarded a pension at the French Academy in Rome from 1763 to 1768. *Agréé* at the Paris Academy in 1769, Lagrenée the Younger was received there in 1775, with his ceiling decoration *Hiver,* which he painted for the Galerie d'Apollon in the Louvre. He was more specialized than his brother in history painting (as early as 1771, he painted for the Carthusian monks the charming *Présentation au temple,* today at Versailles, Grand Trianon, Chapelle), but, as bad luck would have it, the many works he exhibited regularly at the Salons until 1804 are today, for the most part, in poor condition, inaccessible or lost. Let us cite, however, in addition to the ceiling painted in 1779 for the theater of the Petit Trianon *(Apollon, les Grâces et les Muses),* the *Mariage antique* (1776, Angers); the two canvases of the ensemble from the chapel at Fontainebleau (1781), *Baptême du Christ* and *Noces de Cana* ; the *David et Goliath* (1781, Caen); the *Saint Jean-Baptiste prêchant* (1782, Grenoble); *Moïse sauvé des eaux* (1785, Chambéry, Préfecture; *modello* in Dijon, Musée Magnin); and *Ulysse arrivant au palais de Circé* (1787, Tourcoing). Among his later paintings, which have become particularly rare, are *Ulysse et Alcinoüs* (1791, Narbonne, sketch at Saintes) and *Phèdre accusant Hippolyte* (1795, Moscow), both of a particularly rigid construction, and finally *Psyche in her Palace* (No. 114). Lagrenée the Younger, who for a long time had worked at the Sèvres porcelain factory, seems to have been curious about new techniques: he engraved in the manner of a wash and painted on glass as well as on marble. Nothing more about his life is known after the Empire. On the whole, his style is distinguished from that of his brother by its more accentuated draughtsmanship and a more minute but perhaps less pleasant execution. A. S.

114
Psyche in the Enchanted Palace*

"Psyché dans le palais enchanté"
Plate p. 148
Canvas; 69 × 91; s.d.l.l. *J. J. Lagrenée an 6*
Salon of 1798, no. 231
Paris, Private Collection

The catalog from the Salon describes as follows the subject borrowed from the famous fable told by Apuleius: "Psyche in the enchanted palace, where she has been transported by Cupid. Nymphs are attending to her or are preparing for her the most splendid adornments, while harmonious sounds are heard in the background; Zephyr is burning perfume; but in the middle of all these delights, Psyche remains sad and pensive, for she does not see anyone, not even Cupid who is contemplating her. In the background is Venus, who goes to complain to Jupiter."

The painting demonstrates both the persistence through the Revolution of a painting based on graceful subject matter and the limits of the influence of the grand heroic style. The vocabulary is decidedly based on antiquity, such as the great peristyle cutting across the surface of the painting, and the archeological interest in the details of the furniture. But Lagrenée the Younger's is a gentle, tender sort of antiquity, painted in pleasant colors and in a smooth and brilliant pictorial style.

PROVENANCE
Sale, Hôtel Drouot, room 1, November 1966 (no catalog).

EXHIBITION
1798, Salon, no. 231.

A. S.

Louis-J.-F. Lagrenée (called Lagrenée the Elder)
1724 Paris 1805

Born on 30 December 1724, Lagrenée the Elder became the pupil of Carle Van Loo, as did most of the history painters of his generation. After having won the Grand Prix at the Academy in 1749, he stayed for a brief time in Rome in 1751. In 1755, he was received into the Academy (*Enlèvement de Déjanire,* Louvre), where he had a fine career, eventually earning the post of rector (1785), after having directed the French Academy in Rome (1781-85). From 1760 to 1762, he was at the Russian court. Back in France again, he experienced a great success. His abundant production until his death in 1805 is known in detail, thanks to his *livre de raison* (Bibliothèque d'Art et d'Archéologie, MS. 50, published with several small errors by E. and J. de Goncourt, 1877 and 1878). As a history painter, he did works for churches (*Assomption,*

1759, at Saint-Pierre's in Douai; *Saint Ambroise, 1764*, at Sainte-Marguerite's in Paris; *Saint Germain et sainte Geneviève*, at Saint-Thomas-d'Aquin's in Paris) and especially for the King. He helped in the decoration of the Château de Choisy (1765), *La Justice et la Clémence*, and *La Bonté et la Générosité* (both at Fontainebleau), the Château de Bellevue (1767-68, *Mars et Vénus surpris par Vulcain*, Nîmes), the Château de Trianon (1769, *Cérès et Triptolème*). Up until the time of the Revolution, the superintendent d'Angiviller regularly had him participate in the large commissions involving historical paintings. Among these paintings, which are dispersed in provincial museums, and which, for the most part, are not exhibited, are: *Fabricius refuse les présents de Pyrrhus* (1777, Libourne), *Popilius* (1779, Lille), *Les Deux Veuves d'un officier indien* (1783, Dijon), *La Mort de la Femme de Darius* (1785, Angers), *Alexandre consulte l'oracle d'Apollon* (1789, Montpellier; see two articles by M. Sandoz, 1961).

To tell the truth, as did Diderot (who, by the way, liked Lagrenée very much): "The more his canvas stretches out, the more his talent diminishes" (Salon of 1767). He comes across much more effectively in paintings of medium or small proportions, as distantly removed from the systematically artificial pastoral scenes in the manner of François Boucher, as from the new tension of the grand style. He painted mythological themes or historical subjects which were coming into fashion with the same fresh colors, such as the fine ensemble dating from 1770-71 preserved at Stourhead and published by M. Sandoz (in *The Burlington Magazine*, CIII, September 1961, pp. 392-395). A virtuoso of fine craftsmanship, with a smooth and creamy facture, he was fond of painting on copper; his best works are very small paintings, especially those from around 1770. His fresh coloring and brilliant execution (but without excessive attention to minute detail) certainly affected two history painters, seemingly so remote from him, but who were in fact his students: Armand Caraffe and Jean-François Peyron.

A. S.

115
Pygmalion and Galatea

Pygmalion
Plate p. 64
Canvas (oval); 58 × 48; s.d.u.r. L. *Lagrenée/1781*
The Detroit Institute of Arts, Gift of Mr. and Mrs. Benjamin H. Long

Ovid's story of the mysogynist Pygmalion, in love with the statue that he sculpted (see *Metamorphoses*, X, pp. 243-297), has intrigued artists over the centuries. Lagrenée chose to depict the moment when the statue, animated by the will of Venus, descends from its pedestal. The artist often represented this subject, either for its own sake or as an allegory of Sculpture, sometimes as a pendant or in a series with representations of Painting, Architecture, etc. Even though the catalog of the Aubert sale (2 March 1786, no. 69) points out an example by the artist dating from 1762, the subject of Pygmalion does not appear explicitly until after 1772 in his account book, or *livre de raison*, which mentions a small painting on leather painted for the Duc de Liancourt and known through an engraving by F. Dennel (see M. Sandoz, 1961b, ill. p. 8). In 1777, Lagrenée signed a more important canvas (104 × 85), which was in the Péreire sale (6-9 March 1872, no. 64), and which, as M. Sandoz has suggested, might be the painting that is today in the Helsinki museum, although this painting bears neither a signature nor a visible date (M. Sandoz, *ibid.*). The dimensions of the two works are identical and the description in the Péreire catalog is in agreement with the description of the Helsinki painting. This is to be identified as no. 266 in the *livre de raison*, intended as the middle painting of a series of three executed for the Marquis de Véry in 1776 and 1777.

If the Detroit painting corresponds to no. 301 in the *livre de raison* (an example which does not include a pendant), its provenance is difficult to untangle because of the existence of two pendants, a *Pygmalion*, on the one hand, and *La Peinture et les Grâces*, on the other (nos. 31 and 30 in a sale in Paris on 23 March 1908, ill.). The composition and the dimensions of the *Pygmalion* are identical to those of the Detroit painting, but the pendant, according to the catalog, was signed and dated 1772. Two solutions seem possible: either Lagrenée exactly repeated in 1781 a composition dating from 1772 and the Detroit version is not to be confused with the one sold in 1908 (this painting and its pendant would then correspond to nos. 392-393 in the *livre de raison,* which could hardly be the case; see A. Schnapper, 1975); or else the paintings sold in 1908 were not truly pendants, and on one of them the date "1781" had not been read. Both hypotheses are complicated and unsatisfactory; we learn toward the second, because, at this time, no exact duplication in the work of Lagrenée is known, and the style of the Detroit painting with its simplified background, is more "modern' than Lagrenée's style appeared to be in 1772, namely, in the *Pygmalion* painted for the Duc de Liancourt.

PROVENANCE

Perhaps no. 31 in a Paris sale, 23 March 1908 (see above). Paris then New York art market in 1972.

REFERENCES

"Livre de Raison," E. and J. de Goncourt, ed. 1877 and 1878, probably no. 301 *(Pygmalion)* ; A. Schnapper, 1975 (at press). On the paintings in the 1908 sale, see J. Seznec and J. Adhémar, v. I, 1957, p. 43 *(Pygmalion,* ill. 95, confused with a painting of 1759); M. Sandoz, 1961a, p. 133; M. Sandoz, 1963b, p. 60 and n. 60.

A. S.

Charles-Paul Landon

1760 Nonant (Orne) - Paris 1826

After 1785, as a student of François-André Vincent and Jean-Baptiste Regnault, he won the Grand Prix in 1792 with *Eléazar aimant mieux mourir que de manger des viandes défendues* (Paris, École des Beaux-Arts). He was unable to go to Rome, and later regularly exhibited at the Salon from 1791 until 1812. He was particularly fond of pleasant, graceful subjects, treated in bright, clear colors: *Léda,* Salon of 1806 (Fontainebleau, Château); *Vénus sur les eaux,* Salon of 1810 (Nice); *l'Enfance de Paul et Virginie,* Salon of 1812 (Alençon). Toward the end of his life, he turned to themes involving national historical events, such as *Saint Louis fait rétablir les tombeaux des rois ses prédécesseurs dans le chœur de l'église de Saint-Denis* (Sacristy of the Abbey of Saint-Denis).

Landon, however, was better known as a man of letters than as a painter; during the 1790s, he wrote numerous reviews of works exhibited at the Salons, in which he extolled the superiority of drawing and of idealization. Even more important, he was the publisher of the *Annales du musée de l'Ecole Moderne des Beaux-Arts...* (1st ed., 17 vols., Paris, 1801-09 ; 2nd ed., 44 vols., Paris, 1823-35), which are the basis for any study concerning the Salons during the Empire and the Restoration. Mainly with the help of the engravers M.-C. Le Bas and C. Normand, he published numerous commentaries on works of art preserved in the Musée Napoléon, and in the museums of Versailles, the Musée des Monuments Français and the Petits Augustins. It should be noted that each description and review of a work of art was accompanied by a line engraving reproducing it, generally without reversing the scene. But it is especially the second edition of the *Annales du Musée...,* which was, in part, published posterhumously, that is the most valuable. In addition to descriptions of Italian, Flemish, Dutch, German and French works (old and modern schools), which were then at the Louvre and have since been widely dispersed in the provinces, it includes volumes devoted to the Salons that took place between 1808 and 1835, which provide us with inestimably valuable information on the paintings exhibited during this period and are often the only source available to us.

J. V.

116
Daedalus and Icarus

"*Dédale et Icare*"
Plate p. 154
Panel, 54 × 44
Salon of 1799, no. 176
Alençon, Musée

Exhibited at the Salon the same year as Pierre-Narcisse Guérin's *Retour de Marcus Sextus* and Anne-Louis Girodet's *Portrait de Mlle Lange, Daedalus and Icarus* was praised chiefly for its pleasant composition, the "suavity of its colors," and "the finesse of its drawing and handling." The painting is a nice little cabinet picture, in which the historical subject, more modest in size than usual and treated with a great economy of means, leans more toward anecdotal description than toward the heroization which one would expect.

Landon, as a good student of Regnault, executed his works with a fine technique and with delicate, clear colors, of which this painting, very much in the feeling of the *Allégorie de la Peinture et de la Poésie* (Agen), is one of the best examples.

PROVENANCE
Acquired by the Louvre, probably following the Salon of 1799; appeared in 1810 in the Napoleon Inventory (Arch. Louvre I DD 18 no. 1900); placed in 1861 in the Alençon Museum (*ibid.*, P. 11, 1861, 6 January).

EXHIBITION
1799, Salon, no. 176.

REFERENCES
Coll. Deloynes, v. XXI, no. 567, pp. 273-274; no. 570, pp. 370-371; no. 571, pp. 372-374; no. 580, pp. 431-432; no. 582, pp. 553-555; C.-P. Landon, 1803, v. II, p. 125, ill. no. 63; Landon sale, Paris, 15 November 1826, p. 2; C.-P. Landon, 1833, v. XXII, pp. 13-16, ill. 5; mus. cat., 1862, no. 59; Bellier and Auvray, v. I, 1882, p. 897; mus. cat., 1909, no. 53; Thieme and Becker, 1928, v. XXII, p. 299; mus. cat., 1938, no. 90.

RELATED WORKS
Engraved for the Société des Amis des Arts by Louis-Augustin Boucher-Desnoyers; line engraving by C. Normand in Landon (1803, II, pl. no. 63; 1833, XXII, pl. no. 5).

J. V.

Jean-Louis Laneuville

1748 ? Paris 1826

This student of David, of whom only a few works are known, specialized in portraiture and executed a fine series of Conventional portraits: *P.-F.-J. Robert* (Versailles), *P.-Ch. Ruamps de Surgères,* 1972 (New York, private collection), *J. Delaunay,* Salon of 1793 (Versailles), *L. Legendre,* Salon of 1795 (Paris, private collection), or political figures from the 1790s: *Le Ministre de l'Intérieur J.-B. Paré,* Salon of 1795 (Paris, Musée Carnavalet).

His portraits, for a long time confused with those of David, have often given rise to very severe judgments: "His cold, dry and tight talent is not made to please" (P. Dorbec, 1907, p. 49). In spite of everything, one must return Laneuville to his proper place; depicted in front of monochrome backgrounds of a rare quality, and directly based on and inspired by David, his portraits suggest the exactness of psychological analysis, a proven technique in which the exact precision of line (*Portrait of Barère de Vieuzac*, No. 117), exists alongside the mellow softness of the paint (*Portrait of L. Legendre*) which helps in understanding the confusion that existed between his works and those of his illustrious master. Laneuville was, along with such artists as Antoine Vestier, Joseph Ducreux, Joseph Boze, and

Henri-Pierre Danloux, one of the artists who renewed the art of portraiture which, according to the analysis of J.-A. Leith (1965, pp. 173-175), was of prime importance during the Revolutionary period; it must be noted, in fact, that between 1789 and 1799, portraiture itself constituted more than one-quarter of the works exhibited at the Salons, more than paintings of ancient, mythological and contemporary history.   J. V.

117
Portrait of Bertrand Barère de Vieuzac **

Portrait de Bertrand Barère de Vieuzac
Plate p. 126
Canvas; 130 × 98
Bremen, Kunsthalle

Although the attribution to Laneuville had been proposed as early as 1883 by J.-L.-J. David and then confirmed by P. Dorbec and G. Brière (see References), this painting has often been published, even as recently as 1966, as a work by David. One can only agree with the arguments of these three authors despite the letter that Barère de Vieuzac himself wrote on 31 July 1834 at the time when he gave his portrait to his lawyer, M. Lebrun: "allow me to make a present to you of a large portrait in oil and framed, which has no price because it is the work of the immortal David, my former colleague and friend, who was the first painter of Europe" (cited by J.-L.-J. David, 1883, p. 16). If J.-L.-J. David attributes the error of Barère to "a specific lapse of memory" while letting it be understood that he might have confused the study that David did of him for the *Serment du Jeu de Paume* with the present portrait, we would tend to believe that Barère de Vieuzac had a practical interest in giving, as reimbursement for legal fees, a portrait by "David" rather than a work of a then-forgotten painter.

Elected deputy of Bigorre at the National Assembly in September 1792, Barère de Vieuzac (1755-1841) was a member of the General Defense Committee (4 January-5 April 1793) and was named to the first Committee of Public Health (7 April-17 July 1793). A friend of Robespierre, he worked toward the consolidation of Montagnard power and was arrested after the 9 Thermidor. Imprisoned at Saintes, he later escaped and from that time withdrew from political life. Included in the list of regicides, he was exiled to Brussels, where he rejoined David, and did not go back to France until 1830.

This portrait has always been described as the one of Barère before the tribune of the Convention, demanding the death of Louis XVI. If it is true that on Friday, 4 January 1793 he pronounced a résumé of accusations which were being leveled against the King (see A. Soboul, 1966, pp. 163-171), then this would bear no agreement whatsoever with the painting's inscription, seen on the paper on which he rests his right hand: "*Liberté/ Egalité. Le Vendredi 4 janvier 1792. L'an 2ᵉ | De la République Française une et indivisible | discours sur le jugement | de Louis Capet | Citoyens | Ce que....*"

It must be noted, on the one hand, that the year II of the Republic only began on 22 September 1793, and, on the other hand, that the trial of Louis XVI began on 11 December 1792 and ended on 17 January 1793 with his being condemned to death; the execution was carried out on Monday, 21 January. Therefore, the facts are in complete contradiction with the inscription which should have been worded accordingly: "On Friday 4 January 1793. The year I..." Despite everything, the portrait itself must date from before the fall of Barère on 9 Thermidor, year II (27 July 1794), and it is incredible that Laneuville confused at this point the dates of the trial of the King and the agreement between the old and the Revolutionary calendars. It is quite possible, therefore, that the inscription has been repainted.

Finally, let us point out a fine engraving of Vivant Denon, based on a drawing by Jean-Baptiste Isabey, representing *Barère à la tribune*, which does not appear in the catalog of the engraved works of Vivant Denon (*Catalogue des estampes gravées par le citoyen Vivant Denon*, Paris, 1803), perhaps so as not to revive the memory of a person who was then in full disgrace. The engraving was mentioned by J. Renouvier (1863, p. 151).

PROVENANCE
Barère de Vieuzac Collection; given by Barère to M. Lebrun, a lawyer in Tarbes, in 1834? (L.-J. David, 1883, p. 17); Paris, Gustave Rothan Collection, his sale, Paris, Galerie Georges Petit, 29-31 May 1890, no. 138, 7,100 francs (attributed to David); Brussels, Baron Lambert Collection, his sale, London, Christie's, 4 December 1964, no. 82 (attributed to David); gift of the Bremer Landesbank/Staatliche Kreditanstalt Oldenburg-Bremen, 1965.

EXHIBITIONS
1878, Paris, no. 71 (attr. to David); 1883, Paris, no. 37 (idem); 1900, Paris, no. 82 (idem); 1931, Paris, no. 20 (idem); 1965, Bremen, no. 28 (attr. to Laneuville); 1968-1969, Paris, no. 273 (idem).

REFERENCES
J.-L.-J. David, 1883, pp. 13-17 (attr. to Laneuville); P. Dorbec, 1907, pp. 133-134, ill. opp. p. 140 (idem); P. Dorbec, 1907, pp. 316-317 (idem); F. Haack, 1913, p. 42, ill. 13 (attr. to David); F. Haack, 1937, p. 167, ill. 2c (idem); K. Holma, 1940, p. 120, n. 8 (idem); G. Brière, 1945-1946, p. 171 (attr. to Laneuville); R. Huyghe in 1948, London, p. 29 (idem); A. Humbert, n.d., ill. 24 (attr. to David); E. Berl, 1965, p. 49 (idem); F. Antal, 1966, pp. 10-11, ill. 23b (idem); G. Busch and J. Schultze, 1973, ill. 85 (attr. to Laneuville); J. Starobinski, 1973, p. 35, ill. 33 (idem); R. Verbraeken, 1973, pp. 13, 17 (idem).

J. V.

Hippolyte Lecomte

1781 Puiseaux (Loiret) - Paris 1857

Lecomte became the son-in-law of Carle Vernet through marriage to his daughter, Camille. He collaborated with Carle and his brother-in-law Horace Vernet in the *Sujets militaires* (lithographs), and with Horace in the illustrations for the *Fables* of La Fontaine (1818); later, he was often tempted by equestrian subjects (Salon of 1831). He also worked with the painters Philippe Budelot and Victor de Grailly (an example is in Paris, Musée Marmottan), whose landscapes he sometimes animated with groups of figures. He was apprenticed to Jean-Baptiste Regnault to learn history painting and to Antoine-Pierre Mongin to learn landscape. He exhibited widely and regularly in the Salons from 1804 to 1847. Lecomte was almost exclusively a painter of history. However, two pure landscapes were exhibited at the Salon of 1819, *Effet de pluie, paysage,* and *Effet de matin, paysage* which would perhaps reveal a surprise, if one were to find them, as would such a subject à la Swebach-Demarne, *Charrette chargée de foin, vue prise sur les bords de la Seine, à Epinay* (Salon of 1824). Up until about 1835, Lecomte painted numerous *troubadour* paintings: *Deux chevaliers croisés partant pour la Terre Sainte se détournent de leur chemin pour faire une prière à la Vierge* (Salon of 1804, bought by Empress Josephine for Malmaison), *Jeanne d'Arc recevant une épée des mains de Charles VII* (Salon of 1808; Blois), *L'Ecuyer Blondel, sous l'habit d'un pauvre troubadour, raconte à Marguerite de Flandres les aventures et les exploits du Roi Richard en Palestine* (Salon of 1810, placed by the Louvre at the French Embassy in Tokyo in 1914, still there?), two paintings of *Troubadours* (Salons of 1812 and 1814), *Charlemagne passant les Alpes* (1826) for the Galerie de Diane at Fontainebleau. One of the most important groups of *troubadour* painting of the period was created between 1818 and 1826 for Fontainebleau by Lecomte, Régnier, Granet, Richard, Bouton, Révoil, Laurent, Haudebourt-Lescot, Millin de Perreux (these works are still in Fontainebleau). The paintings intended for the Gallery (which later became a library) were removed in the mid-19th century and dispersed. This group included paintings by Ronmy (Rouen), Chauvin (Amboise), Bidauld (Valence; another, location unknown), Millin du Perreux (Pau), Watelet (Sens), Boisselier (Vienne, and one not located), Dunouy (Clermont-Ferrand), Florent Bourgeois (Villeneuve-les-Avignon), Mongin (location unknown), V. Bertin (Béziers), Rémond (Soissons). Lecomte's last painting with a medieval subject was shown at the Salon of 1835, *Sujet tiré de Charles le Téméraire, roman de Walter Scott* (another picture taken from Walter Scott, *Robertson et Jenny,* Salon of 1827, was placed by the Louvre at the Ministry of War in 1876; its present location is unknown). Lecomte also became the official painter of the tragic history of Cinq-Mars and of De Thou (Salons of 1833 and 1834). He also drew upon subjects of contemporary events; in the same Salon, he could exhibit a little painting in the *style troubadour* next to a Napoleonic military feat (for example, at the Salon of 1810,

Napoléon à Asthora se fait présenter les prisonniers anglais, Versailles; and *Henri IV et le paysan*).

From 1836 on, Lecomte worked chiefly for the historical museum at Versailles: 15 battle scenes retracing the great military feats of the Republic and of the Empire, exhibited at the Salons from 1836 to 1847; pictures for the Galerie Louis XIII and the Salle de Marengo; watercolors (42 military costumes dating from the Empire period) for the Salle des Aquarelles. He also did book illustration (*Fables* of La Fontaine, see above; *Contes* of Perrault); costume studies (*Costumes civils et militaires de la Monarchie française, depuis 1200 jusqu'à 1820;* 380 lithographs); *Costumes de théâtre, 1670-1820,* originals at the library of the Opéra, Paris, 104 lithographs; *Costumes italiens, espagnols, grecs, suisses.* The Cabinet des Dessins, Louvre, has a number of military sketches done from life (notably in 1806 during the Prussian campaign). Other paintings by Lecomte are in the Wellington Museum, London; on deposit from the Louvre at Chambéry (*Louis XIII à Suse,* Salon of 1819); in Cherbourg (*Paysage*) ; in the Louvre (*Prise de*

Villefranche en 1792, Salon of 1840); at Sceaux (the *Château de Neuilly,* s.d. 1823, a little masterpiece with an exquisite naïveté somewhere between Post and Valloton !).

His talent, so original and arresting at the beginning, rapidly gave way to correct and prolific production which, perhaps under the withering influence of both Vernets, fell into the stiff banality and monotony of "mechanical" repetition. A surprising exception to his lack of conviction and absence of any stylistic renovation is his *Josephine at Lake Garda* from Malmaison (No. 118). He created a documentary elegance (and boredom !) in the manner of Vernet for subjects of contemporary history (*Entrevue de Louis XVIII et de la Princesse des Deux-Siciles,* 1817, Versailles). In such paintings as the *Prise de Salo en 1796,* intended for Versailles under Louis XVIII, he did not have the excuse of his youth for his former savory archaisms and could only ape and make slick the delightful and naive stylizations of *Josephine at Lake Garda.*

A.-B. L. and J. F.

118
Josephine at Lake Garda

"Vue du lac de Garde"
Plate p. 194
Canvas; 111 × 192; s.d.l.l. H^{te} Lecomte. /1806
Salon of 1806, no. 332
Rueil-Malmaison, Musée National du Château

The catalog of the Salon of 1806 usefully specifies the subject by giving this commentary: "In the foreground, one sees the great road from Peschiera to Desenzano. In the Year IV, Her Majesty the Empress was headed through danger and vicissitudes of war for Desenzano, when her carriage was stopped by some army officers who warned her that the enemy was down the road, and offered her horses so that she could return more quickly to Peschiera; at that very moment, enemy cannon launched fired on her carriage." Very nearly the same text was restated by Soulié in 1859; it also appears in an inscription on the stencil affixed to the back of the canvas under Louis-Philippe (but avoiding the anachronism of designating Josephine Bonaparte as Empress in 1796). The episode is authentic. Modern biographers of Josephine such as

Fr. Masson, A. Castelot, A. Gavoty have referred to the incident (without additional information or stating their sources), by relating the testimony of Hamelin, the financier who aspired to become supplier to the armies and who followed Josephine from Paris; his *Souvenirs* were not published until 1926. (We are grateful to M.G. Hubert for having furnished us with a long documentary note on this problem.) It occurred during the Italian campaign, while Bonaparte was on his way to take Mantua and to win the victories of Castiglione and Lonato. The precise date was the morning of 30 July 1796 (12 Thermidor, Year IV). Josephine had arrived in Milan from Paris on 13 July 1796; on the 23rd, she was asked to rejoin Bonaparte as quickly as possible.

On the morning of the 29th, Bonaparte and Josephine

were lunching at Verona in the company of Hamelin when they saw the Austrians under General Wurmser coming down the mountains. We are grateful to M. G. Hubert for his note on the episode:

Immediately, Bonaparte sent Josephine with Hamelin and a maid, Louise Compoint, on to Peschiera, defended by General Guillaume, by the road that crosses Castelnuovo (Castelnuovo on the road from Verona and not Castelnedolo on the road from Mantua to Brescia, as incorrectly believed by L. Garros who relied on Hamelin in *Quel roman que ma vie ! Itinéraire de Napoléon Bonaparte* Paris, 1947, pp. 100-101). Josephine spent the night of the 29th to the 30th in Peschiera, completely dressed and in the greatest anxiety. The morning of the 30th, Junot escorted Josephine, Hamelin, and Louise Compoint, not toward Castelnuovo, as the biographers stated, but to Desenzano, along Lake Garda, as Hippolyte Lecomte correctly indicated in his commentary. It was then that the carriage was a target for the Austrian cannon. A dragoon from the escort was hit. Junot had the women get out and sent the empty carriage off at a gallop ! Josephine and her companions trudged along the ditches on foot, and then once out of danger got back into the carriage. In passing through Desenzano, which was encumbered with the dead and wounded, Josephine must have caught a glimpse of Bonaparte, who had established his headquarters there for several hours, after having been at Montechiaro the night of the 29th. As Brescia was in the hands of the Austrians, she followed Bonaparte, who, it seems, was coming back toward Castelnuovo by another road. Bonaparte then sent her to the South with Hamelin: on the 30th at five in the afternoon she went through Goïto, avoided the town of Mantua under siege, crossed the Pô at Borgoforte, and dined in Parma with Fesch. She had been saved.

The selection of such an unusual episode could obviously have come only from Napoleon who, in this way wanted to associate his wife with this veritable pictorial display of his grand feats with which he was in the process of decorating his palaces. Unfortunately, it remains impossible for the time being to specify the exact source to which Lecomte had recourse (perhaps the verbal testimony of Hamelin).

Chaussard was practically the only critic to have commented on the painting, praising "the lively and brilliant color, the bright sky [which] suggests at the same time the heat of the season and the climate of beautiful Italy." As for the figures, they "are expressive and cleverly drawn, but they are too sharply outlined against the background and do not turn enough." This last observation is quite correct. The charm of this painting is to be found in is its somewhat precious and delicate naivité, its hard and fine light, its nervously-tapered lines so well suited to contain the sharp coloring, its formal clarity, bringing Lecomte close to Nicolas-Antoine Taunay. In this context, the stiffness of the figures is most effective. The landscape, with its crystalline and unreal lighting, shows a freshness and an astonishment of vision which are as delightful as that of the Primitifs and the minor realist masters of the 1800s influenced by Dutch art (Drolling and Mallet in France; Hendriks, Jelgerkuis, Troostwyk in the Netherlands; Koepke in Denmark; Gärtner in Germany, etc.). It is understandable that Lecomte, paralleling his contemporary history paintings, turned to this *troubadour* genre (his seemingly awkward "primitive" esthetic position was basically the same as Fleury Richard's !), exhibiting notably in the Salon of 1804 (no. 283) a *Paysage, effet de soleil couchant* with "two crusaders leaving for the Holy Land" who turn off the road to offer a prayer to the Virgin. This painting, with a slight variation, is close to the subject treated by Pierre Athanase Chauvin (No. 21) also acquired by Josephine for her gallery at Malmaison. Lecomte sent works to all the following Salons dealing with Napoleonic themes, as well as with the traditional subjects of national history in the manner of Fleury Richard (Louis XIV and Mlle de La Vallière, Jeanne d'Arc, Henri IV, the Troubadours). These paintings prompted the bitter reproach of the anonymous critic of *La Vérité au Salon de 1812* (p. 23) who, concerning the *Reddition de Mantoue* (Versailles), declared about Lecomte: "Why constantly give this painter pictures to do ? Where do they put them ? I have not seen any anywhere. He cannot draw, his colors are crude, he has a detestable execution. I have seen only a few passable landscapes by him." There was, in fact, in the art of Lecomte a meeting between an archaizing "primitivist" style and a certain type of historical painting, especially that manner which was inherent to the *gothique troubadour*. His combination of these modes here, in the depiction of a contemporary subject, is all the more unexpected and convincing. The critic from the 1812 review did not realize Lecomte would soon abandon his unique, naive style to become a trite and prolific follower of Carle Vernet, as fastidious as he was correct and commercial, which is shown by numerous battle pictures in the galleries at Versailles.

PROVENANCE
Acquired by Napoleon at the Salon of 1806 for 3,000 francs (Arch. Louvre, P⁶, 3 May 1807); in December 1808 in the Pope's apartments in the Tuileries (serving then as the lodgings for Prince Eugène); put back into storage in the Louvre during the Restoration (see F. Boyer, 1966); at the Tuileries in 1831; at the Château de Compiègne in 1832;

at the Château de Versailles in 1834; placed at Malmaison in December 1909 (INV 5775; MV. 1479).

EXHIBITION
1806, Salon, no. 332.

REFERENCES
P. Chaussard, in *Le Pausanias français,* 1806, pp. 452-453; Ch. Gavard, v. IV, p. 44, no. 712; E. Soulié, 1859, v. I, p. 462, no. 1479 (wrong dimensions); F. Boyer, 1966, p. 279; Y. Cantarel, 1973, pp. 314-315, 785.

RELATED WORK
Small, mediocre copy at the Thiers Library in Paris, coming from the collection of the historian Frédéric Masson.
J. F.

Robert Lefèvre (called Robert-Lefèvre)

1755 Bayeux - Paris 1830

The son of a Bayeux cloth merchant, and perhaps a relative of Joachim Rupalley, a painter active in that town, Robert Lefèvre worked as a law clerk for a prosecuting attorney in Caen. He was determined to study painting and when still quite young he went to Paris. He might have worked in the studio of Pierre de Lesseline, an obscure portrait painter from Caen, and seems to have quickly made a reputation for himself as a painter in the Normandy area. He decorated the manor house of La Motte d'Airel for the Marguerye family with grisaille paintings and worked on portraits in Saint-Lô, Coutances, Cherbourg. Lefèvre came to Paris about 1784 and entered the workshop of Jean-Baptiste Regnault, his elder by only one year. It was in Regnault's workshop that Lefèvre and Charles-Paul Landon struck up a very close friendship and, in fact, actually became inseparable companions. They both fell in love with the same woman; Lefèvre gave her up because of his devotion for his friend (C.P. Landon, 1833, pp. 30-31).

He exhibited six paintings at the Salon of 1791, which were received very favorably, and at the Salon of 1795, he exhibited a sculptural and Rubensian *Vénus désarmant l'Amour* (Fontainebleau). The artist traveled and continued to paint portraits in Normandy. He drew vignettes for the *Lettres d'une Péruvienne* by Mme de Graffigny and for the *Histoire de Manon Lescaut et du Chevalier des Grieux* (Didot the Elder edition, 1797). But it was as a portraitist that the artist really came into

his own. In 1801, he painted a canvas showing *Le Premier Consul et le général Berthier à la bataille de Marengo,* the background of which was executed by Carle Vernet. Joseph Boze, charged with exhibiting the picture to make money, showed it in Amsterdam and in London, claiming to be its author and going so far as to have it engraved by Cardon under his name. A long controversy ensued between Lefèvre and Boze's wife which appeared in the *Moniteur Universel* (see No. 13). In 1804, his *Portrait de Napoléon en costume de Premier Consul,* painted for the Dunkerque city hall (destroyed in 1817), was described as a chef-d'œuvre; it was even thought, for a moment, that the artist had copied a painting by David. Robert Lefèvre's activity in the field of portraiture was, from this point on, amazingly prolific: protected by Denon, he was the official portraitist of the Imperial family and of high dignitaries of the Empire. He painted numerous replicas of somewhat showy, set portraits for foreign countries, for French municipalities and for dignitaries: his *Portrait de Napoléon en costume impérial* (1806) was requested 37 times. The Emperor appreciated the artist's portraits for their good likeness. But the quality of the painter's works suffered under this quasi-industrial production. Lefèvre tried to execute the repetitions of his paintings himself. In November 1814, Lefèvre exhibited at the Salon a *Portrait de Louis XVIII,* executed "from memory." The flattery had its effect: in 1816, he was named First Painter to the King, and he executed all portraits of the royal family.

He had a studio frequented by ladies of high society and again tried his hand at history paintings: *Baptême du duc de Bordeaux* in 1821 (destroyed ?), an *Assomption* for the church at Fontenay-le-Comte. The missionary Fathers from Mont Valérien commissioned him to do a *Christ en croix* for their church: Lefèvre was accused of having accepted as payment a plot in their cemetery. The large painting, exhibited at the Salon of 1827, was never delivered and was offered to the Musée de Caen by the painter's sons. The last work of Lefèvre, an *Apothéose de Saint Louis* is still in the cathedral of La Rochelle. Aged, suffering from nervous exhaustion and upset perhaps by the Revolution of 1830, in which he lost his titles, the painter committed suicide in 1830.

It is in certain portraits of friends and artists that Lefèvre, in whom his contemporaries saw the "French Van Dyck," gave the best of himself, namely the *Portrait of Guérin* (No. 119), *Carle Vernet* (1804, Louvre), *Percier* (Versailles), *Grétry* (1809, Versailles), *Denon* (Versailles); certain female portraits, like the one of *Pauline Bonaparte* of 1806 (London, Wellington Museum; Versailles) also are to be included among his successes.   J.-P. C.

119
*Portrait of Guérin**

"Portrait du citoyen Guérin"
Plate p. 178
Canvas; 109 × 80; s.d. (date is difficult to read) R. *Lefèvre/An 9*.
Salon of 1801, no. 287
Orléans, Musée des Beaux-Arts

Without any doubt, this one of the finest portraits by Robert Lefèvre, in any case his most famous and, as such, the one most frequently exhibited. The painting shows clearly that the artist, a specialist during the Empire and Restoration, in conventional, heavily costumed official portraits was, at the beginning of his career, capable of fine work. It is in his portraits of artists that Lefèvre is revealed as a painter of great distinction, as in *Carle Vernet* (Salon of 1804, Louvre), solid and stiff in his gray-green costume or in this canvas with its sober nuances of pale gray tones.

Lefèvre must have known Pierre-Narcisse Guérin (see Nos. 93-95), who was 19 years younger, in the studio of Jean-Baptiste Regnault, which they both frequented. The relationship between the two painters was a friendly and lasting one: Guérin took care of Lefèvre at the end of his life and attended him during his last hours (Notice..., 1831, p. 8). At the time Guérin was 27; his name had become famous for his painting of *Marcus Sextus* (Louvre), which was exhibited at the Salon of 1799.

Lefèvre's painting was well received by the critics, who were unanimous in their praise of the perfect likeness of the portrait: for the *Mercure de France*, it was "one of the best works of its author" (Deloynes Coll., XXVI, no. 693, p. 591). *Le Moniteur Universel* praised its "real and transparent" color, even if it reproached " the hands which are too strong and too articulated" (Deloynes Coll., XXVI, no. 695, pp. 698-699). Elsewhere, another critic commented, "The subtlety of coloring and that of expression; an effect that is broad and sharp and especially bright, and the freedom of the brush, are all unified in this fine portrait." (*Examen des ouvrages modernes de peinture*... Deloynes Coll., XXVII, no. 710, p. 464).

The canvas was again exhibited at the Salon of the year X (1802) near Guérin's *Phèdre et Hippolyte,* as indicated in a letter from Mme de Vandeul, the daughter of Diderot, addressed to J.-H. Meister, Grimm's secretary and successor: "The painters brought back last year's *Portrait of Guérin* by Lefèvre, and it was very close in its resemblance. It was placed next to the painting. A singular fatality ! This young artist is thin and weak; one fears he is consumptive. It is, therefore, certainly fair to hasten to lavish praise upon him since, perhaps, he will not have long to enjoy it..." (M. Tourneux, 1912, p. 140).

The nervous elegance and the simple pose of the

model, the intensity of his look, his disheveled hair, his expression—at once haughty, dreamy and a bit dandyish—struck Lefèvre's contemporaries and, although he is elsewhere frequently banal and stiff, earned him the nickname of the "French Van Dyck."

PROVENANCE

Collection of Léon Cogniet, pupil of Guérin, bequeathed to the Musée d'Orléans by Mme Cogniet and Mlle Thévenin in 1892.

EXHIBITIONS

1801, Salon, no. 287; 1802, Salon, h. c.; 1900, Paris, no. 345; 1933, Paris, no. 60; 1947-1948, Brussels, no. 9; 1962, Rome, no. 130, ill. LIX; 1967, Montauban, no. 277; 1972, London, no. 182.

REFERENCES

Coll. Deloynes, v. XXVI, no. 690, p. 327; no. 692, pp. 381-382; no. 693, p. 591; no. 965, pp. 698-699; no. 704, pp. 331-332; no. 705, p. 337; no. 710, p. 464; *Almanach des Muses*, 1821, p. 49; *Notice...*, 1831, p. 5; C.-P. Landon, 1833, p. 32; G. Lavalley, 1902, pp. 6, 79, 84, 176; M. Tourneux, 1912, pp. 126, 140; J. Vergnet-Ruiz and M. Laclotte, 1962, p. 110; G. Wildenstein, 1963, p. 36.

J.-P. C.

General Baron Louis-François Le Jeune

1775 Strasbourg - Toulouse 1848

In 1792, along with all the other students in the Beaux-Arts group in Paris, Le Jeune joined the Champagne army. He took part in several campaigns in Belgium and, in 1794, in Holland. He studied with P.-H. de Valenciennes from 1795 to 1798. Then, called to the war department in Paris, he was a captain in the Corps du Génie, attached to the Minister of War, General Berthier, and became his aide-de-camp (cf. his *Autoportrait* in the Strasbourg museum). He fought at Marengo and painted a panorama of the battle (Salon of 1801, Versailles), then followed the Boulogne camp and the Austerlitz campaign, from which he took four principal episodes as subjects of as many large wash drawings which were exhibited at the Salon of 1806. He was promoted to major. Returning from Vienna, he passed through Munich where he learned from the Senefelder brothers about the newly-invented lithography process. In 1807, he followed the Prussian campaign (*Episode de la campagne de Prusse,* Douai) and witnessed the battle of Eylau. His sketch of the battle (Louvre, Cabinet des Dessins) was used as a model for the famous competition which was won by Antoine-Jean Gros. After the peace of Tilsitt, he was sent to Spain as lieutenant-colonel. He fought at Somo-Sierra (*Bataille de Somo-Sierra en Castille, le 30 novembre 1808,* Versailles) and became colonel after the taking of Saragossa in 1809. He returned to Austria, took part in the taking of Ebensberg and was covered with glory at the Isle of Lobau. Sent again to Spain, he

was taken prisoner (the episode of the painting shown here, no. 120), escaped and again went into the service of Berthier. At the battle of Moscow (painting in Versailles), he was promoted to general, then to major-general for Maréchal Davout. In 1813, he took part in the battles of Lützen and Bautzen.

At the same time that he was pursuing this amazing (even for that time) military career, he never stopped painting and exhibited almost regularly at each Salon beginning in 1798. Lebreton commented in 1808: "One must have a great deal of natural talent and good principles to merit such an honorable place in a difficult art, while giving it only a portion of one's time and attention. He was to continue under the Restoration and during the July Monarchy until 1845, after having been named in 1837 as director of the École des Beaux-Arts and curator of the museum.

As the years continued, he asserted himself as a true painter. A comparison of his early works, such as the *Esquisse de la Bataille du Mont Thabor,* or the *Esquisse de la Victoire d'Aboukir,* simple indications of troops in movement, with the *Battle of Guisando* exhibited here or the *Vue de l'attaque du grand convoi près Salinas* makes apparent Le Jeune's progress. Besides, it must be said that under the Restoration his success was great, and he needed Horace Vernet whom he must have influenced (as he did Swebach) to take from him, according to the expression of Vieillard (1825, p. 16), "the scepter of the battles."

A thesis on the artist by Mlle Gabrielle Vienne, accepted in 1948 at the École du Louvre, has disappeared; one can read the commentary by Eugène de Monglave on this artist, published in 1850, that of Le Jeune *fils,* published in 1860, and the article by L. Sonolet which appeared in the *Gazette des Beaux-Arts* in 1905.

J. L.

120
Battle of Guisando

"Vue du Monastère et des Taureaux antiques de Guisando, sur les bords de l'Alberge en Castillet"
Plate p. 248
Canvas; 210 × 260; d.l.l. *Paris. 1815.,* inscribed l. m. on rock: *Evenement / du / 5 avril / 1811.*
Salon of 1817, no. 3
Versailles, Musée National

The painting depicts an episode in the Peninsular War in which the painter himself was a hero. In 1850, Monglave wrote: "The painting represents the moment when General Lejeune, having had his horse killed from under him, is stripped of his clothes by the enemy. Several guns were aimed at his chest and if Providence had not wanted them to hesitate, he would undoubtedly have perished. The leader of this band of guerillas was Don Juan, whose nickname was "El Medico"; he is wearing a blue uniform and is turning aside the iron point which one of his men levels toward the general.

" Several weeks earlier, about 60 Frenchmen had been killed at this very spot, and their unburied bodies, which one sees on the left, had become the prey of vultures.

"In the background of the landscape: the convent of Guisando occupies the center, and the elevated mountain peak which dominates the background is called the Mountain of the Eagle. The river which extends through the valley is the Alberja, and over it hang the ruins of a bridge that leads to the town of Avila. The colossal images of the bulls are classical in origin. Livy and Polybius mention them. Hannibal's army contained many Spaniards who, in one of his encounters with Fabius, almost fell into the hands of the enemy. Having escaped this danger to return to their home in Spain, they commemorated their liberation by the image of six gigantic bulls which they had carved out in the rock" (1850, pp. 20-22).

For many reasons (the evocation of the Napoleonic campaigns, the pleasingly anecdotal and specific character of the scene), this painting was very much appreciated at the Salon. It was exhibited anonymously, although everyone realized who the artist was. For the critic of the *Moniteur Universel:* "Of all the paintings in the Salon, the one which the crowds seek out most eagerly is the Battle of Guisando... We would say... frankly that this painting appeared to us to contain some good and bad points; but we must add with the same sincerity that the good points outnumber the bad. There are many elements which animate the composition: in fact, there are too many, which make viewing it seem fatiguing. Rather than just to put elements together on the same canvas and on a somewhat limited surface, [the artist has included] a wild, hilly site; a torrent, colossal figures of bulls carved in the round from the very blocks of the mountains; a storm, rain, a rainbow; a battle between cavalry and infantry; a kneeling, naked man pierced with a sword; the dead; the dying; cadavers, sad remains from a previous battle, with dogs gnawing at them; and close beside, actually in the very front of the painting, a vulture which, unafraid, snatches with its claw the remains of a skeleton: this accumulation of elements reaches the point of improbability.

"These naked bodies are not very well drawn; one feels their dryness; the horses also fall short both in their drawing and brushwork. But, on the other hand, the site is well laid out and arranged: the grandiose landscape, the effect of the light on the countryside is lively and correct, the figures are to be admired for their active movement. The courage of all the people fighting is expressed in all its heat, the general tone is firm, and the brush well nourished; the arrangement of the countryside is certainly variegated. Fewer accessories, fewer false elements, less affectation in the means of inciting terror, and this painting would have merited only praise." The long commentary from the *Journal de Paris* is almost identical and recognizes that "the eagerness of the public... is certainly justified by the talent which M. Lejeune has displayed in this work, a talent of the most original sort."

In his *Essai sur le Salon de 1817,* Miel noted: "The variety of the incidents surpasses the imagination, and all the scenes are of a frightful truthfulness... one certainly thinks that such paintings must have attracted the crowds, who never get their fill of strong emotions; no painting has had such a rich success." Finally, Gault de Saint-Germain called the painting "remarkable" and wrote: "With genius, invention, warmth and the imagination hit with so many elements all at the same time, it is difficult not to be abundant and rich; the author in fact certainly is, and with a success disheartening for our illustrious painters, who can do no more than mere summaries drawn out on immense canvases. The color in this picture is seductive, air circulates freely throughout; the painter, however, could perhaps be reproached for not having made enough sacrifices to the rules of art in his handling of *chiaroscuro*."

PROVENANCE

Purchased for Baron Le Jeune (son of the artist) in 1861, along with twelve paintings and one watercolor for the Musée de Versailles (100,000 francs were paid for the group —see Arch. Nat., F²¹ 155).

EXHIBITION

1817, Salon, no. 3.

REFERENCES

Arch. Nat. F²¹ 155; T..., in *Le Moniteur universel,* 6 June 1817, pp. 619-620; (Anon.), in *Le Journal de Paris,* 10 June 1817, P.-M. Gault de Saint-Germain, 1817, pp. 24-25; Miel, 1817, pp. 354-356; E. de Monglave, 1850, p. 8; L. Sonolet, 1905, pp. 292-294; J. Borge, 1960; Ch.-O. Zieseniss, 1970, p. 130.

RELATED WORKS

On 6 March 1968, Paris, Hôtel Drouot, room 10, a watercolor of Le Jeune was sold, *Cavalier jeté à terre et dépouillé de ses vêtements par d'autres soldats* (23 × 18.5), annotated on the mounting: *cet événement est arrivé à l'auteur de ce dessin entre Tolède et Madrid près de Illescas le Sauril 1811 à Midi.*

J. L.

Nicolas-Bernard Lépicié

1735 Paris 1784

The son of François-Bernard Lépicié, engraver to the King and permanent secretary of the Academy, Nicolas-Bernard Lépicié was a pupil of Carle Van Loo. He won a second prize in 1759 and became an *agréé* at the Academy in 1764. Academician in 1769, adjunct professor the following year, professor in 1777, Lépicié exhibited regularly at the Salons beginning in 1765. In 1784, he died at the age of 49, leaving an important production of quite diversified subject matter, religious paintings, portraits, genre scenes, etc., which was studied some 60 years ago by Philippe-Gaston Dreyfus (published posthumously in 1922) and Florence Ingersoll-Smouse (1923-27).

As Georges Wildenstein (1928, pp. 199-200) has correctly observed, in 1773 Lépicié painted his masterpiece, *Le Lever de Fanchon* (Saint-Omer), and this painting signals the new direction of his works. Indeed, he presented to the Salons of 1775 an *Education de la Vierge* (lost); 1777, a *Courage de Porcia* (Lille); 1779, his immense *Régulus partant pour Carthage* (Carcassonne); 1781, a *Pitié de Fabius Dorso* (Chartres); and 1783, the *Zèle de Mathathias tuant un juif qui sacrifiait aux idoles* (Tours), but these paintings had little success, and both critics and public alike preferred his *Vieillard lisant, Départ de Braconnier,* and *Enfant au milieu des amusements de son âge,* in which he excelled. From that moment on, he concentrated on genre scenes, whereas up to that time, he had had the ambition of becoming, above all, a history painter. It is surprising that just at the moment in which historical themes were enjoying an unquestionable revival, an artist, who deliberately turned his back on this respected current, encountered his greatest successes in genre scenes. The large religious or historical compositions of the period were conventional and unimaginative and Lépicié, in his fine and detailed manner, knew how to restate with faithful observation the style and vocabulary of 17th-

century minor Dutch masters, who were then so appreciated by French collectors.

P.R.

121
Interior of a Customhouse

"L'Intérieur d'une douane"
Plate p. 48
Canvas; 98 × 164; s.d. in the center on a bale *Lépicié 1775*
Salon of 1775, no. 23
Lugano, Thyssen-Bornemisza Collection

This painting was one of the attractions at the Salon of 1775 and aroused numerous comments, First of all, there are the words of a reserved Diderot: "Ah! Here is another Lépicié, it is the *Interior of a Customhouse* done entirely from nature. The principal figure is a portrait, that of the painter. Still, if there were only some resemblance and truth! He put his head on the shoulders of someone else. The piece cannot possibly please me, and I do not believe that it will captivate any true amateur; nevertheless, there has been a lot of noise being made about it; he put together, so they say, all his best talents: his natural and ingenious composition, his correct and fine draughtsmanship, his bright and real colors, a harmonious balance. So be it." According to the *Courtes Réflexions* (cited by J. Seznec, 1967): "One clearly distinguishes there the suffering figure of a traveler whose trunk is being examined by the haughty figures of the clerks who open it up and take everything out in order to better study its contents." It is the painting's "truth" and "soft" color, its luminous and very harmonious balance that the critic admired above all.

No one seemed inclined to identify the site. While Diderot wrote that the painting "is done entirely from nature," this indication must not be taken so literally. M.M. Gallet has kindly furnished us with the following specifics. The Paris customhouse was located on the Rue du Bouloir. Repeatedly, during the course of the 18th century, the question of moving it had been raised. Thus, in 1767, Soufflot "had been given the responsibility of studying the installation of the customhouse and the Hôtel des Fermes in the area of the Library, on the Rue de Richelieu and the Rue Neuve-des-Petits-

Champs." These plans were never completed but the "Lugano picture is related by an incontestable synchronism. The circular gallery and its arcades are less evocative of Soufflot than of the Halle au Blé constructed in 1763-66 by Le Camus de Mézières." The pendant, *Vue de l'Intérieur d'une grand halle,* M. Gallet added, contained specific references to Les Halles in Paris: the astrological column of the Halle au Blé and the Fontaine des Halles." Thus, rather than do a topographically accurate painting, Lépicié wanted to represent a spot very well-known to contemporary Parisians, while at the same time idealizing and modernizing it. He animated the scene with various groups of travelers or customs people. Thus, in the center, in addition to the artist himself (a later self-portrait is preserved in Abbeville, another was represented at the Salon of 1777 and is today in Lisbon, the Gulbenkian Foundation) is the man who commissioned the painting, the Abbé Terray, a great collector of paintings, whose portrait was executed by Roslin (1774, Versailles).

The Salon of 1775 marked a turning point in the career of Lépicié. He thought of himself as a history painter and would not completely give up this mode. But he knew, from this point on, that he would owe his greatest success to the portrait (*Savant,* Salon of 1777; Lisbon, the Gulbenkian Foundation) and especially to genre scenes (*Atelier du Menuisier,* Salon of 1775, New York, Wildenstein Gallery). The *Interior of a Customhouse,* which unites under the topographical view of fantasy portraiture and genre, is a kind of "French" response to the equivalent Dutch, Roman, or Venetian attempts.

PROVENANCE

Commissioned by the Abbé Terray (1715-1778), Head Comptroller of Finance and Director General of Royal Buildings until August 1774; posthumous sale, 20 January 1779, no. 9 (3,821 *livres,* with its pendant, *Vue de l'Intérieur d'une grande halle*). Acquired by Dubois, sale of the Marquis de Ménars, Marquis de Marigny, end of February 1782 (postponed until 18 March), no. 54 (3,000 pounds with its pendant). Sale Claude-Joseph Clos, 18-19 November 1812 (no. 23, 984 francs with its pendant). Given by M. de Tarade (d. 1880) in May 1874, to Tours (mus. cat. 1881, no. 101). The gift was rescinded and the town had to give the painting to Tarade's widow, née Anne Limousin (*Inventaire général des Richesses d'Art de la France, Province, Monuments civils,* V. Plon, 1891, pp. 309-310). Tarade sale, 6-9 October 1881, no. 365 (21,500 francs with its pendant). Comte Daupias sale, Paris, 16-17 March 1892, no. 28 (bought again for 19,500 francs the pair). Sale at the Galeries de l'Universelle, 13-15 March 1893, no. 54, ill. (the last sale in which the two paintings, the *Halle* and the *Interior of a Customhouse,* appeared together). Mme C. Lelong sale, 27 April-1 May 1903, no. 36, ill. (9,200 francs to Marius Paulme). Henri de Rothschild Collection, then James de Rothschild; sale, 1 December 1966, no. 127. Acquired in 1966 by the Thyssen-Bornemisza Collection.

EXHIBITIONS

1775, Salon, no. 23; 1968, London, no. 429, ill. 166.

REFERENCES

Coll. Deloynes, v. X, no. 158, p. 481; no. 160, p. 559; no. 162, p. 615; no. 163, p. 643; no. 164, p. 21; Diderot, 1775, cf. J. Seznec, 1967, v. IV, pp. 235, 244-245, 281; L. Bachaumont, 1775 (ed. 1780), v. XIII, pp. 199-200; Ph. Gaston-Dreyfus, 1922, pp. 206-207, no. 182; Fl. Ingersool-Smouse, 1923, v. XLIII, p. 132; 1926, v. L, p. 293, 1927, v. LI, p. 182; Ch. Sterling, 1969, pp. 187-188, no. 163, pl. 312.

RELATED WORKS

The pendant, *Vue de l'intérieur d'une grande halle,* exhibited at the Salon of 1779 (no. 29), belongs to the collection of the Marquis de Ganay's descendants, Paris. A preparatory group drawing of the Swiss painting, with several variations in detail, in the Albertina in Vienna (17430; it most likely concerns no. 406 of Ph. Gaston-Dreyfus (1922), which came from the posthumous sale of Lépicié of 10 February 1785, no. 46). Another group drawing, but less finished which, like the painting, came from the James de Rothschild sale (no. 111 in the 1966 sale) and is located in the Thyssen Collection. A detail study (no. 110 of this same sale, cf. Ph. Gaston-Dreyfus, 1922, no. 407) is preserved in Paris, private collection (exhibited at the Galerie de l'Œil in 1969, no. 27 in the catalog, ill.). A study for the two seated female figures on the extreme left of the composition was reproduced in a recent catalog of the Schab Gallery in New York (1967, no. 36 with pl.). P. R.

Alexandre-Isidore Leroy de Barde

1777 Montreuil - Paris 1828

Exhibited in the Salon of 1817 were six large watercolors belonging to the King (see here No. 122) by a certain Chevalier de Barde. Despite the fascination of his still lifes of minerals and birds, he was never very well-known; no work concerning still life even mentions him. His work is comparable to Audubon, with a purity à la Berjon, an objectivity rivaling that of Van Dael, Redouté and Spaendonck. The artist's unique and highly competent exactitude is moving and, in the end, poetic. This alliance of the scientific and the artistic is very typical of the period of the Chevalier de Barde, whose style was formed at the end of the 18th century.

From an old Picardian family established in the Boulonnais, Leroy de Barde (who gave himself the title and signed his name "Le Chevalier de Barde"), emigrated at the age of 15 with his father and brothers because of strong Royalist convictions. Being a member for a time of the Army of the Princes (under the Duc de Bourbon), he shortly thereafter went to England.

Absolutely nothing is known about his training —for once perhaps we have a truly self-taught man !— the fact remains that in early 1797 he appeared at the Royal Academy as an "honorary" exhibitor (i.e., an amateur whose works were not for sale) with two watercolors, *Fruits* and *Raisins,* followed by three others in 1800 (still at the Royal Academy): *Double Narcisse et Lys de la Vallée, Branche de lilas, Chêne vert;* in 1801, *Fleur de Marronnier d'Inde;* in 1803, *Branche de lilas d'après nature* and *Mites et papillons.* That same year, he began his great series of watercolors representing curiosities from the Bullock Museum, described in the 1814 catalog. This catalog, which contains Thomas Bewick's engravings after certain of these watercolors, attests that they were exhibited together with the natural history curiosities which they represented; shown again in the Salon of 1817, these works of Leroy de Barde became the property of Louis XVIII and are preserved today in the Cabinet des Dessins in the Louvre: from 1803, the *Coquillages;* from 1804, the

Oiseaux (with an eagle-owl as the central motif), pendant to the 1810 *Still life with Birds* (No. 122); from 1813 (Braquehay, who in 1896 published a remarkably informative short treatise on the artist, says 1812, but the Louvre watercolor bears the date 1813), the *Vases grecs et étrusques* and the *Minéraux en cristallisation ;* finally, from 1814, the *Tigre Royal étouffé par un Boa,* inspired by the menagerie of Bullock and the reading of Buffon, and also reproduced by Thomas Bewick (see the 1814 catalog), of which this was one of the most renowned engravings.

About 1804, Leroy de Barde entered the Society of English Watercolorists, which was founded at that time. This fact, as well as the artist's relations at that time with the famous engraver Thomas Bewick (1753-1828), inventor of wood engraving (the process which replaced the traditional process of woodcut), proves that the artist was well assimilated into English life. Upon his death, according to Braquehay, at least 20 *clichés* of Bewick were found that were executed after drawings by Leroy de Barde, but only one has been preserved; reduced by one-fourth, it served as a frontispiece for the Bullock catalog of 1814 (assemblage of birds, snakes, shellfish, minerals and antique vases reproduced in Braquehay's short pamphlet).

One must ask whether Leroy de Barde belonged to the English art colony. It is difficult to categorize such an isolated, singular person, a sort of French Audubon (but one must admit that Audubon and, in general, all "scientific artists" like Redouté or Pancrace Bessa, for flowers, were so immersed in their fascinating objectivity that they do not exhibit characteristics of a "national" school). But one must call attention to the fact that Leroy de Barde, who had a veritable little aristocratic salon at 42 King Street in Covent Garden, always remained a confirmed émigré and signed himself as "Chevalier de Barde;" he kept his works for France so that they could become part of the royal collections, and frequented a society of Royalist French émigrés. He had close ties with Jacques Delille who, like himself, also lived in England: the meeting between Leroy de Barde and the great late 18th-century pastoral poet was in this regard quite significant, and Delille dedicated several verses to the artist's memory after his death. The poetry is lost today, but is pointed out in the *Feuilles d'affiches, annonces, et avis divers de l'arrondissement de Montreuil* dated 12 May 1829 (cited by Braquehay). In 1814, the artist returned to France with the Restoration of the Bourbon line, and at the beginning of 1815, he became lieutenant in the Scottish company of the King's bodyguards, commanded by the Duc d'Havré, and then accompanied Louis XVIII to Ghent during The 100 Days. But he was discharged in 1815 because of his short stature and placed on inactive duty at the disposition of the Ministry of War. He again resumed his watercolors by painting large landscape decorations for the Château de Recques-sur-Course near Montreuil which belonged to the Comte de Montbrun. Braquehay recorded a rather harsh judgment by one of his friends, for whom the colors were too sharp, not mellow enough, and the lines too heavy and obvious. Landscape was not his field. It is difficult to have an idea of the value of these decorative works on the basis of such an individual esthetic judgment. Three of the five are dated 1816 and 1817. Whether or not this is so, these works certainly seem to have been almost the only ones undertaken by the artist after 1815.

Named in 1816 by the King as a Knight of Saint Louis, and then his first painter of natural history (see the *Feuilles d'affiches,* of 1829, cited above), Leroy de Barde was still exhibiting in 1817: a miniature *(Portrait de Femme)*, and in 1819, *Minéraux du Cabinet particulier du Roi* (a watercolor which should not be confused with those of 1817), while at the same time entering the collections of Louis XVIII and being placed in his *cabinet minéralogique* (cf. in the Arch. Louvre, a letter dated 1822 from the appraiser of the royal museums to Forbin, director-general of the museums, concerning the appraisal of this watercolor at from 1,200 to 1,500 francs), and a *Fleur de marronnier d'Inde,* which had already been shown in London in 1801. In 1822, he re-exhibited his *Minéraux du Cabinet particulier du Roi.* Having completely given up his military career in 1818 (he was then eligible for a period of two years to receive funds specially earmarked for those who had left the military service), he married in 1821 and divided his time between his Paris residence and his château in the Boulonnais (Château de Bernieulles), gardening, trying his hand at sculpture and inventing a mill to grind apples. In 1822-23, his last important act was to sell his rich collection of natural history subjects that revealed his curiosities (2,400 pieces, of which 235 were exotic birds, 225 indigenous birds, 250 shellfish, etc.) to the town of Boulogne-sur-Mer. It is significant that while this collection also comprised 80 antique vases, it did not include a single painting. The purchase was ratified in 1825, and the museum was opened that same year.

J. F.

122
Still Life with Birds

"Réunion d'oiseaux étrangers placés dans différentes caisses"
Plate p. 205 and color pl. p. 25
Watercolor and gouache on paper; 126 × 90; s.l.l. *le chev*ᵣ. *de Barde pinx*ⁱᵗ *;* d.l.r. *1810*
Salon of 1817, no. 196
Paris, Musée du Louvre, Cabinet des Dessins

The exceptional inclusion in the present exhibition of paintings of this watercolor (if we can consider it as such) with its elaborate finish, extreme precision and the very mention of the group in the Salon catalog (which, by mistake perhaps, specifies that "These pictures belong to His Majesty")—reflects the attitude of its own time, since at the Salon some drawings, probably very finished and complete, were catalogued and shown in the midst of paintings.

The composition, which contributes to the unusual quality of this assembly of birds represented so faithfully in life-size, was moreover a painter's idea. The device had already been used by Northern or German painters, amateur virtuosos of trompe-l'œil like Johann Hainz, who painted a composition of precious ivories arranged in compartments on different levels (1666, Hamburg). But one must seriously doubt that any outside influence could have been exerted on such a self-taught, isolated painter as Leroy de Barde, so loyal to his subjects that he deliberately falsified perspectives and arbitrarily systematized shadows in an effort to make more legible the ingenious classifications he adopted. Great credit must be given to Leroy de Barde for perfecting an admirable formula to achieve a decorative effect that was almost unreal. His ingenuity becomes even more evident when one compares the intelligent clarity of his painting with the trees loaded with imaginary birds by Snyders and Kessel, or with the natural history scene painted in 1619 by an anonymous Frenchman, a veritable tangle of birds, in the Musée de Strasbourg (Haug, mus. cat. 1964, no. 51, ill.).

The birds in this work are all identified in the 1814 catalog of the Bullock museum in which Leroy de Barde's watercolor, like the "pendant" in the Louvre (see Related Works) and a third work of shellfish, is engraved with numerical references, listed here below. In the upper compartment around a large hyacinth macaw (4), moving clockwise, are a spurwinged water hen (6), a ringed plover (7), an aricari toucan (1, very

long beak), a Virginia nighthawk or nightjar (2, wings spread out), a golden pheasant (3, the fattest bird on the branch), a spotted tanager (5, the small bird perched underneath the pheasant), a rock manakin or rock Guinea Fowl (10, a bird with a tuft of feathers) and finally, to the right below the large macaw in the center, a gray phalarope (9), and to its left a taylor bird (8). In the cases, proceeding from bottom left to the top and then down the right side, are a waxwing chatterer on a branch (17), a great-tailed dove (18), on top a ruff-necked sandpiper (11), a grenadier grosbeck (12), a crested kingfisher (14), a spotted manikin (13), and finally a common bee-eater (15) and on the far right a crescent stare (16). Moving down to the small case on the left is a Brazilian finch (35, long back feathers) on a stick inserted into the wall of the case, in the small case on the right, a pair of amaduvade finches (36). The bird on the floor of the case is the female (37). At the extreme bottom right is a fat puffin hawk (38) and the head of a black-skinned skimmer (39). The central case of the lower area contains four more birds: a caurale snipe (20, with a long neck and striped feathers): a papual long (22, with very long feathers); a cut-throat sparrow (19, top right); and a bullfinch (21, top left). The eggs, too, were enumerated by Bullock. The biggest is obviously an ostrich egg (25), then, proceeding all around, starting at the right, a duck egg, surmounted by a pigeon egg; next, from right to left, a blackbird egg; a speckled egg that is probably that of a moor-game bird (31); flanked by two little eggs in front, either a chaffinch egg (30); an all-white chicken egg (29) and a wren (28). Then there are a speckled egg to the left of the hen's egg, and a plover egg in front of a big cassowary egg (24). Placed above and leaning against the ostrich egg is a guillemot egg (23, lightly tapered). The miniscule egg separated from the others in the foreground is that of a hummingbird.

The 1814 catalog recalled that the 27 birds represented here came from the Lever Museum, just like those in the 1804 watercolor cited below (the naturalists Latham and Shaw described it) and also like the 1803 *Coquillages*. This collection, according to the 1814 booklet, had been augmented by Parkinson and by the famous naturalist, H. Constant Jenning. These last two names are again found with those of John Mawe, Latham, Bournon—one will note the presence of this Royalist French emigrant, obsessively fascinated with minerology, whom Leroy de Barde must often have visited—and Humphrey and the British Museum, among the former owners or lenders of the 40 *Minéraux en cristallisation* reproduced in the 1813 watercolor (Salon of 1817, Louvre). As for the 1812 *Vases grecs ou étrusques* (Louvre), the catalog specifies that they were drawn from the collections of Thomas Hope (see here No. 162) and from the British Museum, and for the most part, came from the famous collections of Sir William Hamilton (1738-1818), English ambassador to Naples, whose collections the French archeologist, Millin, had partially described. The fame of certain of the names cited here attests to the publicity effort exerted by Bullock on this occasion.

PROVENANCE
At the Salon, already part of the collection of Louis XVIII; brought out of reserves and transferred in 1969 to the Cabinet des Dessins; exhibited with the other Leroy de Bardes, in the study rooms of the Cabinet des Dessins and the Rothschild collection (INV. 23692).

EXHIBITIONS
1814, London; 1817, Salon, no. 196.

REFERENCES
Catalogue of the different subjects represented in the large water-colour drawing by the Chevalier de Barde now exhibiting at Mr. Bullock's Museum; the Egyptian Hall, Piccadilly, London, London, 1814, pp. 7-13, ill. I (engraving by T. Bewick, see below); Bellier and Auvray, 1882, I, p. 43; A. Braquehay, 1896, pp. 26-27, 33.

RELATED WORKS
Engraving by Thomas Bewick, 1811 (published in Bullock's catalog of 1814).
Pendant—so called because of the subject matter, the dimensions, and the identical system of representation of birds which appear to be enclosed in wooden cases—also shown the Salon of 1817 (no. 194: *"Caisses contenant des oiseaux,"* s.d. 1804, Paris, Louvre, Cabinet des Dessins).

J. F.

Guillaume Guillon, called Lethière

1760 Sainte-Anne (Guadeloupe) - Paris 1832

In Paris, as a pupil of Jean-François Doyen, he placed second in the 1784 Prix de Rome competition with *La Cananéenne aux pieds du Christ* (Angers), and then stayed in Rome from 1786 to 1790; in Paris, he later exhibited regularly at the Salon from 1793 to 1831. Succeeding Suvée as director of the French Academy in Rome (1807-16), he had numerous pupils, including Ingres, with whom he became quite friendly. Ingres drew an important series of portraits of members of Lethière's family: in 1808, Mme Guillon-Lethière and her son Lucien (New York, Metropolitan Museum); probably from the same year, a portrait of Mme Lethière alone (Cambridge, Mass., Fogg Art Museum); in 1815, Lethière's son Alexandre with his wife and daughter (Boston, Museum of Fine Arts) and a portrait of Alexandre alone (Bayonne); finally, from 1818, the drawing of his grandson Charles (Paris, Musée des Arts Décoratifs). In 1819, Lethière was named professor at the École des Beaux-Arts in Paris and in 1825 a member of the Institute. Tempted especially by the neo-classical esthetic, in drawings (four drawings on the subject of the *Mort de Caton d'Utique* in the Musée de Quimper) as well as in paintings: *Brutus condamnant ses fils à mort* (1811, Louvre), he nevertheless dealt with subjects in the *style troubadour: Saint-Louis visitant les pestiférés de Carthage* (1822, Bagnères-de-Bigorre) and was also sensitive to landscape: *La Chasse de Didon* (1819, Tourcoing), *Paysage à la cascade* (Saint-Lô). He can be considered as a neo-classicist who, in a painting such as the *Mort de Virginie* (1828, Louvre), extended too far into the 19th century formulas which had already become outdated.

J. V.

123
Philoctetes at Lemnos

Philoctète à Lemnos
Plate p. 151
Canvas: 34 × 44
Brest, Musée des Beaux-Arts

In question here is the sketch of the large painting by Lethière, *Philoctète dans l'île déserte de Lemnos, gravissant les rochers pour avoir un oiseau qu'il a tué,* which was exhibited at the Salon of 1798 (no. 278) and which, after having been awarded a prize by the jury of the arts on 13 March 1799, entered the national collections (see Related Works). In 1872, it was placed in Cluny (Saône-et-Loire). This sketch differs considerably from the final painting: the head of Philoctetes is not shown here in profile, and a goat is seen instead of the dead bird. These differences, however, do not cast doubt on the attribution, especially since there was another version of this work, perhaps an autograph repetition (see Related Works), which also showed several variations in the form of the arch, the position of the bird, and the rendering of the trees. The same subject was represented by Achille-Etna Michallon (No. 130) and by Nicolas-Didier Boguet, with the collaboration of François-Xavier Fabre in a fine gouache representing *Philoctète tuant un oiseau* (Musée Sabatier).

PROVENANCE
Acquired by the museum in 1972.

REFERENCE
J.-P. Cuzin, 1972, p. 467, pl. II.

RELATED WORKS
The large painting, 315 × 315 (see above), placed by the Louvre at the Cluny museum (Saône-et-Loire) in 1877.
A version with several variations formerly in the collection of Lucien Bonaparte (see *La Galerie de Lucien Bonaparte,* London, 1812, no. 13).

J. V.

Jean-Baptiste Mallet

1759 Grasse - Paris 1835

A pupil of Simon Julien in Toulon and then of J.-F.-L. Mérimée and Pierre-Paul Prud'hon in Paris, Mallet first made his reputation with paintings and works in gouache (a technique of which he was particularly fond) of everyday subjects, often with libertine overtones in the elegant taste of Philibert-Louis Debucourt and Nicolas Lavreince, as well as of the elder Boilly. However, Mallet rescued himself from the banality of this genre by the precision and ingenuity of his decors, by turns "Egyptian," gothic, classicizing, Directory or Louis XVI (with surprising sculptural inventions in the style of Lequeu). In this vein, Mallet is one of the best chroniclers of furniture and interiors at the end of the 18th century. Good examples of this style can be seen at the Musée Cognacq-Jay and the Musée des Arts Décoratifs in Paris and also in Valenciennes. It is the type of work which often appears in public sales (the Goncourt brothers had a beautiful series of such works in their collection). Mallet, however, handled various genres with great diversity, although he seldom did portraits (*Chénier,* Carcassonne) or history (*Famille royale au Temple* in the collection of Lady Mendl and *Talma et Mlle Georges jouant Britannicus,* sold in Paris, Hôtel Drouot, 23 February 1968, no. 55, ill. in the catalog). He worked most often in the rustic genre or the *genre galant,* with bathing nymphs and antique nudes in the style of Jacques-Antoine Vallin (e.g., the small picture, *Bacchante dans un paysage,* which entered the Louvre in 1934). Some well-known compositions, such as the *Amour les conduit* and the *Amitié les ramène* (1811), engraved by Prud'hon *fils* and representative of Mallet's graceful mythologies, place the artist among the last and most fortunate survivors of the Hellenizing and neo-classical genre that derived from the art of Joseph-Marie Vien and the Lagrenées. Finally and most important, although this fact has perhaps not been sufficiently stressed, Mallet was an excellent painter of the *gothique troubadour* style and of Dutch interiors, rivaling Fleury Richard, Martin Drolling and Marguerite Gérard. He derived his style from Gérard Dou, Gabriel Metsu, and Gérard Terborch and with charming insolence juxtaposed accessories and masterfully interwove decorative elements and styles (Dutch chandeliers, rugs like those used by Metsu, gothic vaults, antique statues, etc.). In this regard, must be mentioned the *Intérieur de ménage* once in the collection of Josephine at Malmaison (see S. Grandjean, 1964, no. 1228, p. 168).

Mallet exhibited at the Salon from 1791 to 1824; among the various identified works are: in 1800, an *Antiquaire,* very probably the painting from the Paris sale of 24 March 1939 (Charpentier, no. 35, ill. in the catalog); it is one of the finest examples of the fusion of *troubadour* and Dutch-derived elements; in 1808, the *Nymphe au bain environnée d'amours,* which Landon en-graved; in 1810, the *Gothic Bath* (No. 124); for 1814, the *Intérieur de l'atelier de Raphaël* (Grenoble), engraved by Landon; in 1817, the *Éducation d'Henri IV* (Pau), engraved by Landon; in 1819, the *Nature et l'Honneur* (Marseille) and perhaps the *Bénédiction nuptiale* (Dijon, Musée Magnin); and in 1824, the last Salon in which he exhibited, *Geneviève de Brabant en prison baptisant son enfant* (Cherbourg). J.-B. Mallet was a second-class medallist in 1812 and a first-class medal winner in 1817. To the provincial museums of France already cited by J. Vergnet-Ruiz and M. Laclotte as owning works by Mallet (Carcassone, Cherbourg, Clamecy, Dijon [Musée Magnin], Grenoble, La Fère, Marseille, Pau [Château], and Valenciennes), we add Dieppe (see No. 124) and Grasse (the *Départ du volontaire,* which might well correspond with the painting for the Salon of 1793, i.e., the *Sacrifice à la patrie ou Départ d'un volontaire*).

Mallet's work was made widely known through engravings; among his engravers were Dissart, Levachez, Jazet, Allais, Prud'hon *fils,* Alix *(style troubadour* series for the story of *Beau Dunois),* Prot, Girard *fils,* J.-P. Simon (on the very popular Atala theme), Cardon and Benoist, Choubard, Bonnet, Mixelle, Copia, De Sève, Moithey, etc. J. F.

124
Gothic Bath

"Salle de bain gothique"
Plate p. 206
Panel; 40.5 × 32.5
Salon of 1810, no. 531
Dieppe, Château-Musée

The painting is easily identifiable as Mallet's *Salle de bain gothique* in the Salon of 1810, as proposed by the clipping of an old sales catalog pasted on the reverse of the panel. The work seems to have attracted hardly any attention from the critics, despite the appeal of its subject for the public. It is nevertheless a small masterpiece in the "Dutch neo-gothic" taste (the two realistic styles are often mingled) of these years, and it is certainly one of Mallet's most characteristic and happiest creations. Suffice it to mention the eclectic (sometimes even chronologically contradictory) and virtuoso multiplicity of accessories and details (there is even a ring on the letter lying on the little table !): the groin vault (like that in the *Antiquaire* of the 1939 sale, cited below), which is faintly romanesque and, in any case, visibly *haute époque.* The medieval window in the background is decorated with medallions of a completely different taste that are symbolic emblems for the female nude in the foreground. They illustrate couples from Ovid's *Metamorphoses:* below, Glaucus and Scylla (with a triton, cf. Spranger's famous picture in Vienna); above, Leda and the Swan (the sole episode not derived from Ovid); above, to the left, Pan and Syrinx (reeds are visible); and finally, on the right, Salmacis and

Hermaphrodite. The painter has skillfully and suggestively masked the other medallions with a curtain, while the armorial bearings at the top of the window provide the indispensable chivalrous tone. The sepulchral ambiance (surprising in such a subject—a bath) is accentuated by the back lighting (cf. Mallet's *Baptême* of 1824, sold Paris, 15 December 1922, no. 47, ill. in the catalog), as is also found in the medieval crypts so obligingly described by François-Marius Granet and later by Charles-Marie Bouton (cf. Bouton's 1828 lithographs in *Recueil d'intérieurs,* where the artist made frequent reference to the "carolingian" crypt of Saint-Médard de Soissons and included a "gothic" bath). Further tributes to Dutch 17th-century painting are the "medieval" setting, the ivoried nude à la Van der Werff, the occasional table and the Empire coffee pot (beautifully neo-classical piece, far from G. Dou's baroque ewer in his *Femme hydropique,* in the Louvre), and especially the "antique" armchair (so close to those of the Rembrandt milieus like the *Chambres de méditation* and the *Philosophes ;* cf. G. Dou; J. Van Vliet; Staveren, whose *Savant* was in the Louvre from 1793 on) are further tributes to Dutch 17th-century painting. Here, the Dutch models for Mallet were not so much Metsu and Terborch (so dear to Marguerite Gérard and Louis-Léopold Boilly), Kalf and Adrian Van Ostade (favored by Marie-Marc-Antoine Bilcoq and Martin Drolling) but rather the school of Leyden after the young Rembrandt and Dou, with its preference for enamel-like painting, cold and pure light and extreme meticulousness.

Mallet's Dutch *troubadour* style, with its apparent eclecticism, obviously approaches that of Fleury Richard, who was its great initiator from 1802 on (*Valentine de Milan,* Salon of 1802, location unkown) and it is not only the acid green of the curtain (which Richard's critics were quick to note) which derives from Richard.

In the œuvre of Mallet (his paintings are not as rare as P.G., in an article on Mallet in *Connaissance des Arts,* March 1957, p. 33, would have us believe) one usually finds a strong Dutch "exercise" comparable to that of the painting exhibited here. For example, his *Toilette de la mariée* (Frédéric Mallet sale, Paris, Hôtel Drouot, 9 February 1938, no. 154) features a Rembrandt-like armchair, lateral lighting from the window, a rich luster à la Dou and the smooth and graceful nude. The female type seen here, with her pure features and smooth chignon, as well as her pose (she is seen from the back with her head turned elegantly three-quarters toward the spectator) recur in figures depicted in many prints done after Mallet, such as the *Bain* in a crystal bathtub (by Girard *fils*) and the small preparatory line drawings, with a significant linear schematization, sold in Paris, 21 May 1937, no. 72, which form a complete series in which it is interesting to follow Mallet's progress as a neo-classicist). In opposition to this half-Dutch, half-Gothic manner (although this is no more than indicative of Mallet's fundamental eclecticism, which touches several esthetics simultaneously), the *Nymphe au bain environnée d'amours* (again the famous crystal bathtub with its fascinating transparency) from the Salon of 1808 (see C. Landon, 1808, II, pl. 31), with its mythological and gracefully antique genre deriving from Lagrenée the Elder, Jacques-Antoine Vallin, and Pierre-Paul Prud'hon, is a total stranger to the decorative and glossy bric-à-brac of the 17th-century Dutch minor masters of interiors.

PROVENANCE
Sale, Paris, Hôtel Drouot, 9 December 1926, no. 45, ill. in the catalog; Paris, Galerie Marcus, 1968; acquired from the latter by the Dieppe Museum in 1968.

EXHIBITION
1810, Salon, no. 531.   J. F.

125
The Bathing of the Infant Saint John the Baptist

La Toilette de saint Jean-Baptiste enfant
Plate p. 261
Canvas; 23 × 19; s.d.l.l.: *Mallet / 1820*
Paris, Private Collection

Unpublished until the time of its sale in 1974, this charming little picture enriches the small group, still little-known and too limited, of religious subjects painted by Mallet. In spite of his reputation, he must not be judged only by his dimension as a painter of gallant and libertine subjects executed during the waning 18th century. Early in his career, Mallet had produced works in the moralizing style of Jean-Baptiste Greuze (the *Catéchisme,* gouache, 1791, sold Paris, 1 June 1949, no. 29, pl. VIII; and a *Distribution des rosaires* of 1793, not to be confused with the *Couronnement d'une rosière* of the Salon of 1793, sold Paris [Galliera], 18 March 1966, no. 7, ill. in the catalog, after appearing in a New York sale, Parke-Bernet, 27 April 1963, no. 20, ill.). In 1824, Mallet represented at least twice the *Baptême* set in a "gothic" church with back-lighting in the Dutch style, somewhat like that of the painting in Dieppe (gouache, dated 1824, sold 15 December 1922, no. 47, ill. in the catalog), and especially like that seen in the famous small masterpiece in Cherbourg, *Geneviève de Brabant en prison baptisant son enfant,* well-known because of its appearance in the exhibitions at Brou (1971) and London (1972).

In its Italianate features (the trellised pergola, the view into the landscape, the costume and head-dress of the servant who holds the little Saint John—numerous elements recalling the style of A.-C.-H. Haudebourt-Lescot), and in its pure female types and its delicate precision of lighting, *The Bathing of the Infant Saint John the Baptist* comes very near to the family genre scenes at which Mallet excelled, for example the *Heureuse famille italienne* (gouache, sold in Paris, Palais Galliera, 19 March 1966, no. 6, ill); the *Amour maternel* (gouache, sold in Paris, 3-4 December 1934, no. 22,

ill., in which the mother has the same Greek profile and smooth chignon as does Elisabeth in the work exhibited here); and the *Famille,* gouache, in Rouen, Dr. Payenneville Collection (see *La Renaissance,* 1929, ill. p. 208). These works by Mallet are less overtly "Dutch" and "antiquarian"; here, he is more drawn to an "antique" dignity, and even approaches the moving manner of Pierre-Paul Prud'hon and Nicolas-André Monsiau. This somewhat timeless mood of dignity and grace, which contrasts with the rather showy affectations of the *style troubadour,* are seen again in the *Prière* (engraved by Prot) or in the *Hymen* (sold in Paris, Palais Galliera, 27 June 1963, no. 215, ill.), in which young people are crowned by a long-robed figure symbolizing marriage under a trellised pergola comparable to that of the work exhibited here.

By escaping pastiche and up-dating such thoroughly Dutch concepts (that is, to the eyes of an era which thus chose its references and ideals) of the finished, the velvety, the precise, the suave, Mallet attained here (as in his *Geneviève de Brabant* in Cherbourg) the perfection of his style. He well deserves Landon's evaluation of the picture in 1824: "There is no room in which one would not be happy to encounter a painting by this artist."

PROVENANCE

Sale, Paris, Palais Galliera, 26 March 1974, no. 18, ill.; withdrawn from the sale and still in its original collection.

J. F.

François-Guillaume Ménageot

1744 London - Paris 1816

The son of Augustin Ménageot, little-known as a painter but well-known as a dealer, François-Guillaume Ménageot was born in London in 1744 and came to Paris as a child. He entered the Royal Academy, where he was a pupil of J.-B. Deshays and, later, of François Boucher. He obtained the second Grand Prix in 1765 with his *Tullie faisant passer son char sur le corps de son père* (Nancy). In 1766, he won the Grand Prix with *Thomyris faisant plonger la tête de Cyrus dans un vase plein de sang* (Paris, École des Beaux-Arts) and then spent

three years at the École des Élèves Protégés before leaving in 1769 for Rome, where he spent five years.

Accepted into the Academy as a history painter in 1777, he exhibited at the Salon of that year *Les Adieux de Polyxène à Hécube* (Chartres), a huge composition which was warmly acclaimed by the critics. This marked the beginning of an auspicious period for the artist, who received numerous commissions. Religious commissions included: *La Justification de Suzanne* and *La Peste de David,* for the abbey at Anchin, exhibited at the Salon of 1779 (church of Saint-Pierre in Douai); *L'Adoration des Bergers*, for the Dames de Saint-Chaumont (Paris, church of Saint-Eustache); *La Naissance du Christ*, for the church of Neuilly (church of Villeneuve-sur-Yonne). Commissions for buildings included: *La Mort de Léonard de Vinci dans les bras de François Ier* (Amboise), the painter's masterpiece, which was immensely successful and made him the uncontested champion of the Salon of 1781; *Astyanax arraché des bras d'Andromaque* and *Cléopâtre rendant le dernier hommage à Antoine* (Angers), shown respectively at the Salons of 1783 and 1785. Commissions for the City of Paris included: *Allégorie à la Naissance du Dauphin* (sketch or reduced copy, Versailles) and *Allégorie à la Paix de 1783*, now lost, in 1782 and 1785.

Ménageot also did a number of easel paintings, now mostly known only from sale catalogs. The choice of subjects, frequently drawn from gallant mythology, moreover indicates to what extent this history painter was tied to the 18th century.

Ménageot was admitted as a member to the Academy in 1780 with *Learning Holding Back Time* (No. 126) and, in 1781, he was made an adjunct professor. The year 1785 marks a turning point in his career: David's *Horaces* was triumphantly hailed at the Salon, and Ménageot's *Cléopâtre* was eclipsed.

From 1787 dates *La Continence de Scipion* (Zidlochovice Castle, Czechoslovakia), composed like an antique relief and clearly neo-classical. The same year, Ménageot was named director of the French Academy in Rome. He sent *Méléagre supplié par sa famille* to the Salon of 1791 (Louvre). Although absent from Paris, he was named professor at the Academy in 1790.

The Revolutionary spirit did not take long to arouse the many Frenh artists in Rome. Ménageot, who was very close to his students, tried vainly to calm them

and finally resigned in 1792. He settled in Vicenza, where he must have painted to earn a living, but very few works from his stay there are known: *La Madone aux Anges* (Vicenza, Monte Berico), an *Autoportrait* (Florence, Galleria degli Uffizi), very close to the one in the Montpellier museum. In 1797, he was made a professor at the Florentine Academy of Fine Arts.

On his return to Paris, he again took up his post as professor at the National School of Painting and Sculpture in May 1801. He was made a knight of the Legion of Honor in 1804 and was elected a member of the class of the Fine Arts of the Institute in 1809. He devoted himself to the workings of the academies and occupied a prominent place within them. These honors perhaps compensated for his misfortunes in the realm of painting.

Ménageot did not have, or no longer had, the vigor requisite to the taste of the times; two works, now lost, shown at the Salon of 1806 were harshly criticized. *Le Mariage d'Eugène de Beauharnais*, commissioned that year for the Tuileries Palace (now, Versailles), proved unsatisfactory to the Emperor. *Dagobert Ier donnant des ordres pour la construction de l'église Saint-Denis* (recently lost) is his last large history painting. He died in 1816.

Ménageot's work is known above all for the large historical and religious paintings which demonstrate his sense of composition, color and beautiful drapery. His few extant sketches, however, have a freedom of movement and a spontaneity which illustrate how much more at ease the artist was in the warmth of the 18th century than he was with the discipline of neo-classicism, which he interpreted with a certain rigidity. This 18th-century painter played an important role, albeit a transitional one, in the return to the "grand manner"; he was outdistanced by the Davidian movement which he had helped to set in motion.

N. W.-B.

126
Learning Holding Back Time *

" *L'Étude qui veut arrêter le Temps* "
Plate p. 65
Canvas; 225 × 184
Salon of 1781, no. 152
Paris, École des Beaux-Arts

Learning Holding Back Time is a simple allegory with two protagonists: Time, in the guise of an old man

holding a scythe and an hour-glass, and Learning, represented by a seated woman with an open book before her. On the table are books, a pen, an inkwell and a lighted lamp; the scene thus takes place at night while Learning is still at work. At her feet are more books, a map of the world, a palette and brushes, a collection of prints, a ruler and a compass—traditional attributes of Science and the Arts. In her left hand, Learning is holding Time's cloak in an attempt to stop his course, but it seems her hold has just given way: the old man has already knocked over one of the two small genii in his way, while the other kneels on some architectural plans, trying to protect them and hence the monuments they represent.

This picture was required of Ménageot for his reception into the Academy. Accepted in 1777, the painter had exhibited the sketch at the meeting of 5 August 1780. On 30 December of that year he "had delivered the piece which had been requested of him" and "the Academy received Sr. Ménageot as a member" (*Procès-verbaux de l'Académie..., * IX, pp. 30, 45). Bachaumont commended the work in eulogistic terms and admired the "ingenious composition, the delightful tonality, the firm and velvety handling, and the excellent taste in the drapery" (*Mémoires secrets,* coll. Deloynes, XII, no. 247, p. 4). Shown at the Salon of 1781, *Learning Holding Back Time* was highly appreciated by the critics who added their praise to Bachaumont's. The painting "provides rare beauties; an ingenious composition, beautiful tonality, a happy choice of drapery, broad and facile brushwork, and a good measure of harmony" (*Réflexions joyeuses d'un garçon de bonne humeur,* coll. Deloynes, XII, no. 264, p. 325). However, the head of Learning "is too genteel" opined *La Vérité* (coll. Deloynes, XII, no. 260, p. 181) and Time "could be a bit more correct" (*idem,* no. 267, p. 386).

The painting entered the Academy's collections and was exhibited in the Salle de l'Assemblée. At the beginning of 1794, while Ménageot was residing in Vicenza, the painting was placed in danger of destruction following the reading of a report from Citizen Wicar "on the infamous conduct of several artists... now in Italy." Read at the meeting of 26 Nivôse, Year II (15 January 1794) of the Société Populaire et Républicaine des Arts, this report initiated a lively discussion, during the course of which it was proposed that the reception pieces of Ménageot and Gabriel-François Doyen be destroyed (H. Lapauze, *Procès-Verbaux de la Commune générale des Arts,* Paris, 1903, pp. 202-203). Fortunately, the matter was carried no further.

A comparison of the various known stages of the work—the drawing in Bayonne, the Montpellier sketch and the finished work—shows the artist's development of the intensity of movement he desired to achieve in this allegory. The rather static drawing for the figure of Time is the study of a man whose action is unclear—is he walking, stopping or turning back? The sketch, on the contrary, is animated by quick movement. Time jostles everything in his path, the small genius throws himself forward to bar the way and Learning prepares to stop Time. The painting itself contains a presentiment of destiny: Time advances powerfully, having already passed by Learning; the child cannot impede his course.

The figure of Time recalls the figure of an old man in the *Mariage de l'Amour et de Psyché* (Louvre, Cabinet des Dessins, R.F. 4552), seated near two cupids who place garlands on his scythe. The figure of Learning is very classical and beautifully draped. It is inspired by 17th-century Bolognese artists whom Ménageot, while director of the Academy in Rome, constantly referred to as models for his students. The small genii carry a hint of the 18th century. The large area of luminous silvered white, background for the action, the clear and very brilliant coloring, the blade of the scythe and the satin quality of Learning's drapery, the harmony of blue and gold set off by the red tonalities—all are constant features of Ménageot's œuvre. The artist executed *Learning Holding Back Time* at the age of 36, when he had reached the height of his career. The equilibrium of the work expresses the meridian of the author.

PROVENANCE
On 5 August 1780, at the meeting of the Royal Academy, Ménageot presented the sketch for *Learning Holding Back Time,* which had been required of him as a reception piece; on 30 December 1780, the painter was received into the Academy upon presentation of this painting. Collection of the Royal Academy; 1794, revolutionary confiscation; 1801, Musée Spécial de l'École française, no. 150; 1810, Musée Napoléon, no. 2122, Arch. Louvre, I DD 18, p. 550); decorated the Salle des Nobles, Grand Trianon (*idem,* I DD 55, p. 104); lent to the Gobelins factory (*idem,* I DD 65, p. 46); returned to the Grand Trianon and sent to the Louvre, 30 November 1836 (*idem,* 3 DD 21, p. 44); (INV. 6599); on 3 October 1873, sent from the Louvre to the École des Beaux-Arts.

EXHIBITION
1781, Salon, no. 152.

REFERENCES
Procès-verbaux de l'Académie..., 1889 ed., v. IX, p. 30, 45;

coll. Deloynes, v. XII, no. 247, p. 41; no. 255, p. 67; no. 257, p. 81; no. 259, p. 148; no. 260, p. 181; no. 262, p. 253; no. 263, p. 293; no. 264, p. 325; no. 267, p. 386; no. 269, p. 432; no. 277, p. 690, v. L; no. 1339, p. 142; Diderot, 1781, J. Seznec and J. Adhémar ed., v. IV, 1967, pp. 295, 301, 330, 370; C.-M. Pahin-Chamblain de La Blancherie, 1783, p. 243; C.-P. Landon, 1801-1809, v. III, p. 252; *Notices des tableaux... composant le musée spécial de l'École française,* 1801, p. 39, no. 150; H. Delaroche, 1816, pp. 1, 3; Ch. Blanc, 1857-1858, v. II, p. 311; *ibid.,* 1865, v. III, appendix pp. 32-33; A. Tornezy, 1895, p. 172; Franqueville, 1895, v. I., p. 159; H. Lapauze, 1903, p. 203; A. Fontaine, 1910, pp. 91, 191; G. Rouchès, 1924, p. 97; N. Ivanoff, 1967, nos. 1-2, p. 175.

RELATED WORKS

Painted sketch (panel; 27 × 21); purchased by the City of Montpellier (INV. 55-7-1). Sketch for the painting for reception into the Academy (heightened drawing, 44 × 31) in Calais, destroyed by fire following bombardment of the museum, June 1940.

Preparatory drawing for the figure of Time, black chalk heightened with white, on gray-beige paper (29 × 16.6), inscribed l.l. *G. Ménageot,* and l.r. *Ecole Française,* formerly in the Chabrillac Collection, later Bonnat Collection; bequeathed by the latter in 1922 to the Musée Bonnat, Bayonne (INV. 111).

Etching by Jean-Jacques Avril, Salon of 1791, no. 517.

N. W.-B.

Charles Meynier

1768 Paris 1832

A pupil of François-André Vincent, Charles Meynier received the Grand Prix in 1789, at the same time as Anne-Louis Girodet, with *Joseph reconnu par ses frères* (Paris, École des Beaux-Arts; sketch, Paris, private collection, exhibited by Cailleux, 1973, no. 27). Because the French Revolution forced the Academy pensioners to disperse, Meynier could stay only a short time in Rome. After returning to France, he began to exhibit at the Salon in 1795. His easy, amply decorative style, for which he drew largely on a Greco-Roman vocabulary, was soon established, as we see in the series of *Muses* painted for Boyer-Fonfrède of Toulouse (Salons of 1798 and 1800; *Apollon, Polymnie, Diane, Mercure ;* grisailles, dating from the Year III, Ministry of Foreign Affairs). Large imperial commissions gave Meynier the opportunity to exercise his talent in the "modern" style: *Marshal Ney and the Soldiers of the 76th Regiment* (No. 129), the *Entrée dans Berlin* (Salon of 1810, Versailles), and the *Empereur dans l'île de Lobau* (Salon of 1812, Versailles). Occasionally, Meynier executed portraits (*Ney* and *Cardinal Fesch,* Versailles) or religious paintings (*Dédicace de l'église de Saint-Denis* for the sacristy of Saint-Denis, Salon of 1812; *Communion de Saint-Louis,* Salon of 1817, Grand Trianon, Chapelle). But above all, he was one of the great decorators of the neo-classical period. In 1806, Meynier provided some large drawings (Louvre) for reliefs and figures for the Arc de Triomphe du Carrousel, the monumental entrance to the Tuileries. These were realized by a team of sculptors: Deseine, Cartellier, Ramey, Le Sueur, Clodion and others.

The first Restoration commissioned Meynier to do a number of ceiling decorations: *Naissance de Louis XIV* for the Grand Salon of the Tuileries (Salon of 1819, now in Amboise, Mairie) and especially for the Louvre: *La France protégeant les arts* (1819, Salle Percier; sketch, Dijon, Musée Magnin); *Triomphe de la peinture française* (1822, Salle Duchâtel; drawing in Coutances; sketch in the Louvre); *Les Nymphes du Parthénope* (1827, Salle G. of Egyptian Antiquities; drawing, Louvre); *La terre recevant des empereurs Adrien et Justinien le code des lois romaines* (1828, Salle des Empereurs).

Meynier was also the author of the grisaille paintings which decorate the right side of the main room of the Paris Stock Exchange (1826). One of his last works is the spirited, Rubenesque *Saint Michel* (1828), a masterpiece still located in the chapel of the Boulard asylum in Saint-Mandé.

Meynier's very beautiful drawings, strongly individualistic, usually drawn with a heavy, energetic stroke of the pen and heightened with wash, have been highly esteemed for some time.

J.-P. C.

127
*France Encouraging Science and the Arts**

La France triomphante encourageant les Sciences et les Arts au milieu de la guerre
Plate p. 132
Canvas; 65 × 74
Boulogne-Billancourt, Bibliothèque Marmottan

Three resolutions of the Committee of Public Safety in Floréal, Year II (August 1793) provided for a competition open to all artists. The painters could themselves choose for their sketch "the most glorious epochs of the French Revolution." A "Jury of Arts" with 27 members (for painting, sculpture and architecture) included among the painters in particular, Fragonard, Vien, Robert, Mérimée, J.-L. Lagrenée, Isabey and Pajou *fils*. The judgment and conferring of prizes was delayed (see J. Renouvier, 1863, pp. 21-22). The list of painted sketches was submitted to the Jury (Notice des ouvrages, Coll. Deloynes, LVI, pp. 193-246) without the authors' names. However, no. 99 on the list (p. 50 of the notice, *ibid.*, p. 244) is *La France protégeant les sciences et les arts, tab. allég. avec explication, 31 po larg. 24 haut.* In the bill of the "Jury of Arts" which proclaimed the awards (in all, 205,000 *livres* for the painters: François Gérard won the first prize, François-André Vincent the second; among the second-place prizes, under no. 99; was *Meynier, de Paris, chez le citoyen Vincent, aux Galeries du Louvre ;* the artist won 8,000 *livres* for the execution of a painting "of his own choice" (coll. Deloynes, LVI, no. 1735). There seems to be no doubt that the sketch in the Bibliothèque Marmottan is the one from the contest, despite a slight difference in dimensions (66 × 85 instead of 65 × 74).

Thus, it was the very idea underlying the competition that Meynier, flatteringly, selected as the subject for his sketch. This was noticed by Landon (1833, p. 60), who described the allegory as follows:

France, surrounded by instruments of war and crowned by the genius of Victory, is represented by a young woman wearing a helmet; she tramples underfoot the Furies which today recall the discord which prevailed for so long among the French. Painting, Sculpture and Architecture urge her to honor their works; after them come several Muses and two Genii, who celebrate the glory of France or record the history of her great deeds. Above these groups, we see Abundance distributing her gifts and Apollo who indicates to the Muses the reward promised to their favorites; this reward is Immortality, represented by an oak tree from which several Genii suspend medallions inscribed with the names of those who merit the approbation of posterity. In the distance, the artist has placed the image of battle, to reinforce the idea he wishes to suggest....

Landon's description calls for some comment. In the painted sketch, France wears a Phrygian bonnet, while Landon's text, like the accompanying engraving by C. Normand (see Related Works), gives her a helmet. This could represent a deliberate wish to generalize the scene or is simply a mistake of the engraver (who also neglected the trumpet held by the victory at the far right). On the other hand, the half-human, half-serpent monster lying behind the figure of France, could simply symbolize the armed coalition of foreign countries. The crown and sceptre she tramples could represent the allied foreign sovereigns rather than the fall of the French monarchy.

An important preparatory drawing, which features a surprising inscription attributing the sheet to Prud'hon, was acquired by the Alençon museum (see Related Works). It was studied by Arlette Sérullaz in the catalog of the exhibition *Le néo-classicisme français ; dessins des musées de province* (Paris, Grand Palais, 1974). It varies only slightly from the definitive composition; the most notable change is the appearance in the foreground, of the hybrid being who appears at the far left in the painting. It seems even more apparent, on the basis of this drawing, that the figure represents the defeated coalition.

The canvas in the Bibliothèque Marmottan is one of the earliest extant works of Meynier, who had just returned from Italy and was to exhibit for the first time in the Salon of 1795. The young pupil of Vincent here produced a picturesque painting, gracious and vibrant, gaily colored, still very 18th-century in spirit, as seen in the clusters of chubby putti, and somewhat in contradiction to the austere Revolutionary aspect of the theme. The artist later evolved toward a more ample and sculptural manner, but all the elements of his style—the physical types of his figures, the rich and varied colors, the taste for picturesque decor—have already been brought together in this allegory.

PROVENANCE

Paul Marmottan Collection; given to the Institute with the rest of his collection in 1932.

REFERENCES

Coll. Deloynes, v. LVI, no. 1736, p. 227; C.-P. Landon, 1833, v. II, pp. 60-61, ill. 32-33; Nagler, v. X, 1907, p. 292; P. Fleuriot de Langle, 1938, p. 71, no. 104.

RELATED WORKS

Drawing, pen and wash, 60 × 75.8, inscribed l.l. *P.P. Prudhon l'an 2*, from Lyon, private collection, Musée d'Alençon (acquired in 1974).

Engraving by C. Normand in Landon, v. II, pls. 32-33.

J.-P. C.

128
Napoleon on the Battlefield of Eylau

Napoléon sur le champ de bataille d'Eylau
Plate p. 197 and color pl. p. 22
Canvas; 93 × 147; inscribed l.r. *Gros*
Versailles, Musée National

In the spring of 1807, 26 painters each provided a sketch for the competition for the execution of a large painting representing Napoleon on the battlefield of Eylau. Among them were Meynier, Roehn, Brocas, Pajou, Thévenin, Debret, Hersent, Lafond, Franque, and Gros—Gros having decided to compete only at last moment, upon the request of Denon.

The battle of Eylau (8 February 1807) was one of the bloodiest of the Empire. Denon, director of museums, in a notice to the competitors, dated 17 March "from the Grand Army," proposed as the subject for their paintings "the moment in which Bonaparte, visiting the battlefield, comes to bring help and consolation to the innumerable victims of combat." An appended notice further specified the subject; a rough sketch of the battlefield, perhaps by Denon himself, was to be at the disposal of the artists (see P. Lelièvre, 1955, pp. 53-54). A committee selected by the fourth class of the Institute was asked to judge the sketches, shown in the Galerie d'Apollon; this committee, chaired by François-André Vincent, gave the first prize of 16,000 francs to Antoine-Jean Gros (sketch, private collection, which may well have led to the masterpiece exhibited at the Salon of 1808 and today in the Louvre) and gave two honorable mentions (awarding each a gold medal and 600 francs), to Meynier and Charles Thévenin.

Meynier thus received the first honorable mention with this sketch, done in a sober harmony of gray-green tones and browns relieved by a few red touches. The overall composition (determined, apparently, by the drawing submitted to the artists) strongly approaches that adopted by Gros, even if Meynier's composition is more congealed and harshly "neo-classical." The artist, in the foreground of his picture, placed an assembly of cadavers, represented nude, unlike Gros. It is this aspect of the program which appears to have been particularly interesting to the competitors and to have struck their imaginations. A police report even protested: "The artists have accumulated all sorts of mutilations, the varieties of a vast butchery, as if they had been specifically requested to paint a scene of horror and carnage and to render war abominable" (Arch. Nat., O² 842; see P. Lelièvre, 1942, p. 114, no. 29). The political outcome thus seems to have been the reverse of what was intended.

This sketch, which bears the false signature of Gros, was only recently reattributed to Meynier, thanks to an incisive intuition of M. Boris Lossky (see exh. cat., 1959, Tours, no. 72), who compared it with other works by Meynier. Meynier's easily recognizable style—a marked graphic quality and characteristic facial types with prominent nose and chin. There is a large, signed, preparatory drawing, now in the Louvre (see

Related Works), which differs from the Versailles canvas in a few details: in the drawing, the lower zone devoted to the cadavers is perceptibly more important, and the landscape and sky are less developed.

EXHIBITION
1959, Tours, no. 72, ill. 25 ("éc. française, 1807").

REFERENCES
C.-O. Zieseniss, 1960, pp. 213-220, ill. p. 214; G. Van der Kemp, 1965, p. 48, ill. 6; C.-O. Zieseniss, 1970, p. 93; Y. Cantarel (1973), pp. 381-387.

PROVENANCE
One of the sketches for the competition of 1807; in a château in the environs of Confolens (Charente) until 1942; Mme Paulette Rogeon Collection, Tours; acquired in 1960 by the museum at Versailles (MV. 8128).

RELATED WORKS
Preparatory drawing, pen and wash, gray over charcoal outlines, squared in sanguine, heightened with white; 58.4 × 94.1; s.d.l.l. *C. Meynier*; Louvre, Cabinet des Dessins, INV. 30987 (see. Ch.-O. Zieseniss, 1960, pp. 213 and 220, fig. 2, p. 215).

J.-P. C.

129
Marshal Ney and the Soldiers of the 76th Regiment*

"Les soldats du 76ᵉ régiment de ligne retrouvant leurs drapeaux dans l'arsenal d'Instruck..."
Plate p. 198
Canvas; 360 × 524; s.d.l.l. on a step *C. Meynier pt. 1808*
Salon of 1808, no. 429
Versailles, Musée National

This huge painting is one of 18 canvases commissioned by a decree 3 March 1806, to illustrate the "German Campaign" of Napoleon's troops. This commission had been prepared through various reports sent by Denon to the Emperor. From among these exist three rough drafts, one undated, one from 19 February, and another from 20 February 1806. The matter had thus been studied, reported and settled in a fortnight (on this commission, see P. Lelièvre, 1942, pp. 60-69).

Nine large paintings were entrusted to (besides Meynier), Gautherot, Hennequin, Lethière, Gérard, Girodet, Gros, Guérin and Monsiau; nine panels of half the size were assigned to Taunay, Ménageot, Berthélémy, Dunouy and Demarne, Perrin, Hue, Le Jeune, Bacler d'Albe, and Peyron (No. 141). The subject given to Meynier seems to have been chosen by Napoleon himself. A report by Denon of 3 June 1806 indicates that he had seen the artists, given them preliminary drawings from his files, enlightened them on the events to be represented and was waiting for them to submit their sketches in order to settle with each the composition for his panel. Another report from Denon, from two years later (15 August 1808), indicated that 13 of the 18 paintings were completed and ready for the opening of the Salon, 14 October 1808; those of Lethière, Gérard, Gros and Bacler d'Albe were missing.

The subject of Meynier's composition is an episode from the campaign of 1805, just prior to the entrance of the French troops into Vienna. On 7 November the sixth army corps, commanded by Ney, took the city of Innsbruck, in the Tyrol. The 76th line regiment retrieved from the arsenal three flags that had been lost during the campaign of 1800.

The 76th line regiment had lost three flags in the Grisons. This loss had for a long time been the symbol of a profound suffering. These brave fellows knew that Europe had not forgotten their misfortune, even though no one would deny their courage. These flags, the subject of such noble remorse, were found in the arsenal in Innsbruck. An officer recognized them and all the soldiers gathered round immediately. When Marshal Ney restored them, tears gushed from the eyes of all the old soldiers, and the young conscripts were proud to have played a part in the recapture of the standards taken from their elders. His Majesty the Emperor had asked that this touching scene be commemorated in painting. (Catalog of the Salon of 1808.)

A medal was struck to commemorate the moment; executed by Brenet from a drawing by Denon, it bears the legend: *Les Autrichiens vaincus. Les drapeaux français repris. Insbruck le XVI Brumaire an XIV. MDCCCV.*

Denon approved highly of Meynier's painting; in his report to the Emperor on 15 August 1808, satisfied at seeing the large canvas finished before the opening of the Salon, he wrote: "The artist has made the very best of a subject which presents great difficulties. He has expressed well the enthusiasm and love of the French soldier for his flags, and in order to mitigate the shame of having lost those which are being returned to them, he has placed the old soldiers so as to show the scars they had received in defending them to their utmost ability." The mystique of the flag is, in fact, one of the emotional catalysts of the imperial period; suffice it to mention David's *Distribution des Aigles* (Versailles).

The critics in general were very favorable. "This picture, with its proud draughtsmanship and vigorous painting, does honor to the broad and mature brushwork of this great artist. It is one of the most beautiful at the Salon" (*L'Observateur au Museum,* coll. Deloynes, XLIII, no. 1137, pp. 18-19). And, "...groups here are drawn with precision, the hues well distributed, the coloring is pleasant" (*Le Nouvel Observateur au Musée Napoléon,* coll. Deloynes, XLIII, no. 429, p. 11). The critic of the *Observation sur le Salon de l'an 1808* congratulated Meynier on avoiding monotony by varying the military costumes; he admired the area "in the foreground, where there is a wounded soldier, whose arm is supported by a large sling, and which produces an excellent effect"; he nevertheless objected to "a too-uniform tonality," and a "brick color" (coll. Deloynes, XLIII, no. 1139, pp. 674-676). In the *Examen critique et raisonné des tableaux* (coll. Deloynes, XLIII, no. 1143, p. 17), the critic admired the "beautiful" and "happy" ideas of the soldier who presses a flag to his breast, the one who shows the scar of a wound received defending the flags, and another who marks the wall to commemorate the event, and the old sapper with the somber look, whose "memory of the loss of the flags outweighs his joy at their recovery;" finally, "...the general ordering is well understood, the groups are artfully disposed and interrelated; the color is agreeable, although not vigorous enough." The critic of the *Exposition des ouvrages de peinture, sculpture, architecture et gravure des artistes vivants* (coll. Deloynes, XLIV, no. 1146, pp. 298-301) praised the canvas, in which he found "pomp, light, movement, activity," and also "pleasing ideas... difficult costumes executed with a good deal of taste and style, lively and varied expressions, beautiful attitudes." But he objected to "the entire composition [being] overridden by a tumult which forbodes a revolutionary scene rather than the satisfaction and joy of these victorious soldiers... some of the heads seem to be those of savages, and we do not see why the artist has made the hair of almost every soldier stand on end." He also found fault with the drawing and harshly concluded, "This painting, it cannot be disputed, is done from inspiration." Likewise, Ducret du Ménil, the editor of the *Journal des Petites Affiches de Paris,* reproached Meynier for "an excess of heat in his composition" (coll. Deloynes, XLIV, no. 1149, pp. 518-521). During the conferring of decennial prizes awarded in 1810 for the fourth class of the Institute, Meynier's large painting received an "honorable mention [in the] ...category of the best painting representing an honorable subject regarding the national character."

The large format permitted the painter to use a frieze-like composition, accented by the rhythmic elements of the architecture and enlivened by the play of diagonals in the weapons and in the flag staffs. The national colors form the basis of the color harmony: reds, pinks, oranges, browns and violet-grays, contrasted with blues, slate tones and bluish-grays. The canvas, both "inspired" and adhering to a strict Neoclassicism, distinguishes itself as one of the great successes of Meynier, who more often is conventional and illustrative.

In Alençon is a very beautiful sketch that already shows the composition in its broad outlines (see Related Works). The principal variation is in the face of the Marshal, here less individualized and wearing a feathered bicorn. Feverish, transported, violent and energetically executed, the Alençon sketch in some aspects recalls Géricault.

PROVENANCE
Palais de Compiègne, 1809; Gobelins manufactory, 1810; Musée du Luxembourg, 1819; Château de Versailles, 1835; exhibited in 1837, room 63.

EXHIBITIONS
1808, Salon, no. 429 ("Les soldats du 76e de ligne retrouvant leurs drapeaux dans l'arsenal d'Inspruck, les reçoivent des mains de leur général, Monseigneur le Maréchal de l'Empire Ney, commandant le 6e corps de la Grande Armée"); 1830, Paris, Luxembourg, no. 178.

REFERENCES
Coll. Deloynes, v. XLIII, no. 429, p. 11; no. 1137, pp. 18-19; no. 1139, pp. 674-676; no. 1143, p. 17, v. XLIV; no. 1146, pp. 298-301; no. 1149, pp. 518-521; C.-P. Landon, 1808, v. I, pp. 39-40; A.-Ch. Quatremère de Quincy, 1837, p. 119; E. Soulié, 1859, v. I, p. 485; F. Benoit, 1897, p. 198; G.-K. Nagler, v. X, 1907, p. 292; P. Lelièvre, 1942, pp. 61, 64-65; Y. Cantarel, 1973, pp. 386-395.

RELATED WORKS
Paintings. Sketch, 48 × 81, Alençon museum, from the Denon Collection; acquired in 1863 (mus. cat., 1938, no.132, p. 45).
Drawings. Drawing of the overall composition (lost), Meynier sale, November 1832, no. 16, "pen and sepia drawing for the painting in the Luxembourg gallery." Four drawings (lost) *ibid.*, no. 45, "Four studies for the flags of Innsbruck... taken from nature."

Prints. C. Normand, line engraving (in Landon, Salon of 1808); A. Tardieu, line engraving (*Ambroise Tardieu direxit*); Châtaigner (*Dessiné par Marchais, gravé à l'Eau-forte par Châtaigner, terminé par Oortnan*); David (*Dessiné par Mounet, gravé par David*); and Wolff (in Gavard, *Galerie Historique de Versailles*, no. 783).

J.-P. C.

Achille-Etna Michallon

1796 Paris 1822

This painter was the son of the sculptor Claude Michallon (1751-1799). An orphan at an early age, he studied with P.-H. de Valenciennes, J.-V. Bertin, A.-H. Dunouy and J.-L.. David. A gifted pupil, he exhibited at the Salon as early as 1812 and received a second-class medal. In 1817 he won the Grand Prix for historical landscape, a category which had been created for him in 1816 by Vaublanc, Minister of the Interior. The paintings which he sent from Italy as a pensioner at the Villa Medici were criticized by the Institute, then under the influence of Quatremère de Quincy. However, judging the works of his last year, the Commission of the Academy of Fine Arts urged him, "now that he seems so well nourished and imbued with the masters of art, to devote himself unhesitatingly and with confidence to the study of Nature" (Arch. Académie des Beaux-Arts, E 12). The works he sent to the Salons of 1817, 1819 (*La Mort de Roland,* Louvre) and 1822 were favorably received by critics such as Gault de Saint-Germain, Kératry, and Forbin. He was the first teacher of Jean-Baptiste Corot. It was thought that he would be the "modern Poussin," when death claimed him at the age of 26.

M. Pierre Lamicq is currently preparing a monograph on Michallon.

J. L.

130
Philoctetes at Lemnos

Philoctète dans l'île de Lemnos
Plate p. 267
Canvas; 67 × 98; s.d.l.r. *Michallon/1822*
Montpellier, Musée Fabre

This work was probably begun in Rome, although this is not verified in the archives of the Academy of Fine Arts. The composed landscape is strongly reminiscent of the work of Pierre-Henri de Valenciennes and Jean-Charles-Joseph Rémond. P. Lamique has also noted Michallon's repeated use of identical elements in various works; here we see the same large rock formation as in sketch of *La Mort de Roland* in Strasbourg. Once again, Michallon has chosen a subject (here the wounded Philoctetes dragging himself over the rocks to retrieve a dove brought down with his arrows) to provide a pretext for a tragic effect. The painting appears to be an example of the dramatic landscape (see M. Brion, 1967, pp. 97-144) popularized in Germany at the beginning of the century by Joseph-Anton Koch and which, according to the region, took a variety of forms.

PROVENANCE
Gift of François-Xavier Fabre to the museum in 1825 (Fabre is known to have acquired several of Michallon's works at the artist's posthumous sale with the aid of Bertin the Elder; we do not, however, know which works these were (see L.-G. Pélissier, 1896, IX, pp. 230-233).

REFERENCES
G. Lafenestre and E. Michel, 1878, v. I, p. 222; L.-G. Pélissier, 1896, v. IV, p. 333; G. d'Albenas, mus. cat., 1910, no. 404; A. Joubin, mus. cat., 1926, no. 685; J. Vergnet-Ruiz and M. Laclotte, 1962, p. 2.

RELATED WORKS
P. Lamique has pointed out to us a smaller copy (anonymous) in a private collection in Paris. No drawing study can presently be linked with this work. We should note that the subject was illustrated frequently in this period (cf. No. 123).

J. L.

Georges Michel

1763 Paris 1843

The little information we have concerning the painter Georges Michel comes from the account which his second wife (whom he married only in 1828) gave in 1849 to the art lover and critic Alfred Sensier. "An enthusiastic confident of romantic landscapists" (R. Bouyer), Sensier was anxious to gather information about this obscure artist whose existence would otherwise have been known only through a few rare references to paintings and drawings. His researches resulted in the first monograph on Michel (1873), a work that covers the essential facts and has never been superseded.

The son of an employee at Les Halles, Michel was apprenticed at the age of 12 to the history painter Leduc, adjunct professor at the Academy of Saint Luke, but he soon escaped from the studio in order to draw landscapes from nature. He is mentioned at the age of 15, as giving lessons himself and as having abducted a young laundress! There is no mention of him again until 1783, at which time he was the father of five children. Up to about 1789 he had to give drawing lessons in order to provide for his family, sometimes in Paris (to Mlle de Chalue and to M. de Grammont-Voulgy), sometimes in the provinces (in Normandy, to Colonel de Berchigny) or abroad (to the Duc de Grammont in Switzerland and to the Duc de Guiche in Germany). It was probably at his time that he met Baron d'Ivry, the great art lover, future patron of Alexandre Decamps and Nicolas-Louis Cabat, and himself a painter, who encouraged and supported Michel and was for a certain period his only buyer. Around 1790, the artist became friends with Lazare Bruandet, a landscapist accustomed to working from nature. Georges Michel was ideally suited to understanding the vagabond painter; he was independent to a fault and, like him, passionately interested in landscape and nature. He visited him often up to his death in 1804. Throughout his life, Michel painted, as did Bruandet, the environs and various sections of Paris, especially Montmartre. He detested traveling and, like Rembrandt who made fun of the obligatory trip to Italy, was fond of saying, "Anyone who cannot spend his whole life painting four spatial sites, is only an oaf who is looking for the mandrake and will find only the void. I ask you, did the Flemish and Dutch ever travel? Nevertheless, they were good painters, the worthiest and boldest and most objective."

Michel participated in the Salons between 1791 and 1814. The critics in general remained indifferent, if not hostile, to his works, and Michel finally abandoned these official exhibitions. The work *Un défilé d'une armée* (s.d. *Michel et Swebach 1797*) reveals his collaboration with the painter from Lorraine. Around 1800, the art dealer Lebrun provided him with commissions for copies of the landscapes of Ruisdael, Hobbema, Rembrandt and other Dutch painters. He restored paintings for Cardinal Fesch. For Vivant Denon, he assisted in the important restoration of Dutch and Flemish pictures in the Louvre, where he was given lodgings. Around 1808, he was running a sort of school for painting, but he soon abandoned this project. At one point, he opened an antique shop, only to close it shortly after. From 1821 until his death in 1843, he was a recluse who no longer attempted to exhibit his work. He thus condemned himself to an undeserved obscurity. During the seclusion of his last 20 years, his life was regulated in an immutable way: he painted at home from seven in the morning until three in the afternoon; then, with his wife, he strolled through the streets of Paris and drew as he went. The account of his wife reads, "He rarely painted from nature, but he drew the views which pleased him on little squares of paper; we would then return home through Montmartre...; he made hundreds and hundreds of little drawings." A sale of his studio in 1841 disclosed his prolific production: more than 1,000 paintings on paper and 2,000 drawings, which altogether brought 2,500 francs. He died, totally forgotten, in 1843.

The rediscovery of Michel is fortunate. It was not until 1848 that the painter emerged from total oblivion, when Paul Lacroix published the first fairly accurate biographical sketch. In 1872, an exhibition at Durand-Ruel in London brought Michel public notice. The following year Sensier put together his catalog of Michel's work. He dedicated the book to Jules Dupré, Charles-Jacques and the Barbizon painters—who claimed Michel as their precursor and paid him homage. The artist was saved from oblivion.

Sensier inventoried only 150 pictures. The number of lost works is therefore large. Their chronology presents difficult problems, since almost none of his works are signed or dated (see No. 131). Regarding

signatures, Michel used to say to his friend Jean-Louis Demarne: "Do what you wish; as for me, you know what I think of a signature. I never put one on a painting, because painting should speak for itself, and the signature is only a cajoler aiming at deceit and seduction; the painting should be pleasing without recourse to a name or a label. We should follow the ancients, who did not sign and whose signature lay in their talent." The paintings exhibited in the Salons and listed in the Salon catalogs might constitute points of reference were it not that their titles are too vague. The titles themselves—*Marché de chevaux et d'animaux* (Salon of 1791), *Vue en Suisse* (Salon of 1793), *Cour champêtre, Défilé d'une armée*—link Michel to his skillful contemporaries (Nicole-Antoine Taunay, Jean-Louis Demarne, Jacques-François Swebach), but occasionally a title such as *Effet de pluie* (Salons of 1798 and 1808) discloses his unspoken preferences. In any case, the "Ruisdael of Montmartre," as Paul Mantz called him, who lived only for painting, created, along with contemporary English landscape painters like John Crome, Richard Bonington and John Constable, at the beginning of the 19th century, a new type of landscape which commands attention and respect today for its epic breadth, staunch independence and occasionally poignant evocation of the Dutch vision.

A.-B. L.

131
Storm

L'Orage or *Animaux à l'abreuvoir*
Plate p. 140
Canvas; 39.5 × 57; s.d.l.l. *G. Michel/3e année* (the signature is almost invisible today because of bitumen damage)
Nantes, Musée des Beaux-Arts

Paintings by Georges Michel that are signed—more especially signed and dated—are extremely rare. For that reason, the work in Nantes, which was singled out at an early date and which appeared in a collection formed before 1810, is of particular interest. In catalogs up to 1876, the poorly-legible signature was interpreted as that of the painter Pierre-François Michel, about whom nothing is known and who is categorized as a follower of Salomon Van Ruisdael. On the basis of a correct reading furnished him in 1873 by Coutan, curator at that

time, Alfred Sensier, commented extensively on this work. He interpreted the still-legible inscription as "*3e année*," Year III of the Republic or 1794-95. In 1913, M. Nicolle was unable to find the date, but suggested that it was covered by the frame. The brevity of the notices in the Salon catalogs prevents any identification of the Nantes picture as being one of the works exhibited in the Salons of 1795 or 1796. Since a signature and date are so rare with this artist, he probably did consider it important and most likely it did appear at a Salon. In 1887, O. Merson proposed that the *Storm* was one of the three paintings from the Salon of 1796 described under no. 332 as "a genre painting and two landscapes with figures and animals." This interpretation of the date seemed feasible and was accepted by all subsequent writers. The only other work clearly dating from the same period is the *Convoi* or *Défilé d'une armée* doubly signed "*Swebach-Defontaine G. Michel, 1797, l'an 5*" (panel, 56 × 76) which at the time of Sensier's writing was in the Du Mesnil-Marigny Collection (Sensier, 1873, pp. 123-125 and catalog no. 1, p. 136), and by 1927, was in the Christian Lazare Collection (G. Michel exh., Paris, Hôtel J. Charpentier, 1927, no. 3; G. Michel exh., Paris, Galerie G. Stein, 1938-1939, no. 46). Sensier catalogued another landscape, *Entrée de bois,* (s.d. 179..., last digit illegible), in the collection of Alfred Renaud. But he did not reproduce the work, and its present location is no longer known. With so few signed and dated works, it is difficult to reconstruct the development of the artist's style. Sensier's subdivision of his work into three periods runs the risk of appearing somewhat artificial. The Nantes picture does resemble the one in the Lazare Collection in its overall disposition—a somber belt of land in the foreground acts as a foil to the vast, illuminated horizon under the tremulous sky, all seen from a slightly elevated and ideally panoramic viewpoint. Apparently having suffered somewhat, the Nantes picture appears less incisive and less meticulously detailed than the 1797 work, and thus does not correspond well to the somewhat tight and labored early style defined by Sensier. If the Nantes picture does date from 1795, it demonstrates Michel's powerful "Dutch" manner, his loyal and yet liberating adherence specifically to the manner of Ruisdael, more strongly visible in this painting than in other works where the influence of Hobbema or of Rembrandt is felt. On this subject, see the significant account of the Michel painting, *Paysage avec figure, genre de Ruisdaël* in Boilly's inventory of 1795 (cf. B.S.H.A.F., 1929, p. 24). It would undoubtedly be wrong to imagine that Georges Michel could remain a timid creator of pastiches for long. Already the sweeping rupture of the sky in the Nantes painting foreshadows the boldness of the works generally assigned to the artist's second and third periods,

which as R. Lebel indicated in his thesis of 1923 (a very brief summary of which appeared in the *Bulletin des Musées de France,* 1929, pp. 215-216), should be placed much earlier than is usually believed: "Michel was aware of his true character from the beginning of the 19th century." Conversely, the works dated later, like the 1832 watercolor exhibited at the Galerie G. Stein, Paris, 1938-39 (no. 69, ill. in the catalog; also at this exhibition there appeared another dated work, a painting of 1829, *Nuages d'orage sur la plaine,* which was not reproduced in the catalog) and the painting *Relais de la diligence* (s.d. 1822, sold in Paris, Galerie Charpentier; 29 January 1957, no. 27; ill. in the catalog) show a somewhat petty precision which in theory should rule out dating them some 20 years after the Nantes picture. This observation demonstrates the fragility of the various hypotheses on Michel's evolution; several styles seemingly can co-exist very well in one artist at the same time !

It is difficult to precisely attribute the figures, given to Taunay according to tradition (in the older catalogs of the museum). They do not stand out sufficiently and, in any case, do not have the rounded and pleasantly sculptural quality of Taunay's figures. Coutan and Sensier therefore rightly ignored this freely interpreted attribution. Even so, it is true that occasionally Michel collaborated with other painters, such as Demarne and especially Swebach, as evidenced by the doubly-signed picture from the Lazare Collection.

PROVENANCE
Former collection of M. Fournier, Inspector-Surveyor of Nantes, who died in 1810 valued at 220 francs in inventory, cf. O. Merson, 1887, p. 46); acquired from his widow with the rest of the Fournier Collection (47 paintings, mostly from the 18th and early 19th-centuries, including works by Bruandet, Hue, Schall, Loutherbourg, Caresme, Oudry, Chancourtois, Auger Lucas, and Philastre, some northern works, and two still lifes signed by Mather).

REFERENCES
Mus., cat., 1859, no. 158 (as Pierre-François Michel); A. Sensier, 1873, pp. 125-127, cat, no. 2, p. 136; mus. cat., 1876, no. 841 (G. Michel); Bellier and Auvray, v. II, 1885, p. 87; O. Merson, 1887, mus. cat., p. 46; R. Bouyer, 1897, p. 308, note 3; M. Nicolle, 1913, no. 1106, p. 128; R. Bouyer, 1927, p. 242; L. Larguier, 1927, p. 67; G. Pudelko, 1937, p. 241.

J. F.

Antoine-Pierre Mongin

1761 or 1762 Paris - Versailles 1827

Trained in the Royal Academy from 1782 to 1785, Mongin was a frequent exhibitor at the Salon from 1791 to 1824. His work, largely unstudied, with the exception of numerous gouaches which made him Moreau the Elder's best disciple, covers a wide range of subjects: landscape and city views, scenes from military life, animals, sentimental genre, literature (*Robinson Crusoe*) and French national history from Joan of Arc to Napoleon. The few paintings by him which are preserved include a group of eight park scenes and landscapes (dated 1793, 1795, 1796) and two genre scenes located at Schwerin; *La Bénédiction de troupeaux partant pour les Alpes* (Salon of 1814, Marseille); two military events from Napoleonic history, *Le Bivouac de l'Empereur, près le château d'Ebersberg le 4 mai 1809* (Salon of 1810, Versailles) and *Passage de l'Armée de réserve dans les défilés d'Albarède, près du fort de Bard* (Salon of 1812, Versailles). As in *Curiosity* (No. 132), these works suggest that Mongin's art was based on a direct and unpretentious naturalism that recorded the data of city and country life with precise detail and a simple compositional clarity.

R. R.

132
Curiosity

"*Le Curieux ; étude d'après nature*"
Plate p. 270
Paper on canvas; 43.5 × 34.6; s.d.l.l. *MONGIN 1823*; an earlier inscription, *Bertin 26* (?), was removed during cleaning
Salon of 1824, no. 1236
Cleveland, Mr. and Mrs. Noah L. Butkin Collection

Signed and dated *MONGIN 1823*, this little painting is probably to be identified with "*Le Curieux ; étude d'après nature*," exhibited at the Salon of 1824 (no. 1236), together with what, judging from its title, must have been its pendant, *L'Intrigue sur les toits ; étude d'après nature* (no. 1235). A young man, precariously perched on the top of a ladder, is seen spying over the wall of a girls' school, whose inscription—INSTITUTION DE JEUNES DEMO[ISELLES] DIRIGÉE PAR MME. WACHSAM—adds a further joke in the choice of the directress' German name, Wachsam, which means "watchful." The amusing narrative incident is unexpected in what would otherwise be an uneventful window view of treetops, rooftops, and chimneys familiar to the more informal traditions of French landscape painting of the late 18th and early 19th centuries; but it is exactly this surprising intrusion which lends the subject its piquancy and wit. In its modest way, Mongin's painting translates into prosaic terms the sentimental adventures of a lover perched upon a ladder and scaling a garden wall in Fragonard's *Progrès d'Amour* series, substituting perceived fact (as "*étude d'après nature*" makes explicit) for rococo fantasy.

The freshness and directness of observation here coincide closely not only with the growing naturalism of French landscape painting in the 1820s, but with the revelation of English landscape painting visible at the same Salon. A critic of the Salon of 1824, Pierre-Ange Vieillard, recognized that Mongin's entries were "marked as much by wit as by delicacy"; but to this should be added, on the basis of *Curiosity*, the artist's intuitive sense of a classicizing order in his unforced yet lucid disposition of architectural and landscape elements in a space undefined by a ground plane. In this, Mongin's painting recalls many of Corot's own landscapes of the 1820s.

EXHIBITION
1824, Salon, no. 1236

REFERENCE
P.-A. Vieillard, 1825, p. 19.

PROVENANCE
Wendell P. Colton and Victor D. Spark.

R. R.

Nicolas-André Monsiau

1755 Paris 1837

Monsiau was a pupil of Peyron in Paris. Assisted by the Marquis de Corberon, his first sponsor, he left for Rome in 1776 and remained there for four years, frequenting the studios of David and Valenciennes. After returning to Paris, he exhibited at the Salons de la Correspondance of 1781 and 1782. In 1787, the Academy accepted him on the basis of an *Alexandre domptant Bucéphale,* and in 1789 he was made an academician, with the *Mort d'Agis.* From that time on until 1833 he exhibited regularly at the Salon. He often submitted drawings and watercolors along with his paintings. In 1792, he married the daughter of his second protector, M. Daucourt, *directeur des fermes.* In 1793 and in 1794 respectively, Monsiau's two protectors were hung. Monsiau was deeply affected by this and stopped painting for some time, devoting himself instead to drawing vignettes illustrating Ovid, Rousseau, Florian, Delille and Gessner. In 1798, he exhibited a *Zeuxis choisissant ses modèles* (engraved), much influenced by Vincent's composition depicting the same subject. He dealt with subjects and episodes taken from ancient history (*Éponine et Sabinus,* Salon of 1804, Autun; *Aspasie s'entrenant avec les hommes les plus illustres d'Athènes,* Salon of 1806, Louvre) as well as subjects from recent history (*Molière lisant le Tartuffe chez Ninon de Lenclos,* Salon of 1802; *Poussin reconduisant le cardinal Massimi,* Salon of 1806). At the Salon of 1808, there appeared one of Monsiau's most ambitious works, *Les Comices de Lyon* (1802). This masterpiece, unfortunately not well-known, is an impressive collection of contemporary portraits and an imposing historical document, handled with a delicate harmony of gray-violet and brown (Versailles, Château). Later in 1814, the artist executed one of the huge paintings done for the sacristy of the church of Saint-Denis, a *Prédication de Saint Denis.* The Louvre owns a beautiful self-portrait (1827).

The last years of Monsiau's life were saddened by illness, by the death of his only son at the age of 22, and by all sorts of difficulties. At the Salon of 1833, the last in which he participated, he exhibited a painting with the significant title: *Le chagrin monte en croupe et galope avec lui.* Monsiau suffered increasing dementia and died, at the age of 83, in a highly tortured state.

The work of this little-studied artist is not very innovative. Nevertheless, it provides an interesting example of illustrative painting, most often didactic and sentimental, but precise and highly finished and of a learned, eclectic and cultivated inspiration. Thus Monsiau, without noticeably altering his style, spanned the ages of Louis XVI and Louis-Philippe. J.-P. C.

133
*Devotion of Monseigneur de Belzunce**

" Admirable dévouement de M. Belzunce, évêque de Marseille, durant la peste qui désolait cette ville en 1720 "
Plate p. 257
Canvas; 130 × 160; s.d.l.l. *Monsiau/1819*
Salon of 1819, no. 849
Paris, Musée du Louvre

A *"Notice sur la vie et les ouvrages de M. Monsiau,"* published at the beginning of the catalog of his posthumous sale (30-31 August 1837), gives a moralizing account of the circumstances of the execution of this picture: "The story of this painting is no less beautiful than the work itself." The artist, ill for two years, had begun working on his *Devotion of Monseigneur de Belzunce ;* he was told that he had been seized with renal colic and that he urgently needed an operation. The painter, however, according to his biographer, defied the danger and was determined to finish his painting before the operation. "If this delay... proves to be the cause of my death, my last work will at least be a tribute to virtue," he explained. "The *Devotion of Monseigneur de Belzunce* was finished," the account continued, "and at the same time as the public was eulogizing the work, the painter was undergoing a most painful surgical operation with resolute calm" (*Notice...,* 1837, pp. 6-7.)

The plague of Marseille in 1720, with scenes of the devotion on the part of the Chevalier Roze and of Monseigneur de Belzunce which the subject entailed, provided the theme for works by several artists: J.-F. de Troy (Marseille); Dandré-Bardon (a painting attributed to the artist in Rouen), Gérard (Marseille), Paulin-Guérin (idem), Comte de Forbin (Salon of 1834). It is also the theme of David's famous painting (No. 28). Here, Monsiau represents the Bishop of Marseille, Monseigneur Belzunce (1671-1755), near the fort of Saint-Jean, administering extreme unction to the dying. Such a subject combines, in accord with the taste of the Restoration, the theme of *exemplum virtutis* with the practices of the Catholic Church. The pyramidal composition, enlivened by diagonals, with repoussoir figures in the foreground is scarcely neo-classical. Monsiau, however, was not an innovator; he followed instead the sturdy principles of Jean-Baptiste Jouvenet and Gabriel-François Doyen. The careful modeling, the smooth and regular pictorial treatment, and the color scale, with its overall mauve-gray tones, are characteristic of the artist. These features were criticized by certain writers; the *Journal de Paris,* after noting the "excellent composition and meaningful details" objected "that his technique is too slack and his color untruthful" (24 October 1819, 13th article).

PROVENANCE
Acquired by Louis XVIII at the Salon of 1819 for 2,500 francs; Paris, Musée du Louvre (INV. 6774); allocated to the museum in Marseille in 1872; returned to the Louvre in December 1972.

EXHIBITION
1819, Salon, no. 849.

REFERENCES
Notice..., 1837, pp. 6-7; Bellier and Auvray, v. II, 1885, p. 112; Nagler, v. X, 1907, p. 469; Ph. Auquier, mus. cat. 1908, p. 196, no. 346.

RELATED WORKS
Wash drawing (19 × 24); annotated on the mounting, l.l.: *Monsiau;* Saint-Tropez, private collection. This delicately and carefully executed drawing, which was pointed out by Nathalie Volle, differs significantly from the definitive composition, particularly in the landscape.

J.-P. C.

Louis-Gabriel Moreau, called Moreau the Elder

1739 Paris 1805

The artist, brother of Jean-Michel Moreau the Younger (born in 1741), was a pupil of P.-A. Demachy. He exhibited at the Salon de la Jeunesse in 1760 and in 1761, and was admitted to the Academy of Saint Luke in 1764. He exhibited there in 1764 and 1774. In 1778, he took part in the Salon de la Correspondance and was named painter to the Comte d'Artois. In this capacity, he participated in the elaboration of the Bagatelle Gardens. In 1787 and 1788, he sought admission to the Royal Academy, but was not accepted and had to wait until access to the Salon became unrestricted before exhibiting there in 1791, 1793, 1795, 1796, 1799, 1801 and 1804. Known chiefly for his gouaches and watercolors, which constitute the most important part of his work, Louis-Gabriel Moreau was also a sensitive printmaker. His freely-handled etchings, especially the four series of six landscapes which appeared in 1779, are related to etchings such as those by Jean-Honoré Fragonard and Gabriel de Saint-Aubin. Although a contemporary of Hubert Robert, he did not go to Italy, dealing uniquely with the landscape of the Ile-de-France. Little is known regarding Moreau's paintings; to be cited are the lovely group in the Louvre, the *Collines près de la Seine,* formerly in the collection of Veil-Picard; the charming *Maison de campagne,* The Hague, Mauritshuis; and the *Vue du Parc de Saint-Cloud,* Salon of 1804 (now in the Los Angeles County Museum of Art). The last-mentioned work is hardly distinguishable from the others previously cited and demonstrates how Moreau, at the dawn of the 19th century, continued to paint in the style he had in the 1770s.

His watercolors and gouaches were collected primarily by MM. David David-Weill and Arthur Veil-Picard, and they represent a calm and friendly nature, populated with jagged trees and accessory figures—(the figures were often executed by artists like F.-G. Casanova, N.-A. Taunay, J.-D. Dugourc or the painter's brother Jean-Michel). These more or less imaginary landscapes are characterized by a light and fluttery execution. Among the watercolors should be mentioned the *Vue du château de Madrid* (Rouen), exhibited at the Academy of Saint Luke in 1774 and later engraved (along with

some of his other views of the Paris environs) by Élise Saugrain and, among the gouaches, an important unpublished *Paysage* in Avignon (in the album donated by the Marquis de Cambis), the *Maison du jardinier,* 1786 (formerly the Veil-Picard Collection), and the *Entrée des Champs-Elysées,* 1795, sold in Paris, Hôtel Drouot, 6 May 1955 (no. 51).

Recent critics have tended to see Moreau as a precursor of the French school, from Georges Michel to Jean-Baptiste Corot himself, and also of the English school and of Richard Bonington in particular. Even if this opinion is possible in connection with the paintings, it cannot be maintained for the major part of his work or especially for the gouaches. In fact, even though Moreau was isolated and misunderstood in his life time (he was virtually unknown after his death) he was thoroughly representative of his own century. A contemporary of P.-H. de Valenciennes, whose studies anticipated the freedom of 19th-century landscape, Moreau was directed, rather, to a graceful and idyllic 18th-century rococo style. Francesco Guardi can provide a more relevant comparison with Moreau, whose typically small format and fluid style align him more loosely with the Venetian master than with Romanticism, which is not yet discernable in his work.

J. V.

134
Landscape*

Paysage
Plate p. 95
Canvas; 76 × 130
Nîmes, Musée des Beaux-Arts

Unknown to G. Wildenstein (1923), this important landscape must, in accordance with its traditional attribution, be reassigned to Louis-Gabriel Moreau. It seems on several accounts to be typical of this artist's work. To be noted first of all is the importance given to the sky, where the modeling of the clouds recalls that of those in the *Vue du château de Vincennes* in the Louvre. The form of the trees and vegetation and the treatment of the rock formations at the right are typical

of Moreau's manner, as seen especially in his vibrant gouaches. In conclusion, we point out the slight importance given to the figures, in the foreground, who are introduced into the landscape without becoming a significant element.

PROVENANCE
Charles Tur Bequest, 1948 (INV. 48.2.42).

J. V.

Jean-Laurent Mosnier

1743 or 1744 (?) Paris (?) - Saint Petersburg 1808

Mosnier was a student at the Academy of Saint Luke in 1766, "painter to the Queen" ten years later, *"agréé"* in 1786 and two years later received as a member of the Academy with portraits of the sculptor Charles-Antoine Bridan (Paris, École des Beaux-Arts; another version, Chartres) and of Lagrenée the Elder (Versailles). Mosnier left France at the time of the Revolution and went to London, where he exhibited regularly at the Royal Academy from 1791 to 1796, then to Hamburg, where he spent four years, and finally to Saint Petersburg where he died the recipient of many honors.

Trained as a miniaturist (there are nine extant miniatures in the Louvre, four are dated), Mosnier devoted himself particularly to portraiture. We have, from his French period, the *Portrait de Bailly* (Salon of 1789, Bordeaux, Chamber of Commerce), as well as the works in Évreux *(Portrait de Mlle de Banastre)* and Mâcon (1762), his first known work.

A few limited details of his English sojourn are known from Danloux' *Journal* (published by R. Portalis, 1910, pp. 247-248, 328, etc.) and from the recent study of G. Marlier (1959), who reproduced some of the 32 portraits shown at the Royal Academy (that of the Chevalier d'Eu is unfortunately not known).

In Hamburg are two Mosnier portraits, *Mme Élisabeth Hudtwalcker* (1798), and the poetess *Christine Westphalen* (1800), which Mosnier painted in that city along with, apparently, the *Portrait d'homme* (1797) in the Pau museum. Other works, noticably reflecting the influence of J.-H.-W. Tischbein, are in a private collection in Brussels (see G. Marlier, 1959) and in the Kiel and Potsdam museums.

Mosnier arrived in Russia in 1801, after Francesco Lampi and Jean Voile had disappeared from the scene. Mme Vigée-Lebrun left Saint Petersburg at the end of 1801, after a stay of six years, and Mosnier thus soon came to the fore. He was accepted at the Academy in 1802 and made a professor in 1806, the year of the death of another émigré, the history painter Gabriel Doyen. Louis Réau (1928, pp. 206 and 246) catalogued some ten Mosnier portraits in major Russian collections. The painter's success is borne out by the importance of his sitters (members of the Stroganov and Youssoupov families, as well as the Emperor Alexander I, the Empress Elizabeth ...). Mosnier died in 1808, four years before Napoleon's entrance into Moscow.

P. R.

135
*Portrait of the Artist in his Studio**

"M. M(osnier), Portrait en pied"
Plate p. 76
Canvas; 230 × 175; s.d.l.l. *J.L. Mosnier f. 1786.*
Salon of 1787, no. 226
Leningrad, The Hermitage Museum

D. Roche, in his fundamental article on Mosnier (1921), hesitated to identify the Hermitage painting with the one exhibited at the Salon of 1787, the first in which Mosnier participated. Among other things, he objected to the date, believing the Russian picture to be dated 1790, although it clearly reads 1786. However, the reviews of the Salon allow us, in agreement with G. Mar-

lier (1959), to propose that the portrait of "M. M." in the Salon of 1787 is indeed the Hermitage painting. The *Mercure de France* (cited by Roche) speaks of a "portrait where the painter is represented with two of his sitters." The commentator in the *Inscriptions pour mettre au bas des différents tableaux exposés au Salon du Louvre en 1787* (coll. Deloynes, XV, no. 387, p. 607) provides a curt description of the work in his mediocre jingle: "Au Salon pourquoi donc paraître / Dans sa robe de chambre en riche petit maître."

In general, even though the critics were favorably disposed toward the painting, Mosnier was criticized for his facile treatment and advised "not to make too just a counterpart to Mme Guiard's painting" (No. 112) and "not to make satin look like mother-of-pearl" (*La Plume du Coq de Micille, ou Aventures de Critès au Salon,* cited by D. Roche). The fashion for portraits of artists in their studios, surrounded by their pupils (here the painter's two daughters) seems to have been popular at the end of the 18th century. We note particularly the picture of Mme Labille-Guiard, dated 1785, exhibited here.

The other works (all portraits) which Mosnier exhibited at the same Salon, notably those of *"Baron de Breteuil"* and *"M. de M..., Portrait en pied"* (Mme Mosnier; see Related Works), are no longer known, except for the portrait of *"M. Bridan, Sculpteur du Roi et Professeur à l'Académie"* (Paris, École des Beaux-Arts).

It is not surprising that Mosnier did not wish to part with his work and that he proudly took it with him to England, where he exhibited it at the Royal Academy in 1791, and later to Russia.

PROVENANCE
Collection of Mme J.-B. Florand, daughter of the painter. Given to the Saint Petersburg Academy at the request of the Czar Nicholas in May 1832. Kouchelev-Besborodko museum. Hermitage, INV. 3699.

EXHIBITIONS
1787, Salon, no. 226; 1791, London, Royal Academy, no. 6.

REFERENCES
Coll. Deloynes, v. XV, no. 387, p. 607; D. Roche, 1921, pp. 171, 173, note 1, 176, ill. p. 169 (dates the work 1790); L. Réau, 1924, p. 295, ill. 29 ("1796"); L. Réau, 1928, p. 206; Thieme and Becker, 1931, v. XXV, p. 186 ("1796"); mus. cat., 1958, v. I, p. 311; G. Marlier, 1959, p. 407.

RELATED WORKS
A study for the portrait of the artist, from the Jules Féral Collection (sale, 17 December 1949, no. 75, ill.), at Cailleux' (canvas; 83 × 64, see G. Marlier, 1959). A *Portrait de "M. de M..."*, the painter's wife, slightly smaller and hence an approximate pendant to the Russian picture also appeared at the Salon of 1787.

P. R.

Henry-François Mulard

1769 Paris (?) - Paris 1850

Among the 300 students whom Delécluze cites as having attended David's studio, a goodly number are now no more than names to which we cannot attribute a single painting. Henry-François Mulard was among these quickly forgotten artists. He was born on 13 November 1769, probably in Paris. He was 20 in 1789 and became strongly influenced by Revolutionary ideas. Delécluze remarked that, with Claude Gautherot, he was the only pupil to use—in reference to the revolutionary spirit of confraternity—the familiar form of address with his teacher (E.-J. Delécluze, 1855, p. 53). We have uncovered a long letter addressed to David by Mulard, in which he revealed his staunch adherence to the new ideas and urged David to continue his task: "There is a feeling among the people to entrust the preservation of Liberty only to hands that are pure and worthy of Her. Know that this daughter of heaven has descended among us; she wants only virtuous spirits among her cult..." (Arch. Nat. F17 1009 A d. 1810, dated 22 Nivôse, Year II, 12 January 1794). In 1797, Mulard was still in the master's studio, along with the brothers Pierre and Joseph Franque, Jean Broc and many others. According to Delécluze, he was not a brilliant student: "The senior pupil because of his age, he is the inferior to most in his talent." He further reported that "David objected to Mulard's feeble drawing and cold coloring" (Delécluze, *op. cit.,* pp. 55-56). He continued, "Mulard-*bavard* [Mulard the Babbler] was the rhymed epithet always added to his name, according to schoolboy usage where the truth is crudely stated. Mulard was one of the most highly taught practitioners, but was unimaginative and not outstandingly talented. He exhausted his few ideas, bearing out, with his endless prattle, the epithet tacked onto his name" (*ibid.,* p. 49). Mulard probably competed several times for the Prix de Rome, but could win no more than a second prize in 1799, with *Manlius Torquatus condamnant son fils à mort* (Algiers museum, formerly attributed to Anne-Louis Girodet).

Biographical information on Mulard is sparse. We know that he was married three times: the first time to Françoise Brion; the second—in 1824—to Madeleine Sauvé, who came from a family of copperplate engravers (Arch. Nat. C 1 1001; information supplied by Marc Simonet-Lenglart), and finally, in 1833, to Marie-Louise Daniel, whom he had known for a long time.

The number of Mulard's inventoried works is limited. He took part in only four Salons, submitting only one work each time. He first exhibited in 1808, with *l'Empereur fait présent d'un sabre au chef militaire d'Alexandrie* (Salon no. 443, Versailles). The work was well-received and earned him a medal. Landon wrote that "the painting is highly effective; the figures on the left are handled with a great deal of talent, the light is skillfully distributed and the drapery is well designed and characterized," but he objected to Mulard's "faulty treatment of the figure of the Emperor" (C.-P. Landon, 1808, p. 100). To the Salon of 1810 the artist submitted the *l'Empereur reçoit au quartier général de Finkenstein Mirza...* (Salon no. 591, Versailles). This work, along with the preceding one and the *Trophées* (Arch. Nat. O 884, 1813), were taken to decorate the throne room in the Palais des Tuileries. In 1812,

Mulard again dealt with a subject from contemporary history: *La Reprise de Diégo* (Salon no. 669, Versailles).

His last appearance at the Salon, in 1817, was with *François Ier dormant sur l'affût d'un canon à la veille de la bataille de Marignan* (Salon no. 591, lost). At the beginning of the Restoration, Mulard entered the service of the Gobelins factory as an inspector of works and he remained there until 1848. Aside from the painting commissioned by the King in 1818 to decorate the Trianon (*Hector reprochant à Pâris sa mollesse ;* Arch. Nat. O 1404, MR 4014, deposited at Clermont-Ferrand by the Louvre in 1876), the *Portrait of a Woman* (No. 136), and the portrait of *Mlle d'Herbez de Saint-Aubin en bergère suisse* (Versailles, MV 6564), hardly any other works by Mulard are known. The archives, nevertheless, provide us with the titles of some of his paintings: *La Mort de Bertrand Duguesclin* (Arch. Nat. O 1389, 1814) and *Mercure et Aglaure* (Arch. Nat. O 1395, 1400, 1818; these references were kindly supplied by Marc Simonet-Lenglart).

In some measure, the work of this uncompromising and devoted follower of David calls to mind that of Anne-Louis Girodet. Mulard had a certain sense for illumination, a sometimes vigorous manner and a rather beautiful craftsmanship. His work certainly deserves further study.

I. J.

136
Portrait of a Woman

Portrait de femme
Plate p. 213
Canvas; 99 × 80; s.l.l. *Mulard*
Fort Worth, Kimbell Art Museum

Little is known of Mulard's career. One may suppose that, like David and Ingres, he did not wish to be considered a portraitist, but rather a history painter. In fact, only one other portrait of the artist has been located, that of *Mlle d'Herbez de Saint-Aubin en bergère suisse* (Versailles). The painting shown here is a charming example of the many portraits executed by David's students, and it would never have been attributed to Mulard without the clearly legible signature at the lower left of the picture.

This painting depicts a captivating young woman

with an ingenious charm, her head inclined forward inquisitively. The silhouette of the languid and supple pose emerges clearly from the subtle gray-wash background, which is completely unadorned and recalls the Spartan austerity of numerous portraits by David (cf. *Mme de Verniac*, Louvre). The young woman wears an Empire dress of glistening white satin that could rival the silver dresses of paintings by Gérard Terborch. The silk Scottish plaid scarf is casually knotted at her breast; the Medici collar and the peacock-eye embroidery of the sleeves date this painting to about 1810 (information kindly supplied by Yvonne Deslandres, director of the Center for Costume Documentation, Paris). The discreet extravagance of the dress and of the jewelry (the pair of earrings illuminate the face in an intriguing way), the direct image, the sincerity of observation and the delicately fresh palette make this the most poetic work of all those known to be by Mulard.

PROVENANCE
Paris, Normand Collection; New York, Newhouse Galleries; purchased by Mr. and Mrs. Kay Kimbell in 1958; 1965, Kimbell Art Foundation, Fort Worth, Texas (INV. ACF 58.6).

REFERENCE
Mus. cat., 1972, pp. 164-165.

I. J.

Jean-Charles Nicaise Perrin

1754 Paris 1831

A student at the Academy in 1772, Perrin shared the second prize for painting (réservé) in 1775 with Jean-Baptiste Regnault for his *Aman confondu par Esther devant Assuérus* (Paris, École des Beaux-Arts). He did not reach Rome until November 1780; when he left in 1784, he was ill. While there he copied Caravaggio and Guercino. He was congratulated by the commissioner of the Academy, "who encouraged him not to abandon his noble simplicity." *Agréé* in 1786, he was received into the Academy the following year with his *Vénus faisant panser la blessure d'Enée* (Paris, École des Beaux-Arts, Inv. 7166). He succeeded Jean-Jacques Bachelier in 1806 as the head of the Free School of Drawing.

Perrin exhibited regularly at the Salon from 1787 until 1822. In 1787, in addition to his reception piece, he exhibited the *Cyanippe* (Lyon) and the preparatory drawing (on the New York art market attributed to Peyron) for the *Sophonisbe recevant la coupe empoisonnée que Massinissa est forcé de lui envoyer*. This work is now in Toulouse, along with its pendant *Alexandre et Timoclée ;* both were painted in Rome about 1782 "for Monseigneur d'Apollonie, nephew of Cardinal [de Bernis]." The three works Perrin submitted to the Salon of 1789 (see No. 137) are still known to us. The *Portrait de Mme Perrin* from the Salon of 1791 is in Valenciennes; the *Cyrus condamné à périr par l'ordre d'Astiage, troisième roi des Mèdes* (Louvre) from the Salon of 1802 is in the Louvre and the beautiful painting from the Salon of 1806, *La France appuyée par la Religion consacre à Notre-Dame de Gloire les drapeaux pris sur l'ennemi* is in the Val-de-Grâce. Various portraits by Perrin are at Versailles (see further, the *Couple* from the Fournès sale, 27 June 1935, no. 46). There is also a *Nativité* (1784) in the church of Saint-Louis-en-l'Ile (pendant to a painting by Peyron) and an *Assomption* in the cathedral of Montpellier.

There has been no study—old or recent—on this worthy artist.

P. R.

137
Death of the Virgin

"Mort de la Vierge"
Plate p. 88
Canvas; 216 × 366 (enlarged at the top by 15 cm. and by 11 cm. on the three other sides); s.d.l.l. *PERRIN, 1788.*
Salon of 1789, no. 116
Versailles, Grand Trianon, Chapelle

The church of the Carthusians (which occupied the current site of the Institut d'Art et d'Archéologie, Paris, and was destroyed around 1800), no longer had room to exhibit the paintings which it continued to collect and decided to rearrange them in the chapter house, around Philippe de Champaigne's *Christ en Croix* of 1674, now in the Louvre. The artists Étienne Jeaurat (painting now in Saint-Bernard-de-la-Chapelle),

Nicolas-René Jollain (work lost), Jean-Jacques Lagrenée the Younger (*Présentation au temple,* 1771, now also in the Trianon) thus received commissions for this room. As a pendant for the last-named picture, the Carthusians asked Perrin, then aged 34 and not yet an academician, to paint for them a *Death of the Virgin.*

Perrin exhibited his painting at the Salon of 1789 along with two others: a *Mort de Sénèque* now in Dijon (mus. cat., 1968, p. 67, no. 291) and a *"Thésée prend en horreur le crime de son épouse et déplore la perte de son fils Hippolyte"* (Milan, private collection). The work was an unqualified success. Though some wished his angel, "had been lighter in form and color," he was praised for the talent he exhibited in the composition, draughtsmanship and color, and for "his well-draped figures." "The painting exudes religious sorrow." The editor of *Observations tirées des petites affiches de Paris* (coll. Deloynes, XVI, no. 420, p. 281) summed up the general opinion thus: "everything about this painting recalls Poussin."

Perrin rarely succeeded in being totally convincing or bringing a personal touch to his work, such as we know it today (or at least in the painting exhibited in the Salon of 1806 and now in the Val-de-Grâce). Perrin not only studied the masters of the 17th century (in addition to Poussin, Le Sueur and especially Le Brun—the mourning figure in the foreground seems directly inspired by the latter's Magdalene), but also, like Jean-François Peyron, he tried to create an original language, one that was not only austere and sculptural but also realistic, as we see here in the commendable, moving face of the Virgin . Like Peyron, Perrin had copied Caravaggio in Rome. It is possible to conceive of Perrin here as eager to take up the challenge of this Italian master, whose painting on the same subject he could have admired in the royal collections.

PROVENANCE
Chapter house of the Carthusian church in Paris; confiscated during the Revolution; depository of the Petits Augustins in 1795; entrusted to Naigeon in Nivôse, Year VII; sent to decorate the Chapel of the Trianon at Versailles in 1800 (MV. 8184; INV. 7165).

EXHIBITION
1789, Salon, no. 116.

REFERENCES
Coll. Deloynes, v. XVI, no. 409, p. 28; no. 410, p. 88; no. 412, pp. 135-136; no. 415, pp. 174-175; no. 416, p. 215; no. 420, p. 281; no. 421, p. 310; no. 422, p. 346; no. 423, p. 384; no. 426, p. 409; [Plon.], v. II, 1883-1897, p. 258, no. 232 and 341, no. 6; J. Wilhelm, 1963, p. 7; B. de Montgolfier, 1964, p. 213; cat. Grand Trianon, 1966, n.p., ill.

RELATED WORKS
Stands out in a fine watercolor of the Salon of 1789 by Charles de Wailly (Paris, Musée Carnavalet; see J. Wilhelm, *op. cit.,* pp. 6, 7). A moving painted study of the Virgin's head (canvas, 35 × 45, Valenciennes; mus. cat., 1931, p. 116, no. 313). A preparatory drawing in Valenciennes (pointed out by J. Vilain) with some variations from the painted study in the same museum (pen and wash with India ink; 18.5 × 33.7; D. 128; mus. cat., 1903, no. 263).

Jean-François-Pierre Peyron

1744 Aix-en-Provence - Paris 1814

"He opened my eyes." These are the words pronounced, according to Emeric David, by Jacques-Louis David at Peyron's funeral in 1814. They demonstrate the importance accorded to the artist by his contemporaries. Peyron was not highly inventive in his compositions, but he was a gifted and ambitious colorist. He was overwhelmed by David's personality, even though he was David's major, if not only, rival over a period of 15 years.

Born into a well-to-do family in 1844 (hence David's senior by four years), Peyron frequented the atelier of M.-F. Dandré-Bardon and later, in Paris, that of Lagrenée the Elder. Of the latter's style, he retained only his taste for clear, boldly juxtaposed colors. In 1770, Peyron won a medal at the Academy and took part in the competitions of 1771 (in which Suvée won over David and 1772 (P.-C. Jombert and A.-C.-G. Lemonnier), before winning the Grand Prix in 1773 with his *Mort de Sénèque* (lost, but known from a line engraving and a drawing in a New York private collection), again placing ahead of David (Petit Palais, sketch and large painting). He left for Rome in December 1775 and stayed at the Villa Mancini until October 1782. Noël Hallé had just been replaced as director by Joseph-Marie Vien. These Roman years were to prove fundamental to Peyron's career and were also his most productive. There he painted his best works *Hagar and the Angel,* No. 138; *Belisarius,* No. 139 and its pendant *Cornélie, mère des Gracques; Cimon et Miltiade* (Louvre and Guéret; drawings at Alençon, Besançon and Guéret) and *Socrate détachant Alcibiade des bras de la Volupté* (Guéret; drawings in Guéret and Chapel Hill, N.C.), the *Athéniennes* (1778, Salon of 1783, London, Wellington Museum; drawings in Aix, Marseille, and England, private collection).

His protectors and defenders, Cardinal de Bernis and the Marquis d'Angiviller, wavered between Peyron and David but prolonged the former's Roman sojourn so that he might perfect his education. After returning to France and painting a *Résurrection* (1784), today in the church of Saint-Louis-en-l'Ile, he exhibited his masterpiece, *La Mort d'Alceste* which etudes a deep", sad silence" (Louvre, drawings in Edinburgh and in private collections in Paris and New York) at the Salon of 1785. Unfortunately for Peyron, this Salon was also that of the *Horaces* ("David was the true winner...," said Cochin), but to the eyes of the critics at the time, the day was not yet lost for the Provençal painter. That day came, however, two years later (despite his reception piece for the Academy, the *Curius Dentatus refusant les présents des Samnites,* 1786, Avignon, study in Marseille, drawing in Grenoble) with his *Mort de Socrate* (Denmark, private collection); drawing, Vienna, Albertina), which could not withstand comparison with David's masterpiece (No. 32). Despite the severity of the critics, Peyron did not give up until two years later, after the failure of the large version of the same theme (Assemblée Nationale).

After 1789, Peyron, ill and little tempted by new ideas, virtually stopped painting. From these years are his *Ulysse et Nausicaa* (Salon of 1791, today in the Schwerin museum), *Belisarius* (1796; see No. 139), *Étude et la Renommée* (1799, Louvre; sketch, Paris); *Time and Minerva* (No. 140), *Paul Émile* (now destroyed, formerly in Caen; sketch of 1802 in Budapest, drawings in Béziers, Caen, 1808), *Death of General Valhubert* (No. 141); and drawings for illustrations in Aix (Musée Arbaud) and Paris (Petit Palais). After exhibiting two now-lost paintings at the Salon of 1812, he died in 1814, on the eve of Napoleon's fall.

Today Peyron's known œuvre constitutes 20 paintings, as well as a few prints and some elegant and perfectly executed drawings. Does this constitute a sufficient foundation on which to claim Peyron as a great artist? A fervent admirer of Poussin, whose works he collected (cf. the sale after his death, 1816) and copied (*Martyre de saint Erasme,* 1781, lost since 1872), Peyron composed his works with the same care he lavished on their execution. He knew better than any of his contemporaries how to use space and to set his figures off against large, somber backgrounds. His boldly harmonized colors are outstanding in their refinement. However, he too often sacrificed his overall composition to detail, and he lacked that inspiration of "invention" which makes a truly great artist. A personality engaging in his intellectual honesty, moving in his incessant struggles to conquer that creative spirit so, indispensable at that time, Peyron did not merely continue the glossy trend, à la Adrian Van der Werff, so fashionable under Louis XVI—he was not a mere representative of a refined Neo-Classicism. He was, by his very failure, proof in counterpoint of the innovative and stimulating genius of David.

P. R.

138
Hagar and the Angel

Agar et l'Ange
Plate p. 56
Canvas; 55 × 38; traces of a signature and date l.l.
Paris, Private Collection

This painting is not only one of Peyron's earliest works, but also one of the rare examples in which he attempts a Biblical rather than antique theme. The subject is well-known: Sarah, Abraham's wife, believed herself to be sterile and presented Abraham her servant Hagar. After bearing a son, Ishmael, Hagar and her son were cast out into the desert by Sarah. When Ishmael was about to die of thirst, he was rescued by an angel who showed him a well of spring waters. (See L. Réau, I, 1956, p. 134 for other artists' treatment of the scene.) For this painting, Peyron executed three studies which are quite close in composition to the finished work (see Related Works); the differences, in fact, between the drawings and the painting are minor. In the two more highly worked drawings can be found the arrangement of the prostrate figure of Ishmael with his empty jug and bowl, and the admirable flying angel, who, with his profoundly moving expression touches, as in an *Annunciation,* Hagar's left arm. These two figures, who occupy almost the entire composition, emerge from a penumbra, a sort of gray and leaden veil, which is taken from Poussin's *Déluge* and where there is "more slate then pearl." The immense wings of the angel, a counterpoint to Hagar's elegantly ordered drapery, constitute a strange note within this finely colored work. Peyron "stirs the cauldron in his combination of the brown and gold of Hagar's garments with the pale mauve of the angel's tunic."

In 1779, the date of one of the drawings and almost certainly of the painting as well, Peyron had been in Rome for four years. The preceding year he had painted his *Jeunes Athéniens et Athéniennes tirant au sort* (London, Wellington Museum) and, in 1777, had had the opportunity of doing a favor for Joseph-Marie Vien and d'Angiviller by doing a drawn copy (Louvre) of a relief of dubious authenticity (now at Versailles) offered to the new King by Abbot Ferdinandi. More important, in Rome he was able to study Poussin (copying his *Martyre de saint Erasme*) as well as the antique.

On 10 April 1779, the secretary of the Academy read out the report of the commissioners selected to examine the works sent by students at the French Academy in Rome (*Correspondance,* XIII, p. 421), "M. Peyron has painted his academic figure in a fine manner; his color is truthful and subtle in the various tonal transitions... the style of his sketch is noble... we feel we must, in giving him the greatest encouragement, advise him not to increase the number of folds in his drapery, since this gives them too papery a character." Could not these words apply to the *Hagar?* As Mirimonde has written, the painting is "a distinguished work [with] intimate charm... [it must have] delighted the contemporary intelligensia... [and] bore the promise of artistic renewal then eagerly awaited."

PROVENANCE
Acquired by the present owner at the Hôtel Drouot, Paris, June 1947, in an uncatalogued sale, where there also appeared the sketch (Paris, private collection; A.-P. de Mirimonde (1967, pp. 139-140, ill.) for the *Étude et la Renommée,* painted in 1799 in a tympanium of the Salle des Antonins in the Louvre and another painting of Peyron, titled *Un Peintre de l'antiquité,* known only through a description provided by M. Erard-Gilles (1969-1970).

REFERENCES
A.-P. de Mirimonde, 1950, pp. 266-269, ill.; M. Erard-Gilles, 1969-1970, pp. 66-67, T. no. 3.

RELATED WORKS
Drawings. For the two main figures, Nancy museum (A.-P. de Mirimonde, 1950, p. 266, ill.); formerly in the collection of the Marquis de Chennevières; pen with wash and heightened with white. Complete drawing, Vienna, Albertina (15395). S.d. *P. Peyron f.,* same technique as above. Complete drawing, Darmstadt (HZ 2543), s.d. *P. Peyron f. rom. 1779,* same technique as above. A second drawing of the same subject in sanguine, also in Darmstadt (HZ 5397).

P. R.

139
Belisarius

Bélisaire recevant l'hospitalité d'un paysan qui avait servi sous lui
Plate p. 55
Canvas; 93 × 132; s.d.l.r. *P. Peyron Pens. du Roy f. Roma/1779* (not 1773 as stated by H. Rachou, 1920)
Toulouse, Musée des Augustins

Done in Rome in 1779, this painting brought Peyron great success. Joseph-Marie Vien wrote to d'Angi-

viller, 8 December 1779 *(Correspondance),* "Mr. Peyron had a painting, which he had done for the Abbé de Bernis and which represents *Belisarius accepting the hospitality of a peasant who had served under him*, which brought him much honor. I observe with satisfaction that this Academy has taken a new turn in Rome, and if the Director who is to come after me (Lagrenée was very soon to replace Vien) wishes to take his task seriously, art will benefit a great deal." D'Angiviller answered Vien on December 27, saying in regard to the *Belisarius* and its author, "he is one of those on whom I am counting to re-establish our painting." The well-known subject became popular with the publication in 1767 of Marmontel's novel, which was censored and condemned by the Sorbonne. The writer, in his *Mémoires* (ed. 1857, p. 328), recalls how the idea of this theme occurred to him, "I was given a print of Belisarius taken from Van Dyck's painting... I was astonished that the poets had not drawn at all upon this moral subject." In 1767, Gravelot and Jollain (Salon no. 153) in turn treated the subject and were followed by Louis-Jacques Durameau (1775) and François-André Vincent (No. 199), before David (no. 30), and later, François Gérard, in their turn, attempted the subject.

Peyron chose to represent the moment in which one of Belisarius' former soldiers, now a peasant, having recognized the blind man roaming the countryside, presents him to his family. The artist must have been particularly pleased with his painting, since he submitted a sketch (now lost) to the Salon of 1785 (when he also exhibited his masterpiece, the *Mort d'Alceste,* Louvre) and a highly successful replica to the Salon of 1796 (see Related Works).

The perfectly constructed frieze-like composition, with its bold coloring and subtle lighting, contrasts with Vincent's painting; but David's work, in its monumentality and simplicity, reaches a completely different dimension.

A refined artist, more precious than powerful, J.-F.-P. Peyron preferred to touch rather than to move, to please rather than to teach, to reveal rather than to convince. It is in this very modesty and reserve that the greatness of this rare and learned master lies.

PROVENANCE
Commissioned by Cardinal de Bernis, from 1769, French ambassador to Rome, where died in 1794 (cf. *Correspondance des Directeurs de l'Académie,* XIV, p. 119). Transferred from Albi, where Bernis had been archbishop from 1764, to Toulouse, 14 June 1792, by the mayor of Albi, M. Gorsse. Deposited in the former archbishop's palace in Toulouse and placed "under the care of Citizen Lucas Cadet." Early possession of the museum (*Bulletin de la Société de l'Histoire de l'Art français,* 1909, p. 285).

EXHIBITION
1967, Montauban, no. 287.

REFERENCES
Correspondance (1779-1781), t. XIII (ed. 1904), pp. 478, 481; v. XIV (ed. 1905), pp. 4, 119; Georges, mus. cat., 1864, p. 144; Georges, mus. cat., 1873, p. 124; E. Lamouzèle, 1909, p. 285, no. 27; J. Locquin, 1912, pp. 216, 253; H. Rachou, 1920, p. 108, no. 195; L. Hautecœur, 1954, pp. 44, 52, 61; J. Vergnet-Ruiz and M. Laclotte, 1962, p. 247; H. Bardon, 1963, p. 222; M. Erard-Gilles (1969-1970), pp. 68-70, v. no. 4.

RELATED WORKS
A sketch, now lost, of the Toulouse painting, measuring 1 *pied* 8 *pouces* by 2 *pieds* 3 *pouces*, belonging to M. de Fonds de Colombe, appeared in the Salon of 1785 (no. 180). A second version, with significant differences, on panel (50 × 65), s.d. 1796, today in a private collection, Paris, appeared in the Salon of 1796, no. 370, and was rewarded, after the Concours solennel, Year II (13 March 1799). The painting in the Montauban museum (D. Ternois, 1961, no. 219, ill.) is only, in our opinion, an old, mediocre copy. A drawing signed *P. Peyron f. Roma* belongs to the Albertina (12899). Is this the composition wanted by d'Angiviller and sent by Peyron to the Academy in 1778 (letter from Vien to d'Angiviller, Correspondance, XIV, p. 4), or is it the one from the Bruun-Neergaard sale (August 1814, no. 300)? The work in the Peyron sale (10 June 1816, no. 38), dated 1778, measured 20 *pouces* by 31 *pouces* and is no longer known. Several recent exhibition catalogs (*Le dessin toulousain,* 1954, Toulouse, Musée Paul-Dupuy, p. 106, and exh. cat., 1967, Montauban, p. 165) point out that Ingres, during his stay in Toulouse with Briant, drew a copy of this painting. Ingres' drawing, then belonging to M. G. Garrisson, may have appeared at a retrospective exhibition in Montauban in 1862, no. 571, M. P. Barousse (written communication) assures us that it was in 1877 and under the indication of no. 378 that a drawing catalogued as "Ingres (J. D.) *Bélisaire dessin lavé,* M. G. Garrisson" was exhibited in Montauban. This drawing, now untraced, cannot in any case be confused with the one which (with a different provenance and also attributed to Ingres, but copying instead Gérard's *Bélisaire*) was recently exhibited in the United States (P. Hattis, *Ingres' Sculptural Style. A group of unknown drawings,* Fogg Art Museum, Harvard University, 1973, no. 8, ill.).

P. R.

140
Time and Minerva*

Le "Temp(s) et Minerve, qui n'accordent l'immortalité qu'à ceux qui ont bien mérité de leur patrie"
Plate p. 156
Canvas; 200 × 130
Salon of 1799, no. 252
Paris, Ministère des Armées

The subject of this picture deserves an explanation. The Salon catalog describes the painting: "Time and Minerva, who grant immortality only to those who have served their country. Solon, as a Sage and Lawmaker, submits to their judgment; Plato, the disciple of Socrates, will soon undergo it. Wisdom proposes and Time points out the place which the Great Men will occupy in the Temple of Remembrance. The Genius of History awaits their decision in order to pass it on to Posterity." This picture—one of Peyron's last works and for a time considered lost—was not received by the critics at the Salon of 1799 with unqualified acceptance. The "Peintre" from the *Revue du Museum* (coll. Deloynes, XXI, no. 562, p. 159) commented about the painting and its sketch: "They are by Peyron and are as sick as their author." Damon queried "Why does this artist bother to give to the Republic an allegorical painting when there are so many national subjects to be depicted?" The "Peintre" replied, "It is perhaps because the Republic paid him allegorically." The critic of the *Journal des Arts* (coll. Deloynes, XXI, no. 567, pp. 220-222) wrote, "When there is no action, the heart cannot be moved," and added, however, that this "painting seems nonetheless intelligently composed..." C. Chaussard (*Journal de la Décade,* coll. Deloynes, XXI, no. 580, pp. 397-398) regretted that Peyron had chosen Plato and Solon to represent the great men, "Were there none from French history?" Peyron has, in fact, reused here the basic composition of one of his earlier works (now known only through engraving): an *Allégorie à la Gloire des peintres de Genre,* engraved by Jean-Antoine Pierron in 1791, after a lost drawing by Peyron of "ten by eight *pouces,* taken from the collection of Citizen Lebrun, Painter and Art Dealer." The medallions in the print are not those of Plato and Solon, but rather celebrate "Gérard Douw," "Van de Velde," "Rembrandt Van Ryn," "Ph. Wouwermans" and especially the "Chev. A. Van der Werf."

The tribute made in this painting holds a double interest for us. It might come as a surprise to see Peyron, confirmed history painter, allegorically glorifying genre painters whom one would expect to see him deride and disparage. On further consideration, however, the choice of artists—only those painters which the France of Louis XVI was so fond of are included here—is revealing and no doubt intentional. Adrian Van der Werf, who did history painting and is overly neglected at the present time (although cf. recent exhibitions in Munich and Rotterdam), but justifiably appreciated in Peyron's, is placed in the foreground. This explains Peyron's choice (one would be too hasty in seeing the artist as directed exclusively toward Italy) to pay homage to a master from whom he borrowed not only a polished and highly finished technique, but also one whom Peyron could admire for his unusual, lively colors carefully chosen and played off against each other with a certain controlled boldness.

The painting exhibited here—its format exceptional in the œuvre of Peyron—thus represents an ambitious attempt to combine two schools with, what seems at first irreconcilable esthetics. The engraving was to be used as the frontispiece of the third volume of Lebrun's (former husband of Mme Vigée) *La Galerie des peintres flamands, hollandais et allemands* (1792-96).

PROVENANCE
In the Year III (by decree of 9 Frimaire) was a competition, designed to represent the most glorious events of the Revolution, which brought together some of the noteworthy painters of the time. Peyron exhibited there the large, now-lost drawing *La Patrie reconnaissante couronne la valeur et l'héroïsme républicain.* The Jury des Arts, convening in Fructidor, Year III (September 1795), awarded him a *prix d'encouragement* of 8,000 *livres* to do a painting of his own choosing. This was the *Time and Minerva* shown at the Salon of 1799, which is mentioned in Villot's inventory of the Louvre (INV. 7180). It was sent on 1 Ventôse, Year IX (Arch. Louvre, 3 DD 22, p. 50) to the Ministère des Armées, where it still remains, hanging in a corridor of the Hôtel de Brienne.

EXHIBITION
1799, Salon, no. 252.

REFERENCES
Coll. Deloynes, v. XXI, no. 252, p. 50; no. 562, p. 159; no. 567, pp. 220-222; no. 580, pp. 397-398; M. Erard-Gilles (1969-1970), pp. 119-120, T. no. XII (lost).

RELATED WORK
A "sketch of the same subject, differently composed" appeared at the same Salon (1799, no. 253).   P. R.

141
Death of General Valhubert

"La mort du Général Valhubert"
Plate p. 200
Canvas; 228 × 278 (without the additions on the four sides: 180 × 220.
The engraving by C. Normand gives an exact idea of the painting with its original dimensions).
S. d. on the rock, at the bottom center *P. Peyron Inv. et pinxit/ 15 aoust 1808.*
Salon of 1808, no. 470
Versailles, Musée National

The catalog of the Salon of 1808 indicates the subject of the painting: "the brave general [Valhubert was born in 1764 in Avranches] at the battle of Austerlitz [2 December 1805] was struck down by the explosion of a shell which wounded him in the left thigh and within a few days ended his glorious career. The orders given were that the wounded were not to be carried off the field until the battle was over. The general's grenadiers and M. Desdorides, his aide-de-camp, found him in a sea of blood and came forward to take him away; he staunchly repelled them with his saber, reminding them of the orders and berating them for their weakness and cowardliness. They did not succeed in picking the general up until after they had disarmed him."

Peyron's painting was deemed unsatisfactory both in the Galerie de Diane at the Tuileries, for which it had been commissioned in 1806, and in the Cabinet de l'Empereur at the Trianon, where it was sent in 1809, as well as at the Salon of 1808. This is attested by a very reserved letter (cited by Y. Cantarel, 1973, p. 535) concerning the painting, from Denon to Napoleon, "This artist, already old and infirm, has busied himself with this work and done all that he could do to be worthy of being chosen to execute this painting; it is not inferior to his works of 20 years ago, which gained him his reputation, but the School has progressed so far in the past six years that his work which at one time would have been outstanding, can now be seen only as a pass-

able performance." In the Salon of 1808 the painting was hung "in a light so weak that one can barely make out the disposition of the figures" (coll. Deloynes, XLIII, no. 1157, p. 654). It was, in fact, difficult for the Salon critics to see it. Although they all praised the color, the critics generally found fault with the artist for not clarifying the action of his subject. "Valhubert has the look of a man who is scared of being trampled by his horse rather than that of a hero who knows he is about to die, but nevertheless spurns the assistance offered him...."

The critics were also surprised by the subject matter; Peyron had virtually never before used a subject from current history. Landon remarked that even though the painter "had few rivals among his contemporaries" in his "very beautiful works drawn from Greek and Roman history" with their "quiet and imposing masses, tranquil groupings, solemn or touching expressions, beautiful drapery motifs and noble background architecture which he could combine to great effect, there are very few artists with a gift for depicting the character of war." "The picture lacks... the energy requisite to history painting," wrote Ducret Dumesnil, editor of the *Journal des petites affiches de Paris* (coll. Deloynes, XLIII, no. 1149, p. 516). Quite considerably modified by enlargements, the Versailles picture nevertheless remains one of the strangest military works of the Empire. Averse to rendering movement, carrying his concern with stylization to the extreme, backing off from realism and emotion itself, Peyron above all emphasized the color, with its acid and precious affectation, which gives the porcelain-like canvas an unreal aspect and an almost surreal poetry. This quality accentuates the crystalline and sun-drenched atmosphere, and the frightened look of the horse which stands out against the eerie cloud of dust and powder.

PROVENANCE
Commissioned, along with other paintings illustrating the German campaign, by a decree of 3 March 1806, to decorate the Galerie de Diane at the Palais des Tuileries for the fee of 6,000 *livres*. It was not exhibited when the court moved to the Palace in December 1808. Sent to Versailles 19 April 1809. In December 1810, it was hung in the Salon de l'Empereur at the Trianon, but was taken down upon Napoleon's arrival. In the Louvre and then in Versailles from 1833 on. Enlarged in 1835, at the time of its installation

in the Musée de l'Histoire de France, Versailles, by Louis-Philippe.

EXHIBITION
1808, Salon, no. 470.

REFERENCES
Coll. Deloynes, v. XLIII, no. 1129, p. 535; no. 1136, p. 617; no. 1139, pp. 680-681; no. 1149, pp. 514-516; no. 1157, pp. 654-656; C.-P. Landon, 1808, v. XXIX, p. 58; mus. cat., 1837, no. 798; Bellier and Auvray, 1885, v. II, p. 259; mus. cat., 1931, v. I, no. 601 (A. Pérat é and G. Brière); Ch.-O. Zieseniss, 1967, pp. 209, 212; C.-O. Zieseniss, 1968, pp. 272, 286, 294, 297; M. Erard-Gilles (1969-1970), no. 21; Y. Cantarel, 1973, v. II, pp. 583-589.

RELATED WORKS
Engraved by C. Normand, in Landon, Salon of 1808, II, p. 43. A copy, "due to Alaux and Brisset in 1835," was catalogued at Versailles in 1837 (no. 799).

P. R.

Pierre-Paul Prud'hon

1758 Cluny - Paris 1823

Son of a stonecutter, Prud'hon was sent in 1774 to the drawing school in Dijon, headed by François Devosge. His patron in Dijon was Baron de Joursanvault. He married Jeanne Pernet in 1778 (that union was a failure); as early as 1780, he left for Paris, where he stayed for three years. In 1783, he returned to Dijon to prepare his competition piece for the prize of the Academy of Dijon, which he won the following year. The three years he was then able to spend in Rome proved decisive to his formation. As Marmottan pointed out, "In Rome, he separated himself from the mode recommended by Lagrenée, and from that of Drouais; to the Davidian style which dominated these painters, he preferred the approach brought to Italy at that time by the Germans, Raphael Mengs and Angelica Kauffmann" (1880, p. 310).

He returned to Paris, where he allied himself with revolutionary elements, probably in excess, since in 1794 he abruptly left for Franche-Comté and settled in Gray. He painted portraits of local personalities; *M. Anthony* (Dijon) and *Mme Anthony* (Lyon). In 1796, he returned to Paris where he earned a living by executing for Didot and various editors drawings intended to illustrate such works as *L'Art d'Aimer, Paul et Virginie, Nouvelle Héloïse*.

The support of his compatriot Frochot, future Prefect of the Seine, during the Empire, opened the door to high society. The famous financier Lanois entrusted him with the decoration of his residence. The wife of Bonaparte commissioned him to decorate the ceiling of her living-room on rue Chantereine. After the great success of his *Triomphe de Bonaparte* at the Salon of 1801, he began to receive various commissions from the government. In 1803, the ceiling in the room of Greek sculptures in the Louvre, then, portraits of the *Imperatrice Joséphine* and *Napoléon*. And on numerous occasions, Prud'hon was the great designer of celebrations given by the city of Paris, ranging from the Emperor's coronation and the treaty of Tilsitt to the wedding of Napoleon and Marie-Louise.

The years from 1808 to 1815 marked the height of his career. He painted his masterpieces: *Innocence préfère l'Amour à la Richesse, Justice et la Vengeance poursuivant le Crime* (1808, Louvre, a second copy in Saint-Omer), *Psyché enlevée par les Zéphyrs* (1808, Louvre), *Portrait de M. Vallet* (1812, Louvre) *Roi de Rome* (1812, two versions, one in Parma), *Entrevue de Napoléon Ier et de François II* (1812, Versailles), *Le Jeune Zéphire* of 1814 (No. 143), *Portrait du Comte Sommariva* (1815, Milan, Brera). He was official designer of subjects used for imperial furnishings (projects in Paris, Musée Carnavalet). He became the drawing instructor for the Empress and was at last recognized (and discovered) by critics (Boutard thought he was a young artist). His life ended sadly. The paintings sent to the Salon seemed old-fashioned. In 1821, his student Constance Meyer, who wished to marry him, committed suicide. While he still painted numerous portraits (e.g. *Mme Jarre,* 1822, Louvre), with the exception of two religious works, *Christ expirant sur la Croix* (Louvre) and *Assomption* (Louvre), he could not complete the large compositions he had planned: *Louis XIV recevant une députation, Minerve guidant le génie des arts vers l'immortalité, L'Ame brisant les liens qui l'attachent à la terre.*

A legend then evolved in which the painter became the very image of the desperate romantic artist. It was confirmed by Prud'hon's last writings (published in *Les Annales de la Société libre des Beaux-Arts,* 1832, pp. 77-78) and by the impressions of his contemporaries. Characteristic is the following judgment, published at the time of the Salon of 1824, regarding the Félix Trézel painting of the *Atelier de Prud'hon:* "As for myself, if I had to treat such a subject, I would have done it another way. First, I would have steeped myself in the character and kind of talent of the artist I had to represent, and I would have wished that he be recognizable by the melancholy of his features, exhausted by his passions and by the study of his art, as well as by the fleeting spark which only the sight of his work brought to his eyes, dulled by illness... he would have been working on [an image of] a dying person.

Thrown into the corner of the studio, this painting should have been placed on an easel.... This dying person... would have appeared to him as an omen of his fate, and he would have turned to his beloved, searching in her eyes for a less painful thought. This is what I would have done, had I painted Prud'hon in his studio with Mlle ..." (Ferd. Flocon and Marie Aycard, 1824, pp. 24-26).

The critical success of the artist is astonishing. Despite Guiffrey's opinion, Prud'hon was in point of fact an artist whose glory was in eclipse. The ambiguity of his œuvre (which reflects the ambiguity of the era) has probably been the cause of a misunderstanding further supported not only by the appearance of numerous drawn or painted copies, but also by the condition of paintings which the artist wished to save from the ravages of time by protecting them with a varnish of his invention, which in fact hastened their ruin. Therefore, it is often difficult for us to appreciate the "grâce indéfinissable" and "charme" (Lebreton, 1808, p. 67) of this artist, considered by some of his contemporaries (Quatremère de Quincy, Bruun-Neergaard, Blanc) to be the French Correggio and whom Stendhal compared to Mozart.

No recent comprehensive work on Prud'hon has been published, and the excellent catalog by Jean Guiffrey, following the books of Charles Clément and Edmond de Goncourt, should be brought up to date. However, the entries by Hélène Toussaint in the catalog of the *Age of Neo-Classicism* (London, 1972) should be cited.   J. L.

142
*Portrait of Vivant Denon**

Portrait du baron Dominique-Vivant Denon
Plate p. 219
Canvas; 61 × 52
Paris, Musée du Louvre

The subtlety of Prud'hon's art was marvelously well suited to conveying the character of this witty and ironic personality. As an artist, diplomat, administrator and collector, Vivant Denon had an extraordinary career (see the thesis by P. Lelièvre, published in 1942, and the recent work of J. Châtelain, which appeared in 1973).

Born in Chalon-sur-Saône in 1747, Denon was first an engraver, in charge of the collection of engraved gems which Mme de Pompadour had bequeathed to the King. Later he was named "Gentleman of the Privy Chamber" and secretary to the embassy in Saint Petersburg. Upon the death of Louis XV, he became an envoy to Sweden. In the service of the Comte de

Vergennes, Minister of Foreign Affairs, he was entrusted with a mission to the Helvetian Cantons, before accompanying the Comte de Clermont d'Amboise, the French ambassador to Naples. He spent seven years there as a minister's deputy and, during his stay, was in charge of illustrating *Voyages Pittoresques de Naples et de Sicile,* begun by the Abbé de Saint-Non. After returning to France, he left diplomatic service to devote himself exclusively to his penchant for the arts. In 1787, he became a member of the Academy of Fine Arts. During the Revolution, he was saved from the guillotine by David. Denon was an indispensible member of Bonaparte's scientific team in Egypt and he returned to France to do his great two-volume illustrated work, *Voyages dans la Haute et Basse Égypte,* Paris, 1802.

In 1802, Napoleon named him General Director of Museums, and a period of intense activity began. He reorganized the Louvre and added to it the works being collected from abroad, presided at the Salons, and watched over the imperial factories. But the Restoration intervened. During the time of repossession of the works in the Louvre garnered from all of Europe, he courageously defended this exceptional museum. Defeated, he retired from public life and henceforth devoted himself to his famous collection (its catalog, in three volumes, comprises no fewer than 3,178 items, often with several works listed under one item !, see No. 57).

This painting, in which Vivant Denon wears the sash with the cross of Saint Anne of Russia, dates from 1812. It was cut from an unfinished portrait. According to J. Guiffrey (1924, no. 498), the drawing from the Marcille-Chevrier Collection might have been a preparatory study for this portrait (see Related Works). There Vivant Denon is seen turned three-quarters to the left seated in an armchair at his desk, with his legs crossed, his head almost frontal, wearing knee-breeches

and a coat fitted at the waist. His left hand is on his hip and he holds a medal in his right; a small statue is placed on his desk and busts appear in the background.

PROVENANCE
Is this the portrait thought to have been of Prud'hon which was listed as no. 49 in an anonymous sale, 19 March 1853 and which is described in the catalog as follows: "Portrait of the famous artist, open collar, ruffled shirt, green suit, wearing two decorations" ? Laperlier Collection; Laperlier sale, Paris, 11-13 April 1867, no. 48 (2,000 francs); acquired by the Louvre at this sale; (MI. 723).

EXHIBITIONS
1934, Venice, no. 159; 1938, Paris, no. 268; 1949, Paris, no. 412; 1952, Rueil-Malmaison, no. 16; 1958, Agen-Grenoble-Nancy, no 35; 1962, Dijon, no. 238, pl. VIII; 1964, Chalon-sur-Saône [no no.]; 1969, Paris, Grand Palais, no. 257.

REFERENCES
E. de Goncourt, 1876, no. 19; H. Mireur, 1912, v. VI p. 76; Ch. Saunier, 1922, p. 312; J. Guiffrey, 1924, no. 497, ill. XVII; R. Régamey, 1928, pp. 39-40, ill. 43; G. Grappe, 1943, p. 5; P. Lelièvre, 1959, ill. p. 18; Ch. Sterling and H. Adhémar, 1961, v. IV, no. 1522, ill. 589; G. Wildenstein, 1963, p. 31; G. Bazin, 1967, p. 177, ill. 89; P. Pradel, 1974, no. 1, ill. p. 75.

RELATED WORKS
The picture was engraved by Huot in 1871 for the Chalcographie du Louvre. J. Guiffrey (1924, no. 498) noted a drawing by Prud'hon (black and white chalk on blue paper; 25 × 20), as an early study for the work shown here. At that time, it belonged to the Chevrier—Marcille Collection; reproduced by G. Grappe (1943, p. 5). A portrait attributed to Prud'hon, where Vivant Denon is depicted half-length, almost frontal, wearing a brown coat, embroidered vest and white tie (32 × 23), appeared at the Beurnonville sale, 5 June 1884, no. 73 (500 francs).
There are innumerable portraits of this celebrated figure, both by painters (Robert Lefèvre, Isabey, Paulin-Guérin and Peroux) and by sculptors (Bosio, Chaudet, Boichot and J.-C. Marin). Among the most striking is the *Portrait allégorique* (wash, 49 × 40) by Benjamin Zix in the Cabinet des Dessins, Louvre.   J. L.

143
Young Zephyr

Jeune Zéphire se balançant au-dessus de l'eau
Plate p. 224
Canvas; 128 × 97
Paris, Musée du Louvre

This camaïeu must have been the model for the painting *Le Zéphire* exhibited at the Salon of 1814

(no. 771), from which it gets its title. Here, in fact, we see only a child, playing at the water's edge, and who would carry no mythological connotation except for the inclusion of certain attributes (wings and drapery). This was noticed by Landon in his commentary on the Salon (1814, pp. 49-50):

At first glance, without knowing its title, one would think that this lovely picture of M. Prud'hon's was intended to represent nothing more than a nine or ten-year-old child who is getting ready to bathe and who holds two branches to ease his way into the water. Instead, Prud'hon seems to have hit upon an unforeseen idea in mid-course and to have transformed the child into Zephyr, giving him butterfly-wings and an airy drapery which flutters about his shoulders. This supposition seems even more sound when we consider that the Zephyr need only move his wings to hover above the water; his effort in grasping the branch, in order to support himself in mid-air, completely destroys the idea of weightlessness which should, instead, characterize him.

Why this metamorphosis? Perhaps it says that without the mythological allusion the work would hold no interest. But then there is Landon's elaboration of the theme: "Zephyr, the son of Æolus and Astraea, was thought by the Greeks to be the West Wind, whose breath brought a gentle breeze to their scorching climate. The poets, in order to indicate his benevolent influence on all of nature, gave him the features of a young man with a serene and gentle mien, butterfly-wings and a wreath composed of all variety of flowers." Thus, we clearly see here the ambiguity of a work and, beyond that, an era which still favored an art full of allusions, and used ones which were no longer understood: academism fast was approaching. Modern taste makes the sketch preferable to the finished work (which is admittedly in worse condition), even though to the painter it was no more than a study. The current taste for the preliminary work is not new and in fact dates to the late 19th century. In 1863, Lagrange wrote, "Forget the polish, forget the golden glazes which burnish the grisaille—the moonlight which illumes the Zephyr would turn to sunlight; but you will find neither a lighter movement nor a greater candor or smile in the eyes and mouth of this child, who plays with his reflection at the bottom of a mysterious grove. All the poetry is in the sketch. The perfected work has nothing to add to this first moment of inspiration." Similarly, Anatole France, pondering Prud'hon's art, noted:

When he had decided that his composition, preceded by a sufficient number of studies, was ready to be carried out, he painted in grisaille on the canvas. Did he proceed in this manner because he believed, rightly or wrongly, that Correggio, the painter he most admired, had done the same? He was not at all afraid, in fact, to stray from the god's path. He was, moreover, guided by his own genius to carry out his work in this way. Grisaille is all chiaroscuro and nothing but chiaroscuro. He makes use of it here, in this first effort, to great effect. Some of the paintings he left in this state, are veritable masterpieces, especially the Zephyr suspended above the water.

PROVENANCE
Posthumous sale of the artist, Paris, 1823, no. 6 (700 francs); Constantin Collection; Duc de Morny Collection; Duc de Morny sale, Paris, Palais de la Présidence du Corps Législatif, 31 May 1865, no. 110 (500 francs); Comte de Boisgelin Collection; anonymous sale, Paris, 20-21 May 1898, no. 201 (700 francs); Baron Basile de Schlichting; bequest of Basile de Schlichting to the museum in 1914 (INV. R.F. 2158).

EXHIBITIONS
1860, Paris, no. 229; 1874, Paris, École des Beaux-Arts, no. 62; 1900, Paris, Centennale, no, 528; 1958, Paris, Jacquemart-André, no. 41; 1973-1974, Paris, no. 20.

REFERENCES
L. Lagrange, 1863, p. 395; G. Duplessis, 1874, p. 572; E. de Goncourt, 1876, pp. 109-110; A. France, 1911; H. Mireur, 1912, v. VI, pp. 75-78; J. Guiffrey, 1924, no. 208, p. 77; L. Hautecœur, 1929, v. I, p. 43, ill. 53; R. Graul, 1933, v. XXVII, p. 432; J. Guiffrey, 1 January 1933, p. 2; R. Regamey, 1940, pp. 35-39, ill. 46; G. Grappe, 1958, p. 263, mus. cat., 1972, p. 307.

RELATED WORKS
Engraved by L. Lagrange. This grisaille is a study for the painting of the Salon of 1814 (no. 771; canvas, 130 × 98; Paris, Musée du Louvre). Guiffrey (1924) catalogued under nos. 209-215 the sketches and studies which relate to this work:
No. 209: Reduced version of the painting from the Salon of 1814 (canvas; 21 × 16), London, Wallace Collection. Under this number, Guiffrey points out a "large painting" (present location unknown), an "old copy" (in the Mir Collection in 1922; present location unknown), and a copy by Guet (Leipzig, museum).
No. 210: Grisaille sketch (canvas; 32 × 24), present location unknown.
No. 211: Study for the Salon painting (canvas; 80 × 64), present location unknown.
No. 212: Retouching for the Salon of 1814 picture. Black and white chalk on blue paper (59 × 37), present location unknown.

No. 213: Figure study for the same picture (same technique as no. 212; 18 × 15), present location unknown.
No. 214: Figure study for the same picture (same technique as no. 212; 18 × 15), present location unknown.
No. 215: Study for the head of Zephyr (same technique as no. 212), present location unknown.

To this list can be added a drawing in charcoal heightened with white (42 × 27), a figure study for the Salon picture, acquired in Paris, Hôtel Drouot, 4 November 1970, by the Dijon museum.

J. L.

144
*Venus, Hymen and Cupid**

Vénus, l'Hymen et l'Amour
Plate p. 259
Panel; 44 × 33
Paris, Musée du Louvre

In this painting, Venus is seated on a chair covered with green drapery, while Cupid is asleep at the left with his head on the goddess's knees. Hymen stands behind them, with a torch in his right hand trying to awaken Cupid.

To Hellenistic, probably Pompeian, reminiscences, the artist has added evocations of the art of the Italian Renaissance: the smile of Leonardo and the attenuated outlines of the mannerists. The work holds a certain fascination in its very awkwardness. The disposition of the figures, the imbalance of the lighting and the opposition of gray and gold in the coloring work together to produce an eerie composition, practically a nightmare. This painting has the evocative effect produced by certain works of Fuseli. In the combination of its classical inspiration and its function as an expression of the Romanticism of the years 1815-20 the work succeeds in evoking, in regard to its subject, the writings of the Abbé Delille and the "antique" verses of Casimir Delavigne, rather than those of André Chénier, as Clément suggested (1872, p. 396).

This work is considered a study for a definitive version, lost since 1845. It thus belongs to the very bizarre series of sketches which reminded Clément (*op. cit.* p. 380) of the difference in technique of Prud'hon and his contemporaries. While David and his pupils proceeded by aligning and juxtaposing their colors without mixing them, Prud'hon prepared his canvases in grisaille, applying color to the different areas. He would thus finish the work with a number of overlaid glazes.

It is also possible that this sketch might have served as a decorative model, which would explain its former possession by the Sèvres painter J.-B. Parent. Its oddly built-up composition, where the figures are so carefully grouped, and its "chic" style serve to reinforce this hypothesis. But the research of Mme T. Préaud, archivist of the Sèvres manufactory, established that this could not be the case.

PROVENANCE
This picture was probably given to J.-B. Parent; Talleyrand Collection; Talleyrand sale, 9 March 1847, no. 81 (500 francs); Breithmayer sale, Paris, Hôtel Drouot, room 3, 1 March 1869, no. 30 (4,500 francs); S. Richard sale (dimensions transposed), 20 June 1873, no. 60; Coltinet Collection; Édouard Kann Collection; Wildenstein Gallery; acquired by the Algiers museum; allocated to the Louvre by the Algiers museum (INV. DL 1970-18).

EXHIBITIONS
1874, Paris, no. 81; 1921, Wildenstein Gallery, no. 37; 1922, Paris, no. 7; 1922, New York, Wildenstein Gallery, no. 11.

REFERENCES
Ch. Clément, 1872, p. 396; Goncourt, 1876, p. 134; H. Mireur, 1912, v. VI, p. 76; J. Guiffrey, 1924, no. 190.

RELATED WORKS
Related works are catalogued by Guiffrey, 1924, nos. 189, 191-193:
No. 189: *Vénus, l'Hymen et l'Amour*, canvas, 125 × 65, Vasserot sale, 18-19 February 1845, no. 114 (1,301 francs), present location unknown.
No. 191: *Vénus, l'Hymen et l'Amour,* early study for the Louvre picture; black and white chalk on gray paper; 44 × 35; present location unknown.
No. 192: Study for the group *Vénus et l'Hymen ;* black and white chalk on bluish paper; 26 × 20; present location unknown.
No. 193: Study for the figure of *Vénus ;* black and white chalk on bluish paper; 26 × 18; present location unknown.

J. L.

145
Andromache and Astyanax

"Andromaque"
Plate p. 278
Canvas; 132 × 170; s.l.l. P.-P. Prudhon
Painted in collaboration with Ch. de Boisfremont (1793-1838)
Salon of 1824, no. 1384
New York, The Metropolitan Museum of Art, Bequest of Collis P. Huntington

The subject is taken from Racine's play *Andromaque* (Act II, scene v). The Salon catalog explains, "Hector's widow is lamenting the fate of her son, whose features vividly recall those of her husband: 'It is Hector,' she exclaims as she kisses him, 'Here are his eyes, his mouth, and already his courage. It is Hector himself. It is you, dear husband, whom I embrace."

This picture was scheduled for the Salon of 1817 (no. 623), but it did not appear there and was not exhibited until seven years later. The painting originally involved an allusion to the situation of Marie-Louise, as we learn from a letter written from Schoenbrunn, 8 December 1814, in which the former Empress approved the composition Prud'hon had submitted to her (E. de Goncourt, 1876, p. 116).

With the exception of the commentaries of the *Journal de Paris* (31 August 1824) and those of Flocon and Aycard, the opinions concerning this work were generally severe. (Although it was not explicitly stated, the severity was probably caused by too-recent historical reference; the figure of Astyanax does recall the King of Rome !) Some saw the work as only a simple sketch (Voïart, 1824, p. 24), and others claimed, perhaps justifiably, that the figures of Pyrrhus and Phoenix had been finished (and poorly so) by Boisfremont. Chauvin wrote, "Hector's widow and son make an interesting group, gracefully and very tastefully arranged. It is outrageous that the present owner of the work has seen fit to finish the two uncompleted figures. These figures detract from the whole and betray the fumbling of a more officious than experienced hand."

Furthermore, the affectation of the scene's self-conscious pathos was found to be disconcerting. According to N.-B.-F. P... (Fabien Pillet ?), "This *Andromache* is not at all a good piece. The sort of merit one finds in it is entirely inappropriate to the nature of the subject. Nothing so tender, nothing so flowery, nothing so fuzzy as these female complexions !

Andromache is young and pretty; she would certainly make a pleasing nymph or an enticing Eucharis; but can we, in good faith, see this figure as Hector's widow, or feel genuinely touched by this pathetic scene?" For the editor of the *Journal des Débats* (15 September 1824), "The mother's head, in the opinion of Prud'hon enthusiasts, is one of the most pleasing he has ever done, even though they frankly admit that its type and expression have nothing to do with the given character. I do not have a decided preference for Prud'hon's work and could never form an opinion on the true worth of this artist." The critic M[iel] wrote: "He has portrayed the scene in a mincing style; it is a thousand times too weak to move us as it should."

In conclusion, Jal gives us a dialogue between the Artist and the Philosopher, upon encountering one another at the Salon:

The Artist: It is a picture worthy of the artists reputation, but not, however, without its faults. Andromache is a good mother, but she does not measure up to being Hector's widow. She eagerly contemplates the features of the child who resembles her lost husband; she is happy to have a living portrait of the man she mourns. But in the midst of this joy, I would wish to see a little more grief. Otherwise, this desolate widow is a little coquettish.

The Philosopher: Yes, but she is very pretty. She almost makes me hate Pyrrhus, since I myself am past the age for romance. Astyanax is delightfully innocent; the two women, one of whom stands behind Andromache's chair, while the other gives the child to his mother, are almost as beautiful as King Æetes' daughter.

The Artist: The conception and execution of this piece leave little to be desired. Moreover, one scarcely notices its faults when one is under the spell of the gracefulness which dominates its composition—Greek in subject and French in style—and which allows one to pronounce it a little masterpiece. Prud'hon's premature death has no doubt deprived us of many precious works ! !...

These commentaries, a rather complete cross-section of the criticism of the time, provide a better understanding of the taste of a public which was not unanimous in recognizing Prud'hon as the greatest interpretor of Racine (it is true that many other artists, including Pierre-Narcisse Guérin, were also interested in illustrating theatrical scenes). The public probably wanted not the sort of pleasant and conventional neo-classical *mise en scène* (Joseph-Marie Vien's *La Marchande d'amours* comes to mind), but a truly dramatic interpretation of that kind of tragedy whose interest was still strongly alive and which had nothing of the "scholarly" about it. Contemporary art historians (such as Focillon and Seznec) are thereby able, without the reticence of 19th-century critics (including even Clément in 1872), to consider the work as one of the best possible representations of Racine.

PROVENANCE
Prud'hon sale, Paris, 13 May 1823, no. 1 (6,000 francs); Charles Leboulanger de Boisfremont Collection; acquired directly from Boisfremont by Laperlier; Laperlier Collection and sale, Paris, Hôtel Drouot, 11 April 1867, no. 38 (10,000 francs); sale [Baron Rivière], Paris, Hôtel Drouot, 22 March 1869, no. 37 (7,150 francs); M. Paradis Collection; Laurent-Richard sale (9,300 francs ?); Secrétan sale, Paris, Sedelmeyer, 1 July 1889, no. 66 (10,100 francs); Baron Gérard Collection; Baron Gérard sale, Paris, 1824; Collis P. Huntington Collection; bequest of Collis P. Huntington, in 1925.

EXHIBITION
1824, Salon, no. 1384.

REFERENCES
M[iel], 1817, p. 6 [Anon.], in *Le Journal de Paris,* 31 August 1824; [Anon.], in *Le Journal des Débats,* 15 September 1824; L'Amateur sans prétention, 1824, v. VII, p. 208; Flocon and Aycard, 1824; A. Jal, 1824; p. 221; N.-B.-F. P.***, 1824, pp. 34-35; Voïart, 1824, p. 24; M. Chauvin, 1825, p. 89; M***, 1825, p. 121; Ch. Clément, 1872, pp. 401-403; E. de Goncourt, 1876, pp. 116-118, no. 47; H. Mireur, 1912, v. VI, pp. 75-78; J.-J. Guiffrey, 1924, no. 249, p. 89; H.-B. Wehle, 1925, pp. 147 ff., ill. 178; H. Focillon, 1927, v. I, p. 70; J. Seznec, December 1944, pp. 354, 358, 361, ill. 13; Ch. Sterling, 1955, pp. 201-203, ill.

RELATED WORKS
Guiffrey (1924) provided a list under nos. 250-258 of sketches and drawings for this composition:
No. 250: Sketch (canvas; 19 × 25); present location unknown.
No. 251: Early study (black and blue chalk on bluish paper; 21 × 33), present location unknown.
No. 252: Drawing of the definitive composition of the Salon painting (black and white chalk on bluish paper; 37.5 × 45.5); Louvre.
No. 253: Large line drawing on canvas, conforming to the Salon painting (graphite; 76 × 90); present location unknown.
No. 254: Figure of Pyrrhus (black and white chalk on bluish paper; 34 × 27); present location unknown.
No. 255: Half-length study for the follower, Céphise (black and white chalk on bluish paper; 29 × 21), present location unknown.
No. 256: Figure of the nurse (black and white chalk on bluish paper); present location unknown.
No. 257: Two studies for Pyrrhus' arm (black and white chalk on bluish paper); present location unknown.
No. 258: Study of feet and arms (black and white chalk on bluish paper); present location unknown.
Under the last number, Guiffrey added a number of studies and sketches, mentioned in 19th-century sales catalogs, but impossible to identify today.
Sterling (1955, p. 202) has reconstructed the evolution of the work, based on Guiffrey's catalog. The first study seems to be no. 251, followed by nos. 253, 250 and 252.

J. L.

Abel de Pujol

1785 Valenciennes - Paris 1861

The artist was admitted at the age of 12 to the Valenciennes École des Beaux-Arts (founded by Mortry de Pujol, Baron de La Grave, his natural father, whose name he took in 1812). He worked there under the direction of Momal (whose works may be seen in Valenciennes). He then entered David's studio after receiving a grant to study in Paris. In 1810, he won second prize for painting and then in 1811 Grand Prix with his *Lycurgue présente aux Lacédémoniens l'héritier du trône* (Paris, École des Beaux-Arts). He spent only one year studying at the Villa Medici, showing "alarming signs of homesickness," according to Couder (1861, p. 2). He exhibited at the Salon regularly between 1808 and 1855 and at the same time received numerous commissions for secular buildings (Louvre, Luxembourg and Versailles palaces and the Stock Exchange) as well as for religious buildings (church of Saint-Sulpice). In 1822, he received the medal of honor at the Salon and the same year was named a knight of the Legion of Honor. He became a member of the Academy of Fine Arts in 1835.

No study has been devoted to Abel de Pujol since the eulogies which appeared at the time of his death (note especially those of Couder and G. Rouget). The only exceptions to this are the dictionary entries (Rosenthal, 1900, and Focillon, 1927) which mention him only

briefly. Therefore, it is not possible to catalogue here the large body of work by this artist. The paintings now in museums (Amiens, Auxerre, Cahors, Château-Gontier, Douai, La Rochelle, Lille, Saumur, Sens, Troyes, Vervins and especially Valenciennes) reveal an inconsistent artist who imitated Gros (and curiously enough, plagarized some of his work in grisaille). His painting *Philopoemen reconnu lorsqu'il coupait du bois dans la cuisine de l'ami qui l'avait invité à dîner* (admired by David) must be found in order to judge the artist fairly, to understand his changes of style and technique, and, finally, to appreciate the importance of his successful paintings, the *Mort de Britannicus* (Salon of 1814, Dijon) and the *Lapidation de saint Étienne* (Salon of 1817, Saint-Étienne-du-Mont).

J. L.

146
Self-Portrait

Autoportrait
Plate p. 192
Canvas; 71 × 55; s.l.r. *Abel/1806*
Valenciennes, Musée des Beaux-Arts

The sadness of this young man's expression, the studied gestures and the theatrical costume are all surprising. The desire to accentuate the tragic tone of the portrait through the coloring is astonishing for its date and calls to mind the late works of Géricault, the series of *Fous*; yet, this painting is exceptional in Abel de Pujol's œuvre and must have been painted during one of the frequent periods of depression to which he was subject as a youth. We have only to compare it with another *Autoportrait,* dated 1812, in the Valen-

ciennes museum, which presents the conventional image of an already established painter.

PROVENANCE
Gift of Julien Dècle in 1891 (INV. 46. 1-293).

REFERENCES
J. Pillion, mus. cat., 1909, no. 111; Ad. Lefranc, mus. cat., 1931, no. 319; J. Vergnet-Ruiz and M. Laclotte, 1962, p. 248.

J. L.

Jacques Réattu

1760 Arles 1833

Jacques Réattu, nephew of Antoine Raspal, painter in Arles, was born in Arles on 11 June 1760. Upon his arrival in Paris, he probably became the pupil of Simon Julien and in 1778 entered the atelier of Jean-

Baptiste Regnault. After receiving the Prix de la Figure in 1789, he obtained the Prix de Rome in 1790 for his *Daniel faisant arrêter les vieillards accusateurs de la chaste Suzanne* (Paris, École des Beaux-Arts). He arrived in Rome in 1791 and studied at the Academy until January 1793. The assassination of the French representative, Hugou de Basseville, and the ensuing events forced him to flee to Naples. There he was reunited with Pierre-Charles Bridan, Anne-Louis Girodet and Claude-Matthieu Delagardette. With the protection of a French merchant, they pursued their studies. Delagardette, Réattu and the English painter George Augustus Wallis left together for Paestum. There Réattu made several sketches and a painting, *Temples à Paestum* (Arles, Musée Réattu). On 11 November of that year, he returned to France.

Academic studies and landscapes exist from this period, as well as several mythological or historical paintings, such as the *Mort de Tatius* (Girodet painted the same subject for the Prix de Rome in 1788, now in Angers; surely, Réattu unsuccessfully entered his painting in the same competition: information kindly provided by Jacques Vilain), the sketch of *Prométhée déroulant le feu du ciel* and *Orphée aux Enfers*. Also in the Musée Réattu (Arles) are six sketch books.

The neo-classical formation of the artist is evident in the paintings of that period: there are few figures, the action of the participants occurs on one plane and the background creates the impression of a stage.

While in Rome, Réattu signed a petition to the Convention demanding more freedom for Academy students. Already sympathic to Revolutionary ideas in his letters prior to 1793, Réattu was profoundly affected by the events in Rome, and upon his return to France became an ardent Republican.

Réattu first settled in Marseille, where he received several city commissions to glorify the Revolution. In 1794, he was commissioned to transform the Église des Prêcheurs into a *"Temple de la Raison."* Imitating bas-reliefs, the sketches for the 11 grisailles he was asked to execute show *Le Génie des temps anciens et la Gloire des Vertus républicaines* (Arles, Musée Réattu). Because of the political situation, the temple was never used to glorify Reason and was reinstated as a church in 1806. Still in Marseille, he painted *La Ville de Marseille faisant construire le lazaret,* a project for the theater ceiling (Arles), and probably the portraits of Lucien and Joseph Bonaparte. Around 1797, Réattu left Marseille for Paris, where in 1798 he sketched *La Liberté parcourant le monde* in 1798 (Arles, Musée Réattu). The grouping of the figures and vigorous movement of this large composition mark the end of his bas-relief style.

Unsuccessful in Paris, Réattu returned to Arles. Between 1800-16, he did not execute any official commissions. In 1805, however, Michel-Robert Penchaud, the architect for the Bouches-du-Rhône, suggested that he join him and the sculptor Barthélemy-François Chardigny in decorating the city of Marseille for the triumphal visit of the Emperor. One can imagine that Réattu refused the offer. Perhaps it was then that Réattu the Republican ceased to paint, not wishing, as one of his friends suggested to him in a letter, to replace in his paintings the figure of Liberty with that of the Emperor. In 1816, Réattu returned to work for cities in Provence. In the years following, he did several projects for ceilings like *Le Cours du soleil à travers les saisons* (sketch of the ceiling of the great hall in the Hôtel de Ville, Marseille, now in Arles, Musée Réattu), and *Apollon et les muses traversant les Champs Élysées en distribuant des couronnes et montant au temple de Mémoire* (1829, project for a curtain for the large theater at Lyon). Toward the end of his life, Réattu began a series of six paintings of the life of Saint Paul commissioned by the city of Beaucaire. It is one of the rare times when he depicted religious subjects.

The number of official commissions attests to the esteem in which he was held. In 1804, he became an associate of the Marseille Academy and in 1824, a corresponding member of the Institute. David praised him in the following terms: "We hasten, Citizen Minister, to repeat that Citizen Réattu has already established his reputation. Eight years ago, he won with distinction the *grand prix* from the aforementioned academy of painting. The works he has executed since he began to exhibit under our eyes have only added to the special esteem we already had for his talent" : *"Rapport concernant le Citoyen Réattu peintre fait par Citns David, Berthélemy et Hue, convoqués à cet effet par une lettre particulière du ministre de l'Intérieur, frimaire, l'an VI"* (Arles, Bibliothèque Municipale, Réattu correspondence). The remainder of his life was spent mostly in Arles.

K. S.

147
Triumph of Civilization

Le Triomphe de la Civilisation
Plate p. 133
Canvas; 98 × 130
New York, Private Collection

This painting, previously given to David, was attributed to Réattu by Jean-Pierre Cuzin. This attribution is confirmed by a description appearing in Réattu's manuscripts (Arles, Bibliothèque Municipale, Réattu correspondence). In view of the complexity of the subject, the artist deemed necessary to provide an explanation: "The principal subject is the Triumph of Civilization. Time writes on a column the progress of Civilization crossing the Ocean; the Genius of France protects it and hurls lightening against vices and abuses; the major French cities eagerly move toward Civilization; as day rises, darkness sinks into the Ocean; the Matronne [sic] crowned with olive branches symbolic of peace, holds in her hand the emblem of harmony: two clasped hands encircled by myrtles represent the Union protected by Hercules, symbol of material strength, and united to Temperance, Prudence and Vigilance, virtues that characterize force; following is Justice, who supports and consoles Misfortune; below Science crushes Ignorance and Error, and with her other hand holds the large book of learning where the Genii, Astronomy, Poetry, Painting, Sculpture, Mathematics and Music come to learn; at the bottom, the Ocean, personified by an old man lying on a dolphin, offers his resources to the Union; he is surrounded by tritons and receives the waters of the Meuse, into which flows the Rhine (representing the borders of France); sunk into shadow, under the arm of the Genius is Victory, who holds palm leaves and crowns in her hands and protects the army, represented by a soldier who has not yet drawn his sword from its sheath."

Despite its restricted format, this is an extremely ambitious composition. Réattu executed very few paintings with so many figures. The dramatic illumination of Civilization, Science and the group of Justice comforting Misfortune distinguishes this work from his earlier paintings, where the lighting was more uniformly distributed. Here, Réattu relinquished orthodox composition to play on diagonals; thus, the groundline and the line of the throne recede into space. The influence of antiquity is profound, as evident in the figures of Hercules and the Union, as well as the bust protected by Victory and the marble head in the foreground. The outstretched arms of the allegorical group of the principal French cities recall the women in David's *Serment des Horaces*. The painting's style and date closely relate it to *Liberté parcourant le monde* of 1778.

PROVENANCE
Acquired by M. Balan in a sale, Vienna, between 1927 and 1930, as a David.

RELATED WORKS
Sketch (canvas; 32 × 46), Arles, Musée Réattu (INV. no. 868-1-34).

K. S.

Jean-Baptiste Regnault
1754 Paris 1829

Regnault was precocious; from the age of ten he distinguished himself copying designs in the Cabinet Bataille de Montval. He soon followed his father to America; he remained a cabin boy for five years. When he returned to Paris, he frequented the atelier of Ambroise-Marguerite Bardin and accompanied him to

Italy. Returning to France, he won in 1775 the second painting prize with *Aman confondu par Esther devant Assuérus,* and the next year took the Grand Prix with *Diogène visité par Alexandre* (Paris, École des Beaux-Arts). He traveled to Rome, where his works were very much admired; his *Baptême du Christ* (sketches in Dijon and in Paris, private collection; engraved by the artist himself) was praised by Raphaël Mengs, who affirmed when speaking of the young painter, "This one is one of us."

Regnault was admitted to the Academy in 1782 with *Andromède délivrée par Persée* and was received as an academician the following year with the *Éducation d'Achille* (Louvre; smaller replica in Avignon), a painting which quickly became famous and was popularized by the engraving. At the Salon of 1785, a *Mort de Priam* (Amiens) and a *Psyché et l'Amour* (Chicago, Art Institute; smaller version in Angers) were shown. In the same year, for the Salon des Nobles, Versailles, he painted two overdoor panels, *Pygmalion amoureux de sa statue* and *La Naissance de la peinture.*

In 1787, he exhibited *Oreste et Iphigénie en Tauride* (Marseille); in 1789, a *Deposition* and the *Deluge* (here, Nos. 148 and 149); and in 1791, *Socrate arrachant Alcibiade des bras de la Volupté.* In 1799, the painter had a one-man exhibition at the Louvre and showed three pictures: *La Mort de Cléopâtre* (Düsseldorf), *Les trois Grâces* (Louvre, his only eternally famous work), *Hercule et Alceste* (lost). Under the Empire, Regnault executed enormous paintings, among them a *Marche triomphale de Napoléon Ier vers le temple de l'Immortalité,* a gigantic canvas (nine meters long!), including many female allegories (during the Restoration, Regnault himself painted over the figure of the Emperor and replaced it with an allegorical figure of France); the *Mariage de Jerôme Bonaparte et de Catherine de Wurtemberg* and the *Sénat recevant les drapeaux pris à la Campagne d'Autriche,* both at Versailles. Under the Restoration, he painted an allegory of the return of the Bourbons, *l'Heureux événement,* to day a ceiling decoration at Fontainebleau. Until the end of his life, he liked mythological subjects, borrowed often from Ovid's *Métamorphoses:* four small pictures of this subject were recently bought by the Mobilier National; an *Io* (1827) was acquired by Brest, a *Danae* is in a private collection. The artist was, in addition, a fine portraitist: *Portrait de jeune femme* (Madame Regnault?) of 1791 in Ponce; *Madame Arnault* (Versailles); *La Reine Hortense* (Malmaison); *Le Comte Bachasson de Montalivet, ministre de l'Intérieur* (1809, Versailles); two portraits of the artist's sons (one, 1815; sale, Paris, Galerie Georges Petit, 2-5 June 1913; the other, London, Heim Gallery, exh. 1972, no. 11); *Portrait d'un officier,* exh. 1972, London, no. 12, today at Yale University, Art Gallery.

Other important canvases of Regnault are the *Persée* (c. 1785) in Louisville, J. B. Speed Museum; *Acceptation de la Constitution par Louis XVI* (sketch, Versailles, Musée Lambinet); *Cérémonie nuptiale chez les Romains* (1788, Riom); *Ariane et Thésée* (Rouen); *Vulcain et Proserpine* and *Achille et Briséis* (Leningrad, Hermitage); *Enlèvement de Déjanire* (Moscow, Pushkin); *Mort de Desaix* (versions in Clermont-Ferrand and Versailles); *La Toilette de Vénus* (New York, Chrysler Collection). There are additional works by Regnault in Montpellier, Orléans, Chartres, Dijon (Musée Magnin), Le Puy, Avignon, Troyes, Valenciennes, Calais, Metz, Auxerre.

The style of Regnault owes as much to the study of the great painters of Bologna as to the antique. While it is complex and refined, it scarcely changed during his career. His taste for round, supple forms, his velvety and blurred modeling, his soft brushwork, his luminous colors—rich with suave and disconcerting nuances—make his paintings distinctive. The mythological or allegorical language he favored permitted him to evoke a delightful world of adolescents, children and young women. He enriched this world with pearly or rosy flesh tones contrasted with the sharp bright blue, ochre or green of the draperies. He thus created a smiling and refined universe, sometimes slightly simpering, but original and completely opposed to the world of David.

J.-P. C.

148
Deposition

"Une Descente de croix"
Plate p. 91
Canvas; 425 × 233; s.d.l.l. *Regnault. De Rome./P 1789.*
Salon of 1789, no. 90
Paris, Musée du Louvre

In 1786, the *Trinité,* a large canvas by Jean Dubois (1642) which decorated the main altar at Fontainebleau, appeared to be in very bad condition and had to be restored (A. Leclair-P. Rosenberg, 1973, p. 261 and n. 2). Two years later it was decided to replace Dubois' composition with a canvas of the same size on a related subject. In 1788, the Comte d'Angiviller commissioned Regnault to do the *Deposition,* which was one of the sensations of the Salon of 1789. The artist completed the work in Paris, and not in Rome as is often said and as one is led to believe by the signature: *Regnault de Rome,* by which the painter simply wished to recall his long formative period in Italy. He had returned from Rome and had settled down in Paris as early as 1782. The *Trinité* of Dubois remains in place today. It should be noted that several years before (1779) the chapel had been the object of a big commission for 40 oval pictures for the piers, done by Renou, Bardin, Jollain, Robin, Durameau, Taraval, J.-J. Lagrenée, A. Van Loo. Twelve of the paintings appeared at the Salon of 1781; Durameau could show his two canvases only later at the Salon of 1789, not far from the large painting by Regnault (cf. A. Leclair-P. Rosenberg, *op. cit.,* p. 264). At the Salon critical reaction to the canvas by Regnault was eulogistic; the critics continually compared the painting to the greatest successes of the Bolognese. For example, the writer of the *Entretien entre un amateur et un admirateur* marvelled, "... and the local color of this painting, how mysterious and well suited to the subject !... In its characteristics, it seems close to a beautiful Guido creation" (coll. Deloynes, XVI, no. 412, pp. 133-134).

The critic of the *Année littéraire* was more complex: he praised the canvas for "its excellent taste in the drawing of the expression, a soft and fine touch...," but added that he "would have wished for more harmony" and criticized the idea of the holy woman embracing the cross, which really must have been, he thought, an object of horror for the disciples of Christ

(coll. Deloynes, XVI, no. 422, p. 347). But, the *L'Observateur au salon de l'année 1789* was ferocious: "... exclamations made me look up, everywhere viewers were shouting how bad it was, what livid flesh, what distasteful tones, and this *Deposition* is the work of an Academician ?... It is impossible... the best advice that one could give to M. Regnault would be to paint over his picture, to cover up all the figures, at least they would no longer make faces at us" (coll. Deloynes, XVI, no. 418, pp. 248-249). Later, Quatremère de Quincy (1837, pp. 39-40) was to insist again on the link with Bolognese painters: "The general appearance of this painting relates it with the work of the Carracci in its vigor, or perhaps because of its style, to the school of Guido. It is the master's manner of painting in a firm, pure, brilliant technique; it has the style of his draperies with their broken folds; it has the slightly cold precision of his brush, especially in the Virgin. It has an expression without depth. But the figure of Christ stretched out dead in the foreground is undoubtedly the most commendable part...."

The relation to Bolognese painting, stressed by the critics, is quite obvious; the concern for realism in the anatomical depiction of the body of Christ recalls Géricault as much as Caracci, and one is reminded of the malicious nickname of "Père La Rotule" which his fastidious preoccupation with anatomical exactitude later won Regnault as professor. The canvas is not unrelated to the *Déposition de croix* by Jean-Baptiste-Marie-Pierre, shown at the Salon of 1761 (cathedral of Versailles), which shows a similar group, with the cross against a somber sky and a realistic dead body lying in front; but curiously, as Leclair and Rosenberg noted (*op. cit.,* p. 261), the face of the Virgin turning to the rear with her eyes raised to the sky, seems directly inspired by the same figure in the canvas by Jean Dubois.

The color harmonies of the canvas, which disconcerted some critics, still have a surprising audacity, as recent restoration has revealed. The magnificent shades of violet-gray of the cadaver stand out against the white drapery, the deep blue of the Virgin's robe, contrasted with the white and yellow of the Magdalene (with such delicate mauve edges, vibrating on the pale yellow !), and the red juxtaposed at the right to the green of the mantle of Saint John, orchestrate subtle dissonances played out against the sky.

The picture was very much admired and frequently copied (the whole composition, and even more often, the isolated bust of the Virgin); several copies were also commissioned during the Second Empire (P. Angrand, 1968, p. 306).

PROVENANCE
Commissioned by d'Angiviller in 1788 for the Chapelle de la Trinité in the Château of Fontainebleau; never hung. Musée du Luxembourg; Louvre (INV. 7381).

EXHIBITION
1789, Salon, no. 90.

REFERENCES
Coll. Deloynes, v. XVI, no. 412, pp. 133-134; no. 418, pp. 248-249, no. 422, p. 347; C.-P. Landon, v. VI, 1804,
p. 1; J.-B. Chaussard, 1806, pp. 247-248; J. Delécluze, 1815, p. 301; A. Chr. Quatremère de Quincy, 1837, pp. 39-40; F. Engerand, 1901, p. 409; R. Rosenblum, 1964, note 116, p. 83; F. Angrand, 1968, v. I, p. 306; A. Leclair - P. Rosenberg, 1973, p. 261.

RELATED WORKS
Bust of Virgin, canvas, 60 × 49; perhaps a copy rather than the original replica; Dijon, Musée Magnin (mus. cat., 1938, no. 835). Incomplete lithograph by Julien in charcoal and chalk, published by De la Rue in Paris, without a date (about 1840 ?).
Sketch (or smaller copy), sold after Regnault's death, 1 March 1830, no. 28 ("Christ descended from the cross, a small picture produced from the large one, done for the Chapel of Fontainebleau"...); the posthumous inventory of the artist gives the dimension of the picture: 22 × 12 *pouces* (information communicated by C. Sells). "Finished sketch" (same as the preceding one ?), Blondel sale, 12 December 1853, no. 113. "Study of the head of the dead Christ", *idem,* no. 114. Painted study of the bust of the Virgin, posthumous sale, no. 91 ("Bust of the Mother of Sorrows, study completed for the lovely painting of the Descent from the cross"). Drawn study for the Virgin, posthumous sale, no. 108 ("Two drawings, the Virgin of Sorrows and...").

J.-P. C.

149
The Deluge

"*Le déluge*"
Plate p. 92
Canvas; 89 × 71 (format transformed in the 19th century to a round one; restored to its original dimensions)
Salon of 1789, no. 91
Paris, Musée du Louvre

Exhibited by Regnault at the same Salon as his large *Deposition* (No. 148), this "easel painting" received the positive votes of critics, who were unanimous in praising the sense of pathos with which the artist expressed the theme of the *Deluge* (for this theme, see also Nos. 26 and 63): the man carrying his helpless father to save him from the water and seeing his wife and young son carried off by the current; "the unhappy man faces the horrible choice to save one or the other, to lose his father or to sacrifice his wife and son" (P. Chaussard, 1806, p. 249). "The subject... is of the greatest interest. It has furnished the artist with the opportunity to paint all ages in extraordinary poses" (*Observations*
critiques sur les tableaux du Salon de l'année 1789, coll. Deloynes, XVI, no. 410, p. 21). The chronicler of the *Vérités agréables ou le Salon vu en beau* was less placid: "He sees himself forced either to throw his father into the torrent or to abandon his wife to it... what a deplorable situation ! What dreadful anxiety !... One's soul is moved, one's heart is broken and tears briming in the eyes of all tell the creator of such a beautiful work that he is worthy to be placed among the most famous artists" (coll. Deloynes, XVI, no. 415, pp. 171-172).

Christopher Sells informs us (written communication) that the prototype of the painting is a print by Coiny from a drawing by Regnault; it involves one of the plates illustrating an edition of Ovid's *Metamorphoses*, translated by the Abbé Banier and published by Didot the Elder in 1787. Regnault later repeated the composition several times (see Related Works). In fact, the canvas became very famous; it was re-exhibited at the Salon of 1791 and "... many artists considered this painting Regnault's masterpiece" (A. Chaussard, 1806, p. 250). The theme reappeared in A.-L. Girodet's masterpiece of the Salon of 1806 (Louvre; see G. Levitine, 1970 and J. H. Rubin, 1972, pp. 211-238). The silky finish of Regnault's painting; the refinement of the color palette, limited to of blue-grays, violets and ochres, with a most luminous note of blue in the belt and of yellow-ochre in the pants, even the elegance of the postures, make this little canvas a delightful masterpiece, still very much "Louis XVI" in spirit, despite the horror of its theme.

PROVENANCE
Sale, Paris, 2 April 1794 ("a fine collection of paintings of the French School gathered through the efforts of Citi en Godefroi"), no. 25 in the catalog; sale, Paris, 17 December 1821 ("a collection of choice pictures... gathered by the late M. Paignon-Dijonval and continued by the Vicomte de Morel Vindé") no. 89, bought for 277 francs, by M. de Langeac (note on the copy of the sale catalog in the Doucet library); acquired by Louis XVIII from M. de Langeac in 1822; Château de Saint-Cloud; Louvre (INV. 7380). (Information communicated by Christopher Sells.)

EXHIBITIONS
1789, Salon, no. 91; 1791, Salon, no. 211.

REFERENCES
Coll. Deloynes, v. XVI, no. 410, p. 21; no. 415, pp. 171-172; C.-P. Landon, v. III, 1802, ill. 21; J.-B. Chaussard, 1806, pp. 249-250; A.-Chr. Quatremère de Quincy, 1837, p. 49; G. Levitine, 1970, pp. 142-144.

RELATED WORKS
Paintings. Another version, height about 45; C.-P. Landon, III, 1802, pp. 49-52; lost. Small version (panels, 215 × 160), recently acquired by the Mobilier National with three other panels of the same dimensions by Regnault; probably a much later replica.
Drawings. Pen and wash; 35 × 25; s.l.l.; Fabre bequest to Montpellier. Drawing (same as the previous one?) sold after Regnault's death, 1 March 1830, no. 102 (framed drawings): "Scene of the deluge... This very important drawing has great dramatic interest." Drawing, in Paris sale, 8 March 1813, no. 127, "done in Italian chalk, on white paper," sold at the same time as the plate by Ingouf (see below) for which it had served as model (reference indicated by Christopher Sells).
Engraving. By Ingouf, 1796, left unfinished; finished by Croutelle, 1817.

J.-P. C.

150
Liberty or Death

"La Liberté ou la Mort"
Plate p. 137
Canvas; 60 × 49; s.d.l.r. *Regnault l'an 3me*
Salon of 1795, no. 424
Hamburg, Kunsthalle

At the Salon of 1795, Regnault showed two versions of his painting *Liberty or Death*; the small version is exhibited here; the larger version (no. 421 of the Salon catalog), given by the artist to the Nation, was on view between 1799 and 1805 in the Salle du Conseil des Cinq-Cents in the Palais-Bourbon. In the mid-19th century, it was found in the reserves of the Louvre and in 1872 was deposited in a provincial museum. To date, all efforts to locate it have been unsuccessful.

The genesis and iconography of this work make it one of the most perfect illustrations of Revolutionary ideas. At the center, the Genius of France, with tri-colored wings, soars over the terrestrial globe, expressing the universal call of the ideas of 1793. To his left is Death. To his right is the Republic with its symbols: the square signifying Equality, the fasces standing for Fraternity; the Phrygian hat representing Liberty, the serpent biting his tail symbolizing Eternity. The Genius of France is derived from the Mercury of the Farnesina. Its reversed appearance here is explained by the existence of an engraving of the Farnesina fresco. One can also compare it with an engraving representing the Genius of France executed in 1794 by C. Schule from a design by Schubert. Such grandiose representation, a worthy extension of the huge allegorical "machines" of the Enlightenment, actually originated in opera; scene VI of the opera, *a Triomphe de la République* by Marie-Joseph Chénier with the score by Gossec (1793), could be considered as one of the sources of Regnault's work.

But the painting's most interesting aspect is certainly its theme, which illustrates the motto of the Constitution of the Year III (10 August 1793): Liberty, Equality, Fraternity or Death. In a weaker form, this later became the motto of the French Republic. Here again the work can be related to the radical maxim, Liberty or Death, expressed by Revolutionary hymns such as *Le Chant de Guerre pour l'Armée du Rhin* (1792) by Rouget de Lisle with the music by François-Joseph Gossec which later became the French national anthem with the name of *La Marseillaise, l'Hymne de mort* (1793) by Jean-Baptiste Louvet or *Le Chant du départ* (1794) by M.-J. Chénier, brother of the poet, with music by Etienne-Nicolas Méhul. It was surely this radicalism expressed in the motto that earned Regnault the criticism which he received. Completed at the end of 1793, *Liberty or Death* revived the intransigent ideas of Robespierre. Although the painting expressed the pure and violent ideology of the Terror, formed in response to civil and foreign wars, the picture was not shown until the Thermidorian Convention (July 1794-October 1795),

that is to say, during the sober stage of the Revolution which followed the fall of Robespierre on 27 July 1794 and led to the accession of the Directory on 26 October 1795. Obviously, the political import of the subject, "suitable for flattering Robespierre and his henchmen" (coll. Deloynes, XVIII, no. 469, p. 406) constituted an anachronism for which Regnault was reproached.

PROVENANCE
Acquired in Hamburg in 1818 by O.-C. Gaedechens; then given by him to the Hamburg Kunsthalle in 1846.

EXHIBITION
1795, Salon, no. 424.

REFERENCES TO THIS WORK
C. Caubisens, 1961, p. 373, ill. 3; mus. cat., 1966, p. 128, no. 510, ill.; J.-H. Rubin, 1972, chap. III and IX; J. Heusinger von Waldegg, 1972, pp. 3-4.

RELATED WORK
Larger version of subject, now lost (see above).

REFERENCES
Coll. Deloynes, v. XVIII, no. 469, pp. 405-408; no. 472, pp. 549-550; no. 476, p. 594; no. 478, pp. 605-610; no. 479, p. 611; no. 480, pp. 613-615; [Anon.], *Examen critique et concis...*, 1795, p. 6; P.-J.-B. Chaussard, 1808, p. 249; J. Renouvier, 1863, p. 23; F. Boyer, 1935, p. 80; J.-A. Leith, 1965, p. 140.

J. V.

151
Physical Man, Moral Man...

L'homme physique, l'homme moral et l'homme intellectuel
Plate p. 220
Canvas; 159 × 131
Brest, Musée des Beaux-Arts

Everything about this canvas, one of the most spetacular purchases of the dynamic Brest museum, is intriguing and disconcerting. Christopher Sells, who is presently studying the work of the artist, has generously shared his information about the painting. It appeared in the painter's will of 12 May 1829 in the following terms: "The allegorical painting depicting physical man, moral man and intellectual man will remain deposited with my elder son, until time and circumstances allow him to make it known to its advantage. However, if my elder son is not married, the painting will be deposited with Franchesco to be returned to the elder

when he marries or with Carle, if one or the other should have died." Until recently, the canvas remained in the Regnault family. (For its subsequent history see Provenance.)

The painting's peculiar subject challenges easy analysis. There seems to be no doubt that it is a Masonic allegory. M. Roger Cotte has very kindly helped with the clarification of some of the obscurities. The main figure, dressed in the antique manner, and seated to the left on the clouds, represents the initiate, who possesses the light (the pot of burning embers in the center foreground) and has access to power over things terrestrial (the globe rising under his extended right hand symbolizing absolute power). In his immediate vicinity are a *cornue*, a curious musical instrument that is something between a lute and a hand-organ, an astronomical spyglass and a tablet covered with geometrical signs which allude to the knowledge of the physical world and perhaps refer more particularly to certain of the liberal arts; the knowledge of which is indispensable to the Freemason. The presence of the terrestrial globe and the insistence placed on the number five (five strings in the musical instrument, five petals on the flower) could indicate the member's rank (second), which is linked to the discovery of the universe. The crown of laurel in the left foreground, symbolizes victory over the self and could constitute an allusion to the fourth rank. The geometrical configuration visible on the tablet behind the pot appears to be a demonstration of the Pythagorean theory: it is the symbol of Masonic science, which one finds engraved on the gems of "Ancient Venerables." Since antiquity, the peacock has been identified as a symbol of immortality.

The group on the right, composed of two women who protect two children, seems to signify the required mutual help which is the basis of Masonic morality. The presence of the women in the intermediate distance is perhaps significant, since in the 18th century, women could not undergo complete Masonic initiation, and "adoptive lodges" were reserved for them. Behind the female group are three disturbing figures. The bearded man who lifts an open book and a bloodstained dagger appears to represent religion, the agent of superstition: he is the false priest, as opposed to the initiate; his two grimacing associates, one holding a broken mirror and a mask, the other with eyes bound, could be allegories of obscurantism and blindness.

At the top, in a blue-tinged penumbra, three seated figures dominate the scene. At the center, the Supreme Being, "Grand Architect of the Universe," crowned with nine stars, is depicted as an old bearded man holding a scepter; at the right, a nude woman, face and shoulders hidden by a veil, probably represents Isis; at the left, another woman who hammers with a mallet on a sculptor's chisel (symbol of active intelligence) represents perhaps Freemasonry, in opposition to Isis. The initiate points to the Supreme Being and the woman at the left, while the false priest points to Isis. Thus, the picture is divided into two halves, left and right, which recall the two columns, J. and B., of the Temple of Solomon that are common components of Masonic

iconography. All of these elements recall Lachnith's opera, *Les Mystères d'Isis* (1801) which at the time had wide repercussions, not to mention Mozart's *Magic Flute*.

The title which Regnault himself gave the painting in his will summarizes its contents well and corresponds to the work's three points of interest: the domination of man over the universe, throught the arts and sciences ("physical man"), the requirement of mutual help ("moral man") and the omnipotence of intelligence ("intellectual man"). The fact that the initiate has the artist's own features adds to the interest of the work. The catalog of the sale of 1912, which undoubtedly repeats a family source, attests to this fact at a time when the precise sense of the work was already lost (or purposefully disguised ?): "the master depicted himself as seated on the ground with an astrologer's features surrounded by numerous figures." The resemblance with known portraits of Regnault is also evident. Therefore, the painter was a Freemason. Thus, the work signifies a manifesto and constitutes a genuine profession of Masonic faith. The entire picture is thus a self-portrait; certainly one of the most ambitious ever painted.

The apparent age of the model is the main component by which one can judge the date of this painting. Regnault appears rather old, but decidedly younger than in certain very late portraits, such as in the lithograph by Jules Boilly of 1820, where the features are clearly aged and puffy. Thus, a date of about 1810-1815 seems reasonable.

A scale of blues joined by ochre or orange tones was favored by the artist at the end of his life; here, as in his admirable *Io* of 1827 (another masterpiece recently acquired by Brest), the painter contrasted tender and luminous blues with milky whites and little accents of bright rose. Throughout his career, Regnault enjoyed adopting a secret allegorical language, complicated by multiple subtleties. The masterpieces of this vein are the allegory, *Liberty or Death* (No. 150), the *Cortège de Napoléon* (Versailles) and the *Heureux événement* (Fontainebleau). *Physical Man, Moral Man...* is a new and fascinating example of this ambition.

PROVENANCE

Kept by the artist until his death; listed in the posthumous inventory of his son Jean-François ("Franchesco"), with the same title, while belonging jointly to Jean-François and to his older brother Antoine-Louis. After the death of the latter (1856), who never married, the work was put up for sale for the first time in Paris, 24 January 1957, no. 32; repurchased under the title *Sujet allégorique, l'homme physique, l'homme moral et l'homme intellectuel,* along with a *Hercule enlevant Alceste* and a *Mercure*. Together with these two latter paintings, it was repurchased by the family of Marie-Sophie Regnault, daughter of Jean-François, wife of Adolphe-Antoine Deforge. At the sales of 14 December 1912 (Paris, Hôtel Drouot, Room 1, no. 104) and June 1920 (Paris, Hôtel Drouot, no. 82) it appeared with the same painting and was repurchased by the family. It appeared with the *Mercure* (really *Persée,* as demonstrated by Sells, 1973; this painting now in the J.-B. Speed Museum, Louisville), at the Sale, 19 December 1971, Paris, Hôtel Drouot, Room 2, no cat. Bought by the Musée de Brest in 1972 on the Parisian art market.

REFERENCES
J.-P. Cuzin, 1972, pp. 468-470, nos. 36 (p. 469), 37, 38 (p. 470), ill. 16; C. Sells, 1973, p. 1.

J.-P. C.

152
Judgment of Paris

Le jugement de Pâris
Plate p. 221
Canvas; 280 × 175 (octagonal); s.d.l.l. (on the gourd) *ch. Regnault*
The Detroit Institute of Arts, Gift of Mr. and Mrs. Henry Ford II

Recently acquired by the Detroit Institute of Arts, this canvas constitutes one of the principal paintings of the last period of Regnault's career. It is not dated and was not exhibited at the Salon. It was however engraved (see Related Works) in the *Salon de 1812* of C.-P. Landon, who noted, "the artist permitted us to copy the work in his studio at the moment he had just applied the finishing touches," and thus we have the date of the execution of the work.

The octogonal form is that which the artist had already adopted for his *Trois Grâces* (Louvre). However, the painting is most likely not, as believed the annotator of the catalog of the sale of the contents of the artist's studio, in a pendant to the *Trois Grâces,* which was executed 12 years before and smaller in size. This type of mythological composition was important to Regnault throughout his career. Here he seems to treat the theme of the judgment of Paris with a sense of humor, insisting on the shepherd's smug and naive expression, on the hard gaze of Venus and on the angry and confused looks of the losing goddesses. The taste for dance-like poses, sinuous and decorative complexity—light draperies, curled locks, Minerva's serpents, or Juno's peacock—enriches the painting with delicate effects. The brushwork anticipates the more ambiguous creations of Bouguereau and Cabanel. A strange painting, it disconcerts the viewer by the unreality of its color scale, fascinating in its "bad taste," and well-made to seduce us.

One is struck here by the evolution of the artist's style since the *Deposition* (No. 148), strongly marked by the Caravagesque influence and the Bolognese School. Here, Regnault seems to have turned to Rubens; his taste for sensuous curves and counter-curves and his silky and transparent paint surface recall the Flemish master. But a sense of Greco-Roman antiquity is always present: the well-endowed form and pose of Venus recalls the *Venus Esquiline* (Rome, Palazzo dei Conservatori); the attitude of the shepherd recalls that of Paris in the Vatican (Museo Pio-Clementino). The Detroit painting is related to Regnault's *Mort d'Adonis,* an important canvas dated 1812, sold in Paris in 1913 (sale, Baron de C., 20 December 1913, no. 68) and now lost; a fine sketch for this composition has just generously been given anonymously to the Louvre (1972).

PROVENANCE
Inventory of the studio of Regnault, November 1829 (Arch. Nat., *Minutier Central, étude* XIII*, liasse* 641); posthumous sale of the artist's studio, 1-3 March 1830, not in the catalog, but noted on the copy in the British Museum: "The Judgment of Paris, pendant to the painting of *Les Trois Grâces,* 4,000, withdrawn for bidding"; collection of Jean-François Regnault, third son of the artist (posthumous inventory, Minutier Central, *étude* XLIV*, liasse* 984); sale, Paris, Hôtel Drouot, 2 July 1928, bought by a M. Roger, Paris, M. Colombier Collection, 1953; Collection Le Peletier, Paris, 1954; Walter P. Chrysler, Jr. Collection, New York; Shepherd Gallery, New York; purchased for the Detroit Institute of Arts by Mr. and Mrs. Henry Ford II in 1972 (the above information generously provided by Christopher Sells).

EXHIBITIONS

1956, Portland, no. 71; 1960, Dayton, no. 4.

REFERENCES

C.-P. Landon, 1812, v. II (1830), p. 78, ill. 57; *Journal des Artistes...,* 1829, p. 333; A. Lenoir, 1830, p. 31; A. Chr. Quatremère de Quincy, 1837, p. 49 ("Grands tableaux"); *G.B.A.,* Feb. 1973, suppl., no. 474, ill.; C. Sells, 1974 (at press).

RELATED WORKS

"Finished sketch" 12 × 12 *pouces,* in the inventory of Regnault of 1829, lost. "Bistre drawing," 15 × 8 *pouces ;* sketch for the *Judgment of Paris." Idem ;* lost. Noted, like the preceding painting, by Christopher Sells (written communication).

"Drawing on tinted paper." Sale after Regnault's death, 1 March 1830, part of no. 121 ("... and the *Judgment of Paris ;* two charming drawings on tinted paper"); lost. "Bistre drawing." *Idem ;* part of no. 169 ("... the *Judgment of Paris,* bistre drawing..."); probably the one cited in the inventory; lost. Drawing, "graphite and chalk," sale, Paris, 31 March 1943, Room 7, no. 59, "Paris et Vénus"; 14.5 × 18; related to the Detroit painting; present location unknown. Engraved by Mme Soyer, in C.-P. Landon, Salon of 1812, ill. 57.

J.-P. C.

Pierre-Henri Révoil

1776 Lyon - Paris 1842

Révoil first studied with Alexis Grognard at the drawing school at Lyon; and then, in 1796, entered David's studio in Paris. There, together with another Lyonnais, Fleury Richard, he distinguished himself by his taste for medieval subjects. He returned to Lyon in 1807, where he was professor of painting until 1818, when he moved to Aix-en-Provence. In 1823, he resumed his professorship at Lyon and exerted an enormous influence on the Lyonnais school of painting before retiring in 1830.

Although Révoil made his Salon debut in 1804 with a painting of Napoleonic history (*Passage de l'Empereur Napoléon à Lyon,* destroyed in 1814), his first success came at the Salon of 1810 with *L'Anneau de l'Empereur Charles Quint* (Versailles, on loan to the French Embassy, Madrid), a work whose scrupulous accuracy of historical detail reflects the collection of medieval and renaissance objects and furniture that Révoil had formed and that Charles X acquired in 1828. Révoil's fascination with the Middle Ages and the Renaissance even included a study of Old French *(la langue romane)* and the invention of medieval romances (e.g., *La Blanche Marguerite).* Such a reconstruction of medieval life, which earned Révoil the title, *peintre de la chevalerie,* is clearly exemplified in his entry at the Salon of 1812, *Le Tournoi* (Lyon), a scene of medieval pageantry which, in its small format and punctilious description of costumes and decor, reveals, like the work of Richard, the influence of late medieval painting and manuscript illumination. He continued to exhibit, until 1841, themes taken primarily from medieval history and legend, ranging from moments in the lives of Tancred and Giotto to Joan of Arc and Mary Stuart. He also executed religious paintings (*Christ en croix ; Adoration du sacré-cœur de Jésus,* Lyon, Saint-Nizier). Révoil's later work, such as his entry at the Salon of 1838 (*Charles Quint à l'abbaye de Saint-Just,* Avignon), tends to lose the miniaturist precision that characterized the *style troubadour* during the first two decades of the century, a mode also practiced by Richard, Laurent, Vermay, Coupin de la Couperie and Ingres.

R. R. and M.-Cl. C.

153
François 1 Knighting his Grandson, François 11

"François Ier faisant chevalier son petit-fils François II"
Plate p. 280
Canvas; 140 × 180; s.d.l.r. *P. REVOIL. 1824.*
Salon of 1824, no. 1428
Aix-en-Provence, Musée Granet

Révoil was famous for paintings of French national history, which he had begun to exhibit as early as the Salon of 1810 (*L'Anneau de Charles Quint,* Salon no. 672). The description in the Salon catalog carefully identifies all present in the painting exhibited here : The child, presented by his aunt and godmother, Madame Marguerite de France, is knighted by the King. He [the child] is surrounded by Eleanor of Austria, his grandfather's second wife; the Comtesse de Saint-Pol; the Duchesse de Guise and the two Duchesses de Nevers. Behind are the Dauphin, Henri II (father of François II), and to the left his brother Charles, Duc d'Orléans; Odouart du Biez, the Dauphin's godfather; the gallant Frœlich, Swiss colonel in the Battle of Cérisoles; the Venetian ambassador; and the dauntless Charles de Cossé-Brissac who, lance in hand... stopped the entire Spanish garrison at Perpignan. Next to the throne are the ministers, the virtuous Admiral d'Annebaud and the Cardinal de Guise, called *Le Magnifique*.

This reconstructed portrait gallery depends in part on well-known 16th-century portraits of the personages represented: e.g., François I is based on the Titian portrait (Louvre), of which Révoil made a drawing (Béziers); and Henri II is based on the Clouet portrait (Florence, Galleria degli Uffizi).

Under the Restoration, such subjects were encouraged, especially those which dealt with Anglo-French dynastic connections. Already at the Salon of 1822, Révoil had exhibited *Marie Stuart séparée de ses fidèles serviteurs* (Salon no. 1081); and this scene of the infancy of François II, who was to become the husband of Mary Stuart in 1558, may have continued to contribute to the growing interest in the relations between England and France in the 16th century.

Révoil's inclusion (to the left and right of the arch) of the two great Raphaels from the collection of François I—the *Holy Family* and *Saint Michael* (now both in the Louvre)—is also characteristic of the frequent reminders under the Bourbon Restoration of artistic patronage by the French kings and other monarchs. As early as the Salon of 1814, Anicet-Charles-Gabriel Lemonnier exhibited *François Ier recevant dans la salle des suisses à Fontainebleau, le tableau de la Sainte Famille, que Raphaël avait exécuté pour lui* (Rouen). Indeed, under Charles X, who commissioned Révoil's painting, the Louvre was decorated with scenes of heads of State and Church as art collectors and patrons, including Alexandre-Évariste Fragonard's *François Ier reçoit les tableaux rapportés d'Italie par le Primatice* (1827). And at the Salon of 1824, one could see not only Révoil's painting of François I, but Ingres' painting of Leonardo da Vinci dying in the arms of that monarch (No. 106).

Although Révoil's over-all composition recalls the grand manner of 16th and 17th-century painting (especially such analogous subjects as Poussin's illustrations of the story of Moses, where an infant is presented by a group of women), the dry and meticulous rendering of details of portraiture, costume and decor evokes an earlier pictorial style. Such careful surface description was typical of many early 19th-century French paintings of late medieval and renaissance history, of which Ingres' own scenes from the lives of Charles V, François I and Henri IV are the best-known examples. Critics were usually negative about this archaizing style, often inspired by late medieval painting. Thus, A. Jal complained of the stiffness of the postures and of the metallic quality of all surfaces, whether flesh or armor, and noted that Révoil substituted "the microscopy for the art of seeing nature." It was exactly this *"microscopie,"* however, that permitted the demonstration, in such history paintings, of the artist's learned reconstruction of the historical past, and that conjured up, furthermore, the jewel-like richness and pageantry of a distant century.

PROVENANCE
Commissioned by the Comte d'Artois, later Charles X (Arch. Nat. O³ 1413); loaned from the Louvre (INV. 7475) to Musée Granet, Aix-en-Provence, 1907.

EXHIBITION
1824, Salon, no. 1428.

REFERENCES
Journal des Débats, 8 September 1824; C.-P. Landon, 1824, v. II, pp. 51-52, ill. 55-56; A. Jal, 1824, pp. 434-435; F. Pillet, 1824, p. 45; P.-A. Vieillard, 1825, p. 19; J.-B. Dumas, 1839, II, p. 108; E.-C. Martin Daussigny, 1842, p. 25; P. Marmottan, 1886, p. 257; M..., 1825, pp. 434-435.

RELATED WORKS
Watercolor (21 × 26, s.l.l. *Révoil*), Montpellier, Musée Fabre (INV. 836-4-261). For the theme, *Portrait de François Ier* (lead pencil; 29 × 22; s.l.r. *P.R.*), Béziers (INV. 439); *François Ier* (black wash; 22 × 27; s.l.l. *P.R.*), Paris, private collection.

R. R., M.-Cl. C.

Fleury-François Richard

1777 Lyon - Ecully 1852

Along with Michel Grobon and Pierre Révoil, Fleury-François Richard was one of the founders of what was called, about 1820, "the Lyonnais school." Too often, the artist has been referred to under the erroneous name of Richard Fleury. It should be recalled here that Fleury was indeed a very common first name in the Lyon region—for example, the landscape painter Fleury Epinat and Fleury Chenu.

In the spring of 1789, Fleury Richard entered the Lyon drawing school, where he took courses from Alexis Grognard and was trained as a painter of flowers for silk firms. In May 1795, he left for Paris and in September 1796 was admitted to David's workshop, where he remained for three years. Richard exhibited regularly at the Salons from 1801 to 1824. He did not appear there again until 22 years later with *Comminge et Adélaïde,* a painting begun about 1822 and finished in 1846. Between 1805 and 1810, Empress Josephine bought seven paintings from him for her gallery in Malmaison and named him "Painter to Her Majesty" in 1808. Queen Hortense also liked Richard's paintings; before inheriting some of those owned by her mother, she had acquired two herself (*Gil Blas chez le chanoine Sédillo,* Salon of 1810, location unknown; *Mlle de La Vallière,* Arenenberg, Musée Napoléon) and even copied several (one was recently found at Arenenberg). In 1814, Richard received the title of "Peintre de genre de Monsieur," and, in 1817, "Painter to His Royal Highness." From 1817 to 1819, he worked solely on one commission, *Tannegui Duchastel sauvant le Dauphin,* done for the Galerie de Diane of the Château de Fontainebleau (still in situ). His career was spent almost entirely in Lyon, where he replaced Pierre Révoil as professor. After 1820, his success seemed to diminish and when, in 1824, he suffered a stroke, he in effect ceased to paint. He was 47 years old. In his last years, he drafted his *Souvenirs,* which have remained unpublished (although a portion was published by the author himself in the *Revue du Lyonnais* in 1851.

Richard's total œuvre is thus quite small. Moreover, he labored long over his works, conceived his paintings with care and gathered documentation which demanded years of studies. Attracted by history painting, Richard found the subjects of his first works in Roman antiquity: *L'impératrice Irène relevant les monuments de la religion chrétienne* (lost, but known through a drawing) and the *Mort de Constantin* (lost), c. 1800, (now lost). But together with Révoil, Forbin and Granet, Richard soon formed a separate group in David's studio. He became a regular visitor of the Musée des Monuments Français, consulted medieval manuscripts and turned to the nation's past. At the Salon of 1802 (no. 243), he had a tremendous success with his *Valentine de Milan* (lost). This work was followed by genre scenes illustrating the history of France, created before Ingres or the Restoration. Richard situated his figures in interiors, emphasized perspective, and lateral lighting. Less often, he placed his figures in a landscape done from nature (*Mort de saint Paul ermite,* 1810, Digne). He liked the anecdotal, but he was also absorbed by historical documentation, owning studies of architecture, costumes, furniture (his collection included gothic and renaissance examples). One from life or from miniatures, as shown by his sketchbooks (Mépieu, Richard Collection). To this erudite taste, very new at the time, Richard added a sentimental or moralizing tone. An example is his depiction of La Vallière as a repentant Magdalene in *La Vallière, carmélite* (1805, Moscow, Pushkin Museum), where he wished to "paint an idea," creating an intellectual work which combined various symbols.

A native of Lyon and admirer of Michel Grobon (he devoted a note to him in the *Revue du Lyonnais* of 1851), Richard emphasized contrasts of light and shadow which stressed the main group, or placed an oblique light on figures and accessories. He was attracted by the genre scenes of the Dutch golden era (in his writings, the names of Pieter de Hooch, Emmanuel de Witte, Gérard Dou reappear several times) and took lessons from the Lyonnais painter Pierre-Toussaint Déchazelle (he published a biography of that artist in the *Revue du lyonnais* of 1851), who taught him to paint in the Dutch manner and to use very fine glazes. Richard painted smoothly and precisely; his excessively detailed style, his polished technique, his worship of the ideal, his desire to educate, his need to leave nothing to the imagination but to study everything carefully, led to the asceticism and symbolism of Victor Orsel and to the sermonizing art of Paul Chevanard.

M.-Cl. C.

154
Deference of Saint Louis to his Mother

"La Déférence de saint Louis pour sa mère"
Plate p. 202
Canvas; 97 × 97
Salons of 1808, no. 495 and 1814, no. 786
Arenenberg, Napoleonmuseum

The subject is inspired by the *Histoire de Saint Louis* (chap. CXIX) by Joinville (1224-1319) : Louis IX, fearing the jealousy of his mother Blanche de Castille, went to see his wife, Marguerite de Provence, without the Queen Mother's knowledge. If the latter were to appear, the guard of the chamber was instructed to make the dogs howl in order to warn the King. "However, once the King was with the Queen, his wife, who was in danger of death because she had been maimed by the birth of a child. At that moment, Queen Blanche appeared, took her son by his hand and said to him: 'Go away, you can do nothing here.' When Queen Marguerite saw that the King was leaving, she cried, 'Alas ! alive or dead, you will not permit me to see my lord ?' and then she fainted. Everyone believed she had died and the king, who thought that she was dead, turned toward her, revived her with great difficulty."

The episode of Louis IX with its image of a weak king —"a schoolboy of 16 who trembles before the rod of his master" (Vict. F....) was apparently seldom depicted by painters. The single exception is the engraving by Moreau the Younger, *Docilité de Saint Louis à l'égard de sa mère, année 1238* (A. Dingué, *Figures de l'histoire de France,* Paris, 1790-Year VII, no. 137). After the Salon of 1802, Richard had turned to the nation's past, taking from French history pathetic scenes, capable of moving the public, such as *Valentine de Milan pleurant la mort de son époux,... Charles VII écrivant ses adieux à Agnès Sorel avant de partir combattre les Anglais....* With the *Deference of Saint Louis* he forced the spectator to feel sympathy for Marguerite de Provence; a critic (Vict. F...) praised "the natural expression" of the young woman, "persecuted, suffering, but noble in her grief."

Instead of using declamatory gestures to describe the scene, Richard used restraint. The figures are somewhat frozen in the feelings they express, such as in the gesturing of Blanche de Castille or Saint Louis, immobilized in the movement traced by his lines.

The critics were sensitive to the precise description of the accessories and the presentation of little known historical fact. A "knowledgeable painter" (coll. Deloynes, XLV, p. 592), Richard described costumes and furniture minutely. The model for the bed "in the style of the period ?" must have been a composite, made up of elements of the architecture and furniture with which his notebooks were filled. The Virgin and Child are very close to the "Virgin in wood which could date back to the 17th and 18th centuries" in the ante-room of the Musée des Monuments Français (cf. *Vues pittoresques et perspectives des salles du Musée des Monuments Français,* engraved by Réville and Lavalée, Paris, 1816, pl. 3).

Richard revived a type of composition which he cherished *(François Ier et Marguerite de Navarre,* Salon of 1804, no. 377; Arenenberg, Napoleonmuseum): a frieze-like placement of figures, a lateral window for light, the accentuation of the impression of depth created by the view to another room and by the receding tiles of the floor. He heavily emphasized the light to sharply define the main group, the white areas of drapery and Queen Marguerite; it lingers over small, precious details and highlights the man and the dogs in the rear who, far from being a superfluous anecdote, directly illustrate the episode related by Joinville. The play of light ("he reveals himself to be the worthy emulator of Rembrandt," *Examen critique...*) is mixed in his work with a linear gothic sensibility. To the effects of light, Richard here added rare tones, like the almond green of the coverlet, colors reaching almost a grating pitch, an unusual effort for Richard.

EXHIBITIONS

1808, Salon, no. 495; 1814, Salon, no. 786; 1867, Rueil-Malmaison, no. 53; 1969, Rueil-Malmaison, no. 63.

PROVENANCE

Acquired for 12,000 francs by Empress Josephine and placed in the music room of Malmaison (cf. Auguste Garnerey, *Le Salon de musique,* watercolor, Château de Malmaison). In 1816, Queen Hortense inherited the painting, then valued at 4,000 francs (*État général des tableaux échus en partage à Mme la duchesse de Saint-Leu,* certified as genuine by Baron Devaux, 1816, Paris, Arch. part.). The painting remained in the possession of Queen Hortense (cf. *Le salon de la reine Hortense à Augsbourg,* wash-drawing, Paris, Bibl. Thiers), then became part of the collection of Napoléon III (see exh. 1867, Malmaison, no. 53; see Lescure, 1867).

REFERENCES

Coll. Deloynes, v. XLIV, p. 65; v. XLV, pp. 63, 216, 592; *Examen critique...,* 1808, p. 20; Vict. F..., 1808, p. 368; C.-P. Landon, 1808, v. II, p. 96; Malmaison, cat., 1811, p. 24, no. 190; F.-S. Delpech, 1814, p. 149; J.-B. Dumas, 1839, v. II, p. 109, XV; F. Richard, 1847-1850, MS., pp. 33, 68, 69; Bellier and Auvray, 1882, v. II, p. 169; Morel de Voleine, 1883, p. 321; M. Audin and E. Vial, 1919, v. II, p. 372; S. Grandjean, 1964, p. 156, no. 1122; M.-Cl. Chaudonneret, 1972, p. 169; M.-Cl. Chaudonneret, 1973, no. 17.

M-Cl. C.

155
Madame Elisabeth de France Distributing Milk

"Madame Élisabeth de France, sœur du roi"
Plate p. 251
Canvas; 134 × 175
Salon of 1817, no. 649
Versailles, Musée National

The Salon catalog described this painting as follows: "Her Royal Highness helped with the distribution of milk, as she did daily in her house at Montreuil; Madame de Bombelles and Madame de Raigecourt, honored with the princess' friendship, helped her in her good works. Madame Elisabeth had sent for a cowherd, named Jacques, from Fribourg to look after her cows. The young boy, far from his homeland, grieved for a Swiss girl he had wished to marry. Madame Elisabeth sent for the young girl, who became her dairy maid, and rewarded the loyalty of the fine couple by arranging their marriage."

This episode from the life of Elisabeth (1764-1794) is probably taken from the *Eloge Historique de Madame Elisabeth de France* by Antoine Ferrand (Paris, 1814): in 1781, Louis XVI purchased the Montreuil estate for his sister, where she had the custom of distributing milk to orphans (p. 42). A note by Mme de Bombelles (*ibid.,* p. 155, n. 32, 1795) mentions the story of the cowherd Jacques and his milkmaid and notes that on that occasion, Mme de Travanet "wrote the tune of 'Pauvre Jacques,' which has become so well known since." The theme was repeated by Mlle Delaval (Salon

of 1824, no. 644) when she painted the Swiss girl at Montreuil singing the "romance of poor Jacques."

With the Restoration, artists chose subjects suited to reestablish the credibility of the royal family. Richard here portrayed a virtuous trait of Madame Elisabeth: "Everything here recalls the image of charity" (Miel). At the same Salon (no. 414), Louis Hersent showed the *Deference of Louis XVI* (No. 100).

Carefully realistic, Richard did the face of the princess from a portrait belonging to the Marquis de Bombelles (cf. Richard, MS.) The composition, which Miel did not like, is very clear, with the columns dividing the work into three distinct scenes: Mme Elisabeth attending the poor children of Montreuil, the milkmaid carrying out the distribution of the milk, and the milking of the cow. This division permits a successive reading of the group, each placed separately but linked by a common theme.

Richard granted the architecture an important role; he emphasized the backlighting of the arcades and distributed a soft and oblique light over all. These effects would reappear in his *Jeanne d'Arc à Vaucouleurs* (Salon of 1819, no. 951 of the Louvre) and recall such

Lyonnais work as those of Duclaux, Épinat and Dunouy. (Dunouy had a certain influence on Richard. In his *Souvenirs,* Richard noted that at the time of his apprenticeship in Paris, about 1794, he received advice from this artist).

Richard used an imposing setting in this painting for the first time; he did not, as was his custom, describe figures in the intimacy of an interior scene, typical of the Dutch genre which had won him so much success during the Empire, but once again treated the anecdote in the manner of Louis-Léopold Boilly and, in so doing, anticipated Constant Desbordes (*Scène de vaccine,* Salon of 1822, no. 348, deposited by the Louvre at Douai).

PROVENANCE
The painting was only shown in the last days of the Salon of 1817 (C.-P. Landon, 1817, p. 111). In his inventory of 1852 to 1860, Villot mentioned the painting as part of the collection of Louis XVIII, although Richard in his *Souvenirs* (p. 48), cited it as belonging to Charles X: "In 1817, I was working on a painting which I was doing for His Royal Highness, the King's brother... I received the title of *Son Altesse Royale Monsieur* by offering him the picture of Mme Élisabeth which I exhibited at the Salon... His Royal Highness paid me 12,000 francs for it as a tribute of his satisfaction with my chosen subject, which was the portrait of his beloved sister." The work does not figure in the former inventories of the Louvre relating to the acquisitions of Louis XVIII and Charles X (Arch. Louvre. 2 DD 1, 2 DD 2). In 1879, the painting was at Versailles, where it hung in the apartment of the Sous-Régisseur (letter of Charles Mauricheau-Beaupré, n.d., Mépieu, Arch. Richard). Inventoried for the first time under Villot (INV. 7481), it was taken in 1880 to the Louvre (letter of Ch. Mauricheau-Beaupré, *idem*) and was sent to Versailles on 11 January 1893 (MV. 5271), after being inventoried in 1890 as R.F. 646; Villot's inventory number was forgotten.

EXHIBITION
1817, Salon, no. 649.

REFERENCES
Annales encyclopédiques, 1817, v. II, p. 367; *Journal des débats,* 1817; *Le Moniteur Universel,* 1817, p. 532; N.-F. Cochard, 1817, p. 152; C.-P. Landon, 1817, p. 111; E.-F.-A. Miel, 1817, pp. 195, 299; J.-B. Dumas, 1818, p. 37; J.-B. Dumas, 1839, v. II, p. 110, XXVI; F. Richard, 1847-1850, MSS., p. 48; E. Bellier and L. Auvray, 1882, v. II, p .372; M. Audin and Vial, 1919, v. II, p. 169; M.-Cl. Chaudonneret, 1973, no. 25.

RELATED WORKS
Engraved in Miel.
Madame Élisabeth de France, sœur du roi, canvas, 68 × 87; s.d.l.l. *F.-F. Richard, Fac. Lug., M.DCCC.XVI;* Mépieu, Richard Collection (M.-Cl. Chaudonneret, 1973, no. 25).

M.-Cl. C.

Hubert Robert

1733 Paris 1808

In the registry of deaths of the 1st *arrondissement* of Paris, for the date 15 April 1808, is the following notice: "Robert (Hubert) called Robert des Ruines, painter." To his contemporaries, and to us today, Hubert Robert owed his reputation to that genre.

Born in Paris in 1733, he overcame his parents' objections and entered the studio of the sculptor M.-A. Slodtz, who taught him drawing, according to Paillet, before recommending him to G.-P. Panini when Robert went to Rome in 1754, accompanying the ambassador, the future Duc de Choiseul.

In fact, it is the influence and the imitation of Panini which made Robert a "painter of architecture and of ruins." The catalog of the posthumous sale which took place 5 ff. April 1809 states: "This group of 25 paintings by the hand of Panini... was considered by Hubert Robert as the treasure of his studies, repeating daily that he owed to them, after Nature, the greatest part of his success."

In these years, Rome was, with Paris, the center which witnessed the development of a new esthetic, seeking its inspiration and forms in antiquity. Thus, Robert was less sensitive to the influence of the *visionnaires* (the preceding generation of Frenchmen in Rome, grouped around Piranesi—Le Geay, Le Lorrain, Jardin, Petitot, the Challes) than to that of his companion architect friends, and even more the true archeologists—Peyre, Moreau, De Wailly, J.-D. Le Roy.

He limited himself to this somewhat facile genre, descended from classical landscape, but emptied of its intellectual content in favor of the literary influence. The painting of ruins seemed at that time like a Roman version of the *Vedute,* ennobled with moral allusions. Ruins, tombs, maxims engraved on broken pediments, all were in happy accord with contemporary taste, the sentimental reaction matching, it seems, the trend of Reason, Enlightened Philosophy and the Spirit of Progress.

Thus, Diderot, a propos of the paintings by Robert shown at the Salon of 1767, defined the poetry of ruins as follows: "The ideas which the ruins awake in me are grand. Everything vanishes, everything dies, everything passes, only time endures... I see the marble of tombstones fall into dust and I do not wish to die !" Ruins are a reminder of man's fragility but are also the ideal setting for revery. "In that deserted sanctuary, unbelievably solitary and vast, I have broken with all the obstacles of life; no one pushes me, no one hears me; I can talk out loud to myself, grieve, shed tears without constraint...."

The personality of the artist, "the most joyful, the most spiritual and inoffensive lad in the world" (as he is described by his biographer Gabillot, after the contemporary memoires of Elisabeth Vigée-Lebrun, Pierre-Alexandre Wille, Louis-Etienne Watelet) pushed him, undoubtedly, toward the most profound in what today we recognize to be pre-romanticism. He knew how to express the sensibility of his own day not only in his paintings and his red chalk drawings and water-colors, but also in the gardens which he designed; the shrubbery at Versailles (which earned him the title "Dessinateur des jardins du Roi" in 1778) and the park of Méréville for the banker Laborde.

But, more than as a painter of ruins—whose art, which exercised so considerable an influence on the taste of his time and which seems to us today faded through repetition and bad imitations—it is as a chronicler of Parisian life that he remains interesting. Fires, urban projects, festivals—few events escaped his chalk and brush.

And, always an art lover, Hubert Robert remains the first of the *"gardes du tableau du Roi"* at the Museum, a post to which he was named in 1784 and which he resumed in 1794, just released from the Revolutionary prisons, as a member of the Conservatoire du Museum National (1795-97), and then of the Conseil de Direction of what was to become the Louvre.

J.-F. M.

156
Demolition of the Houses on the Pont au Change

La démolition des maisons du pont au change
Plate p. 85
Canvas; 86 × 159 (restored to its original dimensions)
Paris, Musée Carnavalet

The Pont au Change, linking the Ile de la Cité to the north bank of the Seine, between the Conciergerie (whose clock tower can be seen in the center) and the Châtelet—had been reconstructed between 1639 and 1647, an era of great urban projects and intense construction in Paris.

On either side of the central causeway, Jacques Androuet du Cerceau had built two rows of houses on a uniform plan.

In 1782, Sebastien Mercier began a grass-roots campaign, for esthetic and hygenic reasons, to demolish these houses, as well as those of the Pont Notre-Dame, built on the same principle. "The river Seine remains hidden in the center of the city by ugly and narrow houses which have been built on its bridges. It is high time to give the city both its view and its flow of air, a principle of health" (*Tableau de Paris,* Amsterdam, 1782, p. 198). The demolition was undertaken on the Pont Notre-Dame in 1786 and on the Pont au Change in 1788. Hubert Robert made it the subject of a pair of paintings.

In contrast to his predecessors—Raguenet, a little limited by his scrupulous vision, or Pierre-Antoine Demachy, whose views of monuments are not without dryness—Robert, his eye always alert, excelled in his accounts of Parisian life—festivals, fires, all types of work—in rendering the effect of movement and light. Indeed, his sketches have the same evocative charm as those of a Gabriel de Saint-Aubin.

While the pendant is close to a traditional presentation, the axial vision of this painting creates a surprising effect. The scale of the figures, a little reduced in relation to that of the buildings (according to a method taken from Piranesi and which Robert, like

Joseph-Benoit Suvée, often used in his views of ruins), accentuates the impression of intense activity given by the men demolishing and salvaging the materials.

The documentary interest of the scene is wedded to a successful visual solution: the brushwork and paint happily render the piles of debris, while the light of the setting sun, reflected on the bank which it illuminates, colors the scene.

PROVENANCE
Breteuil Collection; Revolutionary confiscation at the home of "l'émigré Breteuil, rue du Dauphin, section des Tuileries." Assigned to the Ministère des Finances (Paris, Arch. Louvre, IDD6); Musée de Versailles; deposited at the Musée Carnavalet in 1898 (INV. P. 172).

EXHIBITIONS
1889, Paris, no. 597; 1933, Paris, no. 151.

REFERENCES
A. Bonnardot, 1856, pp. 29-30; Ed. Soulié, 1878, no. 787; A. Tuetey, v. I (1902), p. 342; Ch. Sellier and Pr. Dorbec, 1903, no. 173; J. de Boisjolin, v. XVIII (1905), p. 303; A. Dayot, 1908, p. 203; P. de Nolhac, 1910, ill. opp. p. 114; L. Réau, 1927, p. 216; P. Sentenac, 1929, p. 43, ill. 35; B. de Montgolfier, 1964, pp. 12-13, ill. 9.

RELATED WORKS
Sketch included in the posthumous sale of the artist in 1809, (Paris, 5 ff. April 1809, no. 134); signed replica, Paris, private collection.
Pendant, *Démolition du Pont Notre-Dame* (Paris, Musée Carnavalet); sketch in the Louvre (R.F. 1947-8) and replica in Munich.

J.-F. M.

157
*Project for the Arrangement of the Grand Gallery of the Louvre**
Projet d'aménagement de la Grande Galerie du Louvre
Plate p. 79
Canvas; 46 × 55
Paris, Musée du Louvre

As "Custodian of the Paintings of the Museum of the King" in 1784, then as a member of the Conservatoire du Museum and of the administrative council of the Musée Central des Arts, Hubert Robert was constantly involved in the problems posed by the Louvre's Grand Gallery, where it was planned to exhibit royal and later national collections, not only to artists but to the public as well.

The project of creating a museum at the Louvre arose at the end of the reign of Louis XV (see Bachaumont, *Mémoires secrets,* 14 November 1773); to replace several public rooms at the Luxembourg opened from 1750 on. In 1778, d'Angiviller appointed a committee to investigate the question and, in 1785, the Academy of Architecture undertook a summary of the problems involved (Paris, Arch. Nat., O¹ 1171 and 1235-1238).

On 14 August 1786, Cochin supported a solution which proposed overhead lighting imitating palatial galleries and ancient public baths (*idem,* O¹ 1239). Later, d'Angiviller summed the principles to be followed —their realization required nearly two centuries. "The gallery should not be divided by any decoration... It will be illuminated by daylight through elevated openings. These openings should be put at the top of the vault as several apertures in rectangular form..." (*idem,* O¹ 1671, p. 161).

The sketch by Robert shown here sums up exactly all the proposals of d'Angiviller. Because of the costumes worn by the people and the presence of Swiss and Orientals, it is best to date the composition 1786 or very close to that year, and not in 1796, as stated by all the authors cited below, following G. Brière and J.-J. Marquet de Vasselot. This sketch is only a much earlier idea for the great painting shown by Robert at the Salon of 1796, no. 392: "*Project for lighting the Gallery of the Museum through the roof and for dividing it without taking away the view of the length of the premises*" (formerly Russian imperial collection, today New York, private collection), in which Robert, curator of the Museum National, summarized d'Angiviller's projects. The actual sketch for the project of 1796 was published by M. Roland-Michel (1963, fig. 2). It has exactly the same setting and features in particular the double arches on pairs of columns, an idea which was taken up by Charles Percier and Pierre-François Fontaine in the remodeling done between 1806 and 1810. Furthermore, it is around this period and not in 1792 (perhaps just before the remodeling in 1800-1805) that it is necessary to date the other project in the Louvre (again, in this case, the costumes provide proof to document this dating, RF. 2050, gift of Maurice Fenaille), which summarizes all of the elements of the project of 1796.

But all of these plans were not implemented immediately, and it was not until the Second Empire that the vault was broken through and only in 1947 were the pilasters put in place around the niches. Through the vicissitudes of time the artist, convinced of the superiority of overhead lighting for exhibiting paintings because he had (probably before 1786) painted a gallery lighted in that manner where only his works were shown (Louvre, RF. 1938069), remained faithful to the principle that he was not able to adopt.

But Robert was also a curious and exact reporter, since at least four times he gave views of the Grand Gallery so precise that they can be dated:

—About 1794-95, showing the Louvre when opened to the public 10 August 1793. It was closed and left unchanged in November and thus this work was probably painted after the liberation of Robert, who was imprisoned on 8 Brumaire, Year II (29 October 1793) until 9 Thermidor, Year II (27 July 1794). (Louvre, RF. 1948-36, gift David-Weill.)

—On 30 Frimaire, Year VI (20 December 1797) at the time of the banquet given for Bonaparte by the Directory, the Conseil des Anciens and the Conseil des Cinq-Cents, in honor of the victories of the army in Italy (Paris, Musée des Arts Décoratifs, Émile Peyre bequest).

—At the time of the work to put the museum in order before the reopening which took place 18 Germinal, Year VII (7 April 1799). (Louvre, RF. 1946-29.)

—And finally, after 14 July 1801, when works of art brought back from Italy after the Treaty of Tolentino were shown in the gallery that was then entirely open. (Louvre, RF. 1964-34.)

It is not possible, unfortunately, to identify the works which Robert has represented on the walls of this sketch. It even seems that, unlike the painting of the Salon of 1796, where the identification of what Robert

has depicted hanging on the walls is confirmed by a contemporary report (see coll. Deloynes, v. XVIII, no. 482, pp. 617-664), and as proven by the uniformity of formats, none of the series acquired by d'Angiviller, *La Vie de saint Bruno* by Le Sueur or the *Ports de France,* by Vernet, are included. But in this case it is only a question of a more vast project, which, until the end, would guide the curators of the Louvre in the arrangement of their most prestigious gallery.

PROVENANCE
Camille Groult Collection from 1899; Félix-Jean Groult; bequest to Louvre in 1952; (R.F. 1952-15).

EXHIBITIONS
1889, Exposition Universelle, Paris, no. 589; 1900, Paris, Centennale, no. 4600; 1947, Paris, no. 7; 1952, Rueil, La Malmaison, no. 27; 1960, Paris, no. 678; 1964-1965, U.S.A. and Canada, no. 15; 1967-1968, Orangerie, Paris, no. 371; 1972, Louvre, Paris, no. 45.

REFERENCES
P. de Nolhac, 1910, ill. opp. p. 84; E. Dacier, 1914, p. 217, note 1; G. Brière and J.-J. Marquet de Vasselot, 1920, p. 247; L. Réau, 1927, p. 222; Ch. Sterling, 1933, no. 167; J.-J. Marquet de Vasselot and M.-L. Blumer, 1946, pp. 41-42, no. 83 (description inexact); Ch. Aulanier, (1947). Bulletin des musées de France, p. 10, list 2; Ch. Aulanier, s.d. [1947], p. 19; G. Isarlo, 1953, p. 28, section 29, no. 8; M. Roland-Michel, 1963; p. III, B. de Montgolfier, 1964, p. 35, note 44; G. Bazin, 1967, p. 178, ill. 91; *I maestri del Colore,* 1968, ill. XVIII and color cover; H. Coulanges and J. Cailleux, 1969, ill. XVIII and color cover; V. Noël-Bouton, 1972, no. 45; mus. cat., 1972, p. 333; mus. cat., 1974, v. II, pp. 94, 126, no. 748.

RELATED WORK
A painting, somewhat similar, in a Parisian private collection (see Ch. Aulanier, *op. cit.,* p. 19, ill. 26). A very similar drawing has been attributed to Fragonard (*ibid.,* ill. 28). (The other views and projects for the Grand Gallery by Hubert Robert are cited above.)

J.-F. M.

158
*Ruins of the Grand Gallery of the Louvre**

Ruines de la grande Galerie du Louvre telle que Hubert Robert l'avait conçue
Plate p. 142
Canvas; 35 × 40
Paris, Musée du Louvre

Here, Hubert Robert again takes up all the elements of his plan for the display of the royal then national collections in the Grand Gallery of the Louvre in compliance with all requirements: lighting through the roof and the division of the immense hall without interrupting the perspective (see No. 157). But here, the walls are bare, the niches empty, the vault has caved in and already vegetation has invaded the ruins.

This is a theme often treated by Robert. Thus, among "the brilliant studies made in Italy by this artist," certainly between 1754 and 1765, which were represented at his posthumous sale (Paris, 5 ff. April 1809), one finds under no. 67: "The Ruins of an immense gallery with an open vault"; that painting, executed in Italy, cannot be connected with the painting of 1796, as has been erroneously suggested in the exh. cat. 1967-1968, Paris, no. 372. At the same sale, under no. 78, a work was also exhibited which could have inspired our painting: "A frontal elevation... showing the ruins of a palace where a statue of Apollo can still be found. The center of the foreground is enlivened with a group of nine figures, including soldiers playing cards." Without making a list of the frequent appearance of the theme in public sale catalogs, which would demand a critical study, we can nevertheless cite the canvases of the Salons of 1767 (nos. 106 and 107), 1789 (no. 34) and those described in the posthumous inventory drawn up on 18 August 1821, of Robert's sale, under nos. 237, 240, 244, 250.

Here, however, the artist adds an additional dimension by contrasting a pessimistic vision with his sketches that illustrate the progress of the work he conducted and the ideal arrangement he dreamt about for the Grand Gallery. Instead of another fantasy in a mode he often practiced, here is the declaration of a man whose universe, pleasant to the point of levity, the world of the Comte de Vaudreuil and of Mme Vigée-Lebrun (No. 197), had been completely overturned by the Revolution.

Alone, intact in the midst of the ruins, stands the very symbol of Beauty according to contemporary taste, the Apollo of Belvedere, which in fact the French were about to find in Rome and exhibit in a place of honor in the Louvre.

PROVENANCE

M. de Viefville Collection? (see Service d'étude et de documentation, Louvre, file for the painting); sale, Paris, Hôtel Drouot, 31 May 1961, no. 109, pl. IV; acquired by the Louvre (R.F. 1961-20).

EXHIBITIONS

1967-1968, Paris, no. 372; 1972, Paris, no. 48, ill. 48.

REFERENCES

Mus. cat., 1972, p. 333; mus. cat., 1974, v. II, pp. 95, 216, no. 750.

RELATED WORKS

The painting shown here is almost the exact sketch for the canvas shown at the Salon of 1796, no. 393, which was in Russia and is now in New York, private collection.
The two works have been connected to a drawing (see 1933, Paris, exh. cat., no. 58, ill.), which in fact seems to be related to the many versions of the theme of the ruined gallery rather than this particular composition.

J.-F. M.

159
Young Girls Dancing Around an Obelisk

Ruines anciennes: une ronde de jeunes filles autour d'un obélisque brisé devant les pyramides et le sphinx de Gizeh
Plate p. 152
Canvas; 120 × 99; s.d.l.l. *H. ROBERT/ 1798*
Montreal, Museum of Fine Arts, Lady Davis Bequest

"In the Spring of 1798, despite the precautions taken to avoid disclosing the project, the rumor ran all through Paris of a foreign campaign, undoubtedly in Egypt..." writes Jean Chatelain (1973, p. 77), who reports the words of the poet Arnault: "The desire to leave for Egypt soon became a general fever" *(ibid.).* And the impact of that campaign on the arts of the time was considerable (see Nos. 201, 204).

The date of this painting by Hubert Robert reflects this furor. However, Robert had been interested in Egyptian art, which he discovered in Rome, for a long time. He made numerous drawings after obelisks, sculptures, sphinxes, etc., which had been brought by the ancient Romans and which excavations were bringing to light, just as he often returned to the pyramid of Caius Sextus. In 1760, still in Rome, he signed and dated a *Paysage égyptien* (Moreau-Chaslon sale, 1884, no. 37; Ribes Christophe, Paris, Galerie Georges Petit, 10 December 1928, no. 98, ill.; exh. 1933, Paris, Orangerie, no. 1 and 1935, Copenhagen, no. 187; anon. sale, Paris, Hôtel Drouot, 9 June 1936, no. 25, ill.). The composition, of a more visionary inspiration than usual, is due, no doubt, to the architects who, from Jean-Laurent Legeay to Charles Moreau, had just preceded him to Rome. He returned to the same composition, with some changes, in his undated painting today at the Smith College Museum of Art (Northampton, Mass.).

A letter sent to his daughter by the poet Boucher, who was imprisoned with Robert at Sainte-Pélagie, attests to the artist's interest in Egypt, even in those anguished days. "An artist celebrated for an art which you love, citizen Robert, is here. He is completely bored, because a painter cannot work anywhere like a man of letters. Unable to paint, he wishes to read, and as his imagination enjoys living through ruins... send him that famous Egypt in which the past can be rediscovered in Savary." Robert's answer is significant. "I will now, thanks to your generous attention, travel once more through Egypt with Savary" (cited in P. de Nolhac, 1910, pp. 80, 82).

However, nothing in the present painting would indicate any direct influence from that reading or corresponds to the precise descriptions by Claude Savary (*Lettres sur l'Égypte,* Paris, 3rd ed., 1785-98). Furthermore, Robert evidently did not consult either the *Voyage d'Égypte et de Nubie par M. Frédéric-Louis Norden* (Copenhagen, 1755)—which nevertheless was perhaps a source for the canvas dated 1760 noted above—or the *Antiquities and Views in Greece and Egypt...* by Richard Dalton (London, 1791), or the *Voyage dans la haute et basse Égypte* by C.-S. Sonnini (Paris, year VII), which had just appeared.

Of Robert's research, only the essential elements remain here: the three pyramids and the Sphinx. It is interesting to note that the Sphinx is presented entirely cleared of sand, although at that date only the head was uncovered and is, in fact, only a reproduction of one of those which he had seen in Rome.

PROVENANCE

Kept by the artist until his death; posthumous sale, Paris, 5 ff. April 1809, no. 79: *"un monument composé offrant un obélisque brisé autour duquel dansent des jeunes filles"* ; acquired by Castelli for 193 francs; Montreal, Lady Davis Collection; bequeathed to Montreal, Museum of Fine Arts in 1964.

EXHIBITIONS

1960, Montréal, no. 139, ill.; 1966-1967, Sarasota, Buffalo *et. al.,* no. 80, ill. and detail on the cover; 1969, Kansas City, no. 22, ill.

REFERENCES

C. Gabillot, 1895, p. 262; [Anon.], *Art Quarterly,* 1964, p. 373, ill. p. 383, no. 3 [Anon.], *Canadian Art,* 1964, p. 301, ill.; [Anon.], *G.B.A.,* 1965, p. 22, no. 106, ill.

RELATED WORKS

Perhaps related is a painting in the collection of Vivant Denon, which figured in his sale (Paris, 1-19 May 1826, no. 179): "an architectural painting offering obelisks, and diverse Egyptian monuments tastefully composed... There are several groups of figures on differents planes (canvas, 66 × 52)," proportions similar, but reduced by half.

J.-F. M.

Léopold Robert

1794 La Chaux-de-Fonds - Venice 1835

In 1925, Boy de la Tour remarked, "During his lifetime, Robert knew success and, after his death, the infatuation with him became general, but his vogue was fleeting and soon became one of indifference and then disdain."

In 1810, he learned engraving in Paris with his Swiss compatriot Charles Girardet and at the same time attended the Académie des Beaux-Arts and David's studio. In 1814, he won the second prize for copperplate engraving. Two years later, he competed again, but because the Canton of Neuchâtel was returned to Prussia, he was considered a foreigner and eliminated from the list of competitors. With David's departure in exile, Robert studied briefly with Gros and then returned to Switzerland. Thanks to the generosity of one of his countrymen, Roulet de Mézerac, Robert was finally able to visit Italy in 1818. From that moment on, he was to devote himself to painting.

He found in Rome his friends Jean-Victor Schnetz, François-Joseph Navez, and François-Marius Granet who, at that moment, exercized an enormous influence on him. An event was to permit him to change his style. The robbers of Sonino, brought to Rome in 1819 and confined in the Castel Sant'Angelo were to serve as models for him, as well as for Schnetz (No. 166).

Beginning in 1822, after an exhibition which took place in Rome, he exhibited more or less regularly at the Salon until 1835. The genre paintings he showed were inspired by Italian prototypes. After the relative failure of the *Improvisateur napolitain* (bought by the Duc d'Orléans, damaged in 1848 during the sack of the Château de Neuilly, the central part preserved at Neuchâtel, Musée d'Art et d'Histoire), he produced innumerable small folkloric canvases of robbers, shepherds and *pifferari,* eagerly snatched up by patrons. And during his short career, he executed no less than 160 to 170 paintings on such subjects, often repetitious (Feuillet de Conches knew of 14 versions of *La femme du brigand veillant sur le sommeil de son mari* with more or less important variations; G. B. Ségal has located eight of them (museums in West Berlin, Dresden, La Chaux-de-Fonds, Leipzig, London [Wallace Collection], etc.). Many of these works belong to Swiss museums (in Basel, Geneva, and Neuchâtel, particularly), and to French museums, such as Lille (*Jeune fille assise sur les rochers à Capri,* 1827); and especially Nantes, which owns *L'Ermite de Saint-Nicholas à Ischia* (Salon of 1827); *Deux Baigneuses en costume de San Donato* (Salon of 1827), *Les Petits pêcheurs de grenouilles dans les marais pontins* (Salon of 1831). Once he was famous, Robert wished to do four large compositions which would symbolize the *Seasons* and which, following *L'Improvisateur napolitain,* would classify him, if not as a *peintre d'histoire,* at least a *peintre de style* (an expression appearing at the time). *Pilgrims Returning from the Feast Day of the Madonna dell' Arco* (No. 160) dates from 1827; *L'arrivée de moissonneurs dans les marais pontins* had a great success in 1831 and Charles Clément (1875, p. 270) recalled that the school of David "recognized the painter as one of them and the romantics claimed him as a precious recruit." He never finished the third painting of the *Seasons, Le Carnaval à Venise* (an allegory of winter), which he modified into *Pêcheurs de l'Adriatique* (Musée de Neuchâtel). It should be noted that this was not the first time that Robert changed his subject radically: already in 1822, after studies for *Corinne improvisant au Cap Misène,* he created the *Improvisateur napolitain* (cf. Boy de la Tour, 1925).

The reasons for his suicide are not known, but it was undoubtedly inspired by that of his elder brother Alfred in 1825; it is not necessary to find an explanation for them. It is more interesting to place the painter's art with his time, as well as ours.

In 1836, a very successful posthumous exhibition was held. Shortly afterwards, the works of E.-J. Delécluze (1838) and F. Feuillet de Conches (1848) were published. Charles Clément wrote in his monograph of 1875: "Coming during a period of transition, he brought to the execution of genre subjects the knowledge which he had acquired in David's studio and the serious work habits which he had learned there. On the other hand, influenced by modern ideas, he sought and found in the direct and sincere study of nature, her nobility and beauty. He was an intelligent and truthful interpreter of contemporary Italy, and although some prefer to consider him a *peintre de costumes,* he seized upon the basic features of the people he depicted with a perspicacity and a sureness that denote an observer of the first order; thus, his paintings are at once very distinguished works of art and moral documents worthy of the greatest interest" (p. 53).

Admired by Thoré, Viardot (who compared him to Poussin; *cf.* 1877, pp. 337-338), he still interested Rosenthal in 1898, but in 1927 was barely mentioned by Focillon. Florentin (1934) and D. Berthoud (1936) devoted monographs to him. In 1964, the exhibition at La Chaux-de-Fonds showed his work to the modern public. Finally, in 1973, a thesis was published by G.-B. Ségal (done at the University of Basel), a fundamental work which will now permit the entire œuvre of the artist to be reviewed.

J. L.

160
Pilgrims Returning from the Feast Day of the Madonna dell'Arco

"Le retour de la fête de la Madona de l'Arc, près de Naples"
Plate p. 295
Canvas; 142 × 212; s.d.l.l. *Lld. Robert/Rome. 1827*
Salon of 1827-28, no. 1722
Paris, Musée du Louvre

The pilgrimage to the Madonna dell'Arco, a chapel built in a small village some distance from Naples, took place at the feast of the Pentecost. The people, dressed in their most beautiful costumes, went as a crowd to pray to the Virgin to bless their harvest. Robert had planned a series of paintings to illustrate an allegory of the four seasons, shown by typical scenes from different Italian regions. This work symbolized Naples and Spring; *Les Moissonneurs des marais pontins* (Salon of 1830, Louvre), Rome and Summer; the pictures entitled *Vendanges* (symbolizing Florence and Fall) and *Le Carnaval à Venise* (symbolizing Winter and northern Italy), were never completed.

Letters published by Clément (1875) make known the intentions of the painter. Struck by the feast of the pilgrimage, he wrote in 1826, "It gave me such pleasure that I wished to give an idea of the sensations I felt. It represented ancient bacchanals to me, and it seemed that it recalled them entirely: my motif is one of those great, well-decorated chariots pulled by oxen... in the foreground are two dancers and a woman holding a tambourine. Of the six or seven figures in the chariot, the two principal ones are two newlyweds; all the figures are crowned with flowers and foliage like Madonnas and strongly exhibit the characteristics which I find in the paintings of Pompeii and Herculaneum, the background is Vesuvius seen from fairly close, as it is often represented in views of Naples, but it seems to me that I could not find a backdrop better suited to give a poetic quality to the subject."

Shown at the Salon of 1827, this painting was certainly appreciated, but with some slight differences of opinion. In a letter to Navez (cited by Clément), Robert wrote, "In general it is said that I have run dry and that I paint like a German." Indeed, Béraud (1827) noted that "some people [among them Jal, see below] reproached him a little for dryness in the contours," but, he added, "this fault does not exist for those who remember that the pure, light air of southern Italy does not create indefinite lines which the foggy air of our climate produces and that there objects are clearly outlined against the sky." He spoke of the "charming picture," the "poetic scene," and asked, "In the costume closest to us (and how picturesque it is !) couldn't you imagine a Bacchanalian feast, as they have been recreated on medals and antique reliefs, as they are admired in some of the immortal compositions of our Poussin ?" and concluded, "The excellent painting by M. Léopold Robert possesses all the proper qualities: a well-chosen subject, a well-presented composition, correct and witty drawing, vigorous coloring." The anonymous critic of the *Moniteur Universel* wrote: *"Pilgrims returning from the Feast Day of the Madonna dell'Arco, near Naples,* is one of those pleasant and instructive passages which reveal an experienced interpretor, respectful of the original meaning, and at the same time free and proud in his style. It is not a servile copy, nor a fantastic imitation. The former is unpleasant; the latter questionable; it is the intimate and mysterious union of nature and art which combines truth, the realm of the imagination and choice. But to what extent is the painter still indebted to native costume and climate ! Who [else] would attempt to show with elegance the return from a feast day in a village ?... it is impossible. The work done would certainly offer nothing of the ideal or color of the antique. In place of this charming *Return from the Feast day of the Madonna,* so well executed... you would have gotten, I suppose, a Teniers, a Callot, a Boilly, that is to say a *bambocciate,* instead of a naïve and graceful painting. This is how a student can profit from the time he spends in Rome."

Finally, Jal advised Lord D...: "You need a Léopold Robert; I will see if the delightful painting *Pilgrims Returning from the Feast Day of the Madonna dell'Arco* is still for sale, which I doubt, for a morsel of its merit should have found more than one bidder. For ten thousand francs you would have the work, and in truth you would make a good buy; grace without affectation, naturalness without triviality, characters with true and noble heads, charming poses, observation of the customs of the country, a firm touch, vigorous coloring, straight-forward effects; do you believe you can pay too much for these qualities, scarcely marred by a little hardness in the way in which the silhouettes are outlined against the sky?" And, in 1831, the same critic recalled that it was "one of the most complete genre paintings produced by the French school, which explains its superiority over M. Roger, who exhibited in the same year an episode of the *Feast of the Madonna dell'Arco,* a very pleasant work."

Thus, as the biographers of Léopold Robert have noted, the painter's reputation dates from this work. And, without doubt, this picture should continue to give pleasure. The super-realistic composition and strident color do not make a perfect example of fashionable *kitsch.* The work is important because it shows a forgotten German influence in French art of the 1830s which was transmitted via Italy. Furthermore, it is an example of an impossible Romanticism, too elaborate and artificial, which, at the time, attracted other artists of the period as well (see L. Rosenthal, 1914, pp. 208-209).

PROVENANCE

Acquired at the Salon 4,000 francs for the Musée de Luxembourg; transferred to the Louvre, 24 July 1835 (INV. no. 2 7664).

EXHIBITIONS

1827, Salon, no. 1722; 1962, Naples, no. 85; 1964; La Chaux-de-Fonds, no. 63, ill.

REFERENCES

A. Béraud, 1827, pp. 124-125, ill. 54; Ch..., in *Le Moniteur Universel,* 1 March 1828, p. 255; L.V., 8 March 1828, p. 255; A. Jal, 1828, p. 459; A. Jal, 1831, p. 149; Ch. Lenormant, 1833, p. 102; E.-J. Delécluze, 1838; F. Feuillet de Conches, 1846, p. 8; E.-H. Gaullieur, 1847, pp. 81-94, 161-175; Ch. Lenormant, 1847, pp. 137, 140-142; F. Feuillet de Conches, 1848, pp. 82-87, 153, 155; G. Planche, 1853, pp. 10, 15, 16-18, H. Gérard, 1867, p. 117; *Souvenirs de Mme Vigée-Le-Brun,* 1869, t. I, p. 219; Ch. Clément, 1872, pp. 5-6; Ch. Clément, 1875, pp. 211-238; *Lettres adressées au baron F. Gérard,* 1886, t. I, p. 299; L. Rosenthal, 1898, pp. 289, 293; L. Rosenthal, 1900, pp. 167, 180, 230, 323, 326; C. Brun, 1908, t. II, p. 650; L. Rosenthal, 1914, pp. 208-209; H. Focillon, 1927, p. 214; D. Berthoud, 1934, pp. 137, 140, repr. opp. p. 128; N. Roger, 1935; Ch. Sterling and H. Adhémar, 1961, v. IV, no. 1648, pl. 647; H. Kogina, 1969, p. 225; Louvre, mus. cat., 1972, p. 334; G. Ségal, 1973, p. 33, pp. 158-160, G. 103.

RELATED WORKS

A sketch, squared (canvas, 38 × 46), signed and dated 1826, is conserved at the museum of Neuchâtel; this museum also owns an *Etude de bœuf* for the painting (G. Ségal, 1973, G. 104 and 105).
Engraved by Frenny and by Z. Prévost, Pichard and Joubert; lithograph by Duniez.
A copy by Aurele Robert belongs to Marcotte. Note also, on the same subject, the watercolor by Bodinier (13 × 12) in Angers.

J. L.

Alexandre Roslin

1718 Malmö - Paris 1793

Born in Malmö, Sweden, a student of Georg Engelhardt Schröder in Stockholm, Alexandre Roslin sojourned in Bayreuth from 1745-47, then spent four years in Italy—Venice, Bologna, Florence (where he joined the Academy), Naples and Parma. He arrived in Paris in 1752 and got to know Joseph-Marie Vien and François Boucher, whom he painted in 1760 (Versailles). In 1753, he was admitted to the Academy with *Collin de Vermont* (Versailles) and *Jeaurat* (Louvre); and he participated regularly in the Salon with portraits of architects (*Adeluantz,* 1754, Stockholm; *Rehn,* 1756, Bellinga,

private collection), portraits of painters and sculptors (*Vernet,* 1767, *Pajou,* 1767, both in Stockholm, private collections), and portraits of scholars and writers (*Marmontel,* 1767, Louvre; *Linné,* 1775, Stockholm).

In 1759, he married an artist who worked in pastels, M.-S. Giroust, whom he often depicted. In 1774, Roslin made a brief "triumphal tour" of Sweden, then traveled in 1775 to the court of Catherine II in Saint Petersburg. In 1778, he returned via Poland and Vienna to Paris, which he never again left.

A portraitist of the first rank, Roslin certainly

considered himself a Swede, but the essential part of his career is Parisian and his work, comparable to that of a Duplessis or a Danloux, belongs to the tradition of French portraiture, which was so brilliant in the second half of the 18th century.

The catalog of his œuvre, drawn up by his biographer, G.W. Lundberg, comprises some 625 entries, most of which are portraits.

P. R.

161

Portrait of Daubenton

"Portrait de M. d'Aubenton qui paraît vérifier avec le microscope la finesse de ses laines"
Plate p. 124
Canvas; 80 × 65; s.d. middle l. *Pt p. Le chev^r Roslin,/1791.*
Salon of 1791, no. 23
Orléans, Musée des Beaux-Arts

This portrait was exhibited twice in 1791, the year of its execution. It was first shown at the Salon, the last in which Roslin participated and to which he loaned his *Autoportrait,* destined for the collection of the Grand Duke of Tuscany, and today in Florence, and *Une jeune demoiselle ornant de fleurs la Statue de l'Amour.* (Is this a repetition of the Louvre painting from the Salon of 1783?) The second exhibition was "works of painting... shown at the Louvre [remember that Roslin lodged there] by order of the National Assembly" in September. The portrait of Daubenton is listed in the catalog between a *"Portrait d'homme par M. François"* and *"Un portrait de femme peint jusqu'aux genoux par M. David"* along with seven other canvases by Roslin.

The model is well-known. Louis-Jean-Marie d'Aubenton, called Daubenton (1716-1799) was born, like his colleague Buffon, the naturalist, in Montbard. He participated in the preparation of the latter's *Histoire Naturelle.* He collaborated especially in the chapters devoted to mammals. Relations between the two scholars were not always easy, one being flamboyant and rhetorical, the other modest and precise. Daubenton taught general zoology at the Collège de France, became a member of the Academy of Science in 1760, entered the new Institute in 1795, and became a member of the Conservative Senate in 1799. The title of Roslin's portrait in the catalog of the Salon "qui paraît vérifier avec le microscope la finesse de ses laines" refers to the two recent works by the scholar: *Instruction pour les bergers* (1782) and *Mémoire sur le premier drap de laine superfine du cru de France* (1784), as the label *"Troupeau*

de Montbard" refers to the first Merino sheep raised in Burgundy.

The Orléans canvas is one of the artist's last, along with the *Portrait d'Henriette Begouen* (1792) today in Jacksonville, Fla., the *Portrait du miniaturiste Perrin* (1791) in Rheims and the *Autoportrait* known in two versions (Florence, Galleria degli Uffizi and New York, private collection). The painter has lost nothing of his precise attention to detail: clear forms, lively colors boldly juxtaposed, the gold of the microscope and the lilac of Daubenton's costume. A cold light, like Bellotto's, outlines the contours and gives the canvas a brilliance and the model a presence, a *"vérité,"* unique to the great Swedish painter.

PROVENANCE

In 1878, Ferdinand-Charles-Nicolas Vaussin Collection, a descendant of Daubenton. Given by Mme Ernest Petit, daughter of the chief of medicine of the Hôtel-Dieu d'Orléans, to the Orléans museum.

EXHIBITIONS

1791, Salon, no. 23; 1791, Paris, Louvre, no. 718; 1878, Paris, no. 565.

REFERENCES

H. Jouin, 1879, pp. 121-122, no. 565; O. Fidière, 1898, p. 56 (erroneously at Versailles), pp. 111-112; O. Levertin, 1899, p. 154; O. Levertin, 1901, p. 51; G.-W. Lundberg, 1935, p. 28 (erroneously at Versailles); G.-W. Lundberg, 1957, v. I, pp. 257-259, with pl.; v. II, p. 106, no. 616.

P. R.

Jacob-Henri or Jacques Sablet

1749 Morges (Switzerland) - Paris 1803

Jacques Sablet, brother of the painter François (see below) was first a student of his father Jacob (1720 Morges-Lausanne 1798), who became an art dealer at the end of his life after an early career as a house painter. Very soon, however, Jacques left home for Lyon, where he worked with the house-painters Dubois and Cocher, finally arrived in Paris and entered the atelier of Joseph-Marie Vien, where his brother had already preceded him. In 1775, he followed Vien to Rome, and as early as 1777 received a prize from the Roman Academy of Saint Luke. A document in the archives proves that he was still in Rome in 1779. In 1781, he painted two allegorical pictures for the city of Bern. Roman engravings of 1786 and portraits painted in 1788 (Louvre and Zurich) attest to his continuing stay in Rome, as does the painting of *Colin-Maillard* with its Italian flavor, done in 1790 and shown at the Salon of 1796 (is this the "Taunay" sold in Paris, Hôtel Drouot, 23 March 1966, today in Paris, Galerie Pardo?). In 1791, he competed for the Grand Prix of the Academy of Saint Luke but placed only second. In 1793, he became a member of the Florentine Academy. The serious anti-French demonstrations began in Rome at the beginning of 1793 (sack of Palazzo Mancini; then the siege of the French Academy; 13 January, the massacre of Hugou de Basseville, French representative; and the imprisonment of Chinard, Rater and many Frenchmen). The chargé d'affaires Cacault, who was very close to the Sablet family, as attested by his collection now in the Musée de Nantes, pointed out in a famous letter to the minister Lebrun (written from Florence, 1 March 1793) that the Sablets must have fled from Rome (rather than from Naples, as stated by P. Marmottan, 1927, p. 195), because all artists who were French or who worked in the French style were not well thought of there (*Correspondance des Directeurs de l'Académie de France à Rome*, XVI, 1907, p. 273). On 26 April, Cacault included the Sablets among the artists who had the wherewithal to leave Rome (*ibid.,* XVI, p. 286). Undoubtedly, Jacques Sablet first went through Switzerland with his brother; he then settled in Paris and exhibited regularly at the Salon from 1793 until his death (first exhibit-

ing in 1791 with a *Scène familière* and a *Paysage orné de figures et d'animaux*). He married about 1794-95, but separated from his wife several months later. He received lodgings at the Louvre and a pension from the French government. At the concours of Year III, he won a second prize of 4,000 francs: the painting he selected for purchase by the State was *Paysannes de Frascati* (Louvre, INV. 7084). In 1795-96 (Year IV), he again painted a portrait of Cacault (Paris, Musée Marmottan), which could indicate that he made another trip to Italy (however, a portrait can always be done from memory and the painting is not expressly signed and dated from Rome). In 1799, he was perhaps in touch with Lucien Bonaparte (through Fesch or Cacault?) through whom he was able to witness the famous proconsular meeting of 18 Brumaire, Year VIII (9 November 1799), which he depicted in a well-known picture in Nantes (he represented himself extending an arm to Pauline Bonaparte, sister of Napoleon and wife of General Leclerc). The fact remains that he accompanied Lucien Bonaparte on his mission to Spain in 1800-01, which undoubtedly allowed him to execute the portrait called *Dame à la mantille,* known today by Parboni's engraving and reputed to represent the Marquise de Santa Cruz, great friend of Lucien Bonaparte. But the portrait of Lucien in a garden decorated with antique fragments, seen by Marmottan at the town hall of Ajaccio (at present in the museum?), could be by François or Jacques Sablet, depending on whether it is dated before or after 1803, the year Jacques died (Marmottan inconsistently dates it in 1805 or 1806 and attributes it to Jacques!). In Spain, Sablet and Guillaume Lethière were requested to buy pictures for Lucien's collection. Jacques also worked for Cardinal Fesch on several occasions (15 pictures, mostly genre scenes, including many of Neapolitan inspiration, appear in the sales catalogs from 1843 to 1845, preceded by the initial J.) He was entered posthumously in the Salon of 1804 with a *Bacchante*.

His work is often confused with that of his brother François, in spite of the frequent signature, "J. Sablet," which would seem to clearly designate Jacques, but, admittedly it is sometimes difficult to distinguish between the initials J and F (see also No. 162). His work is relatively varied and includes history and allegory paintings : *La Suisse et Minerve à l'autel des Beaux-Arts* (Bern; sketch in Lausanne) and *La Justice* (in the town hall of Morges), as well as those done for Bern in 1781. There are group portraits: *Artiste dans son atelier avec ses parents* (Lausanne museum, s.d. 1791, not 1781; it is interesting to note that Sablet here shows himself left-handed) and individual portraits: *Autoportrait,* (Lausanne); *Portrait de Gessner peignant* (s.d. 1788, and not 1787; Zurich); *Portrait de Cacault* (Paris, Musée Marmottan, s.d. Year IV [1795]) and another in Nantes, etc. In addition, there are Italianate landscapes enveloped in a warm light which perhaps earned Sablet his name of "painter of the sun": *Paysannes de Frascati,* (c. 1794, Louvre); *Arbres près d'un étang,* (s.d. 1793, Paris, Galerie Marcus, ill. in *Art et Curiosité,* July-August 1967), and elegant genre scenes: *Scène de la vie romaine* (Lausanne). Few of his Salon paintings can be identified with certainty, except for the *Portrait du citoyen... visitant le tombeau de son père avec son épouse* (Salon of 1797) which corresponds to a painting of the same subject that was in the Chabert Collection in 1927 (ill. by Marmottan, 1927, opp. p. 200, with an incorrect and unjustified attribution to François in the text); also the *Départ d'un officier de la 200ᵉ demi-brigade légère* of the Salon of 1802 is confused with a painting in the museum in Ajaccio (incorrectly attributed by Marmottan to François, *op. cit.,* pp. 205-206; note that this article by Marmottan should be used with caution: it is full of errors and the confusion between the two brothers recurs continually).

In addition, there are two paintings by Jacques in the Louvre (including a portrait of an artist that bears little resemblance to the *Autoportrait* of 1791 at Lausanne), and others at the Musée Marmottan, and five in Nantes (including an alleged *Autoportrait*— a painter working in the Campagna, s.d. *J. Sablet, Rome 1789*); London (No. 162), Winterthur; a drawing at Alençon *("portrait-charge")* ; a *Femme assise dans sa cuisine* at Semur; *Deux hommes dans un cimetière protestant de Rome,* s.d. 1791, in Brest (but the J is hard to read and could also be an F—the distinct style is very close to that of a painting by François, s.d. 1791, Lausanne); the two Italian scenes mentioned by Thieme-Becker in the Château of Drottning-Holm near Stockholm; a *Repas de fiançailles napolitaines* sold in Paris, Hôtel Drouot, 9 February 1973 (no. 8, ill. in the catalog, as Léopold Robert, but given to Jacques by P. Rosenberg); and a *Portrait d'homme peignant* sold in London,

Christie's, 1 July 1966 (no. 40, ill. in the catalog as Boilly, again reattributed by P. Rosenberg). Jacque's work is also known by his engravings (well inventoried in 1888 by the Marquis de Surgères, who wrote a fundamental treatise on the Sablets which should be consulted as much if not more than the article by Marmottan), especially eight done in Rome in 1786, which carry a J in the signature; eleven engraved after him by C. Ducros, here again related to Italian subjects; and finally some engravings by Copia (e.g., the *Maréchal-Ferrant de la Vendée,* curiously described by Marmottan as a work by F. Sablet from the Salon of 1791) and L. Portman.

Sablet was a delicate landscapist who was fascinated, like so many, by Italy. At the beginning of his career, he seemed to have been tempted by history painting (his workshop shown in the painting at Lausanne dated 1791 includes a great number of little historical sketches). But he was most successful in little full-length portraits set against the background of an Italian landscape. His style, characterized by an extreme delicacy of tones, fine light, and freshness of atmosphere, often puts Sablet on the level of Gauffier who, after all, was in Italy at the same time. That stylistic affinity alone, as well as the circumstances of his life which brought him to France in his last years, allow Jacques Sablet to be included very legitimately in the French school.

One cannot discuss Jacques Sablet without also talking about his older brother (baptized Jean-François, but simply called François according to Surgères). Born in Morges in 1745, he died in Nantes in 1819. His stays in Italy earned him the name "Sablet the Roman." From 1767, he was in Paris, attended Vien's workshop and went to Rome in 1776 (some say 1768). Married in 1777, he spent some time in Paris, where he specialized in portraits (he might have collaborated with Mme Vigée-Lebrun, painting faces while she painted costumes) and made a great deal of money. He then lived in Rome, as shown by his handsome family portraits of 1791 in Lausanne (see below), which show a great closeness in style to contemporary paintings by Jacques, like the Brest picture (also of 1791), and the *Portrait of Thomas Hope* (No. 162) and various works mentioned below under No. 162, to the point where during this period the distinction between the two brothers is really difficult. In 1793, François was in Italy with Jacques (Cacault noted their joint departure from Rome in April) and went to Switzerland (passport delivered in Lausanne in July), returned to Paris in August, had himself received as a member of the Société Républicaine des Arts which sat at the Louvre, exhibited at the Salons of 1795 and 1799 (thereafter, only in 1804 and 1817, *Vue d'une portion du port de Nantes* [in the city museum] and 1819). Some scholars believe he was in Italy from 1796 to 1798. About 1805, following the architect Crucy, with whom he was very close (Sablet made many portraits of the Crucy family; an *Autoportrait* of François, dedicated "à son ami Crucy" was given to the Nantes museum in 1934 by a Crucy), he settled in Nantes, where he remained until his death. His principal claim to glory in that city was the decoration of the great hall of the Stock Exchange (built by Crucy) with six large canvases commemorating the arrival of Napoleon in Nantes, a decoration commissioned in 1809, finished in 1812, which disappeared in 1815 (sold to an American who was to ship it at Lisbon, according to Surgères). From 1809-10 date the ten design projects and the 80 preparatory portraits relating to this decoration and kept at the Musée

Dobrée in Nantes. Shortly after 1812, Sablet fell ill and worked less.

His œuvre, no less varied than that of Jacques (interiors, religious and history paintings, views of Lausanne and Italy, such an his *Eloge Funèbre*), is conserved principally in Nantes (Musée des Beaux-Arts: 11 paintings; Musée Dobrée: *Portrait de Dobrée* and drawings), at Lausanne (seven paintings including an *Autoportrait* and two ravishing family portraits against a background of a Roman landscape, dated 1791); Marseille (Musée Grobet-Labadié); at the Academy of Fine Arts in Stockholm, *Portrait du sculpteur Masreliez*, s.d. Rome 1782 (it could be by Jacques); in the collection of the Comte de Bourbon-Chalus (*Portrait du Comte d'Artois en colonel des suisses,* 1774), in a sale in Paris, Hôtel Drouot (16 May 1924, no. 116; *Portrait de femme*). Finally, several engravings after F. Sablet are known, two by L. Perrot (1785 and 1786), a *Guillaume Tell* and a *Viala* by Alix and a *Portrait of Comte d'Estaing* engraved under the direction of Gaucher. J. F.

162
Portrait of Thomas Hope Playing Cricket

Thomas Hope d'Amsterdam jouant au cricket avec des amis
Plate p. 128
Canvas; 57.5 × 47.5; s.d.l.l. *J. Sablet Roma 1792*
London, Cricket Memorial Gallery

Thomas Hope (1769-1831) was one of the greatest English supporters of Neo-Classicism at the beginning of the 19th century. He was a great traveler, passionately fond of Turkey and the Middle East (in 1798, he had himself portrayed as a Turk by Beechey, London, National Portrait Gallery), an insatiable collector of antiques (several hundred vases of the Hamilton Collection, among others, bought in 1801, cf. No. 122) and paintings (he had the sense to acquire in about 1798 the extraordinary *Death of Adonis* by Rubens, which came from the liquidation of the Orléans Collection; the painting is today at Duits in London). He was a client and protector of Thorwaldsen, Canova and Flaxman, patron of West, Westall and John Martin, virtuoso designer of architecture and furniture, polemical art

critic (like Percier-Fontaine and Viollet-le-Duc), who published illustrated works on interior decorating (1807) antique costumes (1809) and modern fashion (1812), tireless writer, both obscure and profound and briefly famous for his involved autobiographical novel *Anastasius* (1819) which appeared anonymously and was attributed to Byron. Two recent biographies have just focused attention on this original personality with his immense cultural eclecticism, at once the epitome of the universalism of the Enlightenment and an astonishing prefiguration of the *Musée Imaginaire,* dear to the generations of the 20th century: see biography of Hope by Sandor Baumgarten (Paris, 1958)—very alert and informed as to the archival sources and Hope's literary and social milieu—and one by David Watkin (London,

1968), perhaps less rich in literary and historical data, but more focused on the artistic issues (that transcends the particular instance of Hope) and remarkably illustrated (a number of reproductions of the interiors of Duchess Street and of Deepdene conceived by Hope).

The Hopes were an active and famous family of bankers of Scottish origin established in Holland in the 17th century and settled in England in 1794-95 because of the anti-Orange, Francophile Revolution. He was the grandson of the founder of the Hope bank, Thomas Hope (1704-1779), and nephew of Henry Hope (1736-1811), the close friend of William V of Orange and the banker of Catherine II, the same who appears on the great painting of the Hope family by Benjamin West in the Boston Museum (toward the end of the 18th century the Hopes played an international politico-financial role similar to that of the Rothschilds around 1815-50). An uncle, Olivier, close to the Cardinal Albani, was the traveling companion of Winckelman—the theoretician par excellence of Neo-Classicism!—and visited Greece in the 1760s. That the family environment of the Hopes was very cultivated and inclined to the arts can be judged by the renown of the Hope gallery, rich in 17th-century Dutch paintings and praised by Reynolds, which was formed by Jan and Henry, loaned in 1819 to Thomas by his brother Henry Philipp (d. 1839), returned after 1839 to Henry Thomas and ended by being sold by his heir Lord Francis Pelham to Asher Wertheimer, in 1898, and then dispersed (on the Hope collection, see the introduction by A. Wertheimer to his book on the Hope paintings, London, 1898, and the entry for the painting by Potter, London, National Gallery, no. 2583 in the catalog by N. MacLaren, London, 1960, p. 300).

Thomas Hope was the most eccentric of the family. Impassioned by architecture, he made a "grand tour" between 1787 and 1795, visiting France, Germany, Egypt, Turkey, Greece and of course Italy (*Anastasius* is in great part based on this trip). Certainly this "grand tour" was not a continuous voyage. It is known that Hope was in Amsterdam in 1790, April 1791, March 1793, July and October 1794, etc., that in 1792 he went to Sicily, accompanied by George Wallis, the "English Poussin." Another eloquent testimony to Hope's activities is the letter which Flaxman wrote from Rome in 1792, where he noted that he received from Thomas Hope the commission to restore the Belvedere Torso (Watkin, 1968, p. 30). It is not surprising that in 1792 Hope struck up a relationship with Jacques Sablet, as well as with Louis Gauffier;

both artists were involved a little later in the sumptuous installation planned by Hope about 1800 for his collection of furniture, sculptures and antique vases at Duchess Street in London. The other great estate of Thomas Hope, at Deepdene, was also arranged by him in an extravagant neo-classical style. A painting by Sablet, *Ruines avec figures* (Watkin, 1968, p. 116, attributed it to "François-Jean Sablet" without, however, giving any proof and ignoring the present painting) was in fact exhibited between the windows of the Egyptian Room, while a *Repos de la Fuite en Égypte* by Gauffier appeared above the fireplace and, on the opposite wall, a *Vanité* by the same artist, dated 1791. Hope seemed to be more interested in Gauffier than in Sablet (he owned three other paintings by Gauffier which appeared in the sale of 1917, see Watkin, 1968, p. 44: a *Hector faisant des reproches à Pâris,* an *Œdipe et le Sphinx* and a *Ulysse et Nausicaa* of 1798, which is very probably the painting acquired in 1969 at Christie's in London by the Poitiers museum and published in 1972 by J.-P. Cuzin, 1972, p. 466, ill. p. 467).

The painting exhibited here depicts Hope and others playing cricket, an essentially English game that did not take hold in France until the 19th century. That Hope played cricket indicates he was already anglicized by his friends in Rome. While Sablet included in the painting a wicket and cricket bat, additional equipment necessary for serious games—leather padding, steel-toed shoes, etc., is not shown here.

The attribution of this painting poses problems, since it has been given at various times to both Sablet brothers. The Provenance and Reference sections below show that recent studies have given the work to François unhesitatingly, even though the painting's signature contains a J rather than an F. This is also true for the *Double Portrait dans le cimetière protestant de Rome* in Brest, painted in Rome and dated 1791, recently published as a work by François (J.-P. Cuzin, 1972, p. 466, ill., p. 467; note, however, that at the sale in Vienna in 1970 and in the London exhibition of 1972, no. 229, the painting was again given to Jacques). Does this mean the François also signed with a J, because he was baptized Jean-François (see biography above)? One senses all the fragility of this idea, especially as there are some works signed properly signed "F. Sablet," like the two female portraits of 1813 and 1815 in Lausanne, or "J.-F. Sablet," like the *Portrait de J.-B. Ceineray* and the *Peccot* in Nantes; or even "J.F.S.," like the drawing in Dijon, Musée Magnin. Provisionally, while awaiting a systematic inquiry, it seems sensible to agree that a painting signed J. Sablet stands a much better chance of being by Jacques than by François.

Unless the Sablet brothers were like the Le Nains, they themselves must have wished to avoid confusion, since they obviously influenced one another. Thus, in the Hope portrait, the firm luminosity, the taste for elegant silhouettes on a clear and delicate landscape background, the effective restrained coloration of certain isolated elements like the red waistcoat or the yellow pantaloons and a sort of tender and delightful realism are related to François' Lausanne portraits. Yet, other works by Jacques exhibit the same pure and elegant atmosphere, such as the Brest painting referred to above, the *Couple avec une petite fille* in Winterthur, the *Scène de la vie romaine* in Lausanne, or the elegiac *Portrait de la Princesse Victorine Spinola rendant hommage au buste du Prince Auguste d'Arenenberg*, dated 1795 and sold in London on 4 May 1970. Most characteristic of Jacques Sablet are a sweetness and a very subtle, soft touch; this is certainly the case in the present painting. François exhibits a more naive stiffness, a more graphic outline, a greater insistence on silhouette, construction and relief, as in the admirable family portrait, in which two young children prepare to dance to the sound of a violin before their parents, with an Italian port in the background (canvas, 65 × 81; now at Speelman's, London, for a long time attributed to L.-L. Boilly and given to François by P. Rosenberg). In their Roman portraits, both Jacques and François, along with Gauffier, rise to the level of Boilly, but with the unexpected and touching charm conferred by the pleasant background landscapes of Italy in a pure light, reviving the Arcadias of an Adriaen van de Velde or a Karel Dujardin (one should add, for the Hope portrait, the modulated skies of Philips Wouwerman and the refined clarity of Joseph Vernet). Once again, the Neo-Classicism of the epoch comes via a Dutch detour.

PROVENANCE

Collection Thomas Hope (d. 1831); given to his elder son, Henry-Thomas, whose daughter Henriette-Adèle married the 6th Duke or Newcastle (Henry-Thomas was married in about 1851, shortly after the death of his mother, to a French woman he had known for, many years, Adèle Bichat); sold with the collection of the house of Thomas Hope at Deepdene, London, Christie's, 20 July 1917, no. 69, and apparently bought back by the family; on loan to the Marylebone Cricket Club in London from 1957 to 1968; sold by order of the trustees of Henry Pelham Archibald Douglas, 7th Duke of Newcastle, London, Christie's, 21 June 1968, no. 89, ill. in the catalog (as Jean-François Sablet, see References); acquired through the National Art Collections Fund for the Imperial Cricket Memorial Gallery, London.

EXHIBITIONS

1929, Nothingham; 1970, London, Grosvenor House.

REFERENCES

Christie's Review of the Year, 1967-1968, ill. p. 68 (as François Sablet); *National Art Collections Fund, 65th Annual Report,* 1968, color ill.; S. Searight, 1969, ill. 168; R. Bowen, 1970, pp. 71-72, 267, ill. 10; J.-P. Cuzin, 1972, p. 466 (as François Sablet).

J. F.

Jean-Frédéric Schall

1752 Strasbourg - Paris 1825

Schall was first trained in Strasbourg, about 1768, at the Public Drawing School, where he studied under the brothers Pierre and Henri Haldenwanger. In 1772, he was admitted to the Royal Academy in Paris, where he studied until 1779 with, among other teachers, Nicolas-René Jollain and Nicolas-Bernard Lépicié. Especially before the Revolution, his work typified a belated extension of the rococo in which *fêtes galantes,* scenes of amorous intrigue, illustrations of dancers, and erotic allegories were presented in a style that, judged by the standards of Fragonard, often seemed awkward and provincial. The lighthearted tenor of these works, disseminated and popularized through many engravings, was rarely altered, although Schall's left-wing political loyalties during the Revolution were responsible for the painting exhibited here (No. 163). Such a patriotic subject, however, was exceptional in his œuvre, even during the 1790s, when he exhibited erotic subjects at the Salons of 1793 and 1798. He was nevertheless able to accommodate himself in his later career to a growing interest in the illustration of literature and historical legend, and made a series of prints based on narrative events in the stories of Christopher Columbus, Mme de Lavallière, and Don Quixote. His style also changed, probably under the influence of Marguerite Gérard, and his late rococo fluency of facture was replaced by a more painstakingly descriptive style that approached the domain of Dutch genre painting. Although his art may have seemed extremely retardataire by the time of his death, it ironically became at just that time a major source for the revival of the rococo in the work and thought of the younger Romantics, especially the brothers Achille and Eugène Devéria.

R. R.

163
*Heroism of William Tell**

L'Héroïsme de Guillaume Tell
Plate p. 135
Panel; 45 × 54.5; s.d.l.l. *F. Schall. l'an 2*e
Strasbourg, Musée des Beaux-Arts

The story of William Tell's heroism in fighting for Swiss liberty against foreign oppression is told in great detail in the inscription on Romain Girard's engraving of 1797 after Schall's painting. The particular episode depicted takes place after Gessler (or Gristler, as he is named on the print), the cruel Governor of Uri, has attempted to take Tell as prisoner to his castle at Küssnacht. A storm on Lake Lucerne has led the boat to an unknown shore, where Tell has escaped into a mountainous region. Gessler embarked at Brunnen, but en route to Küssnacht was sighted by Tell, who shot him with his bow and arrow. This is the moment shown by Schall, who includes two astonished pages supporting the dying Gessler and, in the background, two soldiers who signal in Tell's direction. It was a moment decisive in the future expulsion of the tyrannical governors (1 January 1308) and the foundation of the Swiss Republic after two centuries of subjugation.

As the inscription on Girard's print makes clear, Schall's choice of Tell's courageous assassination of a political tyrant was closely related to French Revolutionary propaganda. Already in 1791, a new opera, *Guillaume Tell,* by the composer most closely associated with the Revolution, André Grétry (libretto by J. M. Sedaine), was performed in Paris; and in 1793, when Schall himself was participating in Revolutionary activities, Tell had been made an official Jacobin hero. Indeed, a law of 2 August 1793 decreed that Antoine-Marin Lemierre's play of 1766, *Guillaume Tell,* be performed three times a week at the Republic's expense. Subsequently, the most famous dramatic and operatic interpretations of the legend were to be those by Johann Schiller (1804) and Gioacchino Rossini (1829).

Artists of the late 18th and early 19th centuries were often inspired by the Tell legend. The Swiss, Johann Heinrich Füssli, in addition to executing a painting for the Zurich Rathaus, *The Oath on the Rütli* (1778-79), subsequently painted (c. 1787) the scene of Tell's escape from Gessler's boat, a lost work which was engraved in Paris by the Bavarian printmaker, Carl Guttenberg, before 1790. This engraving bears a long inscription in German and French that emphasizes the Revolutionary implications of the story (see G. Schiff, *Johann Heinrich Füssli, 1741-1825,* I, Zurich, 1973, no. 719). And in 1798, Füssli made two versions (a drawing and an etching) of the same subject illustrated here by Schall (a drawing and an etching) of the same subject illustrated (*ibid.,* nos. 982, 1001). In France, François-André Vincent was commissioned in 1791 to paint *Guillaume Tell renversant la barque sur laquelle le gouverneur Guesler* [sic] *traversait le lac de Lucerne,* a work which was probably inspired by Guttenberg's print and which was exhibited at the Salon of 1795 (Salon no. 528; Toulouse, Musée des Augustins); and David himself included Tell in his project of 1793-94 for the theater curtain of the Opéra (drawing; Paris, Musée Carnavalet). On

7 July 1794, the sculptor Pierre-Nicolas Beauvallet offered a plaster bust of Tell to the Jacobin Club, which displayed it in the Tell section of the Temple. Another version of this bust was then exhibited at the Salon of 1795 (no. 1001), together with Vincent's painting. Under later and different political circumstances, Charles Steuben exhibited at the Salon of 1822 *Guillaume Tell s'élançant de la barque de Gessler* (no. 1204, illustrated in C.P. Landon, *Salon de 1822,* Paris, 1822, I, fig. 44) and *Le Serment des trois Suisses* (no. 1205) both works which, unlike Schall's, make a greater effort at historical accuracy of costume.

Inspired by the circumstances of the Revolution, Schall's painting is, in fact, exceptional in his career, which was dedicated mainly to the perpetuation of such rococo erotic subjects as dancers, *fêtes galantes* and allegories of love. He did, however, design prints illustrating the stories of Christopher Columbus, Mlle de Lavallière, and Don Quixote; and in their choice of more dramatic narrative and picturesque historical costume, these works bear some analogies with the *Heroism of William Tell.* In Schall's painting, the *troubadour* costumes, the diminutive scale of the figures, the nervous brushwork and the irregularity of the landscape all suggest a belated rococo style at odds with the heroic subject; indeed, Tell's bow and arrow seem only a momentary substitute for the Cupid's bow and arrow so ubiquitous in Schall's other work. Nevertheless, in his choice of a highly dramatic medieval subject and in his attempts to intensify the mysteries of a rocky landscape, Schall's little picture also prophesies the narrative and pictorial passions aggrandized in later French romantic painting, as exemplified by such an historicizing landscape as Achille-Etna Michallon's *La Mort de Roland en 778* (Salon of 1819; Louvre).

PROVENANCE
Acquired in Paris, 1930 (INV. no. 1232).

EXHIBITIONS
1930, Strasbourg, no. 6; 1947, Basel, no. 187; 1948, Strasbourg, suppl. no. 893; 1952, Sarrebruck, no. 43; 1958, Bordeaux, no. 66.

REFERENCES
Affiches..., Year V (1797), p. 3812; A. Girodie, 1927, pp. 32, 61, note 168; *Compte rendu...,* 1927-31, p. 10, ill. 11; *mus. cat.,* 1938, no. 433; P. Guth, 1954, p. 19; R. Rosenblum, 1967a, p. 80, note 105.

RELATED WORK
Engraving by Romain Girard: *"publié en Floréal l'an V de la Rép. fr. et Avril 1797 (vieux style)."*

R. R.

Ary Scheffer

1795 Dordrecht - Argenteuil 1858

Born of a German father and a Dutch mother, Scheffer was nevertheless always a part of the French school, throughout his career. His father, who died very young in 1809, taught him basic drawing principles. The precocity of his talent is demonstrated by the *Portrait de vieillard,* inspired by Rembrandt, which he showed in 1807 when he was scarcely 12 years old (Dordrecht). Attracted to Paris after the death of her husband, Cornélie Scheffer took her three sons to the capital permanently; Henry became a painter like Ary, and Arnold was to become a very important journalist and art critic, one of the first to make known the name of Théodore Géricault.

About 1810, Scheffer attended the studio of Pierre-Paul Prud'hon; in 1811, he entered the École des Beaux-Arts and worked in the studio of Pierre-Narcisse Guérin, a liberal teacher well-liked in his day. The first subjects which Scheffer tried were entirely Davidian: *Hannibal jurant de venger la mort de son frère Hasdrubal* (1810, Dordrecht), *Mort de Pline l'Ancien* (1811), *Pyrrhus cherchant à intimider Fabricius* (1812). He exhibited for the first time at the Salon of 1812 with *Abel, étant sorti avec Thirza de sa Cabane au lever du soleil, chante les louanges du Seigneur.* But the painting shown at the Salon of 1814, *Orphée et Eurydice,* of a dry and brilliant palette (Blois; sketch owned by Dordrecht), marks his rupture with the esthetic of David. *La Dernière communion de saint Louis* (Salon of 1815, Paris, Saint-Louis-en-l'Ile) is the first of a series of three paintings about the life of the saint (*Mort de saint Louis,* Salon of 1817, same church), *Saint Louis atteint de la peste visite des soldats malades,* Salon of 1822, Paris, Saint-Jean-Saint-François).

Here Scheffer created grave and simple scenes, dominated by religious sentiment. In 1817, he won the prize for sketches or compositions (*Les Sept Chefs devant Thèbes,* Paris, École des Beaux-Arts). At the Salon of 1819, he demonstrated a fine feeling for violence in the *Dévouement patriotique de six bourgeois de Calais* (Paris, Assemblée Nationale). With *La Veuve du soldat* at the following Salon (1822), Ary began a series of little genre scenes of readily popular subjects, in a sentimental vein like that of Pierre-Roch Vigneron *(Convoi du pauvre)* or Horace Vernet, inspired by the idea of the family menaced in its happiness. These paintings drew the interest of the critics, who abandoned at the same time the disturbing *Massacres de Scio* and were highly successful with the female public. In this vein, with a lachrymose sentimentality that anticipated Octave Tassaert, he presented *La Veuve du soldat* at the Salon of 1822, *Jeune Fille à genoux auprès d'un tombeau, Pauvre femme en couches,* the *Enfants égarés,* the *Enfant malade,* the *Retour du jeune invalide* at the Salon of 1824; *Scène d'inondation, Champ grêlé,* the *Sommeil du grand-père* at the Salon of 1827. "These paintings, lithographed by the artist himself, are sober in form and concise in detail, like a song by Béranger" (Charles Blanc).

Furthermore, Scheffer did not disdain large compositions, the principal one being *Gaston de Foix trouvé mort après avoir remporté la victoire de Ravenne* (Salon of 1824, Versailles; a beautiful sketch at the Hermitage, ill. in color in the book by V. Bérézina, 1972, p. 109), a great energetic and somber scene, painted in long strokes, in which he enjoyed overdoing the impasto and imitating all the liberties and roughness of romantic painting. The critics viewed the painting as the exception in his work; it was indeed a contrast to the dull and grey canvases which preceded it.

A sensitive poet, Ary was active in the philhellenic movement which was interesting the intelligentsia of the time. The poets Casimir Delavigne, Hugo, Béranger, as well as painters like Delacroix, supported the cause of the oppressed Greeks; Scheffer painted several pictures at the time: *Jeunes filles grecques implorant la protection de la Vierge pendant un combat,* the *Femmes souliotes* (Louvre), *Les débris de la garnison de Missolonghi au moment de mettre le feu à la mine qui doit les faire périr,* all three shown at the Salon of 1827. These works inspired some critics to name Scheffer the leader of the romantic school: in 1827, the *Femmes souliotes,* today spoiled by bitumen, must have been more colorful and splendidly impetuous.

Scheffer was a great portraitist. Rosenthal has brilliantly shown how this deserter from Romanticism often remained romantic in his portraits; this field perhaps best reflected his talents. Because of his many political and literary friendships, he was one of the most visible figures of the intelligentsia during the Restoration and the reign of Louis-Philippe. He was associated with the Carbonari, with the liberal party grouped around Lafayette, with the editors of the *Globe* (the journal of the Saint-Simonian religion) and the *National* (the journal of Thiers and Armand Carrel), and even with the Orléans family. As early as 1821, Scheffer was the drawing master for the children of the future Louis-Philippe. Also, passing through his studio were a number of political figures, whose portraits he did: *Lafayette* (Rouen), *Destutt de Tracy, Manin* (Venice, Museo Correr), *Franklin, Maréchal Lobau* (Nancy), *Prince Talleyrand* (Chantilly), the *Duc d'Orléans* (Chantilly), *Dupont de l'Eure* (Évreux); a number of artistic or literary personalities: *Béranger* (Paris, Musée Carnavalet), *Hersent* (No. *165*), *Liszt* (Weimar), *Gounod* (Versailles), *Lamennais* (Louvre), *Lamartine* (Bergues), *David d'Angers* (Le Mans).

As a history painter, Scheffer showed himself to be one of the most literary men of the 19th century. "Ary Scheffer was a transposed poet; Dante, Goethe and Byron were more his masters than Michelangelo, Raphael or Titian" (Théophile Gautier). An intimate friend of the poet Béranger, an enthusiast of Goethe, he often found subjects for his paintings in literature. The *Ronde d'enfants* was inspired by the *Orage* of Béranger, the only French poet to whom the artist was attracted; the *Antiquary* of Walter Scott inspired the *Famille du marin* (1823) and the *Mort du fils du pêcheur* (1824). He was drawn to Shakespeare (a sketch of the *Apparition des trois sorcières à Macbeth,* 1827), and to Byron (*Le Giaour,* Salon of 1833). But it was especially German poetry, Goethe in particular, which inspired this northern artist. Ary greatly admired *Faust,* considering that tragedy the highest expression of art; in 1831, he exhibited *Faust dans son cabinet* and *Marguerite au rouet;* "each of these figures was the portrait of the soul" (see Blanc). These paintings had such success that from then on Ary became the "painter of Marguerite" (before he became the painter of Monique or Mignon). Poems by Burger, ballads by Schiller, writings by Ludwig Uhland gave rise to *Léonore* (1829), the *Plaintes de la jeune fille* (1837) and *Eberhard, comte de Württemberg, dit le Larmoyeur* (Salon of 1831, Louvre), another canvas ruined by bitumen. The witticism by

Charlet: "Lunch with the colorists and dinner with the draughtsmen," could well apply to Scheffer. He became increasingly famous and prolific after 1830 (in all, an œuvre of more than 400 paintings) but moved more and more toward painting with a message, to "*idées pures*" (Gautier), with a reserve dhandling which in the end approached the restrictive stylized ideal of Ingres. The "sublime," even "Calvinist" approach chosen by this Dutchman, not very Dutch at heart, was far from the romantic pictures of his beginnings. Scheffer thus abandoned the prestige of appearance and the pleasures of color to seek a sort of transparency of painting and attained an immense success that is explained by the profound sentimentalism of the period.

A.-B. L.

164
Saint Thomas Aquinas Preaching During a Storm

"Saint Thomas d'Aquin prêchant la confiance en Dieu pendant la tempête"
Plate p. 274
Canvas; 353 × 295; s.d.l.l. *A. Scheffer 1823*
Salon of 1824, no. 1539
Paris, Chapelle de l'Hôpital Laënnec

The iconography of the painting is deceptively simple, because the episode of Saint Thomas Aquinas soothing the passengers of a ship buffeted by the tempest seems totally invented; at least it is not mentioned in any biography of Saint Thomas Aquinas nor in his rich iconography (on this subject see B.-H. Molkenboer, O.-P., *De H. Thomas Van Aquino in de Schilderkunst,* Ghent, 1927; also L. Réau, *Iconographie de l'art chrétien,* Paris, 1959, III, pp. 1277-1280). It is absent during the Counter Reformation, and in the popular series engraved by C. Boel, E. Van Paenderen, G. Swanenburg and C. Galle from the drawing of Otto Voenius in 1610. According to Father Raffin of the Dominican Order (written communication), there may have been a more or less intentional confusion or intermingling with the life of another Dominican saint, the Blessed Pierre Gonzalès (c. 1190-1246), patron of Spanish and Portuguese seamen, who called him Saint Elmo or Saint Telmo (because of another saint invoked during storms at an even earlier time whose name, Erasmus, could have evolved into Ermo or Elmo). Actually, Saint Gonzalès was often shown in a boat in the middle of a storm but with a candle in his hand; furthermore, his biography includes an episode of a sermon menaced by a sudden storm which the saint calmed by his prayers, while reassuring his audience. However, the scene does not take place at sea but beside the ocean, precisely at Bayonne of Galicia. Thus, it is easier to suppose that Scheffer invented a scene modeled on that of Christ calming the storm (Gospels of Saint Luke 8: 22-25; Saint Mark 4: 35-41; Saint Matthew, 8: 23-27). After all, the theme of trust in God was certainly appropriate for Scheffer's strong Protestant pietism.

The violence of the lighting and the play of forms in the painting, the expressive eloquence of the figures must certainly have surprised and upset someone like Stendhal, with his belief in strict Davidian formalism. Thus, Stendhal's sharp attack on this painting, curiously discerning in it the memory of Restout and his "negligent" manner, seen as a veritable return to a period before the French school was so felicitously revived by David: "it is the tentative effort of an artist who has not mastered the basics of the composition, form, and action of each muscle, who does not draw from the nude, who does not observe the sound Davidian principles;" nevertheless, Stendhal could concede that paintings like *Saint Thomas Aquinas* have a certain picturesque fire and spirit." Aside from this criticism, the painting was very well received by the critics of the Salon of 1824 who praised its "composition, full of vigor and enthusiasm... "very effective drapery" (*Revue critique...*), its "great purity of design," the Saint's "admirable pose" and the contrast of the passengers, "bowled over by despair and fear, while he dominates them with majesty" (Flocon and Aycard); the simplicity and veracity of the expressions and poses of the figures, "the profound sensibility that softens their vigorous and masculine faces... the great nobility in the forms... the totally ideal beauty, without insipience, without uniformity... a great elevation of style and a profound talent for expression" *(Le Constitutionnel)*. This critic concluded that "M. Scheffer is a painter eminently qualified to paint history in the new manner"

Jal was also very favorable; he reiterated such descriptions as "nobility... character... force," and he had great praise for the painting's color: "The general harmony is somber as is appropriate for the subject; the color is severe, sustained, and yet mysterious." One objection made by Jal seems pertinent, if one thinks back to the *Radeau de la Méduse* by Géricault of the Salon of 1819: "I am sorry that the space is so narrow; the accessory figures scarcely have room; Thomas Aquinas himself does not have enough space to extend himself; there is too little sky and sea for the storm to be truly frightening." The comparison to Géricault is indeed possible for this heroic scene; the handling, still more nervous and dense in the Dordrecht sketch (see Related Works), reinforces the comparison with Géricault, as does the subject, a simple religous version of the theme of Hope that animates the *Radeau de la Méduse*. Coexisting rather successfully in his work are the virile and monumental lesson of Géricault (great history painting, 17th-century chiaroscuro, from the Bolognese to Van Oost and Jouvenet, significant gestures of Rubens or Lebrun) and moving sentimentality which characterize so many charming paintings of Scheffer's youth, as well as so many minor masters of realism in the romantic era, from Johannot to Biard and from Duval le Camu to Poterlet.

But the painting's genuinely romantic quality confirms that in 1824 future painting would not be limited to Delacroix, and that Scheffer, like Delaroche, could still not foresee the wise and reassuring evolution that his art would increasingly take after 1830. It is true that Scheffer crossed easily from one group to the other, demonstrating a certain indecision and inconsistency of style that certainly did him harm. Various critics of the Salon of 1824 had already marked this tendency, notably Flocon and Aycard and Jal, who much criticized Scheffer's *Gaston de Foix* in the same Salon, as did the anonymous writer of the *Revue Critique*.

PROVENANCE

Acquired by the City of Paris even before the Salon of 1824 (see C.-P. Landon, who stated that the painting was already hanging in a Parisian church); Church of Saint Thomas Aquinas (in 1876, Paul de Saint-Victor indicated that the painting was in the Chapelle des Cathéchismes, whereas it "had formerly been inside the church"); removed in 1880, put into storage; loaned to the chapel of the Hôpital Laennec in October 1943 (according to the documents of the Direction des Beaux-Arts of the City of Paris, which M. Henri Cazaumayou generously consulted for us; taken down for "work" (sic) in the nave in 1974 (on these curious operations by "vandals" which have aroused a lively and legitimate controversy, see Yvan Christ in *L'Amateur d'Art,* 11 April 1974).

EXHIBITION

1824, Salon, no. 1539.

REFERENCES

C.-P. Landon, 1824, v. I, p. 67; Stendhal, 1824, p. 58; F. Flocon and M. Aycard, 1824, pp. 39-40, lithograph by Feillet between pp. 32 and 33; A. Jal, 1824, p. 209; X***, *Revue critique des productions de peinture... exposées au salon de 1824*, 1825, pp. 15, 344; *Le Constitutionnel,* 2 September 1824 ("Salon de 1824") 3rd article); *Le Moniteur universel,* 8 September 1824 ("Salon de 1824", 2nd article); P. de Saint-Victor, 1876, p. 246 (title inexact, dimensions wrong); Six, 1934, p. XXI; Scheffer, mus. cat., Dordrecht, 1934, p. 98 (list of works by Scheffer inscribed on black record book of the Marjolin-Scheffer beguest: see no. III); M. Kolb, 1937, pp. 296, 297, 471 (wrong dimensions and always located at Saint-Thomas d'Aquin !).

RELATED WORKS

Sketch (canvas; 45 × 36) in Dordrecht, Musée Scheffer (mus. cat. 1934, no. 21, ill. VIII); lithograph by Feillet appeared in the work by Flocon and Aycard on the Salon of 1824 (see References).

J. F.

165
Portrait of Hersent

Portrait du peintre Louis Hersent (1777-1860)
Plate p. 299
Canvas; 117 × 90; s.d.m.l. *A. Scheffer/1830.*
Grenoble, Musée de Peinture et de Sculpture

Louis Hersent was associated with Scheffer, whom he met, most notably, in the brilliant salon of Gérard (Kolb, 1937, p. 120). Like Scheffer, he was a member of the commission of artists named in 1831 by Louis-

Philippe to study a certain number of reforms of the fine arts; thus, the two artists both appeared in the collection of the Duc d'Orléans before 1830 (*ibid.*, p. 83, no. 3). It is also conceivable that Hersent's painting, the *Mort de Bichat* of the Salon of 1817 (Faculté de Médecine, Paris), influenced Scheffer when he painted the *Mort de Géricault* (Louvre) in 1824. Whether or not the friendship between the two artists is relevant here, this portrait is striking in its lack of academicism and conventionalism and reveals a typically romantic, restless and convincing presence. Far from the pure and perfectly smooth Davidian polish, with its occasionally heavy, even murky impasto, the brutally frontal effigy shows the effect which the liberating shock of Géricault brought to so many young painters (including Horace Vernet) in the years 1815-20. The pose has affinities to the broad and direct manner of the English portraitists from Sir Joshua Reynolds to Sir Thomas Lawrence.

Here again, Scheffer was not going to continue along this fertile path after 1830. His innumerable subsequent portraits show, on the contrary, a careful and correct execution, an element of perfect coldness, in contrast to the impressionistic intransigence of the present portrait, certainly one of his greatest successes.

PROVENANCE
Sale of the collection of M. Lizé of Rouen, Paris, Hôtel Drouot, 25-28 March 1901, no. 386; gift of Général de Beylié, 1901.

EXHIBITION
1935, Paris, no. 131.

REFERENCES
L. de Beylié, 1909, ill. p. 105; mus. cat., 1911, no. 426; Renckens, in Scheffer, mus. cat., Dordrecht, 1934, p. 115 (list of portraits painted by Scheffer); M. Kolb, 1937, pp. 13, 413, 487.

J. F.

Jean-Victor Schnetz

1787 Versailles - Paris 1870

Schnetz' family was originally from Soleure, Switzerland, but he grew up in France. Restrained by his brother, who served as his tutor, he was first a notary's clerk, but his passion for drawing soon conquered him and at the age of 21, he exhibited for the first time at the Salon of 1808 with a military subject, *Valeur d'un soldat français* (the scene, placed in Calabria, presaged his predilection for Italy). In 1810, he left Versailles and the Salon catalog listed him as a student of Jean-Baptiste Regnault. *La mort du général Colbert* (destroyed in Douai) was noted by C.-P. Landon, who reproduced it. In 1812, he also engraved one of the three pictures which Schnetz showed that year, *L'amitié secourant l'homme dans le voyage pénible de la vie au moment où, accablé sous le poids du malheur, il est prêt à succomber.* In his *Notice sur Victor Schnetz* of 1871, Beulé reported (p. 3) that Schnetz composed this allegory in homage to a "remarkable woman of Versailles," who had advised him to enter David's atelier, where he was in 1812. He even served as a model for the Greek seated at the

feet of Leonidas in David's *Léonidas aux Thermopyles* (Louvre). He failed to win the Prix de Rome in 1813 and 1816, regularly frequented the studios of Gros and Gérard and left for Italy in 1817. He experimented for sometime, sent to the Salon of 1819 some religious paintings, among them the *Samaritain secourant le blessé de Jéricho* (Paris, church of Saint-Gervais), and an early picturesque study from nature, *Un petit voleur de raisin.*

Rewarded with a first-place medal in 1819, he began an official career marked by commissions for churches, monuments and museums; for example, *Saint Martin coupe son manteau pour en donner la moitié à un pauvre* (Salon of 1824, cathedral of Tours), *Les adieux du consul Boetius à sa famille* (Salon of 1827, shown subsequently in a room of the Conseil d'État of the Louvre, then at the Musée du Luxembourg; now at Toulouse), *Des malheureux implorant le secours de la Vierge* (Salon of 1831, Louvre) and *Une famille de Contadini surprise par un prompt débordement du Tibre* (Salon of 1831, Rouen). He also produced numerous compositions for the museum of Versailles. Besides these large works, he became famous for his small paintings depicting, like those of his friend Léopold Robert, scenes of the life of the Italian people, especially after 1822. He loved sentimental and tragic scenes and showed a romantic taste in such subjects as *Une femme assassinée* (Salon of 1824, Quimper).

Knight of the Legion of Honor in 1835, he was elected to the Institute in 1837 to replace Gérard, then directed the École des Beaux-Arts in Paris from 1837 to 1841, when he again left Paris, to which he had returned in 1832, for Rome. He was director of the French Academy in Rome from 1841 to 1847 and again from 1853 to 1866, exercising a great influence on the evolution of academic teaching. A thesis on Schnetz has been written by Geneviève Domino at the École du Louvre.

G. L.

166
Vow to the Madonna[*]

"Une vieille femme et une jeune fille en prière devant une madone"
Plate p. 292
Canvas; 100 × 75; s.l.l. *V*^{or} *Schnetz*
Salon of 1827-1828, no. 955
La Rochelle, Musée des Beaux-Arts

Schnetz "visited Italy on foot, with a pack on his back, where he penetrated into the lairs of brigands and slept on the ground" (Beulé, 1871, p. 2). He had arrived there in 1817 and the following year met Léopold Robert, with whom he had the occasion in 1819 to study the people of the village of Sonnino while staying in Rome at the Castel de Sant'Angelo. Sonnino had been the hold-out of brigands who had rendered the road from Naples impassable and whom it had been necessary to imprison in Rome. Some of the prisoners became professional models, indispensable to Schnetz, who was "a firm believer in realism, always worked with models," (*ibid.*, p. 9). But the painter did not hesitate to seek inspiration even in the mountain villages, where he was well received by the brigands "to whom he brought glory." From Rome, where he was to remain until 1832, he sent numerous paintings on the theme of the Italian peasant, which appeared at the Salons of 1822, 1824, 1827-28 and 1831. On 13 December 1823, David wrote him: "Close your ears to the gigantic proposals of the proponents of the antique with whom I am associated; my taste for it has always been natural. As for your taste, it is not inferior when it can be translated into works of art such as yours..." (cited by Beulé, *op. cit.*, p. 5). Indeed, these genre scenes, comparable to those of the painter Bonnefond

of Lyon, were very successful in an era thirsting for sentimentality. In 1828, Jal cited the painting of the "little sick girl, presented by her mother at the altar of the Virgin" as "one of the most perfect works I know in this style." He had already noted that it was "the best picture of its type at the Salon. Interest, expression, design, arrangement, touch, color, I find all excellent... the beautiful contrast of the two heads of the old woman and the young girl in prayer before an image of the Virgin! The wrinkles of one and the freshness of the other, the difference between the brown tones of the elderly woman and the charming tones which color the cheeks of the little girl, the straightforward and fine relief of hands and faces, the grace and brightness of the costumes, make this study of natural grandeur delightful." Anthony Béraud noted: "Each time that we stopped before this excellent painting, we increasingly admired its exquisite naturalness, the touching simplicity of character, the truthfulness of expression and colors." However, he would have preferred "less harsh contours and more broadly rendered details."

The *Vow to the Madonna* represents a theme which for the next half century was to inspire artists who traveled in Italy, such as Montessuy and Lebel. In this painting, Schnetz did not portray modestly dressed peasants as he would in the huge composition exhibited at the Salon of 1831, *Des malheureux implorant le secours de la Vierge* (Louvre) but rather two women wearing rich country costumes. He painted rings, earrings, lace and embroideries in minute detail. He emphasized the single group of figures, indicating the setting, a chapel, simply by the edge of the altar (with no visible image of the Madonna), and by the ex-votos hung on the wall at the back: small paintings referring to avoided catastrophes, illnesses, drownings, falls, or heart-shaped offerings and rosaries rearranged in the same frame. The two peasants bring the same offerings. Through the interplay of glances and gestures, the addition of carefully selected accessories (lamp, candles, ex-voto) Schnetz depicted a scene of popular Italian life that he had probably observed, but which he certainly composed in conformity with the teachings of David.

PROVENANCE
Bequest of the Baron de Chassiron to the Musée de La Rochelle, 1872.

EXHIBITIONS
1827-1828, Salon, no. 955; 1900, Paris, no. 606.

REFERENCES
A. Béraud, 1827, pp. 131-132; A. Jal, 1828, pp. 348-349, 459; Th. Guédy, n.d., p. 247; L. Rosenthal, 1900, p. 105; L. Bénédite, 1904, p. 150, ill. p. 143; P. Moisy, mus. cat., 1942, p. 64.

G. L.

Xavier Sigalon

1787 (not 1788) Uzès - Rome 1837

Born into the large, impoverished family of a schoolmaster whose school was established in Nîmes in 1796, Sigalon was a difficult and stubborn child. Furthermore, his biographers emphasize the unfinished and somewhat disappointing character of his life: his restless solitude, his passion for work, hampered by too many principles and hesitations, his misfortune, his intransigent artistic integrity, the very noble and elevated conception he had of his role and duties as an artist. Entering the central school of drawing in Nîmes in 1798 (it closed in 1802), Sigalon distinguished himself by his zeal and gleaned his first artistic ideas from Monrose, a student of David. (Delécluze notes that Monrose was a member of the "Barbus" group alongside of Maurice Quaï). Even before 1818, he had already produced several portraits and religious paintings (*Mort de Saint Louis,* cathedral of Nîmes; *Sainte Anastasie,* church of Russan, near Nîmes; a huge *Descente du Saint-Esprit* in the dome of the church of the Penitents of Aigues-Mortes).

When he had acquired enough money, Sigalon finally went to Paris in 1818 and became associated with the atelier of Pierre-Narcisse Guérin, which he soon left, first to rent a studio with a compatriot from the Gard region, Souchon, then to follow a solitary and autodidactic course by studying passionately the lessons of the old masters, especially the Venetians, at the Louvre. His slow maturation ended in a bold stroke with the *Jeune Courtisane* of the Salon of 1822, which received immediate commendation for its finely measured Venetianism (Louvre; the work has aged considerably because of the use of bitumen). Also at this Salon was the *Portrait de Rossi* (also at the Louvre). In 1824, there was the famous *Locusta* of the Nîmes museum (its sketch is shown here, No. 167) and *"plusieurs portraits,"* not specified and under the same number. The triumph of *Locusta,* for which he received a gold medal (see No. 167), was followed by the unparalleled harsh criticism of his *Athalie faisant massacrer ses enfants* of the Salon of 1827 (acquired by the State in 1833 through Thiers and sent to the museum in Nantes; a handsome preparatory drawing is in Nîmes). This work, undoubtedly Sigalon's masterpiece (according to Thoré, in the *Introduction* to his *Salon of 1846)* in its ambitious fury as well as its richness of composition and its gigantic size (428 × 600), revealed the passionate and imposing temperament of the artist. Huge scale was also the prominent characteristic of two important religious compositions begun in these years, the *Baptême du Christ,* commissioned in 1826 for 3,000 francs by the council of the cathedral of Nîmes and finished in 1829 (in situ, 392 × 289), and the *Christ en Croix,* commissioned in 1828 by the Ministry of the Interior for the church of Yssingeaux (Haute-Loire), but finished only after 1830 and exhibited at the Salon of 1831 (still in situ, 500 × 300). The latter painting was shown at the Salon of 1831 at the same time as the *Vision de saint Jérome* (see below) commissioned by the King for the Maison du Roi in 1825 and dated 1829 (438 × 265). The artist was paid 7,000 francs for these two paintings and the subjects were left to his choice; for them, Sigalon won the decoration of the Legion of Honor. Also exhibited at the Salon of 1831 was the *Vision de saint Jérôme,* commissioned by the King for the Maison du Roi in 1825 and dated 1829 (438 × 265). It was exhibited for a long time at the Musée du Luxembourg and then at the Louvre; it was then deposited in 1923 in the church of Château-Renard near Montargis (still there; a lovely sketch in Nîmes was reproduced in color in Alauzen, 1962, p. 138, fig. 60). Among Sigalon's religious paintings is a *Délivrance de Saint Pierre* at the church of Robiac near Alès (1823; see Bosc, 1876, no. 10, p. 436).

After the failure of *Athalie,* Sigalon no longer obtained large commissions. Quite discouraged and scarcely able to meet his expenses, always restless and unhappy, Sigalon returned to a cloistered existence in Nîmes. Abandoning large history painting almost completely (note, however, a *Barque de Dante,* drawing of 1833 in Bagnères-de-Bigorre), he devoted himself to the more commercial venture of portraiture. The Musée de Nîmes contains a beautiful set of his portraits done with an obstinate and noble realism, notably an effigy of his friend Numa Boucoiran, the mother of Diaz and especially a self-portrait (another remarkable example in the Louvre), halfway between Géricault and the great masters of the Florentine Renaissance such as Bronzino or Pontormo. At the Salon of 1833, he showed the *Amour Captif,* perhaps painted earlier, which was acquired by the banker Laffitte, then given to the Louvre in 1862 by Adolphe Moreau *fils,* the father of Étienne Moreau-Nélaton (deposited by the Louvre in Nîmes in 1952). After 1833, on the initiative of Thiers, a great friend and admirer of Sigalon and the future founder of the Musée des Copies, Sigalon was commissioned to copy Michelangelo's *Last Judgment* in Rome, a colossal task which completely absorbed him, perfectionist as he was. At first, Sigalon was assisted by Souchon; when the latter quarreled with him, Boucoiran took his place. The copy, finished in 1837, was exhibited first at the Baths of Diocletian in Rome with great success (Pope Gregory XVI came to see it); it was sent, in the same year, to the École des Beaux-Arts in Paris, and was hung by Sigalon in the chapel in February (still there).

Perhaps already weakened by the intense work, Sigalon was to die soon after his return to Rome of cholera in August. He left unfinished his copies of the Sistine pendentives (they were completed by Boucoiran). Today, they are installed in the Salle de Melpomène of the École des Beaux-Arts in Paris. Nor did he have the time to paint a *Mort de Claude,* for which he left a powerful drawing (Nîmes).

J. F.

167
*Locusta**

Locuste remettant à Narcisse le poison destiné à Britannicus en fait l'essai sur un jeune esclave
Plate p. 276
Canvas; 85 × 107
Nîmes, Musée des Beaux-Arts

This is a sketch for one of the most sensational paintings of the Salon of 1824. It was saluted by Thiers in his article in the *Constitutionel* in quasi-prophetic terms: "A great painter is born in France." As the Salon catalog indicates, the subject is borrowed from Racine's *Britannicus* (1669). The cited verses are spoken by Narcisse to Néron, in Act IV, at the beginning of scene 4: "She caused the death of a slave before my eyes/ Iron is less quick to cut down a life/ than the new poison she entrusts to me." Racine is therefore the source for Sigalon's liberties with the text of the *Annals* of Tacitus, to which he was to be more faithful a little later in his *Mort de l'Empereur Claude* (1837, drawing in Nîmes). The freed Narcissus is characterized as a depraved, viciously mean counselor who directly plots the death of Britannicus with Locusta as poisoner. In Tacitus, however, although Narcissus first has Messalina (first wife of Claudius, soon replaced by Agrippina) killed and serves as a protection for Claudius, he later opposes Agrippina and appears on the whole in a favorable light. He disapproves of the assassination of Claudius and the accession of Agrippina. It is she and not Narcissus who has solicited the help of the famous Locusta to liquidate her aged husband Claudius. He finally lets Agrippina drive him to suicide long before the assassination of young Britannicus. The preliminary testing of the poison on a slave is also Racine's invention: Tacitus (*Annals*, XIII, 15) only mentions that Nero threatened Locusta with torture because her poison had failed in an earlier attempt; Suetonus (Nero, XXXIII) specifies in more detail that Nero himself beat Locusta and forced her to make the poison under his eyes... But Racine's invention could only represent a greater plastic force for the imaginative Sigalon. It is true that Wakefield (1973, p. 19) found such devotion to Racine exceptional among the romantics, but whether Sigalon was a true romantic remains debatable.

Sigalon knew perfectly how to exploit all of the psychological and dramatic aspects which could be deduced from the new situation created by Racine. The critics of the Salon of 1824, where the large painting was extremely successful, did not weary of analyzing the appropriateness of each figure, the dramatic intensity of the scene which represented a truly significant triumph for a painting of literary history (and for an art criticism with the same perspective which saw in Sigalon a new Lebrun). This point of view is very outmoded today but it explains, by the very breadth of the critical commentaries, how Sigalon's *Locusta* could demonstrate and justify a certain legitimacy. From Jal to Favien Pillet, from Stendhal to Chauvin, from Thiers to the anonymous writers of the *Globe* and the *Revue des productions les plus remarquables...*, there were impassioned discussions of the merits of the design and pose of each figure: were they correct, were they well thought out, should they have been dressed so simply without court finery ? But, stated the author of the *Revue critique des productions de peinture exposées au Salon de 1824* (p. 307),

"If one would make Narcissus into an affected courtesan with gold in all his drapery, one would see what would become of the scene and how it would become the dullest and most unbearable spectacle that a painting could be." Was it necessary to bare the wasted bosom of Locusta ? Was it necessary to depict Nero ? Certainly not, according to Jal ! Chauvin admired the cold, calm pose of Narcissus, in contrast with the outburst of Locusta: "M. Sigalon composes with intelligence, he can draw without exaggeration and simulate without distortion. What will the admirers of twisted figures say ?" (1824, p. 25). And again, "The composition is well conceived: here all is simple, natural, expressive" (*Revue des productions les plus remarquables...*, 1824, p. 25).

F. Pillet noted that the slave dies "without daring to revile the instigators of his death" (1824, p. 34). Another critic remarked on how Narcissus uses Locusta "but does not tell her his secret and holds her at a distance" (M..., *Revue critique des productions des peintures... au Salon de 1824,* p. 17). This painting had the fortune of uniting moderates and avant-garde in its favor, of mixing boldness and sublimity with academic correctness and with verisimilitude. Stendhal liked it because of its intelligence, because Sigalon followed primarily "the truth of feeling," which "almost all the celebrated paintings of the present time lack," because in the name of artistic logic "he had the courage to reject all the semi-philosophy which poisons the arts. His soul imperiously dictated to him that pictorial truthfulness which required Locusta to be first of all a woman with hideous features [here Stendhal contradicts himself, for later he regretted the hideous and too visible bosom of Locusta] and then that she be half-crazed by the effect of the crime... Here are the figures that painting needs..." (*Journal de Paris,* 7 October 1824).

There are of course several variations between the sketch and the great painting, few of which are fundamental. The architecture plays a more important role in the preparatory version. An especially pronounced difference is the figure of Locusta, who in the sketch leans more imperiously toward Narcissus in a beautiful motion that is much weaker in the large painting, a loss which some have regretted (see Nîmes mus. cat., 1869 ed.). Bent three-quarters forward, her face is very schematic (in the final painting, Sigalon enjoyed emphasizing the quasi-satanic physiognomy of the poisoner). In the sketch, Locusta does not bare her chest, a detail some critics would have preferred to the final decision: e.g. Stendhal would protest, "M. Sigalon lacked taste in presenting the chest of this figure in the nude, such horrors should be left to Rubens" (*Journal de Paris,* no. 242, 31 August 1824, first article); the same remark was repeated in the *Revue des productions les plus remarquables...*: "True art can avoid such repulsive objects" (p. 40), in response, Jal wrote spiritedly: "I have heard M. Sigalon reproached for the temerity of these long-hanging breasts; it has been said that this nudity is repulsive; I am far from agreeing. This is a mad woman, practiced in poisoning; I want everything about her to be hideous; I want her features to be decomposed, her eye to be frightening, her breath to be imagined as foul, so that everything about her proclaims: keep away if you do not want to die" (A. Jal, 1824, p. 95). In contrast, the poses of Narcissus and of the slave remained unchanged.

Sigalon actually liked to make sketches, but in the process, he became weakened as he approached the final execution. This can certainly be felt in this sketch and even more so in his very beautiful sketch of *Saint Jerôme* at Nîmes (for the painting of the church of Château-Renard), the nervousness of which seems to bear witness to Subleyras ! In the sketch for *Locusta,* the drawing of the slave, as energetic as one could wish, demonstrates Sigalon's perfect classic culture (cf. an equivalent pose in the *Stanze* of Raphael: the *Expulsion of Heliodorus,* and in the tapestry of the *Death of Ananias*—from the series of the Acts of the Apostles), used by a very intriguing and expressive restlessness that should not, however, be called romantic (as did Jal as early as 1824 !), since stylistic tendencies overlapped one another so closely at this time. Moreover, the sketch could not (or would not) specify the setting of the crime, which adds even more to the sense of infernal horror and that attracted critical commentary. As Leon Rosenthal very aptly described it : "a cavern which the moon lights with a sinister luster, a cavern where owls fly and on the floor of which serpents slither... The fact is that the impressions of literary Romanticism presided over this work. Shakespeare is sponsor and the sorceresses of the Scotch heath are the older sisters of Locusta. All that the imagination can conceive of as mysterious, monstrous or horrible crossed Sigalon's mind. It is a nightmare which haunted him, and his passion pushed him to the extremities of his dream" (1900, p. 246). This very incisive and just commentary echoes the original observations of Stendhal: "[Locusta] recalls the Meg-Perillies of Walter Scott" (*Journal de Paris,* 31 August 1824) or those of the critic of the *Globe:* "The *Locusta,* whom he creates as a Canidia, nevertheless recalls the witches of Macbeth" (article of 9 October 1824). Finally, to judge the profound and honestly virtuous originality of Sigalon, we need only compare his *Locusta* with a slightly later painting of the same school, academically perfect, which depicts almost identically the Raphaelesque pose of the slave: the *Éducation à Sparte* by Luigi Massini (1869), deposited by the Louvre in 1886 in Montauban (D. Ternois, 1965, no. 205, ill.). While it presents the same admiration of the past, the same taste for narrative historical painting, it is an empty, powerless image, with disunified passages, altogether gloomy and lifeless, unalleviated academicism. Sigalon equals rather the grandiose academicism of Chenavard, with his ardent study of the past. Chenavard and Sigalon stand out as two isolated figures, strange, unhappy and misunderstood prophets !

PROVENANCE
Gift of M. Rossi in 1838, with two other Sigalons (a portrait and a drawing for *Athalie*). Rossi, originally from Nîmes, was a dentist working in Paris and a friend of Sigalon; the artist painted his portrait in 1822 (Louvre), and they corresponded in 1831 (see E. Bosc., 1876, pp. 451-452). Rossi often helped and encouraged Sigalon in the course of his Parisian years (*ibid.,* pp. 435-436). According to Charles Blanc (Sigalon entry, 1865, p. 3), it was Rossi who had the *Jeune courtisane,* a work which Sigalon, discouraged, had left abandoned in his studio, exhibited at the Salon of 1822.

REFERENCES
J.-F. Perrot, 1840, v. I., p. 287, no. 89; mus. cat., 1844, no. 67; *ibid.,* 1869, no. 76; Bellier and Auvray, 1885, v. II, p. 502; A. Pieyre, 1886, v. I, p. 108; mus. cat., 1895, no. 92; *ibid.,* 1940, no. 169; J. Vergnet-Ruiz and M. Laclotte, 1962, p. 252.

RELATED WORKS
Painting of the Salon of 1824 (no. 1571), at Nîmes from April 1830 (canvas; 220 × 290); one of the paintings by Sigalon most often cited in the literature and described at length in the old catalog of the museum (1844, no. 56; 1854, no. 65; 1869, no. 1; v. 1885-1886, no. 89; 1940, no. 163). A selection of criticism is given above in the body of the present entry, cf. also: Jeanron, 1837, pp. 9-11; J.-F.-A. Perrot, 1840, I, pp. 278-279; Saint-Maurice, 1848, pp. 15-18; Schœlcher, biographical entry on Sigalon in all the 19th-century catalogs of the Nîmes museum; Ch. Blanc, III, 1865, Sigalon entry, pp. 3-4; L. Rosenthal, 1900, pp. 167, 246; R.-P. Huet, 1911, pp. 94-95 (interesting note on the dramatic quality of the landscape); D. Wakefield, 1973, pp. 18, 92, 105-106, ill. 31.
There are several stories about the finished painting's history before it entered the Musée de Nîmes. Michel Nicolas and Alphonse Artozoud, local biographers of the artist (cited by P. Clauzel, 1900, p. 601) claim that the banker Laffitte bought it for 6,000 francs on the second day of the exhibition, then concealed it from Sigalon in exchange for the *Amour captif* of the Salon of 1833. Others, such as Jeanron, a student of Sigalon who wrote about his teacher

as early as 1837, affirm that, on the contrary, the *Locusta* was left in the shop of the artist and that Laffitte came to buy it afterwards while Sigalon was working on his *Athalie* of 1827. He bought it to help the artist; but because his wife was unable, according to Jeanron, to bear "the sight of such a cruel scene," he returned the painting to Sigalon in exchange for another painting of Sigalon's choice. As early as 1829, in any case, Sigalon was negotiating with the mayor of Nimes for the sale of his *Locusta,* which was concluded effectively in May of the same year for 5,000 francs.

J. F.

Gérard van Spaendonck

1746 Tilburg - Paris 1822

Of Dutch origin (although Tilburg is in the Brabant not far from Antwerp), Spaendonck studied in Antwerp under Herreyns, then worked for a time in Breda as a painter-decorator, before journeying finally to Paris in 1770 (sone say 1768), where under Watelet's protection he rapidly earned a reputation as a painter of flowers and miniatures. In 1774, he became miniature painter to the King. In 1775, he was made *agréé* and in 1781, an academician. *Vase rempli de Fleurs,* his reception piece, transferred to the Louvre during the Revolution, was stored in the 19th century in the Ministry of the Interior (it was still there in 1879), but is lost today (Louvre INV. 1857). In 1781-1782, he succeeded Madeleine-Françoise Basseporte (who died in 1780) as draughtsman at the Jardin des Plantes (collection of the Vélins du Roi); in 1788 he was named consultant to the Academy, succeeding Quentin de La Tour. His position as a specialist was so well established that it was maintained during the Revolution, when he became administrator and professor of iconography at the Jardin des Plantes, which became the Museum of Natural History. In 1795, Spaendonck was appointed a member of the new Institute, for which he had been invited to draw up regulations. When François Gérard painted the portrait of the director Larevellière-Lépeaux (No. 67), former professor of botany, he naturally turned to Spaendonck. Towards 1800, his composition *Fleurs dessinées d'après nature* appeared and was engraved by P.-F. Legrand. From that time on, surrounded by pupils, laden with honors, one of the first to receive the Legion of Honor in 1804, designated a count in 1808, the celebrated painter lived out his life besieged with work. His portrait by Nicolas-Antoine Taunay is in Versailles.

He participated in the Salons at the Louvre from 1777 to 1796 while he also exhibited in 1779 at the Salon de la Correspondance. But few of the paintings shown at the Salons have been identified, except for the reception piece for the Academy (Salon of 1781) and the picture from Fontainebleau exhibited here (Salons of 1785 and 1787). However, one of the works exhibited in 1789 can possibly be identified with the *Fruits et Fleurs* dated from the same year, belonging to the Louvre (INV. 1855), a work which was unfortunately stored in 1931 at the French Embassy in Berlin and which disappeared during the last war (nevertheless, a splendid copy on porcelain executed in 1837 by Jacobber is in the collection of the Sèvres museum). Another work of Gérard Van Spaendonck, belonging to the Louvre, burned in the fire at Château de Saint-Cloud in 1870-1871 (INV. 1856; thus has it been with three out of four Spaendonck paintings at Sèvres since the inventory of Villot towards the middle of the 19th century... their eminently decorative qualities have served them rather ill !). At any rate, the work of Spaendonck is present in the celebrated collection of manuscripts of the Museum of Natural History and in that of such museums as Angers (although the signature may be that of his brother, Cornelis Van Spaendonck), Bagnères-de-Bigorre, Dunkirk, Montpellier, Épinal, as well as in the city hall of Tilburg.

As a teacher, he had a considerable influence, if only on Van Dael, who had himself buried near him in Père-Lachaise cemetery, Paris, and on P.-J. Redouté, his most famous pupils. Among many others, let us mention the names of Chazal, who painted the *Tombeau de Spaendonck* in 1830 (deposited in the museum of Tourcoing by the Louvre); Lesourd de Beauregard, Thérèse Baudry de Balzac, Adèle Riché, the Marquise de Grollier, Alexandre Véron, Pancrace Bessa, Jacobber, W. Van Leen, Henriette-Gertruida Knip, etc. The publication in 1826 by Chalons d'Argé of *Les Souvenirs de Van Spaendonck ou Recueil lithographiés d'après les dessins de ce célèbre professeur, accompagné d'un texte rédigé par plusieurs de ses élèves* constituted a veritable monument to his memory.

We must finally add a word about the brother of Gérard, Cornelis Van Spaendonck (1756 Tilburg-Paris 1840), who followed him to Paris and painted in a style very similar to that of his brother. He was made an academician in 1789. His reception piece, formerly preserved in the Louvre, also disappeared in Berlin (INV. 1858 while that of INV. 1859 was burned at Saint-Cloud in 1870-71). Today only one work remains in the Louvre, part of the gift to the museum by the Princesse de Croy in 1930. Cornelis Van Spaendonck was to work a great deal for the Sèvres factory (several of his paintings are still preserved there) and exhibited at the Salon from 1789 to 1833.

J. F.

168
Basket and Vase of Flowers

"Tableau représentant un piédestal d'albâtre, enrichi de bas-relief, sur lequel est posée une corbeille de fleurs, et à côté un vase de bronze"
or *Corbeille et vase de fleurs*
Plate p. 73
Canvas; 117 × 91; s.d.l.l. *G. Van Spaendonck. 1785*
Salon of 1785, no. 64
Fontainebleau, Musée National du Château

The painting was very much admired at the Salon of 1785, if we are to judge by the remarks collected by Deloynes; however, they confine themselves to tedious repetitions on the influence of Huysum. *Le peintre anglais au salon de peinture* (coll. Deloynes, no. 327) even considered that "Vanuisum [Huysum] whom he [Spaendonck] has carefully studied is moreover less dry and has a more varied touch." For comments on the naturalistic illusion and a comparison with examples from the antique such as Zeuxis and Parrhasius, see the *Discours sur l'origine, le progrès et l'état actuel de la Peinture en France* (coll. Deloynes, no. 324) or the *Promenade de Critès au Sallon* (coll. Deloynes, no. 353). "These types of work," according to *Minos au Salon ou la Gazette infernale* (coll. Deloynes, no. 345), "have reached the sublime heights of art. He [Spaendonck] is as elegant and varied in his subjects as he is delicate and certain in his touch. He paints nature; and nature, thus meticulously rendered, retains all its glory." Or again, according to the *Espion des peintres de l'académie royale* (coll. Deloynes, no. 337): "Here is an artist whose works confirm my opinion in this respect by his sensitive and triumphant effects of opposite things ! In truth, he limits himself to painting only flowers and inanimate objects; and in this genre, the painter attains the very limits of his art."

Even more interesting is the commentary of the *Ami des Artistes au Salon de 1787,* quoted by Faré (1962, I, p. 192), "If we examine the arrangement of the flowers, the elegance of their groupings, we are even more impressed by the beauty of their colors, of their nuances, and truthfulness and the art with which they stand out against the background. Several insects and droplets of water which we find there make the illusion complete. The low-relief of the marble and the vase in which the roses are set proclaim how familiar the artist is with antiquity." The comment of Faré: "Where then will the antique find a place ?", seems unnecessary. It is precisely in the contrast of vegetable and mineral, in the very careful treatment of what is living and what is not, in the very delicate and even light caressing all the elements of the composition that the great charm of this still life lies. One of the grandest and richest compositions ever conceived by Spaendonck, it is immediately apparent that it was a royal commission upon which the artist devoted much care. Considering the antique motifs, one could certainly compare this work with the picture formerly in the Guggenheim Collection (from 1887), sold at Christie's in London, 22 April 1966, ill. in the catalog), but the disposition of the elements is not as harmonious: the Fontainebleau painting seems indeed to be an exception in the usual production of the artist. It is this presence of the antique, visible in the tripod vase to the left, very typical of the neo-classicizing atmosphere of the time (can one reproach a painting for being of its time !), that confers a certain originality on the works of Spaendonck. (In this respect, it is difficult to distinguish, except in the case of a signed painting, between Gérard and Cornelis—whose very beautiful work, dated 1791 and featuring a neo-classical color scheme, is in the collection of the Musée Pescatore in Luxembourg.)

Even if most of the elements (the nest, the selection of flowers, the somewhat neutral background) are taken from Huysum whom Spaendonck often closely copied, there are significant differences. In Spaendonck the persistence of verticals, emphasis on sculptural details, decentralized composition—not massed in the center as Huysum would have done—the focus divided among several motifs spread out widely in opposite directions (two vases of roses and the lilacs at the bottom right) resulting in a static and almost ceremonious calm (similar to a large and very beautiful composition by Redouté; cf. Faré, 1962, color ill., p. 13), contrast with the still largely baroque and unified conception of Huysum, who bends and gathers his flowers into a massive spiral. In the neo-classical perspective the smooth finish and the illusionist rendering of objects (e.g. the admirable drops of water) can be seen more than the direct influence of Mignon, Ruysch and Huysum that contemporary critics blindly repeated. Rather we are presented with an original and genuine contribution, closer to Berjon, and subsequently, to Saint-Jean, than to Huysum; on the whole, like Van Dael and Redouté, Spaendonck's documentary, analytical style, his poetry drawn from the real, is more modern than that of Mme Vallayer-Coster, who was too attracted to Chardin, and to the charm of pictorial substances.

Many of the characteristics of this painting are shared by most of the northern flower painters of the 18th century, many of whom journeyed to Paris. Curiously, painters from Antwerp particularly perpetuated this "Dutch" post-Huysum tradition, like Van Dael, Eliarts, W. Van Leen, Redouté, C.-J.-C. Van Os (the son of Jan Van Os), and outside of France, smooth, clear painters like Paulus-Theodorus Van Brussel, Linthrost, Albertus-Jonas Brandt, Jan-Evert Morel and W. Hendricks.

PROVENANCE
Exhibited at the Salon of 1785 and acquired by Louis XVI in the same year, the picture is described in the catalog as being "for the King," but it was not immediately exhibited at the Salon, no doubt because the artist was still in the process of completing it, if we believe the *Journal de Paris* in coll. Deloynes (XIV, no. 350, p. 827); in the inventory of the Louvre compiled during the Restoration (INV. no. MR 2596), according to which the picture was already at Fontainebleau, but also appeared at the Ministry of the Interior. According to the account published in 1841, it was placed in the Château de Fontainebleau in the bedchamber of an apartment in the Louis XV wing; in 1869, the picture was hung in the passageway opposite the bathrooms of the great apartment; see Lossky, 1968, p. 132; (INV. no. INV. 1854).

EXHIBITIONS
1785, Salon, no. 64; 1787, Salon, no. 84.

REFERENCES
Coll. Deloynes, v. XIV, no. 325, p. 38-39; no. 327, p. 22; no. 331, p. 21; no. 337, pp. 27-28; no. 345, pp. 18-19; no. 348, p. 755; no. 350, p. 827; no. 353, p. 45; (Stanislas Koska, Count Potocki), *Lettre d'un étranger sur le salon de 1787,* p. 151 (*cf.* M.-H. Zoltowska, 1974); Notice des peintures... de Fontainebleau, 1841, no. 224; F. Engerand, 1901, pp. 499-500; M. Faré, 1962, v. I, pp. 191, 244 and note 928, p. 341; B. Lossky, 1968, pp. 132-133; P. Mitchell, 1973, p. 242, color ill. 322, p. 229.

J. F.

Joseph-Benoît Suvée

1743 Bruges - Rome 1807

For a century and a half, the name of Joseph-Benoît Suvée has most often been associated with his role as director of the French Academy in Rome. Today, however, historians, dealers and the interested public are rediscovering the artist, not only through his views of Italy; they are recognizing the important place

in the generation born between 1740 and 1750 accorded to Suvée by the official institutions and critics of his time.

Suvée was born in Bruges, in 1743 a part of the Austrian Netherlands. He received his early training there at the recently established Academy, modeled after the one in Paris. It preserved a definite activity in a declining artistic climate, in which French influence was tempered by a certain naïveté.

A recipient of the first prize in the three competitions of 1763, Suvée left the same year for Paris, where he was introduced to the atelier of Jean-Jacques Bachelier. He frequented the Royal Academy, competing for the Grand Prix in 1768 (when he obtained second prize), in 1769 and in 1771, when he won with his *Combat de Minerve et de Mars* (Lille, sketch in Rouen), surpassing Jacques-Louis David and Jean-Joseph Taillasson.

Before leaving for Rome, he carried out several commissions of religious subjects for the churches of Notre-Dame in Ypres, Saint-Germain-de-Charonne in Paris, Saint-Aubert in Cambrai and the Bishopric of Limoges. Arriving in Rome late in 1772, Suvée found the Academy under the direction of the aging Natoire in a state of crisis. It was only with the appointment of Joseph-Marie Vien in 1775 that the Academy again assumed its rightful place in Roman artistic life. Like the rest of his colleagues (Vincent, Bardin, Berthélemy, David, Taillasson, then Peyron and Regnault), Suvée was greatly influenced by the antiquarian current of the time. From his trips in the Roman environs, he brought back views in red chalk, and later in black chalk, in which a taste for ruins and the picturesque, derived from Hubert Robert, is combined with an archeological accuracy and an emphasis on monumentality inspired by Piranesi.

Returning to Paris in 1778, Suvée was made an associate member and then an academician in 1780. He exhibited at the Salon from 1779 to 1796, advancing regularly in his academic career until his election as director of the French Academy in Rome in 1792, a position which was soon afterwards abolished by the intervention of David. Imprisoned in 1794, Suvée recovered a position of honor in 1796, with his nomination to the board of directors of the Musée Central des Arts.

Suvée was finally able to take his position at the Academy in Rome at the close of 1801. He was responsible for moving the institution from Palazzo Mancini to the Villa Medici, and devoted himself with such energy and selflessness to the task that, praised by all his contemporaries for his devotion, he nevertheless completely neglected his painting in his later years.

Suvée's œuvre is divided between official commissions for the King and tapestry cartoons for the Gobelins factory (*La Vestale Émilie*, 1781, Louvre; *L'Été, ou la Fête à Palès*, 1783, Rouen); *Énée et Créuse*, 1785, Douai; *Death of Admiral de Coligny, Cornelia, Mother of the Gracchi* (Nos. 169-170). His decorative work for private individuals was less important, with the exception of the *Dibutade ou l'invention du dessin* in Bruges.

On the other hand, he was responsible for a notable production of religious work, very revealing of the evolution of his personality. In the cycle for Notre-Dame in Ypres, *Dévotion au Scapulaire* (church of Chambray), and the *Saint Denis* in Senlis, the artist created a vision characterized by a very simple presentation, an idealized image of his subjects and a serious and restrained level of emotion that foreshadows the religious painting of the mid-19th century.

Suvée was also a portraitist of a probing psychological intensity and the very numerous examples he painted are slowly coming to light. His smooth and dry execution, his great simplicity of composition, his preference for singular, dense combinations of colors, his often unusual subject matter and taste for emotional scenes, are typical of the period but are done with great restraint and are characteristic of this very attractive artist.

J.-F. M.

169
Death of Admiral de Coligny

"L'amiral de Coligny en impose à ses assassins"
Plate p. 80
Canvas; 325 × 260; s.d.l.r. *J. B. Suvée f. 1787.*
Salon of 1787, no. 16
Dijon, Musée des Beaux-Arts

Frappez, ne craignez rien, Coligny vous l'ordonne,
Ma vie est peu de chose et je vous l'abandonne,

J'eusse aimé mieux la perdre en combattant pour vous.
Ces tigres, à ces mots, tombent à ses genoux:

L'un saisi d'épouvante abandonne ses armes,
L'autre embrassant ses pieds qu'il trempe de ses larmes
Et de ses assassins ce grand homme entouré
Semblant un roi puissant par son peuple adoré...

The above verses are from the second canto of *L'Henriade—La Ligue ou Henry le Grand—poème de M. de Voltaire,* which appeared as early as 1723. Suvée chose to illustrate them as an example of the virtue and courage of a hero of France (see J.-S. Berthélemy, No. 2; N.-G. Brenet, No. 15, L.-J. Durameau, No. 55).

Gaspard de Coligny, born in 1517, was one of the most valiant officers under François I and Henri II. After the unfortunate siege of Saint-Quentin in 1557, which he courageously defended, he returned to his estate to live quietly and to study religious questions, which eventually led him to Protestantism. After Condé's death, the persecutions against Coligny's fellow Protestants encouraged him to become their leader, and in 1571 he drafted the treaty of Saint-Germain. On his return to Paris, he was wounded on 22 August 1572 by one of the men of the Duc de Guise. This was one of the reasons for the Saint Bartholomew's massacre two days later, of which Coligny was one of the most illustrious victims. Ambushed in his home near the Louvre by a group headed by Besme, Coligny was assassinated and his body, thrown out the window, was hung from the gallows of Montfaucon.

When religious tolerance was one of the most sought-after freedoms, it was not easy to illustrate such a theme. In the only official edition, which appeared in France in 1751, Eisen had illustrated the second canto of *La Henriade* by a scene foreshadowing the *troubadour style* in which one can see Henry IV relating to Elizabeth I of England (!) : "The story of the misfortunes of France goes back to their origin and recounts the details of the massacre of Saint Bartholomew." Both Jean-François de Troy (in the edition printed in London in 1728, whose plates were again used for the Amsterdam and Rouen editions between 1752 and 1779) and Gravelot (for the Geneva editions of 1768 and 1775) limited themselves to a massacre scene in a street where one can distinguish in the background a body thrown from a balcony. C.-N. Cochin, in 1750, was the first to show this episode in the dark of night, in a scene for *L'Abrégé chronologique de l'Histoire de France* by Président Hénault. He most probably inspired Charles Monnet, whose drawing does not seem to have been engraved (Paris, private collection); and Moreau the Younger, illustrator of the 1785 Kehl edition of Voltaire's works).

Joseph-Benoît Suvée probably knew of these earlier works, but was able to produce a more dramatic effect in his composition. Led by Besme, an armed band finds its way into the house on the Rue de Béthisy. The surroundings are not precisely depicted but the tiles and the architectural detail suggest a gallery leading to the private apartments of the Grand Admiral. This composition is divided into two groups on either side of a diagonal accented by a torch which clearly lights the scene and accentuates the contrasts between the masses and tints of the two sections. The Visitors to the Salon of 1787 were astounded by this lighting effect, popular in the 17th century, which was revived at the end of the 18th century by a taste for "dark" themes —death scenes, nocturnal visits to crypts and cemeteries, ghostly apparitions or descents into Hell (see F. Pupil, 1974). As early as 1783, Jean-Simon Berthélémy had exhibited *Maillard tuant Étienne Marcel,* which featured a bright torchlight effect. Nevertheless, critical articles of the time mention both the surprise caused by the *Death of Admiral de Coligny* and its success.

Critics, however, noted several compositional errors, in particular the hero's slightly stiff pose, so typical of Suvée. Some mocked the "Parisian bourgeois surprised in his nightshirt" (see coll. Deloynes, no. 376, p. 265), yet compared it to David's *Death of Socrates* (No. 32) or Taillasson's *Virgile lisant l'Énéide,* the *Death of Admiral de Coligny* already seems like a romantic statement. It is not really an exaltation of courage but rather, in a night scene reviving an episode of the national past, the evocation of a hero faced with a cruel and unjust destiny.

PROVENANCE

Commissioned by the Administration of Royal Buildings on 7 May 1786 *"pour le Salon de 1787"* and bought for 3,000 *livres* (Arch. Nat., O¹ 1931), Louis XVI Collection. Accepted as a cartoon for the Gobelins tapestries on 1 Sans-Culotides, Year II (17 September 1794). "The theme recalls all the horror evoked by fanaticism, intolerance, and the memory of Charles IX. This is a painting to be preserved for art's sake." In the Louvre reserves from 1809 to 1855; exhibited from 1855 to 1870, permanent loan to the Dijon museum in 1872 (INV. 465).

EXHIBITION

1787, Salon, no. 16.

REFERENCES

Coll. Deloynes, v. XV, no. 371, p. 94; no. 372, pp. 131-132; no. 373, pp. 154-155; no. 374, pp. 192-193; no. 375, pp. 234-

235; no. 376, p. 265; no. 378, pp. 307-309; no. 379, pp. 360-361; no. 381, pp. 409-410; no. 382, pp. 454-458; no. 384, pp. 517-518; no. 385, p. 542; no. 386, pp. 581-582; no. 387, p. 599; no. 389, p. 641; no. 390, p. 730; no. 394, pp. 755-756; no. 395, pp. 803, 806; no. 396, p. 825; no. 397, p. 870; no. 400, pp. 913-920; *Mercure de France,* September 1787, p. 170; *Journal de Paris,* 1787, pp. 1135-1136, 1191; Bachaumont, v. XXXVI [1787], pp. 357-359; J. Lebreton, 1807, p. 57; C.-P. Landon, 1808, v. I, pp. 16-18; N. Ponce, 1808 and 1826, pp. 4, 407; A. Jal, 1867, pp. 82-90, 1159; J.-J. Guiffrey, 1873, p. 112; mus. cat., 1883, no. 465;; Bellier and Auvray, 1885, v. II, p. 535; F. Benoit, 1897, p. 294; J.-J. Guiffrey, 1897, p. 365, no. 75; J. De Meyer, 1897, p. 16; F. Engerand, 1901, p. 448; M. Fenaille, 1903-1924; v. IV ,p. 372 and v. V, pp. 85-86; J. Guiffrey, 1910, p. 349;

L. Gillet, 1911, p. 181; *I.G.R.A.F.,* 1913, v. IV, p. 150; G. Brière, 1924, p. 337 (251); P. Bautier, 1953, p. 207; mus. cat., 1968, p. 75, no. 335; F. Pupil, 1974, p. 60 and n. 16.

RELATED WORKS
A framed sketch on canvas, 16 × 13 *pouces*, was part of the posthumous sale of the artist (Paris, 4-7 November 1807, no. 28). This painting was used as a cartoon for four Gobelins tapestries: the first, sold to Boursault in 1797, is most probably the one in Marble House, Newport, Rhode Island; the second, given to Murat in 1807 is preserved in Capodimonte, Naples; the third, given to Prince Wilhelm of Prussia in 1808, is now lost; and the last one remained the property of the Mobilier National in Paris.

J.-F. M.

170
Cornelia, Mother of the Gracchi *

"Cornélie, mère des Gracques"
Plate p. 139
Canvas; 318 × 420; s.d.b.l. J.B. SUVÉE P./L'*An 4, (1795.)*
Salon of 1795, no. 458
Paris, Musée du Louvre

"A woman from Campania, during a visit to Cornelia, ostentatiously displayed her jewels and attire. Invited to show off her own, Cornelia pointed to her children returning from the public school with their teachers and replied, 'Here are my riches and my loveliest ornaments'." Thus is this scene described in the catalog of the Year IV (taken from Valère-Maxime, Livre IV, chap. 4). The subject had earlier met with great success in the composition of Hallé (No. 96), shown at the Salon of 1779.

Suvée's painting was much noted at the time of its exhibition at the Salon, particularly for its volontary archaism: "Is the work finished? Is it merely sketched after Greek vases?" (Coll. Deloynes, v. XVIII, no. 473); "The disposition of this scene is wisely considered, the apparel, the nature of the fabrics, the character of the heads and of the architecture: all recall the manners, the habits, and the spirit of the ancient Romans" (ibid., no. 459).

The painting's extreme simplicity—especially striking because this work must have been painted for the Comte d'Artois, who had just commissioned the *Amours de Pâris et d'Hélène* from David—was well thought out and slowly achieved. The sober chromatism, seductive in its deliberate naïveté, is found again, in spite of the luminist effect, in *Dibutade, ou l'invention du dessin,* a roughly contemporary work. The version commissioned in 1791 (Bruges, Musée Grœningue) must be a bit later, probably commissioned by Boutin, kept by the artist, and exhibited at the Salon of 1793.

The studied archaism which Suvée displayed in these years—the last of his career as a painter, for we know nothing by him after 1797—leads to a sort of "primitivism" which was the doctrine of the "Barbus" surrounding M. Quay, so little known today. This tendency carried further characterizes the art of certain pupils of Ingres, of the Nazarenes, and even of the Pre-Raphaelites.

PROVENANCE
In a letter dated 27 May 1790, Suvée wrote to the Comte d'Angiviller: "I have a painting to do for the Comte d'Artois; circumstances force me to leave it roughly finished after having taken much trouble over the studies" (Paris, Arch. Nat. O¹ 1920, p. 66; O¹ 1914-1921); in another letter dated 3 June 1790, D'Angiviller asked the subject (*ibid.,* O¹ 1947,

p. 143); Suvée responded on 4 August: "A Campanian lady", cf. infra (*ibid.*, O¹ 1920, p. 85); on 8 April 1792 Suvée said that he hoped for the commission for the King and had reason to believe "that [he] would not be disappointed" (*ibid.*, O¹ 1925 b, p. 17); the 29 November 1792: "Statement of a painting commissioned by M. de Laporte, controller of the civil list, from M. Suvée, King's painter, and executed by him during the year 1791 and the first six months of 1792, such painting destined to be executed in tapestry at the Gobelins, 13 feet by 10 feet, representing Cornelia... estimated 6,000 livres ((*ibid.*, O¹2053); 11 messidor, an II (29 June 1794) "Citoyenne Suvez appears at the Conservatory of the National Museum of Art and announces that the painting of C^{en} S., her husband, is lodged in the Galerie d'Apollon..." (Arch. Louvre, P.V. du Conservatoire..., p. 41, no. 94); 11 September 1795, request for "a frame for the exhibition of a history painting which C^{en} Suvée is about to complete for the Republic "(*ibid.*, p. 6); chosen in 1799 to decorate the Council room of the 500 at the Palais-Bourbon; kept at the Louvre, but deposited in 1872 at the Musée de Bourges (INV. 812-1-6); returned to the Louvre in 1972 (INV. 8075).

EXHIBITION
1795, Salon, no. 458.

REFERENCES
Coll. Deloynes, v. XVIII, no. 469, pp. 401-402; no. 473, p. 563; J. Le Breton, 1807, p. 57; A. Michiels, 1854-1876, v. X, p. 511; J. Renouvier, 1863, p. 24; J.-J. Guiffrey, 1873, p. 132; Bellier and Auvray, 1885, v. II, p. 535; J. Guiffrey, 1897, p. 294; F. Engerand, p. XXXIV; M. Fenaille, 1903-1924, v. V, pp. 284-285; F. Boyer, 1935, p. 80; P. Bautier, 1945, p. 25; H. Bardon, 1963, p. 232; R. Rosenblum, 1967a, p. 62, note 42.

RELATED WORKS
Sketch very close to the exhibited work, but smaller in both dimensions (Paris, Private Coll.); this sketch on a paper-covered panel, 36 × 46, is clearly inferior to that on canvas which was part of the sale which took place after the artist's death (Paris, 4-7 November 1807, no. 26 - 17 × 22 inches). A markedly different version (Besançon, Musée) (131 × 196), seems to have come from the collection of P.-A. Pâris who took over the interim directorship of the Académie de France in Rome after Suvée's death; nevertheless this version does not appear in the *état des lieux* at the time of the death. It served as model for a tapestry woven at the atelier Cozette between 1804 and 1809 and placed in the Galerie de Diane at the Tuileries at the time of Napoleon's marriage to Marie-Louise in 1810. Offered to the Grand Duke of Wurtzburg on the occasion of the baptism of the King of Rome, it may be at Palazzo Vecchio in Florence (cf. M. Fenaille, op. cit.).

J.-F. M.

Jacques-François-Joseph Swebach

1769 Metz - Paris 1823

His father, a painter, sculptor, engraver, and mineralogist, taught him the elements of drawing. At a young age, he left his native province with his family for Paris. From whom, and by what influence, did he acquire his devotion to hunting and military scenes, affirmed in the years 1788 and 1791-93 (cf. the titles of paintings in the Salons)? It was certainly not from the portrait painter Joseph-Siffred Duplessis whose student he had been, according to André (author of the best article on Swebach, *G.B.A.*, 1904), since his arrival in Paris, but rather from Michel Hamon Duplessis, the excellent popularizer of Wouwermans. In his signatures, Swebach followed his name by "Fountein" or "Desfontaines" (French translation of his family name), fearing that the Germanic sound of Swebach would prevent him from attaining acceptance. The career of this artist was little based on official commissions; instead, he worked principally for individuals. However, he did receive a commission from Joséphine for Malmaison in 1800 (*Cavalcade et promenade en calèche*, Montpellier —at least in the museum catalogue, for such a painting does not appear in the inventory published by Grandjean). Named by Napoleon the chief painter at the Manufacture Nationale de Sèvres, he designed a great many patterns for cups, saucers, and plates (the services called encyclopedic of 1805 and 1810, the *Service de l'Empereur*, 1807-1810, the *Service Égyptien* of Wellington, 1812). It was not until 1821 that he finally received a commission from the Ministry of the Interior (*Paysage, Vue du Tyrol*, Salon of 1822, Lyon, Musée).

This relatively uneventful life filled with innumerable commissions was interrupted by travel in 1809 to the Tyrol, the Black Forest, and the banks of the Danube. Swebach also spent many years in Russia, having been called by Alexander I in 1815 to occupy the post of chief painter at the Imperial Porcelain Manufactory of

Saint Petersburg. From the long visits that he made to Russia each year until 1821, he brought back a considerable store of drawings and sketches which later found their places in numerous small paintings. One sees these sketches reappearing in the *Souvenirs de Russie,* an album of 24 lithographs published in 1822.

There are two directions characteristic of this artist, summarized by the critics' appelations: "the Wouwermans of his time" (Gault de Saint-Germain) and "Carle Vernet in miniature" (Charles Blanc). The stylistic distinction is arbitrary, but we can distinguish two levels of subjects. Certainly the Wouwermans of his era, Swebach delighted in depicting training schools, watering places, wayside stations and encampments, horse markets (a fine example in Metz), cavalry outposts, supply convoys, wagoners at the door of an inn, in short: military scenes. In the manner of the Dutch painter, all revolves around the horse, which plays an obligatory role in his work. As examples of the Dutch style one can cite *L'escarmouche* (Dijon), a masterpiece of vivacity and nervous energy, and *Le Camp du Prince de Condé à Saint-Omer en 1788* (Versailles, Musée, sketch at Cailleux). The pastiche of Wouwermans is even greater when Swebach gives Louis XIII uniforms to his cavaliers, as in *L'arrivée au Cabaret* and *Les Palefreniers* cited by Charles Blanc (referring to the Salon of 1812?). His paintings exhibited at the Salons were always greeted with favor by both the critics and the public. Swebach thus acquired a specialty and received many commissions. He was almost condemned to redoing the same pictures, so dependent was he on the money which those commissions brought (see the correspondance exchanged with Larcher de Saint Vincent, cf. the previously cited article by André.) The genre painter ventured now and then into landscape, as evidenced by the paintings shown in the Salons of the Year VI and VII and by the landscape *(Vue du Tyrol)* of the Musée de Lyon, cited above.

Elsewhere, this prolific artist lived the Revolution intensely. The spectacular events of the period gave him the opportunity to indulge his brilliant draughtmanship. His drawings were the source of many engravings and lithographs, illustrating the following albums: *Collection complète des tableaux historiques de la Révolution française, composée de cent-douze numéros en trois volumes,* 1802 (numerous drawings engraved by himself, by Pierre-Gabriel Berthault, or by the etcher Duplessis-Bertaux); *Campagne des Français sous le Consulat et l'Empire: Album de cinquante-deux batailles et cent portraits de maréchaux* (in collaboration with Carle Vernet). The wash drawing, engraved by Lecœur, that represents *La Fête de la Fédération* is justly regarded as one of the most reliable documents of that historic event. The *Journal* by Wille (ed. Duplessis, 1857, v. II, p. 259) confirms the scrupulous care taken by Swebach in the representation of revolutionary events. In addition to those previously mentioned, Swebach produced a quantity of drawings and engravings relative to this period, now in the Hennin Collection (Paris, Bibliothèque Nationale, Cabinet des Estampes). Desiring to be free of the commissions which forced him to repeat himself so often and wanting to be known as a history painter, Swebach at last conceived the ambitious project of representing the great victories of Bonaparte. Two paintings and a sketch of the *Bataille du Mont Thabor* justify the reputation of their creator at the Salon of 1802, but the critical response did not match his expectations. Swebach later painted a *Bataille de Rivoli,* a work long considered his masterpiece. His popularity was enormous by virtue of his technical perfection as well. One can give as an example the case of the city of Grenoble which wanted a work by Swebach for its museum: the inhabitants raised 4,000 francs in 1799 to buy a *Mort de Bayard.* The artist's specialty brought him into collaboration with other painters; he provided, for instance, the figures in certain landscapes of Bruandet or Georges Michel (*Défilé d'une armée,* 1797, by Swebach and Michel, private coll.).

The talent displayed by this contemporary of Taunay, Demarne, and Carle Vernet is that of an observer: the ability to group a great many persons on a single surface, the variety and vivacity of the figures, the extraordinary art of subordinating details to the general effect. This is all rendered by precise drawing, a fine touch, and a vivid coloring indicative of quick vision and able, rapid execution. The Salon critics noted as early as 1791 his skill in enhancing details, his sense of anecdote, which did not abandon or detract from the whole. To the lists of Vergnet-Ruiz/Laclotte and Thieme/Becker one can add three paintings—two hunting scenes and a delivery coach—in the Musée Nissim de Camondo, as well as two gouaches of military scenes and two paintings, including a *Château de la chaussée près de Bougival* of 1822 (Paris, Musée Marmottan). Swebach left a son, Bernard-Édouard (1800-1870), who produced some paintings and many lithographs (hunts, steeplechases, horse studies) in his father's style. Bernard also followed his father to Russia and collaborated with him on a number of watercolors.

A.-B. L.

171
Unloading of a Ferry Boat

Le Coche d'eau
Plate p. 226
Canvas; 53 × 67; s.l.l. *Swebach*
Private Collection

A formerly unpublished work, but characteristic in every respect of the precise and skillful manner of Swebach, this painting illustrates the artist's accurate and elegant brushwork, his delicate gray tones, his feeling for landscape and his careful execution, a style close to that of Jean-Louis Demarne and Louis-Léopold Boilly. Swebach more typically depicted military subjects (army convoys, skirmishes, cavaliers at rest), horse races, hunting scenes or horse fairs; he appears to have treated this subject less frequently. (In graphic work, we find only a *Bac transportant des chevaux,* a lithograph after Swebach by Godefroy Engelmann, published by Alphonse Giroux.) But *Unloading of a Ship* nevertheless contains all the elements of the artist's personal repertory, particularly his ability to set off to advantage the elegance of the white steed, like Philips Wouwermans, but a Wouwermans more sensitive to the neoclassical modeling of forms than to the quality of light or pictorial smoothness. Swebach was a realistic and incisive Wouwermans, like Kobell, almost to the point of naïveté (see Gerson, 1942, p. 115, who makes this interesting comparison between the two artists). Swebach was as adept as Boilly in describing the picturesque narrative detail of a village stopping place; the greetings of the villagers, the games of the children, the conversations of the small groups, the contrast of elegant travelers with the local inhabitants.

This work is difficult to date because of the lack of similar references in a rather repetitive œuvre, but from the appearance of the costumes, the painting can perhaps be placed around 1810-1820.

PROVENANCE
Acquired at an uncertain date, but apparently long ago, by the family of the present owner.

RELATED WORK
It should be noted that in the Salon of 1814 a *Débarquement de marchandises* was exhibited. Perhaps this was a comparable subject, but with such imprecise data one cannot attempt a definite identification.

J. F.

Jean-Joseph Taillasson

1745 Bordeaux - Paris 1809

Taillasson is among those artists whose talent came to light in a provincial school (cf. J. Locquin, 1912, pp. 135-136). He was admired by connoisseurs such as Lebreton and Bruun-Neergaard, but among many of his contemporaries was considered a minor artist compared to those of his generation like Ménageot, Vincent, Suvée, Peyron and, it goes without saying, David. His work, which has been only partially studied, in 1891 by Charles Marionneau and in 1921 by the Abbé Charles, must be re-examined; it is currently the subject of a thesis in preparation by J.-P. Mouilleseaux.

Briefly, his career can be resumed as follows: in 1764 he entered Joseph-Marie Vien's atelier. Failing twice in the competition for the Prix de Rome, he finally obtained only a third prize in 1769 with *Achille déposant le cadavre d'Hector aux pieds de celui de Patrocle.* In 1784, he was made an academician with his painting *Ulysse et Néoptolème enlèvent à Philoctète les flèches d'Hercule* (Blaye). He exhibited regularly at the Salon from 1783 to 1806; among his more important works are *La Naissance de Louis XIII* (1783, Pau, Musée du Château), *Virgile lisant l'Énéide à Auguste et à Octavie* (1787, recently acquired by London, National Gallery), *Sapho, ne pouvant se faire aimer du jeune Phaon, se précipite du rocher de Leucate* (1791, Brest), *Pauline femme de Sénèque rappelée à la vie* (1793, Blaye), *Timoléon à qui les Syracusains amènent des étrangers* (1796, Tours; sketch in Montauban), *Hero and Leander* (No. 172) and *Olympias* (1799, Brest). With the exception of the *Naissance de Louis XIII,* more in the tradition of the works of Nicolas-Guy Brenet, Taillasson's paintings are influenced by Vien, but transformed by a certain "tragic sentimentalism," a merit, according to Lebreton, that makes one forget the many inaccuracies of these theatrical compositions.

Taillasson was also a writer. He was responsible for the *Danger des règles dans les arts, poème suivi d'une traduction libre, en vers, d'un morceau du XVIᵉ chant de l'Iliade* (1781), a *Traduction libre des chants de Selma d'Ossian, suivi des Dangers des règles dans les arts* (1802), and especially *Observations sur quelques grands peintres dans lesquelles on cherche à fixer les caractères distinctifs de leur talent avec un précis de leur vie* (1807).

J. L.

172
*Hero and Leander**

"*Héro et Léandre*"
Plate p. 150
Canvas; 253 × 318; s.l.r. *Taillasson*
Salon of 1798, no. 383
Blaye, Musée

The Salon catalog explains: "Leander, a young man from Abidos, swam the Hellespont to go see Hero, the priestess of Venus. A torch lit at the top of a tower served him as guide. For a long while Love rewarded his efforts, but at last, just on the point of reaching the shores so dear to him, he met his death in the waves. Hero could not envision living on without him."

A study is soon to be published by Jean-Pierre Mouilleseaux (to whom gratitude must be expressed for his help in verifying the details of this text) on this subject so often treated by artists at the end of the 18th and the beginning of the 19th centuries. Taken from the Greek and Latin authors (Musaeus, Ovid, and Virgil), the theme inscribes itself in the tradition of the essential myth of the struggle of fire and water and at the same time in the tradition of the great civilizing myths. In fact, to recall Landon (1803, p. 115), "Each night Hero lit a torch which she placed at the top of a tower. Guided by this flare, which was, it is said, the first one ever raised, Leander crossed the sea."

Neo-classical in inspiration and even in certain stylistic details—the academic figure of Leander, for example—the picture is already romantic by virtue of its taste for drama which evokes certain frenetic passages in English gothic novels of the 18th century. It bears witness to the development of art in this period and more particularly to the evolution of the painter: one needs only go back to the sketch of 1796 where the gesture of Hero seems not desperate, but theatrical.

Leith (1965, p. 127) reminds us that this work was created for a competition. This contest, which deserves to be studied in greater depth, was established by the Committe for Public Safety in Floréal, Year II (May 1794) at the suggestion of Barère, influenced by David and Fourcoy (see J. Guillaume, IV, 1901, p. 259). After the report of Thibaudeau in the name of the Committee of Public Instruction, 9 Frimaire, Year III (29 November 1794, cf. *Le Moniteur Universel,* 2 December 1794, p. 632), the jury having met the 26 Frimaire, Year III (16 December 1794), the prizes were officially conferred the 14 Fructidor, Year III (31 August 1795). The rules of the contest specified that painters had to represent "the most important events of the Revolution." Taillasson chose as his subject *La Liberté ramène au peuple la Justice et la Vérité.* It seems, however, according to Leith, who refers to series F¹⁷ 1056 and F¹⁷ 1057 in the records of the Archives Nationales, that many painters, given the evolution of the political regime, changed subjects (notably the case with Garnier, No. 64, and Peyron, No. 140) and illustrated an episode of ancient history or mythology (seemingly without contemporary reference). Each of the winners of the competition were paid by the government in advance for the large compositions which they had to produce. Thus, Taillasson received 6,000 *livres*. Leith believed completely that the artists never executed the Revolution-inspired canvases and that the government went along with this.

A new reading of official documents, however, now that many works have reappeared, calls for more precision. The texts say, in effect, that after the competition" 22 artists have won second prizes, that is to say that each of them has to provide a painting of his own choice which is to be acquired in advance by the nation." The first-prize winners, Gérard and Vincent, were required to realize their sketches (respectively, *La Journée du 10 Août* and the *Héroïne de Saint Withier*). It seems logical to offer, in contradiction with Leith, the following hypotheses: on the one hand, the second prize winners, just like the 117 other contestants, were subsidized in their sketches of Revolutionary subjects, but the government, which had use for two, but not for 80 large works, seized the opportunity to encourage the best artists, in the hope of establishing an interesting collection for the country; on the other hand, might not the projects in many cases have been submitted as drawings (Gérard, for example)? According to this hypothesis, a sketch or a drawing which did not have a Revolutionary subject would not have been submitted to the contest (Garnier's *La Consternation de la Famille de Priam,* for example). The winning artists had only to profit from their money to realize long-planned larger works (Garnier) or concede before the results were announced; this, then, was the case of Taillasson, who did a sketch of *Hero and Leander* dated 1796.

Whatever the various hypotheses, Taillasson's painting was well received at the Salon and was even given a distinction by the National Institute (cf. Arch. Nat., F^{17} 1056 and 1057 [Leith, *op. cit.*] and Arch. Nat. F^{17} 1232, folder 11, p. 92). In the *Journal de Paris,* Lebrun included this painting "among the best" exhibited. The anonymous writer in *Mercure de France* wrote: "You well express what you wish to paint, Taillasson, and even though your coloring is weak, and even sometimes doubtful, you are a painter. Hero's crying is well done; the body of Leander leaves something to be desired. Some observers prefer the original sketch to the same work in the Salon." For Chaussart, in *Le Décadaire,* "This composition is beautiful and simple, but perhaps a little weak. It was not like this that the

Greek poet represented the drama. The corpse, says Musaeus, is torn to pieces by the points of the rocks. Hero sees this, throws herself from the top of the tower, and the two lovers are joined in death. There is talent here, Taillasson, make good use of it."

For the critic of the *Journal d'Indications,* "This one is a true painter who goes directly to the soul, moves all the senses, excites enthusiasm ! There are the responses caused by those who paint history: others with talent know only how to please the eyes, but the history painter is the only one worthy of transmitting to posterity the traits of the hero, to paint on canvas heroic actions and great virtues. The genius of Taillasson has this year offered to the public Leander and Hero, one of the most interesting subjects of antiquity. The element of gesture is good. There are, nevertheless, certain small reservations: Leander's coloring is not that of a young man, the shadows are too green and the highlights too gray. Hero suffers in the drawing; the right thigh intersects too high. The sea is not transparent."

In 1803, Landon remembered that the painting was "noticed by the public for its simplicity of composition and its truth of expression" and Bruun-Neergaard remarked a few years later that it was generally considered "one of Taillasson's best paintings."

PROVENANCE
Bought in advance by the government, 6,000 *livres ;* placed in the Corps Législatif in 1810; Louvre; sent to Albi in 1872, transferred to Blaye in 1952 (INV. : MR. 2500 - INV. 8080).

EXHIBITION
1798, Salon, no. 383.

REFERENCES
Arch. Nat., F^{17} 1056 and 1057 (cited by Leith, 1965, p. 127); *Arch. Nat.,* F^{17} 1232; coll. Deloynes, v. XIX, no. 534, p. 711; v. XX, no. 541, pp. 227-229; no. 539, p. 121; C.-P. Landon, 1803, pp. 115-116, ill. 54; T.-C. Bruun-Neergaard, 1809, p. 436; *ibid.,* 1810, p. 5; E. Bellemer, 1886, p. 727; J.-L. Charles, 1921, pp. 213-214; H. Bardon, 1963, p. 229; J.-A. Leith, 1965, p. 127.

RELATED WORKS
Engraved by C. Normand.
The Salon catalog of 1798 indicates: no. 384, *"same subject repeated."* Does this refer to a work (canvas; 40 × 30; s.d. 1796) which is in a private collection in Rennes? Or, more likely to one in a Parisian private collection (canvas; 32 × 40, s.l.l.) ? Was this the repetition that Taillasson proposed to do for 600 *livres* to the President of the Society of Friends of Art of the Louvre, 2 Vendémiaire, Year VII (23 September 1798), as a letter published in the *Nouvelles Archives de l'Art Français* in 1872, p. 430, seems to prove,

and which must have been won on 30 Prairial, Year IX (19 June 1801) by the older Lebarbier (see *Le Journal des Arts, des Sciences et de Littérature,* no. 139, 5 Messidor, Year IX)?

There is an important drawing (black chalk with white highlights) in a private collection in Detroit. According to a letter by Taillasson (cited by Charles), his painting was noticed by the director of the Gobelins Manufactory who wanted to make a tapestry of it. M. de Fleurieu, of the State Council, was responsible for asking the opinion of the Emperor. Apparently, the go-ahead was never given to this project.

J. L.

Nicolas-Antoine Taunay

1755 Paris 1830

Son of a chemist, enamel painter at the Manufacture Nationale de Sèvres, Taunay entered Lépicié's studio at age thirteen. He later studied under Brenet and finally with Casanova, whose influence on him was great. He was encouraged by Fragonard, who reportedly bought his first canvas. With his friends Demarne, Bidauld, Bruandet, and Swebach, he executed landscape studies in the forests of Fontainebleau, Saint-Germain, and Compiègne. As skillful at portraying persons as landscapes, he often garnished his friends' compositions with little figures. In 1776, Taunay traveled to the Dauphiné and Switzerland with Demarne. The same year, he illustrated with vignettes the *Journée de l'Amour* of Favart, the Countess Turpin de Crissé, Boufflers, Guillard, and Voisenon. He showed landscapes at the Salon de la Jeunesse (1777, 1779) and at the Salon de la Correspondance (1782). In 1784, Taunay was accepted in the Academy, but he never became a member. The same year, on the recommendation of Vien and Pierre, he obtained a grant to study at the Academy in Rome. He did not win the prize, but took the place left vacant by the death of Jean-Gustave Taraval. Returning to Paris, he exhibited at the Salon de l'Académie in 1787. From then on, until 1827, his works were shown regularly at the Salon. In 1788, Taunay married Joséphine Rondel, the daughter of an architect and niece of the miniaturist Dumont. They had five sons. During the Terror, the artist took refuge in Montmorency. He was named to the Institute at its inception, in 1795. He illustrated *Les Plaideurs* for Didot's great edition of Racine in 1801 (engravings by Duval; the original gouaches were part of the Goncourt collection). Beginning in 1806, the artist worked for the Manufacture de Sèvres, but under the Empire he received commissions chiefly for battle pictures. The Empress Josephine was highly appreciative of his talent and Taunay was part of her intimate circle. After the fall of the Empire, Taunay was invited by the Portugese ambassador in Rio de Janeiro, along with the sculptor Auguste Taunay, his brother, the architect Grandjean de Montigny, the engraver Charles Pradier, and the musician Neucom, to help set up an Academy of Fine Arts. The painter left for Brazil with his family in January, 1816. He stayed there five years. He finished a great number of paintings, mostly for the royal palaces, but returned to France after much disillusionment in 1821. He regained his position at the Institute and ended his career covered with honors.

Taunay's extensive output consisted mainly of landscapes enlivened with small, brilliantly improvised figures (*Quatremère de Quincy,* 1837, p. 60). He favored pictures of Dutch flavor (parades, jugglers, carnivals, charlatans, concerts), usually of small format and often painted on wood. He also treated biblical, mythological, historical, or religious subjects, with the same narrator's enthusiasm and the same convincing charm. He was capable of striking portraits as well (*Portrait d'un enfant* and *Portrait de Félix-Émile Taunay,* Rio, Museum; *Portrait de Van Spaendonck,* Versailles). Forced into large format by the number of commissions he received for battle pictures under the Empire, Taunay proved he could rise above anecdote to paint lyrical and imposing compositions (these canvases now at Versailles).

Taunay, for his contemporaries the "La Fontaine of painting, the Poussin of small pictures" (Notice..., 1831, p. 8), is more than a charming entertainer; he deserves to be reconsidered as one of the great painters of his time.

J.-P. C.

173
French Army Crossing the Saint-Bernard Pass

L'Armée française passant le mont Saint-Bernard
Plate p. 201 and color pl. p. 23
Canvas; 183 × 163
Versailles, Musée National

The painting represents an episode from the crossing of the Saint-Bernard pass by the French army in 1800, in particular the extremely dangerous descent of the troops toward the Piedmont on 20 May through snow, crevices and gulfs. A wounded soldier is seen being attended by a mountain family. This painting cannot be identified, as it generally has been (E. Soulié, pt. II, 1881, no. 1696; Ch.-O. Zieseniss, 1970, p. 41), with a *Passage des Alpes par le Général Bonaparte* exhibited by Taunay in the Salon of 1801 (no. 334). The description of the latter in the *Moniteur* of 14 September 1801: "...General Bonaparte on horseback encourages with a look a soldier carrying one of the wheels of the cannon, who wipes the perspiration from his brow..." establishes clearly that this was not the Versailles canvas. The painting exhibited here was actually an overdoor commissioned in 1808 for the Galerie de Diane in the Tuileries, along with three other paintings by Adolphe-Eugène Roehn, Hippolyte Lecomte, and Charles Thévenin (Ch.-O. Zieseniss, 1966). The four works, commissioned in the spring, were in place by December, and the rapidity of execution perhaps explains the lively and decisive brushwork of Taunay's painting. Its destination as an overdoor explains the very readable character and strong contrasts of the work.

The painting suggests the winter landscapes of César Van Loo and Louis-Jacques Daguerre (Nos. 184 and 25). Taunay, elsewhere a charming storyteller and lively colorist, here presents us with an austere and simply constructed work with strong value contrasts in a stark grisaille of cold grays set off by the orange tones of the fire, its warm reflections on the assembled figures and the rising brown smoke. The large scale of the figures is also unusual for Taunay, as are the free and rapid execution and the lively impasto.

PROVENANCE
See above; at the Palais du Luxembourg during the Restoration; sent to Versailles in 1822; in Saint-Cloud from 1831 to 1833; returned to Versailles in 1833.

REFERENCES
Gavard, *Galeries historiques,* IV, no. 799; E. Soulié, cat., pt. II, no. 1696; Ch. O. Zieseniss, 1966, pp. 201, 213-214; *idem,* 1970, p. 41; Y. Cantarel, 1973, p. 640.

J.-P. C.

174
*Entry of the Imperial Guard into Paris**

"*Entrée de la Garde Impériale sous l'arc de triomphe érigé en son honneur, sur l'emplacement de la barrière de Pantin*"
Plate p. 209
Canvas; 182 × 221
Salon of 1810, no. 755
Versailles, Musée National

At the close of the Prussian Campaign (1806-07), the Imperial Guard received a triumphant welcome from the Parisians. Here Taunay represents the Guard's entry into Paris, with Marshal Bessières at the head, at the Pantin gate on 25 November 1807. The guard is received by the Town Council led by Frochot, préfet of the Seine *department*. A gigantic banquet for the entire army on the Champs-Élysées followed.

The elements of the decor are placed with precision: in the background one recognizes the Villette gate by Ledoux. The triumphal arch was a temporary structure erected for the occasion by the Parisian municipality. The Emperor, driving a chariot with six horses, dominates the monument ornamented with trophies and the names of victories of the Great Army: Berlin, Jena, Danzig; two inscriptions proclaim : *The Emperor has said: Soldiers, I am proud of my great army* and *Soldiers, you will return to your homes only under triumphal arches.* One notices show closely the architecture of this arch resembles that at the Etoile, the construction of which was just about to begin (see Gaehtgens, 1974, for Napoleonic triumphal arches). Taunay satisfied a difficult commission with aplomb. He could not resist putting the animated Parisian street crowd into the foreground, letting his thick but nimble touch pick out the elements of anecdote and pictorial charm: robust young people, plump infants, the entire colorful and joyous world dear to the artist. This is quite different from the world of Boilly, always finer, more delicate, and aristocratic. In spite of the number of persons, in spite of the different scenes and centers of interest, Taunay wisely established a hierarchy of lighting effects, placing the foreground crowd in shadow broken by some bursts of light, lighting the military parade and urban landscape more clearly, unifying the whole with a vast and admirable sky dappled with grey clouds. The only half-sunny character of the scene is accurately depicted; elsewhere a sudden shower descends and the background is flowered with the umbrellas of spectators.

PROVENANCE
Part of the sale of works following Taunay's death, Paris, 28 February-1 March 1831, no. 5, with this note, "worthy of embellishing a gallery or a public establishment"; unsold, it remained in the possession of the artist's widow; acquired by Louis-Philippe in 1835 from the widow; Louvre (INV. 8126); Musée de Versailles.

EXHIBITIONS
1810, Salon, no. 755; 1900, Paris, Grand Palais, no. 631.

REFERENCES
Gavard, *Galeries...*, 1842, no. 988, p. 789; T. Lejeune, v. I, 1864, p. 389; F. Benoît, 1897, p. 348, note 1; A.-E. Taunay, 1912 p. 94; A.-E. Taunay, 1956, pp. 145-146, 200, 210; C.-O. Zieseniss, 1970, p. 98; Y. Cantarel, 1973, v. II, pp. 653-654.

J.-P. C.

175
Sermon of Saint John the Baptist[*]

"Paysage, site du Brésil," also called *La prédication de saint Jean-Baptiste*
Plate p. 255
Canvas; 95 × 147; s.d.l.c. *Taunay / Rio de Janeiro / 1818*
Nice, Préfecture

Taunay painted this during his stay in Brazil. A letter dated 10 November 1818 from Quatremère de Quincy, the permanent secretary of the Academy, to the Count of Pradel indicates that the artist wanted to offer it to Louis XVIII: "a view of the country where the artist lives provides background and accessory" (Arch. Nat. o³ 1398). A document dated 11 December 1818 reveals that the King declined and that the painting was sent back to the museum, to be bought by the institution if the Comte de Pradel thought it good (Arch. Nat. o³ 1400). Shown at the Salon of 1819, the canvas was finally bought by the King for 3,000 francs (record of payment of 21 March 1820, Arch. Nat. o³ 1405).

Taunay painted many landscapes in Brazil. Two entitled *Vue de Rio de Janeiro du Largo da Carioca* (1816) are in the museum in Rio. In the present work, the painter, probably resuming direct studies from nature, sets the religious scene in a large fluvial landscape. Certain of the small figures are perhaps taken from popular Brazilian types. The work thus provides a curious and new exoticism, in which the biblical subject is merely an accessory.

The taste for large landscape unified by light evokes Joseph Vernet, the first master of this technique; reminiscenses of Casanova, Taunay's teacher, are also seen. However, the taste for anecdote, the finesse of execution, and the attention paid to the quality of light bring to mind, above all, certain landscapes with animals by Berchem or Dujardin. Once again the artist's admiration for the Dutch masters is affirmed.

PROVENANCE
Bought by Louis XVIII in 1820; Musée du Louvre (INV. 8116); sent to the Préfecture in Nice in January, 1867 (Arch. Louvre, 3 DD 22, p. 8).

EXHIBITION
1819, Salon, no. 1062.

REFERENCES
T. Lejeune, 1864, p. 389; A. Jal, 1867, p. 1177; A.-E. Taunay, 1912, pp. 115-116; G. Brière, 1924, p. 339; A.-E. Taunay, 1956, p. 169.

J.-P. C.

Louis-Rolland Trinquesse

c. 1746 Paris - ? c. 1800

A student at the Royal Academy in 1758, Trinquesse journeyed to The Hague in 1767 and on his return to Paris, set himself up as a genre and portrait painter. Unsuccessful in his attempt to become an academician, he exhibited at the Salon de la Correspondance in 1779, 1782, 1785, 1787 and in the Revolutionary Salons of 1791 and 1793.

His portraits, *Une jeune femme* (1777, Louvre), *Un jeune garçon* (1777, Amiens), *Portrait de l'abbé Gentil* (1783, Bagnols-sur-Cèze), and particularly, his genre scenes, *Le Serment à l'Amour*, *L'Offrande à Vénus* (1786, Dijon), *Femmes et enfants dans un parc* (1789, Louvre) are in the gallant and bourgeois tradition of J.-F. Schall and

L.-J. Watteau and prefigure, by their smooth, porcelain-like finish and by the satiny treatment of draperies and fabric, the slightly later work of Marguerite Gérard and Louis-Léopold Boilly.

Trinquesse is equally well-known for his drawings: some in charcoal (examples in Valenciennes) and in watercolor, *Femmes et enfants dans un parc* (Paris, Musée Carnavalet; study for a painting in the Louvre) but most often boldly worked in red chalk: *Portrait de Joseph Vernet* (1771), *Portrait du peintre Jean-Urbain Guérin* (Paris, Musée Carnavalet), *L'atelier de dessin* (acquired in 1974 by the Dijon museum).

J.V.

176
Portrait of an Architect

Portrait de l'architecte Jacques-Denis Antoine
Plate p. 138
Canvas; 131 × 96; s.d.l.l. *L.R. Trinquesse p^tx En 1794*
Paris, Private Collection

For many years considered to be the portrait of the architect Victor Louis, this painting was most recently identified as the portrait of Jacques-Denis Antoine (1753-1801), architect of the Hôtel de la Monnaie and the Salle des Pas-Perdus in the Palais de Justice, Paris. It was published as such in the French edition of this catalog.

Monique Mosser and H. Blanc, however, have

brought to our attention the fact that in 1794 Antoine was in prison and that it would seem quite unlikely for him to have had his portrait painted at that time, one, moreover, so grand and so striking in its stylistic freedom and bravura. One must also note that the architecture featured on the left seems quite different from Antoine's, the doorway crowned by an archway having no counterpart in what is known of his work. Finally, the resemblance between the subject of this portrait and that of Antoine engraved by L.-S. Lempereur not being entirely convincing, we must withdraw our previous identification. Jean Cailleux (written communication) has suggested that this painting might be the portrait of the architect Louis Lemit, who was very active during the Revolution (see J. Wilhelm, 1974, ill. p. 63). In any case, the exact identity of the sitter can only be made definite when the architecture represented here is identified. J. V.

PROVENANCE
Albert Laurans Collection; Laurans sale, Paris, Hôtel Drouot, room 6, 18-19 March 1927, no. 43; Armand Sigwalt Collection.

EXHIBITIONS
1932, London, no. 596; 1969, Dijon, no. 54, ill. XIX.

REFERENCES
Thieme and Becker, XXXIII, 1939, p. 404; J. Wilhelm, 1974 (in press).

J. V.

Lancelot-Théodore Turpin de Crissé

1781 Paris 1859

Descended from a famous Anjou family, Turpin de Crissé's grandfather and father were officers in the royal army; the latter was also an artist, who exhibited several paintings and drawings of Roman landscapes in the Salon of 1787, and guided his son at the outset of his artistic career. One of the elder Turpin de Crissé's paintings, *L'Arc de Triomphe de Janus à Rome,* is preserved in the Turpin de Crissé museum in Angers. Little is known about the life of Lancelot-Théodore before 1800. Did he follow his father as an émigré to England (according to Deville, author of a biographical sketch written in 1846 during the lifetime of the artist) or remain in France during these difficult times (according to Bellier and Auvray)? It appears that the lack of financial resources (since the elder Turpin de Crissé had emigrated, his family was automatically ruined), forced Lancelot-Théodore to abandon his amateur status, the man who "had formerly applied himself to painting as a form of relaxation" (Deville). It was at that moment that the celebrated Choiseul-Gouffier (diplomat and archeologist; he preceded Lord Elgin to the Acropolis) financed the young Turpin de Crissé's studies in Switzerland (1803), and subsequently in Rome (1807-08). He also commissioned a number of paintings from the artist. His first entries to the Salon of 1806 *(Les Adieux de René à sa sœur* and *Vue du temple de Minerve à Athènes)* earned him a gold medal as a painter of landscape and architecture.

On his return to France, Turpin de Crissé was favorably received by the court of Napoleon: protected by Queen Hortense, the young painter had the satisfaction of seeing the Empress Josephine buy *Vue prise à Civita Castellana,* a work he had exhibited at the Salon of 1808. The Queen of Naples and Prince Eugène acquired his paintings, and he was even appointed Chamberlain to Josephine in 1809, a position he retained until her death in 1814. During his tenure, he accompanied the Empress on a voyage to Savoy and Switzerland in 1810. He returned with an album of 33 sepia drawings, completed during the journey (Malmaison museum, see the 1935 publication of J. Bourguignon). Many, such as *Prison souterraine de Chillon* and *Cloître de l'abbaye de la Lence, Intérieur d'une chapelle dans l'abbaye d'Hautecombe*, display a delightful *troubadour* feeling.

One of the pictures sent by the artist to the Salon the same year, *Vue de Suisse: dans le Valais* (Boulogne, Bibliothèque Marmottan), has a beautiful decorative quality and a delicate harmony of color, which is almost too pale. Many of his works were selected to decorate the apartments of the Palais Royal: *Vue d'Alexandrie, Vue du Panthéon, Vue du château de l'Œuf à Naples* (Salon of 1819, lithograph in the Galerie of the Duc d'Orléans), *Halte de Voyageurs sur les ruines de Palmyre.*

The Restoration overwhelmed Turpin de Crissé with honors, since Charles X held this Royalist in great esteem. He was named an independent member of the Academy of Fine Arts on 6 April 1816 and subsequently a member of the board of the Fine Arts for the prefecture of the Seine, and of the royal museums; in 1824, he was associated with the King's household as inspector general of Fine Arts (a position he relinquished in 1830) and honorary gentleman of the King's Chamber.

He exhibited regularly at the Salon until 1835 and even participated in 1832 in an exhibition at the Royal Academy in London, sending four paintings. From 1835 on, Turpin devoted himself to his collection, which on his death in 1859, he bequeathed to the city of Angers. It was installed somewhat later in the Hôtel Pincé, a surprising and delightful connoisseur's assemblage recalling the previous century's collections of curios: Egyptian and Greek sculpture, Etruscan and Roman mementos, Italian statues, antique jewelry, alongside of paintings (among which Ingres' celebrated *Francesca et Paolo*, the most "gothic" of his works, whose neo-gothic frame was executed by Chenavard following Turpin's instructions) and drawings, especially the "moderns" Gérard, Girodet, and Percier.

Of the various paintings, exclusively historical landscapes, that Turpin exhibited in the Salons, few have been recovered. To the already cited works, we can add a *Vue prise à Florence sur le Ponte Vecchio* (s.d. 1811; Salon of 1812; stored at the Ministry of War in 1944 by the Louvre), *Le Chasseur de l'Apennin* (Salon of 1822; placed in the Musée d'Angers by the Musée du Louvre), and *Vues des environs de Naples* (same Salon, perhaps the two pictures in the Cologne museum). In addition, the works of Turpin de Crissé are to be found at La Roche-sur-Yon (*Paysage montagneux dans la région de Naples*; s.d. 1841; acquired in 1974 by the Galerie du Fleuve in Paris as *Paysage dans les Dolomites* [sic], no. 25 in the exhibition *Aspects du paysage néo-classique en France de 1790 à 1850*, Paris, Galerie du Fleuve, ill. in the catalog; the landscape is an obvious repetition of one of the two views in Cologne); at the Finance Ministry in Paris (a *Torrent* and a *Paysage avec des daims*, bequeathed to the Louvre by the artist in 1859 and installed shortly before 1879). At Gray is *Le Vésuve* (1827); another at La Roche-sur-Yon, *Cascade dans les Pyrénées* (preparatory drawing at the Musée Magnin in Dijon); at Lisieux, two *Études d'arbres* (1830-31); at Marseille, *Vue de Roquebrune* (1831); at Montargis, *Vue de Venise*; in Nantes, *Ferdinand I à Venise* (1838-48); at Saint-Germain-en-Laye; and finally and especially at Angers are *Bacchanale* (1834), *Intérieur de la Chapelle privilégiée de Saint-Marc de Venise* (1839), *Extérieur de Santa Maria dell'Orto à Venise* (1839), *Intérieur de la Chapelle de Mascoli à Venise* (1840), *Santa Maria dei Miracoli à Venise*, *Ruines* and numerous drawings. We must point out, finally, a very important collection of drawings in the Louvre, and several single pages in Aix-en-Provence, Dijon, Montargis, Orléans, and Nantes. Turpin was also active as a lithographer. In 1826, he published *Souvenirs du golfe de Naples* (39 plates) and *Souvenirs du vieux Paris, exemples d'architecture de temps et de style divers* (30 plates) in 1835.

In 1834, Turpin de Crissé wrote: "It is my duty to acknowledge that the study of my art took up the greater part of my youth and that, in spite of my enthusiasm, I have never been able to make up for what I lacked. I love and respect the sciences, but know little of them. Old mementos charm me, I draw ancient monuments, collect medals, some bronzes and antique vases, but it is only in their relationship to the art of drawing that these objects are precious to me. I have only a vague and general idea of their past history, and no research nor critical appreciation" — a much too modest confession that endears us to the landscape artist and collector.

A.-B. L.

177
Landscape

Paysage avec bestiaux sur une route
Plate p. 195
Canvas; 48 × 65; S.d.l.r. *T. Turpin. 1806.*
Paris, Musée Marmottan

Curiously omitted from the catalog published by d'H. Lefuel in 1934 (the only one which attempts to be exhaustive), this painting is correctly attributed to Turpin de Crissé and Jean-Louis Demarne: Turpin for the landscape, Demarne for the figures and for his admirable preciseness. This is yet another case of collaboration between Demarne and other artists. Completely signed and dated, the work is a rare document on the pictoral activity of Turpin de Crissé, which remains obscure. Certainly this is true of the early work. We know almost nothing of Turpin's training or of his first Salon pictures. We have nothing before 1810 (*Paysage dans le Valais,* Bibliothèque Marmottan) and 1811 (*Vue prise à Florence sur le vieux pont,* kept at the Louvre, Ministry of the Armies since 1944, Salon of 1812). From 1810 also dates the album of a voyage to Switzerland and Savoy (Malmaison, Musée), which furnishes useful points of comparison with the present realist view. By virtue of their motifs taken from direct observation of nature, the views of Switzerland register in the same realist bearing and are as non-Italianate as the view presented here, some countryside of the Ile-de-France or even of Switzerland. Turpin's trip to Switzerland (1803) marked him at the beginning of his artistic career. One remembers the fruitful journey made to Switzerland in 1780 by Demarne. The taste for crude greenery, the subtlety of observation, joined to an esthetic of fine and precisely rendered light (already that of the Italianized Dutch from Dujardin to Velde, from Pynacker to Moucheron, but singularly revivified by the neo-classical tendencies of one such as Boissieu) strongly recalls the art of V. Bertin, Bidauld, and Demarne. The contribution of Turpin de Crissé, at first glance unexpected, but therefore all the more interesting to notice, is to this type of landscape at once classical and realistic.

PROVENANCE

Coll. Paul Marmottan (1856-1932), joined with his collections at the Institut de France which form today the Musée Marmottan in Paris, opened in 1934, and the Napoleonic Bibliothèque Marmottan at Boulogne-sur-Seine. On the collector Marmottan, cf. H. Lefuel, introduction to museum catalog, 1934, and P. Fleuriot de Langle, 1938, pp. 227-249.

J. F.

Pierre-Auguste Vafflard

1774 Paris 1837

Vafflard was a student of J.-B. Regnault. From 1800 to 1831, he exhibited a wide variety of paintings at the Salon. The most successful are his early *troubadour* paintings: *Emma et Eginhard* (Salon of 1804, Évreux, ill. in R. Monsaldy, n.d.); *Le gouverneur de Château-de-Raudon déposant les clefs de la place près du lit de mort de Du Guesclin* (Salon of 1806, Rennes; clearly inspired by Nicolas-Guy Brenet's painting of the *Death of Du Guesclin,* here No. 15); *Le Chien de l'hospice* (Salon of 1810, Arenenberg). Vafflard also illustrated contemporary events such as *La colonne de Rosbach renversée par l'armée française* (Salon of 1810, Versailles), as well as classical subjects such as *Electre* (Salon of 1814, Dijon), *Le Sommeil d'Oreste* (1819, Dijon), and *Pythagore inspiré par les muses* (Salon of 1819, Dijon).

During the Restoration, Vafflard developed a second *troubadour* style and did large paintings of national and religious subjects. In this vein, should be noted in particular *Saint Ambroise sauvant un prêtre de la fureur du peuple* (Salon of 1819, for the Church of Saint-Am-broise), *La Mort de Saint Louis* (Salon of 1819, for the Chapelle de Dreux), *Henri IV à Notre-Dame le jour de son entrée à Paris* (Salon of 1819, Pau), *La Dernière Bénédiction de Mgr Bourlier, évêque d'Évreux* (Salon of 1824, Évreux). Vafflard's late works—e.g. his *Le Repos* (Évreux, possibly a work called *La Paresseuse* and exhibited at the Musée du Luxembourg in 1830) and *L'Attente* (Évreux, possibly *L'Adieu* of the Salon of 1831)—seem to have been influenced by the romantic style of Eugène Devéria.

Vafflard was soon forgotten (only Rosenthal, 1900, mentioned him), no doubt because he was too susceptible to every fashion. This seems unfortunate, since his diverse work provides an instructive guide to the artistic evolution of an entire period—reason enough to warrant a monograph on this artist, since the catalogs from the sales of his work in 1832 and 1837 are far from adequate.

J. L.

178
Young and his Daughter

"*Young et sa fille*"
Plate p. 189
Canvas; 242 × 194
Salon of 1804, no. 467
Angoulême, Musée National

The catalog of the Salon of 1804 described the painting in this way: "Young with his dead daughter in his arms cries out in bitter grief: *O zèle barbare et haï d'un dieu bienfaisant ; ces hommes impitoyables ont refusé de répandre de la poussière sur une poussière*" from the *Quatrième Nuit* (Fourth Night). This extract is a portion of the celebrated poem *Nuits (Night Thoughts)* written by the English poet Edward Young (1683-1765). At the end of the 18th century, critics and readers were engaged in a running discussion of Young's poem: did Narcissa, the dead heroine, ever exist? If the story was true, where did it happen? And when?

Many legends grew up. In a recent article (1967) J. Murard wrote a history of them and offered the following as a probable version of the story. The poem was based on a very real occurrence. While on a trip to France with his family, Young's step-daughter, Elizabeth Temple, died in Lyon on 8 October 1736 at the age of 18 years. Because she was a Protestant, burial in a Catholic cemetery was denied. Permission was granted for burial (at night?) in the cemetery of the Swiss colony adjacent to the Hôtel-Dieu. The burial site was subsequently disturbed, but the black marble tomb plaque still survives in a corridor in the old Hôtel-Dieu.

The intensively dramatized account of the event struck the imagination of those contemporary with the period and no doubt inspired Chateaubriand to write the story of the death of Atala. Such were the sensibilities of the times. In 1800, Guillon-Pastel wrote: "There is pleasure in the memory of that which one has lost and the tears one sheds have an agreeable charm. This sweet melancoly... eases our thoughts of destrucion. It is this condition of the soul that gives rise to the poetry of Gessner, the *Nuits* of Young, the *Poèmes* of Ossian, and in reading them we find a source of tender thoughts that have their pleasure."

In Vafflard's painting, which is distantly related to the frontispiece drawn by Marillier for the second volume of Le Tourneur's edition of 1769, Vafflard succeeded in making his pair of figures, despite their academic qualities, seem realistic. We are today aware of certain deliberate devices used by Vafflard, for example the monochromatic coloring. At the time, the modernism of the painting was startling (putting aside A.-J. Gros' painting [No. 87], P.-N. Guérin's painting of *Clytemnestre* with its dominant reds was not done until 1817).

The reviews were harsh. One has only to read the critiques of the *Journal de la Décade*, the *Journal du Publiciste* and Voïart. Séraphin composed his comments to the tune of *Au clair de la lune:* "*Au clair de la lune/ Les objets sont bleus/ Plaignons l'infortune/ De ce malheureux/ Las ! sa fille est morte/ Ce n'est pas un jeu/ Ouvrez lui la porte/ Pour l'amour de Dieu*" (1804, pp. 5-6). And Landon wrote: "Paternal suffering is expressed with a certain energy; but the two figures need not have the same coloring, and in Young's case it is unnatural. The effects of moonlight have not been captured; never has the light of this heavenly body cast on objects the green tone that spreads through every part of this painting. Certainly one should not try to create harmony at the expense of truthfulness."

One may be surprised that certain critics blamed Vafflard for taking up a subject which had been attempted by other artists, A.-J. Gros for example, as one can see in pages 29r., 29v. and 30r. of his sketchbook now in the Cabinet des Dessins, Louvre. Yet the critic of the *Journal des Petites Affiches de Paris* found the subject lacking in interest, and the writer for the *Critique raisonnée des tableaux du Salon* said that "the author would do better to handle subjects less somber and thankless."

This leads one to think that the success of Young's *Night Thoughts,* while real enough, was no greater than that of other literary works. Francis Haskell and John Whitney have kindly informed us that a systematic review of the Salon catalogs from 1800 to 1848 yields only two works inspired by Young—Gadbois's *Paysage représentant une soirée de Young* done in 1806 and Demahis' *Young écrivant ses Nuits* of 1821.

PROVENANCE
Given in 1838 by M. Ringuet to the museum in Angoulême; (INV. 383).

EXHIBITION
1804, Salon, no. 467.

REFERENCES
Coll. Deloynes, v. XXXII, no. 892, p. 599; [Anon]., *Les Tableaux chez Séraphin...*, an XIII (1804), pp. 5-6; Voïart (1804), Lettre XXII, p. 27; "Calophile", 1804, p. 68; C.-P. Landon, an XIII (1804) v. IV, p. 119; Biais, mus. cat., 1884, no. 68; Thieme and Becker, 1940, v. XXIV, p. 34; J. Murard, 1967, pp. 2-28.

RELATED WORKS
Another, larger version and the sketch for it are indicated in the Vafflard sale in Paris, Salle Lebrun, 5 and 6 April 1832 (nos. 4 and 78 in the catalog).

J. L.

Pierre-Henri de Valenciennes

1750 Toulouse - Paris 1819

At the Royal Academy in Toulouse, Valenciennes was first the student of the history painter, Jean-Baptiste Despax, and of the miniaturist Guillaume-Gabriel Bouton; but not much else is known about him prior to his trip to Italy in 1769 with Matthias du Bourg, member of the Toulouse Parliament. In 1773, upon the recommendation of the Duc and Duchesse de Choiseul, friends of the Du Bourg family, he entered the atelier of Gabriel-François Doyen in Paris. A landscape painter working with a history painter: the paradox is not as great as it might seem, since Valenciennes wanted to raise landscape to the level of history painting. Due to his friendship with the de Choiseuls, on several occasions he stayed at Chanteloup, where he met Hubert Robert; as it is confirmed by one of the seven sketch books at the Louvre, Valenciennes also visited Amboise in 1775, as well as the outskirts of Paris (studies of Compiègne, Fontainebleau, Villers-Cotterêts, etc.). Drawings at the Musée Paul-Dupuy in Toulouse indicate a trip to Provence and Catalonia. Very recently (December 1973) ten landscapes appeared on the Parisian market, studies in oil on paper done from Breton sites and more specifically the mouth of the Rance River and the Saint-Malo harbor; until this moment, it was not known that Valenciennes had traveled in Brittany. These undated studies are difficult to place in his career. Found with the group of works mentioned above were also some Italian studies (especially Roman) done on paper glued to cardboard.

Several of these unpublished sketches went to French museums in 1974 (Saint-Lô, Dieppe, Poitiers, Aurillac) and one was purchased by the *Mobilier National*. They constitute the most important addition to our knowledge of the art of Valenciennes since the de Croy Collection entered the Louvre in 1930 (works left in the artist's studio, numbering nearly 130 painted studies, which led to the rediscovery of the name Valenciennes).

On the other hand, *Réflexions et Conseils à un élève* published by Valenciennes in 1799, indicates that the artist had visited Asia Minor, Greece, Syria, Egypt and the Archipelago Islands. From 1777-81, Valenciennes made his second and most important trip to Italy. The artist traveled through the entire peninsula, from Rome to Sicily, Spoleto to the Borromeo Islands, and brought back a considerable number of sketches and studies painted on paper (Paris, Cabinet des Estampes, and Louvre). The landscape drawings (pen, black ink, brown wash) are very close to David's, only two years his senior. Both artists employed a meticulous and rather cold technique, as well as a hard and clear use of wash with subtle effects.

We do know that Valenciennes was in Rome in 1780 to study "perspective in its most minute details with an excellent professor of mathematics" and that he "filled more than 500 pages in folio, with sketches and perspective figures" (never located). He came back to France in 1781 via Savoy and Switzerland, but returned to Rome the following year. There is no further mention of him until 1787. Perhaps the trips to the Orient mentioned above took place during those five years. Two Roman sites painted on calendars for the years 1785-86 (Louvre) could make us believe that he was in Rome during these years (Département des Peintures, R. F. 2919, 2936).

On 31 March 1787, sponsored by Pierre-Antoine Demachy, Valenciennes was made associate of the Royal Academy of Painting and was received as academician in July of the same year—a great accomplishment— with a landscape representing *Ciceron qui fait abattre les arbres qui cachaient le tombeau d'Archimède* (Toulouse, on loan from the Louvre). At the Salon of the same year, he showed his acceptance piece and three land-scapes: *L'ancienne ville d'Agrigente* (Louvre), *Paysage de l'ancienne Grèce* and *Paysage au fond duquel on aperçoit une ville antique..., sur le devant deux femmes offrant des fleurs aux naïades d'une fontaine.* In 1789, he exhibited several historical landscapes at the Louvre; in addition, the Comte d'Artois, brother of Louis XVI, commissioned him to do two large decorative paintings for the Château de la Muette, *La Cascade* and *Pont de pierre* (today in New York, private collection). He exhibited regularly at the Salons from 1791-1819 (for the Salon paintings, as well as Valenciennes in general, consult the very thorough exh. cat. by R. Mesuret, 1956-57, Toulouse, Musée Paul-Dupuy). During those years, did Valen-ciennes make another trip to Rome, as his two India ink drawings of *Paysages d'Italie*, signed *P.V., 1791* (Le Havre), would suggest? The Salon catalogs showed him as residing in Paris.

From 1796 to 1800, he gave courses on perspective which would result in the publication in 1799-1800 of *Éléments de Perspective Pratique à l'usage des Artistes ; suivis de Réflexions et Conseils à un élève sur la Peinture et particulièrement sur le genre du Paysage* (a greatly enlarged second edition by the author appeared in 1820). In 1812, he followed Pierre-Charles Dandrillon as Professor of Perspective at the Imperial School of Fine Arts. In 1816, the establishment at the École des Beaux-Arts of a Prix de Rome in landscape painting gave him great satisfaction. The prize would continue to be awarded until 1863; the first prize-winner was Achille-Etna Michallon, pupil of David and Valenciennes. In 1817, Valenciennes paid his last visit to Rome, which produced many sketches (see the drawings, signed and dated in Rome, preserved in the Louvre, as well as a painting at Barnard Castle).

The influence of Valenciennes was extensive: "If one went to learn figure drawing at Guérin's, one went to Valenciennes' to learn about landscape; the two schools were really one and were not unworthy of each other" (C. Clément). A first-class instructor, a remark-able and wise theoretician ready with clear advice and successful solutions (Poussin painted his *Funérailles de Phocion* with the "color of feeling," Ruisdael and the Dutch painted with the "feeling of color"), Valenciennes formed a whole generation of landscapists: Chauvin, Castellan, Deperthes, J.-V. Bertin, Michallon, Croze-Magnan, Millin du Perreux, Prévot the painter of Panoramas.

His advice was sometimes almost prophetic, antici-pating the development of 19th-century landscape painting and the triumph of the study of nature: "We encourage the young men who really want to study landscape in all its phases to get up before dawn to know all of its effects... Do not fail to do some painted studies of beautiful trees isolated or in groups. Devote yourselves to all the details of bark, moss and roots...." Or, again, "In the countryside, scrutinize the move-ment of little streams winding through the willows and among the reeds."

But, as fate would have it, in the 19th century, he had to suffer a veritable purgatory, "the Virgil of decadence" (R. Bouyer, 1894), "author of unfortunate pastiches" (Ménard, 1882), real "Campistron" (A. Dayot, 1925), "paintings as devoid of truth as they are of style" (E. Michel, 1906). It is significant that he was most disliked at the time of the rise of Impressionism.

Since 1930 and the revelation of the painted sketches of the de Croy Collection, Valenciennes justly appeared as the forerunner of Corot. It should not be forgotten that he aimed to be the "David of Landscape" by representing an ideal and ennobled Nature, fed by the meditation of the works of Poussin and the Bolognese (the Carracci, the Grimaldi, Domenichino) and by the reading of Virgil, Homer and Plutarch. Must there be an absolute and definitive difference between the nature studies preferred exclusively by modern taste, and large and noble historical landscapes ? In the end, is not this artist more complex and subtle, as reflected by his writings ? A.-B. L.

179
Byblis Changed into a Fountain

"Paysage où se voit Biblia [ou Biblis] changée en fontaine," old title: *Aréthuse changée en fontaine*
Plate p. 131
Canvas; 54 × 79; s.d.l.r. *P. Valenciennes 1792*
Salon of 1793, no. 521 (?)
Quimper, Musée des Beaux-Arts

At the Salon, Valenciennes exhibited a *Paysage où se voit Biblia (ou Biblis) changée en fontaine* (no. 521), as well as *Narcisse se mirant dans l'eau* (no. 331). The catalog indicated the measurements of the first; 20 by 30 *pouces,* which is not absolutely incompatible with the painting exhibited here; even the date of 1792 supports this identification, as does the existence of a pendant in Quimper, *La Mort de Narcisse.* Could the traditional title of the Quimper *Arethusa* be wrong and our pair identical to the paintings of the Salon of 1793? Indeed, if one looks to the usual iconography of the story of Arethusa—like the story of Byblis taken from Ovid— one notices that in the 17th and 18th centuries the nymph Arethusa was almost never reproduced without the river Alpheus pursuing her. It is a dramatic scene which demands movement: Diana intervenes at the appropriate time to spirit Arethusa away from Alpheus by changing her into a fountain; Alpheus had pursued Arethusa across the whole Ionian Sea. Thus, a painting by Pierre-Charles Trémolières represented three grappling figures in a vast landscape bordering the sea (cf. the engraving by Étienne Fessard of 1737, after the painting by Trémolières at Cholet, lost since 1945; see Trémolières exh. cat., Cholet, 1973, no. 20, p. 71, fig. 38 bottom; and the informative list of examples drawn up by A. Pigler, 1956, II, p. 12, particularly the drawing by Michel Corneille the Younger at the Louvre [no. 2385], and the painting by Jean Restout in Rouen—so many versions of the theme of Arethusa with several characters).

None of this is to be found in Valenciennes' picture. A static composition in which a figure lies alone, seemingly abandoned on a rock, it expresses an elegiac sadness of regret and resignation. The story of Byblis was elegantly outlined by Chompré in his famous *Dictionnaire Abrégé de la Fable* (continually reedited since 1727; by 1855 there were 28 editions; Chompré was constantly referred to by artists, as reported by J. Lethève, 1968, p. 20). According to Chompré, Byblis,

daughter of Miletus and the nymph Cyane, "Not having been able to touch the heart of her brother Caunus whom she loved, cried so much that she was changed into a fountain." The limp pose of the figure expresses a desperate sorrow here—indeed, we actually witness water begin to spring from her arms, as if it came from tears.

Naturally, Valenciennes, who had a deep knowledge of Ovid, did not fail to recommend to young landscapists to choose a site or a country relevant to that story: "In Ionia, a famous and very interesting country for lovers of Antiquity [are] the ruins of Heracleus; one must see the fountain of Byblis, immortalized by Ovid," (Valenciennes, 1820, p. 449; this passage cannot be found in the first edition of 1799).

One will also note his interest in the theme of Narcissus represented in the pendant to this painting: "Fortunate is the artist who, giving himself up to the seductive charm of illusion, believes he sees nature as it should be! His delights know no bounds, he experiences the satisfaction and the noble pride of creating, a nature too exceptional in its perfection... His creative imagination, increased and diversified by the reading of poets, for example, on the theme of tempests... He likes to soothe himself by representing Narcissus beside a fountain, its quiet and limpid waters accurately reflecting the image of this unfortunate lover whose languid and faded charms presage the fatal end which will restore peace to his soul" (Valenciennes, 1799, p. 384; 1820, p. 310). A beautiful text which reveals the importance that Valenciennes assigned to *reading* a painting. No longer can we discuss Valenciennes, as had been the case the last 30 years, as the painter of small sketches supposedly done from nature that presage the free and naturalistic 19th-century movement to landscape. (In fact, several of his landscapes were made from memory, and some unfinished sketches, such as the ones in Poitiers, in which space has been provided for a tree, indicated a work process accomplished in the atelier and not on the spot.) In fact, it can be shown that for Valenciennes, historical landscape was not necessarily synonymous with boredom. We have always mistakenly believed that Salon paintings were very large and have tended to confuse historical and decorative landscapes. *Byblis* proves otherwise; example to the contrary not without charm and discreet emotion (especially if it is *read*), it is well balanced and harmonious, fresh and firm, with a single but apt note of brighter color to mark poor Byblis. In contrast with large, ambitious and richly composed canvases like *Agrigente* (Salon of 1787, Louvre), the *Tombeau d'Archimède* (Salon of 1787, Toulouse), the large landscape of the Union Interalliée (from Galerie Marcus, Paris) or a landscape of 1787 (currently in Paris, Galerie Heim-Gairac) the small views of Quimper are much closer to *Mercure et Argus* of 1793 (Barnard Castle). But to the more pretentious and strong influence of Gaspard Dughet and Francisque Millet which affected English painting, is opposed here the more measured strains of a Huysum or a Glauber, well suited to the sad tone of the legends of Byblis and Narcissus, for the expression of the vanity of things and the impossibility or elusiveness of love. One should not forget, especially at the end of the 18th century, the impact of Italianizing Dutch painters of the 17th century, who enjoyed such an enthusiastic public and whom a man of culture like Valenciennes knew how to appreciate—as his book on the art of landscape proves. In a very pleasant way, Valenciennes introduced us directly to the soft and quiet landscapes of Bertin, Dunouy, Bidauld and Boguet (but in Italy, was he sensitive to the works of Simon Denis and Hackert?), in which nostalgic reverie, elegiac images enhance the pastoral and arcadian decor inherited from Poussin, Van Bloemen and Allegrain.

Before his successful compositions, like those in Quimper which are harmonious and modest, one must immediately share the very enthusiastic judgment expressed on the occasion of the Salon of 1793 by the *Petites Affiches* of 21 September: "We must agree that the landscape of our school has reached its highest point of achievement since Claude Lorrain and Poussin...

all of nature is superb, if one knows how to see, select and render it with taste and energy" (cited by P. Dorbec, 1925, p. 7).

PROVENANCE
According to an old label attached to the frame of the painting, it, like its pendant, belonged to the collection of M. Giroux père. In fact, the *Répertoire des catalogues de vente* of Frits Lugt (I, 1938; II, 1953) indicates several Giroux sales in Paris. The first, in 1811, calls Alphonse Giroux a "painter-restorer of Notre-Dame and the Archbishopric of Paris"; the second sale, on 5 June 1830, is of "Alphonse Giroux père, picture dealer"; other sales took place on 16-17 December 1833, 24-25 February 1850, 10 December 1851, 24-25 February 1851, 19-21 February 1857. Silguy purchased his two Valenciennes in the February 1851 sale for 120 francs. Bequest of Comte Jean-François Xavier de Silguy (1785-1864) to the city of Quimper, along with his entire collection of painting and his library; the *"Musée de Silguy,"* built especially to house this bequest, was dedicated in 1873. An extremely productive technician and engineer for the Bridges and Roads (he was responsible for the harbors of Camaret and Bastia, the bridge of Cubzac, the stabilization of the dunes of Gascogne, highways of the Landes, the canal of Saint-Maur, etc.), Silguy amassed a collection of 1,200 paintings (260 were eliminated at the time of the bequest), which form the core of the Quimper museum and which are of a uniformly high quality. On the personality and career of Silguy, see the useful preface by P. Quiniou in the exhibition catalog of the drawings of the Quimper museum, 1971 (INV. 873-1-439).

EXHIBITION
1793, Salon, no. 521 (?).

REFERENCES
Gauguet and Hombron, mus. cat., 1873, no. 592 (Aréthuse); R. Mesuret, 1956-1957, no. XXII ("Biblis changée en fontaine," as a lost work).

RELATED WORKS
Pendant to the so-called *Arethusa,* in the same collection and with an identical provenance (and with the same old label on the back) is the *Mort de Narcisse* (canvas; 54 × 92; s.d. 1792), mus. cat. 1873, no. 591 (INV. 873-1-441).
A pair of drawings, s.d. 1790, at Schab Gallery, New York, 1973-1974, cat. 137, no. 155, illustrating the drawing supposedly of Arethusa; the pendant, Narcissus, is reproduced in a preceding Schab catalog. Both came from a Christie's sale, London, 25 March 1969, listed together under no. 170 and entitled *Aréthuse et Narcisse.* The landscape contains important variations, but the figures are nearly identical to those in the paintings. J. F.

Anne Vallayer-Coster

1744 Paris 1818

Together with Mme Vigée-Lebrun, Anne Vallayer-Coster was certainly the best known female painter of the 18th century in France. Encouragement and early training were to be found at home, for her father was the King's goldsmith and also worked at the Gobelins until 1754, when he left to establish his own studio. Anne Vallayer, who almost always maintained her maiden name as part of her signature (she married Jean-Pierre-Silvestre Coster, a lawyer at the *Parlement,* in 1781, and afterward signed herself "Vallayer-Coster" and very rarely "Mme Coster"), began brilliantly. From 1766 on, she was in full command of her talent, and one is unable to say who helped to form it (the *Brioche* and the *Service à crème,* former David-Weill collection; from 1767, the *Nature morte au jambon,* Berlin). In 1770, at the age of 26, she was elected to the Royal Academy of Painting with the backing of Pierre, the King's chief painter. The two qualifying works, an *Allegorie des Arts* and the *Instruments de musique,* are in the Louvre and were shown at the Salon of 1771. This election was a prodigious debut, for Vallayer was practically unknown before. The art critics, led by Diderot, could not praise her enough. The years 1770-80 were the most productive of her career, as if the artist sought to gain the favor of the public after winning that of the Academy. Participicipating regularly in the Salons, she showed her first flower paintings in 1775. She was to make a specialty of these. In 1777, she became a first-rank artist at the Salon, and Saint-Aubin illustrated all her works in his catalog. In 1779-80, the royal house created special accommodations for her next to the studios of other artists in the Louvre's Grande Galerie. This was done at the recommendation of Marie-Antoinette (and Vallayer-Coster always remained faithful to the Queen and the royalty), whose portrait, now lost, was painted by the artist in 1780. In spite of her Bourbon sympathies, Mme Vallayer-Coster survived the revolutionary years without harm. She started showing at the Salon again in 1795 and was one of the painters to sign the petition in favor of Mme Vigée-Lebrun. Her work was infrequently seen after that. Under the Empire she showed only twice, in 1804 and 1810. She was forgotten

for much of the 19th century. After 1815, Vallayer's last Salon appearance was in 1817 with a *Nature morte au homard* which belonged to Louis XVIII (now kept at the Mobilier National). The painting was probably a gift of the artist to the monarch; the presence of a lily branch seems to indicate a last royalist homage.

Her output was more varied than one tends to think, and includes miniatures (flowers and portraits, an example at the Musée des Arts Décoratifs, Paris, 1808), full-size portraits, *Roettiers* (Versailles, Salon of 1777; other examples in Epinal, 1772, and at Barnard Castle). In this last area the critics were not gentle with Vallayer, who was certainly more successful with still lifes, *Vestales,* allegorical still lifes, *Allégorie des Arts* and the *Instruments de Musique* (Louvre, Salon of 1771), two *Trophées de chasse* (Salon of 1775, sold at Sotheby's, London, 29 November 1961, repr.; Salon of 1783, Toledo), other still lifes of the hunt (1787, Strasbourg and Le Mans; 1769, Reims). For all this, the floral still lifes are the most numerous (only museums cited here, for Vallayer's works are still much scattered in private collections): 1775, Cambridge, England, Museum, Broughton gift (and another copy in the same donation); Carcassonne, Nancy; 1774, Saint-Jean-Cap-Ferrat; 1775, idem; Salon of 1781, New York; 1787, Geneva, Warsaw, Dijon, Musée des Beaux-Arts (according to Marianne Roland-Michel, the painting in the Musée Magnin is of doubtful attribution). The still lifes of vegetables and fruits and those of meal preparations are just as frequent: Salon of 1773, Paris, Musée Nissim de Camondo; 1774, Nancy, Ottawa, Strasbourg; 1767, Berlin; 1781, Toledo, Berlin, another example undated. Vallayer-Coster finally worked for the Gobelins, where all or at least some of her works were used as cartoons for tapestries (at least between 1803 and 1806 and again in 1809; two still lifes of 1766 and 1767 reproduced as tapestries are kept at the Musée Nissim de Camondo). In total, it is an œuvre of nearly 444 paintings, according to the recent catalogue raisonné by M. Roland-Michel (an exact figure is impossible, since the catalog includes works formerly attributed to Vallayer, for example a gouache of flowers done in 1780 in Narbonne, works in tapestry, etc.). For the identification of Salon pictures we must, for lack of space here, refer the reader to the excellent monograph, cited above, which gives all of the necessary details.

Stylistically, Vallayer takes her place among the best representatives of still life in the 18th-century, next to Prévost, Bellengé, and Roland de La Porte, to whom she is closest. Specific comparisons are sometimes to be made with Jeaurat de Bertry, Bachelier, Marcenay de Guy, Collin de la Biochaye, this last by virtue of being a follower. Vallayer follows Chardin in the representation of fruits and meal preparation, and Desportes and Oudry with respect to allegories and hunt-related scenes. The differences with Spaendonck are notable, despite the parallels critics drew. The influence of Chardin is indisputable, even though

M. Roland-Michel had reason to exonerate Vallayer-Coster of the accusation of plagiarism by showing that Vallayer's manner, agreeable and rich with color, is equally precise and firm, less mysterious and more detailed than that of Chardin. Thus she created a pleasant and familiar style, of a reassuring poetic realism, opening moderately to neo-classical influences, even figuring belatedly in the period of the Revolution and the Empire, which joins to the Flemish tradition and to the triumph of "bien peint" so dear to the French 18th century, a rich, thick color with the virtues of subtle lighting and unifying harmony. The quality of the craft—here a source of poetry—surely led to innovation in the work of Vallayer-Coster.

J. F.

180
*Still Life with Sea Shells**

"Une figure de l'Étude, en marbre blanc, groupée avec des madrépores, des coquillages, et des minéraux"
also called *Nature morte aux minéraux*
Plate p. 96
Canvas; 74 × 60
Salon of 1789, no. 48
Paris, Baronne de Saint-Palais Collection

Discovered in the possession of the artist's descendants and published by Marianne Roland-Michel, the author of the first and fundamental monograph on Vallayer-Coster, this painting can perhaps be identified as one of the four shown in the Salon of 1789 (M. Roland-Michel, 1970, no. 266): "Une figure de l'Étude, en marbre blanc, groupée avec des madrépores, des coquillages, et des minéraux." The description corresponds and the dimensions (3 *pieds* × 2 *pieds,* 8 *pouces,* that is: 97 × 86.4) agree if one includes the frame, or if one assumes an error in the Salon catalog (always a possibility), or if one supposes a subsequent reduction of the canvas (less likely, for the composition seems perfectly framed).

One suspects that such trompe-l'œil pictures of minerals and statues responded to both the antiquarian taste and the naturalist curiosity of the era. Few of Vallayer-Coster's works better affirm their relation to the 18th century neo-classical ideal (the Louis XVI commode, the well-known statue of the *Tireur d'épines* a replica of a famous Alexandrine piece, *l'Étude* in the

style of Clodion and Pigalle) and provide such an agreeable contrast to the artist's usual flower compositions in soft, mellow, neo-Chardinesque tones. The paintings of Vallayer-Coster in this delicately abstract style still seem extraordinary. Shells and corals mimic flowers, and how great was the appeal of such ironies ! The inanimate, familiar or exotic, treated with gentleness and appeasement, assumes a new life, one conferred by curiosity, esthetic admiration, or poetic reverie (not until much later, with the influence of Surrealism, are the inanimate and the objective laden with more agressive meaning). One can also cite Roland-Michel, no. 274, *Coquillages, cristaux, éponges et madrépores* (*op. cit.,* ill. p. 181), sold 7 April 1922 at Christie's in London, no. 62, but not to be found today, and the two *Morceaux d'histoire naturelle* of the Salon of 1771 (Roland-Michel, nos. 260 and 261), neither reappearing since the Prince de Conti's sale in 1777. At that time they were described and commented on by Diderot in terms that could apply to the present painting: "I will add that these objects, much more varied in their colors and their forms, such as madrepores, corals, ores and minerals, being for the most part polished substances, augment the difficulty of forming successful groupings. Nothing stops Mlle Vallayer; each object is rendered by itself, finite yet contributing to the effect of the others. They are masterpieces of this genre." At that date, Vallayer-Coster had gone further than other artists, but she did not continue to advance. One thinks more of Spaendonck and certainly Berjon (whose famous *Madrépores* of the Musée de Lyon could not travel to yet another exhibition), Philippine that little known painter from the Manufacture de Sèvres, the Vicomte de Barde, that marvelous self-taught painter whom we know only from his watercolors in the Cabinet des Dessins of the Louvre (here No. 122). Again pointing out this subject matter in the work of Vallayer-Coster, we have the *Vase de Chine environné de plantes et de minéraux* from the Salon of 1777 (Roland-Michel, no. 265, now lost). One will find it certainly less exceptional, although it corresponds to the same inspiration of smooth, polished mineral, that Vallayer-Coster

frequently represented statues, often indirectly by means of an *Allegorie d'Art, de Science, ou de la Guerre,* and bas-reliefs in grisaille and trompe-l'œil, after a taste widespread since the influence of the Dutch (Dou, Miéris), and particularly cultivated in France in the 18th century by Chardin, Sauvage, Spaendonck (here No. 168), Doncre, Boilly, etc. Accordingly, Marianne Roland-Michel, restricting her list to bas-reliefs imitated in paint, has already recorded about fifteen (nos. 240-256).

PROVENANCE
Family of the artist, now belonging to Mme la Baronne de Saint-Palais, the great-grandniece of Vallayer-Coster.

EXHIBITION
1789, Salon, no. 48.

REFERENCES
M. Roland-Michel, 1970, p. 88, no. 267, p. 188, ill. p. 179, p. 270.

J. F.

Jacques-Antoine Vallin

c. 1760 - Paris (?) - after 1831 (1835 ?)

Little is known about Vallin, even his birth and death dates are uncertain. The son of a sculptor, he entered the school of the Royal Academy of Painting around the age of 15, under the sponsorship of Doyen. A student of Drevet in 1779, of Callet in 1786, again of Drevet in 1789, and finishing under Renou in 1791, he did not make his debut at the Salon until 1791, showing first a *Tempête, naufrage* and a *Petit Paysage.* According to J. Magnin (1928, p. 188), he showed himself to be a plagiarist of Claude-Joseph Vernet (cf. the two *Marines* by Vallin shown in Paris in 1925, nos. 321 and 322) and the influence of Vernet, as well as that of Jean-Joseph-Xavier Bidauld, again mark a work of 1793, the *Bergère des Alpes* (Algiers). He quickly found his own way and popular success, with seductive pictures of nymphs and bacchantes in harmonious landscapes (four paintings of this sort were shown in the Salon of 1795),

often bathed in delicate golden light like those characteristic paintings at Tours, Barnard Castle, Chartres, etc. His *Erigones* and *Bacchantes* bring him close to Regnault and are comparable to works by Vestier de Tours. His identifiable Salon pictures include, for 1798, the *Vieillard et sa fille demandant l'aumône,* which may correspond to the *Bélisaire* of the museum in Leipzig; for 1799, *L'Amour conduisant deux amants au temple de l'Hymen* of a subtle coloring inspired by Regnault (Paris, Galerie Pardo; cf. *Connaissance des Arts,* no. 187, September 1967, p. 51, ill. in color, the painting which came from the Comte de Quélen's sale Paris, 9-10 December 1931, no. 22, ill. Sold again in Paris in 1936 and 1967); for 1806, a *Paysage* representing the hunt of Diana (Cherbourg); in 1808, the *Portrait en pied du docteur Forlenze* with a Neapolitan background (London, National Gallery) which invites comparison with

Gauffier; for 1810 (No. 181) and the *Enfant jouant du violoncelle* (Paris, Musée Marmottan) for 1817, the *Descendants de Michau,* a painting related to the legend of Henry IV and known from the lithograph by Charles-Achille d'Hardiviller in the Galerie de la Duchesse de Berry (at this Salon, Vallin presented many other historical paintings in the *style troubadour,* such as a *Paysage représentant le tombeau du roi Dagobert,* another with the *Tombeau d'Amadore de la Porte, grand prieur de France,* etc.). A painting from the Salon of 1819, *Jeunes femmes de Sparte s'amusant à des jeux gymnastiques,* can almost surely be identified with a painting of the same subject, s. d. 1818, sold by P. Gravier in Paris, 3-4 May 1923,

no. 222, ill. in the catalog. This painting is very close to Taunay and, it should be observed, confusion of the two artists occurred repeatedly. Two characteristic Vallin compositions, for instance, were exhibited as Taunays *(Nymphes dans un paysage)* at the castle-museum of Kouskovo near Moscow. The painting *Le Baptême du Christ* of the Salon of 1822 may correspond to a painting of the same subject in the Gaudin Collection, reproduced in *Les Arts* of 1904. At the Salon of 1824, among other works, Vallin exhibited a *Henri IV amusant ses enfants,* later in Cherbourg. In 1827, he showed a *Tentation de Saint Antoine,* which entered the Louvre in 1923. Vallin did not show at the Salon after 1827. J. F.

181
Diana and Actaeon*

"Diane et ses nymphes au bain surprises par Actéon. Effet de soleil couchant"
Plate p. 210
Canvas; 112 × 150; s.d.l.r. *Vallin. 1810*
Salon of 1810, no. 800
Roanne, Musée Joseph Déchelette

At the Salon of 1810, Vallin showed, among others, two works, a *Diana and Actaeon* which can almost certainly be identified as the Roanne painting dated the same year and distinguished by one of those rosy twilights Vallin loved, and a *Hippolyte et Thésée,* which was much less pleasing. Many critics, like the author of *Sentiment impartial sur le Salon de 1810* and certainly the anonymous B... of the *Artistes traités de la bonne manière ou l'Ami des peintres vivants* (1810, p. 2) held up to Vallin's *Thésée* that of Guérin, and reproached Vallin for doing subjects for which he was not fit and which furthermore, had been treated by major talents like Guerin and endowed with a sense of the heroic. On the other hand, his painting of *Diana and Actaeon* was little mentioned and only the critic of the *Sentiment impartial* remarked, not without pertinence, "We have long known that M. Vallin creates pretty landscapes, albeit a bit vaporous; *Diana and Actaeon* is recent proof. But why does M. Vallin abandon a style in which he has been successful to embrace another which does not suit him?" In fact, the theme of Diana, often associated with that of the setting sun, was treated by Vallin a number of times (there were examples in the Salons of

1796, 1806, 1812, 1814) and landscapes were not infrequent in his œuvre: pure like the backward-looking *Parc de Neuilly* (Amiens), with its almost naïve freshness of observation; or composed like the *Baptême du Christ* and the *Chemin dans les bois* (reproduced in J. Munier-Jolain's article on Vallin, *Les Arts,* no. 30, June 1904, pp. 28 and 30), or even the *Bord de mer avec soleil couchant* (Darmstadt). The strong quality of this landscape, whose lighting is at once firm and tender, brings Vallin close to the work of Lethière or Bidauld, while the pure, sculptural, neo-classical nature of his nudes (cf. Taunay) perpetuates the Dutch tradition of Poelenburg, Cuylenborch, and Lairesse (cf. also Vallin's *Bain de nymphes* from the Ney sale, Paris, 27 May 1929, nos. 31 and 32, ill. in the catalog). In this respect, the superiority of Vallin is clearly superior to Mallet, who produced the same landscapes with nude mythological scenes.

PROVENANCE
Acquired by the German authorities during World War II and sent to Salzburg; recovered in Germany after 1945 and returned to the Louvre by the Office of Private Properties, 1950-1951; placed by the Louvre at the Musée de Roanne, 1965 (MNR 149).

EXHIBITION
1810, Salon, no. 800.

REFERENCE
Sentiment impartial sur le Salon de 1810, Paris, 1810, p. 11.

RELATED WORK
A painting by Vallin of the same subject, but treated very differently and in a vertical format, belonged to the Dutch dealer Buma and was then in the Thurkow Collection in The Hague (Photograph at the R.K.D.).   J. F.

Jan-Frans Van Dael

1764 Antwerp - Paris 1840

Van Dael was the best known of the northern artists, including the Van Spaendoncks and Redouté, who came to Paris at the end of the 18th century to carry on the Dutch tradition of flower painting.   It is very interesting to note how faithful these Dutch artists, who were highly successful in France, remained to their early teachings and how little they were influenced by the French.   On the contrary, they imparted to their many students a precise, faultless style—linear, decorative, almost scientific.   Their work was marked with a typically 19th-century flavor, directly inspired by Huysum and different from the darker and more traditional work of Vallayer-Coster.

Van Dael first studied at the Academy in Antwerp, where he won the architecture prize in 1784 and 1785; then, overriding his parents' objections (Roosmalen, the artist's nephew, related that as a young man, Van Dael painted secretly at night), he came to Paris in 1786 where he first worked decorating buildings, helping with the trompe-l'œil effects (like Sauvage, with whom he probably collaborated from this moment on) in the decoration of the palaces of Chantilly, Saint-Cloud and Bellevue (see Roosmalen, 1840).

Shortly afterwards, however, influenced by G. Van Spaendonck (was he really self-taught, learning only from nature and the great masters, as several of his biographers so flatteringly claim?), he discovered his specialty—the painting of flowers—and with that came success.   His first still life, exhibited at the Lebrun gallery, was purchased by the Duchesse d'Ursel of Brussels.   A work dated 1789, *Fleurs près d'une fenêtre,* belonged to the Knoedler Gallery, New York, in 1962.

From the year 1793, when he first exhibited at the Salon, Van Dael was given accomodations in the Louvre; then he lived from approximately 1806 to 1817 at the Sorbonne, as an artist protected by the State, where he met one of his colleagues and friends from Antwerp, who also specialized in flower paintings, Chrétien van Pol (one of his works is in the Montpellier museum).

At the Salon of 1796, he exhibited one of his most famous works, *Corbeille de fleurs* (lost).   "For posterity, the picture was called *Corbeille à Julie*" stated Roosmalen, who described it as follows: "A lover is waiting for his mistress; he has just hung a basket of flowers on an oak branch; in the middle is a note addressed to Julie, whose name is already carved on the tree trunk." The painting, after having belonged to the banker Pillot, was returned to the artist, but did not appear in the sale after his death.   *L'Offrande à Flore,* exhibited in the Salon of 1799, earned Van Dael a *prix d'encouragement* of 4,000 francs.   The painting has since been lost.   Its pendant, *The Tomb of Julie,* from the Salon of 1804, has been found and is exhibited here (No. 182).   In the Salon of 1810, when he won the gold medal, he showed his fourth great work, *Fleurs à la croisée d'une fenêtre,* described by Roosmalen, lithographed by Chazal and kept by the artist until his death.   It was no. 1 in the catalog of the posthumous sale.   But Thieme and Becker specify incorrectly, as Lossky so rightly pointed out (1967, p. 126, n. 1), that the work had been painted for Josephine, because it was missing in the list of 1814. His admirers included Josephine, who had five Van Daels in her collection; Marie-Louise, who also bought two of his paintings (Gabet, 1831, located one in Parma and another seems to have been in the artist's sale in 1840, no. 118); and the Duchesse de Berry.   Confirming the continuing official esteem that Van Dael enjoyed,

Louis XVIII purchased *Fleurs dans un vase d'agate sur une table de marbre* from the Salon of 1817. It is currently in Fontainebleau (s.d. 1816; Louvre INV. 1197) from the Salon of 1819, *Fruits posés sur une table de marbre* (since 1895, on permanent loan from the Louvre to Auxerre, Louvre INV. 1198). At this Salon the artist was awarded the gold medal. A third Van Dael, dated 1811, was purchased by the King in 1819 (Louvre INV. 1196) and a fourth in 1820 (now in Compiègne, Louvre INV. 1200).

From the Salon of 1824, Charles X bought another flower painting by Van Dael, *Fleurs sur une console de marbre avec un ananas* (s.d. 1823; now in Fontainebleau, Louvre INV. 1199). This same Charles X decorated Van Dael with the Legion of Honor; however, although he was a member of many foreign academies, such as those in Antwerp and Amsterdam, and was honored by King Léopold of Belgium at the end of his life, he never was honored by the Institute.

Van Dael exhibited at the Galerie Lebrun in Paris in 1826 and several times outside of Paris, most notably in Antwerp in 1807. The last time he participated in the Salon was in 1833. Quite well-known and esteemed in France and abroad, his portrait was included by Boilly in *L'Atelier d'Isabey* (Louvre; sketch of detail in Lille), and Van Dael was painted by Philippe Van Brée in his studio surrounded by his pupils (exhibited in Ghent in 1820, included in the 1840 posthumous sale, no. 51).

Van Dael's works were quite expensive; a letter of the musician Méhul, a great friend and admirer of Van Dael's, humorously preserves this memory for us: "If I were rich, if I could indulge my tastes in the midst of my garden and your paintings, I would be in an eternal springtime. But money, cursed money, is rarely to be found in the hands of those who could make excellent use of it. In this world, the ones who have gold don't have taste, the others have taste and no gold. That is...why your chefs-d'œuvre remain in your study" (Autograph catalog, Charavay, Paris, September 1973, no. 35750).

In addition to the works already mentioned, Van Dael's canvases can be found in Lyon (two *Bouquets de fleurs* one a *Tubéreuse cassée* (dated 1807), which was greatly admired (because Van Dael repeated the theme many times (see Nos. 1 and 182); the other a *Fleurs dans une corbeille d'osier,* dated 1806. Both works were purchased in 1810 following a policy of systematically buying paintings with floral motifs to serve as models for the craftsmen in the Lyon silk industry. (This explains the presence of so many *"Fleurs"* and *"Natures*

mortes"* in Lyon painted by Heem, Huysum, J.-B. Huet, Desportes, Van Spaendonck). In Melbourne is an almost literal copy dated 1811 of the painting in the Louvre. There are two works in Florence (Galleria degli Uffizi); canvases are also to be found in Lille, Dijon (Trimolet Bequest), Lisbon, Grenoble *(Grappe de raisins),* Rouen (s.d. 1827), Amiens (actually two copies painted by Thierry), Château-Thierry, Leningrad (Hermitage, signed "An X," i.e. 1801-02) Moscow (Pushkin, s.d. 1808, a painting, provenance is Leuchtenberg, therefore Malmaison, entitled *Raisins et pêches,* most probably no. 1134 of the Malmaison Inventory of 1814).

In connection with the collection of Josephine, let us mention another Van Dael, no. 1135bis, *Grappe de raisins noirs,* because this painting is printed in the catalog of the Leuchtenberg Collection. Van Dael's more ambitious works, such as *Flore, The Tomb of Julie* and *La Croisée* were the exception to his more usual compositions of flowers and fruits, mostly in vases placed according to the old tradition, on a stone table. Rarely, Van Dael painted portraits. Thieme-Becker mentioned a female portrait in the Olga Brykczynska Collection at the Château de Gliny exhibited in 1912 in Lvov (called Lemberg before 1914—perhaps it can be found in the museum of this city). Van Dael also treated religious subjects (a *Sainte famille* in the church at Confolens was copied by A. Maurin in 1841, according to the testimony of the archives researched by P. Angrand, see Lossky, 1968, p. 134, n. 1, which corrects what is mentioned above, p. 124, n. 2). In addition, there were several landscapes like the one in Rotterdam, or those from the 1840 sale already mentioned, some even studies from nature like the *Oreilles d'ours* (1840 sale, no. 8). On the other hand, *L'Intérieur* by Van Dael in the Bruges museum mentioned by Lossky (*op. cit.,* p. 124, n. 2) is, according to Bénézit, *La Première dent* by Casimir Van Dael, dated 1855.

Van Dael had a wide-spread influence, judging from the number of students who studied with him, many of whom were women. His students included Mme Millet de Caux and Elisa Bruyère, who did so much work for the Sèvres manufactory (paintings by Mme Bruyère are in Rouen, Valenciennes and Lyon); Mme Nepveu, whose *Grappe de raisins noirs* of 1836 can be seen at Fontainebleau; as well as Mlles Richer and Pilon, Henriette-Gertruida Knip (who returned to her native Holland), and a Mlle Bonneval, who exhibited at the 1796 Salon as a student of Van Dael.

J. F.

182
The Tomb of Julie

Le Tombeau de Julie
Plate p. 186
Canvas; 198 × 150; s.d.l.l. VAN DAEL/AN. XII
Inscribed on the Mausoleum above:
Flos ipsa Julia sicut flores periit (Herself a flower, Julie died like the flowers)
Rueil-Malmaison, Musée National du Château

This is Van Dael's chef-d'œuvre, his greatest and most beautiful flower painting, and the one always mentioned. It is surprising that although this picture has been part of the collection of a great museum since before 1870, it is still unknown. The recent excellent publication by B. Lossky his filled this gap. The dedication to Julie, the description of the theme and the date (Year XII) and the importance of the appraisal price in the 1814 inventory—4,000 francs for the two pendants, while the three other Van Daels were valued respectively at only 500 francs (nos. 204 and 205) and 120 francs (no. 206)—fully justify Lossky's identification of the painting MI 104 with *The Tomb of Julie* of the Malmaison Gallery. Let us note, parenthetically, that Josephine's famous passion for flowers—her renowned greenhouses at Malmaison—was demonstrated by her choice of paintings; included in the Malmaison collection were *Fleurs* by Charlotte, Mme Millet de Caux, G.-V. Spaendonck, Van Os, the watercolors of Redouté, two colored drawings by Mme Vallayer-Coster (about Josephine and flowers, see S. Grandjean, 1964, pp. 35-36, 39, with references also to the specialized bibliography in the subject: Mauguin, Mirimonde, etc.). However, the pendant to *The Tomb of Julie, L'Offrande à Flore* from the Salon of 1799 (no. 324) also measuring 200 × 150 (according to Muxel, 1834, another edition 1846, no. 143, ill. "*Tableau de fleurs*"; Roosmalen, 1840, p. 6, specifies a height of 209) must be considered lost. After the death in 1852 of Duke Maximilian (son of Eugène de Beauharnais), the Leuchtenberg collections left Munich for the family residences in Russia. There is hope that the work is still in the Soviet Union (like the painting by Fleury Richard from Josephine's collection, purchased by the Moscow museum after 1917; or the François Gérard canvas of Josephine on a divan, now in the Hermitage). However, one should remember that the Leuchtenberg paintings were put on the market very early and that all the family possess-ions were not in Russia. For example, a painting by Jean-Louis Demarne from Josephine's collection was included in the sale of President Charles d'Heucqueville in Paris, 25-26 March 1936, no. 82. Concerning *L'Offrande à Flore,* let us remember that it was known not only through Muxel's engraving published by B. Lossky but also through the lithograph of Antoine Chasal, as Roosmalen states in his introduction to the catalog of the posthumous sale of Van Dael. This is a very accurate text, since Van Dael was Roosmalen's uncle and Gérard Van Spaendonck his teacher (see on this subject the letter to the archives of the Louvre published by B. Lossky, 1967, p. 130).

Painted at different times (*Flore* in the Year VII, 1798-99; *Julie* in the Year XII, 1803-1804), the two paintings were, however, visibly conceived as antitheses, facing each other. The statue of Flora, standing on the left is turned toward the right, that is, toward the painting of Julie, which faces the opposite direction. *Flore* opens out, with little architectural detail, onto a huge clear landscape, in contrast to the detailed, enclosed composition in Malmaison; together they constitute a "thought of happiness and glory."

As Roosmalen very aptly said, "The genius of the artist comes alive; he wants to place his young wreaths on the altar of Flora... an antique altar decorated with bas-reliefs is placed before her and receives like incense the richest offerings of her empire." This is in contrast to the present work, where floral grandeur is put into juxtaposition with melancholy death, where the flowers seem to be even more beautiful because they will wither... The inscription on the tomb of Julie merits a comment: who was this Julie—poetic license of the artist, a family memory or, perhaps, an allusion to the famous poetic garland of Julie d'Angennes, Duchesse de Montausiers (1607-1671)? Let us note that the name Julie already appeared in a *Corbeille de Fleurs* in the Salon of 1796 (see Roosmalen, *op. cit.,* p. 6). As for the words of the inscription, they repeat Malherbe's celebrated verses about roses, as well as the powerful warnings of the psalmist and prophet Isaiah in his metaphor on the brevity and fragility of human life, which he compares to that of flowers. The inscription also resembles that of a *vanitas* painter like Joris Hoefnagel, who in 1591 carefully put an inscription into his diptych of flowers and insects in Lille (cf. *XVIᵉ siècle européen,* exh. cat. 1965-66, Paris, no. 167, ill.). But whereas the painters of past centuries tried to express a moral lesson in a bouquet of flowers with a symbolic choice of species and associated objects, an artist of this more pragmatic age, like Van Dael and Redouté, fascinated moreover by the scientific objectivity of things, expressed himself with an eloquent inscription and then gave free rein to his descriptive technique.

A painting so complete and beautifully executed could not miss being noticed by the critics. The author of *La Critique raisonnée des tableaux de Salon* emphasized the intellectual quality of floral painting: "Besides the merits of the actual technique, one must also praise him for having added interest to a genre which lacked it until now. I congratulate him and invite him always to include the sublime and interesting in his works, because it is flattering, even noble and important, to see the tomb of a hero or friend decorated with flowers and fruits, rather than seeing them placed on a table in a basket or in a crystal or alabaster vase like the famous Van Huysum." How better to emphasize the unusual nature of this painting in the œuvre of Van Dael, who usually worked within the simple, traditional formula of well-arranged flowers posed on a stone shelf in front of a dark background?

For the critic of the *Lettres impartiales...,* such a painting could be read as follows: "This fragrant and white tuberose, scarcely more than a bud, is broken on its stem! Ah, don't you see that it is the symbol of Julie!" But his admiration is clouded by certain reservations: "Why is this tomb so close to the eye? There is no distance nor differentiation between the flowers in the vase and those in the foreground." However, this sells short the decorative, descriptive element desired by the artist to emphasize floral beauty! In their large bunches of flowers, Van der Ast and Bosschaert, Brueghel de Velours or Savery, as well as Mignon and Huysum a little earlier in the 17th century, did not place their bouquets on one level as much for a pleasing effect as to render objective detail to each flower. Moreover, what can one think of the criticism aimed at Van Dael that he misrepresented

"the nature of our climate by showing a mixture of fruits and flowers of every season." This anachronism was again the result of artistic license, one that Huysum often used. Finally, *Séraphin (?)* of the *Ombres chinoises au Salon* unjustly finds these flowers "lacking in brilliance and virtuosity; their colors are too dull!"

PROVENANCE

Purchased with its pendant for 16,000 francs (price given by Roosmalen, 1840, p. VII) by the Empress Josephine for her gallery in Malmaison (cf. the 1811 catalog reprinted by Lescure, 1867, no. 203: two paired paintings, and the posthumous list of 1814, published by S. Grandjean, 1964, p. 158: "M. Van Dael: 133 - Item, two pendant paintings, groups of flowers in baskets and vases, valued at 4,000 francs"). In reference to Josephine's gallery, let us remember that among almost one hundred "modern" paintings in the gallery, only a very limited number have been found: thirteen in Arenenberg, two in Moscow, four in Malmaison, one in an American sale, one in the Lefuel Collection. After 1815, the pendants, *The Tomb of Julie* and *L'Offrande à Flore* were separated very early, contrary to what Gabet suggested in 1831, followed by Nagler (1835-1862) who situated the pair in the Leuchtenberg Gallery in Munich. Only *L'Offrande à Flore,* notes B. Lossky (*op. cit.,* pp. 126-128), is printed in the illustrated catalog of line engravings from the Leuchtenberg Gallery in Munich (first edition about 1834; second in 1846). Therefore, it is possible that the two pendants were shared, shortly after 1814, between the two direct descendants of Josephine, Eugène de Beauharnais, Duke of Leuchtenberg, and Queen Hortense. About 1854, Napoleon III made a gift to the Louvre. (This confirms Hortense, Josephine's daughter, as the source. She died in 1837 and most probably bequeathed the painting to her son.) Apparently remaining in storage and not catalogued (moreover, the catalog of northern painting in the Louvre which includes Van Dael, had been completed by Villot by 1852 and was continually reprinted without changes until 1889), the painting was sent to Fontainebleau in August 1889, removed from storage by B. Lossky around 1966-1967 and re-exhibited in the Salon de Jeux du Petit Appartement de Joséphine in Fontainebleau, transferred to the Château de la Malmaison in 1874 (MI. 104).

EXHIBITIONS

1904, Salon, no. 486 (*"Tableau de fruits."* It depicts a monument to the memory of a young lady. The artist supposes that her friends pay homage to her every year and decorate her tomb with flowers and fruits); 1969, Rueil-Malmaison, no. 60.

REFERENCES

Critique raisonnée des tableaux du Salon, 1804, p. 70; *Lettres impartiales sur les expositions de l'an XIII,* 1804, no. 3, p. 8; *Tableaux chez Séraphin ou les ombres chinoises du Salon,* 1804, p. 13; cat., 1811, no. 203 (pendants under the same no.); Gabet, 1831, p. 674; Nagler, 1835-1862; Roosmalen, 1840, pp. VI-VII; Lescure, 1867, no. 203 (not located); Thieme and Becker, 1913, p. 257 (lost); S. Grandjean, 1964, p. 158 (not located); B. Lossky, 1967, pp. 125-130, ill. opp. p. 128.

RELATED WORKS
Lithograph by Antoine Chasal, with a pendant, *Offrande à Flore*, 1835 (Bibl. Nat., Paris, Estampes, AA3, bound sup-

plement). "Finished sketch" of the *Tombeau de Julie*, no. 115 in the artist's posthumous sale, Paris, 19-20 May 1840. (In the same sale were finished sketches of the *Offrande à Flore* [no. 114], of the *Corbeille à Julie* [no. 113] and of the *Croisée* [no. 116]. Van Dael deliberately kept records of his best paintings, like Gerard and Gauffier; thus, the word "sketch" is perhaps inappropriate.)   J. F.

183
Landscape: The Painter's House

Paysage, also called *La Maison du peintre*
Plate p. 296
Canvas; 50 × 61; s.d.l.l. *Vandael 1828*
Rotterdam, Museum Boymans van Beuningen

The date of the painting as well as the "classic" style of the house with its mansard roof serve as evidence that the work, an exceptional landscape by a painter specializing in flowers, was painted in France. There is, however, nothing in the biography of the artist which permits us to localize the site (why speak of an abbey or a convent as does the catalog of the exhibition in Delft-Antwerp?), although it must be in the region of Paris (or in Paris itself, in the quarter of the Gobelins near the Bièvre?). We do know that two "Vues du Val-de-Grâce [peintes] d'après nature" (no. 12 of the sale) turned up at the posthumous sale of the painter's work (19 and 20 May 1840, in his house on the Impasse des Feuillantines), proving that the Rotterdam painting is not the only one of its kind in his œuvre.

Since its entry into the museum collection, this painting has been thought to represent the painter's house (the catalog of the Delft-Antwerp exhibition of 1967 even gives "Artist at the Window" as the title), but the usual identification of the figure seen through the second story window as Van Dael himself in the act of painting seems unfounded. This charming detail (one sees a no less touching note in the bird perched on a wall near the center) lacks precision and may as well represent someone the painter knew. This unique landscape, with its sharp rawness and fascinating legibility (the virtuosity of the ruined wall meticulously analyzed), suffices to place Van Dael alongside the

landscape painters Jean-Victor Bertin, Jean-Joseph-Xavier Bidauld, and Dunouy. Before Corot, these artists began to explore typically "French" sites in compositions of exquisite high finish characteristic of the Italian-influenced Northerners. From the lessons of Potter or Adrien de Velde were transcribed into landscape painting the porcelain-like exactitude and clarity dear to Demarne or to Drolling. But with or without the painter's northern heritage, it is true that only the Danish or German artists of the period attained this poetry of objectivity becoming almost unreal and the charm of a human presence subtly veiled, which are the marks of intimist compositions, examples as deceptively simple and unaffected as this one being extremely rare.

PROVENANCE
Acquired in 1943 with the funds of the D. Seldenthuis bequest; INV. 2193.

EXHIBITIONS
1964-1965, Delft-Antwerp, no. 32, ill. 42; 1967, Dordrecht, no. 27.

REFERENCES
Museum Boymans, Jaarverslag 1941-1943, p. 33; mus. cat., 1943, no. 27, ill. 23; mus. cat., 1963, no. 2193, pp. 35-36; Museum Boymans-Van Beuningen, *Old Paintings 1400-1900, Illustrations,* Rotterdam, 1972, ill. p. 152.

J. F.

Jules-César-Denis Van Loo or Vanloo

1743 Paris 1821

A student of his father Carle and thus one of the last members of the flourishing dynasty of the Van Loos, César was trained at the Royal Academy of Painting and competed several times for the Grand Prix. In 1767, he was admitted on approval and given lodging at the French Academy in Rome, and was then admitted to the Royal Academy of Painting in 1784 with two entries: *Orage* and *Clair de lune*. He was in Rome about 1785, as attested by one of his drawings, now in Hamburg, which J.-F. Méjanès has pointed out. Van Loo returned to Paris about 1789, and in 1790 was the assistant to the head of the Academy. He emigrated to Turin in 1791, where his father had previously worked, and did several paintings for the Court of Piedmont. In 1795, Cacault noted the presence in Genoa of Van Loo, whom he called a "distinguished landscape painter" (as well as a certain Boquet—perhaps Boguet, see No. 5). Cacault also lists him there at the beginning of 1797, although Thieme and Becker stated that he is mentione das returning to France as early as 1795 (see *Correspondance des Directeurs de l'Académie de France à Rome*, XVI, 1907, pp. 393, 496).

César first exhibited at the Salon de la Correspondance in 1779 with a *Vue prise à Tivoli* (later in the collection of the Comte d'Orsay). His first official Salon was in 1785, where he showed a *Temple de la Sybille de Tivoli* and two *morceaux de réception* (lent by the Louvre to the Ministry of Justice in 1876, last seen in 1955 when they were returned to the national storage of art works). He also exhibited many Italian landscapes (Tivoli, Subiaco, the Ponte Molle, etc).

Van Loo participated in all the subsequent Salons except that of 1795. At the Salon of 1789, Cochin called him "the most dynamic" of all the landscape artists in France, ranking him above Pierre-Henri de Valenciennes (see E. and J. de Goncourt, v. II, 1882, p. 378). However, it was only at the Salon of 1799 that one of his winter landscapes was exhibited, which continued the tradition of the northern painters of the 16th and 17th centuries (the Brueghels, the Grimmers, the Mompers, Lytens, Alsloot, Teniers, Asselyn, Jacob Van Ruisdael, Jan Van Cappelle, Adriaen Van de Velde, Wouwerman, Beerstraten, etc.). These landscapes guaranteed a certain success to the artist, who specialized very early in this type of picturesque, seductive winter landscape which was always extremely appealing to the public and that was exploited by painters such as Wallaert, Mallebranche, Pernot (in the bishopric of Langres) and even by more serious artists such as Granet, Bouton and Bouhot. After the Salon of 1800 (in which he exhibited a prize-winning *Soleil couchant*), Van Loo received a new *prix d'encouragement* in 1801 for his Salon canvas *Ruines d'une église gothique avec un pont couverts de neige* (No. 184). The *Incendie* from the Salon of 1802 (another *prix d'encouragement*) was loaned in 1876 by the Louvre (INV. 6393) to the Ministry of War as a decoration for residences of military commanders (present location unknown). At the Louvre are a *Paysage, effet de neige* (from the La Caze Collection) which is supposed to have been in the Salon of 1804. In the Salon of 1814 was the *Ruines de l'Ancienne porte de la ville de Véroli, dans les États du Pape*, s.d. 1812, bought by the Louvre in 1815 (INV. 6394) and loaned in 1875 to the Elysée Palace; it was transferred to Autun in 1900. The last Salon in which Van Loo participated was in 1817.

In addition to the works already mentioned are a *Paysage d'hiver* in Quimper, s.d. 1812, acquired in 1974; a second in Cherbourg; and a third in Saint-Denis-de-la-Réunion (acquired as a work by an anonymous 18th-century Flemish artist). In Toulouse are six Italian landscapes, subtle and delicate like those of Joseph Vernet. One of them, *Ponte Molle,* is similar to the one in the Salon of 1785 (then belonging to M. de Véméranges). All these landscapes were confiscated during the Revolution from the collection of Monseigneur de Bernis, Archbishop of Albi. There are also two Italian scenes dated 1780 (INV. 6390 and 6391) on loan from the Louvre to the Château de Compiègne; an Italian landscape (s.d. 1817) in the Galerie Marcus, Paris, in 1970; a view of a river in moonlight done in a "pre-romantic" style like G. Lantara, also reminiscent of J. Vernet, a painting acquired by Empress Joséphine and now in Arenenberg. There were two other works by César Van Loo in Malmaison (see S. Grandjean, 1964, p. 158); one, an *Auberge au pied des Alpes, effet de neige,* was engraved by Muxel while in the Leuchtenberg Gallery in Munich, but cannot be located today. One of the more unusual works by Van Loo is the little-known portrait of the *Comte de Mirbel, secrétaire de Louis XVI,* s.d. 1780, in Caen (gift of Duchesne-Fournet, 1960).

Outside France, besides the above-mentioned in Arenenberg, are five paintings by César Van Loo in the Turin museum (as well as in the Castello di Stupinigi).

According to L. Dussieux (1876, p. 516), who studied the very rare brochure entitled *César Van Loo aux amateurs des Beaux-Arts* (1817), mentioned also by Bellier and Auvray, César Van Loo also painted a *Cascatelles de Tivoli* for the Grand Duke of Russia, which (with the Leuchtenberg painting) leads us to believe that there might also be paintings by César Van Loo in Russian museums.

J. F.

184
Ruins of a Gothic Church

"Ruines d'une église gothique avec un pont dans le lointain, couverts de neige"
Plate p. 159
Canvas; 137 × 175; s.d.l.l. *César Van-Loo. l'an 99 —*
Salon of 1801, no. 348
Fontainebleau, Musée National du Château

The Salon notice, no doubt registering the artist's own observations, indicates that "the composition is the result of many studies made from nature in the Piedmont." Indeed, Jules-César Van Loo seems not to have concerned himself with snow scenes of this sort until his stay in Turin during the Revolution, these sorts of snowy landscapes being part of a whole Italian tradition popular in the 18th century. Both Giovanni Michele Graneri and Francesco Foschi contributed to the tradition as did Graneri, from Turin, and Foschi, from Ancona, the great genre specialist. (We cite the wintry scenes of Foschi at Marcus's in 1971, at Leonard Koetser's in 1973, in the museums of Lille, Cambrai, Grenoble—signed and dated 1750—Darmstadt, Toulouse, etc.) Italian precedents themselves refer back to the brilliant, well-known exercises of northern painting in the 16th and 17th centuries, illustrated by Pieter Breughel I, then his son Pieter II, Joos de Momper, the Grimmers, Alsloot, F. Napoletano himself influenced by the Northerners in a curious painting housed in Florence (Pitti Palace), Asselyn, and of course Teniers, perhaps the most admired Flemish painter in the 18th century. Even in France, Van Loo had his artistic competitors in this very picturesque genre (the observation of particular climatic conditions subordinate to the sense of a certain pictorial taste or sensibility, in this case; the same sort of curiosity about nature is found in Volaire in regard to volcanic eruptions), artists such as Wallaert (Lille), Taunay (here No. 173), the painter Mallebranche from Caen (Paris, Musée Marmottan) and Bouhot. So completely was Van Loo associated with snow scenes that one of the critics of the Salon of 1801 (Deloynes, v. XXVII, p. 493) felt obliged to save him from reproach for his specialization. In comparison with the other known snowy landscapes of the artist (Louvre, coll. La Caze; Cherbourg; Quimper, signed and dated 1812; Autun, also 1812), this work from the Salon of 1801 may well be one of the most important and most successful, if only for the quality of detail (the pleasing touch of the cat on the roof, for instance). Finesse and truth—the very qualities the era cherished in the work of Boilly or Mallet, Demarne and Swebach, Forbin and Granet, all these names justly brought together with that of Van Loo by the unidentified author of the *Examen* cited above —are the qualities admired most of all in the *Paysage* of Fontainebleau by the *Examen... d'une Société d'artistes* (cf. Deloynes): "Everything in this excellent composition proclaims that it is the result of studies made directly from nature. What truth in the local tone of each object, as much as in the general tone of the whole ! The snow trodden underfoot on the steps of the little stairway, and that which is beginning to melt near the chimney of the forge, is perfectly rendered. The buildings, whose vigorous tones contrast happily with the dominant tone of the painting are touched with much spirit; and the fire of the forge produces a wonderful contrast of its own light with that of the snow." There is no less point in mentioning, in the context of the taste of the time, the Gothic style of the ruined church which forms the principal motif of the painting studied here or its quality of studied picturesqueness.

PROVENANCE

Acquired by the state at the Salon of 1801 (in exchange for the prize of encouragement of 1,500 francs bestowed on the artist for this work); kept at Trianon under the Empire and the Restoration; in Compiègne under the Second Empire; returned to the Louvre in 1875; sent to House of the Legion of Honor in Saint-Denis from 1877-1887; brought to Fontainebleau in 1902. INV.:MR 2557, INV. 6392.

EXHIBITION

1801, Salon, no 348.

REFERENCES

Rubens au Muséum, Paris, Year IX (1801), p. 23; G. Tarenne, Ouverture du Salon...; Coll. Deloynes, v. XXVI, no. 683, p. 129; v. XXVII, no. 707, p. 370; no. 708, p. 385; no. 710 p. 493; X... "Examen des ouvrages... exposés au Salon... par une Société d'artistes," edited by Landon; B. Lossky, 1966, pp. 187-188, ill.

J. F.

Antoine-Charles-Horace (called Carle) Vernet

1758 Bordeaux - Paris 1836

"It is singular how I resemble the Grand Dauphin, son of a king, father of a king, and never king." This last witticism of Carle Vernet, jokingly stated shortly before death, illuminates in a humorous way the personality and family situation of the artist. The third son of Joseph Vernet and Virginia Parker, Carle was born in Bordeaux in 1758, where his father was executing one of the paintings for the *Ports de France* series ordered by the Marquis de Marigny for Louis XV. From the age of five, Carle displayed a precocious talent. After studying the basics in nis father's studio, he entered the atelier of Nicolas-Bernard Lépicié at the age of eleven. Charming portraits by Lépicié representing the young boy (Louvre, Petit Palais) are touching evidence of these years. He became a witty and elegant youth. The son of a famous father, he was received by the intelligentsia, introduced to Rousseau, Voltaire and all the great minds of the era. At 17, he competed for the Prix de Rome for the first time and managed to win second prize, surpassed by David. The winner in 1782, he left for Rome in October of that year. His passion for horses naturally led him to study Raphael, Giulio Romano, Salvator Rosa. He then underwent a profound mystical crisis, which prompted his father to make him return to Paris, as early as May 1783. Upon his return, he resumed a life divided between work and the frequenting of fashionable Salons. His first success was the *Triomphe de Paul-Émile* (New York, Metropolitan Museum of Art), which in 1789 opened to him the doors of the Royal Academy, where for several months he was associated with his father.

The Revolution affected him deeply; he suffered the tragedy of seeing guillotined his sister Emily, wife of the architect Jean-François Chalgrin, who had emigrated. When the storm had passed and a worldly, gay and frivolous life resumed under the Directory, Carle did a series of mischievous sketches, *Les Incroyables* and *Les Merveilleuses,* engraved by Darcis in 1797. He excelled in capturing gesture, expression and a quality of life which he rendered with a technique that was witty, spontaneous and elegant. Vernet was able to express the spirit and the slight touch of madness prevailing under the Directory; his skill was enriched by his observant and imaginative eye, as in his famous series, the *Cris de Paris,* and in the *Costumes* (56 plates, published 1814-16).

His passion for horses and the effervescence of the Napoleonic epoch led him to paint large scenes of contemporary history. He revived the battle picture, giving importance to the strategic element; at the Salon of 1808, he presented the *Bataille de Marengo,* which earned him the Legion of Honor. He also painted the

Matin d'Austerlitz, infused with a real sense of the epic; and the *Reddition de Madrid* and *Siège de Pampelune,* all of these paintings at Versailles.

Carle Vernet courted the new regime by exhibiting at the Salon of 1814 the *Portrait Équestre du Duc de Berry.* From that time, he painted many racing and hunting scenes, such as the *Chasse au Daim pour la Saint Hubert en 1818* (Louvre) or the *Départ de la Chasse* (Paris, Musée de la Chasse). He was the first to frequent racing stables, riding schools and circuses such as Franconi's, to study the supple and refined thoroughbreds.

The manner in which he understood and interpreted this animal's form has nothing in common with that of his predecessors: Carle did not paint heavy Percherons or Boulonnais, but rather noble racers—English, Arabic, Persian or Hungarian. He studied their delicate anatomy, the lithe strength of their musculature, their majestic form, thus opening the way for Géricault, Delacroix and Degas. Much honored by the Restoration, for which he was in a way the official painter, he had, like his father, the pleasure of seeing his son enter the Academy in 1826.

In our time, Carle Vernet is best known by engravings after his drawings and his lithographs; he was one of the first French artists to be seduced by this new process, so well-suited to his productive spirit.   I. J.

185
Riderless Horse Race

Course de chevaux barbes
Plate p. 285
Canvas; 100 × 138; s.d.l.r. *Carle Vernet. 1826*
Avignon, Musée Calvet

The provincial Academies were particularly active in the first half of the 19th century. In 1825, the Academy of Vaucluse offered "l'éloge de Joseph Vernet," famous son of Avignon, as subject for a literary competition. At that time, the Musée Calvet did not yet have a true painting gallery, but featured some paintings scattered among antiques, medals and specimens of natural history. To give the future gallery an illustrious sponsor, mayor Baron de Montfaucon, museum administrator Marquis de Cambis d'Orsan, as well as curator Esprit Requien decided to speak to Carle Vernet, son of the head of the dynasty, Joseph Vernet. As early as 1825, M. de Cambis got in touch with Carle and went to his studio to discuss his project. The artist was then painting *Vue de Montmartre avec un four à chaux en action et une charrette sur le devant.* Cambis offered to acquire the painting as a gift for the Musée Calvet, but the painter, finding the subject matter inappropriate, refused and chose to execute instead the *Attaque de Voleurs en Espagne.* It was decided to hold a festival during which the winner of the 1825 competition would be honored, the painting by Carle formally received and a marble bust of Joseph Vernet sculpted by Joseph Brian, installed in the painting gallery. All things considered, Carle decided to represent a wild horse race, which he finished in July of 1826 (see J. Girard, 1927, pp. 49-50, 52) and the inauguration took place in Avignon on 12 October of that year.

The theme of the riderless horse race (see also Nos. 76, 186) was a subject which could not help but attract the attention of a horse lover like Carle. There is no doubt that during his brief stay in Rome in the spring of 1783, he loved this spectacle, which marked the end of the Carnival. Forty years later, he recreated with surprising fidelity the setting and atmosphere of that event: the Piazza del Popolo, the stands jammed with Roman peasants, masked harlequins and Trasteverene peasants playing the tambourine, the horses excited by prickly balls and sheets of tinsel. He chose to let us witness the final preparations before the race, the moment when tension reaches its height. His point of view was close to the one adopted by Théodore Géricault in the painting of the same subject of 1817 today in Baltimore (Walters Art Gallery). Vernet captured to perfection the breath of life, the gay and dramatic aspects of such a scene, but there is a trifling element, a little arid and prosaic, characteristic of Carle, which makes this painting an amusing and realistic episode, which does not attain the power of the versions of the subject by his son Horace (No. 186) and even less the one by Géricault (No. 76).

PROVENANCE
Given by the artist to the museum in 1826.

EXHIBITIONS
1826, Avignon; 1898, Paris, no. 130; 1961, Rome and Turin, no. 377, ill. 78.

REFERENCES
Guichard, 1826 (cited by J. Girard, 1927, p. 54), mus. cat., 1858, no. 298, pp. 101-102; A. Deloye, mus. cat., 1879, no. 283, p. 117; J. Girard, mus. cat., 1909, no. 395, p. 90; *ibid.*, 1924, no. 400, p. 205; *ibid.*, 1927, pp. 50, 52, 54; G. Bazin, 1932, p. 96.

RELATED WORK
Watercolor (23 × 31), s.l.l., sale, Hôtel Drouot, 5 March 1968, no. 18, ill.   I. J.

Émile-Jean-Horace (called Horace) Vernet

1789 Paris 1863

The third and last member of the illustrious Vernet family, Horace, was born on 20 June 1789, at no. 15, the Louvre, where André-Charles Boulle, celebrated *ébéniste* of Louis XIV, had lived and where Joseph Vernet was lodging. Grandson of Jean-Michel Moreau the Younger and of Joseph Vernet, nephew of the architect Jean-François Chalgrin and son of Carle Vernet, his future was determined, and he drew instinctively. As a young child growing up with the Empire, he made crayon drawings of soldiers, heroes of that modern age. To complete his training, he went to the studio of François-André Vincent, a friend of the family, where he received an academic instruction.

At an early age, he had acquired a true clientele and executed several vignettes, notably for invitations to imperial hunts. In 1810, Horace competed, unsuccessfully, for the Prix de Rome. From 1811-15, his main activity was his collaboration with the *Journal des Modes,* for which he made witty and free caricatures, in a way a charming continuation of his father's series of *Incroyables* and *Merveilleuses*. He made his debut at the Salon of 1812, with *La Prise d'un camp retranché* (Salon no. 951), which attracted public attention and earned a commission for an equestrian portrait from Jérôme Bonaparte. When the enemy troops marched on the capital, Horace took part in its defense, which he depicted in one of his best canvases, the *Barrière de Clichy* (Louvre). As a reward for his courage, Napoleon made him Knight of the Legion of Honor.

At the beginning of the Restoration, his studio became the meeting place for the liberals, the faithful to *l'Autre*. With Antoine Raffet and Théodore Géricault, he was one of the first to use lithography, a process which had just been discovered in Germany by Alois Senefelder. But while the other two infused their prints with a passionate emphasis and dramatic emotion, Horace traced the misfortunes of soldiers of the Grande Armée with a light stroke, mischievious but without any bitterness (*e.g.,* "*mon caporal, je n'ai pu avoir que ça, mon lieutenant, c'est un conscrit*"). He was then the favorite of the Duc d'Orléans, the future Louis-Philippe who, after 1830, showered him with honors. In 1820, Horace made his first trip to Italy: he was well received in Rome and executed *Riderless Horse Race* (No. 186).

In 1822, a major scandal occurred; seven paintings presented by Vernet to the Salon, among them, the *Bataille de Jemappes* (London, National Gallery) and the *Barrière de Clichy*, were refused. Their quality was not in question, but they were criticized for their inflammatory and anti-Royalist themes. Horace then decided to exhibit them at his own studio, along with others. Interpreting this refusal as a sign of the new government's intolerance, the most prominent malcontents of Paris flocked to Vernet's studio. Despite Vernet's opposition to the regime, Charles X did not hold a grudge against him for his conduct and inscribed him on the civil list. In 1826, he was named Officer of the Legion of Honor and became a member of the Institute, where he assumed David's chair, vacated by Jean-Jacques-François Le Barbier. At the Salon of 1827, he exhibited numerous works, among them the *Bataille de Bouvines* (Versailles), *Jules II en conférence avec Bramante, Raphaël et Michel-Ange* (Louvre, ceiling of room B of Egyptian Antiquities, Salle 238) were very warmly received. In 1828, he was named Director of the French Academy in Rome and his studio became one of that city's most fashionable spots, renowned for its gaiety. He fulfilled his duties until 1833, and upon his return from a trip in Algeria became one of the official painters of Louis-Philippe and Napoleon III. Highly respected, he died in 1863, leaving a considerable œuvre. Horace Vernet belongs to that group of skilled and prolific history painters who added to their concern for the anecdote a sense of movement and a neo-classical porcelain finish.

I. J.

186
Riderless Horse Race

Le Départ de la course de chevaux libres
Plate p. 262
Canvas; 46 × 54; s.l.r. *H. V.*
New York, The Metropolitan Museum of Art, Bequest of Catharine Lorrilard Wolfe

The riderless horse race marked the end of the festivities of the Roman Carnival and fascinated many artists (see Nos. 76, 185). Horace Vernet, a passionate lover of horses, was not indifferent to this impressive and dramatic spectacle. This painting is a sketch for a large canvas, *La Mossa (Course de chevaux libres),* now missing, but known from an undated lithograph by P. Wagner published in Karlsruhe after 1865 in his *Œuvres Complètes d'Horace Vernet),* painted in Rome by Horace in 1820 and purchased for 4,000 francs by the Duc de Blacas, French ambassador to Naples and patron of the arts and artists. As his father would do in 1826 (no. 185), Horace faithfully rendered an episode witnessed during his first voyage to Rome. It is said that among the spectators crowded in the stands around the Piazza del Popolo (the starting line for the race), one can recognize the French painters then in the city, among them, Antoinette Lescot, a painter of numerous genre scenes inspired by her long stay in Italy (see Lagrange, 1867, p. 307).

Vernet chose to represent the moment just prior to departure, the moment of greatest excitement of the men and beasts, when the young Roman attendants can hardly restrain the horses aroused by the prickly balls spurring their sides and the clamor of the crowd. Horace, in turn, was captivated by this struggle between man and horse, a subject which a few years before fascinated his friend Théodore Géricault (No. 76), whose influence enabled him to attain a fully romantic expression.

PROVENANCE
New York, Catharine Lorillard Wolfe Collection; bequeathed by her to The Metropolitan Museum in 1887, INV. 87.15.17.

EXHIBITIONS
1952, Hartford, no. 9; 1964, Bristol.

REFERENCE
L. Lagrange, 1867, pp. 296-327; Ch. Sterling and M.-M. Salinger, mus. cat., 1966, pp. 16-17.

RELATED WORKS
Final painting, *La Mossa,* executed in 1820, purchased by the Duc de Blacas, lost and known only by a lithograph by R. Wagner published in Karlsruhe, undated, but after 1865 (P. Wagner, *Œuvres complètes de Horace Vernet).* I. J.

187
Mazeppa and the Wolves

Mazeppa et les loups
Plate p. 284
Canvas; 110 × 138; s.d.l.r. *H. Vernet fecit 1826*
Avignon, Préfecture

When the city of Avignon decided to commemorate its native son Joseph Vernet, it spoke of its intentions to the artist's son Carle. Carle's son Horace, a new member of the Academy, decided to do a painting in honor of his grandfather.

Horace first intended to execute a subject illustrating

local history but was not inspired by any of the themes suggested by the museum curator, Esprit Requien, not even "Laura and Petrarch" (J. Girard, 1927, pp. 51-52). He preferred an episode of the story of the Polish page and squire to King John Casimir, Mazeppa (1640-1709), who had become the lover of the beautiful Theresa, wife of the Count Palatine. Upon discovering his spouse's treachery, the count took revenge on Mazeppa, stripping and tying him to the back of a wild horse which he sent off in a gallop. The dramatic story of Mazeppa, who was to become one of the Ukraine's greatest hetmans, was celebrated for the first time by Lord Byron, who composed his *Mazeppa* in Ravenna during the Fall of 1818; it was translated by Amédée Pichot into French in 1822.

Like many others, Horace Vernet was fascinated by Mazeppa's dramatic ride. In 1825, he painted a scene representing the young man tied to the back of the horse, who had just fallen from exhaustion among a herd of horses, a raven circling menacingly above. The painting had a great success even before its completion (A. Jal, 1828, p. 339). For his gift to the Musée Calvet, Vernet chose to illustrate another portion of Byron's poem:

With their long gallop which can tire
The hound's deep hate and hunter's fire
Where'er we flew they followed on,
Nor left us with the morning sun...

According to Jal, Horace Vernet then had a young domesticated wolf housed in his garden at Enghien-Montmorency (*ibid.,* p. 340). His studies of the animal inspired the representation of Mazeppa among wolves.

There are two identical paintings of Mazeppa in Avignon, both dedicated during the festival to the memory of Joseph Vernet. One of the letters from Horace to M. de Montfaucon dated 10 September 1826 (Musée Calvet, MS. 2971, fol. 139) indicates that the first version had met a small mishap. In fact, while it was still in the studio, the canvas was damaged by a foil, most likely during one of the fencing matches that Vernet and his friends liked to stage (as can be seen in the *Atelier de Horace Vernet,* 1822, formerly Donatis Collection). According to Guichard, the artist undertook to repair the work so it would be "redone in such a way as to make it impossible to tell which is the first and which is the second... [But] the Musée Calvet, aware of this unusual situation and anxious to obtain a work as astonishing [as the first], became the owner of two *Mazeppas,* even though the second had already been

sold to an illustrious person for whom Horace Vernet had to make another painting on a different subject as a substitute."

The museum administrator offered 2,000 francs for the second painting, which is exhibited here. Despite Guichard's statement, Horace did execute a second replica of the painting, which was in the Salon of 1827 (see Related Works).

The critics were unanimous: *Mazeppa and the Wolves* was better than the version with horses of 1825. Louis Vitet wrote in *Le Globe:* "In my opinion, this painting of M. Horace Vernet is much better than his first *Mazeppa...* The horse is too tame and the wolves have a certain melodramatic expression. Nonetheless, the scene is well arranged and the landscape gives an altogether poetic impression of terror, which singularly enhances the subject" (1827, p. 73). Vergnaud exclaimed, "The one pursued by wolves is much better in terms of composition and painting than the one in which the horses are looking on" (1827, p. 73). Jal asserted, "With more simplicity, the rendition of *Mazeppa and the Wolves* is much more dramatic.... All the accessories of *Mazeppa and the Wolves* are excellent; the Venetian sky of this landscape is more poetic than natural in effect, but it is a forgivable sin for a painter who is always truthful to want to show once how easy it is to seduce with conventional tones" (1828, pp. 340-343).

Horace Vernet, known for his battle paintings, allowed himself to be seduced by this theme which, for the romantics, symbolized the transports of the poet carried away by inspiration. The hellish course results in freedom and leads the hero to the realms of genius: the superior life is achieved by going through the ordeal of facing death. Byron's sensibility corresponded to that of Vernet, who illustrated several of the poet's works: *Manfred, The Bride of Abydos, Don Juan.* Also in 1828, Louis Boulanger depicted the beginning of Mazeppa's story (Rouen). Théodore Géricault was fascinated by the mad ride of the young page and did a small *Mazeppa* (Paris, private collection). Much later, Théodore Chassériau represented the episode of the story in which a young Ukrainian woman discovers the unconscious Mazeppa (Strasbourg). This archetypal romantic theme inspired one of Victor Hugo's most beautiful poems from the *Orientales,* as well as Franz Liszt's sixth symphonic poem.

PROVENANCE
Bought from the artist by the Musée Calvet for 2,000 francs; on loan to the Préfecture de la Ville.

EXHIBITIONS

1855, Paris, no. 4158; 1899, Paris, no. 273 (?); 1900, Paris, Grand Palais, no. 653 (?).

REFERENCES

Guichard, 1826 (quoted by Girard, 1927, p. 54); mus. cat., 1858, no. 300, p. 102; A. Deloye, mus. cat., 1879, no. 258, p. 118; J. Girard, mus. cat., 1909, no. 418, p. 94; H. Roujon, 1913, p. 39; J. Girard, mus. cat., 1924, no. 403, p. 205; ibid., 1927, pp. 53-55, 59; ibid., 1931, p. 18; L. Guillet, 1934, p. 34; J. Girard, 1955, p. 30; Flaubert, 1845, ed. 1970, p. 126.

RELATED WORKS

First version (canvas; 100 × 138; s.d.l.r. H. Vernet fecit 1826) commissioned for the Musée Calvet (see above). According to Vergnaud (1827, pp. 12-14), Horace Vernet

entered in the Salon of 1827 a "Mazeppa aux loups," under no. 1031 of the Salon catalog: "Many paintings under the same number."

A Mazeppa (canvas, 100 × 138, dimensions almost identical to those of the Avignon paintings) in sale of the picture dealer Everard 31 March - 1 April 1881, no. 148, sold for 2,550 francs. This might be identical with the painting shown in the Salon.

Another Mazeppa is mentioned as belonging to Maurice Buquet at the time of Les Vernets exhibition, Paris, École des Beaux-Arts, in 1898; but since no details were provided, it is impossible to tell if it was a Mazeppa with horses or wolves.

Engraved by "L.F.M. élèves Laidat de M" (sic). Lithographed by Charpentier and Mellin in Nantes: "Le produit de cette lithographie est destiné à secourir les familles victimes des mémorables événements de juillet 1830."

I.J.

188
Scene of the French Campaign of 1814

Scène de la campagne de France, 1814 (?)
Plate p. 286
Canvas; 51 × 65; s.d.l.c. H. Vernet/1826
New York, Private Collection

This beautiful canvas was exhibited in New York in 1970 under the simple title Guerre. It seems in fact to represent an episode of the French campaign of 1814, which mostly took place in Champagne and around Paris. A young peasant woman, armed with a pitchfork, supports her dying husband and, turning around, casts a look of hate on the soldiers who are burning the farm and driving out the cattle. Vernet was partial to this type of historical painting. He was, until midcentury, the indefatigable poet of the Napoleonic era, and he greatly contributed, especially through his numerous lithographs, to the cult of the Emperor.

For example, his Barrière de Clichy (1820; Louvre), another episode of the French campaign, remains the most famous of its type, easily comparable by its style to the present painting. Lithographers such as V. Adam or Antoine Raffet quickly popularized themes of the campaign of 1814, particularly scenes of looting Cossack troops.

PROVENANCE

Paris, art market, 1968-69; New York, Schickman Gallery, 1970; New York, private collection.

EXHIBITION

1970, New York, no. 42, ill.

J.-P. C.

Claude-Joseph (called Joseph) Vernet

1714 Avignon - Paris 1789

Born on 14 August 1714, the son of a modest coach painter with many children, Cl.-J. Vernet became the pupil of Jacques Viali in Aix-en-Provence. His first

known works were decorations over the door of the Hôtel de Caumont (dating c. 1731). With the support of some art patrons of this southern region of France, the young Vernet went to Rome in 1734, where he was to stay nearly 20 years. Right from his early years he concentrated on landscape and especially seascape, as we see from the list of paintings for which he received orders from 1735 on (L. Lagrange, 1864). In Rome, he was taught by Fergioni and particularly the Lyon painter Adrien Manglard; he studied the works of Claude Lorrain and Salvator Rosa, to whom Vernet owed his picturesque rock arrangements.

His fame dates from c. 1740, thanks to his international clientele. Among these were artists (Solimène, Conca, P. Costanzi, M.A. Slotz), important French personalities, (including the ambassador Saint-Aignan) Italians and especially Englishmen, whose numbers increased from 1745 on. Vernet married an Irishwoman and was a friend of his contemporary Richard Wilson; like Claude Lorrain, he had a great following in England, where many of his works are still to be found. His style became fixed: scenes of sunrises and sunsets (often in mist), moonlight, storms—often designed as matching pairs or sets ("the four parts of the day") for overdoor decorations. Vernet also painted landscapes from life "with waterfalls, rocks, tree-trunks, some ruins and figures in the manner of Salvator Rosa" (an order in 1750 for the Englishman Bouverie, L. Lagrange, 1864, p. 332). From 1746 on, Vernet sent pictures to the Paris Salon, where they were received with enthusiasm; he was a regular exhibitor until his death.

In 1750, he made the acquaintance of M. de Vandières, the future Marquis de Marigny, and received his first orders for the French court. He returned to France in 1753 and was made a full member of the Academy (he had been an associate since 1745). He began to paint for the King a series of *Ports de France* (originally 20 large canvases but finally only 15), which he worked on until 1765; reproduced alsoin en graving, these paintings were to assure Vernet's fame (most of them are today in the Musée de la Marine in Paris).

The enthusiasm of collectors and critics (led by Diderot) can be explained by the fact that Vernet's talent was two-fold: he could render expertly the irregular features of a landscape, the break of a wave, the play of light through mist, and the vaporous red glow of the setting sun; but he was also a thoughtful artist, who composed his landscapes carefully and gave them the dignity of history painting (in his lifetime, he was commonly preferred for this to Claude Lorrain, over whom he had the advantage of being able to paint figures). Furthermore, the 18th-century mind especially loved his shipwrecks, his "horrible" storms, his "hideous and wild scenes of nature."

But Vernet's very success, his enormous output and his many imitators (apart from his own brother, Volaire, Henry, Lacroix de Marseille, etc.) today detract from his reputation, despite the outstanding quality of his best pictures and his historical importance. A. S.

189
Construction of a Highway

"La Construction d'un grand chemin"
Plate p. 46
Canvas; 97 × 162; s.d.l.l. *J. Vernet. f 1774*
Salon of 1775, no. 31 (with its pendant, here No. 190)
Paris, Musée du Louvre

According to Bachaumont, the horseman inspecting the construction is J.-R. Perronet (1708-1790), famous engineer and builder of the bridges of Neuilly and la Concorde, among other things. He oversaw the construction of the Burgundy canal and was the first director of the School of Bridges and Roads, founded by Trudaine. In the work, Vernet carefully constructed the landscape space, delineating successive planes by

zigzags in the road, a method frequently employed in the "heroic" landscapes of the 17th century. As with its pendant (No. 190), the architectonic solidity of the composition is balanced by picturesque detail: twisted stumps (as in works by Hubert Robert or Jean-Honoré Fragonard), the windmill (which makes a curious contrast with the noble architecture of the background), and especially the animated work site whose lively realism is entirely northern in inspiration and prefigures the art of Jean-Louis Demarne or Nicolas-Antoine Taunay.

PROVENANCE

Painted, with its pendant (No. 190) for Abbé Terray, Controller-General of Finances and Director-General of Buildings, from July 1773 until his downfall in May 1774 (see No. 190); the two paintings cost 10,000 *livres* in two installments, 7 November 1774 and 12 January 1775 ("*Livre de Vérité,*" in L. Lagrange, 1864, p. 368, nos. 179-180); sale after the death of Abbé Terray, January 1779, no. 2, sold with its pendant to the merchant Feuillet for 6,000 *livres ;* de Cotte Collection. Acquired by the Chambre de Paris for the Galerie Vernet at the Luxembourg, July 1814; transferred to the Louvre in 1816 (INV. 8331).

EXHIBITIONS

1775, Salon, no. 31; 1934, Paris, no. 239; 1954-1955, London, no. 361; 1964-1965, United States and Canada, no. 17; 1966, Vienna, no. 501.

REFERENCES

Diderot, 1775, ed. J. Seznec, v. IV, 1967, p. 246, ill. 116 and p. 283; Bachaumont, v. XIII, p. 204; L. Clément de Ris, 1859-1861, ed. 1872, p. 285; L. Lagrange, 1864, pp. 198, 466, 481; F. Ingersoll-Smouse, 1926, v. I, p. 29, v. II, p. 25, no. 981; mus. cat., 1972, p. 390.

RELATED WORK

A small copy appeared on the Paris market in 1966.

A. S.

190
Fair of Beaucaire

"*Les Abords d'une foire*" ou *La Foire de Beaucaire*
Plate p. 47
Canvas; 91 × 162; s.d. b. c. *J. Vernet f. 1774*
Salon of 1775, no. 31 (see the preceding number)
Montpellier, Musée Fabre

As A. Joubin observed in 1926, Vernet's setting for the *Fair of Beaucaire* is imaginary but seems to contain recollections of the bridge of Saint-Cloud and Villeneuve-lès-Avignon, and even of Mont Ventoux. The strict classical organization of the landscape, as defined by the architecture, the tree clumps and the cliff to the right, does not prevent the painter from capturing the lively picturesque quality of the small port. Paintings such as this one and its pendant (No. 189) represent a unique synthesis of two, later divergent, tendencies in French painting: the composed historical landscape and the realistic landscape animated by contemporary figures.

PROVENANCE

Separated from its pendant after the Terray sale, January 1779, no. 3, it passed into the Clos Collection; Clos was Lieutenant-General of the Prévôté de l'Hôtel and Grand Prévôté of France (is the description found on a bundle in the painting and addressed to Clos subsequent to or one of the reasons for the acquisition of the work ?); Clos sale, 18-19 November 1812, no. 43 (acquired by Roland for 2,460 francs); de Solirène sale, 5 May 1829, no. 127 (1,124 francs); purchased by Fabre from the merchant Roger *fils aîné,* 28 July 1829; Fabre bequest, February 1837, no. 547.

EXHIBITION

1775, Salon, no. 31.

REFERENCES

Diderot, 1775, ed. J. Seznec, v. IV, 1967, p. 283; L. Clément de Ris, 1859-1861, ed. 1872, p. 285; L. Lagrange, 1864, pp. 198-199, 466, 476, 481-482; mus. cat. (A. Joubin), 1926, no. 790, p. 241; F. Ingersoll-Smouse, 1926, v. II, p. 26, no. 982, ill. 249; M. Laclotte and J. Vergnet-Ruiz, 1962, p. 100, ill. 120 and p. 255.

A. S.

191
*Death of Virginie**

"Le naufrage de Virginie à l'île de France"
Plate p. 93
Canvas; 87 × 130; s.d.l.l. *J. Vernet f. 1789*
Salon of 1789, no. 26
Leningrad, The Hermitage Museum

Vernet was the first of numerous illustrators employed by Bernardin de Saint-Pierre (1737-1814), the author who emerged from obscurity with the publication of his *Paul et Virginie*. At first inserted in the fourth volume of the *Études de la Nature* (1788), this novelette appeared as a separate edition in early 1789. The painter and the author were personally acquainted, and Vernet appears to have participated in the promotion of the book. On 27 January, he thanked Bernardin de Saint-Pierre for sending him 12 copies in exchange for a drawing, which was perhaps a first version of this painting (signed letter, Cap Sale, 1849, cited by L. Lagrange, 1864, p. 458). On 20 May, Vernet presented him with a rough outline of the painting, sketched directly on the canvas (*ibid.,* 2, p. 459).

The book met with tremendous success, and the popular revised edition by Didot in 1806 was enriched with several engravings after Lafitte, Gérard, Isabey and Prud'hon, all illustrating the shipwreck. Edmond de Favières and Rodolphe Kreutzer wrote a play based on this book and it was performed with equal success by the Comédie Italienne in 1791.

The story of two young lovers, enriched by the description of the Ile de France (Ile Maurice) with its luxuriant vegetation and honest customs, captured the hearts of everyone. The ship "Saint-Géran," which was taking Virginia from France, where she had been educated during the previous two years, was hurled ashore and wrecked by the hurricane. The artist represented that moment when the body of Virginie, her hand still clutching the portrait of Paul, is found on the beach, to the great anguish of Dominique.

F. Ingersoll-Smouse (1926) justly stated that this painting is "as significant a work as the *Accordée de village* or similar moralizing paintings by Greuze." The elderly Vernet (he died at the end of the year),

took this opportunity to revive a theme which he had frequently represented for almost 40 years. The exaggerated emotional quality of his usual "storms" or "shipwrecks" (he submitted three "shipwrecks" to the Salon of 1789 alone) is increased by the unambiguous allusion to a story familiar to most of his audience. The principal elements of this painting, the enormous wave breaking on a rocky platform and the three fallen masts, are found in a number of his earlier works (see nos. 352, 498, 733, 831-832, 1090 and 1168 of Ingersoll Smouse, *op. cit.*). Among examples from the same period, which can be cited is a work dated 1783, at the Ponce museum, and another from the Pacully sale (Paris, Hôtel Drouot, 5 July 1938), dated 1787 (*ibid.,* no. 1168), or that of 1788, also from the Hermitage (*ibid.,* no. 1180), which was confused with the present painting in the French edition of this catalog (pl. 51, pp. 649-650).

PROVENANCE
Painted for one of Vernet's most faithful patrons, Girardot de Marigny, for whom Vernet had executed, between 1777 and his death, some 15 paintings, each costing 3,000 francs; acquired by Czar Paul I for the Hermitage, where it remains (INV. no. 1759).

EXHIBITION
1789, Salon, no 26.

REFERENCES
L. Dussieux, 1852, ed. 1876, p. 580; L. Lagrange, 1864, pp. 293-294, 468, 485; A. Durande (1864), p. 54, mus. cat. (Koehne), 1887, v. III, pp. 73-74 (no. 1554); F. Ingersoll-Smouse, 1926, v. I, p. 32, v. II, p. 44, no. 1186, ill. 279; L. Réau, 1929, no. 387, p. 64; mus. cat., 1958, v. I, p. 274.

RELATED WORK
Engraved by Stépan Galaktionow in 1842.

A. S.

Antoine Vestier

1740 Avallon - Paris 1824

Son of an Avallon merchant of the Troyes bourgeoisie, Antoine Vestier must have revealed his predilection for painting at a young age, and very early painted an *Ascension* for the church at Avallon (M. Nizet, 1907, p. 692). In Paris at the age of 20, he worked with Antoine Révérend, master enameler, whose daughter, Marie-Anne, he married in 1764. Next he left the atelier, little by little abandoning enamel for oil painting, and taking Jean-Baptiste Pierre's courses at the Academy. Vestier seems to have specialized very early in portraiture, oils as well as miniatures. It seems that he traveled to Holland and England; he was in contact with William Peters in London and signed a miniature there in 1776. Vestier often used himself or members of his family as models: his wife, daughter Nicole (who would marry François Dumont), son Nicolas-Jacques-Antoine (a future architect). From 1782, the artist exhibited in the Salon de la Correspondance, in company with Louis-Rolland Trinquesse and Henri-Pierre Danloux. He became an associate member in the Academy in 1785 with a portrait of his daughter, and the following year became an academician with the portraits of Doyen (Louvre) and Brenet (No. 192). His *Portrait of Riesener* (Versailles) dates from 1785. In 1788, the artist painted the sober effigies of the *Jeune Homme,* which recently entered the Avallon museum, and of *Monsieur Bernard de Sarrette et Madame de Sarrette* in the Phoenix Art Museum. As Vestier evolved towards an art once more austere and lyrical, he created some of his masterpieces: *Portrait de Jean Theurel* (1788, Tours), *Portrait de Latude* (1789, Paris, Musée Carnavalet), *Portrait de Gossec* (1791, Paris, Musée de l'Opéra).

Vestier also painted some disguised portraits, such as the *Femme couronnée de roses* and the *Bacchante* in the museum in Tours. After the Revolution, the artist was unable to pick up his career and died, somewhat forgotten, during the Restoration.

Vestier's soberly realistic art adheres to the faithful description of the features of the model and is especially attentive to the rendering of clothing and accessories. He may be credited with some of the most sincere portraits from the late 18th century; a great many remain in private collections.

J.-P. C.

192
Portrait of Brenet

"*M. Brenet*"
Plate p. 77
Canvas; 130 × 97; s.d.l.l. *Nicolas Guy Brenet,/peint en 1786/par Antoine Vestier*
Salon of 1787, no. 142
Versailles, Musée National

This painting was executed as a pendant to the *Portrait de Doyen* which Vestier had painted in 1781 (Louvre). The two paintings constituted Vestier's reception pieces at the Royal Academy; the artist was received on 30 September 1786. On the canvas of the Brenet painting is a line sketch of a work exhibited by the artist in the same Salon (1787), *Le jeune fils de Scipion rendu à son frère par Antiochus,* today in Nantes.

Vestier, a new academician, exhibited a great number of portraits at the Salon of 1787 (Salon nos. 141-152), among them the full-length portrait of his wife (Louvre). Criticism was generally favorable, with praise for "the quality of the textures." The portraits of the painters Nicolas-Guy Brenet (see No. 15) and Gabriel-François Doyen (1727-1806) were found to have "a perfect resemblance, good color, beautiful harmony and a great deal of truth" (*Journal de Paris,* coll. Deloynes, XV, no. 394, pp. 770-771); the critic from the *Mercure de*

France (ibid., no. 396, pp. 840-841) found in Vestier's paintings "pleasing color, although soft at times" and judged the portraits of Brenet and Doyen to be the best: "The tone here is firm and the color pronounced. M. Vestier can be reproached only for having sacrificed accessories in order to illuminate the heads."

Even today the *Portrait of Brenet* stands as one of Vestier's most beautiful paintings. Its simple, dignified pose, both natural and noble, the sumptuosity of the coloring which, in sonorous harmony, opposes the somber and luminous red of the clothing to the emerald tone of the linen at the left; the meticulous and vibrant execution, place it among the best portraits from the end of the Ancien Regime.

PROVENANCE

Collection of the Academy; Musée des Monuments Français; Château de Versailles; École des Beaux-Arts, 1826; Louvre, 1887 (INV. 8412); sent to Versailles in November 1920 (MV. 5805).

EXHIBITION

1787, Salon, no. 142.

REFERENCES

Explication des peintures... 1787, no. 142, p. 26; coll. Deloynes, v. XV, no. 367, p. 26; no. 371, p. 87; no. 373, p. 168; no. 374, p. 212; no. 394, pp. 770-771; no. 394, pp. 840-841; A. Jal, 1867, p. 1264; A. Foulon de Vaulx, 1901, p. 394; M. Nizet, 1907, p. 693; P. Dorbec, 1911, pp. 368-369; Ch. Oulmont, 1913, p. 300; M. Sandoz, 1960, p. 35 and n. 2.

J.-P. C.

Joseph-Marie Vien

1716 Montpellier - Paris 1809

Born at Montpellier in 1716, Joseph-Marie Vien received his first training with local artists who are now forgotten. Compelled to earn his livelihood at an early age, he engaged in diverse activities which had little connection with his vocation, such as drawing maps and architectural plans and decorating faïence. By the time he departed for Paris in July 1740, he had certainly acquired some artistic experience. For four years he was under the guidance of Charles-Joseph Natoire, who, unable to admit Vien to his studio since he had too many pupils, nevertheless lavished on him his advice. Vien earned his living at this time, for better or for worse, by making copies for a picture dealer. While studying at the Academy, he obtained various awards, including second and then first place medals for drawing, in 1741 and 1742. A year later, he was admitted to the competition for the Prix de Rome, which he won with *David se résignant à la volonté du Seigneur qui a frappé son royaume de la peste* (Paris, École des Beaux-Arts). The young painter did not leave for Rome immediately, but remained in Paris for another year, assisting his master Natoire.

From 1744 until 1750, Vien studied at the French Academy in Rome under the direction of Jean-François de Troy. Like the other students, he made numerous copies after the masters, Renaissance as well as those of 17th-century Bologna and Rome. He also executed nude academies and landscape drawings, and obtained several important commissions. From this period dates the series of paintings representing scenes from the life of Saint Martha (Tarascon, church of Sainte-Marthe). This little known cycle is of exceptional quality and is the result of a comprehensive study of 17th-century Italian religious painting. Vien became very interested in the baroque revival occurring in Rome with artists such as Pompeo Batoni. He was also concerned with realism, as attested by his vigorous studies from live models and from nature. His celebrated painting *L'Ermite endormi* (Louvre) was warmly received by the public; and the severe presentation of the model, almost devoid of any accessories, attracted the attention of his contemporaries.

When he returned to France in 1750, Vien had some difficulty in gaining acceptance in the Royal Academy. Most members of this illustrious circle had difficulty in accepting his realism. Finally recognized in 1751, Vien was formally admitted to the Academy in 1754 with his *Dédale et Icare* (Paris, École des Beaux-Arts). In its subject and style, this work evidences a new return to the antique. It also explains, among other things, his friendship with the Comte de Caylus, who collaborated with him in his efforts to rediscover encaustic painting. Vien used encaustics in several paintings.

From the 1760s, Vien executed principally religious paintings, often on a grand scale, and in this manner he revived the tradition of great history painting which had been neglected since Jouvenet and Restout. Besides historical paintings, Vien concerned himself with classical subjects, and an increasingly neo-classical style. The famous *Marchande d'amours* (Fontainebleau), which he exhibited at the Salon of 1763, is only one example of an entire series in which, by borrowing classical models and motifs, he attempted to recreate scenes from ancient Greece. These paintings originally belonged to a style referred to as *"à la grecque."* Mme du Barry had Fragonard's decorative paintings removed from one of her salons at Louveciennes and commissioned Vien to replace them with compositions in the current taste, as she wanted to possess a series in the *"style grec."*

Vien was a clever teacher and had numerous pupils. He taught at the Academy, and in 1771 his teaching abilities led to his appointment as director of the École des Élèves Protégés. From 1775 until 1781, Vien was director of the French Academy in Rome, where David was one of his many students. During this period, Vien completed several large paintings for the King, representing in a moving and dignified style, scenes from the history of Troy. Elected chancellor of the Academy after his return to Paris, he was appointed first painter to the King and director of the Academy in 1789, replacing Pierre. Under the Revolution, Consulate and Empire, the aging Vien executed several series of drawings mostly illustrating scenes from Greek antiquity; one complete series is at the Louvre. He also actively engaged in the administration the Fine Arts; Napoleon appointed him to the Senate in 1799, then to commander of the Legion of Honor in 1804, and finally count of the Empire in 1808. He died in 1809 and was interred in the Panthéon. Vien had a profound influence on several generations of French painters; he was called the "restorer of the French School" and David, in his funeral eulogy, declared "...our father has ceased to live."

Th. G.

193
Saint Louis and Marguerite de Provence*

Saint Thibault *"offre au Roi Saint Louis et à la Reine Marguerite de Provence une corbeille de fleurs"*
Plate p. 45
Canvas; 285 × 177; s.d.l.l. *Jos. m. vien./1774.*
Salon of 1775, no. 3
Versailles, Musée National

The painting of Saint Thibault was commissioned by the King in 1767. On 15 October of that year, Louis XV instructed the Director General of Royal Buildings, the Marquis de Marigny, to have two paintings executed, the first for the chapel of the Château de Saint-Hubert and second for that of Marly or Choisy. The King himself selected the subjects: one was to illustrate an event from the lives of Saints Louis and Thibault (see a memorandum of the King on this theme, Arch. Nat., O¹ 1072, in which the event is described in the following manner: "Saint Thibaud [sic] de Marly, abbot of Vaux-de-Cernay; he was of the House of Montmorency and it is to his prayers that France believed herself indebted for the descendants of Saint Louis. Died 6 December 1247.) Cochin, in a letter of 7 November 1767, explained to the Marquis de Marigny that the subject would be suitable for a royal chapel. "If you knew nothing else about this saint, the subject would offer few possibilities for a painting; a tradition holds that France is indebted to his prayers for the descendants of Saint Louis; thus, there is a theme for a canvas in which, under the guise of allegory, you may represent things at once both flattering to the House of Bourbon, and particularly appropriate to the King's pleasure" (see Seznec, IV, p. 242). When Marigny entrusted Vien with the execution of this painting, he outlined the content: "Saint Thibaud [sic], abbot of Vaux-de-Cernay, receives Saint Louis and Queen Marguerite, his wife, in the garden where he works with his monks. He is accompanied by Bouchard VI (or Mathieu III), lord of the House of Montmorency, his cousin. Through a mysterious cloud, the holy abbot shows their majesties their descendants, especially the House of Bourbon. You will see Robert, progenitor of this house, and those of his lineage who were destined to be enthroned, including Henri IV, Louis XIII, Louis XIV and the King."

Vien did not rigidly adhere to these instructions. Instead of presenting the full assembly of the lineage of Saint Louis, he painted only five personnages in the foreground, and these were accompanied by three children. The eleven stems of the fleur-de-lis symbolize the large Royal family.

A small preparatory pen drawing (private collection) is an early compositional study, in which the central group has not yet been organized. Neither has Vien developed the idea of the monk holding the basket of flowers. In place of Thibault is Bouchard VI (or Mathieu III). Another larger drawing, in which Vien realized the final arrangement, was recently sold at Sotheby's (22 November 1973, no. 17). However, this highly worked drawing offers some interesting deviations from the painting; the Royal family is attired in costume of the Louis XIII period, which Vien would subsequently modify.

Was this elaborate drawing destined for presentation to the King or the Director General of Buildings? Marigny asked Vien to submit two pen sketches "to enable the King to make a choice" (see Seznec, IV, p. 242). Was it executed to obtain final approval for the commission? The circumstances are not known. In January 1768, it was decided that Vien's painting would be assigned to the chapel of the new (Petit) Trianon at Versailles, which had just been completed. Vien did not finish the painting until 1774, exhibiting it at the Salon of 1775, the year of his departure for Rome where he had just been appointed Director of the French Academy. The painting was favorably received. The author of *Observations sur les ouvrages exposés au Sallon* [sic] *du Louvre* noted: "Saint Thibault appears to me to be a beautiful painting, vigorous in color and effect, judiciously and nobly composed. The details are drawn with accuracy and truthfulness. I must note that M. Vien has a unique talent for preserving the nobility of his heads, while at the same time imparting to them a truthful character which proves that they were carefully rendered from life, and this was not a common ability." He then made a minor observation that the back wall was a bit too dark, and he justi-

fiably explained that Vien had "no doubt wished to set off the figures in relief."

This critic's analysis captures the stylistic elements which distinguish Vien from his contemporaries. Since his first neo-classical paintings in the 1760s, the simplicity of the composition in relief is characteristic of his technique. Connected with this simplicity is a studied realism of faces and details, qualified by the critics as created "after nature and with exactitude." This feature is an important element in the teaching of Vien which was followed not only by David but indeed by most of the neo-classical painters. The critic of the *Journal encyclopédique* (no. 1332, n. p.) is in agreement with the writer cited above: "We find the wisdom, purity of composition and design of Monsieur Vien, as well as the balance and harmony of color, in a painting which ought to be installed in the chapel of the new Trianon; the subject is successfully and nobly expressed." Diderot, who in his reviews of the Salons, was so often favorable to Vien and considered him one of the best painters of his time, showed less enthusiasm on this occasion. He derided the representation of the young Queen Marguerite de Provence: "And this vexing mien, what can you say about it? Is this our idea of a queen?"

PROVENANCE
Installed on the main altar of the chapel of the Petit Trianon at Versailles in 1775; removed during the Revolution; returned to its original installation between 1806 and 1812; after the restoration of the chapel, up to the present, the painting has been in storage at Versailles (M.V. 7136).

EXHIBITION
1775, Salon, no. 3.

REFERENCES
Coll. Deloynes, v. X, no. 160, pp. 548-549; no. 162, p. 661; no. 165, pp. 718-719; v. XLIX, no. 1332, p. 753; Diderot, 1775, ed. Seznec and Adhémar, 1967); A. Dézallier d'Argenville, 1779, p. 161; F. Aubert, 1867, v. II, p. 186; A. Dutilleux, 1886, p. 134; F. Engerand, 1901, pp. 513-514; Correspondance des directeurs... v. I, 1906, pp. 67-74; P. de Nolhac, 1914, p. 40; J. Seznec and J. Adhémar, v. IV, 1967, p. 241, 275, ill. 103; J. Lugand, 1964, p. 538 ff.

RELATED WORKS
Pen drawing, Paris, private collection, India ink with a bistre wash, paper on cardboard (13.9 × 8.4), on the reverse *J.-M. Vien 36*. Charcoal and pen drawing (36 × 25.5), inscription: *Vien*, Sotheby sale of 22 November 1973, no. 17, from Paris, private collection.

Th. G.

194
Love Fleeing Slavery

"L'Amour fuyant l'esclavage"
Plate p. 89
Canvas; 131 × 161; s.d.l.l. *J.M. Vien 1789*
Salon of 1789, no. 1
Toulouse, Musée des Augustins

A letter of the secretary of the Duc de Brissac (Versailles, Bibliothèque Municipale) informs us that *Love Fleeing Slavery* was commissioned by his master as a pendant to *La Marchande d'amours* (Salon of 1763, no. 23, now at Fontainebleau). The Duc de Brissac presented both to Mme du Barry.

This painting followed *La Marchande d'amours* by many years and is no longer inspired by a classical model. In the first canvas, of 1763, a vendor sells little cupids. In the later work, the cupid has escaped from his cage and flies aways, startling four young women, one of whom attempts to catch him.

La Marchande d'amours had been a great success in 1763; in its subject and style, Vien had succeeded in recreating a classical painting, based on a fresco rediscovered at Gragnano. His paintings in the 1760s contributed to the growing popularity of the taste for *à la grecque,* which was greatly encouraged by Mme du Barry.

The idea of executing a pendant to *La Marchande d'amours* was possibly suggested to the Duke by the painter himself. Two drawings, signed and dated 1772 (New York, private collection), prove that Vien had already considered such a pair.

The Toulouse painting, executed 25 years later, revives a style which Vien had abandoned during his sojourn in Rome as Director of the French Academy.

The early compositional simplicity is replaced by movement and expression. Certain gestures are reminiscent of Vien's paintings illustrating scenes from the *Histoire de Troye* [sic], executed during the same period. The author of *Observations critiques* made an interesting comment: "M. Vien, after having sounded the heroic trumpet, now appears to play with the Graces and Cupid; it is like the aging Homer becoming Anacreon."

PROVENANCE
Commissioned by the Duc de Brissac and presented to Mme du Barry at Louveciennes; confiscated during the Revolution and deposited in the *Musée spécial de l'Ecole française* at Versailles; transferred to Fontainebleau in 1839; returned to the Louvre (INV. 8425). Transferred to Toulouse in 1876 (INV. 800-2-1).

EXHIBITIONS
1789, Salon, no. 1; 1968-1969, Bregenz, no. 460.

REFERENCES
(Anon.), *Les Élèves au Salon,* 1789, p. 6; Mende Maupas, 1789, pp. 7-8; *Mercure de France,* October 1789, p. 81; Aubert, 1867, v. 23, pp. 175-187; E. de Beaumont, 1872, p. 135; E. Molinier, 1900, p. 177; *Procès-Verbaux de la Commission des Monuments,* v. II, 1902, p. 242; E. Roschach, v. VIII, 1908, pp. 23, 148, no. 305; F.-M. Biebel, 1960, p. 226, no. 41; J. Lugand, 1964, p. 598 ff.; R. Rosenblum, 1967a, pp. 19-20, ill. 15.

Th. G.

Joseph-Marie Vien *fils*

1761 Paris 1848

Joseph-Marie Vien, only son of the famous painter of the same name, was born in Paris on 1 August 1761. While his father's works were in the grand manner,

Vien *fils* painted only miniatures and portraits. He received his first lessons in painting in his father's studio in Rome, where the elder Vien was director of the French Academy. Back in Paris, he continued his studies under the guidance of F.-A. Vincent.

Vien *fils* exhibited portraits—both regular size and miniatures—regularly at the Salon from 1794 to 1835. One of his most famous portraits, is that of the Dauphin (1793; Paris, Musée Carnavalet). His portraits are mainly characterized by extremely detailed, meticulous drawing, demonstrating his talent as a miniaturist. This is especially noticeable in his portrait of a *Vieillard en habit rouge* (Narbonne, attributed to Vien *père*), and in that of the *Poète Jacques Delille* (Saint-Germain-en-Laye). The younger Vien knew early fame as a portraitist and received important commissions under the Empire and Restoration, for example a full-length portrait of Jourdan, hung in the Salle des Maréchaux in the Tuileries (it was unfortunately lost in the fire of 1871).

His work has not yet been catalogued. To be mentioned are a portrait of his father as a senator (Montpellier), and a *Portrait de l'artiste et de son épouse* (Rouen), which was exhibited at the Salon of 1808 and is probably his masterpiece. There are also about 100 drawings at Béziers. Vien *fils'* works characterize portrait development during the Revolution and under the Empire. The poses of the subjects often possess classical and romantic qualities and show the influence of great portraitists such as David, Gérard and Ingres.

On 20 August 1791 Vien *fils* married Rose-Céleste Bache (1774-1835), daughter of Général Jacques-François Bache. Rose-Céleste Vien was a woman of letters who wrote a number of poems, and is known especially for a prose translation of the *Odes* of Anacreon, which she did in 1825.

Th. G.

195
*Portrait of Frion**

"Portrait de M. Frion sortant de nager, et reprenant ses vêtements"
Plate p. 190
Canvas; 206 × 130
Salon of 1804, no. 527
Perpignan, Musée Hyacinthe Rigaud

Jean-Baptiste-François Frion (1773-1819) was Inspector of Arts and Crafts and had connections with all the important people of Paris. He was of very large stature, measuring 2.24 m. It has been said that David used him as a model for his *Funérailles de Patrocle* (No. 27; see H. David, *Gamelin*, pp. 44, 117-118); however, Frion's figure cannot be distinguished in the composition.

Frion's exceptional height fascinated his contemporaries. Thus, we read in his obituary: "The structure of Frion's body could have been the object of useful physiological observations. In all his ways, even as far as his whims, he had the tastes and habits of a woman. The idea that his ashes would not be respected and that after his death he would become an object of public curiosity, was ever present in his mind and was the bane of his life" (see *Mémorial administratif*, 1819, p. 190).

The poet Jacques Delille even dedicated to him these lines of poetry:

La Nature envers les humains
Toujours avare et souvent inégale,
Changea l'ordre de nos destins
Et voulut une fois se montrer libérale.
Elle communiqua son projet à l'Amour;
L'Hymen fut de la conférence,
Et pour preuve de déférence,
Le beau Frion reçut le jour.
Les géants sont, dit-on, d'humeur âpre et sauvage.
Le nôtre fut toujours de la plus belle humeur.
Le nôtre sur son front modestie et candeur.
Aussi Frion, dès son jeune âge,
A la force, à la majesté,
Sut réunir par un rare assemblage,
L'esprit, la grâce et la beauté.

Jacques Gamelin had already executed a portrait of Frion in 1796, where he is seen full-length and full-face, wearing a gray coat (cf. exh. cat., *J. Gamelin,*

Carcassonne, 1938, no. 4, ill.). Vien *fils* represented him very differently. Frion's pose in this portrait is rather curious. The figure is seated on a stone block and appears to dry and dress himself after having bathed. He holds a towel in his left hand, his shirt is open, his feet bare. A river flows at the bottom, in which several swimmers frolic around a boat. A town and mountains rise in the background. It is not likely that the artist would have represented Frion in this unusual pose without the model's consent. Unfortunately, we know nothing about this commission.

The sparse comments made by the reviewers when this bizarre "effigy" was exhibited at the Salon of 1804, were harsh: one remarked: "I don't know how the idea of presenting a figure in such an attire could come into the mind of a painter of good sense. How is it possible that he did not realize that the sight of a man who is undressed, and displays his ugly feet, is both tasteless and repulsive?" (coll. Deloynes, XXXI, no. 527, p. 74).

Landon was the only favorable voice. But he reproached the artist for not having adequately expressed the stature of the model. "We find a good likeness and a fineness of color in the portrait of M. Frion by Monsieur Vien *fils*. If the artist had placed a person of ordinary height near this figure, he would have created a better effect of the proportions of this giant" (coll. Deloynes, XXXII, no. 891, p. 556).

PROVENANCE

Fraisse Collection (nephew of Frion); gift to the Perpignan museum.

EXHIBITIONS

1804, Salon, no. 527; 1900, Grand Palais, no. 658.

REFERENCES

Coll. Deloynes, v. XXXI, no. 527, p. 74; no. 867, p. 416; no. 878, p. 833; v. XXXII, no. 891, p. 556; E. Crouchandeu, mus. cat., 1884, p. 94, no. 129.

Th. G.

Elisabeth-Louise Vigée-Lebrun

1755 Paris 1842

Born in Paris 16 April 1755, Marie-Louis-Élisabeth was the daughter of Louis Vigée, a professor at the Academy of Saint-Luke and a portraitist and pastellist of some renown. In her father's studio she was encouraged by Gabriel-François Doyen (1726-1809) and Joseph Vernet (1714-1789). She perfected her training by studying the works by Rubens in the Galerie du Luxembourg, the collection of Flemish painting amassed by Randon de Boisset, and the Italian masterpieces in the Galerie du Palais Royal. She admired Raphael, copied Rubens, Van Dyck, Rembrandt and "several heads of young girls by Greuze as these heads definitely account for the half-tones, which are found in the delicate complexions" (Madame Vigée-Lebrun, 1835-37, I, p. 19).

At 15 years of age, she commenced a brilliant and promising career as a portraitist. Her fashionable and virtuoso talent, more flattering than preoccupied with psychological accuracy, her elegant manner of draping shawls and turbans and her delicate touch quickly attracted a large aristocratic patronage and visits by many traveling foreigners.

In 1779, she completed her first portrait of the Queen, Marie-Antoinette (Vienna), which she reproduced afterwards on more than 20 occasions.

In spite of a fierce intrigue led principally by Jean-Baptiste Pierre (1713-1789) in opposition to her admission to the Royal Academy of Painting (she was a woman and moreover the wife, since 1776, of an art dealer, albeit an important one, Jean-Baptiste-Pierre Lebrun [1748-1813]), she was admitted in 1783, on submission of *Paix qui ramène l'Abondance* (Louvre).

Her salon attracted the celebrities of the period, such as the minister Calonne, the Comte de Vaudreuil (No. 197); her evening parties were greatly appreciated: most famous is her famed Greek supper, improvised after a reading from the *Voyages du jeune Anacharsis,* which she served herself in company with Mme Chalgrin, both attired as Athenians, and presented in Etruscan cups from the collection of the Comte de Paroy.

The novelty of this feast created a lot of talk throughout Europe (*ibid.*, I, p. 97).

In 1789, with the first events of the Revolution, Mme Vigée-Lebrun, endangered by her ties with the court, took refuge in Italy. Her reputation had preceded her and the academicians in Rome, Parma and Bologna accepted her as one of them; she presented a self-portrait (No. 198) to the Galleria degli Uffizi and another to the Academy of Saint Luke in Rome. After a stay at the court of Naples, she left Italy for Vienna (1793-95) and then settled in Saint Petersburg (1795-1801). On each occasion she was received with the utmost warmth and commissions abounded. Upon her return to Paris in 1801, the imperial court solicited a portrait of Caroline Murat (Versailles). Suspected of loyalty to the Bourbons, she preferred to assume a distant position and to travel in England and Switzerland, where she was welcomed in Coppet by Mme de Staël and did her portrait (now in Geneva).

It was Louis XVIII and the new regime who restored her to the favor of the court. Even though she was over 60 when the second Restoration began, her art was less outmoded than has been suggested. She executed a number of commissions, mainly for middle-class clientele. She was well represented at the Salon of 1824. From that time, she led a secluded existence at Louveciennes and died an octogenarian on 30 March 1842, after publishing her *Souvenirs* in 1835 and 1837, an invaluable document on an era in which she was such an intriguing participant. A complete catalog of her portraits and historical compositions might possibly include over 800 entries. Joseph Baillio is currently preparing a thesis on Mme Vigée-Lebrun for the University of Rochester; we are grateful to him for supplying us with a great deal of the information for the Vigée-Lebrun entries in the American edition of this catalog.

N. V.

196
Portrait of Madame Grant (later Princesse de Talleyrand-Périgord)

"*Portrait de Madame Grant*"
Plate p. 70
Canvas; 92 × 72; S.d.l. on the back of the armchair *E.V. Le Brun 1783*
Salon of 1783, no. 117
New York, The Metropolitan Museum of Art, Bequest of Edward S. Harkness

Catherine Worlée, born in the Indies, married M. Grant or Grand when she was 15 years old. She soon settled in Paris, where she led an adventurous existence, and openly maintained a liaison with Charles-Maurice de Talleyrand-Périgord, whom she later married.

The portrait of Mme Grant was favorably received by the reviewers of the Salon of 1783; however, it was considered by some as too mannered and removed from nature (coll. Deloynes no. 312); others admired its "freshness of approach" and "bewitching sensuality" (coll. Deloynes, no. 311). In this flattering and sophisticated portrayal, Mme Vigée-Lebrun supplies us with the key to her worldly success. "I endeavored," she writes, "to capture in the women I was painting, whenever possible, the attitude and expression of their countenance; those who lacked character (they exist), I painted dreaming and in languid poses" (1835-

37, I, p. 54). In spite of the banality of her model, Vigée-Lebrun relied on her proven ability to capture the reflection of the delicate complexion, the fairness of hair, the transparency of muslin and the reflections of silk, to succeed in creating a precious symphony in blue and gray.

PROVENANCE
Jacques Doucet sale, Paris, Galerie Georges Petit, 6 June 1912, no. 190, ill.; acquired for 400,000 francs by Knoedler; Mrs. William Bateman Leeds, later Princess Christophe de Grèce, Paris, 1914-1923; belonged to the De Grèce family until 1934; Knoedler Gallery, Paris-New York, 1934-1935; Mr. and Mrs. E. Harkness, New York, 1935-1940; their gift to the Metropolitan Museum, New York, in 1940; actually accessioned by the museum in 1950 (INV. 50.135-2).

EXHIBITIONS
1783, Salon, no. 117; 1935-1936, New York, no. 55; 1939, New York, no. 127; 1942, New York, no. 66.

REFERENCES

Coll. Deloynes, v. XIII, no. 294, p. 444; no. 295, pp. 471-473; no. 303, p. 775; no. 309, p. 916; no. 310, p. 927; no. 311, p. 961; no. 312, p. 994; J. Tripier Le Franc, 1828, p. 182; Mme Vigée-Lebrun, 1835-1837, v. I, pp. 249 ff., 331; Bellier and Auvray, 1885, v. II, p. 947; M. Tourneux, 1897, p. 455; E. Dilke, 1899, p. 157, ill. p. 158; A. Dayot, 1899, p. 312; P. de Nohlac, 1908, pp. 18, 30, 151, color ill. opp. p. 36; E. Charles, *La Liberté,* 29 October 1910; P. de Nohlac, 1912, pp. 29, 53, 250, ill. opp. p. 46; G. Babin, 1912, *L'Illustration,* 1 June 1912, pp. 477, 479, ill; W. H. Helm, n.d., p. 222; L. Hautecœur, n.d., pp. 32, 40; A. Blum, 1919, p. 157, ill. opp. p. 80; (Anon.), *Art News,* 1942, 41, 15 December, 1942, p. 19; (Anon.), *Metropolitan Museum of Art Bulletin,* no. 10, 1951, p. 64; L. Perry, 1951, p. 83, ill. p. 64; Ch. Sterling, mus. cat., 1955, pp. 185-188, ill.; I. Bischoff, 1967, pp. 709, 711, ill. p. 708.

RELATED WORKS

Small oval-shaped pencil sketch in the Duc de Talleyrand collection. Copy at the Château de Valençay. Copy sold at the Robinson-Fisher Gallery, New York, 21 May 1925, no. 180. Two copies sold at Parke-Bernet, New York, 20 February 1941, no. 132 and 1 December 1943, no. 398. Variant of this painting, probably painted by Mme Vigée-Lebrun, shows Mme Grant in the same pose but wearing an Empire dress; it was formerly in the Vernhette Collection (Paris), then belonged to Wildenstein. Present location unknown. According to the artist's catalog of her own works, she painted two separate portraits of Mme Grant, the present work and one in 1776, in which case the model was only 14, which seems highly improbable.

N. V.

197
Portrait of the Comte de Vaudreuil

Portrait du comte de Vaudreuil
Plate p. 71
Canvas; 179 × 91; Inscribed: *comte de Vaudreuil | grd Fauconnier de France | chevalier des ordres du roi | lieut^t | général et pair de France | né 1740, mort 1817*
Richmond, Virginia Museum of Fine Arts,
The Adolphe D. and Wilkins C. Williams Collection

Joseph-François de Paule, Comte de Rigaud de Vaudreuil, was born in Santo Domingo on 2 March 1740, and died in Paris in 1817. He attained the dignity of Grand Falconer of France, after having fought in the Seven Year War as aide-de-camp of the Prince de Soubise. He was the loyal friend of the Comte d'Artois, whom he joined in 1782 in the siege of Gibraltar. Then in 1789, then went together into exile. Vaudreuil did not return to Paris until 1814. He was then appointed Peer of France and Governor of the Louvre (L.-G. Michaud, *Biographie Universelle,* 3rd ed., Paris and Leipzig, 1870-73, XLIII, p. 26). The Comte de Vaudreuil was above all a great patron of the arts, possessing one of the most remarkable collections of his time (part of it was the object of a public sale organized by J.-B.-P. Lebrun, 24-25 November 1784).

Mme Vigée-Lebrun, whose salon he frequented regularly and with whom he had a very close friendship, wrote, "With the advantages bestowed by a high position in the world, he combines all the qualities, all the charm which make a man amiable; he was tall, well built, his manners had a nobility and remarkable elegance; his eyes were soft and fine, his face extremely alert as were his ideas, and his compelling smile immediately prepossessed those who met him" (Vigée-Lebrun, 1835-37, I, p. 210). When she painted this canvas in 1784 (*ibid.,* p. 332), she strove to give the model a natural and familiar appearance, in contrast to the ostentatious attire of the courtier.

F.-H. Drouais (1725-1775) and Alexandre Roslin (1718-1793) also executed portraits of the Comte de Vaudreuil (paintings in London and Dublin); both were exhibited it London in 1968 (nos. 207 and 621).

PROVENANCE

Vaudreuil Collection; bequeathed to the Clermont-Tonnerre family; Comtesse Blanche de Clermont-Tonnerre Sale, Paris Hôtel Drouot, 10-13 December 1900, no. 1, ill.; purchased for 11,200 francs by Gardner; Adolph C. and Wilkins C. Williams Collection; gift of the Williams family to the Virginia Museum of Fine Arts (INV. 49-11-21).

EXHIBITION
Paris, 1874, no. 295.

REFERENCES

Vigée-Lebrun, *Souvenirs*, 1835-1837, v. I, pp. 97-103, 145, 204, 210-215, 291, 332, v. III, p. 204; Bellier and Auvray, 1885, v. II, p. 948; Léonce Pingaud, ed., *Correspondance intime du Comte de Vaudreuil et du Comte d'Artois pendant l'Émigration*, Paris, 1889, pp. 351-352, frontispiece; P. de Nolhac, 1908, pp. 44, 49-50; W. H. Helm, n.d., p. 223; *Bulletin of the Virginia Museum of Fine Arts*, March 1949; E. de Ganay, 1959, ill. p. 617; *Catalog of the Virginia Museum of Fine Arts*, 1966, p. 43, ill.; P. Verlet, 1967, p. 52, ill.; I. Bischoff, 1968, p. 110, ill.

RELATED WORKS

A three-quarter length portrait (125 × 95), bearing neither signature nor inscriptions, is in a private collection, Paris. It was shown at the Marie-Antoinette exhibition at Versailles in 1955, no. 973. Another *"en habit français"*; Talleyrand sale in Paris, no. 73, 1847.
A series of reductions, perhaps as many as six, were executed by Vigée-Lebrun after the original. An oval bust in a private collection, Paris. An oval bust (72 × 57), from the former Le Roy collection, now in the Musée Jaquemart-André, Paris, INV. 19. An oval bust (72 × 59) was auctioned at an anonymous sale, Hôtel Drouot, Paris, 8 April 1908. According to the catalog, it was "originally in the Clermont-Tonnerre Collection,". M. Sortais purchased it for 6,050 francs. A portrait of Vaudreuil was in the Exposition Rétrospective Féminine at the Lycéum in Paris in 1908. An oval bust of Vaudreuil (73 × 60) was shown at the Heinemann Gallerie, Munich in 1912 at an exhibition entitled "Französische Kunst des XVIII. Jahrhunderts" with no indication as to provenance. An oval bust "from the studio of Vigée-Lebrun" (71 × 57) was auctioned at the Hôtel Drouot, Paris, 3 February 1944. Purchased for 35,000 francs. A miniature copy by an unknown artist was sold at the Bucowski sale, Stockholm, 18 April 1945, no. 542, ill., under the erroneous title *Portrait of Stanislas Poniatowski*.

N. V.

198
*Self-Portrait***

Autoportrait
Plate p. 121
Canvas; 100 × 81
Florence, Galleria degli Uffizi

Mme Vigée-Lebrun recalled the origin of this work in her *Souvenirs:* "The day I went to visit the gallery where the self-portraits of the modern masters are to be found, I was honored to be asked to present mine to the city of Florence, and I promised to send it as soon as I was in Rome" (Mme Vigée-Lebrun, *Souvenirs,* Vol. II, p. 20). On 16 December 1789, Ménageot, the Director of the French Academy in Rome, wrote to d'Angiviller: "Mme Le Brun will set about painting... the portrait which was requested for the Gallery of the Grand Duke in Florence" (*Correspondance des Directeurs de l'Académie...,* 1906, Vol. XV, p. 372). Several months later, on 3 March 1790, he wrote: "Mme Le Brun has just finished her portrait for the Gallery of the Grand Duke in Florence; it is one of the most beautiful things she has done; I found that she has extended her ability considerably since her departure from Paris. This painting astonishes everybody who has seen it thus far; we had no idea of this kind of talent in Rome..." (*ibid.*, p. 401).

In a letter dated 16 March 1790, which is preserved in the Bibliothèque Jacques Doucet (Paris, Institut d'Art et d'Archéologie: box 52, file II), addressed to the painter Hubert Robert and to the architect Alexandre-Théodore Brogniart, Mme Vigée-Lebrun related the success of her self-portrait after its first public exhibition:

As I do not doubt your interest in me, you too shall learn that my painting for Florence has encountered the grandest reception. I would appear conceited were I to explain at length its complete success; I have never been encouraged like this in my life. I am enjoying it even more so since the Romans concede practically nothing to our school, which is easy to say, but really they have expressed great enthusiasm for me, something they have never done before. All the artists came and returned. Princesses of every nation, even the men. In fact, for the past ten days, my morning receptions have been visited by 60-80 people from all ranks and stations in life. I am called Mme Van Dyck, Mme Rubens, other even more exalted titles. There is no end to it. I am receiving verses full of praise. They wish me to remain in Rome for a long time. Naples, where I am expected, also wants some of my dabblings. All this does not make me more vainglorious; you know me well enough to realize that I have not allowed this success to go to my head. It has merely surprized and encouraged me.

Here we have one of Mme Vigée-Lebrun's finest achievements, one of the best examples of her virtuosity. Seated before her easel, where she is sketching the head of Queen Marie-Antoinette, she offers a flattering, although somewhat rejuvenated image of herself. At the time, she was in fact thirty-six. By means of a sober presentation, a restrained scale of colors, limited to browns and deep blacks set off by whites and reds, the naturalistic detail of the brushes held loosely in the model's hand and the elegant disarray of her costume ("I used to twist," she wrote in her *Souvenirs,* "a muslin scarf around my head, as you can see from my portraits in Florence and Saint-Petersburg..."), the painter has created an outstanding specimen of 18th-century self-portraiture. We observe the silky coloring and the delicately rendered complexion which she owed to the study of Greuze and the Flemish. So perhaps after all, the public did not err in comparing her to Rubens.

Previously, she had represented herself wearing a straw hat (a copy of this painting is in the National Gallery, London), recalling a portrait of Helena Fourment by Rubens (also in the National Gallery, London) which she had admired during her visit to Antwerp in 1782 and about which she wrote: "Its great effect resides in the two different types of lighting which are created by means of simple daylight and sunshine, the highlights being exposed to the rays of the sun, and what I must refer to as the shadows, for lack of a better term, is a half-light" (Vigée-Lebrun, 1835-1837, I, p. 83).

PROVENANCE

On 26 August 1791, Mme Vigée-Lebrun sent written notification to the Chevalier Pelli, Director of the Florentine Academy, that she had just shipped her painting to Florence (E. Muntz, 1874-1875, p. 449). The head of the Galleria degli Uffizi wrote Mme Vigée-Lebrun on 19 September 1791: "Madame, according to the letter which I had the honor of addressing you on the 5th of this month, I have been instruct-

ed to inform you that his Royal Highness is pleased to accept your portrait and has granted me permission to hang it in the royal gallery. It is with very great pleasure that I will carry out this order, especially since I value and admire a work which can justly be referred to as a masterpiece. His Royal Highness ... admired your work and was quite pleased with it. All the French here, all the masters who are acquainted with its excellence, and all the patrons of art deem it above all praise and worthy of the celebrated artists of antiquity ...." In the Grand Ducal Collection of self-portraits.

REFERENCES

Vivant Denon, 1792; J.-B.-P. Lebrun, 1794, p. 18; J. Tripier Le Franc, 1828, pp. 187-188; Mme Vigée-Lebrun, 1835-1837, v. I, p. 110, v. II, pp. 20, 38; Ch. Blanc, 1865, v. II, pp. 4-5; P. Larousse, 1873, v. X, p. 294; E. Müntz, 1874-1875, pp. 449-452; Bellier and Auvray, 1882-1885, v. II, p. 948; H. Bouchot, 1898, pp. 51-62, 219-230; Ch. Pillet, 1890, pp. 5, 7, 32, 34, ill. pp. 5, 7; Gerspach, 1898, pp. 322-323, ill. p. 325; *Correspondance des Directeurs de l'Académie,* ed. 1906, v. XV, pp. 372, 401, 403, 412, 413; P. de Nolhac, 1908, pp. 90, 101, color frontispiece; A. Tuetey, 1911, pp. 171, 179; M. Behrend, 1912, v. II; P. Ratouis de Limay, 1921, p. 80, ill.; Thieme and Becker, 1940, v. XXXIV, p. 346; L. Réau, 1938, p. 340 (1971 edition); M. Masciotta, 1949, color frontispiece; V. Golzio, 1956, pp. 182-183, ill.; F. Boyer, 1957, p. 288; L. Hautecœur, n.d., pp. 76, 79, p. 9; W.-H. Helm, n.d., pp. 108-109, 207, ill. p. 182.

RELATED WORKS

Replica. Almost exact, painted by Vigée-Lebrun in 1790 for the Fourth Earl of Bristol, Bishop of Derry, now in the National Trust, Ickworth, England.
Engravings. Very clumsy engraving by Vivant Denon executed around 1790 (M. Roux, 1949, VI, p. 587); Denon removed the head of Marie-Antoinette and substituted the self-portrait of Raphael which Mme Vigée-Lebrun had admired in Florence at Palazzo Altoviti (Vigée-Lebrun, *op. cit.,* II, p. 19). Reproduced in the works of Denon (1792), A. de La Fizelière (*L'Oeuvre originale de Vivant Denon,* Paris, 1873, I, no. 123) and Ch. Pillet (1890, p. 7). Engraved also by P. Audonin in 1804 after a drawing by J.-B. Wicar, for the *Galerie de Florence* published between 1802-1827 (J. Laran, 1930-1933, I, p. 255); also reproduced in Ch. Pillet, 1890, p. 7. Color engraving by an anonymous hand, distributed soon after the portrait was painted, inscribed: *Luisa Elisabetta le Brun n. Vigèe* (sic) *Pittrice, nata in Parigi nel 1755, vive in Roma 290.*
Copies. Boitelle sale, 24-25 April 1866, Paris, Hôtel Drouot, no. 74, "Portrait of the artist, in her youth; she is represented looking in a mirror, seated before her easel with a brush in her hand"; canvas, 79 × 63, 1,000 francs. Small round-shaped copy of head alone, P. Decourcelle sale 29-30 May 1911, Galerie Georges Petit, Paris, no. 3, ill.; sold again at Palais Galliéra, Paris, 9 June 1964, no. 50, ill. Numerous copies are in existence, most of which are poor in quality and none are by the artist herself.

N. V.

François-André Vincent

1746 Paris 1816

Vincent first studied with his father, François-Élie Vincent (1708-1790), a painter of miniatures from Geneva who had settled in Paris. He then became a pupil of Joseph-Marie Vien at the Academy. At the age of 19, Vincent placed second in the Grand Prix competition with *Thomyris* (1766, Bourges) and then two years later he won the Grand Prix with his glowing painting of *Germanicus apaisant la sédition dans son camp* (1768, Paris, École des Beaux-Arts), a work that is reminiscent of both François Boucher and Jean-Baptiste Greuze. Following a brief period at the École des Élèves Protégés, he went to live at the French Academy in Rome (1771-75). During this period, Vincent did many drawings. Of particular note are his remarkable caricatures of his fellow boarders (Montpellier, Musée Atger; Paris, Musée Carnavalet, Louvre; Rouen, Bibliothèque, etc.). He also painted portraits, including of *Houel* (1772, Rouen) and one of *Monseigneur Ruffo* (1775, Naples, Certosa da San Martino).

After his return to Paris, Vincent presented an important group of works at the Salon of 1777, including *Belisarius* (No. 199), and the brilliant *Portrait de Bergeret* painted in Rome in 1774 (Besançon). At the Salon of 1779 he exhibited *Président Molé et les factieux* (Paris, Palais-Bourbon), a painting which illustrated an important event in national history and which met with great success; the *Guérison de l'aveugle* (shown at the same Salon) and the *Paralytique à la piscine* (sketch in the Salon of 1779 and the painting in the Salon of 1783). The last two works are still in the church of the Madeleine in Rouen.

By this time, Vincent had become a famous painter and exhibited frequently at the Salon. In 1781, he showed the *Combat des Romains et des Sabins* (Angers); in 1783 the *Enlèvement d'Orythie*, which was his reception piece (Chambéry, Préfecture; a spirited sketch in Tours, attributed to Regnault); also in 1783, two paintings of *Aria et Poetus* (one of these is in Amiens); in 1787, *Auguste et Cinna* (Czechoslovakia, Zidlokovice Castle); in 1789, *Zeuxis choissant pour modèles les plus belles filles de Crotone* (Louvre; preparatory drawings in Montpellier, Musée Atger); in 1791, *Jeune Pyrrhus à la cour de Glaucias* (Czechoslovakia, Zidlokovice Castle). At the Salon of 1795, he presented the fiery *Guillaume Tell renversant la barque sur laquelle le gouverneur Gessler traversait le lac de Lucerne* (*ouvrage d'encouragement* commissioned in 1791, now in Toulouse; sketch in Guéret, as pointed out by Jacques Foucart), and at the Salon of 1798 *Agriculture* (Bordeaux), a huge Rousseauian work. Like many of Vincent's Salon paintings, the *Mélancolie* from the Salon of 1801, which was in Josephine's collection, has since been lost.

Vincent's health was not good, and in his last years he seems to have done less work. A large portion of his energy was devoted to the enormous enterprise of the *Battle of the Pyramids* (see No. 201). After that, Vincent seems chiefly to have painted portraits: the *Portrait de la famille Boyer Fonfrède* (1801, Versailles) and the *Portrait de Monsieur de La Forest, de sa femme et de sa fille* (1804, private collection) two very original portraits of families in interior settings; the *Portrait d'Arnault* (Salon of 1801, Versailles); the *Portrait d'Andrieux* (1815, Versailles).

Vincent's originality is evident not only in his choice of Roman themes, but in his equally precocious use of subjects concerning the history of France. The two large paintings of the *Vie de La Galaizière* (1778, Nancy), the series of the *Vie d'Henri IV* (Fontainebleau and the Louvre, 1783-1787) and the *Président Molé* form the basis for an important current in history painting of the 19th century. Throughout his career, the artist also showed a marked taste for portraits, both painted and drawn.

He was a brilliant draughtsman whose works were close in the early years to Jean-Honoré Fragonard and then later to Antoine-Jean Gros and Louis-Léopold Boilly (his work was sometimes even confused with the work of these three artists). Vincent's repertory included red chalk and wash drawing, and pen drawings with pencil shading. His technique in painting, characterized at first by vigorous brushwork and then by more precision and attention to contrasts, reflects a well-trained artist, with a broad curiosity and a concern for balance and good taste. Vincent's paintings thus provide an important measure of the transformation in French painting between 1770 and 1815.

Additional paintings by Vincent exist in the French

museums of Angers, Besançon, Orléans, Amiens, Valenciennes, Lons-le-Saunier, Montpellier and Le Mans, Outside France, they can be found in Munich, Lisbon (Gulbenkian Foundation), Amsterdam, Montreal, Algiers and Washington, D.C.

J.-P. C.

199
Belisarius

"Bélisaire, réduit à la mendicité, secouru par un officier des troupes de l'Empereur Justinien"
Plate p. 49
Canvas; 98 × 129; s.d.l.r. *Vincent F 1776*
Salon of 1777, no. 189
Montpellier, Musée Fabre

Vincent exhibited 15 paintings at the Salon of 1777, the first time that his work was shown publicly. As a young artist who had recently returned from Rome and had just been recognized by the Academy, he wanted to surprise and dazzle the public with the quality and variety of his work: Roman subjects (this painting and its companion piece); religious subjects like the *Saint Jérôme* (Montpellier); portraits such as the famous one of *Bergeret* (Besançon) and the now lost portraits of Berthélemy and Rousseau; genre scenes like *La leçon de dessin* (sale, London, Sotheby's, 12 June 1968); studies of common people, of heads and even one of an animal. Only five of these paintings, some of which were executed during the painter's stay in Italy (1771-75) and others executed after his return, are definitely known today. In the margins of his copy of the Salon catalog, Gabriel de Saint-Aubin left some rapid sketches of some of Vincent's paintings, including one of *Belisarius* (see Dacier, 1910, p. 52, pl. 37).

The story of Belisarius had been painted two years earlier by Louis-Jacques Durameau, a work now lost. It was taken up again by Jacques-Louis David and Jean-François Peyron in paintings which became famous (Nos. 30 and 139).

As a companion piece to *Belisarius,* Vincent showed *Alcibiade recevant les leçons de Socrate,* done in 1777, still another theme of exhortation to the austere and virtuous life (this painting is also in Montpellier). A handsome preparatory wash drawing for *Alcibiade* is in the Pontoise museum (exh. cat. 1971-72, no. 102, fig. 22).

The Salon critics were on the whole full of praise for Vincent's works. Referring to the young painters who were exhibiting for the first time, *Le Journal Encyclopé-*

dique stated that "young M. Vincent who has returned from Rome stands at the head" (coll. Deloynes, XLIX, no. 1334, p. 864). In *La Prêtresse ou nouvelle manière de prédire ce qui est arrivé* compliments and criticism were mixed: "What energy, and at the same time what harmony ! The young Vincent... will fulfill my hopes. He will become, unquestionably, a very great painter; but he is not yet at that point: the heads of his principal figures could be more noble.... He is a little too confident of his talent; but one should forget these small faults in favor of the beauty that shines through in his paintings. He draws correctly; he has the great spirit of history; he has good taste in drapery" (coll. Deloynes, X, no. 189, p. 970).

L'Année littéraire, on the other hand, found a certain coldness in *Belisarius:* "His Belisarius receiving alms is laudable in execution, especially in the precise rendering of the contours which are of the greatest accuracy; but the painting seems cold when one thinks of Vandick's and Salvator rose's [sic] paintings of the same subject. The story of the general of the Emperor's armies losing his sight and being reduced to begging for his life after a long prison term is so extraordinary, so moving, that I am surprised that it did not at all warm the spirit of the young artist" (coll. Deloynes, XLIX, no. 1333, pp. 795-796). Vincent was again accused of coldness in *Les tableaux du Louvre, où il n'y a pas le sens commun, histoire véritable:* "Belisarius, who receives alms—he is blind, he is content that he is exempt from seeing the cold face of his benefactor."

Thus, there was some displeasure expressed about the painting's austere and cold quality, the very quality that was new in 1777. Vincent's painting, so strictly constructed, shows what the painter had learned in Italy from the Bolognese masters, in particular Guercino and Guido Reni. The quality of realism, the brilliant handling of paint with thick and rather hard brushstrokes, the vivid and contrasting rendering of volumes, all were qualities that were new at the time, as was the austere moral lesson that the subject conveyed. This still and taciturn painting, where the emphasis is on the intensity of the gaze that the five figures turn on the face of the blind man, is thus one of the first examples of Neo-Classicism in French painting.

PROVENANCE
Collection of the painter E.-X. Fabre (1766-1837); given in 1837 to the Montpellier museum.

EXHIBITION
1777, Salon, no. 189.

REFERENCES
Coll. Deloynes, v. X, no. 189, p. 970; v. XLIX, no. 1333, pp. 795-796; no. 1334, p. 864; J.-B.-P. Chaussard, 1808, p. 100; A.-Chr. Quatremère de Quincy, 1834, p. 26; H. Lemonnier, 1904, pp. 287-298; J. Locquin, 1912, pp. 212-213, 253, 255; J. Vergnet-Ruiz and M. Laclotte, 1962, p. 256; H. Bardon, 1963, v. I, p. 222.   J.-P. C.

200
*Portrait of the Actor Dazincourt**

Portrait du comédien Dazincourt
Plate p. 127
Canvas; 73 × 60; s.d.m.r. *Vincent 1792*
Marseille, Musée des Beaux-Arts

Jean-Joseph-Baptiste Albouy, called Dazincourt (1747-1809), of Marseille, was one of the famous comic actors of his time. Protected by the Duc de Richelieu, he made his début at the Comédie-Française in 1776 and was a success in comic roles, particularly as Figaro. Starting in 1785, he gave lessons in elocution and acting to Queen Marie-Antoinette. Because of his loyalty to the Queen, he was imprisoned in 1793-94. Under Napoleon, Dazincourt, then "Professor of Elocution" at the National Conservatory, became director of the court performances.

In this painting, Dazincourt already shows a marked stoutness of figure. Toward the end of his career, he was to act only in roles that were created especially for him. One should point out among the portraits of Dazincourt two portraits of the actor as Crispin (Paris, Musée de la Comédie-Française), a pencil and gouache drawing (Paris, Musée Carnavalet), and another pencil drawing (Bibliothèque Nationale, Estampes), all anonymous works. Anne Pingeot has brought to our attention Joseph Chinard's handsome medallion which was exhibited in 1909-10 in Paris at the Musée des Arts Décoratifs (exh. Chinard, no. 104) and then included in the Comte de Penha-Longha's sale, which contained only works by the sculptor (Paris, Galerie Georges Petit, 2 December 1911, no. 15, ill.). Chinard's original plaster model is not dated. Dazincourt seems there to be slightly older than he does in Vincent's painting.

In all phases of his artistic activity, Vincent painted many portraits, most often of intimates and friends. Among the portraits done during the time of the Revolution, one should point out those very sober and distinguished examples where the model, painted as a bust or in half-length, poses in front of a plain background: *Petite fille au tricot* (1791, Wildenstein collection); *Portrait de jeune femme* (1792, at a sale in Paris, 20 March 1953); *Portrait d'Homme,* possibly Bernard, the goldsmith from Bordeaux (1793, Algiers); the portraits presumed to be of *M. Baillon* (Amsterdam, Rijksmuseum) and of *Mlle Duplant* (Lisbon, Gulbenkian Foundation); and finally, the *Portrait de Mme Boyer-Fonfrède* (1796, Louvre).

The Marseille portrait, robust and warm, yet full of reserve, is one of Vincent's most successful. The mastery of the artist is clear in the firm, free execution, the vigorous use of color emphasizing the blue of the eyes and the contrast of the vibrant vermilion of the vest with the green tablecloth.

PROVENANCE
Gift of Mlle Michel to the Musée de Marseille in 1887.

EXHIBITIONS
1900, Paris, Grand Palais, no. 661; 1949, Geneva, no. 126; 1954, London, no. 23; 1958, Paris, no. 89; 1962, Versailles, no. 184.

REFERENCES
F. Benoît, 1897, p. 328, n. 4; Ph. Auquier, mus. cat. 1908, no. 617; Memoranda, mus. cat., 1932, p. 12; J. Vergnet-Ruiz and M. Laclotte, 1962, p. 255; mus. cat., 1965, no. 29.

J.-P. C.

201
Battle of the Pyramids

La bataille des Pyramides
Plate p. 177
Canvas; 120 × 180
Gisors, Private Collection

In 1800, Lucien Bonaparte, Minister of the Interior, at the order of the First Consul, commissioned Vincent to paint a *Battle of the Pyramids,* a work that was to be of enormous size (about 800 × 500; see F. Benoît, 1897, p. 166). In January 1803, Denon's report to the First Consul indicated that Vincent had done only "the drawing on the canvas" for the great painting and that he was "in the process of executing an oil-sketch which would be finished within six weeks." Vincent had assured Denon "that if his health opposed no obstacle to his wishes, the painting could be finished within 8 months..." (Arch. Nat., AF IV 1649). However, the artist was ill and losing his sight and was unable, even with constant labor, to finish his painting. From Denon's letter of 21 February 1806 to the Minister of the Interior, we know that Vincent had to abandon the task of finishing the painting (Arch. Louvre, corresp. administrative, 1803-07, p. 195). He was able to deliver only the finished sketch, and he agreed that the commission should be turned over to another artist. P.-A. Hennequin was charged with finishing the task, and his large painting (Salon of 1806) is today at Versailles. The students in the Fine Arts class at the Institute requested Vincent's huge unfinished canvas, in which the figures were represented nude. On 17 January, Vincent offered his canvas to the fourth class at the Institute. What eventually became of this work is not known; it may well have been destroyed. The finished sketch, the only part of the commission that Vincent had been able to deliver, is now in Versailles in a room on the first floor of the south wing where, since the time of Louis-Philippe, it has been part of ensemble of *entre-fenêtres* decoration and where it can be seen only with difficulty. For further discussion of the commission for the *Battle of the Pyramids,* one should consult Yveline Cantarel's recent, important archival work on military painting of the Napoleonic period (1973, pp. 352-359).

A few years later, in 1810, Vincent was commissioned by Berthier to do a large version of the *Battle of the Pyramids* for a gallery in the Château de Grosbois. A.-J. Gros, Pajou *fils,* Ch. Meynier, C. Thévenin, C. Vernet, N.-A. Taunay and A.-E. Roehn were also commissioned to do other battle paintings for the same decorative ensemble. In his Grosbois painting, Vincent followed the Versailles sketch almost exactly. A.-M. Passez has kindly pointed out to us a pen and sepia wash-drawing, preserved by the painter's descendants, which corresponds perfectly with Vincent's Grosbois work.

The abortive undertaking of the *Battle of the Pyramids* left behind a considerable number of sketches and drawings. At the Musée des Arts Africains et Océaniens, Paris, and the Metropolitan Museum of Art, New York, are two splendid complementary drawings, spirited and roughly sketched, one in pen and the other a wash-drawing heightened with white; both were at one time attributed to A.-J. Gros. These appear to be among the first studies that Vincent did for the overall composition (c. 1800-13). The Paris drawing is less tightly organized and is probably earlier than the more complete and thoroughly worked drawing in New York. It is with the latter drawing that one should compare the work exhibited here. They are very similar in the overall design and in many details. In the Versailles sketch, as in the Grosbois version (and probably also the large lost canvas), the composition became clearer and more open, the startling crowd of horsemen at the left was given less importance, and at the center there appeared an Arab rider charging the ranks of French soldiers.

The sketch that is presented here, which Vincent left mainly in a grisaille state, is impressive in the enthusiasm and freedom of its execution. The nervous lines, firmly articulated with the tip of the brush, remind us of Vincent's talent as a draughtsman. The virtuosity of this work, with its eery foreground of horses and riders carried away in the current of the action, prepares the way for the most untamed examples of Romanticism in art. Yet, at the same time, Vincent's piece contains references to other works. One is reminded of the battle scene by Raphael in the Stanza di Constantino in the Vatican, and even more of Charles Lebrun's *Passage du Granique* with its foreground of water and the crush of horsemen at the center. Vincent's painting, bold and seething with life, is first and foremost a work well thought out and planned at great length by a cultivated painter.

PROVENANCE

Posthumous sale, of artist's studio, 17-19 October 1816, no. 37: "Grisaille in oil—First thought for the Battle of the Pyramids" (see also Related Works). Presumably repurchas-ed by the family; kept by the descendants of Mme Griois, Vincent's sister.

RELATED WORKS

Paintings. Large painting (c. 800 × 500) commissioned in 1800 and never finished; now lost.
Finished sketch, 84 × 130; Château de Versailles, south wing; remounted with decorative elements in an *entre-fenêtres* scheme.
Grosbois version, 185 × 340; s.d.l.r. on a canon-carriage: *Vincent, de l'Institut de France, de la Légion d'Honneur, Paris, 1810*; Château de Grosbois, Galerie des Batailles.
Drawings. Pen and wash, heightened with white on sepia paper, 21 × 42; formerly in collections of Comte Rapp, Vicomtesse de Clairval, Duc de Trévise; acquired in 1837 as a work by Gros, Paris, Musée des Arts Africains et Océaniens.
Pen and wash, heighted with white on gray-washed paper, 42 × 75; Major E.-J. Montagu-Stuart-Wortley Collection, Highcliffe Castle, England; acquired in 1951 as a work by Gros, New York, Metropolitan Museum of Art (exh. Paris, 1973, no. 94, ill. 1).
Pen and brown wash on white paper, 46 × 85; France, private collection. In the posthumous sale, 17-19 October 1816: "Framed drawings": no. 61, "La Bataille des Pyrami-des," a very large drawing in pen with sepia wash. To be identified with the drawing in a private collection mentioned above, presumably repurchased by the artist's family? "Unframed drawings": no. 69, "Two large drawings in pen washed with bistre and heightened with white offering two compositions with alterations for the Battle of the Pyramids." To be identified with the above-mentioned drawings in Paris and New York? No. 76, "Two sketch-books..., and the first thoughts for paintings of... the Battle of the Pyramids."

J.-P. C.

202

Allegory of the Freeing of the Prisoners of Algiers

Allégorie de la libération des esclaves d'Alger par Jérôme Bonaparte
Plate p. 191
Canvas; 159 × 204; s.d.l.l. *Vincent. de l'Institut, | de la Légion d'Honneur. Paris. 1806.*
Kassel, Staatliche Kunstsammlungen

Bruno Foucart has pointed out the importance of this rather surprising painting which stands apart from the rest of Vincent's œuvre. It is one of his last works, done at a time when the artist was often ill and produc-ing little. Chaussard, the only author to mention the painting, spoke of it in the following way: "His poor health, even some long illnesses, had interrupted Vincent's work. One sees arise from his adept and trained brush a charming work, composed of two life-sized figures, a Child releasing a Slave; it is executed with his usual vigor. One finds in it all the energy that he had at 30 when he was at the peak of his talent. There is moreover an admirable truthfulness in the expression of the naïveté, the gratitude and the happiness of the slave to whom liberty has been restored" (Chaussard, 1806).

The sweeping view of the harbor of Genoa in the background, with the feluccas bringing home the old prisoners awaited by their families, as well as the Italian inscription on the streamer, seem to indicate that most of the freed slaves were Genoese.

The painting alludes, as Professor Herzog, director of the Kassel Museum, has indicated, to the mission intrusted by Napoleon to his younger brother Jérôme in 1805. The object of this mission was to liberate the French and Italian prisoners in the jails of Algiers. "The goal of your mission is to rescue all the slaves, Genoese, Italian and French, who are in the prisons of Algiers..." (Napoleon's letter to Jérôme on 5 July 1805; cf. *Mémoires,* 1861, I, p. 339). Was the painting commissioned from Vincent by the liberated prisoners to be offered to Jérôme in recognition of his service? Or was it commissioned by Jérôme himself?

The large sunlit painting shows a slave freed of his chains, accompanied by a little girl who carries a crown of oak leaves tied by a ribbon where one can read the words *"La Riconoscenza à Girolamo Bonaparte"* (to Jérôme Bonaparte in Recognition). The little girl symbolizes, it would seem, this gratitude (or, more simply, is she the prisoner's child, who along with her father shows appreciation to Jérôme?). The dog at the left is an allusion to the loyalty owed by the prisoners to their liberator.

It is a bizarre, even incongruous work, at once pathetic in a theatrical way (the scene on the wharf, the melodramatic pose of the freed slave, the tears running down his cheeks), realistic (the face and hands of the man and the mark of the irons on his ankle), and at the same time possessing a quality of unreal strangeness (the allegorical language, the rigid pose of the figures, the absence of the continuity between the parts). This exceptional and ambitious work in "plein-air" has in its strangeness an unusual power to fascinate.

PROVENANCE
Collection of Jérôme Bonaparte, King of Westphalia, Kassel; in Kassel in 1813; no. 969 of the Inventory of 1875.

REFERENCE
P. Chaussard, 1806, p. 107.

J.-P. C.

Pierre-Jacques Volaire (Chevalier Volaire)

1729 Toulon - Naples before 1802, or Lerici 1790 (?)

Chevalier Volaire, as he is customarily called, came from an old artistic family of Toulon. His grandfather, Jean (c. 1660-1721), probably a student of François Puget, specialized in decorative painting for the navy's ships at Toulon but also left some religious paintings, among them a *Pietà* in Saint-Louis de Toulon, signed and dated posthumously 1723; Pierre-Jacques' father, Jacques (1685-1768), was official painter of the city of Toulon (at least from 1729 to 1766) and the Cathedral still contains his large painting of the *Gloire du Saint-Sacrement,* commissioned in 1745. Another of Jean's sons, François-Alexis (1699-1775), was a painter, as was his daughter Marie-Anne (1730-1806), who painted portraits.

Pierre-Jacques Volaire, the only member of the family whose name was really known, must have been trained in Toulon by his father and, in a document of 1755 related to the restoration of two large paintings of 1718 in the Toulon Cathedral, he is cited as "Volaire the son" to distinguish him from Jacques Volaire the father. But his true beginnings date from 1754, when Joseph Vernet arrived in Toulon, instructed by Louis XV to paint the principle ports of France. Vernet made the young Volaire his collaborator and took him along in 1756, when he left Toulon. For eight years, Volaire followed Vernet in his travels and became a close family friend; he assisted Vernet with his famous series of the *Ports de France.*

In 1763, when the commission was nearing its end, Volaire left Vernet to come back to Toulon and take up his own career, continuing to paint in a manner close to his friend's. In 1764, he went to Rome, where he lived until 1769, when he settled in Naples. The many paintings of the eruptions of Vesuvius (see No. 203) in which he specialized earned him an immense reputation. His work, like Vernet's, is based on a perfect finish, an informed sense of the picturesque, the effects of moonlight or intense, precise, artificial light. The theme of Vesuvius encouraged in Volaire a warmer, livelier sense of color; his emphasis on the spectacular knew no bounds, and Vernet was surpassed on his own ground.

A correspondent member of the Academy of Marseilles from 1784, Volaire maintained his relations of friendship and trust with Vernet, as witnessed by a letter of recommendation that Vernet willingly wrote in May 1784 on behalf of Laurent-Antoine Volaire, a brother of Pierre-Jacques (see Ch. Ginoux, 1893, p. 267). In 1786, Volaire attempted through the Comte d'Angiviller, Director-General of Royal Buildings, to persuade Louis XVI to buy one of his views of Vesuvius. This overture does not seem to have been favorably received, according to the very words of his response, d'Angiviller was then busy selecting paintings by only the greatest masters for the Grande Galerie of the Louvre (*ibid.*, pp. 270-273). Nevertheless, the old basement of the Louvre contained several paintings by Volaire (in the Château de Compiègne, two pendants, a *Marine avec pêcheurs,* and a *Rade nocturne avec effet de lune ;* at Vervins, deposited in 1876 but actually on view at the Hôtel de Ville and not in the museum, one *Éruption du Vésuve* and another at Le Havre).

The date of Volaire's death is not known. The year 1802 is often given, but this means only that the registries of the consul general of Naples go only to 1802 (*ibid.*, p. 267, n. 3) and that one does not find Volaire's name there. But the "Voler, painter, native of Nove (?) in Provence" who died at Lerici (near Genoa) in July 1790 from the effects of bad treatment —torture, in effect—inflicted by the Neapolitan *Sbirros* (as pointed out by a certain Merle, professor of French in Naples, in a memoir of 1796) could he be Volaire, as Montaiglon and Guiffrey believed (see *Correspondance des directeurs de l'Académie de France à Rome,* XVI, 1907, p. 89 and p. 90, n. 2) ? Besides which, according to

Merle, this "Voler" had lived in Naples many years. Was Merle himself expelled from Naples in 1792 ? And how much credence should we give these words ?

It is curious that such a sad end should have escaped general attention. However, what does the presence of "Volers, famous marine painter, living in Naples for 30 years" mean on a list drawn up (by Cacault ?) in Florence in September 1793 of French artists "who are in Italy and those who came from Rome to Florence" (*ibid.*, p. 333) ? Is Volaire mentioned only out of habit ? In fact, while the list emphasizes the presence in Naples of artists like Girandet and Jean-Pierre Péquignot, it is not specific about the where abouts of Volaire.

Volaire exhibited little and exclusively in the Salon de la Correspondance: in 1779, *Éruption du Vésuve en 1771* (collection of the Comte d'Orsay; perhaps entering the Louvre during the Revolution through confiscation); in 1783, a large *Éruption du Vésuve avec foule et clair de lune* (collection of M. de Thélusson, Captain of the Dragoons); in 1786, two *Vues des environs de Naples: Bayes et son fort, Temples de Vénus et Mercure* (d'Orsay collection).

Independent of the theme of Vesuvius (an innumerable list and very incomplete in the following entry) at Agen are two pastel *Marines ;* in Avignon, a *Pêche au clair de lune ;* in Clamecy, the *Éléments ;* in Toulon, a *Cascade*—in the Hermitage, Leningrad, four paintings, of which two are dated 1767 and 1769; in New York, Metropolitan Museum, two lovely drawings of Neapolitan figures in the manner of Vernet.

On several occasions, Volaire's works were engraved, notably by Pierre Duflos *(Vue de la Solvaterra),* by Johann Thomas Hauer (*Éruption du Vésuve,* 1771), by Carl-Gottlieb Guttenberg (same subject). Also of note is a portrait etching of Volaire by Vivant Denon.

J. F.

203
Eruption of Mount Vesuvius

Éruption du Vésuve
Plate p. 60
Canvas; 72.5 × 154
Richmond, Virginia Museum of Fine Arts, Bequest of Dr. Bernard Samuels in
memory of Kathleen Boon Samuels

The theme of the eruptions of Vesuvius, already so often admired by the travelers and the curious of the period, became Volaire's great, if not exclusive specialty from the 1760s, when he settled permanently in Naples.

The volcano Vesuvius, after the famous eruption of 79 A.D. which destroyed Herculaneum and Pompeii, was still rather active until 1138-39, when it seemed to settle down for the whole of the Middle Ages. Its catastrophic reawakening in 1631 caused the death of 4,000 inhabitants and 6,000 head of cattle and ravaged Jorio, Portici, Resina, Torre del Greco (again in 1676, Torre del Greco lost 500 people in a new eruption). In the 18th century, the activity of Vesuvius was intense, and one may cite important eruptions occurring in 1707 and 1737 (one of the most spectacular, with bombardments of lava, explosions, spitting flames) as well as in 1751, 1754, 1759, 1766, 1771, 1790, 1794 (with 33 dead and 4,200 head of cattle lost), 1804, etc. For the history of Vesuvius, see a summary sketch by J. Schneer, *Der Vesuv,* Naples, 1895. Thus, the resurgence of violent eruptions starting in 1631 and continuing throughout the 18th century after an extended period of calm, could not but attract attention and stimulate the imagination. That, as much as the scientific curiosity so characteristic of the century of Saussure, Buffon, Bougainville and of the *Encyclopédie,* explains the extraordinary vogue for Volaire's paintings of the eruptions of Vesuvius, of which the list under Related Works gives only a very limited idea. The examples closest to the Richmond painting are those in Le Havre, the one from the 1959 sale and from the Wengraf and Sestieri galleries. Also, 18th-century painters, especially those of the second half, took a lively interest in all picturesque or dramatic manifestations of nature: tempests, fires, shipwrecks, snow, glaciers and cliffs, waterfalls, windstorms—from Honoré Fragonard to Joseph Vernet and Hubert Robert, from Loutherbourg to Jean-François Hue and G.-F. de Lacroix, from Wolf and Lory to Cozens, from Crépin to César Van Loo, and of course not forgetting Joseph Wright of Derby, who was in Naples in 1774 and who visibly came under the influence of the red glows and spectacular illuminations of Volaire (on this subject, see discussion by F. Cummings cited below). In fact, the present painting was originally attributed to Wright; this very significant error was corrected in 1962 by Charles Buckley and seconded by the Toulouse curator, Paul Mesplé. Was it this enormous vogue for Volaire's paintings of Vesuvius that irritated Stendhal and caused him to exclaim disdainfully in front of the *Eruption* in Nantes: "Eruption of Vesuvius by I do not know what 18th-century Italian. It is painted like a theater decoration; also don't I detect the effect—that convenience for the ignorant—the effect of melodrama?" An incomprehensible judgment which instead only empha-

sizes the precocity and vitality of the pre-romantic 18th-century landscape, in opposition to an early 19th-century concept of landscape that was more cautious, decorative and realistic (*cf.* Pierre-Henri de Valenciennes, Jean-Victor Bertin, Jean-Joseph Xavier Bidault, or Georges Michel). If we contrast the sumptuously colorful *Eruptions* of Volaire to the tonal moderation and almost dry draughtsmanship of Alexandre-Hyacinthe Dunouy at Fontainebleau (1817), we can rescind the severe judgment, very representative of a more "neo-classically" advanced esthetic, of Valenciennes in his *Éléments de perspective à l'usage des artistes* (Paris, 1799, p. 280): "We knew in Naples a painter who occupied himself only with painting the eruptions of Vesuvius; but as he did only what was practical, and perhaps painted even in advance, we never found in his works the character of grandeur and truth suitable to the type of effect as pronounced as that of the eruptions. This requires a great deal of genius, sensibility and memory; one must ally the coolness of observation with the innate sentiment of color, in order to execute faithfully the upheavals of Nature, as sublime [a word to remember] as they are terrifying." At least, Valenciennes permits us to retain the acknowledged vogue for Vesuvius, since in the same passage, he includes it as one of the themes possible for a young landscape painter.

Finally, Volaire, like Joseph Vernet (with whom he shared a taste for theatrical settings and moonlight effects), Hubert Robert, Loutherbourg or Casanova (whose vibrant brushwork and facile and lively sense of color Volaire approaches), is a very gifted representative of the "sublime" defined by Kant in his *Critique of Pure Reason* (1790), which Starobinski, in a recent book, *1789: Les emblèmes de la raison* (1973, p. 180) relates usefully to so many landscapes from the end of the 18th century (without ever citing Volaire !). In effect, among the manifestations of the sublime in nature (the word "sublime" was used by Valenciennes above), it is significant that Kant does not fail to cite "the volcanoes in all their destructive power... [along with]... the rocks audaciously overhanging and as though menacing..., the hurricanes that leave devastation behind them..., the high waterfalls of a powerful river," etc., in brief, the whole repertory of a vision of a nature which, while terrible, becomes more attractive and admirable when we can contemplate it safely. "And we say willingly," Kant continues, "of these things that they are sublime because they increase the soul's energy beyond its habitual measure... [and confer upon us]... the courage to measure ourselves with the omnipotence of nature." The "sublime" is not in nature but in our spirit, "in as much as we can be conscious of our superiority over the nature in us and in that way also over the nature outside of us (in so much as it influences us). Everything that awakens this sentiment in us, such as the *power* of nature which solicits our forces, is called sublime: it is only in supposing in us this idea and in relating to it that we are capable of arriving at the sublimity of being..." Thus, the idea of contemplation, at once safe and exalting, is fundamental to this analysis of the moral role of sublime nature, and all the paintings of *Vesuvius* by Volaire justly include, in a very significant manner, people contemplating the great natural phenomenon from afar and from shelter (they are always placed in the foreground, as in the paintings by Caspar-David Friedrich). The volcanic eruption is never represented for itself, in its tragic and inexorable consequences. For once, the confrontation and convergence of the ideas of a philosopher and those of an artist will not be judged, we believe, as fortuitous, but rather as revelatory of a profound spiritual state, one that is full of meaning.

PROVENANCE
Bequest of Dr. Bernard Samuels, Front Royal, Virginia, 1960, in memory of his mother, Kathleen Boon Samuels (as Joseph Wright of Derby), (INV. no. 60-39-11).

EXHIBITIONS
1964, Poughkeepsie, no. 21; Indianapolis, 1964, no. 21, color ill.; 1969, Ann Arbor, no. 87.

REFERENCES
Mus. cat., 1966, no. 59, ill. p. 42; F. Cummings, 1971, p. 478.

RELATED WORKS
Signed and dated 1782 in the museum at Capodimonte, Naples (see *Il paesaggio napoletano,* exh. cat., Naples, 1962, no. 98); the Capodimonte Museum possesses another nocturnal *Eruption* by Volaire, seen from a port and without the motif of the bridge which distinguishes the 1782 version. In the museum at Le Havre (on deposit from the Louvre, 1876, 74 × 160; S. INV. 8489), comparable to the Richmond painting. In a sale at the Galerie Charpentier, Paris, 11 June 1959, no. 133, ill.; 95 × 145; signed and inscribed: *Eruption du mont Vésuve le 14 mai 1771, peint par le Chev. Volaire,* comparable to the painting in Richmond. In London, at John Mitchell's, according to an advertisement appearing in *The Connoisseur,* June 1964, on sale for £ 575, 22 × 18, an example differing strongly from others for it has a vertical format, rare for Volaire. In the Liverpool museum; 103 × 128 (see museum cat., 1966, no. 6130, ill.). In the museum of the Villa Pignatelli, Naples, on deposit from the Capodimonte Museum; 129 × 260 (see *Arte francese à Napoli,* exh. cat., Naples, 1967, no. 41, ill. 37). Example very close to the one in Nantes, 130 × 227; in 1810, in the collection of Cacault, French ambassador in Italy (thus, a painting very probably acquired on the spot) and allegedly representing an eruption of Vesuvius in 1737 (rather than 1717 stated in the old catalogs). In the Radice Collection, Naples (listed as unpublished in *Arte francese a Napoli*; cited above). In the Museo San Martino, Naples (listed as unpublished in *Arte francese a Napoli.* Recently at Galleria Marcello e Carlo Sestiero, Rome; 131 × 264. At the Museo Sannio in Benevento, on deposit from the Capodimonte Museum, cited in *Arte francese a Napoli.*
At Herner Wengraf's Gallery Ltd., London in 1973 and rather close to the Richmond painting. At Agnew's, London, 1967, no. 43; 48.3 × 63.5. In the Château de Cabarieu (Tarn-et-Garonne) and coming from the collection of the farmer-general Bergert de Grancourt of Négrepelisse; 248 × 378 (see -M. Méras, *Gazette des Beaux-Arts,* December 1972, p. 333, fig. 4). In Leningrad, Hermitage; 104 × 210. S.d. 1779 (with an authentic inscription relating to the eruption of 1779); another painting, on the same subject: 242 × 163. In Toulouse; 76 × 160. In Narbonne; 78 × 178. In Rouen; 99 × 65. In Vienna; Academy of Fine Arts. In Vervins, deposited by the Louvre in 1872 (actually in the Hôtel de Ville); 162 × 105 (Louvre INV. 8489 bis).

J.F.

François-Louis-Joseph Watteau

1758 Valenciennes - Lille 1823

Two painters are known by the name of Watteau de Lille: Louis-Joseph (1731-1798), nephew of the great Antoine Watteau and an artist of an agreeable 18th-century virtuosity, and his son, François-Louis-Joseph, who at first copied his father in order later to achieve a strong originality. He had a brother who was a painter, who died in 1783 at the age of 20; his brother-in-law, François-Léonard Dupont-Watteau, also painted.

Trained by his father at the Lille Drawing Academy (founded in 1755), François won the medal of honor in 1774, at the young age of 16. Thanks to his success and some subsidies from the City of Lille, his father was able, the following year, to send him to Louis-Jacques Durameau in Paris, who had just been named professor at the Painting Academy. François returned from Paris about 1786. The nature of his instruction in Paris is not clearly known: one must ask what lessons Watteau de Lille learned from the history painter Durameau. What was the style of the drawing *Fête dans un jardin,* presented at the Exposition de la Jeunesse, Place Dauphine, in 1783? In truth, it is easier to follow the activity of this painter in Lille, where in 1788 he had business dealings with the famous collector from Angers, the Marquis de Livois (Watteau alerted him to northern paintings on the market; see *B.S.H.A.F.,* 1933, pp. 149-158).

François-Joseph Watteau exhibited in the Paris Salons: in 1795 *(Fête de village, Paysage avec figures et animaux, orage ; Paysage, temps calme)* and in 1802 (the *Défaite de Darius par Alexandre).* His responsibilities in the free drawing school in Lille increased: in 1786, he was named adjunct professor to his father; in 1798, he became professor and in 1812, director. Fortunately for our records, François Watteau took part, while still a student, in the Lille Salons of 1773-75; in 1776 he exhibited a biblical scene; in 1780 he sent a *Mort de Socrate,* and in 1781 a sketch for a *Martyre de saint Pierre* (both perhaps done under the influence of Durameau) and in 1783 a print after a painting by his father. His submissions to the Salons of 1784 and 1786 became more numerous. A. de Poncheville, with Paul Marmottan the only art historian to have concentrated on the work of Watteau de Lille, pointed out that François-Louis decorated a salon in Lille (one large composition and five overdoors) around 1786, for a certain François-Joseph Reynart. In the *Kermesse flamande,* as in one of the overdoors, *Ronde enfantine sous un mai,* can be seen the influence of Teniers and Flemish painting. In his *Cahier de Costumes français* (1786), a series of drawings engraved by Bacquoy and Dupin *fils,* Watteau de Lille revealed himself to be a refined painter of courtly fashion, an artist similar to Schall, Lawreince, Debucourt or Mallet (the original drawings are in the Wicar Foundation, Lille, and in private collections in Paris).

The first important painting by Watteau de Lille which is still extant is the *Menuet sous un chêne* dating from 1787 (Valenciennes); this was his acceptance piece for the Academy of Valenciennes. Very close to that canvas is the famous *Réunion dans un parc* (Paris, Musée Cognacq-Jay): the same nostalgia as his great-uncle, Antoine Watteau, the same setting of shadows touched by autumn, the similar elegant assembly, "a gallant *défroque* which recalls the comic-opera and the theater of the Foire Saint-Germain" (Poncheville), people engaged in the pleasures of conversation and the dance, identical witty drawing, delicate but lively and harmonious color, translated by a rascally, affected talent that recalls Debucourt.

A good part of the art of François-Louis lies in these scenes of gallant customs, which relate him to the minor Parisian masters of the turn of the century in their careful, detailed work. Paintings on this theme were numerous and the Lille Salon catalogs have preserved the titles: 1794, *Fête champêtre dans les costumes du jour ;* 1796, *Concert dans un bois ;* 1797, *Fête villageoise* (Marseille); 1798, *Repas champêtre ;* 1800, *Bal champêtre,* etc. Subjects similar to those of Jean-Baptiste Greuze were equally appealing to Watteau: *La satisfaction du mariage* and *Père de famille donnant le saint Nicolas à ses enfants* (Salon of 1788, now in Lille). A certain eclecticism explains two paintings he did in the manner of Jean-Baptiste Fragonard: *Offrande à l'Amour, Sacrifice à Priape* (both in Arras).

But his painting dealing with contemporary life—political, everyday, military—remind us that it is not necessary to place François Watteau, as there is too much tendency to do, within the category of a painter of small gallant subjects in the manner of Huet or Desrais. *La Fête au Colisée* (1791, Lille); *La Braderie* (Year VIII); *La Fête du braquelet* (Year XI); and *La Procession de Lille en 1789* (Year IX, Lille) are all irreplaceable documents of local life, treated in a technique that is both precise and savory. Watteau de Lille was also a painter of battle scenes (*Battle of the Pyramids,* No. 204; *La Défense de Lille en 1792,* Year IV, Lille), showing a magnificent patriotic sweep, and even unexpected naïve pastiches in Lebrun's style, such as *Alexandre et Porus* and *Alexandre et Darius,* dating from Year X, now in Lille).

François-Louis died penniless in Lille on 1 December 1823, after having been one of the founders of the museum and curator since 1810, along with Van Blarenberghe.

A.-B. L.

204
*Battle of the Pyramids**

La Bataille des Pyramides
Plate p. 153
Canvas; 92 × 120; s.d.l.l. *f. Watteau Ft 7e année, r.p.f.*
Valenciennes, Musée des Beaux-Arts

This painting was paired with a canvas showing the *Siège de Beauvais* by the Burgundians in 1472, which includes the famous episode of Jeanne Hachette (see Related Works). Thus, the theme of the pendant was both a lesson in patriotic heroism and an example of "gothic" history, well suited to the taste of the period and a symbolic counterpart to a scene from modern French history like the *Battle of the Pyramids*.

In both pictures (as well as in his *Défense de Lille en 1792* in Lille; see Mabille de Poncheville, 1928, ill. opp. p. 84), F.-J. Watteau was trying to establish himself as a realist painter of contemporary life by exalting the glory and valor of the Nation in a significant political context. Thus, the painter was clearly less concerned with historical accuracy than with giving the scene epic dimensions, exaggerating the size of the flag and the pyramid to make them more striking. In the same spirit, he depicted Mourad Bey, one of the two leaders of the Mamelukes (the other was Ibrahim Bey) as having been captured by soldiers and led before Bonaparte, whereas actually, as Cantarel has pointed out, the Turkish general, although wounded in the head, succeeded in escaping into Upper Egypt on the evening of 21 July. This theme, was also treated by Vincent, Hennequin, Lejeune (in 1806), as well as Gros and Géricault.

Such historical pictures are more numerous than one might think in the work of Watteau, who is known as a minor painter of genre and fashion, and whose style is generally pleasantly unselfconscious, with vigorous shadows and bright, shimmering colors. Most of his military pictures do in fact date from the Revolutionary years and are chiefly known from the catalogs of the Lille Salons between 1790 and 1803, Watteau's great period of politically-inspired painting in Lille. Also to be noted are two other pictures in Lille: an *Escarmouche* and two *Batailles* of Alexander, curious pastiches of Lebrun, which exhibit the same superbly chaotic throng of figures as in the *Battle of the Pyramids*. The

almost naive, obsessive horror of empty space; the warm, bright colors; the epic inspiration that gives huge proportions to this picture of tiny figures; its very inventiveness, just as striking as that of the matching medieval painting of Jeanne Hachette—all this would suffice, even if these were exceptions in his work, to reveal that F.-J. Watteau was a most alert and sincere historical painter of an undeniable pre-romantic inspiration, and by no means just a "minor master" of Flemish-style realism: as he was so unjustly characterized by his most recent biographer, Mabille de Poncheville who dismissed the two Valenciennes historical *visions* as "less than mediocre." Marmottan, although reticent, was surely a better judge when he saw in them "astonishing verve, realism to the point of hyperbole." In the *Pyramids,* Marmottan continued, the painter "shows a torrent gushing past the great pyramid, a kind of Red Sea in which numbers of the combatants are engulfed... There is fire and the energy of action, in his combats... For any other artist, this would be a tour de force; for François Watteau it is child's play."

J. F.

PROVENANCE
Bequest of Mlle Euphrosine Holaind, 1888 (together with its pendant, the *Siège de Beauvais,* see Related Works). Over half (10 out of 19) of the works by F.-J. Watteau in the Valenciennes museum come from Mlle Holaind, either as gifts or by bequest, or from her sister Mme Dubois (INV. no. 46-1.211).

EXHIBITION
1799, Lille, no. 2.

REFERENCES
P. Marmottan, 1889, pp. 55, 60; F. Benoît, 1897, ill. 23; A. Mabille de Poncheville, 1926, p. 229; *ibid.,* 1928, p. 84, painting cat. no. 2, p. 107; mus. cat., 1931, no. 392; J. Vernet-Ruiz and M. Laclotte, 1962, p. 256; Y. Cantarel, 1973, pp. 680, 791.

RELATED WORKS
A pencil sketch (20 × 30) was in the Maurice Lefebvre

collection at Roubaix in 1928 (A. Mabille de Poncheville, 1928, cat. no. 5, p. 111).

Pendant, the *Siège de Beauvais*, 1798-1799, canvas, 92 × 120, in Valenciennes (see reference in A. Mabille de Poncheville, 1928, cat.). On Jeanne Hachette and her cult in the 18th and 19th centuries, see M. Renet, *Beauvais et le Beauvaisis dans les Temps Modernes/Époque de Louis XI et de Charles le Téméraire/Siège de Beauvais—Jeanne Hachette,* Beauvais, 1898, pp. 550-628 (esp. pp. 581-582, with a discussion of paintings Jeanne Hachette). Following Voltaire, Roucher, Lemierre and so many other writers and dramatists of the 18th century the Marquis de Sade wrote a five-act tragedy about Jeanne Hachette, which he read at the Comédie-Française in 1791

and mentioned as proof of his Republican and civic sympathies in his *Lettre à un Représentant du Peuple* of 9 Vendémiaire, Year VIII (1 October 1799), in which he pleaded for his name to be removed from the list of émigrés. There was a famous precedent to Watteau's painting not long before the Revolution, a large canvas by Lebarbier the Elder, which was very successful at the Salon of 1781 and was triumphantly hung in the Beauvais city hall in 1788 (it was destroyed in 1940; see Vergnet-Ruiz, "Une inspiration de Delacroix? La Jeanne Hachette de Lebarbier," *Revue du Louvre,* 1971, no. 2, pp. 81-85, with reproductions of the painting and its preliminary sketch).

J. F.

Pierre-Alexandre Wille

1748 Paris - after January 1821

Son of the famous engraver of Prussian origin, Jean-Georges Wille, Pierre-Alexandre was apprenticed to Jean-Baptiste Greuze in April 1761. Greuze was a close friend of his father and did a famous portrait of him (Paris, Musée Jacquemart-André). Wille then became the pupil of Joseph-Marie Vien, who had him copy the works by Le Sueur at the Carthusian monastery, Paris. But Wille preferred landscape drawing, like his father, and above all realistic scenes and genre subjects inspired by Greuze, whose influence remained predominant. In this style, are several existing works: a *Marché aux poissons* (dated 1761, Paris, sale Hôtel Drouot, 14-15 May 1963, no. 132, ill.), *Scène de marché: la séduction* (1778, Paris, Musée des Arts Décoratifs), *Marchande de bouquets* (1778, Paris, Brasseur sale, 13 March 1920, fig. 22), *L'Essai du corset* engraved by Dennel as a pendant to the *Dédicace d'un poème épique* (Paris, sale, Galerie Charpentier, 30 May 1956, no. 51, ill.), *La Mère indulgente* and *Les Conseils maternels,* engraved by Lempereur (Paris, Galerie Heim, 1968).

P.-A. Wille was recognized by the Academy in 1774 (he was never admitted), which allowed him to exhibit at the Salon, particularly in 1777 and 1779. He exhibited some subjects typical of Greuze (*L'Aumône, Le Couronnement d'une rosière, Le Repos du bon père, Le Seigneur indulgent et le braconnier,* etc.). In addition to the paintings mentioned here, is another work in Cambrai, *Les Derniers moments d'une épouse chérie* (1784).

In 1789, Wille was among the supporters of the Revolution, and became a batallion chief in the National Guard. It appears that from the 1780s he had difficulty selling his paintings. Either because his art had lost its appeal, or because he abandoned it of his own accord, he stopped exhibiting at the Salon from 1789 onwards, and sank not only into oblivion, but also into destitution, at the end of his life. (At the beginning of 1821, he addressed a petition to the Duchesse d'Angoulême for assistance in paying the pension of his wife who had become insane.) His last known works are some drawings, all executed before 1816. Among these are the superb portrait drawings of about 1793-94, preserved in Paris, Musée Carnavalet and recently published by the late K.-E. Maison (*Master Drawings,* 1972, I, p. 34), as well as a large *Fête à la vieillesse* engraved by Duplessis-Berteaux. Other notable works include the *Baigneuses,* drawing dated the Year VII (Kraemer sale, 2-5 June 1913, no. 211, ill.), the detailed execution of which is reminiscent of the *"beau grenu"* of the first lithographs printed in France, the *Concert,* dated 1801, sold recently in Paris, Hôtel Drouot (room 12, 14 June 1974, no. 9, ill.), and finally the drawing representing the *Communion d'un vieillard,* dated 1809 (Paris, private collection). Wille only made one fleeting reappearance, in 1819, exhibiting a watercolor at the Salon.

A. S.

205
Double Reward*

"La Double récompense du mérite"
Plate p. 67
Canvas; 162 × 129; s.d.l.l.: *P.A. Wille 1781*
Salon of 1781, no. 169
Blérancourt, Musée National du Château

In a letter dated 6 May 1782 (Blérancourt museum CFac 327), whose destination is unfortunately unknown, Wille, bemoaning his wretched material condition, alluded to this painting which he wished to sell and proposed to provide it with a pendant. The latter, dated 1785, also at Blérancourt, is entitled *Le Patriotisme français*. It represents a father presenting his sword to his son in front of a bust of the king. Given the date of the first painting, it must allude to the role of France during the American Revolutionary War (although the Salon reviewers did not mention this idea). In fact, a large watercolor drawing (also at Blérancourt) by Wille, s. d. 1776 (that is from the time of the first departures of French volunteers for America), represents a scene of similar inspiration: a young officer taking leave of his family. The year 1781 was the period of the campaigns of Rochambeau and La Fayette, who aided in the victorious battle of Yorktown in October. *Double Reward* shows the return of a young officer of the dragoons who receives from a general officer, at the same time, the cross of Saint-Louis and the hand of his daughter.

The painter tried to raise himself to the level of history painting, while remaining completely faithful to the style based on the touching inspiration of Greuze. Here he provides an optimistic counterpart to the story of the *Fils prodigue* presented by Greuze in 1778. The *"Garçon de bonne humeur"* (coll. Deloynes, XII, no. 264) did not fail to point out at the Salon: "Sensible and honest souls are delightfully moved by these touching scenes, whereas they rebel at the sight of a father cursing his son, because he became a soldier."

If Wille endeavored to ennoble the scene by the inclusion of stately architecture enriched with columns and trophies of war, he did not avoid revealing some deficiencies, for example, the innacurate perspective. It is clear that he was particularly concerned with the pictorial translation of the textures of materials. It is not without justification that the Salon review of 1781 commented particularly on the blue silk dress of the young girl, deploring especially that "M. Wille did not apply himself to rendering a beautiful head rather than a piece of satin" (coll. Deloynes, no. 265).

PROVENANCE
From the former De Maistre Collection. Acquired on the Paris Art Market. In the Anne Morgan bequest to the State, 8 August 1929 (with the Château de Blérancourt); accepted by decree on 4 February 1931 (CFac 226).

EXHIBITIONS
1781, Salon, no. 169; 1783, Salon de la Correspondance.

REFERENCES
Coll. Deloynes, v. XII, no. 255, pp. 70-71; no. 257, p. 88; no. 259, pp. 140-141; no. 260, pp. 177-178; no. 261, pp. 214-215; no. 264, p. 328; no. 265, pp. 337-337 *bis* ; L. Hautecœur, 1909, p. 275 (engraving); L. Hautecœur, 1913, pp. 448, 450, 454-455, 464; L. Hautecœur, 1913, p. 84; Thieme and Becker, v. XXXVI, 1947; mus. cat., 1957, no. 59 (ill.); *ibid.,* 1966, no. 45 (ill.); A. Brookner, 1972, pp. 139-140, ill. 105 (engraving, painting considered lost).

RELATED WORK
Engraved in 1784 by J.-J. Avril, pupil of J.-G. Wille, to whom the print is dedicated.

A. S.

206
Death of the Duke of Brunswick*

La mort du duc de Brunswick
Plate p. 83
Canvas; 135 × 113; s.d.l.l. *P.A. Wille Tedesco pxt 1787*
Salon of 1787, no. 181
Moscow, Pushkin Museum of Fine Arts

Duke Maximilien-Jules-Léopold of Brunswick-Luneburg died 27 April 1785 in Frankfurt, while attempting to rescue the victims of a catastrophic flood of the Oder. This event attracted great attention and was commemorated in a Latin panegyric published the following month in Helmstadt, by F. A. Wideburg, a professor of philosophy. In Paris, the French Academy recommended it as a subject for young poets. On 9 October, J.-G. Wille wrote to the Baron de Sandoz-Rollin that his son hoped "to journey next year to Frankfurt on the Oder, to draw the site where the distinguished but unfortunate Prince of Brunswick perished, and to paint this lamentable event" (J.-G. Wille, 1857, II, p. 131-132). The young Wille did not make this trip, and a family friend, Winckelman, brought from Frankfurt the drawing of the uniform in which the duke is portrayed here (*ibid.*, March 1787, pp. 136-137).

This kind of subject (also depicted in watercolor by Sergent-Marceau and dated 1787, Bibl. Nat., Estampes), was popular for two reasons. Contemporary newspapers regularly published outstanding acts of courage. In 1785, P.-A. Wille himself had illustrated the bravery of the cavalry marshal Gillet who, in a gloomy forest, had rescued a girl being attacked by three bandits; this painting, engraved by P.-G. Wille, was sold in Paris 30 November 1932, no. 126, ill. Moreover, the courage portrayed in the present work was that of a prince. From the 1760s, the most celebrated princely virtues were generosity and love for one's subjects, as manifested by Trajan, Marcus Aurelius or Henri IV.

Partly because of the subject, this painting interested the Salon critics, who dealt harshly with the painter's incongruities: the duke is represented in full dress uniform, and they wondered if the bargeman would not throw him into the water. According to Bachaumont, the subject called for a "sublime expression" beyond Wille's capability. The basic qualities of this painting, such as the execution and the brilliancy of color, were also criticized. According to Potocki, they "create the impression of a large painting in enamel."

PROVENANCE
This little known painting was in the Sytchevka Museum, near Smolensk. According to Mlle Kuznetsova, it most likely came from Doughino, estate of the Panine counts, formerly the Mestchersky princes. Transferred with other Sytchevka paintings to the Pushkin, Moscow, in 1926 (INV. no. 800).

EXHIBITION
1787, Salon, no. 181.

REFERENCES
J.-G. Wille, 1857, v. II, pp. 131-132, 136-137, 150, 161, 166; J. Potocki, *Lettre d'un étranger...*, in Restif de la Bretonne, *Les nuits de Paris,* re-ed. *Revue Universelle des Arts,* v. XVI, 1862, pp. 376-377; *Réponse de M. Denon à une lettre d'un étranger...*, in coll. Deloynes, v. XV, no. 403; see also no. 378, pp. 322-323; no. 379, pp. 379-380; no. 394, pp. 779-780; no. 397, pp. 875-876; Bachaumont, v. XXXVI, p. 380; L. Hautecœur, 1913, p. 449, 455, 465; A. Brookner, 1972, p. 140 (like L. Hautecœur, she believed the painting lost).

A. S.

List of Exhibitions

1826 Paris, Galerie Lebrun, *Ouvrages de peinture exposés au profit des Grecs.*
1828 Londres, *Works of British and French Artists Composing M. Hobday's Gallery of Modern Art, 53 Pall Mall.*
1829 Paris, *Tableaux et objets exposés dans le musée Colbert.*
1830 (février), Paris, Henri Gaugain et Cie, rue Vivienne, nº 2, *Tableaux et objets d'art exposés dans le musée Colbert.*
(mai), Paris, Henri Gaugain et Cie, rue Vivienne, nº 2, *Tableaux et objets d'art exposés dans le musée Colbert.*
Paris, Palais du Luxembourg, *Exposition au profit des blessés des Journées de Juillet 1830.*
1843-1844 Lyon, Palais Saint-Pierre, *Société des Amis des Arts de Lyon.*
1846 Paris, Galerie des Beaux-Arts, Boulevart (sic) Bonne-Nouvelle, 22, *Exposition au profit de la Caisse de secours et pensions de la société des artistes peintres, sculpteurs, graveurs, architectes et dessinateurs* (le 11 janvier 1846).
1848 Paris, Galerie Bonne-Nouvelle, *Exposition des ouvrages au profit de la Caisse des secours et pensions de l'Association des artistes.*
1851 Bordeaux, *Exposition de la Société des Amis des Arts.*
1855 Paris, Exposition Universelle, Palais des Beaux-Arts, *Ouvrages de peinture, sculpture, gravure, lithographie et architecture des Artistes vivants, étrangers et français.*
1860 Paris, 26 Boulevard des Italiens, *Tableaux et dessins de l'École française, principalement du XVIIIe siècle, tirés des collections d'amateurs...*
1861 Marseille, *Trésors de l'art de la Provence.*
1864 Paris, Société nationale des Beaux-Arts, 26 Boulevard des Italiens, *Exposition des œuvres d'Eugène Delacroix.*
1867 Paris, École Impériale des Beaux-Arts, *Ingres* (exposition posthume).
1874 Paris, École Nationale des Beaux-Arts, *Exposition des œuvres de Prud'hon au profit de sa fille.*
Paris, Société de protection des Alsaciens et Lorrains demeurés français. Palais de la Présidence du Corps législatif, le 23 avril 1874, *Expositions au Profit de la Colonisation de l'Algérie par les Alsaciens-Lorrains.*
1878 Paris, Champ de Mars *Exposition spéciale de la Ville de Paris.*
Paris, musée des Arts Décoratifs, *Tableaux anciens et modernes exposés au profit du musée des Arts Décoratifs.*
Paris, Exposition Universelle, Palais du Trocadéro, *Portraits nationaux.*
1883 Paris, École des Beaux-Arts, *Portraits du Siècle (1783-1882).*
Paris, École des Beaux-Arts, *Deuxième exposition de Portraits du Siècle.*
Paris, École des Beaux-Arts, *Exposition Eugène Delacroix au profit de la souscription destinée à élever à Paris un monument à sa mémoire.*
Paris, Louvre, *Exposition de tableaux, statues et objets d'art au profit de l'œuvre des orphelins d'Alsace-Lorraine.*
1889 Paris, Exposition Universelle Internationale, *Centennale de l'Art français 1789-1889.*
Paris, Louvre, Salle des États, *La Révolution française.*
1895 Paris, Palais Galliera, *Centenaire de Corot.*

1896 Vienne, *Wiener Kongress.*
1898 Paris, École des Beaux-Arts, *Les Vernets à l'École des Beaux-Arts, exposition organisée au profit du monument à élever à Joseph, Carle et Horace Vernet.*
1900 Paris, Exposition Internationale Universelle, Grand Palais, *Œuvres d'art. Exposition centennale de l'art français (1800-1889).*
Paris, Exposition Internationale Universelle, Pavillon de la Ville de Paris, *Exposition rétrospective de la Ville de Paris.*
Paris, Exposition Universelle Internationale, Petit Palais, *Exposition rétrospective de l'art français des origines à 1800.*
1908-1909 Saint-Pétersbourg, Galerie Starye Gody, *Les anciennes écoles de peinture dans les palais et les collections privées russes.*
1909 Paris, Palais du domaine de Bagatelle, *Exposition rétrospective de portraits de femmes sous les trois républiques.*
1910 Berlin, Königliche Akademie, *Austellung von Werken Französischer Kunst des XVIII. Jahrhunderts.*
1911 Paris, École des Beaux-Arts, *Exposition de l'œuvre de Paul Huet (1803-1869)...*
Paris, Galerie Georges Petit, *Ingres.*
1912 Saint-Pétersbourg, Institut français, *Exposition centennale de l'art français à Saint-Pétersbourg.*
1913 Paris, Palais des Beaux-Arts (Petit Palais), *David et ses élèves.*
1921 San Francisco, Palace of Fine Arts, *Loan Exhibition of Paintings by Old Masters.*
Bâle, Kunsthalle, *Exposition de peinture française.*
Paris, Chambre syndicale de la Curiosité et des Beaux-Arts, Association franco-américaine d'exposition de peinture et de sculpture, *Ingres.*
1922 New York, Galerie Wildenstein, *Prud'hon.*
Paris, Palais des Beaux-Arts, *Prud'hon.*
1923 New York, Galerie Wildenstein, *Portraits of the French 18th Century.*
Paris, Galerie Charpentier, *L'Art et la vie romantiques.*
1924 Paris, Galerie Charpentier, *Géricault, L'Exposition du Centenaire.*
1925 Paris, Petit Palais, *Exposition du paysage français de Poussin à Corot.*
1926 Amsterdam, Rijksmuseum, *Exposition rétrospective d'art français.*
Bruxelles, Musée royal des Beaux-Arts, *David et son temps.*
1928 Copenhague - Oslo - Stockholm, *De David à Courbet.*
Paris, Galerie Rosenberg, *Delacroix.*
1929 Nottingham, *Clumber House Collection.*
1930 Paris, Hôtel de Sagan, *Exposition Louis Boilly.*
Paris, Louvre, *Centenaire du romantisme, Exposition E. Delacroix.*
1931 New York, Union Leaf Club, *Exhibition of 18th Century Painting.*
Paris, Galerie Paul Rosenberg, *Exposition d'œuvres importantes de grands maîtres du Dix-Neuvième siècle prêtées au profit de la Cité Universitaire de l'Université de Paris.*
Paris, musée Carnavalet, *Paris et la Révolution.*

1932 Londres, Royal Academy, *Exhibition of French Art (1200-1900)*.
1933 Paris, musée Carnavalet, *Chefs-d'œuvre des musées de Province*.
Paris, Orangerie, *Hubert Robert 1733-1808*.
1934 Paris, École des Beaux-Arts, *David, Ingres et Géricault et leur temps*.
Paris, Galerie de la Gazette des Beaux-Arts, *Le siècle de Louis XV vu par les artistes*.
Paris, Galerie Jacques Seligman, *Portraits par Ingres et ses élèves*.
Venise, *XXe Biennale*.
Zurich, Kunsthaus, *Corot*.
1935 Paris, musée des Arts Décoratifs, *Deux siècles de gloire militaire 1610-1814*.
Paris, Petit Palais, *Les Chefs-d'œuvre du musée de Grenoble*.
1935-1936 New York, The Metropolitan Museum of Art, *French Painting and Sculpture of the XVIII Century*.
1936 Paris, Petit-Palais, *Gros, ses amis, ses élèves*.
1937 Paris, Exposition Universelle, Palais national des Arts, *Chefs-d'œuvre de l'art français*.
1938 Amsterdam, Rijksmuseum, *Peinture française au XIXe siècle*.
Leningrad, musée de l'Ermitage, *Portraits* (en russe).
Paris, Galerie de la Gazette des Beaux-Arts, *La Peinture française du XIXe siècle en Suisse*.
Paris, Orangerie, *Bonaparte en Égypte*.
1938-1939 New York, Knoedler et Cie. - Chicago, Art Institute - Milwaukee Art Center - Saint Louis, City Art Museum, *Gros, Géricault, Delacroix*.
1939 Belgrade, musée du Prince Paul, *Peinture française au XIXe siècle*.
San Francisco, Golden Gate International Exhibition, *Masterworks of Five Centuries*.
1939-1940 Buenos Aires - Rio de Janeiro - Montevideo.
San Francisco, De Young Memorial Museum, *Seven Centuries of Painting*.
New York, World's Fair, *Masterpieces of Art*.
1940 Toronto, Art Gallery, *Great Paintings*.
1940-1942 San Francisco, De Young Memorial Museum, *The Painting of France*.
1942 Montréal, Art Association, *Masterpieces*.
New York, Galerie Wildenstein, *Corot*.
1946 Bordeaux, musée des Beaux-Arts, *Bordeaux au temps de la marine en bois*.
Philadelphie, Museum, *Corot*.
1947 Bordeaux, musée des Beaux-Arts, *La vie du musée de 1939 à 1947*.
Paris, Louvre, *Vingt peintures et dessins illustrant l'histoire de la Grande Galerie du Louvre*.
Saint Louis, City Art Museum, *40 Masterpieces*.
1947-1948 Bruxelles, Palais des Beaux-Arts, *De David à Cézanne*.
1948 New York, Galerie Wildenstein, *French Eighteenth Century Painting*.
Paris, Bibliothèque nationale, *La Révolution de 1848*.
Paris, Orangerie, *David*.
Rouen, musée des Beaux-Arts, *Les peintres normands de Jouvenet à Lebourg*.
Strasbourg, château des Rohan, *L'Alsace française, 1648-1948*.
1948-1949 Londres et Manchester, *David 1748-1825*.
1949 Genève, musée Rath, *Trois siècles de peinture française*.

Paris, musée des Arts Décoratifs, *Égypte-France*.
Toronto, *Canadian National Exhibition*.
1950 Bristol, City Art Gallery, *Bristol-Bordeaux, French Week*.
Detroit, Institute of Arts, *French Painting from David to Courbet*.
Philadelphie, Museum, *Diamond Jubilee*.
1952 Londres, Galerie Wildenstein, *Eugène Delacroix*.
Minneapolis, Institute of Arts, *Great Portraits by Famous Painters*.
Rueil-Malmaison, château, *La Direction générale du Musée central des Arts*.
Venise, Biennale, *Corot*.
Paris, musée Carnavalet, *Chefs-d'œuvres des collections privées parisiennes*.
1952-1953 Hambourg. Kunsthalle, Munich, Alte Pinakothek, *Meisterwerke des französischen Malerei von Poussin bis Ingres*.
New York, Metropolitan Museum, *Art Treasures of the Metropolitan*.
1953 Bruxelles, Palais des Beaux-Arts, *La femme dans l'art français*.
Bruxelles, *Chefs-d'œuvres de l'art ancien dans les musées et les collections belges*.
Winterthur, Kunstmuseum, *Théodore Géricault*.
1954 Fort Worth, Museum, *Inaugural Exhibition*.
Londres, Royal Academy, *Le Portrait français de Watteau à David*.
Pittsburgh, Carnegie Institute, *Pictures of Everyday Life*.
Santa Barbara, Museum of Art - San Francisco, California Palace of the Legion of Honor - Kansas City, William Rockhill Nelson Gallery of Art, *The House in Art*.
Toronto, Art Gallery, *European Masters*.
1954-1955 Londres, *European Masters of the 18th Century*.
1955 Rome-Florence, Palazzo Strozzi, *Mostra di capolavori della pittura francesa dell'Ottocento*.
Toulouse-Montauban, *Ingres et ses maîtres de Roques à David*.
1955-1956 Moscou, musée Pouchkine - Leningrad, musée de l'Ermitage, *Art français du XVe au XIXe siècle* (en russe).
New York, Jacques Seligman et Cie - The Minneapolis Institute of Arts - The Cleveland Museum of Art, *Baron Antoine-Jean Gros (1771-1835) Painter of Battles, the first Romantic Painter*.
1956 Moscou-Leningrad-Varsovie, *La Peinture française de David à Cézanne*.
Paris, Orangerie, *Le Cabinet de l'amateur*.
1956-1957 Portland - Seattle - San Francisco - Los Angeles - Minneapolis - Saint Louis - Kansas City - Detroit - Boston, *Paintings from the Collection of Walter P. Chrysler Jr*.
1957 Amsterdam, Rijksmuseum, *Van Gotiek tot Empire. Franse meesterwerken uit het Musée des Arts Décoratifs te Parijs*.
Charleroi, Palais des Beaux-Arts, *Fragonard, David, Navez*.
1958 Agen-Grenoble-Nancy, *Romantiques et Réalistes au XIXe siècle*.
Bruxelles, Exposition Internationale, Pavillon du Saint-Siège, *Imago Christi*.
New York, The Metropolitan Museum of Art, *Paintings from Private Collections*.
Paris, musée Jacquemart-André, *Prud'hon*.
Paris, Orangerie, *L'art français et l'Europe aux XVIIe et XVIIIe siècles*.

1959 Londres, The Arts Council of Great Britain, *The Romantic Movement*.
Paris, Petit Palais, *De Géricault à Matisse*.
Raleigh, North Carolina Museum of Art, *Masterpieces of Art*.
Rome, *Il Settecento a Roma*.
Tours, musée des Beaux-Arts, *L'Art ancien dans les collections privées de Touraine*.

1960 Berne, Kunstmuseum, *Corot*.
Chicago, The Art Institute, *Corot 1796-1875*.
Dayton Art Institute, *French Paintings 1789-1929 from the Collection of Walter P. Chrysler Jr.*
Montréal, *Canada Collects. Le Canada collectionne*.
Paris, Louvre, *Exposition de 700 tableaux tirés des réserves*.

1961 Bordeaux, Galerie des Beaux-Arts, *Trésors d'art polonais. Chefs-d'œuvre des musées de Pologne*.
Recklinghausen, Städtlische Kunsthalle - Amsterdam, Stedelijk museum, *Polarität*.
Rome-Turin, *L'Italia vista dai pittori francesi del XVIII e XIX secolo*.

1962 Dijon, musée des Beaux-Arts, *Napoléon et la Côte-d'Or*.
Rome, Palazzo Venezia, *Il ritratto francese da Clouet a Degas*.
Sceaux, musée de l'Ile-de-France, Orangerie - Bruxelles, Palais royal des Beaux-Arts, *Ile-de-France-Brabant*.
Versailles, château, *La comédie française*.

1963 Bordeaux, *Delacroix, ses maîtres, ses amis, ses élèves*.
Cleveland, Museum of Art, *Style, Youth and the Portrait*.
Londres, Marlborough Fine Art Limited, *Corot*, (Loan Exhibition in Aid of the Royal Opera House Benevolent Fund).
Paris, Louvre, *Eugène Delacroix, 1798-1863, exposition du centenaire*.

1963-1964 Berne, Kunstmuseum, *Eugène Delacroix*.
Berlin, Schloss Charlottenburg, *Meisterwerke aus dem Museum in Lille*.
Bordeaux, Galerie des Beaux-Arts, *La Femme et l'Artiste de Bellini à Picasso*.
Brême, Kunsthalle, *Eugène Delacroix*.
Chalon-sur-Saône, musée Vivant Denon, *Vivant Denon*.
Indianapolis, Herron Museum of Art, *The Romantic Era*.
La-Chaux-de-Fonds, musée, *Artistes de La Chaux-de-Fonds. De Léopold Robert à Le Corbusier*.
Poughkeepsie (New York), Vassar College Art, *Nature and Natural Phenomenon in 18th Century Art*.
Saint Louis, City Museum, *Highlights from the Collection of the Fogg Museum and Harvard Alumni of Saint Louis*.

1964-1965 Delft-Anvers, *De schilder en zijn wereld van Jan van Eyck tot Van Gogh en Ensor*.
Munich, Haus der Kunst, *Französische Malerei des 19. Jahrhunderts von David bis Cézanne*.
Toledo - Kansas City - Nashville - Atlanta - Baltimore, *18th Century France, Twenty Paintings from the Louvre*.
Toledo - Kansas City - Nashville - Atlanta - Baltimore, *18th Century France, Twenty Paintings from the Louvre*.

1965 Bordeaux, Galerie des Beaux-Arts, *Chefs-d'œuvre de la peinture française dans les musées de l'Ermitage et de Moscou*.
Brême, Kunsthalle, *Erwerbungen der Jahre 1961-1965*.
Edimbourg, The Art Council, National Gallery of Scotland, *Corot*.
Moscou, musée Pouchkine - Leningrad, musée de l'Ermitage, *Chefs-d'œuvre des musées de France*.

Palm Beach, Society of the Four Arts, *For Collectors*.
Vienne, *Die Wiener Kongress I*.

1965-1966 Paris, Louvre, *Chefs-d'œuvre de la peinture française dans les musées de Léningrad et de Moscou*.

1966 Vienne, musée du Belvédère, *Kunst und Geist Frankreichs im 18. Jahrhundert*.

1966-1967 Chicago-Philadelphie-Ottawa, *Treasures from Poland*.
Sarasota - Buffalo - Rochester - Raleigh - Philadelphie - Colombus - Pittsburg, *Masterpieces from Montreal*.

1967 Bourg-en-Bresse, musée de l'Ain, *Jean-Jacques de Boissieu 1736-1810*.
Buffalo, (New York), Albright-Knox Art Gallery, *Harvard Club Exhibition*.
Dordrecht, musée municipal, *Fantaisie et réalité, 1830-1850* (en hollandais).
Montargis, musée, *Girodet 1767-1824*.
Montauban, musée Ingres, *Ingres et son temps*, Exposition organisée pour le centenaire de la mort d'Ingres.
Montréal, Exposition Universelle, *Terre des Hommes*.
New Haven, Yale University Art Gallery, *Exhibition of Paintings, Drawings and Sculpture from the Fogg Art Museum Collection*.

1967-1968 Paris, Orangerie, *Vingt ans d'acquisitions au musée du Louvre*.
Paris, Petit Palais, *Ingres*.

1968 Londres, Royal Academy, *France in the Eighteenth Century*.
Mexico, *Œuvres choisies de l'art mondial*.
Paris, musée de la Légion d'honneur, *Napoléon et la Légion d'honneur*.
Rome, Académie de France, Villa Médicis, *Ingres in Italia (1806-1824. 1835-1841)*.

1968-1969, Moscou-Leningrad, *Le romantisme dans la peinture française* (en russe).
Paris, Archives de France, *Les Droits de l'Homme*.
Paris, Petit Palais, *Baudelaire*.

1969 Amiens - Dunkerque, *Napoléon*.
Ann Arbor, University of Michigan, Museum of Art, *The Age of Voltaire*.
Budapest, musée des Beaux-Arts, *Chefs-d'œuvre de l'Ermitage*.
Dijon, musée des Beaux-Arts, *Trois peintres bourguignons du XVIIIe siècle, Colson, Vestier, Trinquesse*.
Kansas City, William Rockhill Nelson Gallery of Art, *The Taste of Napoleon*.
Minneapolis, Institute of Arts, *The Past Rediscovered*.
New York, Galerie Wildenstein, *Corot*.
Paris, Grand Palais, *Napoléon*.
Rueil-Malmaison, Orangerie du château de Bois-Préau, *Joséphine. Parures, Décors et Jardins*.
Tokyo, musée national d'art occidental, *L'Art français du XVIIIe siècle*.

1970 Boston, Museum of Fine Arts, *Masterpieces of Painting in the Metropolitan Museum of Art*.
Gand, musée des Beaux-Arts-Laren, Singer-Memorial Foundation, *Chefs-d'œuvre du musée de Bordeaux*.
Londres, Grosvenor House, *Antique Dealers Fair*.

1971 Bourg-en-Bresse, musée de l'Ain, *Le style Troubadour*.
Bucarest-Cracovie-Jassi-Budapest, *Tableaux célèbres des musées parisiens*.
Paris, Bibliothèque nationale, *Les joies de la nature au XVIIIe siècle*.
Paris, musée Carnavalet, *Dessins parisiens du XVIIIe*.

1971-1972 Los Angeles-Detroit-Philadelphie, *Géricault*.
Pontoise, *Aquarelles et dessins du musée de Pontoise*.
1972 Anvers, Internationaal Cultureel Centrum, *Neoklassieke schilderkunst in Frankrijk*.
Dresde, Staatliche Kunstsammlungen, *Meisterwerke aus der Ermitage Leningrad und aus dem Puschkin Museum Moskou*.
Londres, Royal Academy et Victoria and Albert Museum, *The Age of Neo-Classicism*.
Parie, musée Carnavalet, *Dessins parisiens du Musée Carnavalet*.
Paris, Louvre, *Dessins français de 1750 à 1825 dans les collections du musée du Louvre ; le néo-classicisme*.
Paris, Louvre, *La Grande Galerie du Louvre* (Les dossiers du département des Peintures, nº 4).
1973 Castres, musée Goya, *Les Femmes peintres au XVIIIe siècle*.
Paris, atelier Delacroix, *Delacroix et la peinture libérée* (sans catal.).
Paris, Galerie Cailleux, *Autour du néo-classicisme*.

Paris, Louvre, *Dessins français du Metropolitan Museum of Art. De David à Picasso*.
Pau, musée des Beaux-Arts, *L'autoportrait du XVIIe siècle à nos jours*.
Paris, musée des Arts Décoratifs, *Équivoques*.
Turin, Galleria civica d'arte moderna, *Combattimento per un' immagine*.
1973-1974 Paris, Louvre, *Copies répliques, pastiches* (Les dossiers du département des Peintures, nº 8).
1974 Dijon, musée des Beaux-Arts, *Dessins de la collection His de la Salle*.
Hambourg, Kunsthalle, *Ossian und die Kunst um 1800*.
Londres, Victoria and Albert Museum, *Byron*.
Paris, Grand Palais, *Ossian*.
Paris, Louvre, *Fragonard* (Le petit Journal des Grandes Expositions, nº 10).
Amsterdam, Rijksmuseum, *Franse tekenkunst van de 18de eeuw uit nederlandse verzamelingen*.
1974-1975 Paris (Grand Palais) - Copenhague, *Le néo-classicisme français : dessins des musées de province*.

Bibliography

ABOUT E., *Voyage à travers l'exposition des Beaux-Arts (Peinture et Sculpture)*, Paris, 1855.

ABOUT E., *Rome contemporaine*, Paris, 1861.

ADHÉMAR J., « L'enseignement académique en 1820; Girodet et son atelier », *B.S.H.A.F.*, 1933, pp. 270-283.

ADHÉMAR J., *David, Naissance du génie d'un peintre*, (s.l.) Raoul Solar, 1953.

ADHÉMAR H., « La liberté sur les barricades de Delacroix étudiée d'après des documents inédits », *G.B.A.*, 1954, pp. 83-92.

AIMÉ-AZAM D., *Mazeppa, Géricault et son temps*, Paris, 1956.

AIMÉ-AZAM D., *La passion de Géricault*, Paris, 1970 (rééd. du précédent).

AIMÉ-AZAM D. « Le tragique sécrète de Théodore Géricault », *Journal de l'Amateur de l'Art*, VII, pp. 5-8.

ALAUX J.-P., *L'Académie de France à Rome, ses Directeurs, ses pensionnaires*, Paris, 1933, 2 vol.

ALAUZEN A.-M., *La peinture en Provence du XIVe siècle à nos jours*, Marseille, 1962.

ALEXANDRE A., *Histoire de la peinture militaire*, Paris, 1889.

Almanach des Muses, « Épître à M. Robert Lefèvre », Paris, 1821.

(L'Amateur), « La Matinée perdue », *Journal de Paris*, 30 fructidor an IX.

L'Amateur sans prétention, « Le Salon de 1834 », *Le Mercure du dix-neuvième siècle*, 1834, t. VII.

ANANOFF A., *L'œuvre dessiné de Jean-Honoré Fragonard*, 4 vol., Paris, t. I, 1961; t. II, 1963; t. III, 1968; t. IV, 1970.

ANANOFF A., « Alexandre-Évariste Fragonard et son père (Technique comparative des dessins et nouvelles attributions) », *B.S.H.A.F.*, 1961, pp. 155-157.

ANGRAND P., « L'État Mécène. *Période autoritaire du Second Empire 1851-1860* », *G.B.A.*, 1968, t. I, pp. 303-348.

ANTAL F., « Reflections on Classicism and Romanticism », *The Burlington Magazine*, mars 1936, pp. 131-139; avril 1937, pp. 159-168; 1940, p. 72-78.

ANTAL F., *Classicism and Romanticism*, Londres, 1966.

ARAGON L., « Girodet-Trioson ou le sujet de la peinture », *Europe*, décembre 1949, pp. 185-215.

ARAGON L., *La semaine sainte*, Paris, 1958.

Arlequin chassé du muséum par un artiste ; critique en prose et en vaudeville, Paris, An IX (1801).

Arlequin de retour au muséum, Paris, v. 1801.

AUBERT F., « Joseph-Marie Vien », *G.B.A.*, 1867, 22, pp. 180-190, 282-294, 493-507; 23, 275-287, 297-310, 470-482.

AUBRUN M.-M., « Nicolas-Didier Boguet (1755-1839), un émule du Lorrain », *G.B.A.*, juin 1974, pp. 319-336.

AUDIN M. et VIAL E., *Dictionnaire des artistes et ouvriers d'art du Lyonnais*, Paris, 1919, 2 vol.

AULANIER Ch., *La Grande Galerie du bord de l'eau*, Paris, s.d. (1947).

AULANIER Ch., « A propos d'un tableau d'Hubert Robert : la Grande Galerie avant le Premier Empire », *Bulletin des Musées de France*, mars 1947, pp. 3-10.

AULANIER Ch., *Le Nouveau Louvre de Napoléon III*, Paris, 1953.

AULANIER Ch., *La Petite Galerie du Louvre*, Paris, s.d. (v. 1950-1960).

AUVRAY, voir BELLIER.

AYCARD, voir FLOCON.

BABIN G., « Mme Vigée-Lebrun, portrait de Mme Grand, plus tard princesse de Talleyrand », *L'Illustration*, 1er juin 1912.

BACHAUMONT L. (Petit) de, *Mémoires secrets pour servir à l'histoire de la République des Lettres en France depuis 1762 jusqu'à nos jours ou Journal d'un observateur... par Feu M. de Bachaumont (continué par Pidansat de Mairobert et Moufle d'Angerville)*, Londres, 1777-1789, 36 tomes en 31 volumes.

BALAGNY P., *Le combat de Nazareth d'après le tableau de Nantes*, Fontenay-le-Comte, 1936.

BARDON H., « Les peintures à sujets antiques au XVIIIe siècle d'après les livrets de Salons », *G.B.A.*, avril 1963, pp. 217-250.

BASCHET R., 1948 : voir E.-J. Delécluze.

BASSAN F., *Politique et haute société à l'époque romantique : la famille Pastoret d'après sa correspondance (1788-1858)*, Paris, 1969.

BAUD-BOVY D., *Corot*, Genève, 1957.

BAUDELAIRE Ch., « Le musée classique du bazar Bonne-Nouvelle », *Corsaire-Satan*, 21 janvier 1846 (recueilli dans *Écrits sur l'Art*, Paris, Le livre de poche, 1971).

BAUDELAIRE Ch., *Œuvres Complètes*, Paris, Éd. de la Pléiade, 1961.

BAUDISSIN K. von, *Georg August Wallis, Maler aus Schottland (1768-1847)*, Heidelberg, 1924 (avec « Ossian in der bildenden Kunst », pp. 60-63).

BAUDOT H., *Éloge historique de Bénigne Gagneraux*, avec préface et notes de M.-C. [Chevrot, architecte], Dijon, 1889 (première édition, 1847).

BAUMGARTEN S., *Le crépuscule néo-classique, Thomas Hope*, Paris, 1958.

BAUTIER P., *La peinture en Belgique au XVIIIe siècle*, Bruxelles, 1945.

BAUTIER P., « Quelques peintres brugeois à l'étranger de la fin du XVIe siècle au début du XIXe siècle », *Bulletin de la classe des Beaux-Arts de l'Académie Royale de Belgique*, t. XXXV, 1953, pp. 196-209.

BAZIN G., « La Course de chevaux barbes de Géricault », *L'Amour de l'Art*, avril 1932, pp. 46-53.

BAZIN G., *Corot*, Paris, 1942, nelle éd., 1973.

BAZIN G., « Les fous de Géricault », *Quadrige*, 1946, no. 9, p. 43ss.

BAZIN G., « Duplessis », *Kindlers Malerei Lexikon*, t. II, Zurich 1965, pp. 185-187.

BAZIN G., *Le temps des Musées*, Liège-Bruxelles, 1967.

« Beaux-Arts. Coup d'œil sur le Salon », *La Décade philosophique, littéraire et poétique*, 30 fructidor an X, t. 30, n° 36.

BEAUMONT E. DE, « Deux Mobiliers d'Autrefois », *G.B.A.*, février 1972, pp. 129-139.

BECKER W., *Paris und die deutsche Malerei, 1750-1840*, Munich, 1971.

BÉDOLLIÈRE E. de la, « Paul Delaroche », *Le Siècle*, 7 novembre 1856.

BEHREND M., *Die Erinnerungen der Malerin Vigée-Lebrun*, Weimar, 1912.

BELLEMER Abbé E., *Histoire de la ville de Blaye*, Blaye-Bordeaux, 1886.

BELLEUDY J., *J.-S. Duplessis, peintre du roi (1725-1802)*, Chartres, 1913.

BELLIER et AUVRAY, Émile Bellier de la Chavignerie continué par Louis Auvray, *Dictionnaire général des artistes de l'école française depuis l'origine des arts du dessin jusqu'à nos jours*, Paris, t. I, 1882; t. II, 1885.

BÉNARD R., « Galerie Koucheleff », *G.B.A.*, 1869, t. I, pp. 479-484.

BÉNÉDITE L., *Exposition universelle internationale de 1900 à Paris. Rapport du jury international. Introduction générale. 2e partie : Beaux-Arts*, Paris, 1904.

BÉNÉZIT E., *Dictionnaire des Peintres, Sculpteurs, Dessinateurs et Graveurs*, Paris, 3e éd., 6 vol., 1924-1950.

BENOIS A., « La peinture des époques baroque et rococo », *Starye Gody*, 1908, pp. 720-734.

BENOIST L., *La sculpture romantique*, Paris, 1928.

BENOIT F., *L'art français sous la Révolution et l'Empire. Les doctrines, les idées, les genres*, Paris, 1897.

BENOIT F., *La peinture au musée de Lille*, Paris, 1909, 3 vol.

BÉRAUD A., *Annales de l'Ecole Française des Beaux-Arts*, Paris, 1827.

BÉRÉZINA V., *Musée de l'Ermitage, la peinture française du XIXe siècle. De David à Fantin-Latour* (en russe), Léningrad, 1972.

BERGER K., « David and the Development of Géricault's Art », *G.B.A.*, XXX, 1946, p. 41.

BERGER K., *Géricault und sein Werk*, Vienne, 1952; éd. française, *Géricault et son œuvre*, Paris, 1968.

BERGER K., *Géricault and his Work*, Lawrence, University of Kansas Press, 1955.

BERGER K., « Ingrism and Pre-Raphaelism », *Relations artistiques entre la France et les autres pays. Actes du XIXe congrès international d'histoire de l'art, Paris, 1958*, publié en 1959.

BERGERET DE GRANCOURT, *Voyage d'Italie, 1773-1774*, introduction et notes de J. Wilhelm Paris, 1948.

BERGSTRASSER G., « Zeichnungen von J.-J. de Boissieu im Hessischen Landesmuseum zu Darmstadt », *Kunst in Hessen und Darmstadt*, no 10, 1970, pp. 89-99.

BERL E., *Le neuf Thermidor*, Paris, 1965.

BERTHOUD D., *Vie du peintre Léopold Robert*, Neuchâtel, 1934.

BESSIS H., « Philippe Burty et Eugène Delacroix », *G.B.A.*, 1968, t. II, pp. 195-202.

BEULÉ, *Discours prononcé aux funérailles de M. Brascassat*, Paris, 1867.

BEULÉ, *Notice sur Victor Schnetz*, lue dans la séance publique de l'Académie des Beaux-Arts, le 18 novembre 1871, Paris, 1871.

BEYLIÉ général de, *Le musée de Grenoble*, Paris, 1909.

BIALOSTOCKI J. et WALICKI M., *Malarstwo Europejskie w Zbiorich Polskich 1300-1800*, Cracovie, 1955 (éd. allemande, 1956).

BIEBEL F.M., « Fragonard and Madame du Barry », *G.B.A.*, 56, 1960, p. 207 ss.

BILLIOUD J. et RIPERT P., « Le peintre Louis David et Marseille », *Marseille. Revue municipale*, 3e série, no 24, mai-juillet 1956, pp. 29-33.

BISCHOFF I., « Vigée-Lebrun's Portraits of Men », *Antiques*, janvier 1968, pp. 109-113.

BLANC Ch., *Histoire des peintres français au dix-neuvième siècle*, t. I (seul paru), Paris, 1845.

BLANC Ch., *Le trésor de la curiosité tiré des catalogues de vente...*, Paris, 1857-1858, 2 vol.

BLANC Ch., *Histoire des peintres de toutes les écoles, école française*, 3 vol., Paris, 1865-1869.

BLANC Ch., *Les artistes de mon temps*, Paris, 1876.

BLAUENSTEINER K., *Gérards Bildnis des Reichsgrafen Fries*, Vienne, 1940.

BLONDEL S., *L'art pendant la Révolution*, Paris, 1887.

BLUM A., *Mme Vigée-Lebrun, peintre des grandes dames du XVIIIe siècle*, Paris, 1919.

BLUMER M.-L., *La commission pour la recherche des objets de science et art en Italie, 1796-1797*, Paris, 1934 (Extrait de la Révolution Française, t. 87).

BOIME A., *The Academy and French Painting in the Nineteenth Century*, Londres, 1971.

BOISJOLIN J. de, « Le Musée Carnavalet », *R.A.A.M.*, t. XI, 1902, pp. 137-154; t. XVIII, 1905, pp. 211-222; 301-311.

BONNARDET E., « Comment un oratorien vint en aide à un grand peintre », *G.B.A.*, mai-juin 1938, pp. 311-315.

BONNARDOT A., « Iconographie du vieux Paris », *Revue Universelle des Arts*, IV, 1856, pp. 15-40.

BONNEMAISON (Chev. de), voir *Galerie de S.A.R. la Duchesse de Berry*.

BORDES Ph., « Louis Gauffier and Thomas Penrose in Florence », *The Minneapolis Institute of Arts Bulletin*, t. XIII, 1974, pp. 72-75.

BORENIUS T., *A Catalogue of the Collection of Pictures at Northwick Park*, Londres, 1921.

BORGE J., « Lejeune, premier reporter de l'histoire », *Paris-Match*, 10 septembre 1960.

BOSC E., « Xavier Sigalon. Notes biographiques accompagnées de lettres et de documents inédits avec un essai de catalogue raisonné de son œuvre (1788-1837) », *N.A.A.F.*, 1876, pp. 420-454.

BOUCHOT H., « Le portrait miniature en France », *G.B.A.*, 1894, t. I, pp. 237-252.

BOUCHOT H., « Une artiste française pendant l'émigration, Mme Vigée-Lebrun », *R.A.A.M.*, 1898, pp. 51-62, 219-230.

BOUCHOT H., *La miniature française*, Paris, 1907.

BOURCARD G., *Manuel de l'Amateur d'Estampes* (Dessins, Gouaches, Estampes et Tableaux du 18e siècle), Guide de l'Amateur, Paris, 1893.

BOURGUIGNON J., « Musée de Malmaison, acquisitions récentes », *Bulletin des Musées de France*, octobre 1931, pp. 214-221.

BOURGUIGNON J., *L'album de voyage de l'impératrice Joséphine en 1810 à travers la Suisse et la Savoie avec les trente-trois sépias exécutés au cours du voyage par le Comte de Turpin de Crissé, chambellan de l'impératrice*, Paris, 1935.

BOUVER R., *Le Paysage dans l'Art*, Paris, 1894.

BOUYER R., « Petits maîtres oubliés. Georges Michel », *G.B.A.*, 1897, t. II, pp. 304-313.

BOUYER R., « Georges Michel », *R.A.A.M.* 1927, p. 237-248.

BOWEN R., *Cricket : A History of its Growth and Development throughout the World*, Londres, 1970.

BOYER F., « Le Conseil des Cinq Cents au Palais Bourbon », *B.S.H.A.F.*, 1935, pp. 59-82.

BOYER F., « Les artistes français lauréats ou membres de l'Académie romaine de Saint-Luc dans la seconde moitié du XVIIIe siècle », *B.S.H.A.F.*, 1957, pp. 273-288.

BOYER F., « Le sort sous la Restauration des tableaux à sujets napoléoniens (documents inédits) », *B.S.H.A.F.*, 1966, pp. 271-281.

BOYER F., *Le monde des arts en Italie et la France de la Révolution et de l'Empire*, Turin, 1969a.

BOYER F., « Les débuts du peintre Joseph Boze », *G.B.A.*, septembre 1969b, pp. 135-142.

BOYER D'AGEN, *Ingres d'après une correspondance inédite*, Paris, 1909.

BRAQUEHAY A., *Un peintre d'histoire naturelle. Leroy de Barde et son temps (1777-1829)*, Abbeville, 1896.

BRETON J., *Nos peintres du siècle*, Paris, 1899.

BRIÈRE G., « Nouvelles acquisitions du Musée de Versailles », *Les Musées de France*, 1913, no 5, pp. 69-71.

BRIÈRE G., « Emplacements actuels des tableaux du Musée du Louvre catalogués par F. Villot, Tauzia et retirés des galeries. École française », *B.S.H.A.F.*, 1924, pp. 273-357.

BRIÈRE G., « Sur David portraitiste », *B.S.H.A.F.*, 1945-1946, pp. 168-179.

BRION M., *La Peinture Romantique*, Paris, 1967.

BROOKNER A., « Jean-Baptiste Greuze », *The Burlington Magazine*, t. 98, 1956, pp. 157-162 et 192-199.

BROOKNER A., « Aspects of Neo-Classicism in French Painting », *Apollo*, décembre 1958, pp. 67-73.

BROOKNER A., « J.L. David. A Sentimental Classicist », *Akten des 21. Internationalen Kongresses für Kunstgeschichte in Bonn 1964*, Berlin, 1967, pp. 184-190.

BROOKNER A., *Greuze. The Rise and Fall of an Eighteenth Century Phenomenon*, Londres, 1972.

BRUN C., *Schweizerisches Künstler-Lexikon*, Frauenfeld, 1908.

BRUNET M., « Musée céramique de Sèvres. A propos de la copie sur porcelaine de la Sainte Thérèse de Gérard », *Bulletin des Musées de France*, décembre 1948, pp. 299-301.

BRUNON-GUARDIA G., « Paris et la Révolution au musée Carnavalet », *Beaux-Arts*, mars 1931, p. 18ss.

BRUUN-NEERGAARD T.-C., *Sur la situation des Beaux-Arts en France ou Lettres d'un Danois à son ami*, Paris, an IX (1801).

BRUUN-NEERGAARD T.-C., « Notice nécrologique », *Le Moniteur Universel*, 10 décembre 1809.

BRUUN-NEERGAARD T.-C., « Notice sur M. Taillasson », extrait du *Magasin Encyclopédique*, Paris, février 1810.

BURGER (Thoré) W., « Exposition de tableaux de l'école française ancienne tirés de collections d'amateurs », *G.B.A.*, 1860 (2e article, 15 septembre 1860), pp. 333-358.

BURROUGHS B., « A Picture by Jacques-Louis David », *Metropolitan Museum of Art Bulletin*, juin 1931, pp. 140-144.

BURTY Ph., *Paul Huet. Notice biographique et critique suivie du catalogue de ses œuvres exposées en partie dans les salons de l'Union artistique*, Paris, décembre 1869.

BUSCH G. et SCHULTZE D., *Meisterwerke der Kunsthalle Bremen*, Brême, 1973.

BYRNES J.-B., « A Portrait by Baron Gros », *Los Angeles County Museum, Bulletin of the Art Division*, vol. 4, no 1, automne 1951, pp. 12-14.

CABANNE P., « L'œil de Monsieur Georges [Wildenstein] », *Lectures pour tous*, no 220, mai 1972, pp. 28-37.

CABAT, *Notice sur Brascassat*, Paris, 1868.

CAILLEUX J., *Chefs-d'œuvre de l'art. Grands peintres. Hubert Robert*. Milan, 1968, Paris, 1969.

CAILLEUX, voir aussi CAYEUX.

CALONNE A. DE, « Delaroche et son œuvre », *Revue contemporaine*, t. XXXI, 1er avril 1857.

« CALOPHILE », *Critique raisonnée des tableaux du Salon. Dialogue entre Pasquino, voyageur romain et Scapin*, Paris, an XIII (1804).

CAMESASCA, voir TERNOIS.

CANTALOUBE A., « Les dessins de Louis David », *G.B.A.*, septembre 1860, pp. 284-303.

CANTALOUBE A., *Eugène Delacroix, l'homme et l'artiste*, Paris, 1864.

CANTAREL Y., *Recherches sur les petits maîtres français de la peinture militaire à l'époque napoléonienne*, thèse dactylographiée de l'École du Louvre, Paris, 1973.

CANTINELLI R., *Jacques-Louis David, 1748-1825*, Paris-Bruxelles, 1930.

CAPON G., *The Portrait of Lavoisier and his Wife by Jacques-Louis David*, s.l.n.d. (1924).

CARRIÈRE C. DE, « Sur un tableau de M. Ingres », *L'Artiste*, 26 mars 1848, 3e livraison, pp. 41-42.

CASO J. DE, « Girodet », *The Art Bulletin*, mars 1969, p. 85.

CASO J. DE, « Jacques-Louis David and the Style *all'antica* », *The Burlington Magazine*, t. 114, 1972, pp. 686-690.

CASSOU J., « Ingres et ses contradictions », *G.B.A.*, mars 1934, pp. 146-164.

CASSOU J., *Delacroix*, Paris, 1947.

Catalogue des tableaux de Sa Majesté l'Impératrice Joséphine dans la galerie et les appartements de son palais de Malmaison, Paris, 1811.

Catalogue of Pictures, Works of Art... at Northwick Park, Londres, 1864.

CAUBISENS C., « Peinture et préromantisme pendant la Révolution française », *G.B.A.*, décembre 1961, pp. 367-376.

CAYEUX J. DE, « Watelet et Rembrandt », *B.S.H.A.F.*, 1965, pp. 131-163.

CH..., « Beaux-Arts. Salon (huitième et dernier article) », *Le Moniteur Universel*, 1er mars 1828.

CHABERT Ph.-G., « Le Musée-Hôtel Sandelin de Saint-Omer », *La Revue Française*, supplément au no 240, février 1971.

CHABEUF H., « A propos de la Bacchanale de Bénigne Gagneraux (1756-1795) », *Les Musées de France*, 1913, pp. 77-79.

CHABOT G., *Le musée des Beaux-Arts de Gand*, Bruxelles, 1951.

CHALONS D'ARGÉ, « Nécrologie. Pierre Claude François Delorme, peintre d'histoire », *Revue des Beaux-Arts*, 1859, t. X.

CHAMPFLEURY, « Une visite au Louvre », *L'Artiste*, 1er décembre 1844.

CHAMPFLEURY, « Monsieur Prudhomme au Salon », *Pauvre trompette-Fantaisie de printemps*, Paris, 1847, pp. 33-34.

CHAPTAL Comte, *Mes souvenirs sur Napoléon*, publiés par son arrière petit-fils le Vte A. Chaptal, Paris, 1893.

CHARLES Abbé J.-L., « Un peintre blayais. Jean-Joseph Taillasson (1745-1809) », *Revue historique de Bordeaux*, 1921.

CHASTEL A., « L'année Delacroix », *Art de France*, IV, 1964, pp. 328-335.

CHATEAUBRIAND F.-R. DE, *Mémoires d'Outre-tombe*, Paris, 1849-1850 et éd. de La Pléiade établie par M. Levaillant et G. Moulinier, Paris, 1951.

CHATELAIN J., *Dominique Vivant Denon et le Louvre de Napoléon*, Paris, 1973.

CHAUDONNERET M.-C., « Tableaux de Fleury-Richard à Arenenberg », *Thurgauische Beiträge zur vaterländischen Geschichte*, 1972, 110, pp. 168-174.

CHAUDONNERET M.-C., *Le peintre Fleury-Richard (1777-1852)*, Mémoire de maîtrise (exemplaire dactylographié), Dijon, Faculté des Lettres, 1973 (à paraître).

(CHAUSSARD P.), *Le Pausanias français, ou Description du Salon de 1806 : état des arts du dessin en France, à l'ouverture du XIXe siècle...*, Paris, 1806, 2e éd., Paris, 1808.

CHAUVIN M., *Salon de Mil huit cent vingt quatre*, Paris, 1825.

CHENNEVIÈRES, voir SAINT-SANTIN.

CHENNEVIÈRES Ph. DE, *Souvenirs d'un directeur des Beaux-Arts*, Paris, 1883-1889 (2e partie, 1885).

CHENNEVIÈRES Ph. DE, « M. Eudoxe Marcille », *G.B.A.*, 1890, t. II, pp. 296-310.

CHENNEVIÈRES Ph. and H., « Les Peintres décorateurs du XVIIIe siècle : Louis Durameau », *Revue des Arts Décoratifs*, 1881-1882, pp. 396-398.

CHESNEAU E., *Le mouvement moderne en peinture. Gros*, Paris, 1861.

CHESNEAU E., *La Peinture française au XIXe siècle. Les Chefs d'école*, Paris, 1862 ; rééd. 1864.

CHESNEAU E., *L'Art et les Artistes modernes*, Paris, 1864.

CHESNEAU E., *Les Chefs d'école*, Paris, 1883.

CHOMPRÉ, *Dictionnaire abrégé de la fable, pour l'intelligence des poètes, des tableaux et des statues dont les sujets sont tirés de l'Histoire poétique*, Paris, 1re éd. 1727.

Christie's Review of the Year 1967-1968, Londres, 1968.

CLAPARÈDE J., « Jacques Gamelin, Directeur des Écoles de la Société des Beaux-Arts de Montpellier (novembre 1780-octobre 1783) », *Congrès régional des Fédérations historiques de Languedoc*, Carcassonne, 1952, pub. dans *Bulletin de la Société d'Études scientifiques de l'Aude*, t. LIII, 1952, pp. 195-208.

CLARAC Comte DE, *Description des antiques du musée Royal...* Paris, 1820. Cf. aussi sa *Description des Musées de sculpture antique et moderne du Louvre*, Paris, 3 vol., 1847-1849.

CLARK T.-J., *The Absolute Bourgeois*, Londres, 1973.

CLARK K., « Ingres : peintre de la vie moderne », *Apollo*, mai 1971.

CLAUZEL P., « Xavier Sigalon, Peintre d'histoire (1788-1837) », *Réunion des Sociétés des Beaux-Arts des départements*, 1900, pp. 594-607.

CLAUZEL P., « Note rectificative du mémoire inséré dans le compte rendu de la session de 1900, p. 594 », *Réunion des Sociétés des Beaux-Arts des départements*, 1901, pp. 731-735.

CLÉMENT Ch., *Prud'hon, sa vie, ses œuvres et sa correspondance*, Paris, 1872.

CLÉMENT Ch., *Les Pêcheurs de l'Adriatique de Léopold Robert*, Neuchâtel, 1872.

CLÉMENT Ch., *Léopold Robert d'après sa correspondance inédite*, Paris, 1875.

CLÉMENT Ch., *Artistes anciens et modernes*, Paris, 1876.

CLÉMENT Ch., *Géricault, étude biographique et critique*, 3e éd., Paris, 1879, voir Eitner, L., 1973.

CLÉMENT DE RIS L., *Les Musées de province. Histoire et description*, 1re éd., 2 vol., Paris, 1859 et 1861 ; 2e éd., Paris, 1872.

CLÉMENT DE RIS L., « Musées de Province - Musée de Bordeaux », *Revue Universelle des Arts*, XII, Paris, 1860.

CLÉMENT DE RIS L., « Le musée Henry à Cherbourg », *Revue universelle des arts*, t. XXI, 1865, pp. 197-208.

COCHARD N.-F., *Description historique de Lyon*, Lyon, 1817.

COGGINS C., « Tracings in the Work of Jacques-Louis David », *G.B.A.*, novembre 1968, pp. 259-264.

Collection du Teil Chaix d'Estange (La), Musée de Saint-Omer, Paris, 1925.

COLIGNY Ch., « La vie et la mort de Drouais », *L'Artiste*, 1er mars 1862, pp. 97-101.

COLOMBIER P. DU, « Géricault au musée de Rouen », *La Revue Française*, mai 1963.

COMSTOCK H., « European Art in the Golden Gate International Exposition, San Francisco », *The Connoisseur*, juillet 1939, pp. 28-33, 400.

COMSTOCK H., « The Connoisseur in America. Painting in Los Angeles », *The Connoisseur*, mai 1955, p. 216.

Correspondance de M. d'Angiviller avec Pierre, publ. par M. Furcy-Raynaud, *A.A.F.*, 1905 et 1906, 2 vol.

Correspondance des Directeurs de l'Académie de France à Rome avec les Surintendants des Bâtiments, publiée d'après les manuscrits des Archives Nationales, par A. de Montaiglon et J. Guiffrey, Paris, 1887-1912, 17 vol.

Correspondance des Directeurs généraux des Bâtiments du Roi (Lenormant de Tournehem, Marigny, Terray, d'Angiviller) avec Ch. Coypel, B. Lépicié, C.-N. Cochin, J.-B.-M. Pierre, et J.-M. Vien, publ. par M. Furcy-Raynaud, Paris, 1903-1906.

COULONGES H. et CAILLEUX J., *Hubert Robert*, coll. Chefs d'œuvre de l'Art, Grands Peintres, no 128, Paris, 1969.

COUPIN P.-A., *Essai sur J.-L. David, peintre d'histoire, ancien membre de l'Institut, officier de la Légion d'Honneur*, Paris, 1827.

COUPIN P.-A., *Oeuvres posthumes de Girodet-Trioson... suivies de sa correspondance ; précédées d'une notice historique...*, Paris, 1829, 2 vol.

COURAJOD L., *L'École Royale des élèves Protégés, précédé d'une étude sur le caractère de l'enseignement de l'art français aux différentes époques de son histoire*, Paris, 1874.

COURTHION P., *Delacroix. Journal et correspondance*, Fribourg, 1944.

COURTHION P. et CAILLER P., *Géricault raconté par lui-même et par ses amis*, Genève, 1947.

CROZET R., « Louis Gauffier », *B.S.H.A.F.*, 1941-1944, pp. 100-113.

CUMMINGS F., « Joseph Wright at the National Gallery », *The Art Bulletin*, vol. XXXIV, 1971, no 4, pp. 475-482.

CUMMINGS F., « The Problem of Artistic Style as it Relates to the Beginnings of Romanticism », *Irrationalism in the 18th Century*, Londres-Cleveland, 1972.

CUZIN J.-P., « Nouvelles acquisitions des musées de province. Tableaux de la période néo-classique », *Revue du Louvre et des musées de France*, 1972, no 6, pp. 463-470.

CUZIN J.-P., « Y a-t-il une peinture troubadour ? Notes à propos d'une exposition récente », *L'Information d'Histoire de l'Art*, 1974, no 2, pp. 74-81.

D..., « Beaux-Arts. Salon de 1824. 4e article », *Le Moniteur Universel*, 12 octobre 1824.

D..., « Beaux-Arts. Concours pour le Grand prix de Paysage », *Journal des Débats*, 1er septembre 1825.

D..., « Variétés. Séance de l'Académie royale des Beaux-Arts », *Journal des Débats*, 3 octobre 1825.

D..., « Salon de 1831 », *Journal des Débats*, 7 mai 1931.

D..., « Exposition de 1831 », *Journal des Débats*, 12 mai 1831.

DACIER É., *Catalogues de ventes et livrets de Salons illustrés par Gabriel de Saint-Aubin*, Paris, 1909-1919, 7 vol.

DACIER É., « La Grande Galerie du Louvre, par Hubert Robert au Musée du Louvre », *R.A.A.M.*, 1914, t. II, pp. 215-218.

DARGENTY G., *Le Baron Gros*, Paris-Londres, 1887.

DAUSSIGNY M., *Éloge historique de Pierre Révoil*, Lyon, 1842.

DAVID J.-L.-J., *Le peintre Louis David 1748-1825. Souvenirs et documents inédits*, Paris, 1880; volume de planches non paginé, 1882.

DAVID J.-L.-J., *Quelques observations sur les 19 toiles attribuées à Louis David à l'exposition des portraits du siècle (1783-1883)*, Paris, 1883.

DAYOT A., *L'Image de la Femme*, Paris, 1889.

DAYOT A., *Napoléon raconté par l'image d'après les sculpteurs, les graveurs et les peintres*, Paris, 1895.

DAYOT A., « Le centenaire d'Hubert Robert », *L'Art et les Artistes*, août 1908, pp. 203-209.

DAYOT A., « L'École paysagiste française au XVIIIe siècle », *L'Art et les Artistes*, 1925.

DAYOT A. et PHILLIPS C., *Cent portraits de femmes d'Écoles française et anglaise*, Paris, 1910.

DELABORDE H. et GODDÉ J., *Oeuvre de Paul Delaroche*, Paris, 1858.

DELABORDE H., *Ingres, sa vie, ses travaux, sa doctrine d'après les notes manuscrites et les lettres du maître*, Paris, 1870.

DELACROIX E., « Peintres et sculpteurs modernes. III. Gros », *Revue des Deux Mondes*, 1er septembre 1848.

DELACROIX E., *Journal*, 3 t., Paris, 1932 (préface et notes de A. Joubin).

DELAROCHE H., *Notice des tableaux, dessins, estampes... composant le cabinet et les études de Feu François-Guillaume Ménageot*, Paris, 1816.

DELAROCHE-VERNET H., « Lettres à Paul Delaroche », *La Revue de Paris*, t. VI, novembre-décembre 1910.

DELÉCLUZE E.-J., « Beaux-Arts. Expositions. Salon de 1822 (4e article) », *Le Moniteur Universel*, 18 mai 1822.

DELÉCLUZE E.-J., *Journal... 1824-1828*, publié par R. Baschet, Paris, 1948.

DELÉCLUZE E.-J., *Notice sur la vie et les ouvrages de Léopold Robert*, Paris, 1838.

DELÉCLUZE E.-J., *David, son école et son temps. Souvenirs*, Paris, 1855 (rééd. 1863).

DELESTRE J.-B., *Discours prononcé sur la tombe de Gros*, Paris, 1835.

DELESTRE J.-B., *Gros et ses ouvrages*, Paris, s.d., et 2e éd., 1867.

DELIGNIÈRES E., « Notice sur les tableaux de Louis David et d'Ingres au château de Moreuil en Picardie », *Réunion des Sociétés des Beaux-Arts des départements*, 1890, pp. 489-496.

DELPECH F.-S., *Examen raisonné des ouvrages de peintures, sculptures et gravures exposés au Salon du Louvre en 1814*, Paris, 1814.

DELPHIS H., « Exposition de peinture (2e article) », *Le Mercure du dix-neuvième siècle*, t. XXXIV, 1831.

DELTEIL L., *Le peintre graveur illustré*, t. VII, « Paul Huet », Paris, 1911.

DE MARNE, voir NAPE.

DE MEYER J., *Notice biographique sur J.-B. Suvée*, Bruxelles, 1897.

DENON V., *L'originale e il ritratto*, Bassano, 1792.

DEVLIEGHER L., « J.-B. Suvée en het frans Klassicisme 1743-1807 », *Annales de la Société d'Émulation de Bruges*, 1956, pp. 133-144.

DÉZALLIER D'ARGENVILLE A.-N., *Voyage pittoresque des environs de Paris*, Paris, 1779. (1re éd. 1755).

DEZARROIS A., FÉRAL et MANNHEIM, *Catalogue de la collection du Teil-Chaix d'Est-Ange*, Mâcon, 1925.

DIDEROT D., voir SEZNEC J. et ADHÉMAR J.

DILKE E., *French Painters of the XVIIIth Century*, London, 1899.

DIMIER L., *Histoire de la peinture française au XIXe siècle (1793-1890)*, Paris, 1913.

DIMIER L., « Tableaux qui passent », *Beaux-Arts*, 30 octobre 1930, no 10.

DOIN J., « Marguerite Gérard », *G.B.A.*, décembre 1912, pp. 429-452.

DORBEC P., « Le portrait pendant la Révolution », *R.A.A.M.*, no 118, janvier 1907, pp. 40-52; no 119, février 1907, pp. 133-148.

DORBEC P., « David portraitiste », *G.B.A.*, avril 1907, pp. 306-330.

DORBEC P., « Antoine Vestier », *R.A.A.M.*, XXIX, 1911, pp. 363-376.

DORBEC P., *L'art du paysage en France. Essai sur son évolution de la fin du XVIIIe siècle à la fin du Second Empire*, Paris, 1925.

DORIA Comte A., *Une émule d'Adélaïde Labille-Guiard, Gabrielle Capet portraitiste*, Paris, 1934.

DORIVAL B., « Deux commandes officielles inconnues passées à Ingres en 1803 et 1817 », *Bulletin du Musée Ingres*, no 26, décembre 1969, pp. 5-8.

DORRA H. et REWALD J., *Seurat. L'œuvre peint, biographie et catalogue raisonné*, Paris, 1959.

DU CAMP M., *Les Beaux-Arts en 1855*, Paris, 1855.

DUCHANGE, *Berthélemy, peintre laonnais (1743-1811)*, Laon, 1853 (extrait du *Bulletin de la Société Académique de Laon*).

DUGAS-MONTBEL, *Éloge historique de M. J.-J. de Boissieu*, Lyon, 1810.

DUMAS J.-B., *Compte rendu des travaux de l'Académie royale des sciences, belles-lettres et arts de Lyon, pendant l'année 1817*, Lyon, 1818.

DUMAS J.-B., *Histoire de l'Académie royale des sciences, belles-lettres et arts de Lyon*, Lyon, 1839.

DUNCAN C., « Happy Mothers and Other New Ideas in French Art », *The Art Bulletin*, décembre 1973, pp. 570-600.

DUPLESSIS G., « Le cabinet de M. Gatteaux », *G.B.A.*, 1870-1871, pp. 338-354.

DUPLESSIS G., « Les œuvres de Prud'hon à l'École des Beaux-Arts », *G.B.A.*, juin 1874, pp. 564-576.

DUPLESSIS G., *Catalogue de la collection de pièces sur les Beaux-Arts imprimées et manuscrites recueillie par Pierre-Jean Mariette, Charles-Nicolas Cochin et M. Deloynes... Paris*, 1881.

DU PONT DE NEMOURS, « Lettres sur les Salons de 1775, 1777 et 1779 adressées par Du Pont de Nemours à la Margrave Caroline-Louise de Bade », publ. par Tourneux-Brière, *A.A.F.*, 1908, II, pp. 1-128.

DURANDE A., *Joseph, Carle et Horace Vernet. Correspondance et biographies*, Paris, s.d. (1884).

DURDENT R.-J., *Galerie des peintres français du Salon de 1812*, Paris, 1813.

DUSSIEUX L., *Les artistes français à l'étranger*, Paris, 1re éd. 1852, 2e éd. 1856, 3e éd. 1876.

DU TEIL J., « La collection Chaix-d'Est-Ange », *Les Arts*, no 67, juillet 1907, pp. 2-34.

DUTILLEUX A., « Le Museum National et le Musée spécial de l'École française à Versailles », *Comptes rendus de sessions des Beaux-Arts des départements*, 1886, p. 134.

DUVIVIER, « Arts libéraux et beaux-arts », *Annales de la littérature et des arts*, 1825, t. XXI.

EITNER L., « Two Re-Discovered Landscapes by Géricault and the Chronology of his Early Work », *The Art Bulletin*, XXXVI, 1954, pp. 131-142.

EITNER L., « Géricault's Wounded Cuirassier », *The Burlington Magazine*, t. XCVI, 1954, pp. 254-259.

EITNER L., « The Open Window and the Storm-Tossed Boat; an Essay in the Iconography of Romanticism », *The Art Bulletin*, décembre 1955, pp. 281-290.

EITNER L., « The Sale of Géricault's Studio in 1824 », *G.B.A.*, février 1959, pp. 115-126.

EITNER L., réimpression de Ch. Clément, *Géricault, étude biographique et critique*, 3e éd. 1879, Paris, 1973.

ENGERAND F., *Inventaire des tableaux commandés et achetés par la Direction des Bâtiments du Roi (1709-1792)*, Paris, 1901.

ERARD-GILLES M., *J.-F.-P. Peyron (1744-1814)*, mémoire de maîtrise dactylographié, Paris, 1969-1970.

ESCRAGNOLLE TAUNAY A. d', *A Missão artistica de 1816*, Rio, 1912; rééd. augmentée, Publicaçoes da diretoria de patrimonio historico é artistico nacional, no 18, Rio, 1956.

ERNST S., *Yusupovskaya Galerya-Frantsuskaya Skola*, Leningrad, 1924 (en russe).

F... Vict., « Salon de peinture », *Mercure de France*, octobre 1808, pp. 368-369.

ESCHOLIER R., *Delacroix, peintre, graveur, écrivain*, Paris, t. I, 1926, t. II, 1927, t. III, 1929.

ESCHOLIER R., *Gros, Ses Amis et ses Élèves*, Paris, 1936.

ESCHOLIER R., *La Peinture Française, XIXe siècle*, Paris, t. I, 1941, t. II, 1943.

ESCHOLIER R., *Eugène Delacroix*, Paris, 1963.

Essai sur le Salon de 1817, Paris, 1817.

ESTOURNET O., « La famille des Hallé », *Réunion des Sociétés des Beaux-Arts des départements*, 1905, pp. 71-236.

ETEX A., *Les trois tombeaux de Géricault*, Paris, 1885.

Examen critique et concis des plus beaux ouvrages exposés au Salon du Louvre de cette année 1795, Paris, 1795.

Examen critique et raisonné des tableaux des peintres vivants formant l'exposition de 1808, Paris, 1808.

Examen des ouvrages modernes de peinture, sculpture, architecture et gravure, exposés au Salon, par une Société d'artistes, Paris, An IX (1801).

FABRE F.-X., *Notice des tableaux exposés au musée de Montpellier*, Montpellier, 1828.

FARÉ M., *La nature morte en France. Son histoire et son évolution du XVIIe au XXe siècle*, Genève, 1962.

FENAILLE M., *État général des tapisseries de la Manufacture des Gobelins (1600-1900)*, Paris, 1903-1923, 5 vol.

FEUILLET DE CONCHES F., *Notice historique sur Léopold Robert*, Paris, 1846.

FEUILLET DE CONCHES F., *Léopold Robert. Sa vie, ses œuvres et sa correspondance*, Paris, 1848.

FIDIÈRE O., « Alexandre Roslin », *G.B.A.*, 1898, t. I, pp. 45-62 et pp. 104-116.

FIERENS-GEVAERT, « L'exposition David et son temps au Musée de Bruxelles », *G.B.A.*, mars 1926, pp. 163-174.

FILHOL et LAVALLÉE J., *Galerie du Musée Napoléon*, Paris, 1804-1828, 11 vol.

FIORILLO J.-D., *Geschichte der Zeichnenden Kunste von ihrer Wiederauflebung bis auf die neuesten Zeiten*, Göttingen, 1805, 3 vol.

FLAUBERT G., *Par les champs et par les fièvres - voyage en Italie et en Suisse, avril-mai 1845*, Genève, 1970.

FLEURIOT DE LANGLE P., *Bibliothèque Marmottan. Guide analytique*, Boulogne-sur-Seine, 1938.

FLOCON F. et AYCARD M., *Salon de 1824*, Paris, 1824.

FLORISOONE M., *La Peinture française. Le dix-huitième siècle*, Paris, 1948.

FOCILLON H., *La Peinture au XIXe siècle. Le retour à l'Antique. Le Romantisme*, t. I, Paris, 1927.

FONTAINE A., *Les collections de l'Académie Royale de Peinture et de Sculpture*, Paris, 1910 (rééd. 1930).

FOSCA F., *Corot*, Paris, 1930.

FOUCART B., « The Taste for a Moderate Neo-Classicism », *Apollo* (à paraître en 1974).

FOUCART J., Catalogue de l'exposition *Ingres in Italia (1806-1824; 1835-1841)*, Rome, Villa Médicis, 1968.

FOUCART J., compte rendu de l'exposition *Napoléon Ier*, Amiens, Musée de Picardie, 1969, *Revue de l'Art*, no 8, 1970, pp. 76-77.

FOUCART P., *Brascassat*, Valenciennes, 1887.

FOULON DE VAULX A., « Antoine Vestier », *Le Carnet historique et littéraire*, Paris, 1901a.

FOULON DE VAULX A., « Un pastelliste du XVIIIe siècle : Joseph Boze », *Le Carnet historique et littéraire*, VIII et IX, juin-août 1901b (et tiré à part).

FRANCE A., « P.-P. Prud'hon », *L'Illustration*, 2 décembre 1911.

FRANCIS H.-S., Préface de l'exposition *Baron Antoine-Jean Gros. Painter of Battles. The First Romantic Painter*, Minneapolis-Cleveland, Galerie Seligmann, 1955-1956.

FRANCIS H.-S., « Two portraits by Aved and Gros », *The Bulletin of the Cleveland Museum of Art*, octobre 1964, pp. 196-205.

FRANKFURTER A.-M., « The Apostles of Romanticism », *Art News*, 26 novembre 1938, pp. 8-10.

FRANQUEVILLE DE, *Le premier siècle de l'Institut de France. 25 octobre 1795-25 octobre 1895*, Paris, 1895, 2 vol.

FRIEDLAENDER W., *David to Delacroix*, Harvard-Cambridge (Mass.), 1952, (éd. allemande, 1930).

FRIEDLAENDER W., « Géricault, Romantic, Realist », *Magazine of Art*, t. XLV, 1952, pp. 260-269.

FRIES Comte A., *Die Grafen von Fries*, Dresde, 1903.

FRIMMEL Th. von, « Die werdende Galerie - Haus Lemberg », *Blätter für Gemäldekunde*, t. IV, 1907-1908, pp. 101-103.

FURCY-RAYNAUD M., « Les tableaux et objets d'art saisis chez les émigrés et condamnés et envoyés au Muséum central », *A.A.F.*, 1912, pp. 245-343.

FURCY-RAYNAUD M., « Notes sur les tableaux de *Bélisaire* par David », *B.S.H.A.F.*, 1915-1917, pp. 115-123.

FURCY-RAYNAUD, voir aussi *Correspondance...*

GABET Ch., *Dictionnaire des artistes de l'école française au XIXe s.*, Paris, 1831.

GABILLOT C., *Hubert Robert et son temps*, Paris, 1895.

GABILLOT C., « Les trois Drouais », *G.B.A.*, mars 1906, pp. 246-258.

GAEHTGENS Th. W., *Napoleons Arc de Triomphe*, Abhandlungen der Akademie der Wissenschaften in Göttingen, 1974.

Galerie de S.A.R. la Duchesse de Berry. École française ; peintres modernes (ouvrage sous la direction de M. le Chevalier de Bonnemaison), 3 vol., Paris, 1822.

GALIBERT P., *Chefs-d'œuvre du Musée de Bordeaux*, Bordeaux, 1906.

GALICHON E., « Description des dessins de M. Ingres exposés au salon des Arts-Unis », *G.B.A.*, 1861, t. IX, pp. 343-362; t. XI, pp. 38-48.

GANAY E. DE, « Plaisirs de Trianon », *Jardin des Arts*, n° 58, avril 1959, pp. 612-622.

GARDNER E., « Four French Paintings from the Berwind Collections », *Metropolitan Museum of Art Bulletin*, 1962, pp. 264-271.

GASTON-DREYFUS Ph., « Catalogue raisonné de l'œuvre de Nicolas-Bernard Lépicié », *B.S.H.A.F.*, 1922, pp. 134-283.

GATTEAUX-MARVILLE, E. Gatteaux, Collection de 120 dessins, croquis et peintures de M. Ingres, classés et mis en ordre par son ami Edouard Gatteaux, 1re et 2e séries, Paris, 1875 (photographies de Marville, sans doute avant 1870).

GAUDIBERT P., « Delacroix et le romantisme révolutionnaire : à propos de la Liberté sur les barricades », *Europe*, 1963, n° 408, pp. 4-21.

GAUDIBERT P., *Ingres*, Paris, Flammarion (Petits classiques de l'art), 1970.

GAULLIEUR É.-H., « Léopold Robert d'après ses lettres et ses entretiens », *Revue Suisse*, 1847.

GAULT DE SAINT-GERMAIN P.-M., *Les trois siècles de la peinture en France*, Paris, 1808.

GAULT DE SAINT-GERMAIN P.-M., *Choix des productions les plus remarquables exposées dans le Salon de 1817*, Paris, 1817.

GAVARD Ch., *Versailles, Galeries historiques*, Paris, 1838-1848, 10 vol.

GAUTHIER M., *Géricault*, Paris, 1935.

GEBAUER E., *Les Beaux-Arts à l'Exposition Universelle de 1855*, Paris, 1855.

GEFFROY, « Brascassat » dans Thieme-Becken, t. IV, Leipzig, 1910.

GENSEL W., *Corot und Troyon*, Bielefeld et Leipzig, 1906.

GEOFFROY G., « Corot et Millet », *Studio*, hiver 1902-1903.

GEOFFROY G., *Corot raconté par lui-même et ses amis*, Genève, 1946, 2 vol.

GÉRARD H., *Correspondance de François Gérard* (publiée par GHenri Gérard), Paris, 1867 (précédée d'une notice par A. Viollet-le-Duc).

GERSON H., *Ausbreitung und Nachwirkung der holländischen Malerei des 17. Jahrhunderts*, Haarlem, 1942.

GERSPACHE E., « Les portraits des peintres français à la galerie des Offices de Florence », *Revue Populaire des Beaux-Arts*, octobre 1898, pp. 321-326.

GILARDONI V., *Corot*, Milan, 1952.

GILLET L., *Nomenclature des ouvrages de peintures se rapportant à Paris*, Paris, 1911.

GILLET L., *La peinture française de Poussin à David*, Paris, 1935.

GIMPEL R., *Diary of an Art Dealer*, London, 1966.

GINOUX Ch., « Le chevalier Volaire et les autres peintres toulonnais de ce nom (1660-1831) », *Réunion des Sociétés des Beaux-Arts des départements*, 1893, pp. 262-275.

GIRARD J., « Les souvenirs des Vernet au musée Calvet », *Mémoires de l'Académie de Vaucluse*, 1927, pp. 49-61.

GIRAUD S., *Gustave Ricard, sa vie et son œuvre (1823-1873)*, Paris, 1932.

GIRODIE A., *Jean-Frédéric Schall (Strasbourg 1757-Paris 1825)*, Strasbourg, 1927.

GOLDWATER R.-J., « Gros, Géricault, Delacroix », *Art in America*, janvier, 1939, pp. 36-39.

GOLZIO V., « Il soggiorno romano di Elisabeth Vigée-Lebrun », *Studi Romani*, 1956, IV, pp. 182-183.

GONCOURT E. DE, *Catalogue raisonné de l'œuvre... de P.-P. Prud'hon*, Paris, 1876.

GONCOURT E. et J. DE, publication du livre de raison de Louis Lagrenée, *L'Art*, IV, 1877, pp. 25-26, 136-141, 255-260; reprise dans *Portraits intimes du XVIIIe siècle. Études nouvelles d'après les lettres autographes et les documents inédits*, nouvelle éd., Paris, 1878, pp. 323-362.

GONCOURT E. et J. DE, *L'art du XVIIIe siècle*, Paris, 2e série (Cochin...), 1882; nouvelle éd., 1909.

GONSE L., *Les chefs-d'œuvre des Musées de France. La Peinture*, Paris, 1900.

GONSE L., « Le Musée de Clermont-Ferrand », *La Revue de l'Art ancien et moderne*, 1903, pp. 366-369.

GONZALEZ-PALACIOS A., *David et la pittura Napoleonica*, Milan, 1966; Paris, 1967.

GONZALEZ-PALACIOS A., « La grammatica neoclassica », *Antichità Viva*, 12, 1973a, no. 4, pp. 29-55.

GONZALEZ-PALACIOS A., *Mobili d'arte, Storia del mobile dal 500 al 900*, Milan, 1973b.

GRANDJEAN S., *Inventaire après décès de l'Impératrice Joséphine à Malmaison*, Paris, 1964.

Grands peintres, 1966-1967, voir Gonzalèz-Palacios A. 1968, voir Cailleux J.

GRANGES DES SURGÈRES marquis de, *Les Sablet. Peintres, graveurs et dessinateurs*, Paris, 1888.

GRANVILLE P., « L'une des sources de Géricault révélée par l'identification d'une radiographie », *La Revue du Louvre*, 1968, n° 3, pp. 139-146.

GRAPPE G., « Les amis de jeunesse de Vivant Denon », *Les Beaux-Arts*, 1943, n° 93, p. 5.

GRAPPE G., *P.-P. Prud'hon*, Paris, 1958.

GRAUL R., « Gros », dans Thieme-Becker, t. XV, Leipzig, 1922.

GRAUL R., « Prud'hon », dans Thieme-Becker, t. XXVII, Leipzig, 1933.

GRÉGOIRE J.-A., *Itinéraire de l'Artiste... dans les Églises de Paris*, Paris, 1837.

GRIMAUX E., *Lavoisier 1743-1794, d'après sa correspondance, ses manuscrits, ses papiers de famille et d'autres documents inédits*, Paris, 1888.

GUEDY TH., *Musées de France et Collections particulières*, Paris, s.d.

GUEFFIER P.-F., *Entretien sur les ouvrages de peinture, sculpture et gravure exposés au Musée Napoléon en 1810*, Paris, 1811.

GUERCIO A. DEL, *Géricault*, Milan, 1963.

GUIFFREY J.-J., *Notes et documents inédits sur les expositions du XVIIIe siècle recueillis et mis en ordre par...*, Paris, 1873.

GUIFFREY J., *Histoire de la Tapisserie depuis le Moyen Age jusqu'à nos jours*, Tours, 1886.

GUIFFREY J.-J., « Les modèles des Gobelins devant le jury des Arts en septembre 1794 », *N.A.A.F.*, t. XIII, 1897, pp. 349-389.

GUIFFREY J., « David et le théâtre pendant le séjour à Bruxelles », *G.B.A.*, 1903, t. II, pp. 205-208.

GUIFFREY J., « Joseph-Benoît Suvée, correspondance inédite », *A.A.F.*, 1910, pp. 290-350.

GUIFFREY J., « L'œuvre de Pierre-Paul Prud'hon », *A.A.F.*, 1924.

GUIFFREY J., « Musée du Louvre. Peintures et dessins. Deux nouveaux Prud'hon », *Bulletin des Musées de France*, 1er janvier 1933, pp. 2-5.

GUIFFREY J. et GONSE L., « Louis David, lettres et documents divers (1748-1825) », *N.A.A.F.*, 1874-1875, pp. 373-394.

GUILLAUME J., *Procès-verbaux du comité d'Instruction publique de la Convention nationale*, t. IV, Paris, 1901.

GUILLON-PASTEL C., *Sur le respect dû aux tombeaux et l'indécence des inhumations actuelles*, Paris, 1800.

GUIZOT E., « De l'état des Beaux-Arts en France et du Salon de 1810 », recueilli dans *Études sur les Beaux-Arts en général*, Paris, 1852, pp. 3-100.

GUTH P., « Schall, le peintre des danseuses du XVIIIe siècle », *Connaissance des Arts*, n° 29, juillet 1954, pp. 14-19.

GUTWIRTH S., « Jean-Victor Bertin. Un paysagiste néo-classique (1767-1842) », *G.B.A.*, juin 1974, pp. 337-358.

H. (O.-M.), *L'Amateur au Salon ; Exposition de 1817*, Paris, 1817.

HAACK F., *Die Kunst des XIX. Jahrhunderts*, Esslingen, 1913, rééd. 1937.

HAMEL M., « Compte rendu de l'exposition de tableaux de maîtres anciens au profit des inondés du Midi », *G.B.A.*, t. XXXV, 1887, pp. 244-256.

HAMEL M., *Corot et son œuvre*, Paris, 1905, 2 vol.

HAMILTON G.-H., « Les origines iconographiques de la Liberté sur les barricades », *Studies in Art and Litterature for Belle Da Costa Green*, Princeton, 1954.

HARRISSE H., *L.-L. Boilly, peintre, dessinateur et lithographe, sa vie et son œuvre, 1761-1845*, Paris, 1898 (exemplaire annoté de la main de l'auteur, à la Bibl. Nat., Cabinet des Estampes, Dc 43a).

HASKELL F., « The Old Masters in Nineteenth-Century French Painting », *The Art Quarterly*, printemps 1971, pp. 55-85.

HASKELL F., *An Italian Patron of French Neo-classic Art, Sommariva*, The Zaharoff Lecture for 1972, Oxford 1972.

HAUTECŒUR L., « Le sentimentalisme dans la peinture française », *G.B.A.*, 1909, t. I, pp. 159-176 et 269-286.

HAUTECŒUR L., *Rome et la renaissance de l'Antiquité*, Paris, 1912a (Bibl. des Écoles françaises d'Athènes et de Rome, n° 105).

HAUTECŒUR L., « L'exposition centennale de peinture française à Saint-Petersbourg », *Les Arts*, n° 129, septembre 1912b, pp. 24-32.

HAUTECŒUR L., *Greuze*, Paris, 1913.

HAUTECŒUR L., « Pierre-Alexandre Wille le fils (1748-1821 ?) », *A.A.F.*, 1913 (Mélanges Henry Lemonnier), pp. 440-466.

HAUTECŒUR L., « Les origines du romantisme », *Le Romantisme et l'Art*, Paris, 1928.

HAUTECŒUR L., *Musée du Louvre. École française. XIXe siècle*, t. I, Paris, 1929.

HAUTECŒUR L., *Littérature et peinture en France du XVIIe au XXe siècle*, Paris, 1942.

HAUTECŒUR L., *L'Art sous la Révolution, le Directoire et l'Empire*, Paris, 1953.

HAUTECŒUR L., *Louis David*, Paris, 1954.

HAUTECŒUR L., *Madame Vigée-Lebrun*, Paris, s.d.

HAVERKAMP-BEGEMANN E. et LOGAN A.-M.-S., *European Drawings and Watercolors in the Yale University Art Gallery*, New Haven et Londres, 1970, 2 vol.

HEINE H., *Lutèce*, Paris, 1855.

HEINE H., « Salon de 1831 », *De la France*, Paris, 1833 ; rééd. 1857.

HELM W.-H., *Vigée-Lebrun, her Life and Friendships*, Londres, s.d. [1915].

HERBERT R.-L., *David, Voltaire, « Brutus » and the French Revolution: An Essay in Art and Politics*, Londres, 1972.

HEUSINGER VON WALDEGG J., « Freiheit oder Tod (1794-1795) ; zu einem Gemälde von Jean-Baptiste Regnault in der Kunsthalle », *Ferdinands-Tor-Blatt*, 17 janvier 1972, pp. 3-4.

HOLMA K., *David, son évolution et son style*, Paris, 1940.

HONOUR H., *Neoclassicism*, Harmondsworth, 1968.

HONOUR H., « Canova and David », *Apollo*, octobre 1972, pp. 312-317.

HOPP G., « Le train d'artillerie de Géricault, essai de restitution d'un tableau », *G.B.A.*, 1973, pp. 311-320.

HOURTICQ L., *Delacroix*, Paris, 1930.

HOUSSAYE H., « Un maître de l'école française », *Revue des Deux Mondes*, t. XXXVI, 1879, pp. 374-391.

HOUYOUX R. et SULZBERGER S., « Fernand Khnopff et Eugène Delacroix », *G.B.A.*, septembre 1964, pp. 183-185.

HOWARD S., « A Model of Early Romantic Necrophilia », *Akten des 21. Internationalen Kongresses für Kunstgeschichte in Bonn 1964*, Berlin, 1967, t. I, pp. 217-225.

HUBERT G., « L'Ossian de François Gérard et ses variantes », *La Revue du Louvre et des Musées de France*, 1967, n° 4-5, pp. 239-248.

HUET R.-P., *Paul Huet (1803-1869) d'après ses notes, sa correspondance, ses contemporains. Documents recueillis et précédés d'une notice biographique par son fils René-Paul Huet*, Paris, 1911.

HUGGLER M., « Two Unknown Landscapes by Géricault », *The Burlington Magazine*, XCVI, 1954, pp. 234-237.

HUISMAN G., *Chefs-d'œuvre de l'art français*, Paris, 1937.

HUMBERT A., *Louis David peintre et conventionnel. Essai de critique marxiste*, Paris, 1936.

HUYGHE R., « Genèse du cuirassier blessé de Géricault », *L'Amour de l'Art*, 1931, pp. 69-73.

HUYGHE R., « David le réformateur » (préface de l'exposition *David*, 1948, Paris).

HUYGHE R., *Dialogue avec le visible*, Paris, 1955.

HUYGHE R., *Delacroix*, Paris, 1963.

HUYGHE R., *Delacroix ou le combat solitaire*, Paris, 1964.

INGERSOLL-SMOUSE, F., « Nicolas Bernard Lépicié », *R.A.A.M.*, 1923, t. XLIII, pp. 39-43, 125-136, 365-378 ; 1924, t. XLVI, pp. 122-130, 217-228 ; 1926, t. L, pp. 253-276 ; 1927, t. LIV, pp. 175-186.

INGERSOLL-SMOUSE F., *Joseph Vernet, peintre de marine, 1714-1789. Étude critique suivie d'un catalogue raisonné de son œuvre peint*, Paris, 1926, 2 vol.

Inventaire Général des richesses d'art de la France, Paris, 21 vol., 1876-1907 : 4 vol., *Paris, Monuments civils* ; 8 vol. *Province, Monuments civils*, 4 vol., *Province, Monuments religieux* ; 3 vol., *Archives du Musée des Monuments français*.

ISARLO G., « Hubert Robert », *Connaissance des Arts*, n° 18, 15 août 1953, pp. 28-33.

IVANOFF N., « François-Guillaume Ménageot e una sua opera vicentina », *Ateneo Veneto*, 1967, n° 1-2, pp. 173-179.

JACOB P.-L., (pseudonyme de Paul Lacroix), « David et son École jugée par M. Thiers en 1824 », *G.B.A.*, 1873, t. I, pp. 295-304.

JAL A., *L'artiste et le philosophe, entretiens critiques sur le Salon de 1824*, Paris, 1824.

JAL A., « Mars, Vénus et les Grâces, » *Mercure de France*, 1824, V, pp. 374-382.

JAL A., *Esquisses, croquis, pochades ou tout ce qu'on voudra sur le Salon de 1827*, Paris, 1828.

JAL A., *Salon de 1831. Ébauches critiques*, Paris, 1831.

JAL A., *Dictionnaire critique de biographie et d'histoire...*, Paris, 1867.

JAMES H., *A Small Boy and Others*, Londres, 1913.

JAMOT P., « Delacroix », *Le Romantisme et l'Art* (ouvrage collectif, par L. Hautecœur, etc.), Paris, 1928.

JAMOT P., *La Peinture au Musée du Louvre*. École française. XIXe siècle. 2e partie, Paris, 1929.

JANEAU H., *Le Vendéen La Revellière-Lépeaux, membre du Directoire*, Poitiers, 1953.

JANSON H.-W., « Observations on Nudity in Neoclassical Art », *Akten des 21. Internationalen Kongresses für Kunstgeschichte in Bonn 1964*, Berlin, 1967, t. I, pp. 198-207.

JARRY P., « Les peintures murales du Palais-Bourbon », *B.S.H.A.F.*, 1928, p. 39-41.

JEANRON Ph., « Sigalon et ses ouvrages », extrait de *La Revue du Nord*, no 9, 1837.

J.-G..., « Recent Acquisitions of the Department of Painting », *Museums of Fine Arts Bulletin* (Boston), IX, no 53, octobre 1911, pp. 46-48.

« J.-L. David », *A.A.F.*, I, 1851-1852, pp. 340-342.

JOANNIDES P. et SELLS Ch., « Ossian at the Grand Palais », *The Burlington Magazine*, juin 1974, pp. 358-362.

JOETS J., « Le musée de Saint-Omer », *Bulletin des Musées de France*, no 11, décembre 1937, pp. 180-183.

JOHNSON L., « Some Unknown Sketches for the Wounded Cuirassier and a Subject Identified », *The Burlington Magazine*, t. XCVII, 1955, pp. 78-81.

JOHNSON L., *Delacroix*, Londres, 1963.

JOHNSON L., « Delacroix Centenary in France. II », *The Burlington Magazine*, t. CVI, 1964, pp. 259-267.

JOHNSON L., « Eugène Delacroix et les Salons. Documents inédits au Louvre », *La Revue du Louvre et des Musées de France*, 1966, no 4-5, pp. 217-230.

JOUBIN A., « Études sur le Musée de Montpellier. Cent ans de peinture académique (1665-1759). Morceaux de réception à l'Académie royale », *G.B.A.*, 1924, t. I, pp. 205-214.

JOUBIN A., *Correspondance générale de Eugène Delacroix*, Paris, 1936 à 1938, 5 vol.

JOUBIN A., « Les Modèles de Delacroix », *B.S.H.A.F.*, 1936, 1er fasc., pp. 135-136.

JOUBIN A., « Modèles de Delacroix », *G.B.A.*, 1936, t. I, juin, pp. 345-360.

JOUBIN A., « Logis et ateliers de Delacroix », *B.S.H.A.F.*, 1938, 1er fascicule, pp. 60-69.

JOUIN H., *Exposition universelle de 1878 à Paris. Notice historique et analytique des peintures et sculptures, tapisseries... exposés dans les galeries des Portraits Nationaux du Palais du Trocadéro*, Paris, 1879.

JOUIN H., *Histoire et description des musées d'Angers...*, Paris, 1885.

JOUIN H., « Andromaque, morceau de réception de Louis David », *L'Art*, LXIII, 1904, pp. 215-218.

JULLIAN Ph., *Delacroix*, Paris, 1963.

JULLIAN R., « Géricault et l'Italie », *Arte in Europa, Scritti di Storia dell'Arte in onore di Eduardo Arslan* [Milan, 1966], pp. 897.

KALNEIN W. et LEVEY M., *Art and Architecture of the Eighteenth Century in France*, Londres, 1972.

KOGINA H., *La Bataille romantique*, Leningrad, 1969 (en russe).

KOLB M., *Ary Scheffer et son temps, 1795-1858*, Paris, 1937.

L.A., « Peinture, Tableau du Cit. Girodet », *Journal des Arts, des Sciences, et de littérature*, 30 prairial an X (1802), p. 410-412.

LACAMBRE G. et J., « Ingres à la Villa Médicis. Quelques précisions sur ses envois de pensionnaire », *La Revue du Louvre et des Musées de France*, 1967, pp. 233-238.

LACAMBRE G. et J., « Les élèves d'Ingres et la critique satirique », *Bulletin du Musée Ingres*, no 23, juillet 1968, pp. 19-22.

LACAMBRE G et J., *Champfleury. Le Réalisme*, Paris, 1973.

LACAMBRE G. et J., « La politique d'acquisition sous la Restauration : les tableaux d'histoire », *B.S.H.A.F.*, 1972, pp. 331-344.

LACAMBRE J., « I funerali di Patroclo : Gamelin e David », *Arte Illustrata*, vol. 54, août 1973, pp. 302-303.

LACAMBRE J., Catalogue de l'exposition *Le néo-classicisme français ; dessins des musées de province*, Paris, Grand Palais, Copenhague, Thorvaldsen Museum, 1974-1975.

LACASSAGNE J., « Quand Napoléon perçait sous Bonaparte », *Revue de l'Institut Napoléon*, octobre 1965.

LACLOTTE M., voir VERGNET-RUIZ J.

LADOUÉ P., « Le Musée français des artistes vivants », *G.B.A.*, 1948, pp. 193-208.

LAFARGUE M., *Corot*, Coll. Les Maîtres de l'art moderne, no 8, Paris, 1925.

LAFENESTRE G., *Notice des portraits d'artistes exposés dans la salle Denon au Louvre*, Paris, 1888.

LAFENESTRE G., « Paul Huet et le paysage français », *La Revue des Deux Mondes*, 15 juin 1911, pp. 830-861.

LA FIZELIÈRE A. de, *Granet (François-Marius)*, s.l.n.d. [1850].

LAFOND P., « François-Joseph Heim », *G.B.A.*, 1896, t. I, p. 441-454, 1897, t. I, pp. 27-36.

LAGRANGE L., « Horace Vernet », *G.B.A.*, 1863, t. II, pp. 296-327.

LAGRANGE L. « La Galerie de M. le duc de Morny », *G.B.A.*, 1er mai 1863, pp. 385-401.

LAGRANGE L., *Les Vernet. Joseph Vernet et la peinture au XVIIIe siècle. Avec le texte des livres de raison et un grand nombre de documents inédits*, Paris, 2e éd. 1864.

LAMOUZÈLE E., « Catalogue de la collection du cardinal de Bernis à l'archevêché d'Albi », *B.S.H.A.F.*, 1909, pp. 281-291.

LANDON C.-P. *Précis Historique des productions des Arts*, Paris, an X (1801).

LANDON C.-P. *Nouvelles des Arts*, Paris, an XI (1802).

LANDON C.-P. *Nouvelles des Arts*, t. IV, Paris, an XIII (1804).

LANDON C.-P. *Annales du Musée et de l'école moderne des Beaux-Arts*, 17 vol., Paris, 1801-1809 ; 2e éd., 44 vol., Paris, 1823-1835.

LANDON C.-P. *Salons...*, Paris, 1808-1835 (réédités dans *Annales du Musée et de l'école moderne des Beaux-Arts*).

LANDON C.-P. *Musée royal du Luxembourg, recréé en 1822, et composé des principales productions des artistes vivants*, extrait des *Annales du Musée et de l'école moderne des Beaux-Arts*, Paris, 1823.

LANKHEIT K., *Révolution et Restauration*, éd. française, Paris, 1966.

LANSON R., *Le goût du Moyen Age en France au XVIIIe siècle*, Paris-Bruxelles, 1926.

LAPAUZE H., *Les dessins de J.A.D. Ingres du Musée de Montauban*, Paris, 1901 (1 vol. de texte, 4 vol. de planches).

LAPAUZE H. *Procès-verbaux de la Commune générale des Arts...* Paris, 1903.

LAPAUZE H., *Ingres. Sa vie et son œuvre (1780-1867). D'après des documents inédits*, Paris, 1911.

Lapauze H., « Ingres chez Degas », *La Renaissance de l'art français et des industries de luxe*, mars 1918, pp. 9-15.

Lapauze H., *Histoire de l'Académie de France à Rome*, Paris, 1924, 2 vol.

Laran J., *Inventaire du fonds français après 1800, Bibliothèque Nationale, Département des Estampes,* Paris, 1930-1948, 3 vol.

Larguier L., *Georges Michel (1763-1843)*, Paris, 1927.

Larousse P., *Grand dictionnaire universel du XIXe siècle*, t. X, 1873.

Larroumet G., *Derniers portraits*, Paris, 1904.

Lassaigne J., *Eugène Delacroix*, Londres-New York-Paris, 1950.

Latreille A., *François-Gérard (1770-1837). Catalogue raisonné des portraits peints par le baron François Gérard.* Mémoire dactylographié de l'École du Louvre, Paris, 1973.

Lavalley G., *Le peintre Robert Lefèvre, sa vie, son œuvre*, Caen, s.d. (1902).

La Ville de Mirmont H. de, *Histoire du Musée de Bordeaux (1801-1830)*, Bordeaux, 1899.

Lazard L., « Les peintres de Paris, I, Étienne Bouhot », *Bulletin de la Société de l'histoire de Paris et de l'Ile-de-France*, 1901, pp. 57-66.

Lebel R., « Géricault, ses ambitions monumentales et l'inspiration italienne », *L'Arte*, n.s., XXV, 1960, pp. 327-342.

Lebreton J., « Notice nécrologique sur Madame Vincent née Labille », *Nouvelles des Arts*, an IX (1803), t. II, p. 18.

Lebreton J., « Éloge historique de M. Suvée lu dans la séance publique du 30 octobre 1807 par Joachim Lebreton, secrétaire perpétuel de la classe des Beaux-Arts », *Magasin Encyclopédique*, 1807, t. VI, pp. 55-64.

Lebreton J., *Rapport sur les Beaux-Arts*, Paris, 1808.

Lebrun J.-B.-P., *Précis historique de la vie de la citoyenne Lebrun peintre*, Paris, an II (1794).

Lebrun J.-B.-P., *Galerie des peintres flamands, hollandais et allemands*, Paris, 1796, t. III.

Le Cointe de Laveau G., « Arkhanguelski », *Bulletin du Nord*, 3 mars 1828 (texte repris dans G. Le Cointe de Laveau, 1835.)

Le Cointe de Laveau G., *Description de Moscou*, Moscou, 1835, 2 vol.

Lecoy de la Marche A., « L'Académie de France à Rome d'après la correspondance de ses directeurs (1666-1792); suite des lettres de Lagrenée », *G.B.A.*, 1872, II, novembre, pp. 410-414.

Lecoy de la Marche A., *L'Académie de France à Rome ; correspondance inédite de ses Directeurs*, Paris, 1874.

Ledoux C. et Lebard G., « L'inventaire des appartements de l'empereur Napoléon Ier aux Tuileries », *B.S.H.A.F.*, 1952, pp. 186-204.

Lefebvre L., *Les livrets des Salons de Lille (1773-1788)*, Lille, 1882.

Le Go A., « Beaux-Arts. Pierre Guérin », *Revue de Paris*, 24 août 1833, pp. 260-265.

Leisching E., *Der Wiener Kongress*, Vienne, 1898.

Leith J.A., *The Idea of Art as Propaganda in France, 1750-1799*, Toronto, 1965.

Lelièvre P., « Gros, peintre d'histoire », *G.B.A.*, mai 1936, pp. 289-304.

Lelièvre P., *Vivant Denon, Directeur des Beaux-Arts de Napoléon*, (thèse) Paris, 1942.

Lelièvre P., « Napoléon sur le champ de bataille d'Eylau, par A.-J. Gros », *B.S.H.A.F.*, 1955, pp. 51-55.

Lelièvre P., « Le chevalier Denon... », *L'Œil*, février 1959, pp. 18-27.

Lem F.-H., « Géricault portraitiste », *L'Arte*, n.s., XXVIII, 1963, pp. 59-109.

Lemoisne P.-A., « Quelques tableaux de l'école française du XVIIIe siècle au musée d'Aix-en-Provence », *Les Arts*, no 167, 1918, pp. 2-14.

Lemonnier H., « Notes sur le peintre Vincent », *G.B.A.*, 1904, II, pp. 287-298.

Lemonnier H., « Girodet et les héros d'Ossian », *Séances annuelles des cinq académies du 25 octobre 1913*, Paris, 1913.

Lemonnier H., *Gros*, Paris (s.d.).

Lenoir A., *Journal des Artistes et des Amateurs*, 10 janvier 1830.

Lenoir A., *David. Souvenirs historiques*, tiré à part du *Journal de l'Institut historique*, novembre 1835.

Lenormant Ch., *Les Artistes contemporains. Salon de 1831*, Paris, 1833.

Lenormant Ch., *François Gérard, peintre d'histoire. Essai de biographie et de critique*, Paris, 1847 (2e éd.).

Leris G. de, « Les Femmes à l'Académie de Peinture », *L'Art*, t. XXXXV, 1888, pp. 122-133.

Lescure A.-M. de, *Le château de la Malmaison. Histoire, description, catalogue des objets exposés sous les auspices de S.M. l'Impératrice*, Paris, s.d. (1867).

Lethève J., *La vie quotidienne des artistes au XIXe siècle*, Paris, 1968.

Lettres adressées au baron François Gérard, Paris, 1886.

Lettres impartiales sur les expositions de l'An XIII par un amateur, Paris, An XIII (1804).

Levertin O., *Niclas Lafrensen d.y. och förbindelserna mella u stensk och fransk må larkoust på 1700-tales*, Sveriges allmänna Konstgöreninp publikation. 7. Stockholm, 1899.

Levertin O., *A. Roslin. En Studie*, Stockholm, 1901.

Levey M., voir Kalnein.

Levitine G., *Girodet-Trioson, an Iconographic Study*, Université de Harvard, 1952.

Levitine G., « L'Ossian de Girodet et l'actualité politique sous le Consulat », *G.B.A.*, octobre 1956, pp. 39-56.

Levitine G., « The Primitifs and their Critics in the Year 1800 », *Studies in Romanticism*, Boston, 1962, pp. 209-219.

Levitine G., « Quelques aspects peu connus de Girodet », *G.B.A.*, avril 1965, pp. 231-246.

Levitine G., « Marguerite Gérard and her Stylistic Significance », *Baltimore Museum Annual*, III, 1968, pp. 21 ss.

Levitine G., « Some Unexplored Aspects of the Illustrations of *Atala* : the *Surenchères visuelles* of Girodet and Hersent », *Actes du Congrès de Wisconsin pour le 200e anniversaire de la naissance de Chateaubriand*, 1968, Genève, 1970, pp. 139-145.

Levitine G. « *L'École d'Apelle* de Jean Broc : un « Primitif » au Salon de l'An VIII », *G.B.A.*, novembre 1972, pp. 285-294.

Levetine G., « L'aigle épouvanté de 'l'Ossian' de Girodet et de l'aigle effrayé du Mausolée de Turenne », *G.B.A.*, novembre-décembre 1974, pp. 319-323.

Lewinson-Lessing W.-F., *Meisterwerke aus der Eremitage : Malerei der 17. und 18. Jahrhunderts*, Prague, 1963.

Leymarie J., *La peinture française. Le XIXe siècle*, Genève, 1962.

Lhomme H.-F., « Note des tableaux que M. Vernet se propose d'exposer au salon du Louvre, cette année 1789, autographe dans la collection Raymond Le Ghait », *L'Art*, LXVII, 1907, p. 61.

LIGERET DU CLOISEAU, *Notice historique sur la vie et les ouvrages d'Étienne Bouhot, peintre d'intérieur. Directeur de l'école de dessin de Semur-en-Auxois. Fondateur et Conservateur du Musée de cette ville*, Semur, 1854.

LINDON R., « De la salle de bains de Corot au « Frigidaire » de Bernard Buffet », *G.B.A.*, décembre 1961, pp. 371-377.

LINDSAY J., *Death of the Hero. French Painting from David to Delacroix*, Londres, 1960.

LOCQUIN J., « Notice sur le peintre J.-F. Sané (1732 (?)-1779) », *B.S.H.A.F.*, 1910, pp. 48-60.

LOCQUIN J., *La Peinture d'Histoire en France de 1747 à 1785. Étude sur l'évolution des idées artistiques dans la seconde moitié du XVIIIe siècle*, Paris, 1912.

LOSSKY B., « Œuvres de paysagistes peu connus de la première moitié du XIXe siècle aux musées de Tours et d'Amboise », *B.S.H.A.F.*, 1961, pp. 163-169.

LOSSKY B., « Peintures peu connues du XVIIIe siècle au château de Fontainebleau », *B.S.H.A.F.*, 1966, pp. 177-188.

LOSSKY B., « Léonard de Vinci mourant dans les bras de François Ier. Peinture de François-Guillaume Ménageot au Musée de l'Hôtel de Ville d'Amboise », *Bulletin de l'Association Léonard de Vinci*, n° 6, juin 1967, pp. 43-52.

LOSSKY B., « Le peintre fleuriste Jean-François Van Dael et ses œuvres au château de Fontainebleau », *B.S.H.A.F.*, 1967, pp. 123-136.

LOSSKY B., « Léonard de Vinci mourant dans les bras de François Ier. Tableau d'Ingres au musée du Petit Palais », *Bulletin de l'Association Léonard de Vinci*, décembre 1970, pp. 11-20.

LOSTALOT A. DE, « Henriquel-Dupont », *G.B.A.*, 3e période, LXX, 1892, I, pp. 177-195.

L.P., « Salon de 1831 », Le National, 12 mai 1831.

LUDECKE H., *Eugène Delacroix und die pariser Juli Revolution*, Berlin, 1965.

LUGAND J., « Musée des Beaux-Arts de Béziers; Nouvelles Acquisitions », *La Revue du Louvre*, 4-5, 1964, pp. 269-270.

LUGAND J., « Contribution à l'étude de la vie et de l'œuvre de Joseph-Marie Vien », thèse présentée à l'École du Louvre, 1964.

LUNDBERG G.-W., *Roslin Liv och Verk*, Malmö, 1957, 2 vol.

M***, *Sentiment impartial sur le Salon de 1810*, Paris, 1810.

M***, *Revue critique des productions de peinture, sculpture, et gravure exposées au Salon de 1824*, Paris, 1825.

M. M..., voir MIEL, 1817.

MABILLE DE PONCHEVILLE A., « Les peintres Louis et François Watteau dits « Watteau de Lille », *G.B.A.*, avril 1926, pp. 219-230.

MABILLE DE PONCHEVILLE A., *Louis et François Watteau dits Watteau de Lille*, Paris, 1928.

MABILLE DE PONCHEVILLE A., *Boilly*, Paris, 1931.

MacCOLL D.-S., « Jacques-Louis David and the Ducreux Family », *The Burlington Magazine*, t. LXXII, 1938, pp. 263-270.

MAGIMEL A., *Œuvres de J.-A.-D. Ingres. Gravées au trait sur acier par A. Réveil 1800-1850*, Paris, 1851.

MAGNIN J., *Le paysage français des enlumineurs à Corot*, Paris, 1928.

MAGNIN J., « Un peintre bourguignon, Étienne Bouhot », *Annales de Bourgogne*, t. I, fascicule IV, 1929; tiré à part (consulté), Dijon, 1930.

MALRAUX A., *Psychologie de l'Art*, Genève, 1947-1949, 3 vol., t. I, *Le Musée imaginaire*, 1947.

MANTZ P., « Les Musées de Province. I. Le Musée de Bordeaux », *L'Artiste*, 20 novembre 1846.

MANTZ P., « Exposition en faveur de l'œuvre des Alsaciens et Lorrains. Peinture », 2e article, *G.B.A.*, 1874, II, pp. 193-215.

MARCEL H., « Essai sur l'iconographie de Mirabeau », *R.A.A.M.*, IX, 1901, pp. 269-280.

MARCEL H., *La Peinture française au XIXe siècle*, Paris, s.d. (1905).

MARCUS C.-G., « Un petit maître inconnu, Louis-Philippe Crépin », *Art et Curiosité*, novembre-décembre 1964.

MARET J., *David*, Monaco, 1943.

MARIONNEAU Ch., *Brascassat, sa vie et son œuvre*, Paris, 1872.

MARKHAM F., « Napoleon and his Painters », *Apollo*, septembre 1964, 187-191.

MARLIER G., « Les séjours à Londres et à Hambourg de Jean-Laurent Mosnier », *Actes du XIXe congrès international d'Histoire de l'Art*, 1958, Paris, 1959, pp. 405-411.

MARMOTTAN P., *L'École française de peinture (1789-1830)*, Paris, 1886.

MARMOTTAN P., *Notice historique et critique sur les peintres Louis et François dits Watteau de Lille*, Lille-Paris, 1889.

MARMOTTAN P., «Pierre-Athanase Chauvin, peintre de paysages (1774-1832). Documents communiqués et annotés par M. Paul Marmottan », *N.A.A.F.*, 1889, pp. 126-128.

MARMOTTAN P., *Le peintre Louis Boilly (1761-1845)*, Paris, 1913.

MARMOTTAN P., « Le paysagiste Nicolas-Didier Boguet (1755-1839) », *G.B.A.*, janvier 1925, pp. 15-34.

MARMOTTAN P., « Le peintre Louis Gauffier », *G.B.A.*, mai 1926, pp. 281-300.

MARMOTTAN P., « Les peintres François et Jacques Sablet », *G.B.A.*, octobre 1927, pp. 193-210.

MARQUET DE VASSELOT J.-J. et BLUMER M.-L., « Répertoire des vues des salles du Musée du Louvre », *A.A.F.*, t. XX, 1946.

MARTIN J. et MASSON Ch., dans MAUCLAIR, *Greuze*, Paris, s.d. (1907).

MARTIN-MÉRY G., « Le Musée des Beaux-Arts de Bordeaux », *Les Muses*, n° 40, 24 juin 1970.

MARTIN-MÉRY G., « Le Musée des Beaux-Arts de Bordeaux », *Les Monuments historiques de la France*, 1972, n° 2.

MASCIOTTA M., *Portraits d'artistes par eux-mêmes. XVIIe et XVIIIe siècles*, Florence, 1949.

MASSIN J., *Robespierre*, Paris, 1956.

MATHEY F., Préface dans *Équivoques,* exh., Paris, musée des Arts Décoratifs 1973.

MAUCLAIR C., « L'exposition de l'art et la vie romantiques », *L'Art et les Artistes*, avril 1923, pp. 263-272.

MAUMENÉ Ch. et d'HARCOURT L., « Iconographie des rois de France », *A.A.F.*, Paris, 1931.

MAUROIS A., *J.L. David*, Paris, 1948.

MAX R., « Salon de 1831 », *Le Cabinet de lecture*, 29 mai 1831.

MAXON J., « A David Portrait for Chicago », *Apollo*, janvier 1968, p. 65.

MAXON J., *The Art Institute of Chicago*, New York, 1970.

M.-C.-H., « Paul Delaroche », *Fine Arts Quarterly Review*, II, mai 1864.

MEIER-GRAEFE J., *Eugène Delacroix. Beiträge zu eine Analyse*, Munich, 1913, rééd. 1922.

MEIER-GRAEFE J. et KLOSSOWSKI E., *La collection Chéramy. Catalogue raisonné précédé d'études sur les maîtres principaux de la collection*, Munich, 1908.

Mémoires de Larevellière-Lépeaux, publiés par son fils, Paris, 1895.

Mémoires et Correspondance du Roi Jérôme et de la Reine Catherine, Paris, 1861.

MÉNARD R., « Galerie Koucheleff », *G.B.A.*, 1869, I, pp. 479-484.

MÉRAS M., « Ingres et le baron Vialètes de Mortarieu », *Colloque Ingres*, Montauban, 1969, pp. 115-122.

MÉRAS M., « Deux tableaux retrouvés des collections Bergeret de Grandcourt », *G.B.A.*, décembre 1972, pp. 331-334.

MERSON O., *Inventaire général des richesses d'art de la France. Province. Monuments civils*, t. II, 1897 (*Musée de Nantes*, par Olivier Merson).

MESPLEN P., « David et ses élèves Toulousains », *A.A.F.*, 1969, pp. 91-102.

MESURET R., « Les peintures bordelaises antérieures à 1811 conservées dans les Musées de Bordeaux », *Revue historique de Bordeaux et de la Gironde*, 1955, t. IV, pp. 111-126.

MESURET R., Catalogue de l'exposition *Pierre-Henri de Valenciennes*, Toulouse, 1956.

MICHEL A., « L'œuvre de Corot et le paysage moderne », *Revue des Deux Mondes*, 15 février 1896, pp. 913-930.

MICHEL A., « La peinture française à l'exposition centennale », *G.B.A.*, août 1900, pp. 147-159; octobre 1900, pp. 284-306.

MICHEL É., *Les maîtres du paysage*, Paris, 1906.

MICHIELS A., *Histoire de la peinture flamande*, Paris, 1847-1874, 10 vol.

MIEL E.-F., *Essai sur les Beaux-Arts et particulièrement sur le Salon de 1817, ou examen critique des principaux ouvrages d'art exposés dans le cours de cette année*, Paris, 1817.

MIEL E.-F., « Notice sur Jean-Germain Drouais », *Annales de la Société libre des Beaux-Arts*, 1836, pp. 50-62.

MIEL E.-F., « Notice sur Girodet-Trioson », *Annales de la Société libre des Beaux-Arts*, 1843, pp. 287-300.

MIETTE de VILLARS, *Mémoires de David, peintre et député à la Convention*, Paris, 1850.

MILLER M., « Géricault's Portraits of the Insane », *Journal of the Warburg and Courtauld Institutes*, t. IV, 1941, pp. 152-163.

MIRECOURT E. DE, *Paul Delaroche*, Paris, 1856.

MIRECOURT E. DE, *Eugène Delacroix. Les Contemporains*, Paris, 1856.

MIREUR H., *Dictionnaire des Ventes d'art faits en France et à l'étranger pendant les XVIIIᵉ et XIXᵉ siècles*, Paris, 1911-12, 7 vol.

MIRIMONDE A.-P. DE, « *Agar et l'Ange* de J.-F.-P. Peyron au Musée de Nancy », *Musées de France*, 1950, pp. 266-269.

MIRIMONDE A.-P. DE, « Pierre-Maximilien Delafontaine, élève de David », *G.B.A.*, octobre 1956, pp. 31-38.

MIRIMONDE A.-P. DE, « Esquisses retrouvées (Oudry, Noël, Hallé, Subleyras, Lépicié, Sigalon et Peyron) », *B.S.H.A.F.*, 1967, pp. 131-160.

MITCHELL P., *European Flower Painters*, Londres, 1973.

MOLINIER E., *Le Mobilier au XVIIᵉ et au XVIIIᵉ siècles*, Paris, 1900.

MOMMÉJA J., « La correspondance d'Ingres », *Réunion des sociétés des Beaux-Arts des départements*, 1898, pp. 719-741.

MOMMÉJA J. *La collection Ingres au musée de Montauban, Inventaire général des richesses d'art de la France, Province. Monuments civils*, t. VII, Paris, 1905.

MONGAN A. « Drawings by Ingres in the Winthrop Collection », *G.B.A.*, 1944, pp. 387-412.

MONGLAVE E. DE, *Notice sur les tableaux de bataille peints par le Général Baron Lejeune*, Toulouse, 1850.

MONICAULT C. DE, *Catalogue raisonné des collections publiques. Le musée municipal de Saint-Germain-en-Laye*, Mémoire de maîtrise dactylographié, Paris, 1974.

MONOD F., « L'exposition centennale de l'art français », *G.B.A.*, mars 1912, pp. 191-198; avril 1912, pp. 301-326.

MONSALDY R., *Contre-épreuves des croquis pour les Salons de l'An VII, IX et XII*, Paris, s.d. (1804) (conservé au Cabinet des Estampes de la Bibliothèque Nationale).

MONTAIGLON A. DE, « Lettres écrites par Pierre-Paul Prud'hon à MM. Devosge et Fauconnier pendant son voyage d'Italie », *A.A.F.*, 1857-1858, pp. 164-170.

MONTAIGLON A. DE, et GUIFFREY J., voir *Correspondance des Directeurs...*

MONTGOLFIER B. DE, « Hubert Robert, peintre de Paris au musée Carnavalet », *Bulletin du Musée Carnavalet*, 17ᵉ année, 1964, nᵒˢ 1 et 2.

MONTGOLFIER B. DE, « Les peintres de l'Académie royale à la Chartreuse de Paris », *G.B.A.*, 1964, t. II, pp. 200-216.

MONTIGNY L. DE, *Mémoires biographiques, littéraires et politiques de Mirabeau écrits par lui-même, par son père, son oncle et son fils adoptif*, Paris, 1834-1835, 8 vol.

MOREAU A., *Eugène Delacroix et son œuvre*, Paris, 1873.

MOREAU-NÉLATON E., *Delacroix raconté par lui-même*, Paris, 1916.

MOREAU-NÉLATON E., *Corot raconté par lui-même*, Paris, 1924, 2 vol.

MOREL DE VOLEINE, « Le musée des peintres lyonnais », *Revue du Lyonnais*, 1883, t. VI, pp. 321-333.

MOSELIUS C.-D., *Louis Masreliez*, Stockholm, 1923 (en suédois).

MUNHALL E., « Greuze's Frontispiece for Sophronie », *G.B.A.*, II, 1961, pp. 237-242.

MUNHALL E., « Greuze and the Protestant Spirit », *The Art Quarterly*, 1964, nᵒ 1, pp. 2-23.

MUNTZ E., « Lettres de Mme Le Brun relatives à son portrait de la galerie des Offices (1791) », *N.A.A.F.*, 1874-1875, pp. 449-452.

MUNTZ E., « L'art français du XVIIIᵉ siècle et l'enseignement académique », *R.A.A.M.*, août 1897, pp. 31-48.

MURARD J., « Une visite au tombeau de Narcissa à l'Hôtel-Dieu de Lyon », *Album du Crocodile*, janvier-février 1967, pp. 2-28.

MUXEL J.-N., *Gemälde-Sammlung in München S.K.H. Dom Auguste Herz' von Leuchtenberg*, Munich, s.d. (v. 1834); autres éd., 1846, 1851 (voir Passavant).

NAEF H., « Ingres duelliste », *Bulletin du Musée Ingres*, nᵒ 25, juillet 1969, pp. 17-20.

NAEF H., « Ingres to M. Leblanc. An Unpublished Letter », *The Metropolitan Museum of Art Bulletin*, décembre 1970, pp. 178-184.

NAEF H. et ANGRAND P., « Ingres et la famille de Pastoret, correspondance inédite », *Bulletin du Musée Ingres*, nᵒ 27, juillet 1970, pp. 7-24; nᵒ 28, décembre 1970, pp. 7-22.

NAGLER G.K.N., *Neues allgemeines Künstler-Lexicon*, Munich 1835 - Linz 1914, 25 vol.

NAPE A., « Jean-Louis Demarne. Notice sur sa vie et sur quelques-uns de ses ouvrages », *Revue Universelle des Arts*, t. XXI, 1865, pp. 269-299. (Notice anonyme due au comte de Nape ? présentée par P.-L. [Pau Lacroix] avec la réédition du catalogue de la collection de tableaux de Demarne appartenant à M. de Nape en 1817.)

National Art-Collections Fund 65th Annual Report, Londres, 1968.

Nicolle M., *Catalogue du musée de Nantes*, Nantes, 1913.

Nicolle M., *Le musée de Rouen, peintures*, Paris, s.d.

Nizet M., « Les Vestier », *Congrès archéologique de France*, Avallon, 1907, pp. 691-701.

Noël-Bouton V., « La Grande Galerie du Louvre », *Le petit Journal des Grandes Expositions*, juin-septembre 1972 (Les dossiers du département des Peintures, nº 4).

Nolhac P. de, *Madame Vigée-Lebrun, peintre de la Reine Marie-Antoinette (1755-1842)*, Paris, 1908.

Nolhac P. de, *Hubert Robert*, Paris, 1910.

Nolhac P. de, *Madame Vigée-Lebrun*, Paris, 1912.

Nolhac P. de, *Le Trianon de Marie-Antoinette*, Paris, 1914.

Normand Ch., *J.B. Greuze*, Paris, s.d.

« Notes sur le Salon de 1831 », *L'Artiste*, I, 1831, p. 146.

Notice des tableaux, statues, vases, bustes etc., composant le musée spécial de l'école française (...), Versailles, An X (1801).

Notice sur la vie et les ouvrages de M.-J.-L. David, Paris, 1824.

« Notice historique sur Robert Lefèvre », in *Catalogue des tableaux et du cabinet de M. Robert Lefèvre* (vente après décès, Paris, 7, 8, 9 mars 1831), p. 3-11.

« Notice historique sur Taunay », in *Catalogue des tableaux de Taunay, peintre...* (vente après décès, 28 février-1er mars 1831), Paris, 1831, pp. 3-15.

« Notice sur la vie et les ouvrages de M. Monsiau », in *Catalogue des tableaux, études, dessins, gravures... dépendant de la succession de M. Monsiau* (vente après décès 30-31 août 1837), Paris, 1837, pp. 3-7.

Notice sur la vie et les travaux de M. Garnier, peintre d'histoire, Membre de l'Académie royale des Beaux-Arts de l'Institut, Archives de la France contemporaine, Paris, 1843.

Notice sur le Marat de Louis David suivie de la liste des tableaux dressée par lui-même, Paris, 1867.

« Notice sur le peintre de portraits Joseph Boze (1749-1831) », *N.A.A.F.*, 1872, pp. 407-408.

« Nouvelles des Sciences et des Arts », *Journal des Bâtiments civils, des Monuments et des Arts*, nº 139, 13 nivose An X (décembre 1801).

Observateur au Muséum (L'), ou la critique des tableaux en vaudeville, Paris, 1801.

Observateur et Arlequin aux Salons (L'), Paris, 1822.

Œuvre du baron François Gérard, 1789-1836, gravures à l'eau forte, Paris, 1re partie, 1852-1853; 2e partie, 1856; 3e partie, 1857.

Ojalvo D., « La peinture au musée des Beaux-Arts d'Orléans », *Médecine de France*, 1969, pp. 1-16.

Okun H., « Ossian in painting », *Journal of the Warburg and Courtauld Institutes*, 1967, vol. XXX, pp. 327-356.

Oprescu G., *Géricault*, Paris, 1927.

Oulmont Ch., « Antoine Vestier d'après des portraits de famille inédits », *G.B.A.*, 1913, t. I, pp. 295-313.

Oulmont Ch., *Les femmes peintres du XVIIIe siècle*, Paris, 1928.

Ounaniantz N.-T., *La peinture française à Arkhanguelski*, Moscou, 1970 (en russe).

P..., « Salon de 1831. Peinture (deuxième article) », *Le Moniteur Universel*, 9 mai 1831.

P... CH., « Peinture. Ouverture du Salon », *Le Journal des Arts, des Sciences et de la Littérature*, 30 fructidor An IX, nº 150.

P. N-B-F. (Fabien Pillet), *Une matinée au Salon, ou les peintres de l'école passés en revue ; critique des tableaux de l'exposition de 1824*, Paris, 1824.

Pach W., « Géricault in America », *G.B.A.*, 1945, t. I, pp. 227-240.

Pahin de la Blancherie, *Essai d'un tableau historique des peintres de l'École française...*, Paris, 1783.

Paris, Louvre, 1972, voir exh. 1972, Paris, Louvre.

Pariset F.-G., *Bordeaux au XIXe siècle*, t. VI de *l'Histoire de Bordeaux*, publiée sous la direction de L. Desgraves et G. Dupeux, Bordeaux, 1969.

Pariset F.-G., *L'art néo-classique*, Paris, 1974.

Parlange M., « Fort Central ou Fort de l'île Pelée », *Neptunia*, nº 68, automne 1962.

Passavant J.-D., *Galerie Leuchtenberg. Gemäldesammlung seines Kaiserl. Hoheit des Herzogs von Leuchtenberg in München*, Francfort-sur-le-Main, 1851.

Passez A.-M., *Adélaïde Labille-Guiard. Biographie et catalogue raisonné de son œuvre*, Paris, 1973.

Pélissier L.-G., « Les correspondants du peintre Fabre », *Nouvelle revue rétrospective*, t. IV, 1896,

Pélissier L.-G., *Lettres inédites de la comtesse d'Albany à ses amis de Sienne, 1797-1820*, Toulouse, 1912.

Pératé A., « Les esquisses de Gérard », *L'Art et les artistes*, octobre 1909, pp. 4-7.

Pératé A. et Brière G., *Musée national de Versailles. Catalogue, I, Compositions historiques*, Paris, 1931.

Pérignon, *Catalogue de tableaux, esquisses, dessins et croquis de M. Girodet-Trioson*, Paris, 1825.

Perrier Ch., « Exposition universelle des Beaux-Arts. II, La peinture française. M. Ingres », *L'Artiste*, XV, 27 mai 1855, pp. 43-46.

Perrier Ch., « Paul Delaroche 1857 », *Études sur les beaux-arts en France et à l'étranger*, Paris, 1863.

Perrot J.-F.-A., *Lettres sur Nismes et le midi...*, t. I, Nîmes, 1840.

Pesquidoux L. de, *Voyage artistique en France*, Paris, 1857.

Petroz P. *L'Art et la critique en France*, Paris 1875.

Picard Ch., « Nouvelles et correspondances. L'influence des antiques sur le classicisme de David, d'Ingres et de Delacroix » (compte-rendu de l'article de B. Pollak paru dans *Nederlands Kunsthistorisch Jaarboek*, 1948-1949, pp. 287-315), *Revue archéologique*, juillet-septembre 1952, pp. 105-107.

Picon G., *Ingres*, Paris-Genève, 1967.

Pieyre A., *Histoire de la ville de Nîmes*, Nîmes 1886, t. I.

Pidansat de Mairobert M.-F., « Lettres sur l'Académie Royale de Sculpture et de Peinture et sur le Salon de 1777 », 2e lettre, *Revue Universelle des Arts*, 1865, XXII, pp. 213-233.

Pigler A., *Barockthemen. Eine Auswahl von Verzeichnissen zur Ikonographie des 17. und 18. Jahrhunderts*, Berlin et Budapest, 1956.

Pillement G., *Les pré-impressionnistes*, Paris, 1974.

Pillet Ch., *Madame Vigée-Le Brun*, Paris, 1890.

Pillet F., « Salon de l'an IX », *Le Moniteur Universel*, 6 vendémiaire an X (septembre 1801).

Pillet F., *Une matinée au Salon ou les peintres de l'École passés en revue ; critique des tableaux et sculptures de l'exposition de 1824*, Paris, 1824.

Pillet F., « Salon de 1831 », *Le Moniteur Universel*, 16 mai 1831.

PINET G., *Collection de trente dessins de Maîtres du XVIIIᵉ siècle, Fragonard, Hubert Robert, N. Cochin, Lepaon, Desprès, Pérignon, Carle Vernet, etc. conservés à l'École Polytechnique. Introduction et notes par le commandant Pinet*, Paris, 1910.

PINSET E. et AURIAC J. d', *Histoire du portrait en France*, Paris, 1884.

PLANCHE G., *Salon de 1831*, Paris, 1831.

PLANCHE G., *Portraits d'artistes*, Paris, 1853.

PLANCHE G., *Études sur l'école française*, Paris, 1855.

POLLAK, voir PICARD.

PONCE N., « Notice sur Joseph-Benoît Suvée », *Courrier de l'Europe et des Spectacles*, 27 juin 1808, p. 4, reprise dans *Mélanges sur les Beaux-Arts*, Paris, 1826, pp. 404-409.

PONCHEVILLE, voir MABILLE.

PORTALIS R. et BÉRALDI H., *Les graveurs du dix-huitième siècle*, Paris, 1880, t. I.

PORTALIS Baron R., *Honoré Fragonard, sa vie et son œuvre*, Paris, 1889.

PORTALIS Baron R., « Adélaïde Labille-Guiard », *G.B.A.*, 1901, t. II, pp. 476-494; 1902, t. I, pp. 100-118.

PORTALIS Baron R., *Adélaïde Labille-Guiard*, Paris, 1902.

PORTALIS Baron R., *Henri-Pierre Danloux, peintre de portraits et son Journal pendant l'émigration (1753-1809)*, Paris, 1910.

Pourquoi Le, ou l'ami des artistes, Genève, 1781.

PRADEL P., « Chronique bibliographique », *Revue du Louvre et des Musées de France*, 1974, nᵒ 1, p. 75.

PRAKSOV A., « Matériaux pour un inventaire des collections artistiques des princes Youssoupov », *Le Patrimoine artistique de la Russie*, 1907 (en russe).

PRAZ M., *Gusto Neoclassico*, Florence, 1940, édition augmentée, 1959; trad. anglaise *On Neoclassicism*, Londres, 1969, rééd. 1972.

PRÉCLIN E., *Le XVIIIᵉ siècle*, Paris, 1952, 2 vol.

PRIER et SOULAS, *Notice sur la vie et les travaux de F.-X. Fabre*, Montpellier, 1855.

Procès-verbaux de l'Académie Royale de Peinture et de Sculpture, 1648-1793. Publiée pour la Société d'Histoire de l'Art français d'après les registres originaux conservés à l'École des Beaux-Arts, Paris, 1875-1892, 10 vol. et table.

PROKOFIEV N.-V., *Géricault*, Moscou, 1963.

PRUVOST-AUZAS J., « Le portrait français au musée d'Orléans », *La Revue française*, janvier 1958.

PRUVOST-AUZAS J., *Catalogue de l'exposition Girodet*, Montargis, 1967.

PRUVOST-AUZAS J. et TERNOIS D., « Dessins de Girodet à sujets ossianiques », *La Revue du Louvre et des Musées de France*, 1973, nᵒˢ 4-5, pp. 261-270.

PUDELKO G., « Georges Michel », *G.B.A.*, avril 1937, pp. 232-244.

PUPIL F., « Aux sources du Romantisme, le XVIIIᵉ siècle et les ténèbres », *L'Information d'Histoire de l'Art*, 19ᵉ année, nᵒ 2, mars-avril 1974, pp. 55-65.

QUATREMÈRE DE QUINCY A. Ch., *Recueil de notices historiques lues dans les séances publiques de l'Académie royale des Beaux-Arts à l'Institut*, Paris, 1834; *Suite du recueil de notices historiques...*, Paris, 1837.

QUENOT M., *L'Histoire du Chien*, Paris, 1964.

RACHOU H., dans *Catalogue des collections de peinture du musée de Toulouse dressé par Ernest Roschach avec un appendice de Henri Rachou*, Toulouse, 1920.

RAOUL-ROCHETTE D.R. dit, *Funérailles de M. Garnier*, Paris, 1849.

RAOUL-ROCHETTE D.R. dit, *Notice sur la vie et les ouvrages de M. Garnier, peintre d'histoire*, Paris, 1850.

RATOUIS DE LIMAY P., « Le musée d'Orléans », *L'Art et les Artistes*, décembre 1920, pp. 91-111.

RATOUIS DE LIMAY P., *Les artistes écrivains*, Paris, 1921.

RATOUIS DE LIMAY P., *Le pastel en France au XVIIIᵉ siècle*, Paris, 1946.

RÉAU L., « Greuze et la Russie », *L'Art et les Artistes*, 1920, t. I, pp. 273-286.

RÉAU L., *L'expansion de l'Art français moderne. Le monde slave et l'Orient*, t. I, Paris, 1924.

RÉAU L., « Hubert Robert, peintre de Paris », *B.S.H.A.F.*, 1927, pp. 207-228.

RÉAU L., *Catalogue de l'art français dans les musées russes*, Paris, 1929.

RÉAU L., *L'Europe française au siècle des lumières*, Paris, 1938; rééd. 1971.

RÉAU L., *Iconographie de l'art chrétien*, t. I, Paris, 1955 (Introduction générale); t. II, *Iconographie de la Bible, Ancien Testament*, 1956; *Nouveau Testament*, 1957; t. III, *Iconographie des saints*, 1958-1959.

RÉAU L., *Fragonard, sa vie et son œuvre*, Bruxelles, 1956.

REDMOND R.-L., « Review of the Year », *Metropolitan Museum of Art Bulletin*, 1961, p. 44.

REFF Th., « Copyists in the Louvre, 1850-1870 », *The Art Bulletin*, décembre 1964, pp. 552-559.

RÉGAMEY R., « Hommage à Géricault », *Les Cahiers du mois*, juillet 1924, pp. 1-96.

RÉGAMEY R., *Géricault*, Paris, 1926.

RÉGAMEY R., *Prud'hon*, Paris, 1928.

REGNARD E., « Larevellière de Lepeaux », *Nouvelle biographie générale depuis les temps les plus reculés jusqu'en 1850-1860*, sous la direction de M. le Dr Hœfer, Paris, 1889, t. 29; rééd. Copenhague, 1967.

RENARD R., « Aligny et le paysage historique », *L'Art*, XXIX, 1882, t. I.

RENÉ-JEAN, *Corot*, Paris, 1931.

RENOUVIER J., *Histoire de l'art pendant la Révolution, considéré principalement dans les estampes...*, Paris, 1863.

Revue des productions les plus remarquables de nos beaux-arts exposées au Salon du Louvre en 1824 par une société de gens de lettres et d'artistes, Paris, 1824.

REY R., « Géricault », *L'Art et les Artistes*, avril 1924, pp. 257-264.

REY R., « Gros-Géricault », *Le Romantisme et l'art*, ouvrage collectif, Paris, 1928.

REYMOND M., *Étude sur le musée des tableaux de Grenoble*, Paris, Grenoble, 1879.

REWALD J., voir à DORRA.

RHEIMS M., *Musées de France*, Paris, 1973.

RICAUD T., *Le musée de Peinture et de Sculpture de Bordeaux de 1830 à 1870*, Bordeaux, 1938.

RICHARD F., *Mes souvenirs*, Manuscrit, 1847-1850, Mépieu, coll. Richard (publication prochaine par M.-Cl. Chaudonneret).

RINGBOM S.-L., « Guérin, Delacroix and *The Liberty* », *The Burlington Magazine*, mai 1968, pp. 270-274.

RIPERT E., *François-Marius Granet (1775-1849), peintre d'Aix et d'Assise*, Paris, 1937.

RIS. Voir CLÉMENT DE RIS.

ROBAUT A., *L'œuvre complet d'Eugène Delacroix*, Paris, 1885 (avec la collaboration d'E. Chesnau).

ROBAUT A., *L'œuvre de Corot, précédé de l'Histoire de Corot et de ses œuvres par Étienne Moreau-Nélaton*, Paris, 1905, 4 vol.

ROBISON G., *Revellière-Lepeaux, Citizen Director 1753-1825,* New York, 1938.

ROCHE D., « Jean-Laurent Mosnier et ses portraits à l'huile », *La Renaissance de l'art français et des industries de luxe,* avril 1921, pp. 169-176.

ROCHETTE, voir RAOUL-ROCHETTE.

ROGER N., « La Passion et la mort de Léopold Robert », *L'Illustration,* 30 mars 1935.

ROGER-MARX, *Maîtres d'hier et d'aujourd'hui,* Paris, 1914.

ROGER-MILÈS L., *Album classique des chefs-d'œuvre de Corot comprenant 40 reproductions d'après les toiles les plus célèbres du maître, précédées d'un essai critique de ...,* Paris, s.d. [1895].

ROLAND-MICHEL M., « From the « Museum » to the Musée du Louvre : Schemes and Transformations in Connexion with two Paintings by Hubert Robert », *The Burlington Magazine,* mars 1963, supplément : *L'Art au dix-huitième siècle,* pp. I-IV.

ROLAND-MICHEL M., *Anne Vallayer-Coster. 1774-1818,* Paris, 1970.

ROOSMALEN A. DE, *Notice biographique sur J.-F. van Dael,* dans le catalogue de la vente posthume de l'artiste, Paris, 1840, pp. 1-10.

ROSCHACH E., « Musées de Toulouse », dans *L'Inventaire général des richesses d'art de la France, Province, Monuments civils,* VIII, Paris, 1908.

ROSENBERG P., catalogue de l'exposition *Disegni francesi da Callot a Ingres,* Florence, Offices, 1968.

ROSENBERG P., « Twenty French Drawings in Sacramento », *Master Drawings,* VIII, n° 1, 1970, pp. 31-39.

ROSENBERG P., catalogue de l'exposition *Dessins français du 17e et du 18e siècle des collections américaines,* Toronto-Ottawa-San Francisco-New York, 1972-1973.

ROSENBERG P., « Disegni francesi dal 1750 al 1825 nelle collezioni del Louvre; il neoclassicismo, Parigi, 1972 », *Arte Illustrata,* VI, février 1973, pp. 77-84.

ROSENBERG P. et BUTOR N., Catalogue de l'exposition « *La Mort de Germanicus* » de Poussin du musée de Minneapolis, Les dossiers du département des Peintures, n° 7, musée du Louvre, 1973.

ROSENBERG P. et COMPIN I., « Quatre nouveaux Fragonard au Louvre. II », *La Revue du Louvre et des Musées de France,* 1974, n°s 4-5, pp. 263-278.

ROSENBLUM R., « Moses and the Brazen Serpent: a Painting from David's Roman Period », *The Burlington Magazine,* décembre 1963, pp. 557-558, (complété par la lettre de Jennifer Montagu, *ibidem,* mars 1964, pp. 132-134).

ROSENBLUM R., *Transformations in Late Eighteenth Century Art,* Princeton, 1967a.

ROSENBLUM R., *Jean-Auguste-Dominique Ingres,* New York, 1967b.

ROSENBLUM R., compte rendu de l'exposition *Girodet,* *Revue de l'Art,* n° 3, 1969, pp. 100-101.

ROSENBLUM R., compte rendu de l'exposition *Ingres en 1967-1968, Revue de l'Art,* n° 3, 1969, pp. 101-103.

ROSENBLUM R., « David's Funeral of Patroclus », *The Burlington Magazine,* septembre 1973, pp. 567-576.

ROSENTHAL L., « Léopold Robert peintre de l'Italie », *Revue populaire des Beaux-Arts,* 8 octobre 1898.

ROSENTHAL L., *La peinture romantique. Essai sur l'évolution de la peinture française de 1815 à 1830,* Paris, 1900.

ROSENTHAL L., *Louis David,* Paris, s.d. (1905).

ROSENTHAL L., *Géricault,* Paris, 1905.

ROSENTHAL L., « L'exposition de David et ses élèves au Petit Palais », *R.A.A.M.,* XXXIII, mai 1913, pp. 337-350.

ROSENTHAL L., *Du Romantisme au réalisme,* Paris, 1914.

ROSENTHAL L., « A propos du centenaire de Géricault », *R.A.A.M.,* XLIX, 1924, pp. 225-235.

ROUART L., « La collection de M. Chéramy », *Les Arts,* avril 1907, pp. 2-32.

ROUCHÈS G., *L'École des Beaux-Arts,* Paris, 1924.

ROUJON H., *Horace Vernet,* Paris, 1913.

ROUSSEL, « Mélanges. Doutes historiques sur Sapho », *Le Moniteur Universel,* 19 vendémiaire an X (oct. 1801).

ROUX M., *Bibliothèque Nationale. Département des Estampes. Fonds français. Graveurs du XVIIIe siècle,* Paris, t. II, 1933.

ROZET-SAINT-GENEST C., « Mieux vaut tard que jamais, ou mon opinion sur les esquisses de la bataille de Nazareth », *Le Journal des Arts, des Sciences et de Littérature,* n° 176, 10 nivôse, an X (déc. 1801).

Rubens au Muséum, Paris, an IX (1801).

RUBIN J.-H., « An Early Romantic Polemic: Girodet and Milton », *The Art Quarterly,* 1972, pp. 210-238.

RUBIN J.-H., *Ut Pictora Theatrum, Painting as Theatre: an Approach to Neoclassical Painting in France, 1791 to 1810,* Ph. D. Dissertation, Harvard University, Cambridge (Mass.), juin 1972.

RUBIN J.-H., « Oedipus, Antigone and Exiles in Post-Revolutionary French Painting », *The Art Quarterly,* vol. XXXVI, n° 3, 1973, pp. 141-171.

RUDRAUF L., « Une variation sur le thème du radeau de la Méduse », *Actes du deuxième congrès international d'Esthétiques et des Sciences de l'Art,* 1937.

RUDRAUF L., *Eugène Delacroix et le problème du romantisme artistique,* Paris, 1942.

RYSZKIEWICZ A., « Portrait équestre de Stanislas Koska Potocki par Jacques-Louis David », *Bulletin du Musée National de Varsovie,* n° 3, 1963, pp. 77-95.

RYSZKIEWICZ A., « Jacques-Louis David i Polacy », *Rocznik Historii Satuki,* IV, 1964, pp. 87-112 (avec résumé en français; article repris dans *Francusko-Polskie Zwiazki Artystyczne,* V, 1967, pp. 31-54).

SACY J. Silvestre DE, *Le comte d'Angiviller, dernier directeur général des Bâtiments du Roi,* Paris, 1953.

SAGLIO E., « Un nouveau tableau de M. Ingres. Liste complète de ses œuvres », *La Correspondance littéraire,* février 1857, pp. 75-80.

SAINT-C., « Revue dramatique », *L'Artiste,* V, 1833, p. 213.

SAINT-MAURICE, *Éloge de Xavier Sigalon,* Paris, 1848.

SAINT-PIERRE F., *Quatre portraits pour mon petit-fils,* s.l., 1970.

SAINT-SANTIN (Ph. de Chennevières), « M. Heim », *G.B.A.,* janvier 1867, pp. 40-62.

SAINT-SANTIN (Ph. de Chennevières), « J. R. Brascassat », *G.B.A.,* 1868, t. I, pp. 562-586.

SAINT-VICTOR P. DE, *Inventaire général des richesses d'art de la France. Monuments religieux,* Paris, t. I, 1876 (église Saint-Thomas-d'Aquin).

« Salon de l'An IX », *Le Moniteur universel,* 6 vendémiaire, An X.

« Salon de 1817 », *Le Moniteur Universel,* 14 mai 1817, p. 532.

« Le Salon de 1817 », *Le Journal de Paris,* 10 juin 1817.

« Le Salon de 1822 (1er article) », *Le Journal de Paris,* 25 avril 1822.

« Le Salon de 1822 (10e article) », *Le Journal de Paris,* 22 juin 1822.

« Le Salon de 1824 (1er article) », *Le Journal de Paris*, 31 août 1824.

« Le Salon de 1824 (5e article) », *Le Journal de Paris*, 15 septembre 1824.

« Le Salon de 1827 », *Le Courrier des Théâtres*, 25 novembre 1827.

« Salon de 1831 », *L'Artiste*, I, 1831, p. 174.

SALMON A., « Le *Socrate* de David et le *Phédon* de Platon », *Revue Belge de Philologie et d'histoire*, XL, 1962, nº 1, pp. 90-111.

SANDOZ M., « Nicolas Brenet, peintre d'histoire (1728-1792) », *B.S.H.A.F.*, 1960, pp. 33-50.

SANDOZ M., « Louis-Jean-François Lagrenée, dit l'aîné (1752-1805), peintre d'histoire », *B.S.H.A.F.*, 1961a, pp. 115-136.

SANDOZ M., « Peintures de Louis-Jean-François Lagrenée l'aîné en Finlande », *Ateneumin Taidemuseo. Museojulkaisu*, 6, nºs 1-2, 1961b, pp. 2-11.

SANDOZ M. « Jean-Jacques Lagrenée peintre d'histoire (1739-1821) », *B.S.H.A.F.*, 1962, pp. 121-133.

SANDOZ M., « Le *Bayard* de Louis Durameau (1777). Durameau, peintre d'histoire et artiste préromantique », *B.S.H.A.F.*, 1963, pp. 105-119.

SANDOZ M., « The Drawings of Louis-Jean-François Lagrenée: Notes for a Tentative Catalogue Raisonné », *The Art Quarterly*, printemps 1963, pp. 47-70.

SANDSTROM B., « Bénigne Gagneraux et ses contacts avec la Suède », *Annales de Bourgogne*, nºs 175-176, juillet-décembre 1972, pp. 65-79.

« Sans-Gêne et Cadet-Buteux », *Un tour au Salon ou Revue critique des tableaux de 1817*, Paris, 1817.

SARRAUTE Chanoine G., « Trois tableaux de Gamelin à l'église Saint-Vincent de Carcassonne », *Mémoires de la Société des Arts et des Sciences de Carcassonne*, 4e série, t. V, 1963-1967 (pub. en 1971).

SARRAUTE Chanoine G., « Nouveautés sur Jacques Gamelin », *Mémoires de la Société des Arts et des Sciences de Carcassonne*, 4e série, t. VI, 1968-1970 (pub. en 1972).

SAUERHERING F., « Belisar in Sage und Kunst », *Repertorium für Kunstwissenschaft*, XVI, 1893, pp. 289-295.

SAUNIER C., *Louis David*, Paris, s.d. (1904).

SAUNIER Ch., « David et son école au palais des Beaux-Arts de la ville de Paris », *G.B.A.*, mai 1913, pp. 271-290.

SAUNIER Ch., « Les dessins de Prud'hon », in « L'exposition Prud'hon », *La Renaissance de l'art français et des industries de luxe*, mai 1922, pp. 294-335.

SAUNIER Ch., *Bordeaux*, Paris, 1925.

SCHLENOFF N., *Ingres, ses sources littéraires*, Paris, 1956.

SCHNAPPER A., « Louis Lagrenée et le thème de Pygmalion » *Bulletin of the Detroit Institute of Arts*, 1974 (à paraître).

SCHNEIDER R., *L'Art français du classicisme davidien au romantisme*, Paris, 1939.

SCHNITZLER J.-H., *Moscou. Tableau statistique, géographique, topographique et historique de la ville et du gouvernement de ce nom*, Saint-Petersbourg - Paris, 1834.

SCHOMMER P., « Les voyages maritimes de Marie-Louise », *Neptunia*, nº 67, été 1962.

SEARIGHT S., *The British in the Middle East*, Londres, 1969.

SÉGAL G.-B., *Der Maler Louis-Léopold Robert*, Bâle, 1973, (dissertation).

SEIGNEUR Du J., « Le dernier Drouais », *Revue Universelle des Arts*, XVII, 1862, pp. 47-53.

SEIGNEUR Du J., « Appendice à la notice de P. Chaussard sur L. David ». *Revue Universelle des Arts*, XVIII, 1863, pp. 114-128, 359-369.

SELLIER CH. et DORBEC P., *Guide explicatif du musée Carnavalet*, Paris, 1903.

SELLS Chr., « Jean-Baptiste Regnault in Louisville », *Bulletin of the J.-B. Speed Art Museum*, vol. XXVII, nº 2, avril 1973.

SELLS Chr., « A Regnault for Detroit », *Bulletin of the Detroit Institute of Arts*, 1974 (à paraître).

SENSIER A., *Étude sur Georges Michel*, Paris, 1873.

SENTENAC P., *Hubert Robert*, Paris, 1929.

SÉRULLAZ M., *Mémorial Delacroix*, Paris, 1963.

SÉRULLAZ M., *Delacroix*, New York, 1971.

SÉRULLAZ M. et A., « Dessins inédits de Delacroix pour « La Liberté guidant le peuple » », *Revue de l'Art*, nº 14, 1971, pp. 57-62.

SÉRULLAZ A., Catalogue de l'exposition *Le néo-classicisme français ; dessins des musées de province*, Paris, Grand Palais, Copenhague, Thorvaldsen Museum, 1974-1975.

SEZNEC J. et ADHÉMAR J., *Salons* de Diderot, Oxford, 1957-1967, 4 vol.

SEZNEC J., *Essais sur Diderot et l'Antiquité*, Oxford, 1957.

[SHISSLER Mrs], *European Paintings from the Minneapolis Institute of Arts*, New York, 1971.

SILBERT P., *Notice historique sur la vie et l'œuvre de Granet*, Aix, 1862.

SIMON K.E., « Ausländische Kunst in Polen, übersicht und Eigänzungen zu einen Inventar », *Zietschrift für Kunstgeschichte*, V, 1936, pp. 140-150.

SIX E., *Museum Ary Scheffer. Catalogus der kunstwerken en andere voorwerpen*, Dordrecht, 1934.

SMITH J., *A Catalogue raisonné of the most eminent dutch, flemish and french painters...*, 1837.

SOBOUL A., *Le procès de Louis XVI*, Paris, 1966.

SONOLET L., « Un peintre à la Grande Armée. Le général baron Lejeune », *G.B.A.*, 1905, t. I, pp. 282-302.

SOUBIES A., *Les membres de l'Académie des Beaux-Arts*, 2e série, Paris, 1906.

SOULIÉ E., *Notice du Musée Impérial de Versailles*, 2e éd., Paris, 1859-61, 3 vol.; 3e éd. Paris, 1878.

STAROBINSKI J., *1789, les emblèmes de la Raison*, Paris, 1973.

STENDHAL, *Oeuvres complètes*, Nouvelle édition établie sous la direction de V. del Litto et E. Abravanel, t. LXVII (critique parue dans le *Journal de Paris*, nº 281, octobre 1824).

STENDHAL, *Voyage dans le Midi de la France (1837-1838)* (notes préparatoires aux *Mémoires d'un touriste*, publiées pour la première fois en 1927), Paris, 1930.

STERLING Ch., Catalogue de l'exposition 1933, *Hubert Robert*. Paris, Orangerie.

STERLING Ch., « A Fine David Reattributed », *Bulletin of the Metropolitan Museum of Art*, IX, janvier 1951, pp. 121-132.

STERLING Ch., « Sur un prétendu chef-d'œuvre de David », *B.S.H.A.F.*, 1951, pp. 118-130.

STERLING Ch., *The Metropolitan Museum of Art. A Catalogue of French Paintings. XV-XVIII Centuries*, Cambridge, 1955.

STERLING Ch., *Le musée de l'Ermitage. La peinture française de Poussin à nos jours*, Paris, 1957.

STERLING Ch., dans *The Thyssen-Bornemisza Collection*, Villa Favorita, Castagnola, 1969, 2 vol.

STERLING Ch. et ADHÉMAR H., *Musée National du Louvre. Peintures de l'école française du XIXe siècle*, Paris, 1958-1961, 4 vol.

STERLING Ch. et SALINGER M.-M., *A Catalogue of the Collection of the Collection of the Metropolitan Museum of Art*, New York, 1966, 2 vol.

SUARD J.-B.-A., « Éloge de Drouais », *Mélange de littérature*, t. III, Paris, 1806.

« Suite du Salon de l'an neuf - Gros, Sapho à Leucade », *Le Mercure de France*, frimaire An IX.

SWEENEY J.-J., « Exhibition in New York. Three Romantics: Gros, Géricault and Delacroix », *Parnassus*, décembre 1938, pp. 12-14.

SZCZPINSKA-TRAMER J., « Recherches sur le paysage de Géricault », *B.S.H.A.F.*, 1973 (à paraître).

T..., « Beaux-Arts-Salon (sixième article) », *Le Moniteur Universel*, 6 juin 1817.

Les tableaux chez Séraphin ou les Ombres chinoises du Salon, Paris, an XIII (1804).

TARDIEU A., *Annales du Musée. Salon de 1831*, Paris 1831.

TERNOIS D., *Les dessins d'Ingres au musée de Montauban. Les portraits. Inventaire général des dessins des musées de province*, t. III, Paris, 1959.

TERNOIS D., *Montauban, Musée Ingres. Peintures. Ingres et son temps (artistes nés entre 1740 et 1830). Inventaire des collections publiques françaises*, 11, Paris, 1965.

TERNOIS D., Catalogue de l'exposition *Ingres*, Paris, Petit Palais, 1967.

TERNOIS D., « Ossian et les peintres », *Actes du colloque Ingres*, 1967, Montauban, 1969.

TERNOIS D. et CAMESASCA E., *Tout l'œuvre peint d'Ingres*, Paris, 1971 (Introduction de D. Ternois; documentation d'E. Camesasca).

TERNOIS D., « Addition à Ossian et les peintres », *Bulletin du Musée Ingres*, n° 31, juillet 1972.

TERRIER M., « Musée Carnavalet. Acquisitions récentes », *Bulletin des Musées de France*, 1931, pp. 133-138.

THUILLIER J., *Fragonard*, Genève, 1967.

THIEGHEM P. van, *Ossian en France*, Paris, 1917.

THIEGHEM P. van, « Napoléon Ier et Ossian », *Revue des études napoléoniennes*, janvier-février, 1948, pp. 44-64.

THIEGHEM P. van, *Le Préromantisme*, Paris, 1924.

THIEME et BECKER, Ulrich Thieme et Felix Becker, *Allgemeines Lexikon der bildenden Künstler von der Antike bis zur Gegenwart unter Mitwirkung von 300 Fachgelehrten des In- und Auslandes herausgegeben von...*, Leipzig, t. I-XXXVI, 1907-1950.

THIERS A., « De Monsieur David et de son dernier tableau », *Revue Européenne*, I, juin 1824, pp. 335-339 (reproduit pour l'essentiel par P.-L. Jacob, 1873).

THIERS A., *Salon de 1824 ou collection des articles insérés au Constitutionnel sur l'exposition de cette année*, Paris, 1824.

TH. (OME) (?) A., *Vie de David, premier peintre de Napoléon*, Paris, 1826.

TOMINAGA S., *Ingres, Delacroix*, Tokyo, 1972.

TOMKIEWICZ W., *Catalogue of Paintings Removed from Poland during the Years 1939-1945*, Varsovie, 1950 (édit. anglaise).

TOURNEUX M., *Eugène Delacroix devant ses contemporains, ses écrits, ses biographes, ses critiques*, Paris, 1886.

TOURNEUX M., « L'exposition historique de la Révolution », *G.B.A.*, 1889, t. I, pp. 403-415.

TOURNEUX M., Revue de l'exposition des Portraits de femmes et d'enfants, *G.B.A.*, XVII, 1897, p. 455.

TOURNEUX M., « Lettre de Mme Vandeul, née Diderot, sur le Salon de l'An X », *B.S.H.A.F.*, 1912, pp. 124-140.

TORNEZY A., *Bergeret et Fragonard. Journal inédit d'un voyage en Italie. 1773-1774*, Paris, 1895.

TOUSSAINT H., Notices dans le catalogue de l'exposition *The Age of Neo-Classicism*, Londres, 1972.

TOUSSAINT H., Catalogue de l'exposition *Ossian*, Paris, 1974.

TRÉVISE E. DE, « Géricault », *The Arts*, t. XII, 1927, pp. 183-200.

TRIPIER-LE-FRANC J., *Notice sur la vie et les ouvrages de Mme Lebrun*, Paris, 1828 (extrait du *Journal-Dictionnaire Biographique Moderne*).

TRIPIER-LE-FRANC J., *Histoire de la vie et de la mort du baron Gros*, Paris, 1880.

TUETEY A., « Procès-verbaux de la Commission des Monuments », *N.A.A.F.*, 3e série, t. XVII et XVIII, 1902-1903.

TUETEY A., « L'émigration de Mme Vigée-Lebrun », *B.S.H.A.F.*, 1911, pp. 169-182.

TUIN H. van der, *Les vieux peintres des Pays-Bas et la critique artistique en France de la première moitié du XIXe siècle*, Paris, 1948.

ULBACH L., « Paul Delaroche », *Revue de Paris*, XXXVI, 1er avril 1857.

VAISSE P., « Ossian et les peintres du XIXe siècle. Notes à propos d'une exposition », *L'Information d'Histoire de l'art*, 1974, n° 2, pp. 81-88.

VALORY C. Tochon DE, *Greuze ou l'accordée de Village*, Paris, 1813.

VALABRÈGUE A., « Les femmes artistes du XIXe siècle. Mme Haudebourt-Lescot », *Les Lettres et les Arts*, 1887, I, pp. 102-109.

VALENCIENNES P.-H. DE, *Elémens de Perspective pratique à l'usage des artistes, suivis de Réflexions et Conseils à un Élève sur la Peinture et particulièrement sur le genre du Paysage*, Paris, an VIII (1799-1800); 2e édition revue et augmentée, Paris, 1820.

VALENTINER W.-R., « Meat, Saints and Poetry », *Art News*, mars 1950, pp. 35-37 et 64-65.

VAN DER KEMP G., « Musée de Versailles et des Trianons. Acquisitions de 1950 à 1961 », *La Revue du Louvre et des Musées de France*, 1965, n° 1, pp. 45-50.

VARNIER J., « M. Ingres », *L'Artiste*, 1841.

VAUGHAN M., « Corot in Chicago », *The Connoisseur*, CXLVII, n° 591, mars 1961, pp. 68-69.

VENTURI L., *Les peintres modernes... Corot...*, Paris, 1941.

VENTURI L., *Painters and Paintings*, New York, 1946.

VERBRAEKEN R., *Jacques-Louis David jugé par ses contemporains et par la postérité*, Paris, 1973.

VERGNAUD A.-D., *Examen du Salon de 1827*,[1] Paris, 1827.

VERGNET-RUIZ J., « Une inspiration de Delacroix ? La Jeanne Hachette de Lebarbier », *La Revue du Louvre*, 1971, n° 2, pp. 81-85.

VERGNET-RUIZ J. et LACLOTTE M., *Petits et grands musées de France. La Peinture française des Primitifs à nos jours*, Paris, 1962.

VERLET P., *The Eighteenth Century in France*, Fribourg, 1967.

VIARDOT L., *Les musées d'Angleterre, de Belgique, de Hollande et de Russie*, 2e éd. augmentée, Paris, 1855.

VIEL-CASTEL comte H. DE, « Salon de 1831 », *L'Artiste*, I, 1831.

V. P.-A. (Pierre-Ange Vieillard), *Salon de 1824. Revue des ouvrages* (extrait du *Journal des Maires*), Paris, 1825.

VIGÉE-LEBRUN É., *Souvenirs de Mme Vigée-Lebrun*, Paris, 1835-1837, 3 vol.; Paris, 1869, 2 vol.

VILAIN J., « Un tableau de J.-G. Drouais récemment acquis par le musée du Mans », *La Revue du Louvre et des Musées de France*, 1974, n° 6, pp. 400-404.

VILAIN J., Catalogue de l'exposition *Le néo-classicisme français ; dessins des musées de province*, Paris, Grand Palais, Copenhague, Thorvaldsen Museum, 1974-1975.

VILLARS F. DE, « Les trois Drouais », *Revue Universelle des Arts*, 1859, pp. 310-314.

Visite au musée du Louvre, ou guide de l'amateur à l'exposition des ouvrages... des artistes vivants (année 1827-1828), Paris, 1828.

V.[ITET] L., « Beaux-Arts », *Le Globe*, 8 mars 1828.

VITRY P., *Le musée d'Orléans*, Paris, 1922.

VIVIELLE J., « Les premiers peintres du Département de la Marine », *Bulletin officiel du Yacht Club de France* juin-août 1929, nos 123-124.

VLOBERG M., *Jean Houel, peintre et graveur, 1735-1813*, Paris, 1930.

VOIART, *Lettres impartiales sur les expositions de l'An XIII*, Paris, an XIII (1804).

VOIART, *Notice historique sur la vie et les ouvrages de P.-P. Prud'hon, peintre*, Paris, 1824.

VOLCY-BOZE, *Le comte Joseph de Boze, peintre de Louis XVI, roi de France*, Marseille, 1873.

VOLLE N., Catalogue de l'exposition *Le néo-classicisme français ; dessins des musées de province*, Paris, Grand Palais, Copenhague, Thorvaldsen Museum, 1974-1975.

VOLLMER H., « David », dans Thieme-Becker, *Allgemeines Lexikon*, t. VIII, Leipzig, 1913.

VOLLMER H., « Delorme », dans Thieme-Becker, *Allgemeines Lexikon*, t. IX, Leipzig, 1913.

VOLLMER H., « Drouais », dans Thieme-Becker. *Allgemeines Lexikon*, t. IX, Leipzig, 1913.

VOLLMER H., « Gudin », dans Thieme-Becker, *Allgemeines Lexikon*, t. XV, Leipzig, 1922.

WAAGEN G.F., *Treasures of Art in Great Britain...*, London, 1854, 3 t.

WAKEFIELD D., *Stendhal and the Arts*, Londres, 1973.

WALKER J., EMERSON G. et SEYMOUR C., Jr., *Art Treasures for America, An Anthology of Painting and Sculptures in the Samuel H. Kress Collection*, London, 1961.

WARD-JACKSON Ph., « The Girodet exhibition at Montargis », *The Burlington Magazine*, novembre 1967, pp. 660-663.

WARNOD J., « Une année d'achats au Petit Palais », *Le Figaro*, lundi 9 septembre 1968, p. 20.

WATELIN J., *Le peintre J.-L. De Marne*, Paris, 1962.

WATKIN D., *Thomas Hope and the Neo-classical Idea*, Londres, 1968.

WHITEHILL W.-M., *Museum of Fine Arts, Boston ; A Centennial History*, Cambridge, Mass., 1970.

WILDENSTEIN G., *Un peintre de paysage au XVIIIe siècle ; Louis Moreau*, Paris, 1923.

WILDENSTEIN G., « L'exposition de l'Art français à Londres, le XVIIIe siècle », *G.B.A.*, 1932, t. I, pp. 54-76.

WILDENSTEIN G., INGRES, Paris, s.d. (1954).

WILDENSTEIN G., *The Paintings of Fragonard*, New York, 1960.

WILDENSTEIN G., « Table alphabétique des portraits peints, sculptés, dessinés et gravés exposés à Paris au Salon entre 1800 et 1826 », *G.B.A.*, janvier 1963, pp. 9-60.

WILDENSTEIN D. et MANDEL G., *L'Opera completa di Fragonard*, Milan, 1972.

WILDENSTEIN D. et G., *Documents complémentaires au catalogue de l'œuvre de Louis David*, Paris, 1973.

WILHELM J., « Un projet de Charles de Wailly pour l'aménagement du Salon du Louvre », *Bulletin du musée Carnavalet*, 1963, no 1, pp. 5-10.

WILHELM J., « Les principales acquisitions du musée Carnavalet de 1941 à 1972 », *Bulletin du musée Carnavalet*, 1973, nos 1-2.

WILHELM J., « Les portraits masculins dans l'œuvre de Louis-Roland Trinquesse », *Revue de l'Art*, 1974, no 25, pp. 55-65.

WILLE J.-G., *Mémoires et Journal de J.-G. Wille, graveur du roi, publiés d'après les manuscrits autographes de la Bibliothèque impériale par Georges Duplessis, avec une préface par Edmond et Jules de Goncourt*, Paris, 1857, 2 vol.

WIND E., « A Lost Article on David by Reynolds », *Journal of the Warburg and Courtauld Institutes*, VI, 1943, pp. 223-224.

ZEITLER R., *Klassizismus und Utopia*, Stockholm, 1954.

ZIESENISS Ch.-O., « Napoléon à Eylau, une esquisse de Charles Meynier », *Revue des Arts*, 1960, nos 4-5, pp. 213-220.

ZIESENISS Ch.-O., « A propos des « esquisses » de Gérard », *B.S.H.A.F.*, 1961, p. 171.

ZIESENISS Ch.-O., « Le décor pictural de la Galerie de Diane aux Tuileries sous le Premier Empire », *B.S.H.A.F.*, 1966, pp. 199-235.

ZIESENISS Ch.-O., « A propos de l'exposition Ingres au Petit Palais », *Revue de l'Institut Napoléon*, janvier 1968.

ZIESENISS Ch.-O., « Napoléon et les tableaux du Grand Trianon », *B.S.H.A.F.*, 1968, pp. 253-308.

ZIESENISS Ch.-O., *Versailles, Musée de l'Histoire de France 1796-1815 ; collection des guides du visiteur*, Paris, 1970.

ZOLTOWSKA M. E., « La première critique d'art écrite par un Polonais : *Lettre d'un étranger sur le salon de 1787 de Stanislas Kotska Potocki* », dans *Dix-huitième siècle*, 1974, pp. 325-341.

Credits

Photographs by:
A.C.L., Brussels
Agraci, Paris
Archives photographiques, Paris
The Art Institute of Chicago
The Brooklyn Museum, New York
Brunel, Lugano
Bulloz, Paris
Centre d'optique et d'électronique, Paris
Christian, Chauny
Courtesy of the National Gallery of Ireland, Dublin
C.R.D.P. Photothèque, Clermont-Ferrand
Danvers
Delacroix & Poidvin, Dieppe
The Detroit Institute of Arts
Dräyer, Zurich
Ely, Aix-en-Provence
Evers, Angers
The Fine Arts Museums, San Francisco
Fogg Art Museum (Harvard University), Cambridge, Massachussetts
Gabinetto fotografico, Florence
Gérondal, Lomme-Lille
Hahn J. & Co., Paris and Pézenas
The Hermitage Museum, Leningrad
Kimbell Art Museum, Fort Worth, Texas
Lauros-Giraudon, Paris
Laverton
Leroy, Arras
Lévy, Paris
Los Angeles County Museum of Art
Madec, Nantes
Marylebone Cricket Club, London
The Metropolitan Museum of Art, New York
Millar & Harris, London
The Minneapolis Institute of Arts
Morillon, La Rochelle
Musée d'Art et d'Histoire, Geneva
Musée Calvet, Avignon
Musée de la Marine, Paris
Musée de Picardie, Amiens
Musée Rigaud, Perpignan
Musées Royaux des Beaux-Arts, Brussels
Musées de la ville de Strasbourg
The Museum of Fine Arts, Boston
The National Gallery of Canada, Ottawa
Oeffentliche Kunstsammlung, Basel
O'Sughrue, Montpellier
Pollitzer, New York
The Portland Art Museum
Réunion des Musées Nationaux, Paris
Routhier, Paris
S.P.A.D.E.M. (Resseguié), Paris
Stickelmann, Bremen
Tarascon, Saint-Quentin
Virginia Museum of Fine Arts, Richmond
Witt Library, Courtauld Institute of Art, London

Texts translated by:
Kenneth Bendiner
Rose Cogliati
Hermine Chivian
Ingrid Daemmrich
Martha Dunkelmann
Ross A.C. Fox
Alexander Gaudieri
Francine Goldenhar
Evelyne Mosby
Terry Ann R. Neff
Stark C. Ward
Carolyn Wilson
Stephen Zwirn

Designed by:
Frutiger & Pfäffli, Paris

Typeset and printed by:
Blanchard, 92350 Le Plessis-Robinson, France

List of Lenders

Index to Artists in the Exhibition

according to catalog numbers

264

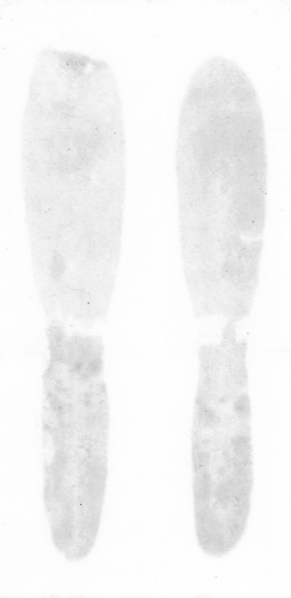

DATE DUE	
APR 27 1997	
DEC 14 1997	
NOV 22 2006	
DEC 14 2007	
DEC 12 2008	
OCT 20 2013	
GAYLORD	PRINTED IN U.S.A.